D0003544

All content plus more can be found at:
www.chambers-associate.com

Chambers Associate 2018-19

OUR education determines our career success – for students this is gospel. But as we transition from student to lawyer and then to leader, there comes a point where knowledge only partly equates to power. Amassing all this knowledge is fruitless if we make bad decisions. So while part of this guide's aim is to build your understanding of the legal market, its true value is revealed in helping you make the right choices, setting you on the path to leadership.

This edition comes equipped with a new armory of decision-making tools. Our new practice area guides are well worth a look: here lawyers from the specialist firms tell their career stories, bringing each practice area to life and helping you find your niche. We then dissect the market by every metric that matters, beginning with the latest associate satisfaction surveys.

Expanding our data research revealed a truth about this market: comparison tools are invaluable for shortlisting, but there is no substitute for speaking to lawyers. The US legal market is uniquely competitive; everything is benchmarked and imitated right through to the recruitment branding. Recruiters tell us getting hired is about finding the right fit, but how do you make progress when the firms won't readily reveal their true character?

Be assured that beyond all the marketing there is true distinction – pretty and ugly. Our research team challenges the platitudes and industry clichés. We ask lawyers the difficult questions that you'd prefer not to ask face-to-face; our lawyer sources speak more openly with their identities concealed. This guide has delved into every aspect of an associate's life in more depth than ever before. Our interviewees help us paint an accurate picture of that elusive thing called 'law firm culture'; bar visiting the firm in person, there is no better way of visualising whether you'd fit in and thrive at each firm. Our interview research is intensive, but we believe worth the effort when it helps you succeed.

The *Chambers Associate* team
June 2018

Our Editorial Team

Antony Cooke

Editor of *Chambers Associate* and *Chambers Student Guide*. Graduated from Durham University in Russian & French. Taught English at St. Petersburg State University. Previously worked at Michelin as a European project manager, and at PricewaterhouseCoopers as an associate in investment management. Fluent in Russian and French.

Antony Cooke
Editor

antonyc@chambersandpartners.com

Paul Rance

Deputy editor. Graduated from Exeter University with a first in English Literature and also spent a year abroad at the University of Toronto to read Canadian literature. He completed his MA in English at UCL in 2010.

Paul Rance
Deputy Editor

paul.rance@chambersandpartners.com

Our Editorial Team *continued*

Sam Morris
Deputy editor. Sam graduated from the University of Leiden, The Netherlands with a first in Political Science in 2008 and from the London School of Economics with an MSc in Comparative Politics in 2009. He has worked for the Dutch Ministry of Foreign Affairs. Speaks Dutch and German.

Tom Lewis
Deputy editor. Graduated in 2015 with a BA in History from the University of Sheffield.

Natalie Bertram
Senior researcher. Graduated in 2016 from the University of Exeter with a BA Hons in English Literature. Freelances as a proof reader in her free time.

Michael Bird
Senior researcher. Graduated from Royal Holloway, University of London with a BA in History. Prior to Chambers, Michael worked for US-based entertainment websites, and continues to review music in his spare time.

Harry Cerasale
Senior researcher. Graduated in 2015 with a BA in History from the University of Nottingham. Has previously worked as an English teacher in Vietnam and Cambodia.

Laura Bishop
Researcher. Graduated in 2017 from the University of Sussex with an MA in Creative and Critical Writing following a BA in English.

Alex Radford
Researcher. Graduated from the University of York with a BA in Philosophy. Previously he worked as a project manager for an engineering firm.

Leah Henderson
Researcher. Graduated from the University of the West of England with an MA in Journalism in 2015, after completing an undergraduate degree in English Language and Literature in 2014 at the University of Glasgow. Previously worked as a business English teacher in Madrid.

Sal Francis Morton
Researcher. Graduated from Queen Mary University of London with a BA in Drama, receiving the Sylvia Perry Prize for Outstanding Contribution. Has previously worked in education.

Annie Robertson
Researcher. Graduated from the University of Sheffield with a BA in Journalism and completed the GDL at the University of Law, Moorgate. Previously a legal recruitment consultant in London. Speaks Hebrew.

A beginner's guide to Chambers research

At every stage in your career planning, the decisions you make should always be based on sound research. This short guide helps you focus and get the most out of our resources. We've stripped away the fat and reduced your job to four steps.

STEP 1:

What kind of lawyer do you want to be?
Practice Area Guides
What are they? We interviewed leading lawyers from each of the main practice areas. They provide an overview of what they do. Cleary's litigators, for example, explained that their practice is all about *"telling a compelling story,"* and added: *"You need to think about what will be persuasive and compelling for the decision maker, be it a judge, jury, or arbitrator."* The personality traits needed to be a litigator will not be the same as those of a capital markets lawyer; life goals and motivations among IP lawyers will differ to those of real estate or private equity lawyers.

Why use the practice area reviews? They will give you a feel for what your job might end up being like, and whether you can hack it. They're full of useful insights like: *"If your eyes glaze over when reading a detailed technical or cost proposal, this is not the area for you"* – a top government lawyer at Hogan Lovells.

Where? Check out **pages 79 to 234** to read our practice area guides.

STEP 2:

Narrowing the field
***Chambers USA* and *Chambers Global* rankings**
What are they? Our parent company, Chambers and Partners, is the authority on researching and ranking law firms around the world. Say you want to view the top firms practicing political law in the US – you can.

Why use them? It's the most efficient way of shortlisting firms by city and the practice areas you're interested in. The site ranks firms and lawyers by every practice area in every significant legal market, and gives an idea of the type of work each office does.

Where? *Chambers USA* is the most immediately relevant, and, if international work is important to you, check out

the US rankings in the *Chambers Global* guide – access to both guides is available via chambersandpartners.com.

Comparison tables
What are they? We compile vital data on firms – salaries, attorney numbers, diversity percentages etc. – and put them into a comparison table.

Why use them? Using the tools on the web page, you can rank firms by certain characteristics, immediately ruling out firms that don't fit what you're looking for.

Where? Follow this link to our website (chambers-associate.com/law-firms/a-to-z-firm-list) and select the firms you want to compare. We analyze more data from our homepage too, in case you want to pick a firm by partner-associate leverage, for example. Data is also listed from p.19 of this guide.

STEP 3:

The Shortlist
The Inside View
What is it? The Inside View is the heart of our guide. It gives you a behind-the-scenes look at the lives of junior associates, examining firms' culture, work and training opportunities, office environments, diversity, hours culture and pro bono.

Why use it? Reading these will help you to see if you're a good match for the firms you've selected so far. Ask yourself: does this firm offer me what I want? Will I fit in? What will my life *actually* be like?

Where? Turn to **page 235** to start reading our Inside View features on over 100 firms.

Managing partner interviews
What are they? As part of our research for the Inside View, we also speak to firms' managing partners.

Why use them? Read these to get an idea of what the firm wants to achieve and where its priorities lie. Could you be part of this firm's future? Do your aspirations match this firm's? To be that candidate is attractive to firms.

Where? Find comments from managing partners in the 'Strategy & Future' sections within our Inside View features. To read full transcripts of our interviews with managing partners, go to our website (chambers-associate.com) and click on the 'Bonus Features' tab on each firm's page.

Associate survey results

What are they? Our survey highlights how associates rate their own firm in areas like satisfaction, benefits & lifestyle, pro bono and diversity. The firms we list are those showing excellent performance.

Why use them? Use this in conjunction with the Inside View and you'll get an idea of whether the firm is simply a cut-throat business, or if it takes a more holistic, pastoral approach.

Where? Check out **pages 8 to 18** to read the results of the 2018 survey in the areas listed above and more.

STEP 4:

Prepare

Return to The Inside View

Why? The Inside View is designed to help you prepare for interview. To know how a firm works and to imagine yourself there will take you far. Your knowledge and enthusiasm come across naturally, and it's clear to a recruiter why you want to be there, and your likelihood of getting a call-back interview skyrockets.

Where? **Pages 235 to 606.**

Get Hired

What is it? We speak to firms' current associates and interview the hiring partners to learn how to pass interview.

Where? Go to chambers-associate.com and click on the 'Bonus Features' tab on each firm's Inside View page.

Learn about the BigLaw hiring process

Just turn to the 'Becoming a lawyer' chapter, on **page 45** in this book, where you'll find pages on different types of law firm, OCI interviews, recruitment trends, clerkships, SCOTUS clerkships and more.

Throughout this guide you'll see how a firm's structure, or the way it generates income, has a direct impact on its culture.

The Associate Satisfaction survey

We asked thousands of junior associates to assess the factors that contribute toward their satisfaction. Here are the top performers.

Most satisfied associates 2018

1	Kramer Levin
2	Clifford Chance
3	Finnegan
4	Seward & Kissel
5	Allen & Overy
6	Gibson Dunn
7	Goodwin
8	Proskauer
9	Thompson & Knight
10	MoFo
11	Cozen
12	Milbank
13	Perkins Coie
14	Latham
15	Weil
16	Cravath
17	Irell & Manella
18	White & Case
19	Alston & Bird
20	Skadden
21	Waller
22	Akin Gump
23	Simpson Thacher
24	Debevoise
25	Munger Tolles
26	Kirkland
27	Paul, Weiss
28	Cleary
29	Jenner & Block
30	Cooley
31	Vedder
32	Crowell & Moring
33	Winston
34	Fried Frank
35	DLA Piper
36	Cahill
37	Morgan Lewis
38	Hogan Lovells
39	Mintz Levin
40	Haynes and Boone

"*WE definitely work very hard, but this is a place that I look forward to journeying to every morning,*" reported an associate at Kramer Levin, the leading firm in our satisfaction chart this year. This associate articulated where the limitations are to any BigLaw happiness survey: we're not talking boundless euphoria here, but contentment in spite of the pressures of the job. So to find the global finance and corporate beast Clifford Chance in the second spot may be unexpected, but the firm has been an outstanding performer for two years now, and this magic circle firm is accompanied by many other global heavyweights in this list.

A Clifford Chance associate told us: "*We had a rough Thanksgiving because we had a ton of work, but we still got together and cooked a couple of turkeys.*" Simple touches like this can make all the difference, introducing some humanity when times are hard. There is no formula for associate satisfaction – if there were, IP whiz Finnegan (3rd) would have patented it by now – but there are common traits. The scholars at Finnegan reduced the equation to "*interesting work and people I like working with.*"

The quality of the work is crucial. In this research you'll always see niche or sector-focused firms performing well – Kramer, Finnegan, Seward, Goodwin and MoFo are there in the top ten. The clients' work was a source of inspiration for Finnegan's associates: "*you get to see some amazing technology on the brink of its field.*" And the prestige of your work as an associate is important, thought Clifford Chance associates: "*huge deals you read about in big journals – that was very exciting to me.*" Gibson Dunn (6th) is the highest ranking US giant in this list and their associates did admit to us that the firm's own accolades were a big draw: "*It's just legal stars up and down the directory!*"

Since we're on the topic of prestige, we should mention the mighty Cravath, where, like Clifford Chance, you might not expect joie de vivre to be a priority, but they perform very well regardless. "*There's something nice about working at a firm that emits a consistent level of quality, competence and dedication to the job.*" When over-achievers find their mothership, all is well.

So it's no coincidence that the happiest feel the most invested in their work. In our interviews associates put a premium on early responsibility, because to see where your career is going – to remove that uncertainty and junior anonymity – is immensely valuable. Lean staffing is how Kramer Levin's associates got to feel valued early on: "*we had client meetings with just me, a partner and another second year.*" And Clifford Chance's associates thought they had the best of both worlds with "*the combination of an extremely large, international firm with the much smaller feel of the relatively small US offices.*" Gibson Dunn makes self-determination a central theme with its free-market system, which "*empowers you to pick and choose how you want your career to look.*" Many firms in this list achieve a similar effect with a commitment to pro bono.

Law firm culture trickles down from the personalities at the top and the legacy working relationships. Our sources at Proskauer (8th) were confident enough that they would aspire to the top no matter what, but thought that "*other firms are too OCD about things and want to harp on about details to the nth degree. The result is that people become bland, dry and lose their energy.*" This seems smart – you have hired a group of natural perfectionists; does perfectionism need to be drilled in so rigorously? Proskauer's

associates stressed that "*to fit in here it's imperative to have a sense of humor.*" Similarly, associates at Goodwin (7th) found an empathetic firm: "*I have messed up a few times and the partners have all been very nice about it – they understand that you learn.*"

But enough of this hugging and back-slapping – isn't ruthless competition the beating heart of the American legal profession? Speaking on behalf of many top firms in this list, Clifford Chance's associates remind us: "*We're competitive in the sense that we want the firm to succeed but we don't compete against each other.*" You'll find firms in this guide where associates are competitive, and others that find the eat-what-you-kill model positively awkward: neither has the edge on the other; both types of firm have their own merits and story to tell.

Methodology

We asked associates to rate their firm on how happy they were, how stressed they were, their intention to stay at the firm, how much the work motivates them, and the firm's value to them in their career. The firms listed are those demonstrating strong performance.

'It's no coincidence that the happiest feel the most invested in their work. In our interviews associates put a premium on early responsibility, because to see where your career is going – to remove that uncertainty and junior anonymity – is immensely valuable.'

The career opportunities survey

Law at the top is hard work, that's a given – but the opportunities to do exciting work which you enjoy, to develop along with a group of peers and to forge a lasting career provide the counter balance. Which firms do best on this front?

Opportunities: The best firms 2018

1	Kramer Levin
2	Clifford Chance
3	White & Case
4	Vedder
5	Crowell & Moring
6	Cozen
7	Proskauer
8	Gibson Dunn
9	Katten Muchin
10	Finnegan
11	Reed Smith
12	Cleary
13	Goodwin
14	Irell & Manella
15	Waller
16	Kirkland
17	Allen & Overy
18	Munger Tolles
19	Duane Morris
20	Patterson Bellknap
21	Norton Rose Fulbright
22	Fish & Richardson
23	Adam Leitman Bailey
24	Snell & Wilmer
25	Morgan Lewis
26	Nutter
27	MoFo
28	Fried Frank
29	Haynes and Boone
30	Perkins Coie
31	Cahill
32	Latham
33	Akin Gump
34	Jackson Walker
35	Alston & Bird
36	Jenner & Block
37	Schulte Roth
38	Simpson Thacher
39	Sullivan & Cromwell
40	Skadden

DESPITE the many fine bells and whistles that law firms offer these days, the experience of associates is still reliant on how a firm approaches the work they do. It's what they spend most of their time doing after all. Keeping the work satisfying relies on dishing out tasks that are stimulating, challenging and allow associates to develop; it relies on having the resources to support associates, and it relies on having a team which functions... as a team, where relationships are respectful, responsibility is shared and associates feel appreciated. Combine these elements, and associates will be presented with fewer barriers to developing their career.

It's the last of those points which helps advertising litigation expert Kramer Levin secure the top spot. It scored exceptionally for fostering teamwork and collaboration across levels. Sources didn't feel isolated from their seniors – *"there's always an open channel of communication"* – and this negated the pressures of the BigLaw workload: *"When people are working they go all in, 100%, but everyone still gets along. There's no yelling."* While an eat-what-you-kill system might work for some firms, it was the fact that *"there's no competitive edge to the culture"* at Chicagoan Vedder (4th) which ensured they had one of the best working cultures around. Rather than concerning themselves with bettering their colleagues in a scrap for the partnership, sources could work safe in the knowledge that *"the firm is rooting for you to succeed and become a shareholder."*

Magic-circler Clifford Chance's associates were also extremely close: *"Everyone seems to be working together to survive – it can be hard at a law firm!"* But they illustrate a more important point regarding career opportunities. Clifford Chance's associates felt extremely aware of the firm's strategic goals. This helps explain the firm's second place spot – the disclosure of the firm's goals suggests to associates that they are going to be the ones to help implement the strategy further down the road. Meanwhile, fellow magic circle firm Allen & Overy was the best rated for allowing associates to establish themselves in a practice area of their choosing.

For those that have very clear ideas about how they want their career to develop, is there anything more important than allowing associates to choose their work? A generous approach in this area benefited Kramer Levin and Gibson Dunn (8th) in our survey. The relatively small Kramer Levin allowed associates to source work *"from asking around or developing relationships with partners. That's possible in an office with just a few hundred people."* Sources at the much larger Gibson Dunn enthused about how the firm had made a free market system work: *"it's like a Goosebumps Choose Your Own Adventure book."*

At Katten Muchin (9th) associates were empowered with the responsibility of frequent and meaningful client contact: *"there's a push for associates to meet people on the client side who are of a similar age and experience: the thought behind this is that the firm can grow with the client."* Crowell & Moring meanwhile, a firm known for its rubber duck mascot, did well in our survey for allowing associates to flourish as individuals. *"Quirkiness is a virtue,"* said sources, with one recalling an admirably chilled approach to a difficult case: *"It was just how I'd pictured it – eating Chinese food with people around a table, trying to figure it out."*

It's stories like these that show there's a clear alternative to barked orders and ruthless competition. There are firms out there who recognize the potential of junior associates, rather than simply seeing them as your go-to for repetitive, menial tasks. Providing them with the tools and experience to build their careers from an early stage can reap huge benefits. All of the firms who succeeded in our survey appreciated this to some degree.

Methodology
We asked associates to give a rating for their level of responsibility, their autonomy in work acquisition, their opportunities to establish themselves in a practice area, the quality of training, their contact time with partners, the travel opportunities, technological support, support on procedural tasks, competition between peers, their stress, whether they're nurtured as future leaders, camaraderie between associates, the communication of management strategy and to what extent they feel comfortable being themselves. The firms listed are those demonstrating strong performance.

'Providing associates with the tools and experience to build their careers from an early stage can reap huge benefits. All of the firms who succeeded in our survey appreciated this to some degree.'

The retention survey

Careers at BigLaw firms can be nonsensically short – but they don't have to be. Associates rate their firms on the factors that prevent juniors rushing for the exit.

Retention: The best firms 2018

1	White & Case
2	Finnegan
3	Proskauer
4	Allen & Overy
5	Katten Muchin
6	Clifford Chance
7	Reed Smith
8	Cozen
9	Thompson & Knight
10	Gibson Dunn
11	Irell & Manella
12	Kirkland
13	Crowell & Moring
14	Kramer Levin
15	Goodwin
16	Munger Tolles
17	Duane Morris
18	Cleary
19	Fish & Richardson
20	Morgan Lewis
21	MoFo
22	Vedder
23	Haynes and Boone
24	Cahill
25	Nutter
26	Patterson Bellknap
27	Waller
28	Adam Leitman Bailey
29	Snell & Wilmer
30	Sullivan & Cromwell
31	Hangley
32	Debevoise
33	Perkins Coie
34	Simpson Thacher
35	Akin Gump
36	Jackson Walker
37	Sheppard Mullin
38	Weil
39	Latham
40	Alston & Bird

ONCE a firm has decided its associates aren't a dispensable part of its pyramidal structure, keeping an associate interested relies upon a potent mix of factors: ensuring juniors can see a realistic, and prosperous career path; ensuring that they're not browbeaten by the hours, expectations, or sterile/hostile environments that law firms are prone to; and ensuring that the grass seems greener on *this* side – a firm's current prestige, or its lofty goals will make a lateral move less tempting.

The firms who topped our survey each provided their own solutions to these problems. At the very top sits White & Case. The international prodigy did excellently in our survey for its market reputation (its ambitious growth strategy has clearly trickled down to associates). Long hours weren't a foreign concept to the top firms – but the key, as at White & Case, was that they were motivated to work hard. *"I'd rather work 2,300 happy hours than 200 at a place I was unhappy with."* A *"team-orientated environment"* provided a more human approach: *"We had a big filing a month or so ago so we broke out the ping pong table to lighten the mood."* And, crucially, frequent training and mentoring ensured associates felt they were progressing towards something more long term. *"There's a good sense of nurturing people to become one of us. Part of that involves putting you on the spot with partners and asking you what you think. People here want you to succeed."*

Our recent study of associate retention found that the quality of training and development corresponded most closely with associates' intent to stay. Fourth placed Allen & Overy (another candidate ripe for future growth) offered quarterly feedback sessions, as well as second year *"'make your mark' training, which gives an introduction to how things operate and the firm's strategic focuses."* Second placed IP maestro Finnegan impressed with, among plenty of other formal training programs, its legal writing course, which *"dives deep into grammar and writing style to make sure everyone's up to speed."* Fifth placed Katten Muchin meanwhile, ensured its associates could see a future for themselves because of its entrepreneurial mantra. *"If you're motivated and want to make your mark you can take it as far as you want. If you try to take the lead, nobody's going to say you're too junior."*

Trusting associates, and demonstrating commitment to them, was key. For some, it's placed at the forefront of their offering. Ninth placed Thompson and Knight "*attracts people who want to be in it for the long haul – they want people who want to make partner here. It's very rare to see people leave.*" Likewise eighth placed Cozen was described as "*a young, energetic, creative law firm that cares about developing its young lawyers and investing in them.*"

The top firms are a mixed bunch, but the presence of IP magnates Irell and Finnegan is notable. They are both market leaders in their specific fields. Associates' perception that their work is the very best they could be doing means there's less motivation to move. The other noticeable point is a general absence of the very largest firms. Size does not typically lend itself to the personal touch. And that, we think, is all important when considering associates' careers. It's a complicated issue, because it's a very human issue. There's no strict formula for success, but across the board, combining the investment of care and attention, and time and money, into the aspirations and welfare of associates pays off – big time.

Methodology

We asked associates to rate their firm on how much value the firm's name added to their resume, their intent to stay at the firm, how it matched their perceptions before joining, the level of responsibility and client contact, their autonomy over work acquisition, their opportunities to establish themselves in a practice area, the quality of training, their contact time with partners, and how much partners were nurturing future leaders. The firms listed showed strong performance across these topics.

'There's no strict formula for success, but across the board, combining the investment of care and attention, and time and money, into the aspirations and welfare of associates pays off – big time.'

The benefits and lifestyle survey

Are a bumper pay packet and a good work-life balance mutually exclusive? Can jet-setting and flexible working policies compensate for long hours? We asked associates to rate their firms on the factors that impact their lifestyle.

Benefits and lifestyle: The best firms 2018

1	Clifford Chance
2	Kramer Levin
3	White & Case
4	Patterson Bellknap
5	Allen & Overy
6	Gibson Dunn
7	Cahill
8	Cleary
9	Crowell & Moring
10	Proskauer
11	Vedder
12	Munger Tolles
13	Irell & Manella
14	Finnegan
15	MoFo
16	Weil
17	Cozen
18	Willkie
19	Kirkland
20	Waller
21	Goodwin
22	Akin Gump
23	Winston
24	Milbank
25	Reed Smith
26	Fried Frank
27	Latham
28	Morgan Lewis
29	Nutter
30	Hogan Lovells
31	Debevoise
32	Arnold & Porter
33	Paul, Weiss
34	Fish & Richardson
35	Sullivan & Cromwell
36	Skadden
37	Cooley
38	Perkins Coie
39	Brown Rudnick
40	Simpson Thacher

MANY of the firms in our top ten are large global/international players, and they are attractive from a lifestyle point of view for the potential travel opportunities they provide. These outfits therefore performed well in this category, but the ones that shone the most were those that could combine international access with a more intimate feel. Take reigning champion Clifford Chance and its magic circle sister Allen & Overy (5th). These British firms offer their US associates plenty of opportunity to hop on a plane (for the likes of global university sessions and summer program sojourns to foreign offices) but also *"smaller, more navigable offices"* in the States, as one A&O source put it. White & Case (3rd) may not have compact domestic offices, but it does meld high travel scores with a reportedly cosy atmosphere: *"Despite being so big and spread out we're still able to feel like a family."*

Most of the top names on our list are known for their demanding hours (*"I'd be lying if I said the hours weren't long. On a crazy day I could be in the office until any time,"* one Clifford Chance junior admitted), so why are they still rated so highly in this survey? Associates at Cahill (7th) may well have given the firm a lower work-life balance score than firms further down the list, but its success in the bonus category sweetened the deal: *"We work harder than other firms, but we get paid more,"* said one junior at the firm. Aside from material benefits, feedback collected from Cahill also shows how cultural factors (like team spirit and widespread adoption of flexible working) help to determine the overall view on lifestyle, as this source's views indicated: *"Flexibility is afforded to associates – there's no face-time requirement and you're not micromanaged. You're respected, and therefore expected to get your work done and handle your own things."*

All of the firms in our top ten offer either four weeks of vacation or an 'unlimited' amount, as well as flexible working policies and caregiver leave periods that fall within the upper end of the scale (nothing below 18 weeks for primary caregivers, and four weeks for secondary caregivers). On the subject of vacation, Patterson (4th) came out on top for making associates feel that they can take a break on their own terms: *"It's easy to take vacation – you just have to write up an email and send it to who you're working with."* It's worth noting that firms with the 'unlimited' option came lower down the list in the vacation category. The issue with this option – as this source from Gibson (6th) explained – is that *"younger associates might feel scared to take vacation"* due to uncertainty over how much to take; figuring out what is culturally acceptable/ normal can be more difficult in firms with this set-up.

Patterson is the outlier here in that it's a smaller, single-site firm with no physical presence overseas. It again took the crown in the work-life balance category: *"I was worried about being a lawyer in New York. I didn't think I'd be able to find a place where I'd enjoy the work and also have a life outside work, but so far I've been able to accomplish both of those things at Patterson."* One possible reason for its high score is that the firm is litigation-heavy; this practice, in contrast to transactional areas like corporate and real estate, typically has more predictable deadlines that are set by the court. In addition, Patterson's scores for bonus received and work-life balance are similar – an alignment that wasn't so equal at other participating firms in the survey, where bonuses appeared to compensate for a balance that was tilted further in the direction of work.

Methodology

We asked associates to rate the bonus they receive against the market, the whole benefits package, the travel opportunities available, the ability to take vacation on their own terms, and their work-life balance/scope for flexible working. The firms listed are those demonstrating strong performance.

Which firms offer the best parental leave?
Will the firm cover health and dental?
Compare all firms on their benefits packages online.

The pro bono survey

For junior associates, pro bono is a great way to get early hands-on experience of advising clients and handling matters. We asked associates to rate their firm for how good it is at supporting pro bono.

The best firms for pro bono 2018

1	Jenner & Block
2	Kramer Levin
3	Patterson Belknap
4	Gibson Dunn
5	Cleary
6	Munger Tolles
7	White & Case
8	Morgan Lewis
9	Allen & Overy
10	Akin Gump
11	Gibbons
12	Irell & Manella
13	Nutter
14	Proskauer
15	MoFo
16	Skadden
17	Dechert
18	Hogan Lovells
19	Crowell & Moring
20	Finnegan
21	Arnold & Porter
22	Fried Frank
23	Goodwin
24	Paul, Weiss
25	Willkie
26	Debevoise
27	Clifford Chance
28	Milbank
29	Cozen
30	Duane Morris
31	Hunton
32	Simpson Thacher
33	Kirkland
34	Perkins Coie
35	Latham
36	Winston
37	Cahill
38	Jones Day
39	Alston & Bird
40	Weil

MANY firms scoring highly in our pro bono survey are those with a legacy of focusing on litigation – for example, Jenner (1st) Kramer Levin (2nd), Patterson Belknap (3rd), Gibson Dunn (4th), Munger (6th) and Gibbons (11th). This reflects common feedback we hear that pro bono is more readily available to junior litigators than their transactional counterparts. This is an underlying trend, but to get to the top of this table, firms have to be doing something rather special. Jenner holds its position at the top of this table, and that should be no surprise, if you listen to their associates: "*What's most important about Jenner's culture is the pro bono. Everyone here has this unwavering dedication to giving back to the community.*"

The advertising litigators at Kramer Levin (2nd) picked up on an important point: that their firm "*both encourages and – more importantly – doesn't discourage doing pro bono.*" The firm has an annual pro bono award, long-standing links to domestic abuse charity Her Justice, and offers a four-month pro bono secondment to Brooklyn Legal Services.

"*It gives me an opportunity to take a lead role, so it's really rewarding,*" said one Patterson Belknap associate of their pro bono experience. "*It's really me doing most of the work and then a partner has an overview of the case. It's much more hands on, because I'm doing everything.*" Gibson Dunn is also a firm which "*puts its money where its mouth is*" on pro bono, associates said. Juniors at the firm told us they'd been working on asylum cases resulting from President Trump's travel ban as well as international matters for Lawyers Without Borders.

Firms with a more transactional focus are often outshone in the pro bono stakes, but several do feature in our pro bono top ten. "*It's okay to take on pro bono and partners don't view it as lesser work,*" an associate at Cleary (5th) told us. "*They accommodate it as though it were billable, although of course if there are deadlines you sometimes have to prioritize.*" Meanwhile an associate at White & Case (placed 7th) praised the efforts of the firm's global pro bono manager: "*I emailed him about trying to meet my pro bono hours and he called me within five minutes to discuss.*" The best firms for pro bono recognize the valuable experience it can give juniors, encourage associates to undertake pro bono, value it equally to billable work, and allow young attorneys to pursue those pro bono matters which interest them the most.

Methodology

We asked associates to rate their firm for how interesting the pro bono work is, whether pro bono helped build their skills, how committed the firm is to pro bono, and whether there is any pressure to NOT do pro bono. The firms listed are those demonstrating strong performance.

"In today's business world, success means helping clients harness extraordinary advancements in technology. I would advise all aspiring lawyers to develop tech-related skills and stay on top of innovation in the space. Virtually every major corporation is deeply dependent on technology, and not just actual tech companies like Google or Amazon."
– Clifford Chance's Americas regional managing partner, Evan Cohen

The diversity survey

Associates rate their own firms' diversity efforts.

Diversity: The best firms 2018

1	Debevoise
2	Waller
3	Proskauer
4	Kramer Levin
5	Crowell & Moring
6	MoFo
7	Weil
8	Fried Frank
9	Clifford Chance
10	Mintz Levin
11	Jenner & Block
12	Finnegan
13	Paul, Weiss
14	Cleary
15	Perkins Coie
16	Goodwin
17	White & Case
18	Gibson Dunn
19	Latham
20	Haynes and Boone
21	Reed Smith
22	Simpson Thacher
23	Cahill
24	Duane Morris
25	Cooley
26	Skadden
27	Vedder
28	Cozen
29	Norton Rose Fulbright
30	Munger Tolles
31	Kirkland
32	Cravath
33	Davis Polk
34	Hogan Lovells
35	Alston & Bird
36	Winston
37	Fish & Richardson
38	DLA Piper
39	Arnold & Porter
40	Milbank

LOOKING down this list, it would be hard to conclude that a certain type of firm does best at diversity: we have global bruisers like Debevoise and Clifford Chance; Waller, a niche healthcare specialist in Tennessee; finance leaders like Weil and Fried Frank; techy firms like MoFo and Mintz Levin. Explore each of these firms, though, and you'll find significant efforts to overcome all the barriers to equality. Our leader for two years in a row, Debevoise, typifies many firms in this list: the firm is famous for its considerate, collaborative working culture, so diversity efforts really are a natural product of that. LGBT leader Jenner & Block (11th) operates on a similar model: "*it's about creating a culture where diversity is normalized.*" That Jenner tops the table for pro bono is no coincidence.

Clifford Chance (9th) and MoFo (6th) are among the firms that have adopted the Mansfield Rule, meaning at least one candidate considered for a leadership role must be a woman. Clifford Chance's London HQ is among the most transparent of the UK firms on tracking diversity. The firm's associates were impressed with their 200-lawyer New York office's breadth of diversity committees, "*with a bunch of sub-committes, e.g. LGBT, African-American, Asian-American and Hispanic groups.*"

Three firms stand out for making it into the top ten for two years running: Proskauer, Weil and Debevoise. "*Over the last five years the firm has done a lot to incentivize women to stay,*" a female associate at Proskauer (3rd) told us. This includes introducing a mentoring program, shared parental leave, and reduced work schedules. Debevoise's associates highlighted "*all sorts of initiatives across the firm*" including diversity mentoring and a "*really fantastic*" Women's Resources Group.

"*The diversity initiatives have improved markedly over the past couple of years,*" associates at second-placed Waller told us, hinting at why the firm has gone up to 2nd place this year. Kramer Levin (4th), has historic ties to LGBT causes, and like many in this group, the firm's overall collaborative, empathetic vibe has made diversity initiatives a no-brainer. However, their associates were echoing hundreds of others across the market when they told us that "*there's room for improvement*" on diversity, noting that "*the partnership is heavily white and male.*" For the record, we hear this at every single firm. So even at the most progessive, campaigning, BigLaw firms in this list – all still have a long way to go before they are truly representative and inclusive.

Methodology

We asked associates to rate their firm on its efforts to recruit diverse associates, inclusivity training, diversity mentoring, diverse staffing, promoting of diverse attorneys, and how hard it is to make partner if you start a family. The firms listed are those demonstrating strong performance.

Law firm comparison data

How do you choose the right firm?

The menu of firms to choose between is bewildering. Researching them all would be a waste of time. Increase your prospect of getting a job by choosing the firm that suits you.

Step 1: work out what matters in your life – not what others expect of you
Consider how you respond to stress, work/life balance, how much autonomy you can handle, what subject matter gets you going, how you build and rely on personal relationships, and whether prestige motivates you. Will you become a pillar of your local business community or a jet-setting deal-maker? Do you thrive in disorder or need to control everything? Are you buttoned-up or dress down? Aggressive or collaborative?

Step 2: refine your search
Shortlist cities and regions. Then pick some practice areas you think you'd thrive in – firms will be looking for someone with focus and passion. The practice area reviews in this guide will make sense of your options. The chambers-associate.com search will round down the firms you should look at.

Step 3: read the introductions
Open the Inside View and read the first few paragraphs. Does it sound like your bag? Remember your wish list from Step 1 and have a look at our reviews of the firm culture, in particular. Bookmark all the firms that stand out.

Step 4: compare your shortlist
Use the comparison function on chambers-associate.com to compare your firms on every factor that counts: salary, pro bono, billables, diversity stats, size of firm, Chambers rankings, international offices, maternity allowance…

www.chambers-associate.com

Hours and Compensation Survey

Firm	1st year salary	2nd year salary	Billable hour requirement	Average billable hours per associate	Average pro bono hours	Billable pro bono hours	Total pro bono hours across US offices
Adam Leitman Bailey	No less than $150,000	No less than $150,000	1,600 target	1,163	U	U	U
Akin Gump Strauss Hauer & Feld	$180,000	$190,000	None	U	105	Unlimited	84,388
Allen & Overy	$180,000	$190,000	2,000 target	1,482	51.5	150	8,745
Alston & Bird	$155,000 - $180,000	$160,000 - $190,000	1,950 target	U	63	150	55,778
Arnold & Porter	$180,000	U	2,000 target	U	117	200	101,438
Axinn, Veltrop & Harkrider	$170,000 - $180,000	$175,000 - $190,000	1,800 required	1,350	35.4	100	3,113
Baker Botts	$180,000	U	2,000 target	U	52.2	Unlimited	34,842
Bracewell	$180,000	$190,000	2,000 target	U	U	100	U
Brown Rudnick	$180,000	$190,000	1,950 required	U	36	Unlimited	9,517
Cadwalader, Wickersham & Taft	$180,000	$190,000	2,000 required	1,665	20	200	6,314
Cahill Gordon & Reindel	$180,000	$190,000	None	U	34.8	Unlimited	10,912
Choate Hall & Stewart	$180,000	$190,000	2,000 required	U	27	Unlimited	5,289
Cleary Gottlieb Steen & Hamilton	$180,000	$190,000	None	U	115	Unlimited	84,269
Clifford Chance	$180,000	$190,000	None	U	U	Unlimited	U
Cooley	$180,000	$190,000	1,950 target	1,928	56.5	U	44,486
Cozen O'Connor	$130,000 - $165,000	U	1,600 - 2,000 target	1,679	31	75	21,372
Cravath, Swaine & Moore	$180,000	$190,000	None	U	51	Unlimited	25,838
Crowell & Moring	$180,000	$190,000	2,000 required	1,830	81	Unlimited	45,530
Curtis, Mallet-Prevost, Colt & Mosle	$180,000	$190,000	2,000 target	1,696	38	Unlimited	5,750
Davis Polk & Wardwell	$180,000	$190,000	None	U	62	Unlimited	54,859
Debevoise & Plimpton	$180,000	$190,000	-	U	102	U	51,788
Dechert	$180,000	$190,000	1,950 target	U	104.1	200	63,390
DLA Piper (US)	$160,000 - $180,000	U	2,000 target	1,831	74	U	117,000
Duane Morris	$140,000 - $165,000	U	1,950 required	U	49.2	100	36,797
Dykema Gossett PLLC	$120,000 - $150,000	U	1,950 target	U	U	40	U
Epstein Becker & Green	U	U	1,950 required	1,664	17.1	100	4,657
Finnegan, Henderson, Farabow, Garrett & Dunner	$180,000	$190,000	2,000 target	U	U	100	11,271
Fish & Richardson	$180,000	$190,000	1,900 required	1,848	56	200	20,662

U = undisclosed

Hours and Compensation Survey *continued*

Firm	1st year salary	2nd year salary	Billable hour requirement	Average billable hours per associate	Average pro bono hours	Billable pro bono hours	Total pro bono hours across US offices
Fitzpatrick, Cella, Harper & Scinto	$180,000	U	2,160 target	U	19.2	U	2,219
Foley & Lardner	$140,000 - $180,000	U	1,900 required	1,852	55	100	45,778
Fox Rothschild	$115,000 - $160,000	U	1,850 (1,900 in litigation)	1,733	9.5	50	8,755
Freshfields Bruckhaus Deringer	$180,000	$190,000	None	U	62	Unlimited	12,927
Fried, Frank, Harris, Shriver & Jacobson	$180,000	$190,000	2,000 target	U	68.2	300	33,291
Gibbons	U	$135,000	1,980 target	1,530	81	50	14,960
Gibson, Dunn & Crutcher	$180,000	$190,000	None	U	126	Unlimited	159,093
Goodwin	$180,000	$190,000	1,950 target	U	67	Unlimited	59,453
Goulston & Storrs	$180,000	U	None	1,850	U	Unlimited	14,170
Greenberg Glusker Fields Claman & Machtinger	$160,000	$165,000	1,850 required	1,414	47	Unlimited	1,541
Greenberg Traurig	$110,000 - $180,000	U	None	U	16	100	25,622
Hangley Aronchick Segal Pudlin & Schiller	$135,000	Varies	None	U	U	0	U
Harris, Wiltshire & Grannis	$178,500	$189,500	None	1,493	108	U	3,593
Haynes and Boone	$180,000	$190,000	1,800 - 2,000 target	1,646	25.9	100	13,043
Hogan Lovells	$180,000	$190,000	2,000 target	U	91.1	Unlimited	102,539
Holland & Knight	$180,000	$190,000	1,900 required	U	60	100	72,742
Hughes Hubbard & Reed	$180,000	$190,000	1,950 target	1,900	123.5	200	32,725
Hunton Andrews Kurth	$160,000 - $180,000	U	2,000 target	1,674	63.3	50	41,964
Irell & Manella	$180,000	$190,000	2,000 target	1,897	101	Unlimited	9,590
Jackson Walker	$180,000	U	1,950 required	1,351	20	0	7,671
Jenner & Block	$180,000	U	2,100 target	U	168.4	Unlimited	90,255
Jones Day	$160,000 - $180,000	U	2,000 target	U	U	Unlimited	159,392
K&L Gates	$120,000 - $180,000	U	1,950 target	U	42	Unlimited	49,138
Kasowitz Benson Torres	$180,000	$190,000	2,150 target	U	39.1	Unlimited	11,749
Katten Muchin Rosenman	$155,000 - $180,000	$160,000 - $190,000	2,000 required	U	67.5	100	14,853
King & Spalding	$155,000 - $180,000	U	None	1,920	37.8	100	36,709
Kirkland & Ellis	$180,000	$190,000	None	U	63.7	Unlimited	118,000+
Kramer Levin Naftalis & Frankel	$180,000	$190,000	1,950 target	1,700	85	Unlimited	25,946

U = undisclosed

Hours and Compensation Survey *continued*

Firm	1st year salary	2nd year salary	Billable hour requirement	Average billable hours per associate	Average pro bono hours	Billable pro bono hours	Total pro bono hours across US offices
Latham & Watkins	$180,000	$190,000	1,900 target	U	111	Unlimited	190,536
Linklaters	$180,000	$190,000	None	U	50	Unlimited	5,867
Mayer Brown	$180,000	$190,000	2,000 required	U	66	Unlimited	58,175
McDermott Will & Emery	$180,000	$190,000	2,000 target	U	47.4	100	37,388
Milbank, Tweed, Hadley & McCloy	$180,000	$190,000	None	U	86	Unlimited	44,215
Mintz Levin Cohn Ferris Glovsky and Popeo	$180,000	$190,000	2,000 target	U	30	Unlimited	14,598
Morgan, Lewis & Bockius	$180,000	$190,000	None	U	62	Unlimited	101,871
Morrison & Foerster	$180,000	$190,000	U	U	90	Unlimited	63,266
Munger, Tolles & Olson	$180,000	$190,000	None	U	135.5	Unlimited	25,696
Nelson Mullins Riley & Scarborough	$95,000 - $170,000	U	1,900 required	1,798	52	U	31,536
Norton Rose Fulbright	$180,000	$190,000	1,800 - 1,900 target	U	U	U	U
Nutter McClennen & Fish	$160,000	U	1,900 required	1,610	53	Unlimited	7,490
O'Melveny & Myers	$180,000	$190,000		U	118	Unlimited	72,092
Orrick, Herrington & Sutcliffe	$165,000 - $180,000	$175,000 - $190,000	2,000 target	U	134	Unlimited	93,617
Patterson Belknap Webb & Tyler	$180,000	$190,000	2,100 target	U	139	Unlimited	23,301
Paul Hastings	$180,000	$190,000	2,000 target	U	U	U	U
Paul, Weiss, Rifkind, Wharton & Garrison	$180,000	$190,000	U	U	100	Unlimited	100,563
Perkins Coie	$105,000 - $180,000	$110,000 - $190,000	1,850 - 1,950 required	1,934	60.8	Unlimited	56,717
Pillsbury Winthrop Shaw Pittman	$180,000	$190,000	1,950 target	U	79.4	Unlimited	42,216
Proskauer Rose	$180,000	$190,000	None	U	56.3	Unlimited	46,755
Reed Smith	$130,000 - $180,000	$135,000 - $190,000	1,900 required	1,839	59	120	56,310
Ropes & Gray	$180,000	$190,000	U	U	119	Unlimited	132,385
Schulte Roth & Zabel	$180,000	$190,000	2,000 target	U	36	200	12,289
Seward & Kissel	$180,000	$190,000	2,000 target	1,509	35	Unlimited	6,028
Shearman & Sterling	$180,000	$190,000	None	U	85.5		35,554
Sheppard, Mullin, Richter & Hampton	$180,000	$190,000	1,950 target	1,851	38	Unlimited	28,669
Sidley Austin	$180,000	U	2,000 target	U	66.8	U	119,323
Simpson Thacher & Bartlett	$180,000	$190,000	None	U	63	Unlimited	48,359

U = undisclosed

Hours and Compensation Survey *continued*

Firm	1st year salary	2nd year salary	Billable hour requirement	Average billable hours per associate	Average pro bono hours	Billable pro bono hours	Total pro bono hours across US offices
Skadden, Arps, Slate, Meagher & Flom & Affiliates	$180,000	$190,000	1,800 target	U	136.2	Unlimited	181,644
Snell & Wilmer	$115,000 - $160,000	U	1,800 - 1,950 required	1,688	29	Unlimited	11,870
Squire Patton Boggs	$135,000 - $180,000	U	1,950 required	U	26	100	18,599
Sterne, Kessler, Goldstein & Fox	$165,000 - $180,000	$175,000 - $190,000	1,900 - 2,000 target	1,838	8.6	U	1,120
Stroock & Stroock & Lavan	$180,000	$190,000	2,000 target	U	50.6	200	15,974
Sullivan & Cromwell	$180,000	$190,000	None	U	58	U	37,818
Thompson & Knight	$180,000	$190,000	1,900 - 2,000 target	2,037	26	Unlimited	3,212
Troutman Sanders	$115,000 - $180,000	U	None	U	23	50	15,317
Vedder Price	$180,000	U	2,000 required	U	U	60	U
Venable	$180,000	$190,000	1,900 required	U	43	50	29,833
Vinson & Elkins	$180,000	$190,000	2,000 target	U	35	Unlimited	21,154
Waller	$130,000	U	1,800 required	1,817	16.6	0	3,801
Weil, Gotshal & Manges	$180,000	$190,000	None	U	42	Unlimited	50,913
White & Case	$174,000 - $180,000	$180,000 - $190,000	2,000 target	U	75	200	68,759
Wiley Rein	$180,000	$190,000	1,950 target	1,971	48	50	13,151
Willkie Farr & Gallagher	$180,000	$190,000	None	1672	79	Unlimited	44,634
WilmerHale	$180,000	$190,000	2,000 target	1,833	118.3	Unlimited	109,629
Wilson Sonsini Goodrich & Rosati	$180,000	$190,000	1,950 target	1,950	72	Unlimited	37,593
Winston & Strawn	$180,000	$190,000	2,000 required	U	73.5	100	65,000

U = undisclosed

To sort and rank firms by this data, visit www.chambers-associate.com

Firms by Size

Firm	Partners	Associates	Domestic offices
Adam Leitman Bailey, P.C.	8	17	1
Akin Gump Strauss Hauer & Feld	267	386	11
Allen & Overy	45	128	2
Alston & Bird	345	366	9
Arnold & Porter Kaye Scholer	299	467	9
Axinn, Veltrop & Harkrider	25	40	3
Baker Botts	243	340	7
Bracewell	158	196	8
Brown Rudnick	85	75	6
Cadwalader, Wickersham & Taft	77	172	3
Cahill Gordon & Reindel	66	201	2
Choate Hall & Stewart	63	97	1
Cleary Gottlieb Steen & Hamilton	108	481	2
Clifford Chance	72	201	2
Cooley	300	600	10
Cozen O'Connor	444	169	24
Cravath, Swaine & Moore	84	42	1
Crowell & Moring	188	149	5
Curtis, Mallet-Prevost, Colt & Mosle	52	74	3
Davis Polk & Wardwell	132	688	3
Debevoise & Plimpton	134	417	2
Dechert	209	371	13
DLA Piper (US)	612	543	28
Duane Morris	397	324	21
Dykema Gossett PLLC	276	141	13
Epstein Becker & Green	132	128	14
Finnegan, Henderson, Farabow, Garrett & Dunner	121	134	5
Fish & Richardson	182	162	11
Fitzpatrick, Cella, Harper & Scinto	49	55	3
Foley & Lardner	482	402	21
Fox Rothschild	497	241	21
Freshfields Bruckhaus Deringer	41	157	2
Fried, Frank, Harris, Shriver & Jacobson	122	298	2
Gibbons P.C.	139	61	5
Gibson, Dunn & Crutcher	317	800	10
Goodwin	318	444	6
Goulston & Storrs	121	70	3
Greenberg Glusker Fields Claman & Machtinger	63	29	1
Greenberg Traurig	992	1051	29
Hangley Aronchick Segal Pudlin & Schiller	32	14	4
Harris, Wiltshire & Grannis	37	13	2
Haynes and Boone,	230	311	12
Hogan Lovells	400	525	14

International offices	Revenue 2016 (millions)	Intake size	Number of summers
0	20	2	2
9	1,039.7	53	71
42	1,980	21	22
2	781.8	46	55
4	951.5	56	65
0	U	7	9
7	731.8	56	103
2	278.7	17	39
2	192.2	8	11
2	408	21	35
1	387.6	38	44
0	236.3	15	15
14	U	120	119
30	1,985	28	20
3	1,007	51	61
3	416	12	29
1	U	92	87
2	418.7	20	21
14	155	6	10
7	U	129	175
7	822	75	95
14	978	48	43
67	2,634	34	65
8	466	15	21
0	212	11	20
0	U	9	10
5	309.1	22	32
1	416.8	17	25
0	U	6	9
3	687	53	81
0	449	18	33
25	1,720	18	14
2	634.9	60	71
0	99.4	-	
10	1,642	100	137
4	1032	50	59
0	176	6	7
-	U	3	3
9	1,477	38	34
0	U	1	-
0	U	4	3
3	397.5	26	47
36	2,036	82	102

U = undisclosed

Firms by Size *continued*

Firm	Partners	Associates	Domestic offices
Holland & Knight	628	493	24
Hughes Hubbard & Reed	82	167	7
Hunton Andrews Kurth	387	372	15
Irell & Manella	46	48	2
Jackson Walker	243	99	7
Jenner & Block	227	179	4
Jones Day	656	843	18
K&L Gates	591	474	23
Kasowitz Benson Torres	90	176	9
Katten Muchin Rosenman	393	263	12
King & Spalding	338	317	10
Kirkland & Ellis	838	1,000	8
Kramer Levin Naftalis & Frankel	98	217	2
Latham & Watkins	502	1,087	11
Linklaters	43	147	2
Mayer Brown	401	417	8
McDermott Will & Emery	472	245	10
Milbank, Tweed, Hadley & McCloy	114	356	3
Mintz Levin Cohn Ferris Glovsky and Popeo	239	219	7
Morgan, Lewis & Bockius	633	762	17
Morrison & Foerster	237	404	8
Munger, Tolles & Olson	84	106	3
Nelson Mullins Riley & Scarborough	362	235	18
Norton Rose Fulbright	309	325	11
Nutter McClennen & Fish	79	39	2
O'Melveny & Myers	186	438	7
Orrick, Herrington & Sutcliffe	299	541	12
Patterson Belknap Webb & Tyler	50	105	1
Paul Hastings	232	58	11
Paul, Weiss, Rifkind, Wharton & Garrison	132	612	3
Perkins Coie	513	497	16
Pillsbury Winthrop Shaw Pittman	297	245	14
Proskauer Rose	235	386	8
Reed Smith	448	395	15
Ropes & Gray	235	879	6
Schulte Roth & Zabel	86	250	2
Seward & Kissel	53	92	2
Shearman & Sterling	-	-	5
Sheppard, Mullin, Richter & Hampton	324	281	10
Sidley Austin	577	808	10
Simpson Thacher & Bartlett	155	602	5
Skadden, Arps, Slate, Meagher & Flom & Affiliates	289	900	8
Snell & Wilmer	202	153	8

International offices	Revenue 2016 (millions)	Intake size	Number of summers
3	848.2	21	34
2	322	18	19
5	541	41	50
0	U	14	20
0	249.4	13	27
1	448.7	33	44
25	U	150	214
22	989.9	51	47
0	U	9	13
2	U	23	33
10	1,140	35	60
5	3,165	251	283
1	387	16	15
19	3,064	163	196
27	1,438	22	23
18	1,313	50	44
8	925.5	34	48
0	916.5	79	63
2	400	14	16
13	U	56	87
8	1,062	58	86
0	234.5	22	20
0	406.4	13	48
47	1958	38	83
0	90	7	7
8	738	44	80
13	929	51	64
0	192.7	2	-
11	1,118.1	59	157
5	1,301.8	101	148
3	786	42	62
7	589.5	37	33
5	890.3	74	63
12	1,119	46	59
5	U	135	175
1	424	38	41
0	U	11	11
16	917	58	56
5	671.1	30	30
10	2,036	155	168
6	1,375.7	105	108
14	U	187	203
1	U	21	20

U = undisclosed

Firms by Size *continued*

Firm	Partners	Associates	Domestic offices
Squire Patton Boggs	262	244	18
Sterne, Kessler, Goldstein & Fox P.L.L.C.	54	63	1
Stroock & Stroock & Lavan	75	172	4
Sullivan & Cromwell	137	476	4
Thompson & Knight	148	79	6
Troutman Sanders	295	267	13
Vedder Price	160	126	5
Venable	306	272	9
Vinson & Elkins	201	340	8
Waller	133	104	5
Weil, Gotshal & Manges	181	538	8
White & Case	186	477	7
Wiley Rein	113	57	1
Willkie Farr & Gallagher	167	476	3
WilmerHale	249	538	7
Wilson Sonsini Goodrich & Rosati	204	438	11
Winston & Strawn	398	428	9

International offices	Revenue 2016 (millions)	Intake size	Number of summers
29	1000	15	30
0	U	4	6
0	251	13	17
9	U	79	152
4	212	7	11
2	509	27	56
2	252	12	13
0	540.5	32	43
8	727.5	68	113
0	U	7	17
9	1390	102	136
43	1,800	108	119
0	U	8	12
6	772	52	55
5	1,137	75	92
4	797	53	48
7	978.5	58	83

U = undisclosed

Law firm comparison data

To rank law firms on all the above data and more, head to the 'Law firms A-Z' list on chambers-associate.com

Work/life and Benefits Survey

Firm	Vacation	Paid parental: primary caregiver	Paid parental: secondary caregiver
Adam Leitman Bailey	3 weeks minimum	12 weeks	U
Akin Gump Strauss Hauer & Feld	4 weeks	18 weeks	10 weeks maximum
Allen & Overy	20 days	18 weeks	4 weeks
Alston & Bird	Flexible	18 weeks	4 weeks
Arnold & Porter Kaye Scholer	Unlimited	18 weeks	6 weeks
Axinn, Veltrop & Harkrider	4 weeks	20 weeks	4 weeks
Baker Botts	3 weeks	18 weeks	4 weeks
Bracewell	Unlimited	18 weeks	2 weeks
Brown Rudnick	4 weeks	18 weeks	4 weeks
Cadwalader, Wickersham & Taft	Unlimited	18 weeks	4 weeks
Cahill Gordon & Reindel	4 weeks	18 weeks	4 weeks
Choate Hall & Stewart	4 weeks	18 weeks	4 weeks
Cleary Gottlieb Steen & Hamilton	4 weeks	18 weeks	5 weeks
Clifford Chance	4 weeks	18 weeks	8 weeks maximum
Cooley	4 weeks	20 weeks	10 weeks
Cozen O'Connor	Unlimited	18 weeks	10 weeks
Cravath, Swaine & Moore	4 weeks	20 weeks maximum	4 weeks
Crowell & Moring	Unlimited	18 weeks	4 weeks
Curtis, Mallet-Prevost, Colt & Mosle	4 weeks	12 weeks	2 weeks
Davis Polk & Wardwell	4 weeks minimum	18 weeks maximum	10 weeks maximum
Debevoise & Plimpton	4 weeks	18 weeks	4 weeks
Dechert	4 weeks	18 weeks	4 weeks
DLA Piper	Discretionary	18 weeks	4 weeks
Duane Morris	4 weeks	16 weeks	4 weeks
Dykema Gossett	Unlimited	12 weeks	6 weeks
Epstein Becker & Green	4 weeks	12 weeks	12 weeks
Finnegan, Henderson, Farabow, Garrett & Dunner	Unlimited	18 weeks	12 weeks
Fish & Richardson	Unlimited	16 weeks	8 weeks
Fitzpatrick, Cella, Harper & Scinto	4 weeks	12 weeks	2 weeks
Foley & Lardner	Discretionary	18 weeks	4 weeks minimum
Fox Rothschild	Flexible	20 weeks	8 weeks
Freshfields Bruckhaus Deringer	20 days	12 weeks	4 weeks
Fried, Frank, Harris, Shriver & Jacobson	4 weeks	18 weeks	10 weeks
Gibbons	3 weeks	12 weeks	12 weeks
Gibson, Dunn & Crutcher	Unlimited	18 weeks	10 weeks
Goodwin	4 weeks	18 weeks	4 weeks
Goulston & Storrs	4 weeks	12 weeks	3 weeks
Greenberg Glusker Fields Claman & Machtinger	U	U	U
Greenberg Traurig	Discretionary	18 weeks	Discretionary
Hangley Aronchick Segal Pudlin & Schiller	4 weeks	Yes U undefined	4 weeks
Harris, Wiltshire & Grannis	Unlimited	17 weeks	3 weeks

Adoption/surrogacy fees	Flexible work arrangements	Retirement plan	Medical and dental plans
U	Yes, case by case	401K	Yes, contributory
Yes	Yes	401K	Yes, contributory
No	Yes	401K	Yes
Yes, up to $10,000	Yes	401K	Yes
Yes	Yes	401K	Yes, both
No	Yes, case by case	401K	Yes, contributory
No	U	401K	Yes, contributory
No	Yes	401K	Yes
Yes	Yes	401K	Yes
No	Yes, case by case	401K	Yes, contributory
No	Yes	401K	Yes, both
No	U	401K; Roth 401K	Yes, contributory
No	Yes	Tax Opportunity Plan for Saving	Yes
No	Yes	401K	Yes
No	Yes	401K	Yes
No	Yes	401K	Yes, both
No	Yes	401K	Yes
No	Yes	401K	Yes
No	Yes, case by case	401K; Defined Benefit Pension Plan	Yes, contributory
Yes	Yes	401K	Yes, contributory
No	Yes	Yes U for partners and counsel	Yes
No	Yes	401K	Yes, contributory
No	Yes	401K	Yes
No	Yes	401K	Yes, contributory (varies by office)
No	Yes	401K	Yes, both
No	Yes	401K	Yes
No	Yes	401K	Yes
No	Yes	401K	Yes
No	Yes	401K	Yes, both
Yes, up to $5,000	Yes	401K	Yes
No	Yes	401K	Yes
No	Yes	401K	Yes, both
Yes, up to $15,000	Yes	401K	Yes
No	Yes	401K	Yes, contributory
No	Yes	401K	Yes
Yes, up to $5,000	Yes	401K	Yes
No	Yes	401K	Yes
U	U	U	U
No	Yes	401K	Yes
No	Yes	401K	Yes, both
No	Yes	401K	Yes

U = undisclosed

Work/life and Benefits Survey *continued*

Firm	Vacation	Paid parental: primary caregiver	Paid parental: secondary caregiver
Haynes and Boone	10 days minimum	12 weeks	4 weeks
Hogan Lovells	Unlimited	20 weeks	12 weeks maximum
Holland & Knight	4 weeks	16 weeks	6 weeks
Hughes Hubbard & Reed	4 weeks	18 weeks	4 weeks
Hunton Andrews Kurth	4 weeks	18 weeks	18 weeks
Irell & Manella	Unlimited	18 weeks	4 weeks
Jackson Walker	Unlimited	12 weeks	U
Jenner & Block	3 weeks	18 weeks	12 weeks maximum
Jones Day	4 weeks	18 weeks	10 weeks maximum
K&L Gates	3 weeks minimum	18 weeks	12 weeks
Kasowitz Benson Torres	4 weeks	18 weeks	4 weeks
Katten Muchin Rosenman	Unlimited	20 weeks	4 weeks
King & Spalding	4 weeks	18 weeks	6 weeks
Kirkland & Ellis	Unlimited	18 weeks	10 weeks
Kramer Levin Naftalis & Frankel	4 weeks	20 weeks	4 weeks
Latham & Watkins	Unlimited	22 weeks	4 weeks
Linklaters	22 days	18 weeks	4 weeks
Mayer Brown	Unlimited	20 weeks maximum	6 weeks
McDermott Will & Emery	Unlimited	18 weeks	4 weeks
Milbank, Tweed, Hadley & McCloy	4 weeks	18 weeks	10 weeks maximum
Mintz Levin Cohn Ferris Glovsky and Popeo	Flexible	18 weeks	8 weeks
Morgan, Lewis & Bockius	4 weeks	18 weeks	18 weeks maximum
Morrison & Foerster	4 weeks	20 weeks	6 weeks
Munger, Tolles & Olson	Unlimited	18 weeks	6 weeks
Nelson Mullins Riley & Scarborough	Unlimited	12 weeks	2 weeks
Norton Rose Fulbright	4 weeks	18 weeks	18 weeks
Nutter McClennen & Fish	4 weeks	12 weeks minimum	12 weeks minimum
O'Melveny & Myers	3 weeks minimum	18 weeks	4 weeks
Orrick, Herrington & Sutcliffe	Unlimited	22 weeks	3 weeks minimum
Patterson Belknap Webb & Tyler	4 weeks	18 weeks	4 weeks
Paul Hastings	4 weeks	18 weeks	10 weeks
Paul, Weiss, Rifkind, Wharton & Garrison	4 weeks	18 weeks	4 weeks
Perkins Coie	Unlimited	26 weeks maximum	4 weeks minimum
Pillsbury Winthrop Shaw Pittman	4 weeks	20 weeks maximum	12 weeks maximum
Proskauer Rose	4 weeks	18 weeks	4 weeks
Reed Smith	4 weeks	16 weeks	10 weeks
Ropes & Gray	4 weeks	10 weeks	8 weeks
Schulte Roth & Zabel	5 weeks	18 weeks	4 weeks
Seward & Kissel	4 weeks	12 weeks	2 weeks
Shearman & Sterling	4 weeks	20 weeks	8 weeks
Sheppard, Mullin, Richter & Hampton	Unlimited	18 weeks	4 weeks
Sidley Austin	U	U	U

Adoption/surrogacy fees	Flexible work arrangements	Retirement plan	Medical and dental plans
No	Yes	401K	Yes
Yes	Yes	401K	Yes
No	Yes	401K	Yes
No	Yes	401K	Yes, contributory
Yes, up to $5,000	Yes	401K	Yes, both; medical contributory
No	Yes, case by case	401K	Yes, contributory
Yes	Yes, case by case	401K	Yes, both
N/A	Yes	401K	Yes, contributory
No	Yes	401K	Yes, contributory
No	Yes	401K	Yes
No	Yes	401K	Yes
No	Yes	401K	Yes
No	Yes	Yes	Yes
No	Yes	401K	Yes, contributory
No	Yes	401K	Yes
Yes	Yes	401K	Yes
No	Yes	401K	Yes
No	Yes	Yes	Yes
No	Yes	401K	Yes
No	Yes	401K	Yes
No	Yes	401K	Yes, contributory
No	Yes	401K	Yes
No	Yes	401K	Yes, contributory
No	Yes	Yes	Yes, both
No	Yes	401K; Roth 401K	Yes, both
Yes	Yes	401K	Yes
No	Yes	401K; Roth 401K	Yes
No	Yes	401K	Yes
No	Yes	401K; IRA	Yes, both
No	Yes	401K	Yes
No	U	401K	Yes, contributory
Yes	Yes	401K	Yes, both
Yes	Yes	401K	Yes
No	Yes	401K	Yes, contributory
Yes, up to $5,000	Yes	401K	Yes
No	Yes	Yes	Yes
Yes, up to $5,000	Yes	401K	Yes
No	Yes	Yes	Yes
No	Yes, case by case	401K	Yes, both
No	Yes	401K	Yes, contributory
Yes, $25,000	Yes, case by case	401K	Yes, contributory
U	U	U	U

U = undisclosed

Work/life and Benefits Survey *continued*

Firm	Vacation	Paid parental: primary caregiver	Paid parental: secondary caregiver
Simpson Thacher & Bartlett	4 weeks	18 weeks	4 weeks
Skadden, Arps, Slate, Meagher & Flom & Affiliates	4 weeks	18 weeks	12 weeks maximum
Snell & Wilmer	Unlimited	12 weeks	12 weeks
Squire Patton Boggs	6 weeks	18 weeks	3 weeks
Sterne, Kessler, Goldstein & Fox P.L.L.C.	Case by case	12 weeks maximum	2 weeks maximum
Stroock & Stroock & Lavan	4 weeks	18 weeks	4 weeks
Sullivan & Cromwell	4 weeks	18 weeks	4 weeks
Thompson & Knight	Unlimited	18 weeks	4 weeks
Troutman Sanders	Discretionary	18 weeks	4 weeks
Vedder Price	4 weeks	16 weeks	8 weeks maximum
Venable	4 weeks	18 weeks	4 weeks
Vinson & Elkins	15 days	18 weeks minimum	4 weeks minimum
Waller	2 weeks minimum	12 weeks	12 weeks
Weil, Gotshal & Manges	4 weeks	18 weeks	10 weeks
White & Case	Unlimited	22 weeks maximum	12 weeks
Wiley Rein	4 weeks	18 weeks	4 weeks
Willkie Farr & Gallagher	4 weeks	18 weeks	4 weeks
WilmerHale	4 weeks	18 weeks	4 weeks
Wilson Sonsini Goodrich & Rosati	4 weeks maximum	20 weeks	12 weeks
Winston & Strawn	Unlimited	20 weeks	20 weeks

Adoption/surrogacy fees	Flexible work arrangements	Retirement plan	Medical and dental plans
No	Yes	Yes	Yes
No	Yes	401K	Yes, contributory
No	Yes	401K	Yes
No	Yes	401K	Yes
No	Yes	401K	Yes, contributory
No	Yes	401K	Yes
Yes, up to $7,500	Yes	401K	Yes
No	Yes	401K	Yes
U	Yes	401K	Yes
No	Yes	401K	Yes, contributory
No	Yes	Yes	Yes
No	Yes	401K	Yes, contributory
No	Yes	401K	Yes, both
No	Yes	401K	Yes
Yes	Yes	401K	Yes
No	Yes	401K	Yes
No	Yes, case by case	401K	Yes, both
No	Yes	401K	Yes
No	Yes	401K	Yes, both
No	Yes	401K	Yes, both

U = undisclosed

Diversity

Firm	% female partners	% female associates	% ethnic minority partners	% ethnic minority associates	% LGBT partners	% LGBT associates
Adam Leitman Bailey	22	40		21	13	U
Akin Gump Strauss Hauer & Feld	20	43	12.2	20.3	2.2	2.8
Allen & Overy	18.2	44.1	9.1	27.9	11.4	4.4
Alston & Bird	23.2	43.3	7.8	27	3	4.6
Arnold & Porter	21.4	51.4	11.7	25	3.3	4.9
Axinn, Veltrop & Harkrider	16	35	4	35	8	8
Baker Botts	20	43	12	26	3	4
Bracewell	22	44.4	8.3	15.8		
Brown Rudnick	18	45	10	22	0	1
Cadwalader, Wickersham & Taft	21	40	11	25	5	4
Cahill Gordon & Reindel	21	42	11	19	6	5
Choate Hall & Stewart	21	49	7	16	6	3
Cleary Gottlieb Steen & Hamilton	19	49	12	34	5	6
Clifford Chance	13	44	15	37	1	2
Cooley	23	53	14	24	2	3
Cozen O'Connor	23	47	6	19	1	3
Cravath, Swaine & Moore	22	39	6	27	4	5
Crowell & Moring	23.3	54	12.2	38.8	3.2	4.6
Curtis, Mallet-Prevost, Colt & Mosle	13	36	21	25	4	3
Davis Polk & Wardwell	20	45	10	31	3	6
Debevoise & Plimpton	21.9	53.6	13.3	35.7	3.8	6.7
Dechert	16	45.4	10.2	26.3	2.9	3.2
DLA Piper (US)	21.7	43.5	16.5	24.9	1.1	1.8
Duane Morris	22.4	39	11	18.1	0.8	1.1
Dykema Gossett PLLC	24	52	10	28	1	1
Epstein Becker & Green PC	30	59	12	21	2	2
Finnegan, Henderson, Farabow, Garrett & Dunner	28	38	15	32	2	2
Fish & Richardson PC	20.3	33.3	13.2	30.9	1.6	4.9
Fitzpatrick, Cella, Harper & Scinto	14	47	8	31	1	1
Foley & Lardner	22.4	43.2	10	21.6	1	5.1
Fox Rothschild	28.5	50.6	7.2	16.2	0.4	3.3
Freshfields Bruckhaus Deringer	22.5	54	7.5	25		3
Fried, Frank, Harris, Shriver & Jacobson	15	42	4	27	1.6	5.4
Gibbons	22	43	6	14	2	8
Gibson, Dunn & Crutcher	20.2	43.7	10.4	22.2	2.2	6.7
Goodwin	22	47	8	25	3	4
Goulston & Storrs	22	57	1	25	3	4
Greenberg Glusker Fields Claman & Machtinger	22	43	10	10	U	U

Firm	% female partners	% female associates	% ethnic minority partners	% ethnic minority associates	% LGBT partners	% LGBT associates
Greenberg Traurig, PA	22.5	47	13.3	22.6	U	U
Hangley Aronchick Segal Pudlin & Schiller	31	50	U	U	U	U
Harris, Wiltshire & Grannis	23	64	17	43	10	7
Haynes and Boone	23	41	11	29	2	3
Hogan Lovells	30	51	15	30	3	5.3
Holland & Knight	23	53	12.8	28.4	2.7	1.8
Hughes Hubbard & Reed	21	51	10	34	2	5
Hunton Andrews Kurth	19.6	50	10.7	18.3	0.7	1.3
Irell & Manella	9	42	16	17	2	2
Jackson Walker	22.4	44.3	11	27.8	U	U
Jenner & Block	29.8	45	8.3	26.5	5	12
Jones Day	25	49	11	19	U	U
K&L Gates	24	43	12	19	2	4
Kasowitz Benson Torres	23.1	43.3	15.4	22.5	1.1	4.2
Katten Muchin Rosenman	24.3	47	17.7	21.1	2.1	5.1
King & Spalding	22.5	47.8	8.3	18.2	1.2	3.0
Kirkland & Ellis	24.6	30	13.1	24	2.3	4.5
Kramer Levin Naftalis & Frankel	15.3	38.6	8.2	25.7	3.1	2.3
Latham & Watkins	22.8	43	9.8	26.6	3	5.2
Linklaters	17.1	45.2	14.6	42.2	7.3	4.4
Mayer Brown	20.3	41.4	10.8	31	2.2	3.7
McDermott Will & Emery	32	49	13	23	3	2
Milbank, Tweed, Hadley & McCloy	14	42.3	12.3	25.5	2.6	3.6
Mintz Levin Cohn Ferris Glovsky and Popeo PC	24.5	48	8.8	22.3	3.3	2.5
Morgan, Lewis & Bockius	23.6	50.3	9	27	2.7	4.8
Morrison & Foerster	23.1	45.9	15.8	37.8	3.4	6.1
Munger, Tolles & Olson	24	45	18	30	2	9
Nelson Mullins Riley & Scarborough	22	44	6	22	1	2
Norton Rose Fulbright	21	47	8	30	1.5	1
Nutter McClennen & Fish	25	59	3	30	1	2.5
O'Melveny & Myers	20.5	48.1	11.1	27.4	3.2	5.6
Orrick, Herrington & Sutcliffe	22.5	47.7	21.8	42.3	2.7	5.1
Patterson Belknap Webb & Tyler	18	43	10	24	12	8.6
Paul Hastings	22	43	22	35	3	3
Paul, Weiss, Rifkind, Wharton & Garrison	21	40	13	22	6	6
Perkins Coie	24.8	48.7	12.1	28.8	2.5	3.9
Pillsbury Winthrop Shaw Pittman	23.5	46.7	11.6	30	3.6	3.9
Proskauer Rose	17	48	8	25.7	1.8	3.3

U = undisclosed

Diversity *continued*

Firm	% female partners	% female associates	% ethnic minority partners	% ethnic minority associates	% LGBT partners	% LGBT associates
Reed Smith	23.3	48.7	12	22.1	2.2	3
Ropes & Gray	24.7	48.5	14.6	28	2.1	5.4
Schulte Roth & Zabel	12	42	11	27	2	4
Seward & Kissel	11	43	92	82	0	1
Shearman & Sterling	17	39.2	25	40.8	0.9	5.3
Sheppard, Mullin, Richter & Hampton	19.6	49.4	12.5	30.5	2.5	3.1
Sidley Austin	25.3	45.8	11.6	30.6	U	U
Simpson Thacher & Bartlett	20	43	11	30	3	5
Skadden, Arps, Slate, Meagher & Flom & Affiliates	22.4	47	8.4	28.8	1.7	4.7
Snell & Wilmer	16.3	42	8	15	1	1.8
Squire Patton Boggs	23	51.6	16	19.7		
Sterne, Kessler, Goldstein & Fox	25.5	27.1	21.8	27.1	1.8	4.3
Stroock & Stroock & Lavan	19	42	9	22	1	2
Sullivan & Cromwell	21	40	10	23	7	7
Thompson & Knight	25	45	8	13	1	3
Troutman Sanders	19.6	50.9	11.5	26.6	1.7	4.9
Vedder Price	18	45	8	24	2	2
Venable	U	U	U	U	U	U
Vinson & Elkins	15	38	9	23	2	4
Waller	18	13	95	85	U	U
Weil, Gotshal & Manges	24	49	11	26	2	4
White & Case	19	50	21	38	2	5
Wiley Rein	27	54	12	26	2	4
Willkie Farr & Gallagher	15	43	8.2	22	3.4	3.7
WilmerHale	25.4	49.6	12.5	25.3	1.2	6.1
Wilson Sonsini Goodrich & Rosati	23.7	42.4	20.2	32.6	1	3
Winston & Strawn	22.5	44	10	26	1.2	3.5

U = undisclosed

Joining the law review

Law firms take law review work very seriously. We spoke to some keen reviewers to learn how to proceed.

When we spoke to **Jim Leipold**, director of **NALP**, he offered up this pearl of wisdom: "*Law firms still hire in very traditional and some would say ancient ways.*" When it comes down to it, "*it's still a credential and prestige-driven market. Despite all the thinking law firms do around hiring, most often it still depends on what school you went to, your GPA and whether you were on the journal. Those credentials are the given.*" In this article, we're going to look at one of the three in particular: participating in your law school's law journal.

We've interviewed current members of some law reviews to get an insight into the experience, to find out whether it's for you, and we've compiled interviews with hiring partners at top BigLaw firms to understand how much of a difference it really makes in getting hired, and why.

What is law review?

Excuse us while we cover the basics: a law journal and a law review are essentially the same thing. The organisations have different names, but whatever they call it, a law review is an academic journal staffed by students of a law school (though it is independent of the law school). Faculties may provide assistance, but students are in control, and do the leg work. Where academic journals within other disciplines institute a strict system of peer review by other academics, in this case it's the students who take charge of both the day-to-day running and publishing of the journal, and the editing of the pieces featured within each release.

Law reviews publish a number of issues each year – ranging from as low as four, to as high as eight – which form one complete volume. Many have some serious vintage; the oldest, The University of Pennsylvania Law Review (originally the American Law Register), was founded in 1852. Traditionally, these publications took a physical form, and that's still largely true – but most can also be seen online, with their archives available for free. Some, with the advent of technology, have expanded their output to include blog posts and other additional content.

The vast majority of law schools have one (we couldn't find one that didn't!), and in fact, many universities have a good number. The usual structure consists of one main law review/journal with a broad focus, and then a number of more specific publications. For example, Columbia Law School has its titular Columbia Law Review, and then 13 more journals, including the Columbia Journal of Tax Law, The American Review of International Arbitration, Columbia Human Rights Law Review and Columbia Business Law Review.

However, when people talk about law review, the shorthand usually refers to the flag-bearing, general review. It's often the oldest organisation, and typically bears the most prestige. Gaining membership of this journal, with its attached prestige, is held in high regard throughout the discipline, from private practice to public interest.

These reviews cover every branch of law, but they usually consider where the law could go in the future. It's all about examining the law as it is, what isn't working, and what should be done to solve problems with the judicial system, or, more widely, problems which afflict society or the economy. As such, the material can make fascinating reading. For example, a recent article in the Iowa Law Review was titled: "*Looks Can Kill: The Dark Side of Indoor Tanning and What States Need to do to Help Protect Young Adults from This Deadly 'Glow.'*"

Articles are written by legal academics, professors, judges or practicing lawyers, with a dizzying array of experience and expertise. Harvard Law Review even managed to snag Obama to write a "*commentary*" in 2017 entitled "*The President's Role in Advancing Criminal Justice Reform.*" That's an unusual occurrence, but it demonstrates the weight and respect reviews can command. They are a mainstay of US legal academia. Articles have been cited in the Supreme Court, used to influence and sculpt legislation, and the past members of the most prominent reviews read like a who's who of legal superstars.

Crucially, students also write content, called 'notes,' which sit alongside the 'articles' written by prestigious legal scholars. It's a key part of the appeal for students, but they're hefty projects. Students have to put in serious work to have even a chance of theirs being published.

Why should you care?

Why should you, a time-pressed, frazzled, finger-in-every-conceivable-pie student, get involved in this review carry-on? Simply put, it could get you a job. Take a look at our hiring partner interviews, which we conduct with firms as part of our annual research. An impressive amount explicitly mention law review as something they'd value.

When asked, 'what kind of extracurricular activities does the firm appreciate?' One hiring partner replied: "*The obvious one with respect to law school is doing law review. Either associates being honored with it, or seeking that out and displaying the aptitude at writing which we think is important. Part of our job is to write well.*"

> *"One of the great things about law review is how universal it is. People across generations, across schools, all know what it means and can relate."*

To hiring partners, it's a credential which speaks volumes. Writing skill, editing skill, critical thinking, attention to detail, gumption, commitment, time management, coordination with others and legal knowledge (especially thinking about how the law might change) – all of these and more could be feasibly attained, and proved, through the experience of being on a journal.

Law reviews have long been magnets for the keen, the talented and the career driven. That means a huge number of successful lawyers participated in their law review – successful lawyers who might be sat on the other side of the interview table. As **Shirin Baradaran**, an editorial board member of the **Virginia Law Review**, puts it: "*One of the great things about law review is how universal it is. People across generations, across schools, all know what it means and can relate. People will ask you what you are writing your note about in interviews. It's a unifying experience that can create a bond in the interview room or once you're working there.*" With OCIs being aimed at students beginning their 2L year, students will just be starting out on the review (you normally begin membership as a 2L, having been selected at the end of your 1L year). However, they will have far more to talk about in callbacks, and even more to talk about when they summer at firms.

It is not unusual to hear of law firms contacting students when they make it onto the review, trying to bag the best talent. It might just be a congratulatory email, but the message is clear: they want you to keep them in mind, and they're letting you know that they're interested, purely as a result of your law review membership. Membership can also aid in gaining a clerkship, another step in the right direction.

Having said all of this, it's important to point out that law review is probably not for everyone. In fact, it categorically isn't; there are only a limited amount of places. So it's just another thing you must weigh up. In addition, while it brings advantages, it is not the only way to demonstrate the aforementioned qualities. Though we have

heard it said that certain firms won't bother with you unless you've made it onto law review (it's not something spoken of widely), we know scores of firms who do not use membership of the law review as a strict cut-off.

How can you get involved?

If you're considering review, it's worth looking at the selection process. Taking place towards the end of the 1L year, the process for gaining membership varies between reviews, but typically relies on two things: your 1L grades, and a writing competition (sometimes referred to as 'writing-on'). Some also offer membership later on to those who have submitted a note worthy of publishing.

Different law reviews weigh these differently. You can gain membership purely because of your grades, or simply because you aced the writing competition. There's normally a number of different ways of achieving membership, but some ask that you take part in the writing competition to express interest. A personal statement may also be required.

Achieving good grades is clear enough, get in the top echelon of your class and you'll be in with a chance (reviews are very vague about numbers). But what does this writing competition consist of? Again, there is variation between reviews, but **Patrick Bradley**, editor-in-chief of the **Duke Law Journal**, tells us: "*It's a casenote. You have to produce an essay about a recently published court of appeals judgment. This year it was a recent Fourth Circuit Court of Appeals decision which implicated various criminal procedure issues, but it changes every year for fairness. You can choose any aspect of it and write an analytical paper on it of about 14 pages. You have two weeks to write the paper.*" So it's no small feat. "*It requires a first level of research just to get to know the substantive law, but it's open-source in terms of what students can consider, in part to test students' research ability.*" Being so open, Patrick tells us that "*it's interesting to see the broad range of what people write. It's freeing. You can be creative but you have to be confident in your approach.*" Though students' work is assessed and graded by members of the law review, the process is anonymous.

> *"You can take something that is really good, make suggestions that help the author, and add in a little more coherence that makes the argument more persuasive."*

It works a little differently at the Virginia Law Review, according to Shirin. Their writing competition "*is made up of two parts. The first is a test of reviewing and updating blue-booking.*" Bluebooking, in case you wondered, is a style guide for legal citation. It's the gospel for law reviews.

"*You're provided with a legal article which has mistakes in it, and you're tasked with identifying mistakes,*" she continues. "*For the second part you're given a closed book of sources and you're asked to write a critical piece about them. If I remember correctly, mine was on the free speech rights of students in schools. That part of the process is trying to focus on your critical thinking and writing ability, as well as how you interact with academic material.*" Students must complete both over the course of a weekend.

The process is always fairly demanding, and for those aiming to partake, Patrick gives a word of advice. "*For students who are participating, the writing contest will immediately follow spring finals. Students should keep that in mind as they are studying – carrying through the most busy time of the year, they should keep some energy in reserve.*"

What do you actually do on law review?
Congratulations. You've made it onto the journal. Now what? A large part of the role of editors in their first year revolves around citation checking. It's an essential component of the editing process, but it can be repetitive. Read around online and the task gets plenty of flack, but it's undoubtedly good preparation for the meticulous approach lawyers have to take throughout their careers.

Fortunately there's more to the experience. People often look to gain more seniority as a 3L. There are myriad positions to be elected to, which normally provide added responsibility and variety. "*I'm an editorial board member,*" says Shirin. "*I get assigned part of a paper that we are going to publish: I make edits, read through the entire paper, making sure it all makes sense. Then I'll make suggestions, both technically and grammatically.*" Doing this, Shirin says,"*made me a stronger writer, but more so a better reviewer of writing, seeing and spotting logical fallacies.*"

As you'd expect, Patrick, being editor-in-chief, as well as the third years who fill other executive board positions, have a little more control. They'll select pieces to go into the issue as well as making substantial edits. "*By the end of going through the editorial process I will have read each piece three or four times. You can take something that is re-*

ally good, make suggestions that help the author, and add in a little more coherence that makes the argument more persuasive."

Hearing this, the question of time commitment looms. How does being on a journal impact students' ability to focus on their law school work? Shirin described her workload: "*I end up doing about six pieces per academic year. I'm therefore working on each piece, one at a time, for about two months, but only two weeks of that are really focused, where I'm doing it heavily. Each piece may take up to 40 hours of work on my end.*"

Senior roles will be more demanding. "*I think you have to prioritise,*" says Shirin. "*You have to make it something that is almost on an equal footing with your school work. Sometimes you may wish you could be doing something else with your time, but you do find enjoyment from the tasks themselves and the academic material. It can be a break – something beyond reading for class.*"

Patrick also weighed it up. "*It adds another ball that you have to juggle going from first to second year, and then you're adding another by taking a board position that can be time consuming. But it's what we are all getting into in terms of our career path. It can be useful, it can be overwhelming. But I like to think that although some of the work is very tedious, it also involves thinking critically about ways to improve articles. Even if the article's not directly about a topic you take in an exam, it is still helpful.*"

So serving on the journal might in fact aid your studies? Shirin adds a word of caution. "*When it comes to school work it's less helpful. This is cutting edge stuff rather than black letter law. There's a disconnect there, but you're still going beyond what you learn in the classroom.*"

The last thing to discuss are notes. On many journals it is compulsory for students to write and submit a note, though not all get published. They must, however, all meet the required standard. Notes are usually more than 30 pages long, and are written with the mentorship of a law professor. "*It's a great opportunity to get to know other professors and to continue getting feedback once you have finished your legal research and writing class,*" says Shirin. "*It's one of the biggest perks. I know a lot of people have worked really hard to get theirs published, and to see it in print was their crowning achievement of law school.*"

Law review provides a chance to hone important skills, and while it involves plenty of work, it serves as an excellent way to boost your recruitment hopes.

Becoming a Lawyer

The trends in legal recruiting

We caught up with James Leipold, executive director of NALP, to learn about the state of recruitment in law.

Chambers Associate: Last year we discussed a 'leveling off' in legal recruitment – has this trend continued in 2018?

James Leipold: I'd say we've seen the trend continue for another year, although I don't want to overstate it as BigLaw's still a robust market. It's not where it was before the recession – we're still about 1,000 summer associate positions shy of peak volume – but in intensity and competition it's close. This year 43% of large law firms said they made fewer offers for summer positions and last year 50% said they made fewer offers. That's the first time since the recession we have had large numbers of firms saying they were making fewer offers. Again, I don't want to overstate this but it does demonstrate that the growth in summer programs has tapered. New York and Silicon Valley were the markets that led the recovery in many ways, and we've seen those two markets slow down a little bit in particular. The fact that they've built back the fastest and have now peaked contributes to this leveling out. In terms of offer rates, we have also seen that the offer rate following callback interviews has tapered off over the last two years and that curve is beginning to head in the other direction. At the largest law firms the median number of offers extended to 2Ls had been 30 before the recession and fell to just 8 in 2008. In 2015/16 it was back to 20, but during this last cycle it dipped back down to 16. We also ask law firms if they've been recruiting 3Ls, and the percentage that said they did so has also come down over the last two years.

CA: How is artificial intelligence affecting the legal profession?

JL: I think we are seeing adoption most quickly in large in-house departments. Law firms are also trying to figure out of to create value and efficiencies with this rapidly evolving technology. Using it for document review is now standard in the industry even for law firms, and in-house departments are using AI for contract management, E-billing and E-signature. And Blockchain is rapidly becoming part of the landscape. Individual law firms are having a hard time balancing the development costs of implementing AI and finding the right return when it comes to creating efficiencies. Law firms are trying to figure out when they need to become technology providers for their corporate clients and when they should be buyers of technology, so you see firms taking different tacks.

CA: How has the Trump administration affected the legal market and profession so far?

JL: I would prefer not to comment specifically on the Trump administration. It's hard to know what the real impact is. We have seen an increase in law school applications after a seven year slide, and that's important, and we've seen the applications go up disproportionately among the highest LSAT bands, which is encouraging. There are people in the industry who attribute that to a 'Trump bump' in light of current affairs, and I don't doubt that's a part of it but we don't have any data to prove that. Law school application volume over time is a series of peaks and valleys and there had to be an upturn somewhere, and the job market for law school graduates has improved considerably since the recession. In terms of the business climate, somewhat counter-intuitively, the market has been strong despite all of the political uncertainty. The current administration has been deregulating and the tax law changes have been very favorable for businesses so we have seen a very healthy marketplace. Certainly it was a very profitable year for many large law firms despite the political climate.

CA: Last year we asked about diversity in BigLaw, and from looking at the stats we haven't seen a major improvement. What's behind this?

JL: There are two reasons behind this. Law firms continue to make modest gains, but they are so modest that you and I will be long dead before we reach parity with women or ethnic minorities. Pay and equity issues have risen in importance in light of the #MeToo movement, the Weinstein scandal and the Hollywood pay gap. The news about the UK requiring companies to report their pay gap has been widely publicized in the US and that's shone a light on the issue. We continue to see women of color being the most underrepresented demographic, and most of the recent diversity gains among associates can be attributed to a rise in the number of Asian associates. In aggregate, however, Asian associates convert to partnership at the lowest rate, in part because they tend to move in-house or into other private sector work. African Americans are actually less well-represented among associates than before the recession. That's where we are at this point. We could deconstruct all of the societal inequities and talk about how the pipeline shows leaks before children even reach elementary school, and we disproportionately lose Latino and African Americans at every stage of the pipeline by failing them at school. Law firms are actually very good at recruiting when it comes to diversity. The percentage of summer associate classes that's diverse exceeds that of the graduating class, so they are recruiting well. The challenges law firms face are more about retention and development, and creating an inclusive environment. At every year after the first year diverse attorneys are leaving law firms at a disproportionately high rate.

CA: Do you see flexible working becoming the norm in the future?

JL: I do think that law firms understand that the millennial generation has different expectations about things like face time and work/life balance. Nowadays you can work from anywhere, and young attorneys don't understand why they should stay in one place. An area where we've seen the most progress is in family leave policies which aren't gender specific, so you see young fathers taking paternity leave alongside women taking maternity leave, which signals a cultural change. You get firms offering it and young men taking it without worrying about any stigma. You do see some flexible working arrangements but management and leadership still have the expectation of face time. It's great to work from home or from Starbucks, but when work is doled out in a free-market way if you're not there you won't get the project. I think firms understand the generational shift and are trying to implement more progressive policies, but family leave is the area where we've seen the most cultural change recently.

CA: Do you think law firms will ever consider offering associates less money for fewer billable hours?

JL: No. Not partnership track associates. But we do see firms offering different kinds of jobs for fewer hours and experimenting with practice-specific staff attorney positions without the same upward career path. Some progressive firms have a career development matrix where associates can step off into a staff attorney role with some opportunity to return later to a partnership track, but they're careful to state that's an exception rather than a rule. As for associates on a partner track: until the partnership structure disappears and firms adopt a more corporate-style ownership structure, billable hour expectations will stay high.

CA: Given how competitive the recruitment process is, how important do you think it is for students to know which specific area of law they'd like to practice in?

JL: I think that depends. For the most part law firms aren't looking for specialization and want flexibility for staffing on the fly. There are exceptions and certainly in intellectual property – which is super important – they do want people to know ahead of time and have STEM (science, technology, engineering and mathematics) backgrounds.

I think that is another factor in the LSAT vs. GRE debate that's going on. One of the reasons schools are accepting GRE results is because it brings in more people who have experience in the STEM fields. This crops up during 'pre-cruiting' where firms try to get to certain kinds of candidates early, and we certainly see more and more early outreach to candidates with STEM backgrounds. That's where specialization is important, and in tax as well there are courses that are important if you want to become an associate in that area. But even if you just make a decision between litigation and transactional work the lines are still blurry and people still have to be flexible.

CA: Do you have any words of wisdom for people thinking about pursuing a career in BigLaw?

JL: I think it's important to take time out between undergrad and law school and do two years of work experience for example. I think that makes you a more fully formed professional and spending time in the job market gives you an advantage that really shows. People who go straight through to law school from university without working are at a disadvantage. Another rule is borrowing as little money as you can so you're not locked into having to take the BigLaw job. There is a lot of tuition discounting at present because competition for the smaller group of applicants has been so keen, so the net cost at many law schools has actually come down over the last five years even though the sticker price is higher. The thing that's the hardest to do – and law firms don't make it easy – is to actually distinguish between firms. Websites and lawyer bios often look the same but they're actually very different culturally. Spend as much time in the pre-offer/acceptance phase making distinctions between firms and ask yourself: 'Will I fit in here? Are there people that I could work with every day and want to get out of bed and spend 18 hours a day working with them?' A lot of people wind up at a law firm without having done that, so I think that's important.

CA: Are there any other issues that you think our readers should be aware of?

JL: There's a recent issue that's bubbled up here recently, where a firm was flagged up for having all of its associates sign mandatory arbitration and nondisclosure agreements regarding sexual harassment. The firm has rescinded the policy but it's an issue we're keeping an eye on. Some associates have said they don't want to interview with firms that have similar policies and it's something that the board will be monitoring. Some people think it's perhaps more of an issue in California because of state laws there, but we expect more firms to come forward and say they're rescinding that policy. It'll be interesting in recruitment to see whether firms change policy or whether they were widely in place, but we're going to be keeping an eye on it.

What type of law firm suits you?

Researching every firm to find the right fit for you would be madness. So here's how to start a shortlist.

Wall Street firms

NEW York, by headcount, is the largest legal market in America. Zone in on NYC and you'll find the city's most elite firms in the borough of Manhattan, either near Wall Street or in Midtown. While they can range in size from under 200 to over 2,000 lawyers, all will house teams of attorneys working on high-value cases and deals for high financiers and big business, which are regularly reported on in the pages of the *Wall Street Journal*. A big pull with these firms is the prestige, but it does come at a cost: young lawyers work long hours, so *"from Monday to Friday, they own you."* New York is also the country's most internationally oriented market, and even though some Wall Street firms may not have legions of lawyers stationed in Chicago, Charlotte or Shanghai, their work can span the nation and the globe. Culture-wise they can be stuffy and hierarchical, even for law firms.

Global firms

Law firms have been 'international' for years. White & Case made the trip from New York to open an office in Paris in 1926, a full year before Charles Lindbergh made the same journey in the Spirit of St. Louis. However, an increasing number of firms are now more than 'international' – they are global. They figure that, in today's world, you need a foothold in every market to have a competitive advantage.

A few early movers like Baker McKenzie have grown organically from small beginnings in other countries. A more recent tactic for expansion – pursued with particular vigor by the likes of Dentons, Norton Rose Fulbright and DLA Piper – is for large outfits to gobble up smaller foreign firms. By October 2017, Dentons had combined with a jaw-dropping 31 firms across the globe over a seven-year period. DLA Piper, meanwhile, recently sated its appetite for mergers by absorbing Danish firm LETT and Portuguese entity ABBC.

Having flooded the Western world with offices, the global firms are now targeting emerging markets: sending delegations to charm the Chinese and Russians, beginning to open offices in Africa and South America, and keeping a close eye on India (currently off limits to foreign firms, but there's talk that the Indian legal market will soon be liberalized – so watch this space).

The work junior associates undertake is not hugely different from their peers at Wall Street firms. What is different is the strategy these firms employ to achieve their goals. This naturally has a knock-on effect on the culture. Like Wall Street firms, the work will have an international flavor.

Multi-site firms

Clients like their lawyers close at hand, so as they've grown, many firms have established networks of offices across the country. At some multi-site firms, offices work together on nationwide matters, while at others each office focuses on matters in its locality. The size of the deals will often compete with the biggest international firms, as do the salaries.

Many of these firms maintain offices abroad (though they generally have less reach than the global firms mentioned above) which have differing levels of integration with the USA (and many multi-site firms are merging with overseas counterparts to move into the 'global' category). A major benefit of a multi-site firm is that as an associate you can move cities while remaining with the same employer.

Regional firms

There can be quite a difference in the culture, working style and practice remit of firms based in different regions. Many firms take pride in the fact they are Californian, Midwestern or Bostonian. All populous states – from New Jersey and Pennsylvania to Arizona and Minnesota – have their own sophisticated legal markets, with a group of leading firms working on complex transactions and cases.

Certain regions are known for certain types of work: corporate, banking and finance in New York; government/regulatory in DC; technology and media in California; energy in Texas; private equity in Boston, etc. Many West

On chambers-associate.com...

- We look at the life of a lawyer in all the major legal markets across the US.

Becoming a Lawyer

Coast firms look toward Asia for business, while Florida firms often work in Latin America. Each region has its own set of traits and it is worth thinking about them. When researching a firm, find out about the local market in which it operates. Typically, these firms are seen as less high-stress than the New York elite, and that's reflected in the salary – which is still good, nevertheless.

Boutiques and specialists

Boutiques are firms that practice in a single area of law – litigation or IP, for example. Some are very small; others have hundreds of lawyers. These firms offer a great opportunity for those who know what they want to do and want to work with like-minded people, but they are not a good option if you are unsure what area of law you want to work in. Specialist firms may offer additional practice areas to support their main agenda.

Outside BigLaw: small firms

Only a fraction of the nation's 50,000 plus law firms employ more than 50 lawyers. The others are smaller businesses doing all kinds of legal work, often with a local focus, in towns and cities from Portland, Maine to Portland, Oregon, and from Anchorage to Key West. We discuss the opportunities offered by these businesses in our small firms feature, which you can find on chambers-associate.com.

"The practice of law when I first started is different from what it is now – you have to be flexible and understand change. There are challenges the next generation of lawyers will face, that we didn't. Our challenge was embracing technology. Something else will impact theirs, but change is good and healthy, and valuable to our clients. They should be sensitive to the changes they experience, but embrace it and don't be fearful."

– Cozen O'Connor managing partner
Vince McGuinness

The big trends in practice areas

We asked thousands of junior associates to tell us about their practice groups. After crunching some data we picked out some trends that might help your decision-making.

The practices junior associates end up in

This is a distribution of where our sources told us they worked. Notable here is a bias toward litigation and corporate. If this lack of variety concerns you, be assured that the market is much less homogeneous and more complex. Take a typical Texan firm: many associates may be working in their corporate departments, but the subject matter will very often be energy, although not ex-clusively. A Silicon Valley firm might have a large team of junior litigators, but they are most frequently serving tech and start-up clients. So this is how associates perceive their work, but if you have your eye on a lesser frequented practice (and to stand out at OCI we recommend that you do), follow our practice areas chapter through to the recommended firms.

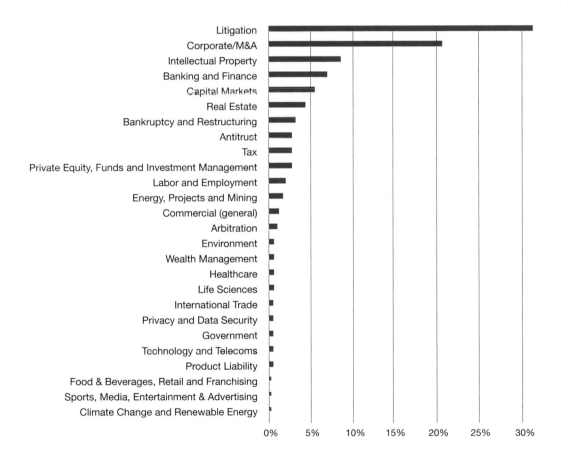

For in-depth reviews of each practice area, turn to p.79

Associate satisfaction by practice area

Every year our research shows a link between niche or sector focuses and lawyer satisfaction. In the table below, the lesser populated areas like climate change, sport, media, tech, and government are producing the happiest associates. Countless factors contribute to a person's career happiness, and we should bear in mind this is a correlation, not a cause-and-effect. But there are variables like responsibility, client and partner contact, subject-matter intrigue, perceived value of your contribution, and work-ing hours, which all have an obvious impact on your enjoyment. And each of these varies depending on the practice area. Finally, don't take this to mean the larger litigation and corporate teams are less happy; our ranking on p.8 features plenty of friendly giants like Gibson Dunn, Latham and White & Case. So given you're most likely to end up in corporate or litigation, it pays to do your homework and get to know the firms.

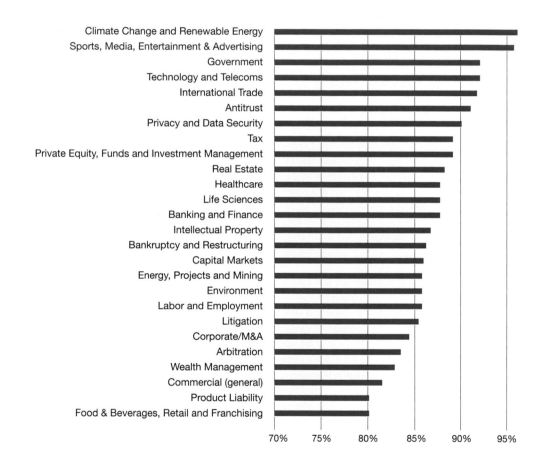

For more data and analysis, join our newsletter from the chambers-associate.com homepage

Lawyer stress by practice area

There is a relationship between lawyer stress and practice group, but note how stress is not the direct inverse of happiness. Given law is the natural habitat of high achievers, stress can, if managed well, be a positive force that gets the best results from lawyers and contributes to career satisfaction. Inevitably we find the most demanding transactional practices toward the top, but perhaps unexpectedly, life sciences and healthcare associates feel the most stressed this year. The picture becomes clearer when you look at international trade in at 3rd and government at 5th: these four practices are most closely related to government, and the US government is not a serene, relaxing place to be in 2018. Before interpreting this data, we'd recommend considering how you respond to stress – does it bring out the best in you?

Career development by practice area

Take what we learnt above about type-A achievers when you put them under pressure and consider the results below: throw the right person into a stressful environment and they will thrive. To be doing work in government or international trade at this point in history is likely to further your career quicker than many other areas. Privacy, data security and tech feature highly because they are among the hottest topics of 2018 in the US and globally, and the work lawyers do this year will make their careers.

Corporate doesn't come off well in the data below, but we should remember these are the largest departments in most firms, and within several you will find junior associates doing the grunt work. The small-cog-big-machine couplet is a familiar gripe and one that has been channelled in this figure for corporate M&A. In defense of this giant sector, we'd urge you to remember that it's a career-maker – those who take the long view and thrive will truly thrive. M&A is an all-encompassing practice and so excellent training for you, and those who reach partnership are among the most influential and well-paid lawyers in the profession globally.

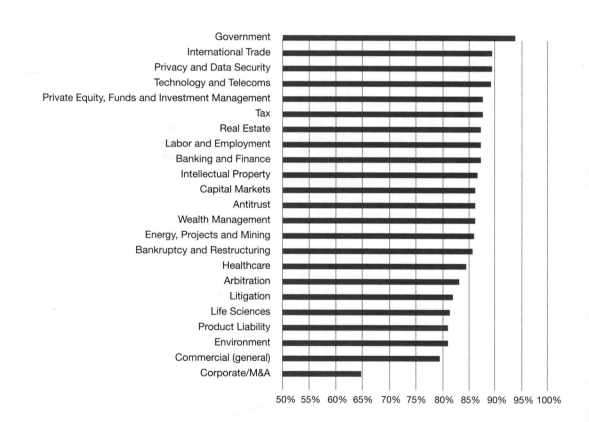

Work/life balance and flexible working by practice area

This conforms to what we hear from lawyers when we interview them – that the transactional practices are the most consistently demanding. In areas like private equity, M&A and finance, hours are the least likely to slacken. And these are the most international areas of business, so conference calls in European or Asian time zones contribute to the need for office sleep-pods, team take-out dinners and midnight cab rides home. In more niche practices like life sciences and tech, there are still some very weighty deadlines, but like litigation, the work is cyclical. However erratic, social life is more possible.

Flexible working is revolutionizing the industry, but is most commonly employed in areas where teamwork and face-time are less of a requirement. A good example is wealth management, where the lawyer and client have a more personal relationship: they might receive a call from a tycoon in Monaco at 3am, but they can take the call in their PJs.

Becoming a lawyer at a global firm

The heavyweights of the legal industry operate seamlessly on a global level, and Skadden is one such firm. A selection of lawyers from its 22 worldwide offices detail the exciting complexity of life at a global firm, and offer advice on what you can do to thrive in an organization like theirs.

IN 2017, Intel, the ubiquitous Silicon Valley chip-maker, bought the Israeli company MobilEye, one of the leaders in autonomous driving tech. Price tag? A cool $15.3 billion. The sizable figure bears significance, as does the context of a furious race towards self-driving dominance – but, more fundamentally, this deal highlights the incessantly international nature of modern business. It's a basic point, but it's nevertheless remarkable.

And who was it that provided Intel's legal advice on this deal? Skadden. That's less remarkable. The New York firm is synonymous with M&A at the very highest level – these days, that means managing a whirling vortex of international interests and diverse jurisdictions. Skadden certainly fits the bill of a 'global firm', with its 22 offices spread across the world's key financial centers, and its demonstrable skill at handling cross-border matters in many practice areas.

Over the last 30-odd years this particular breed of law firm has multiplied. Those that fall into the category are defined by their ability to provide coordinated legal services that accommodate the wide-ranging needs of the global clients they serve. Their rise has become a significant trend in the legal industry, and, fortunately for those pursuing a legal career, they're here to stay.

To examine the career path that will end with you bossing it at a global firm, we've called on Skadden and its attorneys to shine a light on what's involved. For the reasons set out above, they're in a great position to offer some choice words of advice.

Visit our website to read the full feature on what joining a global firm entails. It covers, among other topics, the issues Skadden's attorneys contend with; the international opportunities they have; and, of course, their top tips for forging a successful career as an international lawyer in a global firm. www.chambers-associate.com

Skadden, Arps, Slate, Meagher & Flom LLP & Affiliates

On-campus interviews

We interview the interviewers to help guide you through the OCIs...

The process

HIRING at most top firms follows a similar highly structured pattern: interviews on campus, followed by interviews back at the firms, then (hopefully) a summer associateship. Many components of this process are laid down by NALP's guidelines, and by law schools. Recruitment varies from school to school and from firm to firm, but here we will attempt to give you a rough overview of how the OCI process works, plus tips on how to get through it successfully.

We speak to many dozens of law firm recruiters each year during our research for this guide. Among other things, they tell us what they look for in prospective hires and what questions they're likely to ask during interviews. A number of consistent themes emerge about what they are looking for during these interviews, which we present below with some quotes from hiring partners themselves. Firms' recruiting strategies do differ, of course, and you can find out more about the particular requirements of each in the Get Hired section of our Inside View features.

Bidding

OCIs are aimed at students at the start of their 2L year for summer positions the following summer, between their 2L and 3L years. Although they occur under the banner of 'fall recruiting', OCIs are increasingly held earlier in the year, starting in August and September. Besides BigLaw firms, smaller firms, public interest organizations and government agencies (like the Federal Public Defender's Office, the IRS and Immigration and Customs Enforcement) also recruit on campus. While commercial law firms pay to attend, government and public organizations usually don't.

Students can bid on a certain number of employers (often between 20 and 50), ranking their preferences for firms and office locations. A preset system determines who they interview with: some schools allow employers to select a proportion of the students they interview; others use a lottery system which is entirely based on students' preferences. Bidding deadlines are usually in July.

On chambers-associate.com...

- Good legal writing.

Most schools request that students submit a writing sample alongside their resume when bidding for firms at OCI. This is typically a paper written on a legal subject. Good writing skills are essential for junior associates, as drafting is a big part of their staple diet. The writing sample is more important to some firms than to others. *"This firm is really, really serious about the quality of the writing sample,"* one BigLaw associate emphasized to us. *"People with excellent credentials get turned away because their writing isn't top-notch."*

Besides OCIs, some firms also interview at job fairs with a regional focus (like the Midwest Job Fair) or are focused on a specific minority (like the NBLSA Job Fair and the Lavender Law Fair), or have a specific industry focus, like the Loyola Patent Law Interview Program. Smaller firms often take applicants through a mix of direct applications and OCIs, as they don't have the resources to visit a large number of campuses. A few firms bypass the OCI process entirely. Quinn Emanuel's recruitment 'parties' are the most high-profile example, letting students mingle with the firm's associates and partners at an informal drinks event before submitting resumes.

Resumes

Firms see students' resumes before the interview. A resume should be no longer than a page long, unless you have at least five years' work experience prior to law school, which means you probably don't have space for that paper route you did in 10th grade. It also goes without saying that typos are to be avoided at all costs; even one mistake can make the difference between the 'yes' pile and the rejects, so do enlist someone to proofread your resume. Think carefully about coming up with a clear, punchy layout (there's helpful advice from Harvard here). Keep your resume continually up-to-date, and refine it constantly. Put your strengths somewhere where they can be clearly seen, targeting the five-second glance by a rushed recruiter. And, crucially, think carefully about how to tailor your resume to the jobs you want. It's not enough to say you're passionate about law. Give real and specific evidence which is targeted to the kind of firms you're applying to.

Often a resume will tick the right boxes, but recruiters will want to use the interview to find out if you really live up to your billing. Make sure you have plenty more to say about all the activities, experiences and hobbies you've listed. One interviewer explains that candidates are *"likely to be asked detailed questions about items on their resumes. Their capacity to speak to those topics thoughtfully, compellingly and with some imaginative insight is very important."*

The interview

Most students interview with between ten and 30 firms (assuming they can get that many interviews). OCIs usually last 20 minutes and are conducted by a mix of partners and associates. Some firms have a dedicated group of attorneys (often the hiring committee) which interviews on campus; others let a wider range of attorneys participate. Sometimes interviewers are trained by firms on how to interview and how to present the firm during OCIs.

Whatever's on your resume, it's how you come across during the OCI which matters most to firms. That doesn't just mean your personality – you need to be able to communicate how and why your past experiences make you right for the firm. The interview process itself is a test of character: interviewers will look at the way you speak, answer questions and make an argument to judge whether you have the qualities they are looking for. For example, many recruiters ask about candidates' undergraduate dissertations. They do this to see how well you still recall your main argument, and how well you can summarize your argument briefly for a lay audience. Of course, this ability to think on your feet is itself an essential quality for any attorney. Pay attention to which of its offices a firm is recruiting for on your campus. Some firms recruit for all their offices on all campuses; others allow specific offices to target specific campuses.

Callback interviews

Firms often have a maximum number of students from any school who they will 'call back' for a second interview. 'Callback interviews' usually take place in October. They involve a half-day or whole day spent on-site at one of the firm's offices. Students are usually interviewed by four to six attorneys – a mix of partners and associates. Often there will also be a lunch or coffee event with junior associates.

Be aware that you are being assessed during the whole day, not just during the interviews themselves. Treat lunches and coffee dates as part of the interview process;

On chambers-associate.com...
- What's your greatest weakness? How to handle this annoying interview question.

there's no need to be formal, but you should always keep in mind that you are being judged – showing an interest in your interviewers' work and the firm in general is a good bet. *"Candidates feel more comfortable during lunches with junior associates, so these interviews will often be more illuminating than the office ones. The associates fill out assessment forms in the same way that partners do,"* a BigLaw hiring partner tells us. How you greet and talk to support staff and recruiters when you first arrive can be important too. Hiring committees usually take into consideration the views of staff and junior associates who have met with candidates.

A 'standard' callback interview will see some interviewers ask about your resume, while others might talk about hobbies, sports and academics to find out more about your skills and personality. *"My interviewer put down my resume and said: 'Let's just have a conversation,'"* one junior associate recalled. *"Then we talked about what I liked and disliked about law school, the firm and my connection to the city."* Most firms allow interviewers a lot of free rein in what they ask. *"Different interviewers will put different weights on certain aspects of a student,"* another recruiter pointed out. Some firms employ so-called behavioral interviewing techniques. This ranges from asking questions directly about skills and competencies ('give an example of when you worked in a team') to structured assessments.

For example, Philadelphia's Pepper Hamilton has used an interactive scenario in which interviewers and candidates work though a legal issue. The aim of this was to *"see how comfortable the candidate is in a working situation, how they work in a team and how they might counsel a client."* We predict that this type of interviewing will become increasingly common in future.

If a student is unsure whether to join the firm (or vice versa) they might return to the firm for a 'second look' and meet with a few more attorneys. Candidates are often asked if they want to meet attorneys from certain practice areas during the callback or 'second look'. Make use of this opportunity: asking to meet people from certain departments – even if you're not sure which you want to join – will show you're engaged with the firm's work. A short while after the callback students will hear whether the firm wants to offer them a position as a summer associate. Students have 28 days to accept the offer.

Some top interview tips from hiring partners

"I like to engage students about what their passions are – say what they wrote their thesis on – to see their fluency with language and whether they have a clear world view, sophistication and maturity."

"In interviews we use simple techniques to draw out aspects of someone's personality: when looking at leadership we might ask about past experiences where candidates were put into a leadership role. What was that experience like? Could they describe it in detail? How did you rise to the occasion? And so on."

"We ask about their connection to the city they're interviewing in, about their outside interests and long-term plans, and what they like and don't like about law school."

"One stock question I ask is: what is not on your resume that we should know about you? I like to know what's behind the resume. That's not just personality-related. I want them to go a little deeper so I can find out about their skills as a person. A wonderful response to that question is if someone relates it to a challenge they have overcome or a time when they have shown good judgment."

"The worst answer I have ever had to a question was the person who told me about working on a group project at college where no-one pulled their weight, so they did all the work. They were really proud of it, but it tells me they might not work well in a team."

"Show a serious interest in what the firm does, and what the people you are speaking to do."

"The biggest thing you could do wrong at OCI is not be able to keep up an intelligent conversation for 20 minutes or not have any questions."

"During interviews candidates should have good questions about the firm. Not just questions to which the answers are on our website, but things that show they have done their homework."

"Prepare. It takes more time than some students set aside for it. Practicing to get over the jitters is good, but what's more important is thinking through what you've done in your life to understand what skills you have that can contribute to being a lawyer. When we sense that somebody's done enough thinking about themselves to know which part of their experience to talk about at an interview, we're prone to think they're analytical and will be able to perform the tasks required of them."

"Identify a couple of areas of real interest and educate yourself about those areas, both through law school courses and practice experience. In that way you can distinguish yourself from the mass."

Examples of questions

Here are some examples of OCI and callback interview questions reported by juniors and recruiters:

Why do you want to be a lawyer?

Why are you applying to this firm?

What is it you have heard or read about this firm that made you interested?

What areas of practice are you interested in and why?

Describe to me the central argument of your undergraduate thesis.

What did you enjoy about law school?

Where do you see yourself five or ten years down the road?

What mistakes have you made in your past?

If I called one of your referees now, how would they describe you?

How would your law journal colleagues who worked with you describe you?

Describe a time when you didn't succeed and what you learned from it.

Describe a time you showed leadership. How did you rise to the occasion?

How much time would you spend polishing a draft to get the little points right?

Can you describe a particularly challenging circumstance in your life?

What motivates you?

Are you a team player?

Can you describe a situation where you handled a difficult customer?

Tell me about a time you worked in a team that was dysfunctional.

Tell me about a time you helped successfully produce a certain work product.

Tell me about a time you had to juggle several responsibilities.

Tell me about a time you faced a setback or failure and what you did.

What adversities have you faced in past employment?

Summers

At many BigLaw firms, getting on the summer program is tantamount to getting an associate job. Historically, many firms used the summer program as a final step in the recruitment process: a tough few months' work at the firm would weed out the weaklings, and firms would only give job offers to a certain proportion of each summer class. Some firms still use the old model, but since the recession an increasing number only hire summers who they intend to take on as first-years. Firms now pride themselves on their 100% offer rates – you'd really have to screw up during the summer not to get an offer (the economy aside...).

Summer programs traditionally involved a lot of wining, dining and schmoozing of participating students. This trend, too, is declining. First, a recession-induced squeeze on firms' budgets means less cash to spend on perks for summers. Second, it used to be fairly important for firms to impress (top) students to stop them seeking jobs elsewhere. With the job market as tough as it is, this is barely necessary any more.

Firms now pride themselves on offering students a summer experience which reflects the life of a junior associate.

Recruitment outside OCIs

Aside from OCIs, firms recruit from some schools by allowing students to submit their resumes via a central pool. This is known as a 'resume drop'.

Some firms also accept direct write-in applications outside OCIs. As one recruiter put it: *"If someone writes in to us and they're not from a top-50 school, but they came top of their class and were editor-in-chief of a law journal, that will certainly get our attention."* Networking is also very important if you want to get an associate job outside OCIs. Getting in touch with attorneys at the firm you are interested in either directly or via alumni events is the very least you should do. *"Our attorneys are very involved with their alma maters,"* a hiring partner told us. Networking is also increasingly important if you are applying via OCIs. *"Students need to work hard at networking as more job opportunities are spread by word of mouth than before."*

Some firms like recruiting candidates who have completed an LL.M., especially overseas. Usually though, an LL.M. will do nothing to help your chances of getting a job as an associate.

For more tips from the hiring partners, visit our website, where you'll find interviews with each HP.

"At the bottom of a resume there's space for additional information, and my advice would be to use that for something that makes you stand out, like baking or what you like to read instead of a class you took or being able to use Excel."
– a DLA Piper associate

"We're optimistic about the continued relevance and importance of the legal profession. There are some negative connotations surrounding the future of practicing law that have seeped into the popular mind, and there's some pessimism about whether pursuing the law is a rewarding endeavor. It's challenging at times, but I don't think it's ever been as important in our recent past as it is now, to have the best and brightest promoting the rule of law. I think it's going to be turbulent times ahead, but also important and interesting times to be engaged in the legal realm. I would encourage students to embrace that. When things are challenging, we as lawyers have a special responsibility to promote what's right, what needs to be done, and to protect our clients."

– Dykema CEO Peter Kellett

Summer programs

The halcyon days of extravagant spending might be over, but BigLaw summer associate programs by and large remain a decent mix of solid work experience and merry social jamborees...

SUMMER associate programs are an integral part of BigLaw recruiting. Attrition rates are high across the profession, so firms run annual programs – which usually last from six to 12 weeks – to ensure that a steady influx of first-year associates join the ranks each year. A summer stint effectively serves as a prolonged interview, with clear benefits for applicants and recruiting attorneys alike: the former receive a taste of associate life, while the latter get an up-close and personal view of their potential colleagues in action. Provided all goes well, summers receive an offer to return as a full-time first-year associate upon completion of their law degree.

Recent years have seen summer associate classes composed primarily of 2Ls. Many firms hire a handful of 1Ls each year – often via scholarships or competitions – but the chances of nabbing a spot as a 3L are slim: according to NALP, only 18% of firms in 2017 reported any third-year recruiting activity, with a microscopic quantity of offers made to 3Ls. As such, many law students concentrate on applications during the summer following their 1L year, when the on-campus recruiting season kicks off. Competition is fierce so it's vital that your grades and extracurriculars are up to scratch when you apply – for information about when and how to apply for summer spots, see our feature on the OCI process.

As a summer, you'll likely get the chance to try out work across a variety of practice groups, which *"can be really helpful if you don't have a clear idea of what you want to go into,"* sources agreed. Some firms, like Willkie, Milbank and King & Spalding, even have formal rotation systems in place to ensure summer associates experience a broad mix of assignments. At the end of the program, candidates typically submit a preference for a particular practice group that is taken into consideration at the offers stage.

"I felt really integrated into my practice group when I saw that my work product was actually incorporated into the matters at hand."

The summer associate experience has historically been somewhat artificial, with many firms offering made-up tasks and discrete research assignments that bear only mild resemblance to actual responsibilities. However, the recession prompted an increased reliance on summers at many a cash-strapped firm, and offering 'real' work soon became not only a priority but a necessity across the profession. That trend continues today – most of our associate interviewees now report a relatively *"authentic"* experience as summers.

"I felt really integrated into my practice group when I saw that my work product was actually incorporated into the matters at hand," one associate shared. *"When I returned as a first-year, I was able to pick up one of the projects that was still ongoing and see it through to the end."* Another said: *"Firms now realize the value of allowing summers to get their hands dirty with real tasks; that approach demonstrates how you will actually react under certain circumstances and prepares you for the transition into being a first-year."* Indeed, as one BigLaw hiring partner confirms, *"throwing people into the mix seems to work out best for everyone involved."*

Typical summer duties include small research tasks, drafting memos and attending negotiations or depositions to observe their seniors. The last is an important part of the learning process, according to our sources. *"We make the effort to get people on the phone to listen to the back and forth of arguing a case, and in client meetings so they can witness the kind of behavior that gets things done,"* one hiring partner tells us. In addition, taking on *"pro bono matters can be a real chance to stretch your wings,"* one source reported. *"It was small, short-term work, sure, but it was meaningful too."* When they're not 'learning by doing', students usually attend summer-specific training sessions, and they're often able to opt into CLE classes alongside fully fledged associates. As well as general introductions to the different practices, summer training sessions cover topics as varied as advocacy, due diligence, depositions, legal writing and business development. Summers at some firms even undergo a mock trial.

Becoming a Lawyer

In keeping with the post-recession trend of cutbacks across the legal sector, the culture of lavish wining and dining – a summer staple implemented with the intent of wooing top hires – has slowed down to some extent. *"Anyone summering now will find things aren't as flashy as they used to be,"* sources revealed. Is this a sore spot? *"Not at all; if anything it helps prepare you for the working world,"* one associate said, looking back on their time as a summer. *"They're not trying to seduce you into thinking associate life is something that it isn't – it's not all karaoke, free bars and boat trips down the Hudson River."*

> **"They're not trying to seduce you into thinking associate life is something that it isn't – it's not all karaoke, free bars and boat trips down the Hudson River."**

Still, socializing remains an important part of the summer experience, with lunches, sports events, wine-tastings and theater trips among the standard perks. *"You can still get tickets to a Yankees game, but they won't be behind home plate,"* one source summed up. In any case, attorneys of all levels tend to look forward to the summer since *"that's when the majority of the year's social events take place."* Some of the more exciting traditions we've heard about include trips to Disneyland and a destination hike at Quinn Emanuel, cooking classes and Shakespeare in the Park at Debevoise, and mixology courses and sunset sails at Willkie. *"I'd be a summer forever if I could!"* one insider enthused.

Savvy summers will see these events as more than just a chance to chill out – they're golden opportunities to meet and mingle. Indeed, a hiring partner at a top international firm says: *"I don't care how busy you are or how tired you are, you need to get out there and go to as many events as possible! It's as good a chance to meet and talk to people as you'll get during office hours and the more contacts you're able to make the better."*

Some firms have programs in place that let summers spend time in multiple offices, or even at outside organizations with which the firm has ties. Certain large international outfits allow associates to spend part of their summer in an overseas office. *"Having that opportunity helped me make valuable connections with my international colleagues and offered a good insight into how the firm operates abroad,"* said one source who'd split their time between London and New York. Others offer the chance to spend several weeks working with a local public interest organization, while some run mini client secondments for summer associates.

"I'd be a summer forever if I could!"

When it comes to landing an offer, a good impression is imperative – a summer stint is akin to an audition, after all. Whether you're responding to a partner's request or schmoozing at an event, engage appropriately and keep to your best behavior to show you're taking the opportunity seriously. As one BigLaw hiring partner shares, *"being enthusiastic about the work is just as important as demonstrating you're capable of doing it as far as I'm concerned."* Other interviewees advised summers to *"maintain a positive attitude"* and *"show a genuine interest in what's going on at the firm and where it's heading."* That said, *"there's certainly room to relax"* during the program, sources assured us, *"just don't go overboard with the booze!"* Indeed, the point of offering opportunities for candidates to let their hair down is to assess their personalities, *"including how they interact outside a work context,"* one hiring partner reveals. *"It's a good glimpse into people's attitudes and what it'll be like interacting with them on a day-to-day basis."*

Since the recession, offer rates from summer programs have been high. A tightened grip on financials prompted many firms to limit summer hiring to those they intended to keep on for good, and the ability to claim a 100% offer rate has become a badge of pride on the recruiting side. *"We always aim to keep everyone, and it's rare when we don't end up with offers across the board,"* one hiring partner tells us. *"When that happens, it's because we haven't done our job perfectly and it turns out someone doesn't really fit in or didn't pan out in terms of our expectations."* The latest NALP report shows that 95% of summer associates received offers in 2017.

Becoming a Lawyer

Clerkships

Clerking for a judge is a great way to kick-start your career as a litigator...

What is a law clerk?

A JUDICIAL clerk (or 'elbow clerk') works as a judge's assistant and typically starts after graduating law school. These clerkships normally involve working alongside a single judge. Responsibilities vary from judge to judge, but all clerks engage in research and do copious amounts of writing. Most appointments last one or two years – judges indicate the duration of the commitment at the outset. Whether you want to work in BigLaw or for a smaller outfit, the skills, connections and insights picked up while clerking are invaluable.

Why clerk?

"It's an absolutely amazing experience. If everyone could do it, there would be a lot of better lawyers," one former district court clerk told us. *"It's absolutely hands down the best way to start a legal career,"* says Melissa Lennon, president elect at NALP. *"The training you get – really intense research and writing – is incredibly valuable."* According to retired Judge Joel Pisano of the District Court of New Jersey, *"clerking offers an opportunity to be in on the decision-making process, to understand how the courts work, to be mentored by a sitting judge and to be introduced to the members of the Bar."* Clerks learn how judges react to different briefs and styles of advocacy, and are exposed to a wide range of legal issues.

The educational value of clerkships cannot be overstated, as clerks learn directly from the arbiters of the law. A judge might ask a clerk to write a memorandum or even a first draft of a judicial opinion. *"Certainly, I was writing opinions,"* said an associate who had clerked with the District Court of Maryland. *"My writing got a lot better over the course of a year, because of the benefit of having a judge who sees you every day, guides you and shapes your writing style."* Clerks may get an insight into legal administration too. One source had clerked with a judge who sat on the Judicial Conference of the United States – a body concerned with US Courts administration – and had taken on duties related to the Conference.

The judge/clerk relationship often extends beyond the clerkship term. *"Previous clerks are always encouraged to call if they want to chat or need advice,"* according to Judge Pisano. For some this relationship is career-changing as their judge mentors them on the next step in their career. *"I didn't have a good idea of the legal scene so I*

asked the judge what he recommended," one former clerk told us. *"The firm I'm at now is the first one he recommended."* Clerks also build up a valuable network among members of the Bar, other clerks and judges. This comes in handy when practicing in the same state or district as the judge.

Different courts provide windows into different types of law. For someone who wants to be a criminal litigator, clerking in a state trial court would provide maximum exposure to criminal prosecution. Bankruptcy judges are part of the district court system and have special purview over bankruptcy filings. *"If you are interested in transactional law or corporate governance, working for the Delaware Court of Chancery is significantly advantageous,"* says Melissa Lennon. *"Delaware is the home of corporate law in the US: many groundbreaking corporate and governance issues are decided there."* Equally, those interested in green issues could look into clerking at the environmental division of the Vermont Superior Court (Vermont is one of the few states where courts have specialized environmental divisions).

Types of clerkship
Federal courts

A stint at the US Supreme Court is the most sought-after, hard-to-land position on the clerking circuit. Read our feature on SCOTUS clerkships. While these clerks can practically pick a firm of their choice after this clerkship, several choose to go into academia instead (see endnote 1).

There are 13 federal courts of appeals. Federal circuit court clerks do a lot of research: assessing opposing briefs, going over the trial records, and interpreting application of the law. Many appellate court judges are known as 'feeder judges' as they have a history of having their former clerks hired by the Supreme Court.

There are 94 federal districts in the USA, and federal district courts offer clerkships with either a district judge or a magistrate judge. Federal district clerks have a more varied role than their appellate counterparts as they work in the general trial courts of the US federal system. In addition to the extensive research and writing appellate clerks undertake, district clerks coordinate with attorneys, help resolve discovery-related motions, prepare

Becoming a Lawyer

judges for settlement conferences and attend trial-related hearings.

Budding litigators should note that this is the perfect opportunity to pick up useful skills. Clerking with a magistrate judge is slightly more limited in scope as their remit is constrained by what federal district judges assign them. They do handle a wide range of work: warrants, bail hearings, arraignments, pretrial motions and civil matters related to multiparty litigation. Magistrates also write reports and recommendations to the district judge. Prospective clerks should make sure to find out what matters are referred to a magistrate judge before applying.

There are also opportunities to clerk for federal judges in subject matter-specific special courts. The Court of International Trade is one example; it has jurisdiction over international trade and customs with nine judges who often hire two clerks each (see endnote 2). Each judicial district is also home to a bankruptcy court. Clerks here are exposed to complex commercial cases, including claims made against debtors. The US Tax Court adjudicates tax disputes and arranges settlement payments to the IRS: the court comprises 19 judges, appointed for 15 years each. Other special courts include the US Court of Appeals for Veterans Claims and the US Court of Federal Claims.

State courts

Courts of last resort contribute to the development of state common law and interpret state statute, having a significant impact on state law. Clerks here have similar tasks and responsibilities to federal appellate law clerks. These clerkships are the most competitive to obtain at state level. To be considered for one, high academic standing and some journal experience are essential.

Some states have intermediary appellate courts, which operate along the lines of the federal courts of appeals – resolving appeals arising from the state's lower courts.

Many civil and criminal matters are dealt with at first instance by state trial courts. This grouping includes both general and limited jurisdiction trial courts such as city, county and probate courts. Law students looking to become criminal lawyers might be better off clerking in a state trial court than in federal court. Clerks here gain significant insight into the workings of the local Bar, state procedures and state law while assisting in trial procedures, research and drafting. This is also useful for those

wishing to become public prosecutors in the region. NALP provides a detailed guide on clerkships in select state courts.

Staff attorneys

Some courts hire 'staff attorneys': clerks who work for a group of judges instead of just one. Also known as pool clerks or court attorneys, these positions can be found in both federal and state courts. The core responsibilities of staff attorneys are more limited than those of other clerks and include reviewing appeals, preparing memos and assisting in case management.

Clerkship application

Federal and state clerkships don't abide by the same deadlines. State clerkship deadlines vary from court to court and state to state. Research local deadlines to find out more.

The majority of federal appellate judges hire clerks in the fall of their 3L year. To find out more check out OSCAR, the Online System for Clerkship Application and Review, at oscar.uscourts.gov. This online system allows judges to post vacancies, and students to apply online. OSCAR is currently piloting a two-year hiring plan. The class of 2020 will be able to access OSCAR, research clerkship positions and build applications from February 6, 2019. Applications will be released to judges on June 17, 2019. To get dates for the class of 2021, visit OSCAR's website.

Different judges have different preferences for how they like students to apply. You may be able to find out how the judge you are interested in clerking with recruits by contacting their chambers. Judges usually look for a good writing sample and good personal references. Sometimes schools recommend candidates to judges. Getting a (good) clerkship can often be all about networking, recommendations and connections.

Traditional practice for interviewees has been to accept the first offer they get, as many judges expect an immediate answer. *"The crucial thing is never tell a judge, 'I don't want to work with you',"* one source advised. At the time of writing, base salaries for federal clerks ranged from $50,790 to $72,391, depending on experience level. Salaries for state clerks vary.

Choosing a judge

Once you've chosen which judges you may want to clerk with, finding out more can be a murky process. Unfortunately there is no guide that will list the quirks of each judge, although it is extremely important to collect every last bit of information you can before applying. *"The only place where that information exists is in the halls of law*

On chambers-associate.com...

- How to speak judge: an insider's guide to getting, and surviving, your clerkship.

Becoming a Lawyer

schools," says Melissa Lennon. *"If you're lucky enough to get an interview with a judge, you need to talk to as many people as possible who have clerked or interviewed with that judge. Figure out what the judge is like and how they run their chambers."*

There are also blogs and forums where former clerks discuss their judges, their interviews and clerkships. Some clerks have been known to scoff at attempts to gather information this way but, along with networking, doing a few Google searches is a good way to find out more about a judge.

Talking to former clerks is really the best resource; we spoke with a few associates who had clerked and learned a lot. *"Some judges – like Judge Easterbrook– you just don't apply to,"* said one source. *"He and other judges on the Seventh Circuit only take people who are recommended by certain schools."* Court of Appeals Judge Danny Boggs is known as the trivia judge – he administers a general knowledge test to prospective applicants and three of his former clerks have appeared on Who Wants to Be a Millionaire (see endnote 3). One associate had interviewed with a judge who asked them all about college basketball during the interview. *"They don't just look at your academic performance,"* said one former clerk. *"They know they will be working closely with you and want to find out if they can get along with you on a personal level."*

Should you apply?

A federal law clerk should have completed their JD and be a US citizen. Following that, there are no set academic requirements. Students who secure the most coveted clerkships are often from a highly ranked law school, were in the top quarter of their class, have worked on a law journal and have glowing academic references. Given the importance of personal recommendations, it's never too early to start forming connections with the right faculty members.

If you don't have the best grades or you're not at one of the top schools, take heart from these words from Melissa Lennon: *"It's a big country and there are opportunities for federal clerkships for candidates from different schools, not just the top 20. Judges have loyalty to their own schools."* Given that approximately 480 clerkship positions are offered by just the New Jersey Courts (see endnote 4), it would be a fair estimate that aggregate state and federal clerkships outnumber top-grade applicants, although that doesn't mean that all of those positions are open to all applicants. State judges often have strong ties to the local community, so a strong letter of recommendation from a local school could have more clout than an Ivy League recommendation. *"As with many job applications, showing you have a local link helps,"* one former clerk advised.

If you're desperate for a clerkship but don't have the right grades, journal experience or law school pedigree, try making up with practical experience: intern at a regional firm, work in-house, do pro bono work or work part-time at a small firm (these experiences can also help provide you with the writing samples which judges so love). If you haven't worked on a law journal, highlighting courses in research and writing that you've aced can help too.

Many state and federal courts offer externships to law students, often during 1L or 2L summers. It can be tough to land one of these: you will need the right combination of grades, gumption and connections. Recommendations from these externships can be key to securing a coveted clerkship later on.

Endnotes

1 www.legalauthority.com/articles/70010/Clerkships

2 indylaw.indiana.edu/career/judicialclerkship.htm

3 www.newyorker.com/archive/2001/05/14/010514ta_TALK_DEPT_OF_TRIVIA

4 https://www.judiciary.state.nj.us/public/lawclerks.html

SCOTUS clerkships

Clerking at the Supreme Court, as told by the lucky few who've been there, done that, got the judicial robe...

CLERKING at the Supreme Court of the United States is the holy grail, the most prestigious gig any law grad can get. Only 36 SCOTUS clerkships come up for grabs each year. Only the brightest and very, very best need apply. Over a thousand who consider themselves in this category (and have letters of introduction from distinguished law professors and others to back them up) do so every year. And you don't go to the Supreme Court straight from law school – usually all successful candidates have previously clerked at federal appellate level, and wowed their judges there.

"Nothing else short of being a judge will replicate this experience," one former SCOTUS clerk tells us of their year with a Justice. *"You see directly how things work, which completely changes the way you see cases."*

How do I apply?

At some point during your federal clerkship, bundle your resume, cover letter, transcript, writing sample and letters of recommendation (most Justices require at least three) and ping them to the Court. The Justices decide their own hiring schedules, so keep an eye out for announcements well in advance. *"If you've managed to get a clerkship on the circuit court, you've got some idea that you have both the grades and the recommendations to make you competitive,"* an ex-SCOTUS clerk counsels, encouragingly. A stellar reference from your judge, *"based on the couple months work you've already done for them,"* is essential. *"Many circuit judges have a great record of sending clerks to the Supreme Court."* Aside from this, the application is relatively labor-free – *"it's as brief as a resume and a cover letter."*

Your circuit court judge can help in other ways too: *"Often he can put you in touch with the SCOTUS Justice's previous clerks so you can talk with them about their experiences."* There's a lot to learn, as interviewing style varies as much as the Justices' personalities. Overall, it's important to *"be familiar with their cases and their judicial philosophy by getting your hands on as much of their writing as you can, and by reading their most high-profile cases. You also need to be familiar with all the pending cases the Court is hearing, to demonstrate you have a clear interest in that Court."*

The ex-clerks we spoke to found their interview more relaxed than anticipated. *"It tested whether you can hold an interesting conversation – very different to testing your legal reasoning skills!"* You've made it this far, so they take your legal genius as a given: *"Each Justice interviews ten to 15 people who have extremely good qualifications. They're already confident in you, so their main task is to see if they connect with you on a personal level."* Hopefully this shouldn't be too tricky as the people who recommended you *"already have a relationship with the Justice and have thought about personality and ideological fit – after all, they're sending you to live with someone for a year."* The importance of recommendations from others during the hiring process cannot be overstated: it's *"not just old guys in smoky rooms making the decisions."*

The Chief Justice is authorized to hire five clerks, the eight Associate Justices four and retired Justices one apiece.

So what do SCOTUS clerks actually do?

Something similar to what federal court clerks do. Primarily, their role is to sift through the thousands of petitions and mark the cases worthy of being granted time. *"It's the most basic task, and the constant thing that you do – during the summer it's practically your only task."* The petitions that lawyers write very cleverly argue why their cases should be granted; the clerk's job is *"to screen out those that are legitimate and write bench memos on what we think about the case."* On top of this, there's *"preparing your Justice for argument and conference. You learn very quickly how to handle yourself beyond just thinking 'wow, these people are brilliant!' You learn critical thinking and the big picture, and a sense of professionalism where it would be easy to strongly disagree with folks."*

As term progresses, clerks move *"to the fun part."* Assisting with opinion-drafting is a process that can vary between Justices. *"Sometimes the Justice just wants to talk through an issue, so having a personality that won't be a distraction here is really beneficial,"* says one former clerk. Another enjoyed the close interaction when producing documents: *"We helped a lot with the drafting but ultimately every word that appeared in writing was the*

Justice's. The best learning experience was going back and forth on a piece of writing and seeing it changing."

And what do I get out of it?

Being at the heart of such a profound process gives you tremendous insights, something that BigLaw recognizes by offering eye-popping SCOTUS clerkship bonuses. *"Reading and attending oral arguments is the best imaginable lesson by example you can have on being a good lawyer,"* a former clerk says. *"The practice of law has always been an apprenticeship – you learn best by example. You're privileged to see how your Justice writes out an argument, but you also see what kind of things persuade them. That alone is so beneficial in terms of your own perspective and in terms of knowing what persuades judges for when you go into private practice yourself."*

"Even if you didn't learn how to write or earn a dime during the year, it would be worth it to see a branch of government working." Equally – and altruistically – *"you're performing a public service. The issue at the heart of everything is 'what's the right answer, and how can we put it out there in the most persuasive way?'"*

> *"The level of aggression varies, but generally there's a two-week period where you get taken to lunch by everyone. It's a fairly ego-boosting process."*

After their year at the elbow of a Supreme Court Justice, the 36 are in incredibly high demand. *"You get letters from firms as soon as you start,"* explains one. *"It's up to you and your Justice when you start to interview at firms – usually it's in June or July. The level of aggression varies, but generally there's a two-week period where you get taken to lunch by everyone. It's a fairly ego-boosting process, as they're all so nice to you!"*

Ultimately, most *"assume they'll go into BigLaw – there are loads of student loans to pay off, and the signing bonuses available go some way to making a dent in them."* But not everyone's head is turned by gold: *"It can be a real dilemma for some clerks, who'd prefer to go to a public interest group or go be a professor."*

And what of those bonuses? The latest round of SCOTUS clerks received golden hellos of $300,000 or more from their BigLaw firms (in addition to an approx $185,000 base salary) on arrival as third-year associates.

OK I'm sold. What should I do now to have a shot at a SCOTUS clerkship?

Get top grades, a place on Law Review, and glowing references from your law professors. Then you have a chance of a clerkship at federal appellate level. *"There are three ways to develop these relationships,"* explained one ex-clerk. *"The first is by taking regular classes with particular professors. The second is to get onto particular clinics – some schools have Supreme Court Litigation clinics where professors supervise students in brief writing. The professors are very experienced Supreme Court advocates – by virtue of that, they're very well known to the Justices and are impressive in their own right. These clinics are competitive to get into. The third route is to become a research assistant for a professor who has a relationship with the Supreme Court Justices."*

Depending on their particular school, our sources became aware of clerkships around their second year. *"For me it was more a by-product of the underlying material of law,"* says one. *"The professors at my school were clerkship-focused though, and they managed to convey how important they can be."*

The necessity of excellent personal recommendations means the process *"can be idiosyncratic and slightly opaque, but the overall feeling is that there is some sort of meritocracy in play. The same things students do to make themselves competitive also allow you to meet the recommendation people and have them like you."* Our sources concurred that *"you've got to have a very strong paper record before recommenders will help you."* The ex-clerks we spoke to had *"jumped through every hoop necessary,"* but not just out of a sense of duty. *"I did those things for years because I enjoyed them,"* says one. *"People you meet on Law Review come back and talk about the experience they've had and you learn a lot from it. These things may appear resume-focused, but they're also a lot of fun!"*

At the time of writing, all of our interviewees were working at Jones Day.

Pro bono

Doing your bit for society, or advancing your legal skills – whichever way you look at it, pro bono does a world of good.

IT'S SHORT for 'pro bono publico', which, you won't need telling, means 'for the public good'. Pro bono is essentially voluntary work carried out by legal professionals – drawing on their legal nous to help out those who couldn't otherwise afford legal advice. The work offers up limitless opportunities, from advising struggling artists on the technicalities of IP law, to helping draw up new legal constitutions for war-torn African states.

Why do firms do it?

In a profession that is wedded to the billable hour, it seems even shark-like partners have a soft side. The late Esther Lardent, ex president and CEO of the Pro Bono Institute, stated when we chatted a few years ago: "I think that larger law firms do pro bono for the same reason that many individual lawyers do it. There's a sense that there are problems only lawyers can address – it's a special responsibility." She continued: "Fundamentally, this really is a question of passion and a desire to serve." She certainly embodied that passion (look her up for more info on her fantastic work), but it turns out that giving back to the community is also a pretty smart business move:

1. A top-quality pro bono program attracts top-quality attorneys. Those who enter the profession with dreams of changing the world are more likely to join a firm that lets them run with these projects than one that denies them the chance. Increased pro bono opportunities can seal the deal for gold-standard candidates. Pro bono also serves as an incentive for more senior attorneys or partners to stick around.

2. Pro bono has come to play a central role in training for young attorneys. Juniors tend to be afforded heaps of responsibility on these matters, often taking the lead and liaising with the client directly rather than shuffling papers in the background. Not only is it an effective method of on-the-job training, but it saves both time and money on more formalized programs.

Litigation powerhouse Jenner & Block has long been known for racking up a high average number of pro bono hours per attorney, and 2017 was no exception – each of the firm's US-based lawyers devoted 168.4 hours on average over the year. The firm's previous pro bono chairman, Gabriel Fuentes, explains: "A very big factor in a firm's decision to do pro bono is that it's a great training tool for younger associates, particularly for litigators. Given the type of work that firms like Jenner do – very high-end, with millions or billions of dollars involved in any matter – cases often settle before they go to trial. Sometimes the stakes are so high that the youngest associates don't get the participation they might want." This is where pro bono comes into its own. "The program allows younger attorneys to make decisions about strategy, and learn how to conduct themselves in court under our supervision. They learn all those essential elements of litigation that young attorneys need in order to develop into successful older attorneys and partners."

> "A very big factor in a firm's decision to do pro bono is that it's a great training tool for younger associates, particularly for litigators."

3. The work is also a tremendous morale booster. Few things in BigLaw will seem as worthwhile as getting an innocent man off death row, or reuniting an asylum seeker with their family. Pro bono recognition events aren't bad for team spirit either. It's known as "pro bono glue," Esther Lardent explained. "In terms of goodwill, branding, and the retention of attorneys, large firms have the ability to use pro bono as a rallying force and a source of cross-office collaboration."

4. A healthy pro bono caseload is a PR officer's dream. Even juniors admit that "the website looks better when you can show that pro bono is widely available." Then there's the fact that publicity regarding a pro bono case is cheaper and much more credible than a paid advertisement. It gets the firm's name out into the community, beyond legal circles. Studies have shown that clients are more likely to part with their money if firms are perceived to be involved with worthwhile causes. In this way, pro bono is a nifty exercise in branding.

On chambers-associate.com...

- Ten pro bono organizations you should know about.

For a prime example, look no further than Gibson Dunn. The firm's renowned litigator Ted Olson teamed up with David Boies, his opposing counsel in *Bush v Gore*, to challenge Prop 8, a California state constitutional amendment banning same-sex marriage. His work on the lawsuit earned him a place among *Time 100*'s greatest thinkers, and an ABA Medal (the highest award of the American Bar Association). The case caused such a furore it was even turned into a play, *8*, which saw Olson played by John Lithgow and Martin Sheen, and Boies by Morgan Freeman and George Clooney. Not bad publicity for a bit of pro bono work.

So, from a business perspective, pro bono makes sense. Why, then, do some firms do so much more than others? According to our 2017 figures, US attorneys at Jenner & Block, Munger, Orrick, Patterson Belknap and Skadden stacked up an impressive average of over 130 pro bono hours each. Compare this to Greenberg Traurig, Sterne Kessler, Epstein, Fitzpatrick, Fox Rothschild and Waller, whose US-based attorneys mustered a relatively low average of less than 20 hours per person.

> *"It's really nice to step outside of what you're doing for the big clients and help people who wouldn't otherwise be able to afford it."*

Like so many things in business, this often comes down to the bottom line: there's a clear correlation between gross revenue and the amount of pro bono that a firm racks up. Take Curtis, for instance. This international firm's revenue has gone berserk in recent years, more than doubling between 2007 and 2013 – and ballooning by over 27% in the following three years. Its pro bono contribution has taken a similar gradient, increasing from an average of 17.5 hours per attorney in 2011 to 45 in 2013. In fact, every year firms in the *Am Law100* far outdo those lower down the rankings in terms of pro bono.

This is largely down to a lack of resources. Your Gibson Dunns (126 hours in 2017) and Ropes & Grays (119) can afford to hire a full-time pro bono coordinator or put together a robust pro bono committee. Many of these law firms have also fostered longstanding relationships with public service organizations. At smaller firms, full-time partners are likely to be juggling pro bono coordination tasks with their already hefty workload, which has a knock-on effect on the program's ultimate impact.

The ratio of associates to partners also plays a part, as does geography. If your biggest office is in Phoenix, Arizona – like Snell & Wilmer (29 hours in 2017) – fewer pro bono opportunities are likely to present themselves compared to a firm based in New York or DC like Cleary (115).

Why do attorneys do it?

After a hard week of training, networking and racking up an obscene amount of billable hours, why spend your time rifling through immigration documents when you could be eating chocolate mousse in front of *Unbreakable Kimmy Schmidt*? As one associate put it, *"there are two kinds of time: time you're billing hours that count, and time you could be spending on the couch."*

Well, for starters, doing pro bono work just feels good. One junior associate told us: *"It's really nice to step outside of what you're doing for the big clients and help people who wouldn't otherwise be able to afford it."* Plus, on a more cynical note: *"It's often a more interesting topic of conversation at a party than what financing transaction you just closed."*

Secondly, as we've already mentioned, pro bono projects provide some of the best on-the-job training you're likely to receive as an attorney. Another massive bonus is that juniors can actually seek out the type of skills and experience they want to gain, and make a beeline for those cases.

The integral issue of billable hours complicates things. Every firm has a different policy when it comes to pro bono work. Some count time spent on pro bono in exactly the same way as paid client hours (Cleary, Jones Day). Most only count a certain number of pro bono hours as billable (Haynes and Boone, Gibbons). A select few only begin to count pro bono once juniors have reached their billable hour target, while others don't count time spent on pro bono at all. Of course, within these broad categories fall myriad variations, but generally *"it's considered part of firm citizenship,"* one source explained. All in all, the billable hour/pro bono equilibrium is well worth taking into consideration when choosing the firm to kickstart your career.

State requirements

In 1969, the ABA adopted the Code of Professional Responsibility, which stated: *"Every lawyer, regardless of professional prominence or professional workload, should find time to participate in serving the disadvantaged."* This still stands today, as does the aspirational goal that every lawyer in the USA should spend at least 50 hours a year working on pro bono matters.

In most states, however, these rules aren't enforced (apart from Florida, Hawaii, Illinois, Indiana, Maryland, Mississippi, Nevada and New Mexico). They recognize that attorneys may not be dead on 50 hours each year, but suggest that over the entire course of their career it should pretty much balance out. Some states have also departed from the 50-hour rule, choosing their own aspirational pro bono goal. Virginia, for instance, requires attorneys to dedicate 2% of their professional time to pro bono. In Oregon, the target is 80 hours.

One of the biggest talking points in the pro bono world recently has been New York's adoption of a new hours requirement. On May 1, 2012, New York's then-Chief Judge Jonathan Lippman announced that all applicants for admission to the New York Bar from January 2015 would be required to have completed 50 hours of pro bono. Go online to read more about the impact of this.

What sort of pro bono work is on offer?

The opportunities for pro bono work may as well be endless; some firms have an enormous list of options, and strongly encourage associates to bring in their own projects from outside. Others are more limited in their range, working closely with a couple of organizations or insisting that juniors only take on pro bono work that complements their practice area. A lack of pro bono options is a regular grumble among our transactional-focused associates.

That said, in the past few years we've spoken to associates involved in a whole range of fascinating projects, like assisting with Hurricane Sandy relief efforts, volunteering for a presidential election protection helpline to combat corruption, defending families who are having their homes foreclosed, and helping survivors of sex trafficking have their convictions for prostitution overturned (to name but a few).

But it is true that certain types of pro bono matters are likely to crop up more than most: death penalty, civil rights, prisoners' rights, criminal defense and veterans cases tend be the most common.

Current issues in pro bono

After the recession, the 'justice gap' – the divide between the legal needs of low-income people and the ability of civil legal mechanisms to meet these needs – visibly grew. Already bending under pressure, the system came under additional strain. The Legal Services Corporation (LSC), the largest single funder of civil legal services in the USA, has for several years been reporting on the depressingly low percentages of low-income people with civil legal problems who are actually able to obtain the necessary legal assistance. The March 2013 sequestration didn't help matters.

It's perhaps no surprise then that Jonathan Lippman took arguably drastic measures a few years back and implemented a scheme whereby all applicants to the New York bar must have carried out a minimum of 50 hours of legal pro bono work. The new rule has been active since January 2015, and it was estimated that it would add 500,000 hours of voluntary legal assistance in the area.

One of the hottest pro bono matters recently has been The Clemency Project: an initiative in which lawyers have helped non-violent offenders, who would have likely received a substantially lower sentence had they been convicted today, obtain clemency. During his time in office, President Obama granted clemency to 1,927 individuals. In one case, Hunton & Williams obtained clemency for William Ortiz, commuting his 50-year sentence for non-violent, low-level drug offenses.

Immigration and asylum cases have also been on the rise, and this will likely continue in the foreseeable future. The true effects of President Trump's executive order on immigration are yet to be fully seen. In the meantime, Jones Day associates have got involved with the Unaccompanied Minors project. Families who cross the US borders *"end up subject to removal or deportation with no access to legal representation."* The project aims to help children who have been separated from their families gain Special Immigrant Juvenile Status. Check out our website for more on recent pro bono matters.

Diversity: Jenner & Block

Jenner & Block lawyers talk to us about making LGBT diversity and inclusion *"part of the fabric"* of their institution. Whether you identify as LGBT or not, Jenner's lawyers educate us all about how law firms should approach inclusion, and how you the applicant should proceed.

In BigLaw, diversity is a big concern. Every year many words are exchanged and dollars spent in the hope of making firms more representative of the American population, but only a handful of firms can show a good return. Jenner & Block is one such firm: with 8.3% of associates identifying as LGBT, the firm has the highest figure in the *Am Law 100* and outranks the rest of BigLaw by some degree – the average in our guide is 3.8%. We interviewed a few LGBT lawyers and diversity leaders at the firm to find out why Jenner is getting results where others are not, and what impact it has on the whole firm.

Fighting the cause has been important for Jenner and has sent a strong message to the LGBT legal community. (Go to chambers-associate.com to read more about Jenner's legacy of LGBT advocacy.) Andrew Sullivan commends the firm's commitment to diversity and inclusion. He reflected that LGBT lawyers *"don't have to be the token LGBT person."* When LGBT lawyers don't feel 'token', they feel respected for their LGBT status but not defined by it. As with other areas in D&I, achieving a kind of *"critical mass,"* as Partner (and one of the LGBT Bar's Top LGBT Lawyers Under 40 award winner) Emily Chapuis puts it, makes a huge cultural impact; *"It feels pretty terrific having so many people share and understand LGBT issues."*

To affinity and beyond

Attracting the numbers is one problem, but as we know from tracking the rates of women making partner in BigLaw, the culture must remain open all the way up the hierarchy. Affinity groups are one effective way of keeping up a dialogue, and Jenner, unsurprisingly, has *"a very active LGBT affinity group."* Not only do they offer a 'safe space' for LGBT lawyers to *"not worry about who you are,"* but they're also the vehicle for *"pushing forward LGBT initiatives within the firm."* The group has *"lots of conversations to make sure our internal policies match up to our firm values,"* Chapuis tells us. *"We hit all the check marks for inclusion, but we're constantly trying to figure out ways to do more than that!"*

Jenner's LGBT affinity group houses within it a working group that is focused on trans inclusion. *"Focusing on*

specific groups is a part of being inclusive," says Courtney Carter, the Associate Director of Diversity and Inclusion. *"We emphasize this by hosting a variety of events to help us move the needle."* One recent event led by the working group was a panel on transgender inclusion in the workplace. *"We had two experts in the field,"* including Jillian Wise, who works with the Transgender Legal Defense and Education Fund, and *"our panelists discussed what they're seeing in workplaces and some best practices."* The firm maximized the event's impact by inviting local law students and broadcasting it live across the firm's network. Chapuis tells us, *"We need to share what we can all be doing in order to improve inclusion everywhere."*

Genderqueer pioneer

Jenner has been something of a trendsetter. *"In terms of LGBT inclusion we have long been an industry leader. Jenner offered LGBT-inclusive benefits and policies before most other law firms did,"* Chapuis explains. *"Now those benefits and policies have become standard in many law firms!"* But that doesn't mean the battle for LGBT equality is over; *"trans inclusion is an area we're really trying to push and further establish Jenner & Block as an industry leader."*

Associate Emily McWilliams is the first lawyer at the firm to come out as trans and use gender-neutral pronouns and titles. *"Last year I came out as transgender – as genderqueer and on the trans spectrum,"* they told us, *"and the firm said from day one 'what can we do support you?' and 'what can we do better?'"*

"It is so powerful to have someone who is comfortable to be who they are."

Including people of trans experience in the workplace means promoting specific initiatives, such as using an employee healthcare provider that covers any surgeries and medicine wanted by the individual for their transition, equal bathroom policies, and a standardized system for communicating names and pronouns internally. But listening is probably the best thing an employer can do, thinks McWilliams: *"When I say there are resources I need* on a personal level to be included, they trust me on that. There's only one of me, but it's not contingent on the number of trans people there are here: I work here, I'm a colleague – that's enough for them to take it seriously."

Transgender people still experience severe legal challenges in healthcare, immigration and legal gender recognition, as well as laws that impact daily life such as state-based 'bathroom bills' and exclusive insurance policies. Transgender lawyers bring a fresh perspective and help push the profession forward – Jenner is one firm acknowledging that. As Carter puts it, it's an opportunity for leadership in the profession: "It is so powerful to have someone who is comfortable to be who they are. It's one thing for me to say the firm lets people openly be who they are; it's another to see someone live that out. Emily is a role model and messenger – they are the best of us!"

Diversity: the business case

"We've known for a long time that diversity of all kinds makes our work better," Chapuis tells us. "If you exclude people, implicitly or explicitly, for any reason – you're not getting the best result you can get."

Carter, an expert on the business case for diversity, reminds businesses that fostering inclusivity and diversity is "obviously the moral and right thing to do." But for those that aren't persuaded by moral duty, she implores that diversity "is also a business imperative! And there are hard facts and research that back that up."

Data research and marketing specialists Out Now's 2015 report *LGBT Diversity: Show Me the Business Case* claims that LGBT diversity in the workplace can improve team productivity by up to 30%. Reports on the other main focuses of diversity – women and ethnicity – produce equally persuasive figures. An increasing trend, for example, is being led by the clients who are becoming more demanding about the diversity on legal teams at the point of tender.

"I'm going to be successful in my life, I'm going to create this life for myself."

A study from McKinsey & Company found that companies with diverse leadership generally performed better financially, and another from Deloitte concluded that more diverse companies were perceived to have a significant competitive advantage. The consensus is that diverse teams offer a greater variety of ways to tackle problems; more lived experience means more potential solutions to issues.

"We are people who have faced adversity," says Andrew Sullivan, highlighting a trait LGBT people share with many from other diverse groups. "That background tends to make us fighters, strivers and hard-workers," he adds. Drawing on his own life experience, Sullivan elaborates: "I don't want to generalize – but for me, going through high school I faced a lot of not nice things. It forced me to say to myself: 'you know what? I'm going to rise above this, I'm going to work hard, study hard and I'm going to be successful in my life, I'm going to create this life for myself.'"

"When you face adversity, it propels you," concludes Sullivan. This knowledge should be empowering to LGBT students: most standard OCI questions cover the generic 'tell us about a time you overcame adversity'. This is the moment to draw on your personal experience, and explain why it would be an asset to the firm.

It's the little things

However inclusive a firm is, being a lawyer requires a lot of contact with people outside of the office. Sullivan tells us of the inescapable "implicit or explicit bias of a whole host of people who might not give you a fair shot as a lawyer because of who you are. When you think about going in front of a jury, you don't know who's on the other side of the equation."

Of course, if queerphobia presents itself and an LGBT individual feels uncomfortable or unsafe, firms dedicated to inclusion ought to remove the prejudiced party. However, when it comes to the silent implicit bias of a client, juror, opposing counsel or judge, it can be much harder to even detect a prejudice against LGBT lawyers. Small, almost undetectable prejudices can eat away at an LGBT individual's career confidence.

"You're never going to be able to do your job well if you're not being authentic."

Sullivan says if he's in a situation where he feels the person on the other side might have a bias against LGBT individuals: "I forge ahead and do the best I can. At the end of the day, you're never going to be able to do your job well if you're not being authentic." Though not an option available to everyone, doing your best work in the face of implicit bias shows the world that LGBT people will not stand down for others' prejudices.

In the office, micro-discriminations can occur outside of direct homophobic and transphobic behavior, even in an organization that counts itself as LGBT inclusive. Lack of LGBT management, exclusive language and *that* indescribable vibe that you need to watch what you say can all lead LGBT people to feel they may have no future with an employer. McWilliams tells us: "If you're out as LGBT for long enough, you learn to read signs of disapproval. You *learn the sidelong glances, the phrases."* (Though they are quick to add: *"I've never gotten signals from my colleagues at Jenner & Block that my queerness is a disruption."*)

Such behavior hinders confidence and drive and so decreases business productivity too. In addition, lack of confidence could cost an LGBT individual that important place on a case or deal team, leading to a lower chance of promotion. This in turn leads to fewer LGBT people in positions of power at a law firm, which means fewer role models for those at the entry level.

On the cutting room floor

In a profession like law that relies heavily on interaction and rapport, being open and honest is key. Sullivan tells us: *"If I was editing a conversation with a colleague or client to cut out the fact that I have a partner of 12 years and we just bought our first house or are planning on adopting, I'm not going to be authentic or connect."* This hinders work product for both the individual and the firm. *"Clients need to have trust in their lawyer,"* explains partner Emily Loeb. *"If there are barriers in the relationship, it's harder to provide the best legal services."* Talking about family, friends or social activities is one of the most common ways to build rapport in a business meeting – everyone ought to be open to talking to LGBT people about all these things too. *"People perceive barriers even if they're unspoken,"* says McWilliams.

"At Jenner & Block there's no 'do you have a husband/wife?' – people will say 'partner'."

Firms can promote equality through promoting simple changes to phrasing: *"At Jenner & Block there's no 'do you have a husband/wife?' – people will say say 'partner',"* McWilliams tells us. Trans and non-binary inclusion can be promoted through the avoidance of gendered formal greetings like 'ladies and gentlemen', and the inclusion of custom gender options rather than 'male' and 'female' on application and data tracking forms. *"These are small things that really make a difference in people's lives,"* says Carter.

In addition, *"a lot of it is about signalling,"* McWilliams tells us. *"At orientation for first-years this year, colleagues introduced themselves and gave their pronouns at the same time."* This is a signal that *"in itself says 'hey, we're a trans friendly environment and there's no stigma here'."*

Is it worth it? Let me work it

As an aspiring LGBT lawyer, there are also bigger policies to look into when you're choosing a firm: gender-neutral parental leave, adoption benefits, equal healthcare access, and future prospects.

Before you get to a firm, analyze if senior management are practicing what they preach in terms of wanting LGBT individuals to succeed at their firm. If a firm's LGBT inclusive policies are relatively new then a lack of LGBT people at the top may be a historic pipeline issue. However, it's not a bad idea to ask exactly what is in place to help you succeed and make your way to the top of the firm.

"I made it very clear that I was LGBT to any person I was speaking with."

Carter suggests students *"talk to other lawyers about diversity at the firm. Hearing personal experiences and advice from LGBT lawyers who have worked there is key."* However, Sullivan warns budding lawyer not to take advice from everyone as gospel: *"I had an older lawyer tell me 'you shouldn't get into your personal life in your interviews.' I know that his intentions were good, and he was trying to protect me based on his own experience as an LGBT lawyer – but I did not take that advice."*

In fact, Sullivan did the exact opposite, *"I made it very clear that I was LGBT to any person I was speaking with. I knew if that was a reason that I was going to be treated negatively, I didn't want to work there anyway!"* For those that feel safe and confident doing so, being open and proud is a great way not only to let a firm get to know you better, but to really gauge how accepted you'd be on a daily basis at a firm.

Carter gives us her three golden rules of how to approach the hiring process as an LGBT law student:

- The first is almost a given: "Talk to people and analyze what they say."
- The second requires some detective skills: "Look at the lists of who's best for diversity, and which law firms have been on those lists for some years in a row. It's important that a firm is demonstrating inclusion year after year."
- And third, ask questions: "Ask the firm how they celebrate diversity and inclusion. If people struggle to answer, that says a lot. When a law firm values diversity, people at multiple levels should be able to speak to it."

Loud and proud

LGBT people exist in every profession in every corner of the world. But, Andrew Sullivan says, *"LGBT people cannot be their best and most productive selves when they're hiding a meaningful part of their identity."* Prospective LGBT lawyers should show off their *"unique skills and ability to look at problems through different lenses,"* Loeb says.

As an LGBT student, demand support from your potential employers and let them know that by discounting you, *"it would hinder their work product, quite frankly."* Law students also have the power to change the hearts and minds of their cis/straight counterparts and superiors by asking the right questions about LGBT inclusivity, being their best selves, and existing with pride. *"There's so many ways to make a difference,"* McWilliams concludes, *"and my body in this space makes waves."*

Emily McWilliams, associate

Emily Chapuis, partner

Andrew Sullivan, associate

Emily Loeb, partner

Courtney Dredden Carter, associate director of diversity and inclusion

JENNER&BLOCK LLP

"During the first semester we advise students to focus on their studies and then to research employers as time permits." – Jason McCann, Associate Director of Career Services, Harvard Law School

This is the first formal opportunity that employers have to make one-on-one recruiting contact with law students

"In their first semester students should look at their style of learning but in the second it's imperative to talk about different practice areas and make the most of networking opportunities. People don't necessarily need to know they want to go into project finance, but it's wise to distinguish between litigation and corporate and find something you enjoy." - Rebecca Bradley, hiring partner at Foley & Lardner.

"Here at Cornell we have a series of programs during spring term where firms visit law schools to talk about their practice area." – Now is the time to figure our what kind of lawyer you want to be.

"Recruiters call this period 'The Compression'. There's increased market pressure for recruiters over about three weeks and every firm wants to secure callback interviews at the same time." – Jason McCann, Harvard

Because of the compressed time frame of on-campus interviews, some large firms do a small amount of 'precruiting' in the summer to connect with candidates – and sometimes make offers ahead of OCIs." – Lois T. Casaleggi, Senior Director of Career Services, University of Chicago Law School.

Large firms tend to hire very few first year students. Careers Advisors at Cornell told us: *"Positions with federal judges are very popular for first year interns. We also see a lot of people going to in-house legal departments, government services, the US attorney's office and nonprofits."*

"Many students will have had their initial interviews and a good percentage will have had callbacks before their second year even begins." – Cornell

In most cases students can keep a maximum of five choices open for up to 28 days.

"Typically offers follow callbacks fairly quickly; usually within two weeks." – Jason McCann, Harvard

We heard: *"Firms now realize the value of allowing summers to get their hands dirty with real tasks; that approach demonstrates how you will actually react under certain circumstances."* Hiring partners confirmed: *"throwing people into the mix seems to work out best for everyone involved."*

For more on what it's like to summer at a BigLaw firm, head to chambers-associate.com…

Law school timeline

1L year

August 2018 – Start of fall semester

December 2018 – Fall exam period

January 2019 – Spring OCIs: a much smaller program than fall recruiting, but more likely to include government and public interest organizations.

April/May 2019 – Spring exam period

June 2019 – Most students get grades back

1L summer

July/August 2019 – Bidding for OCIs

Students can bid on between 20 and 50 employers usually using Symplicity.

Summer internships

2L year

August/September 2019 – 'Fall recruiting': OCIs

August/September/October 2019 – Callback interviews / Offers received

January 2020 – Spring term

MPRE (Multistate Professional Responsibility Examination) held in March, August and November – most students take this after they've completed their PR (professional responsibility) class.

2L summer

Summer 2020 – Summer programs at law firms
(these usually last from six to 12 weeks)

3L year

Fall 2020 – begin planning for the Bar Exam

Throughout – work on Bar application

May/June 2021 – Commencement!

Take Bar Exam

Becoming a Lawyer

"One of our existing associates would drive around the States in an Oscar Mayer Weiner car and meet people and connect with them. It made for a very interesting discussion point, but more importantly it really showed how he was able to connect with people of all types, and that is so important at a global law firm. You may think you've mastered the culture around you and then end up dealing with a client who may be from a different country or have a completely different background. Somebody who shows themselves to be very nimble in connecting with people is always impressive to me."

– K&L Gates' recruitment and integration partner, Craig Budner

Practice Areas

Commercial and Industrial

"There'll be changes in this profession, and they'll occur at an accelerating pace over the years to come. It's a great profession, and will always be in demand. People will always need counsel and advice to get from point A to B, or out of difficult situations. It's very gratifying and I would encourage students to stay with it – there'll be disruption to the industry (as there will be with lots of industries), but the need for good, sage counsel will always be present."
– Simpson's chairman Bill Dougherty.

Food & beverages, retail and franchising

In a nutshell

Food and beverages, retail, and franchising law are three overlapping practice areas, which center on the trade of products and services. They encompass the sale of goods and services to consumers, as well as business-to-business (B2B) matters. Attorneys who specialize in these fields must take a holistic approach to their work, as they deal with a wide range of issues; matters can encompass real estate leases, franchise documentation, M&A deals, antitrust compliance and IP regulations. There is a contentious side to these practices, where the work is similarly varied: false advertising class actions, GMO (genetically modified organism) labeling claims and data breach investigations are covered alongside other issues. Practitioners act for an unsurprisingly broad list of clients, including multinational food distributors, international fashion houses, shopping centers and trade associations.

The global flow of products and services, facilitated by the rise of e-commerce, means that lawyers typically have expertise in both international and domestic regulations. The latter are issued by the likes of the Food and Drug Administration (FDA), the United States Department of Agriculture (USDA), the Drug Enforcement Administration (DEA), the Department of Justice (DOJ), and the Federal Trade Commission (FTC).

What lawyers do

Food & Beverages/Retail (contentious)

- Receive instructions from a client who has been accused of false advertising.
- File for a motion to dismiss.
- If it's a class action, conduct 'class' discovery. This involves working with experts to try to defeat class action certification. Attorneys will depose the experts before filing and defending their reports.
- If class certification is granted (or if the case was never a class action in the first place) attorneys carry out 'merits' discovery. They obtain all the relevant documents and conduct depositions about liability and damages.
- Apply for summary judgment. If summary judgment is denied, the case goes to trial. Attorneys determine the evidence and depositions to use, produce the exhibit list, and decide on what sort of discovery or motions to advocate.
- Go to trial. Handle post-trial steps.
- Attorneys for the plaintiff conduct due diligence before filing a complaint, oppose motions to dismiss, defend class action certification and oppose summary judgment.

Franchising (transactional)

- Receive instructions from a franchisor who would like to establish a franchise agreement with a franchisee.
- Draft a franchise disclosure document (FDD) and send it to the franchisee to review.
- Negotiate any revisions to the disclosure document in consultation with the client.
- Apply to have the FDD filed by a state agency if required under state law.
- Draft the franchise contract and ensure that it is signed by both parties.

Realities of the job

- **Miriam Guggenheim**, cochair of **Covington & Burling's** food, drug & device practice group says: *"The issues in the food and beverages industry are quite broad. There is nutrition and public health policy; engaging with Congress and the FDA; considering what consumer advocacy groups and NGOs think about a particular issue; helping companies think through acquisitions and about the value of the brand; giving labeling advice; and preventing consumer fraud litigation."*

> *"There will be enforcement actions and recalls where you need to drop everything and help a client make a decision and interact with regulatory agencies."*

- **Martin Hahn**, a food and beverages partner at **Hogan Lovells**, asserts: *"The typical day is unpredictable. There will be countless calls and people that will stop by your office. There will be enforcement actions and recalls where you need to drop everything and help a client make a decision and interact with regulatory agencies."*
- He jokes: *"I never accomplish what I intend to do when I come into the office!"*
- Food and beverages cases are often filed in California with the US District Court for the Northern District of California, which is fondly referred to as the 'Food Court.'
- Lawyers in this field must maintain a thorough understanding of various acts, especially the Nutrition Labeling and Education Act (1990) and the FDA Food Safety Modernization Act (2011).

Practice Areas

Rankings in *Chambers USA*

Top Ranked

DLA Piper (US)	McDermott Will & Emery
Gibson, Dunn & Crutcher	Morgan, Lewis & Bockius
Greenberg Traurig, PA	Perkins Coie
Jones Day	

Highly Recommended

Foley & Lardner	Latham & Watkins
Goulston & Storrs	Norton Rose Fulbright
Haynes and Boone	Paul, Weiss
Holland & Knight	Pillsbury Winthrop Shaw
Hunton Andrews Kurth	Venable
King & Spalding	Wiley Rein

For more detail on ranking tiers and locations, visit
www.chambersandpartners.com

- An interest in science is essential within the food and beverages domain: *"You have to be willing to engage with scientific studies and grapple with them,"* Guggenheim points out.
- Guggenheim also emphasizes the importance of time management, especially as a regulatory attorney: *"We tend to work on several different matters at a time, compared to litigators or corporate attorneys who might work on one deal for an extended period. I have 14 to 16 client matters on any given day, which is fun but can also be challenging."* However, she also notes that *"the hours are still lower compared to typical litigation or corporate practices."*

"You have to be willing to engage with scientific studies and grapple with them."

- **Deborah Coldwell**, a franchising litigator at **Haynes and Boone**, flags the difference between a litigator's and a corporate attorney's schedule: *"50% or more of my colleagues are transactional lawyers. They are very busy at year end, whereas we are not so busy. However, we work really hard when we are going to trial — 24/7 in some instances."*

- Working with foreign jurisdictions is common for a transactional franchising lawyer. *"We do a significant amount of work for US-based clients expanding internationally,"* states **Stuart Hershman**, a franchising partner at **DLA Piper**. He explains that most overseas jurisdictions do not have governmental franchising agencies: *"You have to comply with laws internationally, including franchise-specific laws in an increasing number of countries, but overall (there of course are exceptions) there isn't government interaction and oversight like there is in the US."* In contrast, franchising litigators find that most brawls tend to be domestic in nature. *"I have not seen that many cross-border court cases,"*
- Coldwell tells us. *"Typically if they are cross-border they end up in arbitration."*
- Many firms actively seek out candidates with professional work experience. **Warren Karp**, chair of **Greenberg Traurig**'s global retail practice, notes: *"We look for people who have taken a year or two after college to go out into the real world, to do volunteer work or gain business experience. We find that when they come into the firm as a young associate they have a different, beneficial perspective."*

Current Issues
Food & Beverages

- There has been much debate and consumer concern over labeling in recent years. Recent attention has been given to what constitutes 'natural' food as, at the time of writing, there is not yet a clear legal or regulatory definition. The past three years have been marked by a sharp rise in the number of lawsuits filed (over 300) that allege misrepresentation on labeling for 'natural' products, including food and other consumer goods like laundry detergents.

"We're seeing a continued interest by consumers to learn more about their food."

- As a result, transparency is on the rise, as Miriam Guggenheim explains: *"We're seeing a continued interest by consumers to learn more about their food. Companies are intending to be more transparent about their products, by stating what the ingredients are and where they come from."* This can, however, create new problems: *"They are using more plain English and can come up against regulatory bodies if they aren't consistent with defined terms."*

Practice Areas

- The rise of artificial methods of creating meat products has led to calls from traditional beef producers to tighten legal definitions and food labeling. Increased consumer interest in artificial meat (both plant substitutes and meat grown in a lab, i.e. 'clean meat'), has prompted the beef industry to petition the US Department of Agriculture (USDA) to exclude artificial meat products from the definition of 'beef' under federal law. Legal wrangles over the very definition of what constitutes a 'meat' product are likely to continue.
- The FDA intends to extend the deadline for when food manufacturers will have to introduce a new 'Nutrition Facts' label for their packaged foods. Manufacturers with $10 million or more in food sales will have until January 2020 to do so, while those with sales under that amount will have until January 2021. Martin Hahn tells us that the introduction of the label has resulted in *"a tremendous economic burden on the industry."*
- He hopes that the new administration will be *"more sensitive to industry concerns."*
- According to Hahn, *"litigation continues to be one of the biggest threats to the food industry. People are looking for new and creative ways to bring actions against the industry. It is a tremendous drag on resources and companies' ability to produce high-quality food products."*
- Like many practice areas, the food and beverages market is becoming increasingly international in its focus. Guggenheim reports: *"Foreign companies are interested in entering the US and domestic companies are looking to acquire foreign companies and bring new food products to the country."*
- The Trump administration has focused on deregulating the industry, by proposing cuts to the likes of the Supplemental Nutrition Assistance Program and delaying the aforementioned 'Nutrition Facts' label deadline. This marks a shift from the stance taken by the Obama administration, which was keen to place responsibility on food manufacturers for tackling issues such as obesity and diabetes – Trump's administration places more of that responsibility on the consumers themselves.
- Recently a number of big industry names in Europe and North America have started dabbling in startup incubators and accelerators to help them develop new products. These include food manufacturer Land O'Lakes, Nestlé and PepsiCo. This has become all the more important as 2017 saw food startups experience significant profit increases along with high growth, while big name brands appeared to struggle more. Professional services firm Moss Adams claims that only 41% of what it defines as 'iconic brands' had any growth during the year. It also predicts that further M&A activity in the sector should be expected, particularly from private equity investors.

- The Pennsylvania Supreme Court announced in early 2018 that it would hear an appeal against Philadelphia's recent tax on sweetened beverages. The tax, which in 2017 raised $78 million, is being collected to pay for community initiatives in the city. The question being dissected by the appeal is whether the city's tax duplicates one already being collected by the state, and therefore violates a law passed in 1932.

Retail

- The popularity of online shopping has inevitably affected the commerce of bricks-and-mortar retailers; retail space in shopping malls has consequently become cheaper.
- Furthermore, the sector has suffered from the lackluster economy, leading to an increased number of companies filing for bankruptcy. A total of 50 US retailers filed for bankruptcy in 2017. These included big names like Toys R Us, and a report by S&P Global Market Intelligence suggests that 15 more companies are at risk, including the parent company of Sears and Kmart, as well as Bebe Stores.
- The digitalization of the retail market (via increased use of mobile devices and the spread of social media) has given rise to many opportunities for lawyers. Warren Karp identifies one important trend in this digitized retail market: *"There is a move from multichannel retailing to consumer-centric, omnichannel retailing where the consumer has multiple choices. They can get products from anywhere, delivered directly from a fulfillment center or store."*
- Intellectual property is an important strand of retail work. Companies often look to protect their designs under trade dress – a constituent of the Lanham Act. In 2012, for example, the fashion designer Christian Louboutin succeeded in protecting his red shoe sole under trade dress in the US.
- Products are also becoming 'smarter' in line with technological developments. E-textiles are of great interest to apparel manufacturers, as well as to the military sector, which accounted for over 26% of the global market share, according to research by Technavio. In addition, US conglomerate DuPont has recently launched a range of 'smart clothing' aimed at the healthcare and fitness industries, which incorporates stretchable electronic inks and films that can trace the wearer's heart and breathing rates.
- The Trump administration's lowering of the corporate tax rate from 35% to 21% should provide many retailers with excess cash at the end of 2018. However, retailers that are already in debt may not experience the benefit, as there are now limits on how much in the way of debt expenses and operating losses can be used to lower the amount of tax paid.

Franchising

- One of the big issues in the franchising market continues to be the 'joint employer' model. It has thrown up the following question: which party is responsible for employees? The franchisor (the owner of the franchise) or the franchisee (the company or individual licensed to operate under the franchise). The saga started in 2014 when the National Labor Relations Board decided that McDonald's could be held partially responsible for its franchisees' employees. Much has happened since then with the 2015 Browning-Ferris case expanding the definition of a joint employer, much to the consternation of franchisors. This was then overturned in the 2017 Hy-Brand case, to industry relief. However, this decision didn't last long, as the case was *also* overturned shortly after in February 2018 – a move that reinstated the Browning-Ferris definition. Watch out for developments in this back and forth of legal ping-pong.

- Stuart Hershman tells us. Consequently, a lot of franchising lawyers are advising on employment dispute resolution matters.

- Elsewhere, Deborah Coldwell notes that technology poses a challenge to the franchising market. She explains that there are laws for everything *"from drone delivery, to online ordering, to website franchise sales,"* adding: *"Keeping up is going to be a challenge for lawyers and companies because technology moves so quickly."*

"I think that in this competitive industry walking into a firm and having a sense of what its individual lawyers do, the types of matters they work on and being able to talk about that helps to make candidates stand out."
– Allen & Overy's New York managing partner,
Dave Lewis

International trade

In a nutshell

The work of international trade lawyers is split between two main areas: the application of domestic law to international trade, and treaty-based international law governing trade flows. On the domestic side, work covers export controls, embargoes and economic sanctions, import relief actions such as antidumping, countervailing duties and safeguards, and customs classifications, valuation and rules of origin matters. In relation to international treaties, attorneys advise on World Trade Organization (WTO) rules, preferential trade regimes such as the North American Free Trade Agreement (NAFTA) and bilateral investment treaties (BITs).

Lawyers advise on the implementation of these domestic and international rules, and counsel clients in disputes related to their violation. Clients include US organizations doing business in foreign jurisdictions and foreign businesses operating in the USA; they include major corporations, trade associations and national and regional governments.

What lawyers do

Domestic

- Lawyers represent clients before the International Trade Commission (ITC) and the Department of Commerce (DOC), the two main bodies that review petitions related to import laws. They are the first port of call for disputes and protests related to issues such as dumping, countervailing duties and safeguards.
- The first port of call for protests over customs classifications, valuation and rules of origin matters is US Customs and Border Protection (CBP).
- Lawyers assist US companies to secure a license from the DOC for the export of 'dual use' goods (with both military and commercial applications), or from the Department of State for the shipment of military goods.
- They also assist clients before the Treasury Department's Office of Foreign Assets Control (OFAC), which administers and enforces economic and trade sanctions against targeted foreign countries, terrorism-sponsoring organizations and international narcotics traffickers.
- Parties can protest determinations made by the ITC, DOC and CBP at the Court of International Trade. This court also hears protests against trade-related worker assistance decisions made by the Departments of Labor and Agriculture.

- Antidumping duties are imposed on imports to combat 'dumping' – selling a product in an export market at a price less than its home market value, which injures a domestic industry.
- Countervailing duties are similar to antidumping duties, but are imposed by a country to counter the effects of subsidies in foreign markets.
- Safeguards are 'emergency' measures in response to an unforeseen increase in imports which damages or threatens to damage a specific domestic industry. Unlike 'unfair' activities like subsidies and dumping, increased shipments by themselves are not deemed to be unfair, so safeguards must be applied in a nondiscriminatory fashion.
- Section 337 of the Tariff Act of 1930 provides an alternative to US court actions to challenge imports that infringe patents or other intellectual property rights. These cases are dealt with by administrative law judges in the ITC.
- Lawyers also assist companies involved in an acquisition of a US target under review by the Committee on Foreign Investment in the United States (CFIUS). Established in 1975, CFIUS (pronounced 'sifius') is tasked with reviewing the national security implications of investment in US assets.

International

- On the treaty side, trade lawyers practice *"global regulatory law,"* according to **Andy Shoyer**, partner and co-chair of **Sidley Austin**'s international trade practice.
- Disputes are the largest source of work. The WTO is the main international arbitrator of trade disputes. Its Dispute Settlement Body makes rulings on agreements made between member states under WTO negotiations. Only sovereign states can bring disputes to the WTO so lawyers for private stakeholders will be involved in lobbying governments to bring cases or in assisting to defend them.
- Neither the US government nor the EU hires outside counsel to represent them in front of the WTO, so US attorneys often find themselves representing other nations, such as Brazil.
- Disputes relating to BITs are heard in arbitral tribunals administered by the International Centre for Settlement of Investment Disputes (ICSID), an arm of The World Bank, or similar arbitration centers.

Practice Areas

Rankings in *Chambers USA*

Top Ranked

Fish & Richardson PC	Skadden
Sidley Austin	White & Case

Highly Recommended

Akin Gump Strauss Hauer	Latham & Watkins
Alston & Bird	Morrison & Foerster
Arnold & Porter	O'Melveny & Myers
Crowell & Moring	Pillsbury Winthrop Shaw
Curtis, Mallet-Prevost	Simpson Thacher & Bartlett
Davis Polk & Wardwell	Stroock & Stroock & Lavan
DLA Piper (US)	Vinson & Elkins
Finnegan, Henderson	Wiley Rein
Gibson, Dunn & Crutcher	WilmerHale
Hughes Hubbard & Reed	Wilson Sonsini Goodrich
King & Spalding	Winston & Strawn
Kirkland & Ellis	

For more detail on ranking tiers and locations, visit www.chambersandpartners.com

- Treaty-focused attorneys will also engage in lobbying to influence the development of new international rules. *"We listen to what companies tell us about the regulatory barriers they face and translate that into potential treaty language. Then we will help businesses affect the negotiations within the US and internationally,"* Andy Shoyer explains.

Realities of the job

- **F. Joseph Warin**, partner and chair of the Washington, DC litigation department at **Gibson Dunn**, advises: *"Adventurousness and a willingness to take risks are necessary in this practice. If you're dealing with, for instance, stock options in Norway, you need a sense of intellectual curiosity to understand and process all this and then give advice that's nuanced to the environment. Cultural sensitivity is a must. Being a good listener is imperative. I urge young associates to be keen listeners and not to leapfrog that step because it's absolutely essential in order to give good solid advice."*
- International trade work is often closely tied to headline-making current events, and associates grapple with key policy as well as legal issues.
- One associate who works in an international trade department told us: *"I had focused on international studies throughout college and demonstrated an interest in international trade."*

- *"Unlike domestic litigation we don't have substantial document production and discovery work in WTO or other treaty disputes,"* Shoyer informs us. *"That saves junior associates from some of the drudge work. But that doesn't mean that lawyers don't have to get on top of the facts! Arbitrations can involve hundreds of pages of documents and younger associates will get involved in that."*
- *"International trade practices with a significant policy focus tend to be partner-heavy because clients demand high-profile advice,"* Shoyer explains. *"It's hard to generate the knowledge base required just by reading the case law: you need to have the experience. You build up your knowledge base slower."*
- Trade lawyers need to be politically aware and keep track of negotiations at the WTO and other multilateral, regional and bilateral regimes. **Joe Dorn**, former partner at **King & Spalding**, says: *"Many WTO cases are very intellectually challenging. You're often covering new ground, so that's very stimulating."*
- Andy Shoyer tells us: *"The greatest challenge and joy in this area is that you are really practicing the law of globalization. You're at the forefront of those business and policy forces that drive the world. Anyone in this practice needs to appreciate that the nexus of law and policy is very important."*
- Shoyer adds: *"While the ability to work comfortably in several languages is so helpful, a fluency with culture is vital. You need to be comfortable putting yourself in the shoes of someone from another culture. Creativity and openness is a must, perhaps more so than in any other area of the law because it's still emerging."*
- F. Joseph Warin says: *"I'm constantly globe-trotting. I'll go to London, then Abu Dhabi, then two weeks later I'll be in New Delhi. It's fascinating but it also keeps me away from my family, so this big plus is also the biggest negative."*

Current issues

- International trade laws increasingly intersect other regulatory frameworks and cut across multiple borders, which makes compliance challenging. **Beth Peters** of **Hogan Lovells** informs us that *"typically regulations within the US, EU, UK and other regions may be triggered simultaneously when trade issues arise, whether that's in international trade litigation or in international trade compliance matters. Some examples are export controls, sanctions, anti-money laundering, cybersecurity and securities reporting regulations."*

Practice Areas

- The Trans-Pacific Partnership (TPP) – currently held between Australia, Brunei, Canada, Chile, Japan, Malaysia, Mexico, New Zealand, Peru, Singapore and Vietnam – was thrown into disarray when the United States withdrew in 2017. Though a partial agreement was put together by the remaining members, the viability of the proposals without US involvement has been called into question.
- US sanctions on North Korea have been strengthened and expanded recently. In September 2017, President Trump signed an executive order permitting the freezing of any assets, organizations or individuals trading with North Korea. Further sanctions were ordered a month later.
- In June 2017, President Trump suspended various aspects of the deal reached with Cuba by the Obama administration; however, diplomatic relations remain open and new policies are being formulated.
- Brexit will completely change the legal basis of Britain's trade links with the world. *"This is an area that requires complex study,"* Peters tells us, as *"the USA and Britain have a very close trade and national security relationship."* Future developments will depend heavily on the negotiations between the UK and EU and the nature of its future relationship: if the UK exits the EU customs union (as the Government intends to) it will be able to negotiate independent trade deals around the world, but doing so could jeopardize its preexisting trade ties.
- **Matthew Nicely** of **Hughes Hubbard** stressed that *"there's always a lot of focus on the origin of goods imported into the United States. This is true with all products, but particularly those that have been subjected to antidumping or countervailing duty cases, which inevitably lead to allegations of transshipment."*

- In the recent past the most frequent target of antidumping and countervailing duty cases was China, but recent cases include *"multiple other countries, including Korea, Japan and Turkey, and others, particularly as the US steel industry has resumed its heavy use of this kind of import relief."*
- Increasingly, both US and foreign clients are becoming more aware that nations outside the USA also have complicated and important trade laws. Beth Peters highlights that *"we've certainly experienced clients addressing trade issues in Singapore, Brazil and India,"* in particular.
- India canceled investment treaties with more than 50 states in 2017, fearing they left too much room for international arbitration disputes – a serious undertaking for one of the fastest-rising economies globally. New treaty terms proposed by India to reduce the potential for international arbitration claims have so far left investors from other countries wary.
- Across the globe, World Trade Organization figures reveal that world merchandise exports have increased in value by more than 30% since 2006, with commercial service exports increasing at more than *twice* that rate.
- Export control and trade compliance are becoming an increasingly busy area due to trade control being seen as a means to exert geopolitical influence. **David J. Levine** of **McDermott Will & Emery** explains: *"In a broader sense, there is a tendency, as our election made clear, for countries to become more insular and retract from global trade deals. People are watching carefully as trade was highlighted during the campaign, and Trump is still talking about how to implement some of what he campaigned for."*

Practice Areas

Labor and employment

In a nutshell

Labor and employment law governs the workplace and the relationships between employers and employees; managers and unions; and employers and the government. BigLaw firms tend to represent employers.

Employment work involves both litigation and counseling. The former tackles claims of discrimination, including age, disability, national origin, race, religion, whistle-blower/retaliation, sex and sexual harassment. Such claims are brought by individuals or administrative agencies like the US Equal Employment Opportunity Commission (EEOC). Other common disputes concern unpaid overtime ('wage and hour' claims) under the Fair Labor Standards Act (FLSA), and claims relating to the Family and Medical Leave Act (FMLA), both of which may be filed with the US Department of Labor (DOL).

Lawyers who offer employment counseling advise on compliance with various employment laws. This involves advising on clients' wholesale employment policies and practices, as well as on 'difficult situations', be they sexual harassment complaints or reductions in force. They will often advise on the employment aspects of business transactions like M&A or restructurings. Attorneys will either provide both litigation and counseling advice, or specialize in one discipline.

BigLaw labor lawyers commonly advise management on union matters governed by the National Labor Relations Act (NLRA), which is administered by the National Labor Relations Board (NLRB). They have expertise in collective bargaining, union and strike avoidance, and strike breaking. They will also advise on Occupational Safety and Health Act (OSHA) matters, which the DOL (via the Occupational Safety and Health Administration) enforces. Labor attorneys may also engage in litigation of NLRA and OSHA disputes.

Employee Benefits, Executive Compensation & ERISA
Many firms have a distinct practice focused on executive compensation, employee benefits and ERISA work. For the uninitiated, ERISA is the Employee Retirement Income Security Act of 1974 – the federal statutory framework that governs the administration of employee benefit plans and the rights of the beneficiaries. **Kyoko Takahashi Lin**, partner at **Davis Polk**, tells us: "*The work we do is really about people: how do you motivate them? How do you get them to be incentivized and work hard and do the right thing and treat employees well? That is what we are*

trying to advise companies on." There is much, much more to this specialization, however.

What lawyers do
Employment litigation
- Receive notice of a charge or complaint filed with the EEOC or DOL, respectively.
- Advise clients on how to respond to the EEOC, DOL or other government investigations.
- Negotiate with the agencies, work with them in investigations, and try to come to settlement in appropriate cases.
- If a class action, oppose class certification.
- If no settlement can be reached, begin discovery – paper and electronic. Settlement can occur at any stage of a case.
- Provided the case is not settled, standard litigation will commence.

Employment counseling
- Review and draft employment contracts and policy documents.
- Advise clients on the steps to take when problems arise.
- Keep clients abreast of new changes to laws and regulations, often by way of newsletters or seminars.
- Advise on the employment implications of business transactions.
- Focus on minimizing risk for the client, by instilling a proactive and preventive approach.

Labor relations
- Act as a liaison between management and unions.
- Lead negotiations between the different sides.
- Litigate cases before the NLRB and in federal courts.

Realities of the job
- Only a small percentage of cases filed in the courts are putative class actions. Most are wage and hour or discrimination cases.
- Cases are heard in state and federal courts, as well as before administrative and regulatory boards.
- Many labor and employment laws will sound familiar: Americans with Disabilities Act, Civil Rights Act of 1964, Equal Pay Act, Age Discrimination in Employment Act and National Labor Relations Act.
- Most charges are found to have 'no reasonable cause' and many others will be settled before litigation.

Rankings in *Chambers USA*

Top Ranked

Alston & Bird	Morgan, Lewis & Bockius
Gibson, Dunn & Crutcher	Paul Hastings
Greenberg Traurig, PA	Perkins Coie
Hunton Andrews Kurth	Proskauer Rose
Jones Day	Waller
McDermott Will & Emery	Winston & Strawn

Highly Recommended

Akin Gump Strauss Hauer	Norton Rose Fulbright
Bracewell	Nutter McClennen & Fish
Cozen O'Connor	O'Melveny & Myers
Duane Morris	Orrick, Herrington & Sutcliffe
Dykema Gossett PLLC	
Epstein Becker & Green PC	Reed Smith
Foley & Lardner	Ropes & Gray
Fox Rothschild	Sheppard, Mullin
Gibbons P.C.	Sidley Austin
Haynes and Boone	Snell & Wilmer
Holland & Knight	Squire Patton Boggs
Jackson Walker	Thompson & Knight
Jenner & Block	Troutman Sanders
K&L Gates	Vedder Price
King & Spalding	Venable
Mayer Brown	Vinson & Elkins
Morrison & Foerster	Weil, Gotshal & Manges
Munger, Tolles & Olson	

For more detail on ranking tiers and locations, visit www.chambersandpartners.com

- The EEOC and NLRB are separate administrative agencies and are not part of the DOL. The best labor lawyers will have good people skills, because they will be interacting with both management and unions. The most successful ones will be able to convince both management and unions that they have common goals.
- According to **Thomas Linthorst**, a partner in **Morgan Lewis & Bockius**' labor & employment practice: "*Those that really can get close to their clients, understand what the client needs, and can think creatively about meeting the client's needs will find that to be a successful approach.*" When the economy is down, clients are concerned about surviving, which often involves downsizing. Advising on reductions in force is never pleasant.
- **Alison Marshall** of **Jones Day** says: "*I do think that we move more quickly in comparison to some of the big commercial litigation cases. Also, our cases are not always as big, so associates often get more responsibility. That is a plus, but juniors need to be prepared to take on that responsibility.*"

- Sometimes the intensity of the workload is high, especially when lawyers are gearing up for a big trial. Being responsive is critical.
- Often lawyers will be dealing with a non-lawyer – an HR professional for example – so they need to be able to translate complex legal principles into clear concepts for them. It's critical to be able to write well, with a view toward addressing practical problems, and not overwhelming the client. This is also true when it comes to explaining elements of a case or situation to the judiciary.
- **Bettina Plevan**, partner at **Proskauer Rose**, says: "*Sometimes clients have pressing emergencies, and you have to be responsive immediately.*"
- **Joseph Costello**, partner at **Morgan Lewis**, warns: "*This is an area of law that requires flexibility and adaptability. Every day there's a new challenge, and the issues are not always predictable: an employee may have a disability that needs to be accommodated; there might be a union-organizing drive; or maybe an employee has complained about a posting on a social media website, which another employee has published. Any of these situations could trigger a call to us.*"
- **Stephen Poor**, chairman of **Seyfarth Shaw**, informs us that in this field, "*there is still that focus on the real world, which can be messier and stickier than the relatively sterile laboratory of the justice system. In other words, success in this field requires a practical bent and a propensity to solve problems rather than win arguments.*"

Current issues

- Following the death of Justice Scalia in 2016, Donald Trump appointed Neil Gorsuch to the Supreme Court. In the employment law context, some predict he will be unwilling to give judicial deference to labor and employment agency regulations and unlikely to interpret statutes in a manner as to benefit employees – his dissent in the Tenth Circuit decision of *TransAm Trucking v. Administrative Review Board* has been cited by some as an example of this. The National Employment Lawyers Association expressed strong opposition to his nomination.
- In February 2018, the Supreme Court ruled unanimously that employees are not protected from retaliation if they report alleged corporate misdeeds unless they take it to the Securities and Exchange Commission. This comes two years after the Whistleblower Augmented Reward and Nonretaliation Act of 2016 (or WARN Act) was introduced, which aimed to strengthen the protections and incentives available to whistleblowers who report financial crimes. Instances of whistleblowing in the US have risen year-on-year since 2011, according to the Annual Report on the Dodd-Frank Whistleblower Program, released by Office of the Whistleblower (OWB).

Practice Areas

- One area that has also been very active is the SEC's stance on policies and agreements that it contends may chill reporting to regulators, such as overbroad confidentiality agreements and nondisparagement provisions. *"The SEC has brought several enforcement actions against companies where it claimed the policies or agreements were overbroad,"*

- Linthorst informed us. *"This means companies are generally reviewing their policies and agreements to make sure they don't preclude or chill employees from reporting potential violations of law to regulators."*

- Another hot area is that of wage and hour claims. A new overtime rule will likely be issued in October 2018, and is predicted to raise the minimum exempt salary threshold level (which exempts workers from qualifying for overtime pay) for white-collar workers above the current benchmark of $23,660. The new threshold could be in the $30,000 – $35,000 range. There are questions over whether the Department of Labor has the power to implement a provision that could allow for automatic adjustments to be made to the threshold, so that the minimum salary matches the rate of inflation; if implemented, employers may have to raise salaries outside of normal time-frames (i.e. not in conjunction with performance reviews and at the end of the fiscal year).

- Linthorst gives us his view on the topic of wage and hour claims: *"There has been lots of class and collective action litigation as everyone seems to be suing for overtime."*

- Some of the claims are being brought by those covered by the 'white-collar exemptions' to the overtime requirements, while others have been brought by employees claiming that they have not been properly compensated for 'off-the-clock' work. *"One of the reasons for this spike,"* explains Linthorst, *"is that under the federal overtime law, the Fair Labor Standards Act, a claim can be filed on behalf of all those who are 'similarly situated' to the plaintiff and, upon a determination by the court that the case is appropriate for notice, notice can be sent to all others 'similarly situated'. When that happens, there can suddenly be hundreds of claims."*

- More generally, Linthorst pointed to *"the rise of labor and employment laws, regulations and ordinances at the state and local level."*

- He continued that *"a lot of state and local governments are passing laws; some of them are around wage theft, some relating to paid sick leave, and some are just new posting requirements for existing laws, but it creates a real challenge for those employers that operate nationally."*

- Experts predict that allegations of sexual harassment in the workplace are likely to increase as the #MeToo movement gains traction, and could extend to claims against managers and executives of all types of companies.

Practice Areas

Product liability

In a nutshell

Product liability involves personal injury or property damage litigation arising from alleged design and manufacturing defects, or information/warning deficiencies, in products. Litigation can consist of individual cases arising from one-off injuries, though in recent years much of it has been conducted through mass torts. Mass torts comprise class actions and/or multiple related individual cases brought by plaintiffs. Most cases within a mass tort do not usually go to trial as they tend to be resolved early through mediation or settlement.

Product liability lawyers also advise on how to avoid litigation, since clients are increasingly interested in prevention and mitigation of the costs and risks of significant product liability litigation. Attorneys are also often required to advise on related, nontraditional product claims, such as government investigations, which frequently arise alongside private claims. This quasi-criminal aspect involves defending the client against suits filed by state attorneys general and investigations conducted by the Department of Justice, often simultaneously.

The major industries that see the lion's share of product liability suits are tobacco, pharmaceutical, consumer products, chemicals and medical devices. BigLaw firms normally defend the manufacturers of the products.

What lawyers do

- Meet with company witnesses to put together the company's defense.
- Fact investigation and discovery – find out what actually happened.
- Product investigation – get to know the product.
- Choose and prepare experts; arrange for experiments if necessary.
- File motions under the Frye or Daubert doctrines to dismiss inadequate plaintiffs' experts.
- Write briefs on evidentiary, class action and dispositive motion issues, as well as legal analysis.
- Take and defend fact and expert depositions.
- Argue cases before juries.
- Manage post-trial steps.

Realities of the job

- Mass torts will typically include some form of consolidation or aggregation of the claims, ranging from a class action – in which plaintiffs have significant issues in common – to a federal multidistrict proceeding coordinating all the cases for pretrial purposes.
- Cases are heard all across the country, though plaintiffs may like certain jurisdictions better than others for tactical reasons. These include East Texas, Atlantic County in New Jersey, and Philadelphia. The 'bank district' in Los Angeles is popular for its history of awarding multimillion and billion-dollar verdicts. It has been described by advocates of tort law reform as *"judicial hell on earth."*
- Not all cases are tried the same way. There are a variety of different trial models that judges are experimenting with, including the bifurcated, reverse-bifurcated and bellwether models. Depending on the model, different strategies will be needed, and will sometimes require a mock jury exercise to see what will work best. Attorneys can suggest alternate trial plans, though the judge has the final say. Once the trial has begun, it is difficult to change how it is tried, though with mass tort, which involves many cases, it is possible to try iterative cases differently. Judges experimented extensively with the thousands of cases in the fen-phen litigation in the Philadelphia courts.
- The main drivers of complex product liability litigation are the business and strategic decisions made by the plaintiffs' Bar, which do not necessarily involve pure scientific analysis of a product.
- Plaintiff lawyers jump from product to product and industry to industry, and try to apply the same model to different cases. The tobacco industry has often seen plaintiffs' innovations before any other, whereafter plaintiffs will experiment with those approaches in different industries.
- Many clients work extensively with the FDA, so current FDA employees cannot be used by the defense as expert witnesses, due to the conflict of interest. Instead, attorneys will work with retired FDA employees to learn about the regulatory and approval processes.
- Much of the work done preparing for trial will turn out to be for cases that never make it to trial, since most mass torts are resolved before then. But attorneys do not know which of the 20,000–30,000 claims filed will actually be tried. There is, however, a winnowing process whereby judges eventually select a smaller pool of cases to be tried.

Rankings in *Chambers USA*

Top Ranked

Sidley Austin

Highly Recommended

Arnold & Porter Kaye	Morrison & Foerster
Baker Botts	Nelson Mullins Riley
DLA Piper (US)	Norton Rose Fulbright
Greenberg Traurig, PA	O'Melveny & Myers
Holland & Knight	Orrick, Herrington & Sutcliffe
Hughes Hubbard & Reed	
Jones Day	Perkins Coie
King & Spalding	Reed Smith
Kirkland & Ellis	Skadden
Mayer Brown	Venable
Morgan, Lewis & Bockius	

For more detail on ranking tiers and locations, visit www.chambersandpartners.com

- There is a large amount of routine paper and electronic discovery required, though many firms use staff and contract attorneys to do this job.
- You don't have to have a background in science to be a product liability lawyer, though to be a successful one you will have to learn about areas outside the law like engineering, medicine and science. You will also have to be able to communicate complicated scientific ideas to a judge or jury in a clear and simple fashion.
- You may work with some of the leading scientists and doctors in the country and the world.
- The job often involves extensive travel for trials and meeting with experts.
- Most product liability work is domestic.

Current issues

- The FDA Reauthorization Act of 2017 has extended the amount of time drug and device manufacturers have to report product malfunctions, from 30 to 90 days for possible safety issues that haven't yet caused serious harm. The change has garnered criticism for potentially increasing the risk to patients who use or come into contact with certain medical products. However, the FDA (Food and Drug Administration) maintains that the emphasis on patient safety is still preserved via measures including the 30-day reporting limit on issues that have already caused serious harm or have been encountered with any product that has been on the market for under two years.
- The possible relaxation of the regulatory framework under the Trump administration could well favor law firms' life sciences clients in the courtroom. For now,

product liability claims in the life sciences sector remain plentiful, so lawyers in the area have been focusing on delivering early advice to their clients in order to reduce the potential for litigation in the future.

- Consumer fraud class actions continue to be on the rise across the United States, particularly in California. These actions tend to be filed when plaintiffs' counsel allege that *"defendants mislead consumers as to the benefits of their products,"* explains **Michael Davis**, former head of **Sidley Austin**'s product liability and mass torts practice. These actions often arise when a product *"claims to be 'natural' or have a specific health benefit, or when there are technical issues with labeling."*
- Some frequently named defendants, in addition to the traditional consumer, food and pharmaceutical companies, are *"energy drink manufacturers who allegedly fail to adequately label their products, helmet manufacturers, and NFL franchises for concussion injuries players allegedly suffered over time,"* according to Michael Davis.
- Another interesting development has been the advent of 'innovator liability'. According to **Paul Boehm**, partner at **Williams & Connolly**, this has been driven *"by plaintiffs' lawyers' desire to circumvent the Supreme Court's decision in Mensing. Since plaintiffs, under Mensing, cannot sue a generic drug manufacturer for failure to warn, plaintiffs' attorneys have advanced the theory that the 'original innovator' of the product, rather than the manufacturer of the product plaintiff actually used, can be liable under state-based 'failure to warn' claims. This theory would represent a fundamental change in some basic principles of tort law. Three state courts have allowed 'failure to warn' cases founded on the theory of 'innovator liability', but most courts continue to reject it."*
- Plaintiffs' attorneys continue to bring cases on purely speculative bases. These actions are often based on supposed economic loss or the mere risk of a loss in future. *"Such cases are often brought when the actual product works as it should, but it is claimed that negative press coverage about possible damage has reduced the product's value,"* according to Davis.
- The development of driverless cars has generated new queries for the practice area – does an accident involving one constitute a product liability case, or is a crash the fault of the, for want of a better term, 'driver'? Current consensus suggests this will indeed be a product liability issue, but the conundrum demonstrates how technology can evolve faster than the law surrounding it. A recent incident in March 2018, in which a pedestrian was hit and killed in Arizona by a self-driving Uber car, will further highlight the issue and raise the demand for tighter regulations on such technology.

Practice Areas

Corporate

"I don't think having a career as a generalist litigator is something I'd recommend to my kid. I'd say, specialize in something. Be a healthcare litigator or a white-collar criminal defense litigator. I think it's now more important than ever that young people find a passion for a certain industry to really help them drive their career path, because our clients are demanding deep industry knowledge. If you want to be successful in this business you really have to be a trusted adviser. The best way to do it is, one, care about your clients, two, understand the industry, then lastly, provide excellent legal service. And I don't think you could start to focus too early on those areas."
– McDermott chairman Ira Coleman

Corporate/M&A – the basics

In a nutshell

Corporate is sometimes defined as a catch-all practice area that includes everything that's not litigation or tax. The higher you go in the BigLaw tree, however, the more corporate becomes synonymous with mergers and acquisitions (M&A) and corporate governance. Some big firms include capital markets and private equity under this umbrella, but these areas are so complex and distinct that *Chambers Associate* prefers to treat them separately.

This practice area can involve advising clients from cradle to grave: from starting up and going public, to raising capital, selling, acquiring and combining businesses, to looking at the overall framework for operations and advising the board of directors on special transactions. Typical M&A work involves advising on selling, combining and acquiring businesses. BigLaw firms often focus on **public M&A**, advising either the buyer or seller in a transaction involving a public company. This area of corporate law routinely provides the biggest deals, is often cross-border and can involve cash and/or stock considerations. **Private M&A** takes place between private companies and can also be multifaceted, particularly where partnerships are involved. M&A lawyers can act as transactional coordinators too, because for every takeover or disposal, there will be employment, antitrust or tax implications to consider.

Corporate governance involves advising companies on crucial board affairs (including director duties) and their relationships with shareholders, which are paramount during transactions or shareholder disputes.

What lawyers do

Public M&A for buyer

- Identify the client's business objectives.
- Identify the legal issues – these vary depending on factors like whether the deal is friendly or unfriendly.
- Build a 'road map' for the client from start to finish, including a timeframe.
- Advise on deal and negotiating tactics.
- Conduct due diligence on other side.
- Determine – with the help of tax attorneys – any tax implications and if they require special structuring.
- Work with antitrust attorneys to assess regulatory obstacles, gain regulatory approval and analyze any other required regulatory approvals.
- If cross-border, work with local counsel. Review all the client's contracts: business, employment, outsourcing, debt instruments, preferred stock, etc.

- Obtain third-party consents from lenders or parties to other contracts.
- Negotiate agreement, sign, announce publicly, close the deal.
- Attorneys for the target decide whether to negotiate, refuse the buyer's overtures, sell, or do a deal with another company.

Realities of the job

- *"The most important thing for a corporate lawyer is to develop an understanding of what's most important to your client – what they are really trying to accomplish and what issues really matter to them and why,"* explains **Victor Lewkow** of **Cleary Gottlieb Steen & Hamilton**.
- **Robert Townsend** of **Cravath, Swaine & Moore LLP** highlights some of the characteristics common to those working in corporate/M&A, which include being *"driven and motivated to maintain a high level of quality. You need to be intellectually curious in order to identify issues, but also practical so that you can figure out how to best solve those issues – that's where we add value."*
- An M&A transaction can feature *"a whole laundry list of tactics to choose from and issues to consider, depending upon what side you're on,"* says **Alison Ressler** of **Sullivan & Cromwell**, meaning that no two deals are exactly the same. Similarly each deal will have a unique life cycle and so some will naturally take longer to complete than others.
- A key part of M&A work is explaining issues in a way that makes sense to the client. *"Lawyers often use enormous amounts of jargon with great expertise and complexity, which is not necessarily helpful for the business people involved,"* Lewkow tells us. He adds: *"Often there is no perfect answer, so some of the time you'll be helping the client figure out what the least 'bad' alternative is."*
- Townsend adds: *"You need to have the ability to articulate your position in a way that is clear and concise so that a business person can understand. It is also important to listen carefully to what your client and the other side are saying in negotiations in order to know how to modify your strategy accordingly."*
- Due diligence will largely fall to associates and, though it can be tedious, it's crucial for attorneys to understand what's in the documents. *"Law students tend to think of us as just reading and marking up documents, but a key characteristic of a top corporate lawyer is the ability to negotiate and construct arguments on your feet,"* states Ressler.

Rankings in *Chambers USA*

Top Ranked

Alston & Bird	Morgan, Lewis & Bockius
Baker Botts	Morrison & Foerster
Brownstein Hyatt Farber	Nelson Mullins Riley
Cooley	Perkins Coie
Cravath, Swaine & Moore	Reed Smith
Davis Polk & Wardwell	Ropes & Gray
Dechert	Sidley Austin
DLA Piper (US)	Simpson Thacher & Bartlett
Foley & Lardner	Skadden
Gibson, Dunn & Crutcher	Snell & Wilmer
Greenberg Traurig, PA	Squire Patton Boggs
Holland & Knight	Sullivan & Cromwell
Hunton Andrews Kurth	Troutman Sanders
Jones Day	Venable
K&L Gates	Vinson & Elkins
King & Spalding	WilmerHale
Kirkland & Ellis	Wilson Sonsini Goodrich
Latham & Watkins	

Highly Recommended

Akin Gump Strauss Hauer	Kramer Levin Naftalis
Allen & Overy	Mayer Brown
Arnold & Porter	McDermott Will & Emery
Baker McKenzie	Milbank
Bracewell	Mintz Levin Cohn Ferris
Cadwalader, Wickersham	Munger, Tolles & Olson
Choate Hall & Stewart	Norton Rose Fulbright
Cleary Gottlieb Steen	Orrick
Clifford Chance US	Paul Hastings
Cozen O'Connor	Paul, Weiss, Rifkind
Crowell & Moring	Pillsbury Winthrop Shaw
Debevoise & Plimpton	Proskauer Rose
Duane Morris	Schulte Roth & Zabel
Dykema Gossett PLLC	Seward & Kissel
Fox Rothschild	Shearman & Sterling
Freshfields Bruckhaus	Sheppard, Mullin, Richter
Fried, Frank	Thompson & Knight
Gibbons P.C.	Vedder Price
Haynes and Boone,	Waller
Hughes Hubbard & Reed	Weil, Gotshal & Manges
Jackson Walker	White & Case LLP
Jenner & Block	Willkie Farr & Gallagher LLP
Katten Muchin Rosenman	Winston & Strawn LLP

For more detail on ranking tiers and locations, visit www.chambersandpartners.com

- Delaware, where many corporations are incorporated, has among the most pronounced and expansive laws on the duties of the board and rules concerning special committees, which have tremendous implications for M&A transactions and corporate governance work. Lewkow confirms: *"Many of the corporate law court de-*

cisions in Delaware influence how we address problems and generally go about structuring transactions."

- Public companies, particularly those in the Fortune 500, are slick operations with considerable legal budgets and expertise, and usually need less hand-holding than smaller, less sophisticated clients.
- The high-pressure nature of the work is a result of *"not only having the chance to be involved in issues that are very important to your client, but also making a genuine difference to those issues,"* says **Adam Emmerich** of **Wachtell, Lipton, Rosen & Katz.**
- *"Many deals have a lot of moving pieces, whereby solving one problem could actually create another problem,"* according to Lewkow. *"What works well for IP purposes, for example, might not work well for tax purposes."*
- Clients often expect transactions to be completed in a matter of days, which can mean working 18-hour days and weekends. This expectation can create an atmosphere of cooperation and expediency among parties. *"You break down the walls between who's doing what, and just dive in and do it,"* **Josh Bonnie** of **Simpson Thacher & Bartlett** says.
- It also means that flexibility is key. *"Sometimes you may have a plan to go on holiday, then find out that you need to be on the spot and fully engaged,"* says Emmerich. However, this comes with the territory of it being *"a dynamic, interesting and exciting practice."*
- *"I don't think there is one style which makes you an excellent or effective M&A lawyer,"* explains **Louis Goldberg** of **Davis Polk & Wardwell.** He adds that at one end of the spectrum you have those who are *"thoughtful, determined and tactical,"* while at the other end there are the 'deal junkies': *"They have the charisma and love the ins and outs of the deal climate."*
- The broader category of corporate finance includes representing borrowers in lending transactions with banks, though most firms organize themselves so that the lawyers who advise the lenders and borrowers are part of the banking and finance team.

Top career tips

George Bason Jr, partner, **Davis Polk & Wardwell**:

"The key to it is that law is a service profession. I think all personality types are welcome, but having that availability and enthusiasm 24 hours a day, 365 days a year is very important – once you accept that as a base line it's a wonderful profession. And, with a few exceptions, clients treat their lawyers with respect and view them as a valued part of the team. It's such a human thing, but a lot of people lose sight of the fact that it's a service business."

Practice Areas

Alison Ressler, partner, **Sullivan & Cromwell:**

"There are three primary courses that students who are interested in corporate law should take. Securities regulation is key – you need to understand securities law and what's involved in issuing securities. A general corporate law course explains the different forms of corporate entities and how federal and state regulations affect mergers. A business combinations or mergers class teaches the case law on mergers and the difference between hostile and friendly takeovers. Two key ancillary courses are corporate income tax and accounting for lawyers."

"The best thing law students can do in preparation is read the Financial Times and The Wall Street Journal while in law school. Those papers will really give you a sense of what's happening in the business world."

Adam Emmerich, partner, **Wachtell, Lipton, Rosen & Katz:**

"Like most things in life, if it's your passion and you find it engaging then it's relatively easy to do well. If you've gotten the idea that it sounds good on paper, or is remunerative or prestigious, that won't carry you through; you actually have to find it interesting."

Victor Lewkow, partner, **Cleary Gottlieb Steen & Hamilton:**

"I think what surprised me the most is how much I actually enjoy being a corporate lawyer. I had no background or experience in business, but quickly discovered that mergers and acquisitions was an interesting and challenging practice that I found fun – and still do."

Current issues

- 18,433 M&A deals were completed in 2017, totaling $3.15 trillion in value. Despite a dip of 3.2% on the previous year, this was the fourth consecutive year the market broke $3 trillion.

- 6459 of those deals were cross-border. The $1.32 trillion value of these was a 13% drop from 2016's cross-border deal total, but the second biggest proportion of global M&A since the financial crisis.

- The US accounted for a 40.2% share of the global value (the lowest percentage since 2012). Meanwhile, Chinese outbound M&A activity hit a record $220 billion in 2016; 2017 saw a relative drop, but forecasters expect the market to bounce back in 2018.

- With 2569 deals struck, the technology sector hit its highest annual deal count since 2001, with the latest developments in the industry including autonomous vehicles and blockchain technology fueling growth.

- AT&T's $109 billion acquisition of Time Warner ran into problems when the United States Department of Justice Antitrust Division filed a lawsuit to block the merger, arguing it would reduce competition. The move came as a surprise as for decades, regulators have mostly been concerned about horizontal mergers, not vertical ones.

- Based on surveys conducted by Deloittes, expectations for M&A deals for 2018 are high for heftier deals. 63% of respondents anticipate the average enterprise size of transactions in the next 12 months will exceed those in the past year while 34% of respondents expect deal size to hold steady.

Practice Areas

Corporate/M&A by Jones Day

Since 2000, Jones Day has done more M&A deals than any other law firm worldwide... so who better to give us the score on what it takes to become a top M&A lawyer?

Chambers Associate: What is M&A?
Stephen Olson, partner: At its most basic level M&A, or mergers and acquisitions, is the buying and selling of business and/or the assets used in businesses around the world. This is true whether you're representing a large public company, a private equity firm, a sovereign wealth fund or any type of buyer or seller. As legal advisers, our role in the M&A process is to provide our clients with true legal risk assessment, to create value through transactional structuring, new governance processes, and the ability to marshal numerous practice disciplines on a seamless and cost-effective basis, frequently in multijurisdictional, even global, transactional settings.

Stephen G. Damato, junior associate: M&A is the process whereby entities are consolidated or divided in order to maximize value.

CA: What kind of work is involved day-to-day?

SO: The day-to-day work involved in M&A depends a lot on whether you are representing the buyer or the seller. If you're representing a seller, the day-to-day in the early stages of a deal can include helping clients populate their data room, advise on deal structures and execute confidentiality agreements with interested buyers; if you're representing a buyer, your duties may include reviewing the target's material agreements and legal matters in order to advise the client on any substantive risks associated with the target's business and operations.

Dotun Obadina, associate: Due diligence is the process of evaluating the operations of the business to identify risks of a transaction by investigating the obligations and liabilities of the selling company. Even when representing the seller, doing sell-side due diligence is important to gain an understanding of the selling company's business and the obligations and liabilities of the selling company. On the buy side, due diligence is critical. Due diligence helps the buyer understand the key risks of the transaction, allows the buyer to value the business appropriately and to consider transaction structures and terms that will provide for an appropriate allocation of pre- and post-closing liabilities of the business.

"No two deals are the same, which keeps the work exciting and fresh."

Ann Bomberger, associate: At the beginning of a transaction, the team is generally focused on due diligence and preparing initial drafts of documents. As the deal progresses, the M&A attorneys, together with our client and colleagues in other disciplines, negotiate and revise the documents to address various issues that arise during due diligence or other changes to the business understanding as a result of negotiations. Depending on the particular deal and client preference, you can do an entire transaction through phone and e-mail or you can end up traveling and hunkering down with your clients and the opposing side until the deal is completed.

CA: What are the highs and lows in this area?

SD: During the first few months at the firm I witnessed my fellow first-years in litigation seamlessly apply the legal research and writing techniques that we all refined during law school. I, on the other hand, was confronted with terminology and assignments which largely appeared foreign to me. However, this same steep learning curve presented by an M&A practice has yielded some of the highest highs of my legal career. For example, there is immense gratification associated with saving a client a significant sum of money by spotting an issue in one agreement after witnessing a partner or senior associate spot a similar issue in connection with a previous transaction.

DO: The highs are the varied nature of the work. You are working in several different industries, like manufacturing, pharmaceuticals, software, consumer goods, retail, etc., and in each deal, there is a different driver, whether it's an environmental, regulatory, intellectual property, tax, inventory, employee benefits or other issue. This is incredibly fascinating as you are exposed to—and are expected to understand—so many different areas of law.

AB: No two deals are the same, which keeps the work exciting and fresh. I enjoy the excitement of resolving complex issues for our clients and bringing complicated deals to fruition. Of course, it is also exciting to see your deals make the headlines. In terms of lows, the hours can occasionally be challenging but I have found that you do not necessarily notice while in the thick of getting a transaction signed and closed.

SO: The highs of an M&A practice are sitting in a board room with your client, your client's financial adviser and the other side and its representatives and negotiating the deal structure and material terms and conditions on the deal. Of course, finally getting the transaction closed is a high as well. The lows are when after months of hard work and long hours, the parties cannot simply agree on the substance and form of a transaction and the deal dies.

CA: What is a partner's typical role in matters?

SO: Leading a multidisciplinary team of lawyers to advise a client on the most effective and efficient way to structure, negotiate and ultimately close the transaction. The lead M&A partner is responsible for coordinating all of the efforts and ensuring that the client receives seamless and timely advice.

CA: What do associates at each level do?

SD: Associates at all levels work collaboratively to ensure each deal is run effectively and that nothing falls through the cracks. While the more senior associates are typically tasked with managing the deal team and drafting the main transaction agreements, it is not uncommon for midlevel and junior associates to step into the role of manager or draft the first cut of a purchase agreement. In fact, because Jones Day handles more deals worldwide than any other firm, associates at all levels are expected to be able to handle anything necessary to move a transaction forward in a way that best serves the client. This only works because of the dedication of all Jones Day associates and their willingness to perform both the smallest tasks and conquer the largest challenges.

AB: Our junior associates are involved at every step of our transactions. For example, at the beginning of a deal, our junior associates assist with due diligence and preparation of diligence reports that flag issues that could affect the transaction and/or should be addressed in the transaction documents. They also assist with initial drafts of transaction documents and completing various tasks that need to be completed in order to close transactions.

"A good M&A lawyer needs to be creative and strategic in order to advise their client on how to effectively structure and negotiate a transaction."

As our associates progress in their career, they will take over responsibility for 'quarterbacking' the transaction – e.g., coordinating with the client and other attorneys on the deal team to ensure that issues are addressed and satisfactorily resolved, supervising preparation of the diligence report and transaction documents, and gradually taking over responsibility for negotiating various documents and getting the transaction across the finish line.

CA: Where can new associates expect to be in five years?

SO: In five years new associates can expect to be second-chairing transactions and taking a critical role in drafting and negotiating the documents involved in the M&A process. They will be active participants in almost all of the deal's calls and meetings.

SD: At Jones Day, mid-level M&A associates frequently operate as senior associates and take on partner-level responsibilities. Of course, they have sufficient guidance, but their days are filled with client contact, managing the deal team and drafting and reviewing deliverables.

CA: What qualities make for good M&A lawyers?

SO: A good M&A lawyer needs to be creative and strategic in order to advise their client on how to effectively structure and negotiate a transaction, and to find innovative ways to solve the unique issues in each transaction. They also need to be excellent project managers, since it is their job to supervise and coordinate all of the multidisciplinary efforts that go into advising a client on a transaction, and be able to distill all of the different advice and clearly communicate it to the client in form and substance so the client can make informed decisions on important issues.

SD: The best M&A lawyer is hungry to learn and focused on the ultimate goal of adding as much value as possible to their team and client. To accomplish this, a good M&A lawyer is thoughtful, unafraid to ask questions, selfless, thorough and communicative. I believe associates are most effective when they look at every task through the lens of, "why does this matter to the client and what can I do to analyze and communicate this most clearly and efficiently?"

CA: What separates the Jones Day team from its peers?

SO: There are two differentiators.

- Our experience: every quarter since 2000, Jones Day has done more M&A deals than any other law firm in the world. In earning this market leading number of transactional engagements, we have developed deep experience

Practice Areas

across a range of issues, jurisdictions, and industries. We can tailor an approach for effective and meaningful due diligence, as well as risk assessment and management.

- Jones Day's cohesive culture serving clients as One Firm Worldwide: Our formidable talent across specialties and jurisdictions provides the foundation for our M&A teams to be composed of lawyers from many disciplines, such as intellectual property, employment, compensation, benefits, tax, environmental, and antitrust who are recognized for their substantive knowledge and creativity. Because parties to M&A transactions are increasingly likely to be based in two or more countries, our global presence, and ability to collaborate seamlessly across jurisdictions is a great benefit to companies involved in such transactions. Nearly half of our practice involves cross-border deals.

Our objective in every client engagement is to bring the Firm's extensive experience and scalable resources to bear on a timely, cost-effective basis. With offices in centers of business and finance throughout the world, and a cohesive and collaborative culture that shares professional values, Jones Day is positioned to do business wherever our clients do.

Julia Feldman, junior associate: The biggest difference I see between my experience at Jones Day and my friends' experience at peer firms is the high level of responsibility I've been given since I started. Since my first deal at the firm, I have had significant client interaction and drafting experience. At Jones Day, if you show that you are diligent and enthusiastic about the work you will not be limited to certain tasks just because those are "typical" of your seniority level. In addition, unlike other firms, Jones Day does not feel overly hierarchical. When I work on a deal with a senior associate and partner, I do not feel like I only report to the associate above me; we all work alongside each other on different tasks which may vary in complexity. In addition, deal teams at Jones Day are staffed across numerous offices and practices, and are unique because of the way we seamlessly collaborate t is not uncommon to be working with colleagues from at least three other offices and multiple practices on any given transaction.

> **"The continued globalization of companies and capital providers will have the most material impact on the M&A discipline over the next few years."**

CA: How do you see the market evolving in the next few years?

SO: The continued globalization of companies and capital providers will have the most material impact on the M&A discipline over the next few years. Buyers and sellers now come from all over the globe, and with fewer and fewer geographical limitations on how companies or capital providers are willing to grow their businesses, the global marketplace for strategic or financial acquisitions and divestitures will continue to become more and more accessible to people from all over the world.

SD: A lot of my recent deals have been in the technology sector and I expect that M&A activity will continue to be active therein. Further, I have noticed that many sophisticated companies are growing increasingly concerned with managing compliance risks, so I anticipate that the market will reflect this heightened awareness of regulatory hurdles.

DO: Representations and warranties (R&W) insurance has become a popular tool in effective private equity transactions. R&W will become increasingly prevalent.

CA: What advice would you give to students interested in the area?

SO: Recognize the teachable moments in each stage of the career of an M&A lawyer. In the early years, paying attention to and asking questions about the documents they're reviewing in data rooms can form the knowledge base on which they will one day be advising clients.

The other piece of advice is to continuously work on their communication skills, both written and oral. The successful outcome of a transaction for your client is going to be based on the documents clearly and articulately covering the issues in the deal so the client can be certain of their rights and obligations and if necessary, the enforcement of the same. Effectively and professionally negotiating on behalf of the client is a critical aspect of communication as well, especially considering that after the deal closes the parties will often be working together again in some capacity. If the deal process was unnecessarily acrimonious or contentious, that could impact the success of the post-closing.

SD: Use your school's resources to stay current on major transactions and pay specific attention to trends and events that are reported on a large scale. Additionally, students should not be hesitant to express interest in M&A even though they do not have a background in finance. The most important thing is to be hungry to learn and add value to your team in any way possible.

JF: Read business news, take an introductory corporate law course and look for a firm like Jones Day, where junior associates work alongside senior associates and partners from day one.

Authors

Stephen Olson
Partner

Ann Bomberger
Associate

Dotun Obadina
Associate

Stephen G. Damato
Junior associate

Julia Feldman
Junior associate

M&A in the middle market by Jenner & Block

With M&A in this segment of the market set for growth in 2018, Jenner's deal-doers tell us that the middle is the perfect place to be: the scope to get creative and navigate various transaction structures awaits those who look to become a lawyer in this thriving area.

Chambers Associate: What is the value range covered by mid-market M&A deals?
Peter Rosenbaum, partner: I think of mid-market M&A as transactions with enterprise value of between US$50 and $500 million.

CA: What do the partners do?

Joseph Gromacki, partner: My practice is generally oriented around public companies and their strategic transactions and other strategic matters. In general, our clients look to me to advise them in connection with structuring and negotiating public and private mergers, acquisitions, divestitures, public securities offerings and other highly complex corporate transactions. A key part of my practice involves counseling companies and their boards on matters of corporate governance, fiduciary duties, crisis management and the like.

H. Kurt von Moltke, partner: We are responsible for taking overall responsibility for the transaction. This starts with helping our clients choose the best overall structure of a deal (asset vs. stock purchase) and use the correct entity (LLC vs. Corporation). We are also responsible for staffing the transaction, negotiating key terms, anticipating potential issues and solving complex issues.

PR: My primary roles as a partner are helping our clients achieve the desired outcome (e.g., buy or sell) and minimizing or limiting the client's risk associated with the transaction. In this regard, I help each client identify key issues in the transaction and lead negotiations in our efforts to manage the risk associated with those issues.

CA: What do the associates do?

Brendan Donahue, associate: Associates draft and review documents and negotiate deals (with supervision from the partners). We also research applicable law and analyze market trends to determine what the contract terms should be.

Amy Inagaki, associate: On a very basic level, I try to be a good team player. As a mid-level, I try and make

the lives of the senior and junior associates, as well as the partners, as easy as possible. This means that I anticipate and plan what needs to be done in the short-term, I prepare drafts of documents for the senior associate or partner to review and assign lower-level assignments to junior associates.

"A typical day includes receiving a contract from opposing counsel, giving the client advice about what parts of it are good or bad for them (in light of typical "market" terms), and negotiating for the changes that are in that client's best interests."

CA: What kind of work is involved in the day-to-day?

PR: In the context of an active M&A transaction, the day-to-day work is typically comprised of phone calls with our client and separate calls with opposing counsel to discuss and resolve issues presented in the transaction and then revising transaction documents to reflect those discussions.

BD: A typical day includes receiving a contract from opposing counsel, giving the client advice about what parts of it are good or bad for them (in light of typical "market" terms), and negotiating for the changes that are in that client's best interests. For example, if we are helping a client sell a business, we might receive a draft of a stock purchase agreement. I would need to make sure that it fits the structure of the deal and achieves the company's defined goals and objectives. I would then make a list of the issues I have identified and work with the client to decide which points they should and should not accept. We would also discuss which issues are worth fighting about and which risks the client is willing to bear in the particular transaction. Following this conversation, I would revise the document accordingly and have a conversation with opposing counsel to work out the relevant issues.

Practice Areas

CA: What are the highs and lows?

HKvM: Highs would include solving complex issues in a manner that allows our client to achieve their goals with limited risk, while lows would include failure to find acceptable compromises on key issues.

PR: For me, the highs are learning the business of our clients and helping them realize their business strategy with acquisitions and divestitures. The lows are when a transaction falls through and sometimes the long hours that it takes to complete a transaction.

BD: The biggest 'high' is when a deal closes and both clients are happy with it. You can look back and feel very accomplished by a project you helped to quarterback and bring to completion. The lows are that M&A or corporate work can be very unpredictable and a bit of a roller coaster ride – you never know what's going to happen or when, but you have to be ready to respond at all times.

"The highs are learning the business of our clients and helping them realize their business strategy with acquisitions and divestitures."

CA: Describe your latest transaction: what were the issues involved? How did you spend your days?

BD: We recently helped a public company in the internet and technology industry acquire a middle-market business that was owned by its founders and a private equity firm. My role involved conducting due diligence on the business to help the client understand what they were buying and what steps were needed to purchase and integrate that company, and then helping to draft and negotiate the primary and ancillary transaction documents.

HKvM: Our client was interested in selling an entire company in a process that would be structured as three separate transactions, each for a portion of the company, to three different buyers. We were responsible for structuring the sale transactions to both maximize their return and to minimize the potential liability to the seller from the transactions and to negotiate with the different buyer groups to develop the structures and timing of the transactions. As the lead Partner, I spent a fair amount of time with our client on the strategy aspects of the sale process, as well as analyzing the different risks and potential outcomes of multiple structures. Once we had the structure in place we desired, we then had to deal with opposing counsel, explaining our structure and rationale, and responding to their questions and concerns and alternative proposals.

PR: My latest transaction involved the divesture of the assets of a healthcare business by a larger corporation. My role was to help our client identify those assets that would be sold, those assets that would be retained and those assets that would be shared by the buyer and the seller and to effectuate that transaction. Most of my days were spent negotiating with opposing counsel on issues about the scope of the assets to be acquired and the related assumption of liabilities related to this acquisition.

CA: What are the current trends in mid-market M&A?

BD: There is a big boom in the volume of mid-market M&A, part of which is the result of recent tax reform. A lot of potential buyers are bringing money back to the US, and they need to find a place to spend it. M&A is the beneficiary of some of this spending, with many of the available opportunities being acquisitions of mid-sized businesses held by strategics, private equity firms, and other investors.

"There is a big boom in the volume of mid-market M&A, part of which is the result of recent tax reform."

JG: The mid cap segment is expected to hold up well in the year ahead, as market fundamentals remain strong and a number of key factors drive deals. Of course, it's important to take a nuanced view of the market, because some industries are faring better than others. Tech-enabled services — whether cybersecurity, the internet of things or software as a service — continue to be strategically important for corporates, although such deals command high multiples. This finding is confirmed by a recent Deloitte survey of M&A trends for 2018. Among the report's findings is that corporate and private equity executives foresee an acceleration of M&A activity in 2018, both in the number of deals and the size of the transactions.

Additionally, one major factor for the bright outlook for public company M&A is ever-increasing competition, which has resulted in sweeping industry consolidation as both serial and opportunistic acquirers have focused on larger strategic transactions with both industry rivals and complementary businesses to strengthen their market positions. The technology industry exemplifies this trend.

HKvM: One of the current trends we are seeing in the mid-market is the increase in purchase price multiples for transactions. There is a lot of activity from both corporate strategic buyers as well as private equity funds looking to deploy capital, which has led to an increase in purchase prices.

Practice Areas

PR: Mid-market M&A continues to be robust. A specific trend that has significantly affected how mid-market M&A transactions are negotiated and consummated over the last decade is the use of representation and warranty insurance policies.

"There is a great deal of flexibility and creativity involved in mid-market M&A transactions."

CA: What personal qualities make a good M&A lawyer?

BD: You need to be able to adapt. M&A lawyers juggle a lot at once and things can change quickly. You need to always be on your toes. You don't always need to know the answer, but you need to know who to ask, since a major component of your role is coordinating with specialists such as accountants and tax advisors. You have to issue spot and ensure that issues are addressed appropriately, even if they're outside of your own wheelhouse.

JG: Commitment to substantive excellence, dedication and attention to detail are the price of admission. But there are many highly qualified lawyers out there. So much of M&A and capital markets work involves collaboration with clients and a thorough comprehension of their strategic imperatives, so being a willing, committed and productive team member is also important. But the truly distinguishing characteristic of an outstanding corporate lawyer is the ability to earn the trust and confidence of your client, through demonstrated capability, judgment and strategic perspective.

HKvM: Good M&A lawyers are smart, diligent, creative and positive. Because of the tight time frames involved in most transactions, there are periods of intense activity, so stamina is also important.

CA: What can students do to prepare themselves for a career in mid-market M&A?

BD: Law students should take substantive classes that are useful for transactional practice, such as corporations, tax, bankruptcy, and secured transactions. Students should also brush up on basic quantitative skills such as financial accounting and corporate finance.

CA: What makes mid-market M&A unique? And by extension, what opportunities are unique to Jenner?

BD: In a mid-market M&A transaction, a lawyer gets a chance to be a generalist. You need to understand and work on every part of the company you are buying or selling; you encounter every area of law. At Jenner & Block, we have a large variety of deals – from $1 million to many billions. In the same day, you could represent a small family business and one of the biggest public companies in the world.

HKvM: There is a great deal of flexibility and creativity involved in mid-market M&A transactions. There is a wide area of what are considered to be market terms, which allows for more creativity to find acceptable solutions to complicated issues.

Jenner & Block is well-positioned in the mid-market M&A space. We view mid-market M&A as a significant area of our focus, and have developed a strong reputation for completing these types of transactions.

PR: Mid-market M&A is different than most other types of M&A because of the focus on the post-closing indemnification obligations of the parties. You need to have a good understanding of how these complex contractual provisions work in order to meet the needs of your clients. I think young Corporate lawyers at Jenner & Block have an outstanding opportunity to get hands-on experience early on in their careers with meaningful deal work that will help accelerate their growth as an M&A lawyer.

Authors

Brendan Donahue
Associate

Joseph Gromacki
Partner

Amy Inagaki
Associate

H. Kurt von Moltke
Partner

Peter Rosenbaum
Partner

Practice Areas

Antitrust meets M&A by Freshfields

Chambers Global places Freshfields among the top two firms in the world for antitrust, and among the top four firms worldwide for M&A. We interviewed associates from the firm's DC and New York offices to learn how these two teams collaborate and what students can do to become lawyers in them…

Chambers Associate: What is corporate law?

Camille Ranadive, corporate associate: We do a lot of cross-border public and private M&A, private equity transactions, venture capital deals and joint-venture arrangements. Then there's general corporate governance: dealing with boards and board appointees, and advising on board decisions. Our work essentially involves working on documentation to achieve a client's goal: that might be deciding to purchase a company or selling assets or a business division.

Paul Humphreys, corporate senior associate: Corporate and M&A are overlapping and the terms get used interchangeably. Corporate, I think of as encompassing everything from M&A, to capital markets to fund formation to more run-of-the-mill corporate maintenance, like record keeping, updating minutes, and corporate secretarial-type activities. M&A, I think of as buying and selling businesses or investing in businesses, and that can be public or private transactions. Our practice is primarily M&A and capital markets.

CA: What is antitrust law?

Justin Stewart-Teitelbaum, antitrust senior associate: Antitrust law is a legal analysis of competition. There are two high-level areas of practice: the conduct side – legal assessment or litigation over business conduct which could be deemed anticompetitive – and M&A approval: regulators in the US and around the world assess planned mergers to determine if their consummation might result in competition issues. The two key US enforcers are the Federal Trade Commission (FTC) and Department of Justice (DOJ).

Ilana Kattan, antitrust associate: Put simply, the antitrust laws aim to preserve competition. Antitrust lawyers advise clients on a wide range of issues, including on mergers, agreements with competitors, and monopolization. We advise clients in the M&A context, in regulatory investigations and litigation, and in private litigation. We also provide advice to clients on antitrust compliance.

> *"You need to really understand the mechanics of the market you're analyzing: the product, players, how it functions."*

CA: What kind of work is involved day-to-day?

CR: Today I am supervising a due diligence project. The firm's legal services center employs trained attorneys who do a lot of due diligence for us, and then we review it. Additionally I'll be doing due diligence myself and updating diligence reports. Thankfully there's also a lot beyond diligence. I'll be working on documentation to add board members to an incentive program and reviewing stock purchase agreement precedents. A lot my time is devoted to phone calls with other offices and clients.

JST: One thing I enjoy about antitrust law is that it's highly fact-intensive – you need to understand the mechanics of the market you're analyzing: the product, players, how it functions, the regulatory framework. You're really digging into what underpins the market. In addition to the legal and factual analysis, I liaise with clients to pursue transaction clearance and work directly with the regulatory agencies – it's their job to review the merger and our job to explain why the transaction should not be considered to present competition concerns.

PH: I manage deal teams, which usually consist of one or two junior associates, maybe a mid-level associate and a partner, depending on the size of the transaction. At Freshfields 99% of what we do is cross-border, so often teams are not just based in the US. As a senior associate I draft, negotiate and solve outstanding issues. The partner takes a senior leadership role and would deal with any tricky relationship issues or very difficult negotiation points.

Practice Areas

"One of the great things about corporate practice is that it's very people focused."

CA: What is the difference between junior-level work and partner-level work?

CR: We all work together all the time, on an hourly basis, not just daily. We're constantly in each others' offices. One of the great things about corporate practice is that it's very people focused – you don't just bury your head in research and not surface for hours. As a junior, you're expected to really get into the details: if you're doing diligence on a company, you need to understand everything about them and tell the partner everything they need to know about that company. They can then condense that into a client-friendly version.

PH: Juniors do a lot of diligence work – reviewing contracts and other key documents – and draft red-flag reports for the client, which highlight problematic legal and commercial issues and recommend what to do about them. Juniors also manage the global diligence team, which for our global practice usually means teams in some locations where we rely on outside counsel. Junior associates do not only do due diligence. At Freshfields, they will be involved in preparing first drafts of transaction documents. We also involve our junior associates in the firm's business development efforts, so you may find a junior preparing a presentation for a client. Our partners often involve the juniors who have done the work in the presentation to the client as well.

JST: As you move up in seniority you become more focused on the tactical and strategic implications of issues arising from diligence. For example, junior attorneys often conduct factual research and analysis and become experts on an area of the matter or the market. Then as a team we'll set the strategic course of action.

"Our roles fit together like puzzle pieces."

CA: How do the antitrust and corporate teams work together?

PH: Almost all transactions we work on in the US involve antitrust filings, as the threshold for making a filing is very low compared to the size of transactions on which we work – so our antitrust people are almost always involved.

JST: The corporate team is very aware that antitrust filings and review are often an important aspect of getting a transaction closed – thus we liaise closely on various aspects during transaction consideration and after signing, often we'll look at the antitrust considerations of a transaction before even discussing various other parts.

CR: As soon as we're aware of an M&A deal we get the antitrust team involved to understand what competition issues might arise in order to give a realistic deal timeline to the client. The worst thing to do would be to assume there are no competition issues and that it's going to be a quick deal process, only to find out you have to do an HSR [Hart–Scott–Rodino] Act filing – that can delay a deal by months, if not years.

IK: Our roles fit together like puzzle pieces. The corporate team organizes the strategy for large M&A deals and shepherds the process from origination of the deal to closing and beyond. The antitrust team works closely with the corporate team, assessing the antitrust risks of the deal and obtaining antitrust approvals for the deal.

PH: The antitrust team also provides training for the M&A team on potential antitrust issues that can arise during a transaction.

"We are getting a lot of questions about how certain political events will affect antitrust enforcement."

CA: What would you say about the future of M&A and antitrust practice?

JST: The proliferation of antitrust law and regulatory agencies around the world means the field will continue to grow. As more jurisdictions come into play and more antitrust laws are introduced, trying to comply with them all can be complex. There may also be an increase in private antitrust litigation, in particular outside of the US.

CR: We at Freshfields see M&A becoming increasingly global and cross border. US companies are realizing that they have to expand beyond the US to stay competitive and relevant. It'll be interesting to see what the next few years bring with Brexit and the new presidential administration in the US, but we have a positive outlook that M&A will continue to grow. 2016 didn't quite keep up with booming 2015, but it almost did. As clients become more global, they need law firms that have a global presence and we have offices around the world that work together on a daily basis.

IK: We are getting a lot of questions about how certain political events will affect antitrust enforcement. For example, how will Brexit affect competition law in Europe? How will antitrust enforcement change under the Trump administration? Despite this uncertainty – or in some cases, because of this uncertainty – companies have been proposing a large number of deals over the past couple of years that raise significant and complex antitrust issues. This merger wave likely will continue.

PH: The regulatory landscape changed a lot for our clients after the financial crisis. Now with the Trump administration many of those new regulations may be removed. That theoretically paves the way for more consolidation and merger activity. But while things are in limbo, everyone may remain in a wait-and-see mode. In particular, in-bound M&A from places like China may wane until the Trump administration's policies are better understood.

The Obama administration was very active in looking at M&A deals from an antitrust perspective – they were willing to fight against deals they believed were anticompetitive and some fell apart. That may change under the Trump administration. There is a lot of talk about renegotiating trade deals – that will affect what foreign investment will look like for cross-border businesses and what type of investments non-US buyers are able to make. Another key trend for businesses in developed economies is the replacement of individual labor with intelligent machines. That will impact productivity but also change the labor force, as workers no longer need to be qualified just to put stuff together but rather to be someone who, for example, develops software. It'll be interesting to see how that drives consolidation, and how it creates opportunities for businesses.

"Summer associates are able to spend two weeks in a foreign office after their time with us in the US."

CA: What particular opportunities are available to antitrust and corporate juniors at Freshfields?

JST: There's definitely the opportunity for international travel – the work we do has a lot of travel built in. Summer associates are able to spend two weeks in a foreign office after their time with us in the US. Training also happens internationally – once or twice a year there is an antitrust training conference somewhere abroad. I have also been on a secondment to London and that has made me feel very close to the people in our team around the world. I know them, they know me, and we work together very closely. The commitment to trainings and secondment to other offices shows the firm's commitment to its unified network approach.

CR: It's good to go abroad and be there on the ground, as you just can't get as much done over the phone or by email as you can when you're in the room. Often juniors are the ones to travel to foreign offices for closings etc.

IK: One of the best things about Freshfields is the firm's focus on training. Several times a year, the junior associates in our antitrust team travel to Brussels from around the world to attend training on particular antitrust topics. These trainings not only allow for associates in the US to have a handle on the approach to antitrust issues outside the US, but also allow associates to get to know their colleagues on a personal level. These relationships continue to be developed as associates become more senior, with trainings scheduled each year for mid-level associates and senior associates.

CA: What's unique about Freshfields' antitrust and M&A teams?

CR: Our corporate team is small – it has about 20 associates and just a handful of partners, so it's very intimate. We all know each other very well and work with everyone closely. But at the same time we have the resources of a large global law firm, so it's the best of both worlds.

JST: Freshfields is considered to have the best antitrust practice in world, but the team doesn't feel overly big or impersonal – either locally or globally. For example, the Washington team is not particularly large compared to many other US antitrust practices – the team is close knit.

PH: We don't think of our international network in the sense that we would say 'oh, we have 15 people in Milan, who handle Italian law issues.' I think of Milan as a partner named Luigi Verga, who I've worked with on cross-border deals on multiple occasions. We don't just outsource non-US issues to a "network" office. We are one global firm, and we work incredibly hard to encourage internal networking and to build actual relationships with colleagues around the globe.

We want our clients' experience with the firm to be the same in Italy as it is in New York. We achieve this through things like global conferences, which start with 'Career Milestones' training for associates in their first and second year, and sector group conferences as you go along. The end result is that we know the individuals with whom we work, and we actually like working with one another. This is a huge benefit for clients as it improves efficiency and ensures the global team – not just the lead partner and lead associate – is committed to helping the client achieve its goals.

It is not uncommon for associates from our offices outside the US to visit the New York office on a vacation or personal trip to the US to meet in person someone with whom they have worked. I just don't think that is so common at other firms, and I believe that is a real testament to the culture of collegiality across borders that we strive to build and maintain.

CA: What's your advice for law students wanting to succeed in these areas?

JST: In terms of seeking positions at law firms, I recommend that you demonstrate your interest in each specific firm. That doesn't just mean knowing how many offices or associates we have, but also understanding the type of work we do. We don't expect you to be an expert on it during the interview process, but make sure you've done your homework – and if you want to know something then make sure you ask a question. Also, in the interview, try to showcase your interests and personality rather than simply reciting talking points.

CR: Take law school classes that are practical: I took seminars on 'the art of the deal' and general M&A which really gave me exposure to what corporate work is and made me familiar with certain terms. M&A seminars given by practitioners are most useful, as they give you a taste of what corporate practice is really like.

Authors

Camille Ranadive is a corporate associate in New York.

Camille Ranadive

Ilana Kattan is an antitrust associate in DC.

Ilana Kattan

Paul Humphreys is a senior associate focusing on cross-border public and private M&A, private equity transactions, venture capital and general corporate governance.

Paul Humphreys

Justin Stewart-Teitelbaum is a senior associate in DC whose practice areas include representing clients in investigations of mergers and acquisitions before the Federal Trade Commission (FTC) and the Antitrust Division at the Department of Justice (DOJ).

Justin Stewart-Teitelbaum

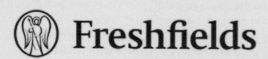
Freshfields

Practice Areas

Antitrust: cartels, pharma and class actions by White & Case

From pet food to plastics to auto parts – White & Case's antitrust lawyers have seen it all. Here three of the firm's savvy associates explain what it's like to become an antitrust lawyer, from the thrill of winning complex cases to the satisfaction of working on novel issues in various industries.

Chambers Associate: Can you describe what the competition/antitrust teams at White & Case do? Are there any specialist areas of work that the group is especially known for?

Kathryn Mims, associate: The White & Case Antitrust/Competition teams advise clients worldwide on every facet of competition laws around the globe. We have extensive experience in complex litigations against governmental authorities and private parties; we advise clients on complex merger control regimes and fight for merger approval through litigation; we counsel clients through global cartel investigations, including parallel Sherman Act class actions, European Union proceedings, and international discovery.

Kevin Adam, associate: Over the last few years, the Competition Group has handled a number of novel pharmaceutical antitrust cases involving allegations of "reverse payments" or "product hopping" and, in the process, has really distinguished itself as one of the "go to" firms for pharmaceutical antitrust work. White & Case is the only law firm to have defended successfully at trial pharmaceutical clients against both FTC and private plaintiff reverse payment suits, and we were counsel in the landmark SCOTUS ruling on reverse payments in *FTC v. Actavis*.

CA: Can you give an overview/examples of the cartel work the practice does?

KA: The Antitrust/Competition Group handles the full range of cartel litigation at the trial and appellate levels, including internal investigations, responding to subpoenas from U.S. and international competition authorities, and defending companies and individuals against both government enforcement suits and follow-on private lawsuits brought by class-action and corporate plaintiffs. Over the past few years, White & Case has secured dismissal of a complaint alleging that Purina participated in a conspiracy to fix the prices of prescription pet food, and defeated class certification motions brought against Toshiba for alleged price fixing of lithium ion batteries.

KM: White & Case has been involved in the leading cartel cases of the last decade, including matters involving pet food, chemicals, plastics, auto parts, and electronic components. For example, White & Case successfully represented Toshiba Corporation in a much-publicized U.S. antitrust jury trial involving allegations of price-fixing in the LCD (Liquid-Crystal Display) industry. Plaintiffs sought over US $2 billion in trebled damages, and Toshiba was completely exonerated by the jury. By way of another example, White & Case defeated the Department of Justice Antitrust Division in a criminal trial against Stolt-Nielsen, which also directly led to a revised Department of Justice amnesty policy.

Kelly Newman, associate: Some examples of cartel work that we have done are the CertainTeed antitrust litigation (dismissed at summary judgment), and the Richard Usher criminal antitrust lawsuit.

> *"By the time you hit your third year, you're taking depositions, and if there's a trial, you're second-chairing trial witnesses."*

CA: What do associates do? What kind of work is involved day-to-day?

KM: White & Case Antitrust/Competition associates are the backbone of our matters. With careful guidance from the partners, associates take lead roles in drafting, interviews/depositions, and organizing and running discovery and diligence teams. Importantly, associates are also very much included in, and central to, legal strategy discussions and decisions. White & Case is a very collaborative environment, and while senior partners and associates have a greater depth of knowledge commensurate with their experience, thoughts and ideas from junior lawyers are not only welcome, but encour-

Practice Areas

aged. On a day-to-day basis, therefore, associates may be tasked with everything from legal research to develop innovative case theories, to drafting probative discovery requests to serve on an opposing party, to helping a more senior associate or partner prepare for the deposition or interview of a key witness or even taking the deposition themselves.

KN: Associates are actively involved in case management and really in all aspects of the case. As a junior associate, you will be heavily involved in deposition preparation and will second-chair depositions. By the time you hit your third year, you're taking depositions, and if there's a trial, you're second-chairing trial witnesses. On the writing front, you're going to be actively involved in developing the briefing strategy at all levels. While junior associates tend to be limited to drafting riders and shorter motions (such as discovery motions), as a mid-level and senior associate, you will be given substantial drafting experience, including drafting motions for summary judgment, *Daubert* motions and oppositions. As a mid-level you'll also likely get a chance to argue lesser motions in court if the opportunity arises.

KA: All of our associates play a major role in our cases, but their responsibilities and day-to-day tasks vary quite a bit depending on the stage of the litigation and the associate's experience. Early on in a case, for example, our associates likely will assist with fact development, such as interviewing client witnesses, and motion practice, such as drafting a motion to dismiss or discovery motions. As our cases move into discovery, associates are often tasked with handling depositions, supporting expert witnesses, and developing our best arguments for summary judgment and trial. When we finally get to trial, the associates that put in the hard work on the case over the previous few years really get their chance to be involved in all aspects of trial preparation, direct- and cross-examination of lay and expert witnesses, motion practice, and development of our overall trial strategy. And because the Competition Group at White & Case tries so many cases, our junior lawyers have an excellent chance to get real-world trial experience early on in their careers.

> **"The work is face-paced and exciting, but you learn quickly that if you want to be successful you'll need to be able to juggle multiple tasks, with various deadlines, on all of your cases."**

CA: What are the highs of the antitrust practice?

KA: This is an easy one – winning big, complex antitrust cases for our clients. By way of example, I spent my early years at the firm working on a case involving a drug called "Doryx." The case went on for a number of years, and the parties really fought tooth and nail over what, at the time, were novel allegations under the Sherman Act. In the end, the court ruled in our client's favor on summary judgment, representing the first-ever victory for a defendant on a full evidentiary record in a so-called pharmaceutical "product hopping" litigation. The Third Circuit Court Appeals affirmed the ruling the following year, creating the only appellate precedent in favor of a defendant in a "product hopping" case. Our White & Case team spent a lot of time on that case, and to have both the district court and Third Circuit rule in our favor on issues and theories we had been litigating over for years was a great feeling, both for us and our client.

KM: There is no better high in the practice of law than knowing that your client trusted you with a "bet the company" deal or litigation and that you secured the best possible outcome. That feeling is only compounded by the nature of our cases – handling some of the largest, most complex, and most legally significant matters for some of the world's largest, most complex, and most significant clients is particularly rewarding; there's nothing quite like seeing your matters and your clients' successes on the evening news.

KN: The highs are definitely the frequent trials. I've been to trial now twice (though my third – a jury trial – is going to trial next Monday, and my fourth – also a jury trial – is scheduled for the fall), and have second-chaired multiple witnesses at trial. In some of the cases that have gone to trial I was able as a more junior mid-level to have a substantive and core-team role in the trial.

CA: And the lows?

KA: The size and complexity of our cases, coupled with tight scheduling orders from the court, can lead to challenging scheduling issues, such as depositions piling up and deadlines fast approaching when the court has yet to rule on earlier motions. The work is face-paced and exciting, but you learn quickly that if you want to be successful you'll need to be able to juggle multiple tasks, with various deadlines, on all of your cases.

KN: The lows are discovery battles and keeping up with the waves of discovery and document productions that accompany any large antitrust case.

CA: What factors are currently driving work in the antitrust group?

KA: Some of the factors driving the work in White & Case's Competition Group are recent developments in the law regarding class actions and class certification; the application of Supreme Court precedent, such as *FTC v. Actavis* (where we served as counsel), to patent settlement agreements; challenges to new-product launches under the Sherman Act; the impact of technology on price-fixing allegations; and the application of the Foreign Trade Antitrust Improvements Act.

KM: I would add that novel governmental applications of monopsony theories in merger challenges is another issue currently driving work in the Group.

"Keep an eye on the popular antitrust legal blogs and websites for news and recent developments."

CA: How can students and associates keep up-to-date with these trends?

KM: Staying up-to-date on the ever-changing antitrust legal landscape is a challenge, but there are a variety of good resources that I would recommend for students and associates. A great place to start would be to become a member of the American Bar Association's Section on Antitrust Law, which offers some insightful publications and hosts the annual "Spring Meeting" – a several day affair with dozens of panels addressing hot topics from the past year, such as landmark cases, trends, and practice pointers.

KA: A good start would be to keep an eye on the popular antitrust legal blogs and websites for news and recent developments. A lot of these websites publish weekly, or even daily, updates about notable decisions and important antitrust cases. Some of my favorites are Law360, PaRR, and Global Competition Review.

CA: What opportunities in antitrust work are unique to White & Case?

KN: Trial, trial trial. I was always told that you never go to trial in BigLaw. But by the end of February, I'll have gone to three trials in four years, and by the end of the fall, four trials in four years. It's a lot of work, but it is so worth it.

KA: The opportunity for junior associates to take on significant responsibility on major antitrust cases is unique to White & Case. Because the cases we handle are so large and complex, oftentimes there are opportunities for jun-

ior associates to step up and master a specific legal issue or set of facts in the case that make that associate indispensable and a key player in developing our overall case strategy.

KM: Another unique feature of the White & Case antitrust practice is its global presence. Unlike firms whose international offices are merely outposts of their New York headquarters, White & Case is truly global, with fully-formed, fully-integrated international offices, and, in fact, more lawyers practicing outside the US than within. This allows us to serve clients not only across the spectrum of legal issues – from governmental criminal investigations to agency enforcement actions to residual civil class actions – but to offer those services around the globe. That means that a US-based antitrust associate might work on a matter for a German client whose US arm is accused of competition violations in Mexico. It also means that by providing global solutions, the White & Case antitrust group gets to tackle unique legal challenges presented by conflicting governments and laws. For example, where one client is investigated by EU Competition authorities and the US Department of Justice, White & Case can develop a legal strategy to succeed in both jurisdictions without conflict, for the best outcome for the client.

"Much of competition law is rooted in economic theory – and indeed, economists are often critical experts in antitrust matters – so even an entry level understanding is helpful for seeing the bigger picture and positioning yourself for success."

CA: What advice do you have for students interested in this area?

KM: My general advice to students interested in antitrust is to take not only antitrust and competition classes in law school but also economics and business law classes. Much of competition law is rooted in economic theory – and indeed, economists are often critical experts in antitrust matters – so even an entry level understanding is helpful for seeing the bigger picture and positioning yourself for success. As for career development – many law students don't develop a particular legal area of interest until well into practicing law, so if you know you want to work in antitrust/competition, you're already ahead of the game.

KA: Students interested in antitrust work should keep an eye on major antitrust cases and recent developments.

Practice Areas

Additionally, meeting and speaking with antitrust lawyers, both in private practice and with government agencies, is a great way to get up to speed on the practice, make good connections, and get a better understanding of what the practice looks like day-to-day.

CA: Where can new junior associates expect to be in five years?

KN: At White & Case, if you work hard, it's likely that after five years you'll be a point associate on major antitrust matters, you'll be taking and defending depositions (both expert and fact), you'll be drafting dispositive motions, and, with some luck, you might get to take a witness at trial as well (I've seen it happen, though I haven't had the opportunity yet).

KA: At White & Case, junior associates can expect to be well-trained and experienced, having likely been staffed on a number of complex antitrust litigations that reached trial. They can also expect to have more real-world litigation experience than most of their peers, given our group's willingness to let junior associates take on substantive work and responsibility early on in their careers. Last, they can expect to have some great connections and relationships, both with partners and associates in the group as well as with our clients, who they will have met and worked with throughout the course of our cases.

Authors

Kathryn Mims
Associate

Kevin Adam
Associate

Kelly Newman
Associate

Practice Areas

Antitrust – the basics

In a nutshell

Antitrust attorneys advise clients on whether their business practices comply with regulations domestically and abroad so that markets function effectively on the basis of fair and open competition. In doing so, they undertake a broad range of different legal activities, including litigation, government investigations, merger advice and counseling.

Within litigation, generally there are cases alleging improper single company conduct and those alleging anti-competitive agreements or collusion among two or more entities. The former refers to claims against a single entity for monopolistic conduct, such as predatory pricing or abuse of monopoly power. The latter refers to an agreement or conspiracy among two or more entities that could include conduct such as boycotting, bid-rigging, price-fixing and dividing markets or customers. Many of these cases are brought by a class of affected customers or consumers. Both types are private and civil.

Government investigation, or enforcement, can be brought as a civil or criminal proceeding. Civil enforcement involves investigating companies for certain conduct, asking them to change their behavior, and sometimes fining them. Criminal investigations revolve primarily around cartels and price-fixing, and carry steep criminal penalties.

Merger advice (often called merger control) is another big piece of antitrust work, whereby attorneys shepherd their client through major regulations associated with M&A transactions, which generally result in a greater market share, the likely elimination of competitors and a greater risk of monopolistic conduct. Counseling involves providing clients with advice about their current and future business practices, such as co-marketing or distribution.

Rankings in *Chambers USA*

Top Ranked

Alston & Bird	Morgan, Lewis & Bockius
Cleary Gottlieb Steen	Norton Rose Fulbright
Davis Polk & Wardwell	O'Melveny & Myers
Dechert	Ropes & Gray
Gibson, Dunn & Crutcher	Sidley Austin
Jones Day	Skadden
Kirkland & Ellis	White & Case
Latham & Watkins	WilmerHale
Mayer Brown	

Highly Recommended

Arnold & Porter	Orrick, Herrington
Axinn, Veltrop & Harkrider	Paul Hastings
Baker Botts	Paul, Weiss
Choate Hall & Stewart	Reed Smith
Cooley	Shearman & Sterling
Cravath, Swaine & Moore	Sheppard, Mullin, Richter
Crowell & Moring	Simpson Thacher & Bartlett
Freshfields	Sullivan & Cromwell
Haynes and Boone,	Thompson & Knight
King & Spalding	Vinson & Elkins
Linklaters	Weil, Gotshal & Manges
McDermott Will & Emery	Willkie Farr & Gallagher
Morrison & Foerster	Wilson Sonsini Goodrich
Munger, Tolles & Olson	Winston & Strawn

For more detail on ranking tiers and locations, visit www.chambersandpartners.com

"A great place to start would be to become a member of the American Bar Association's Section on Antitrust Law, which offers some insightful publications and hosts the annual "Spring Meeting" – a several day affair with dozens of panels addressing hot topics from the past year, such as landmark cases, trends, and practice pointers."

– Kathryn Mims, associate, White & Case

Private equity by Weil

In the high-octane world of private equity, lawyers may only have a bidding window of a few days to get the components of a deal right for their clients. Weil's attorneys tell us about the adrenaline rush, managing risks and why emotional intelligence is key for becoming a successful private equity lawyer.

Practice Areas

Chambers Associate: What does Weil's private equity practice do?

Kyle Krpata, partner: We represent private equity firms and their portfolio companies on a variety of acquisitions, investments and sale transactions. Transactions can be for controlling interests or minority interests, they can be done by a single private equity firm or a group of investors. These are just a few examples of the many different types of transactions that our private equity group covers.

Ramona Nee, partner: Our work doesn't end when we close the initial acquisition – we often participate throughout the entire life cycle of an investment as we assist our private equity clientsand their portfolio companies in monitoring their investments and their ultimate dispositions, whether through a proprietary deal, an auction process or an IPO.

Peter Feist, partner: In addition to the deal side of our practice, Weil has 60 private funds lawyers in the U.S., Europe and Asia who focus exclusively on the formation of private investment funds. Our private funds lawyers cover the full sponsor spectrum, from some of the largest players to the emerging participants and funds of all sizes and investment strategies.

CA: What does Weil's private equity client base look like?

PF: We advise more than 200 private equity clients worldwide, 100 of which are in the U.S. There really isn't a corner of the market that our clients don't play in. Our clients range from growth equity to middle market to the largest private equity funds and pension funds in the world. Our private equity clients also focus on all segments of the market, including buyouts, infrastructure, real estate, growth equity, special situations and credit, and do transactions across all industries.

"We often participate throughout the entire life cycle of an investment as we assist our private equity clients."

KK: On the West Coast in particular, we advise a number of corporate venture capital investors and growth equity funds that focus on the technology space. Our corporate venture capital practice has grown significantly as our public company clients have become increasingly interested in investing in early stage companies to get early looks at innovative technology as well as for the potential financial returns.

CA: What do associates do?

David Gail, partner: Deal work is fast-paced and requires associates to multitask. Associates get involved in every aspect of the deal, from initial market research and diligence to negotiating principal transactions agreements. Our associates are generally coordinating with our clients on day-to-day deal matters from the moment they walk in the door.

RN: Our private equity associates are involved from the ground up. Our recruiting and training is focused on finding and developing attorneys who can hit the ground running – direct exposure to clients with intentionally leanly staffed deal teams creates consistent opportunity for even the most junior associates to gain immediate experience and broad exposure to our clients and to the practice.

CA: What do partners do?

KK: Partners wear a number of hats. First and foremost, we are responsible for making sure our clients are receiving the best-in-class legal service that they expect. This means our private equity partners are actively involved in executing deals and working very closely with associates. We are also very focused on building and maintaining client relationships and making sure our clients meet and are comfortable with their deal teams from the most senior members of the team to the junior associates. We value building long-term partnerships with our clients, and getting the teams together socially is invaluable to building these relationships.

PF: We also offer our clients a comprehensive sense of the market. That really comes with the extensive range of sponsors we work with and transactions we touch. Partners in Weil's PE group are so steeped in the market that they can offer clients perspective on what other sponsors are doing, what deal terms to agree to (and not agree to) and what obstacles and opportunities might be coming down the road.

RN: Getting deals done and managing client relationships goes without saying. Almost more importantly, the partners in our group realize that we have a responsibility to train and mentor our associates.

"The goal is trying to balance achieving the goals of the deal, with managing the risks, and getting to a point where all sides believe the deal is worth doing on the terms agreed."

CA: What is the most challenging aspect of your practice area?

PF: One of the most challenging aspects of transactional work, and also one of the most rewarding, is finding solutions to the constant stream of issues that usually arise among the many parties in a deal, and doing so on invariably a highly time sensitive basis. As lawyers, we have to work with their clients, and the other parties and counsel, to identify the issues for that particular deal and come up with solutions that all parties can accept. Taking a step back, each client is doing a deal because they see the benefits of it – it should be a "win-win" – but there are always risks and concerns on every deal. So the goal is trying to balance achieving the goals of the deal, with managing the risks, and getting to a point where all sides believe the deal is worth doing on the terms agreed.

RN: The execution speed that many types of deals demand is both exciting and challenging. Our private equity clients are constantly assessing new opportunities, so on any given day you might get a call from a client looking to acquire a company with the bidding window closing in a matter of days. Sometimes, at the 11th hour, an issue comes to light that threatens to derail a closing. My job is to figure out what needs to be done, pull together the right resources, and provide the best client service possible – figuring out the right priorities to balance the timing constraints while providing the quality work product that the industry demands. It's pretty challenging to negotiate an entire deal in 24 hours, but it's also a huge adrenaline rush – we're lucky to have the support both within our own practice and among all of our specialist areas to get it done.

CA: What are the differences between private equity and corporate M&A deals? Is it beneficial to work on both?

PF: At a very high level, private equity and corporate M&A are very similar. Businesses are being acquired or sold or are being invested in. It is when you drill down to the nature and purpose of the transactions that you see the real differences. The main difference is that a private equity firm buys a business as an investment – and therefore buys a business with the intent that the business will be sold or will go public within some period of time. When a corporate buys a business, it is usually for keeps. This is a major difference. It means that every time we do a private equity deal, we are not only asking how to get the deal done, but we are looking ahead and asking a lot of questions like "when will our client possibly exit from the investment, will they exit by selling the business or taking it public?" and so on. Very often, what the expectations for the future are will impact the deal today – so, it is truly multifaceted.

KK: On the West Coast, most of our lawyers do private equity and corporate M&A transactions. Personally, my practice is relatively evenly balanced between private equity and corporate M&A and I enjoy the variety. I advise a number of leading private equity firms who play in the middle market, growth equity and venture capital space, as well as large public technology companies on their acquisitions and investments. By focusing on a broader spectrum of transactions, I have developed a more well-rounded perspective and approach to my deals.

"A private equity firm buys a business as an investment – and therefore buys a business with the intent that the business will be sold or will go public within some period of time."

CA: What are the latest trends and developments in private equity? What does the future look like?

PF: The future for private equity is very strong. Private equity firms add a lot of value to the businesses they acquire – helping them to grow, expand and develop. At the same time, investors continue to want to invest in private equity firms as, when done right, the investment returns are overall better than what can be achieved in other investments, like buying stocks of public companies. So expect that private equity will continue to grow!

But at the same time, there are challenges. For example, it is a really competitive deal market right now and the prices our clients have to pay for businesses are very expensive. As a result, private equity firms are not only looking at traditional deals, but are spending a lot of time thinking "outside of the box", and looking for new and innovative types of transactions – ways they can get an edge or differentiate themselves. As a lawyer, this is one of the great things about private equity – it is constantly evolving and adapting, and means that for those of us in the legal industry advising on private equity deals, we have to continually think of new and better ways to advise and assist our clients.

CA: What personal qualities make for a good private equity lawyer?

KK: Having a keen interest in the broader market is crucial as a lot of our work involves providing clients strategic counseling on "what is market" and how they can best leverage such information. The ability to think beyond legal issues to provide strategic advice is a key differentiator in this increasingly competitive market – and one of our greatest value-adds to clients. First and foremost, we are problem solvers and our clients expect us to help them figure out how to get things done rather than simply highlighting issues.

PF: Private equity is an industry that plays into strong people skills and high levels of emotional intelligence. Every deal involves multiple parties and personalities, so pragmatically finding common ground and getting all parties to agree to a common set of terms is a key ingredient for success in executing deals.

DG: A willingness to learn new things every day. Our deals aren't "cookie-cutter", and they require creative

thinking and problem solving. Multitasking, time management and attention to detail are also key to success.

"The ability to think beyond legal issues to provide strategic advice is a key differentiator in this increasingly competitive market."

CA: What preparations should students make in order to succeed in this area?

PF: There is no particular set of classes or experience required to become a part of our team. All the necessary skills will be learned from working with our partners and associates on deals. The nature of private equity is that we aim to build long-term relationships with all our clients and do many deals for them, so our core deal teams become very familiar with our clients' business objectives and their style. Our group also prides itself on training our lawyers to be the best in the business.

DG: The technical skills that you will need to sign and close private equity deals you will learn on the job. However, because we touch on so many areas, it is helpful to have some background in tax and securities law. Also, while no one expects a lawyer to run complex financial models, a basic understanding of and interest in finance is also helpful.

CA: What is unique about Weil's private equity practice?

KK: Weil was one of the first law firms to focus on private equity. Because we have been steeped in the industry since the beginning, we have a longstanding and nuanced understanding of the market. Several of our partners handled the formation of many leading private equity firms and have enjoyed relationships with private equity clients for more than 20 years. Since I've been at the Firm, we've more than quadrupled the number of private equity clients we work with, and we continue to grow year after year.

Authors

Peter Feist
Partner

David Gail
Partner

Kyle Krpata
Partner

Ramona Nee
Partner

Weil

Funds and investment management by Fried Frank

Advising on the activities of hedge and private equity funds certainly keeps lawyers on their toes. For Fried Frank's asset management whizzes, it's the variety and ever-evolving nature of the practice that leads them to recommend becoming a lawyer in the area.

Chambers Associate: What does Fried Frank's asset management group do?
Lisa Schneider, partner: The Fried Frank asset management group represents hedge fund and private equity managers in all aspects of their businesses, including: the structuring and offering of new funds and other products; ongoing operations and strategic planning; negotiations with investors; the structuring of new management companies, and carried interest and compensation arrangements; advising on seed and stake transactions; and negotiating the spin-out of fund teams from larger institutions. We are known for representing some of the most sophisticated fund managers in the industry, combining our technical skills with a commercial and practical mindset in order to best represent our clients.

Bryan Hunkele, associate: We specialize in counseling large sponsors around the world, including Bain Capital, BlackRock, Blue Bay, Brookfield, Fortress, Goldman Sachs, HPS Partners, Permira and many others.

Joanna Rosenberg, associate: Half of the group focuses on hedge fund formation and the other half focuses on private equity fund formation. We also have a regulatory asset management subgroup (which I am a part of), which focuses on Advisers Act issues, as well as certain Investment Company Act and Securities Act issues.

CA: What kind of work can associates expect to do?

JR: Day-to-day, associates draft and revise offering memoranda and governing documents for new private funds and negotiate investment management agreements. Fried Frank also has an active practice in the area of fund manager M&A, and so asset management associates will also assist in due diligence relating to fund managers in which a client is purchasing a stake or the entire business. As a member of the regulatory asset management subgroup, I field regulatory questions about the Advisers Act, Investment Company Act, and Securities Act from the asset management group but also from the M&A group and capital markets group.

CA: What do partners do?

LS: Working as a partner in this practice area is extremely satisfying, both professionally and personally. My day involves reviewing and negotiating complex agreements and offering documents, working with clients to develop sound and innovative solutions to various issues, and providing day-to-day advice on a variety of different topics that touch upon the investment management space.

"Each phase of a fund's life cycle presents unique challenges that require different skills and play to different strengths."

CA: What are the best things about the practice?

BH: Each phase of a fund's life cycle presents unique challenges that require different skills and play to different strengths: (a) the structuring phase is thought-intensive, and it emphasizes creativity and teamwork; (b) drafting the fund documents requires diligence and writing skills; (c) fundraising and investor negotiation involves the use of management and personal skills, as well as the ability to think on one's feet, and (d) the operational phase, in which all the work one has done in the other three phases is applied to real-world challenges, is full of surprises and emphasizes critical thinking.

JR: The regulatory asset management practice at Fried Frank involves working on many different matters on any given day, which keeps things interesting and challenging. There are also certain questions that come up regularly, which creates a nice mix of consistent, familiar work and new issues that require deep and often creative thinking.

LS: Because this practice area often involves providing counsel to hedge fund and private equity managers throughout their lifespans, attorneys are able to grow and develop longstanding relationships with clients. In addition, our practice evolves as the fund industry evolves,

Practice Areas

which is exciting and allows us to continuously work on new and interesting matters.

CA: Which factors are currently affecting the practice area?

JR: The condition of the financial markets can impact our clients' ability to fundraise and to some extent the type of private funds clients are forming. In addition, the recent change in administration slowed the pace of SEC [Securities and Exchange Commission] rulemaking and, to some degree, SEC enforcement action.

"The condition of the financial markets can impact our clients' ability to fundraise and to some extent the type of private funds clients are forming."

LS: The industry has been digesting the new US tax legislation and its impact on hedge funds and private equity funds. It will be interesting to see how the space evolves as a result of these changes.

CA: How can students keep up-to-date with trends in the market?

BH: *The Wall Street Journal* does a great job of covering the business elements of our practice area, while SEC releases and actions relating to the Investment Adviser's Act provide a good avenue for getting to know the latest regulatory focus.

CA: Where can new associates expect to be in five years' time?

BH: With hard work and the right set of skills, associates could be leading the closing of a multibillion dollar fund – the deals which will be in the news for the next three or four years.

LS: One of the best parts of the asset management practice is that associates are offered the opportunity to have direct exposure to clients and to take on as much re-

sponsibility as they are comfortable with early on. It is the perfect practice area for an attorney looking to gain enormous experience, a wealth of knowledge and significant client exposure early in their career.

CA: Which opportunities are unique to Fried Frank?
BH: I think our group provides a unique combination of lean staffing and high-profile matters. At our size, we do not have the luxury to ask associates to review subscription materials and investor questionnaires during their first-year. Of course, there will be some of that, but the professional opportunities our young associates enjoy (with appropriate supervision) are otherwise a year or two ahead of what they might typically see elsewhere.

JR: Fried Frank is a place where hard work and quality work product are rewarded. If associates show a strong work ethic and an interest in the matters they are working on, they are sought out and given more responsibility and more challenging assignments.

LS: Because the Fried Frank asset management group has extremely sophisticated, long-standing clients, I have had the opportunity to develop relationships with wonderful people and work on the most interesting and cutting edge matters. The combination of Fried Frank's legal acumen and the collegiality of the attorneys who work here is unparalleled.

CA: Do you have any words of advice for students interested in this area?

BH: Pay attention to market news and try to understand the business motivations behind what you read. The separation between the practice of law and business is something of a myth, as a good lawyer needs to understand their clients' business goals in order to provide meaningful legal advice.

JR: I would suggest taking a class on securities regulation. It helps to give high level context to the work that asset management associates do at the firm.

Authors

Bryan Hunkele
Associate

Joanna Rosenberg
Associate

Lisa Schneider
Partner

FRIED FRANK

Private equity & investment management – the basics

In a nutshell

Private equity and investment companies operate funds that pool the investments of anybody prepared to part with their money for a sustained period of time. The private equity firm takes this cash – often alongside a large portion of bank debt (making it a 'leveraged buyout', or 'LBO') – to buy companies or other assets with the goal of selling them on at a massive profit. Investment management lawyers, therefore, have two primary functions: they form the funds (which are typically structured as limited partnerships) and help the private equity firm negotiate the terms on which investors contribute their money, and they act for the private equity fund when it buys and sells its investments.

Venture capital is a subset of private equity that sees investors put money into startup companies or small businesses in the hope they will be sold to a private equity firm or taken public. Although this typically entails high risk for the investor, it has the potential for above-average returns. The higher risk compared to private equity proper is offset by investing smaller amounts over a shorter timespan, typically.

Investment management is the professional management of various securities (shares, bonds, etc) and assets in order to meet the specified investment goals of investors. Investment management lawyers may work in any of the specialist areas described below, but ultimately advise on the structuring, formation, taxation and regulation of all types of investment funds.

A **hedge fund** is a private, actively managed investment fund. It aims to provide returns to investors by investing in a diverse range of markets, investment instruments and strategies. Hedge funds' investment strategies aim to make a positive return on investment regardless of whether markets are rising or falling. Expertise on the derivative markets helps hedge funds achieve this.

Rankings in *Chambers USA*

Top Ranked

Cooley	Proskauer Rose
Debevoise & Plimpton	Ropes & Gray
Dechert	Schulte Roth & Zabel
Kirkland & Ellis	Sidley Austin
Latham & Watkins	Simpson Thacher & Bartlett
Morgan, Lewis & Bockius	

Highly Recommended

Akin Gump Strauss Hauer	Paul, Weiss
Choate Hall & Stewart	Seward & Kissel LLP
Cleary Gottlieb Steen	Skadden
Davis Polk & Wardwell	Sullivan & Cromwell LLP
Fried, Frank, Harris, Shriver	Vedder Price
Gibson, Dunn & Crutcher	Weil, Gotshal & Manges
K&L Gates	White & Case LLP
Linklaters	Willkie Farr & Gallagher LLP
Paul Hastings LLP	WilmerHale

For more detail on ranking tiers and locations, visit www.chambersandpartners.com

A **mutual fund** is a collective investment vehicle that pools money from many investors to purchase securities. The term is most commonly applied to collective investments that are regulated and sold to the general public.

A **real estate investment fund/trust** is a publicly traded investment vehicle that uses investors' money to invest in properties and mortgages.

Both hedge funds and mutual funds generally operate as **open funds**. This means that investors may periodically make additions to, or withdrawals from, their stakes in the fund. An investor will generally purchase shares in the fund directly from the fund itself rather than from the existing shareholders. It contrasts with a closed fund, which typically issues all the shares it will issue at the outset, with such shares usually being tradable between investors thereafter.

"Private equity is an industry that plays into strong people skills and high levels of emotional intelligence. Every deal involves multiple parties and personalities, so pragmatically finding common ground and getting all parties to agree to a common set of terms is a key ingredient for success in executing deals."

– Peter Feist, partner, Weil, Gotshal & Manges

Bankruptcy and restructuring

In a nutshell

The essential task of bankruptcy and restructuring lawyers is to avoid a client's bankruptcy. The term 'bankruptcy' itself is a technical term that refers to when financially distressed companies, unable to restructure on their own, file for Chapter 11 to undergo a court-supervised restructuring.

In order to avoid this scenario, a company must restructure it's debt, but the path to financial viability – through court or not – can be convoluted. The legal know-how required and the multitude and variety of actors involved make bankruptcy and restructuring a rather complex practice.

Bankruptcy and restructuring attorneys must be adept at transactionalwork and litigationacross a range of areas like M&A, securities, banking, labor and employment, environment, tax and IP.

Troubled companies will first attempt out-of-court restructuring, or corporate reorganization, in which they try to reach an agreement with their creditors. This has become an increasingly important stage. *"Traditional Chapter 11 cases can be expensive, inefficient and harmful to the business,"* according to **Jay Goffman**, global co-head of **Skadden's** corporate restructuring group. *"This means it's important to advise companies on how to avoid Chapter 11 or shorten their time in Chapter 11 and similar insolvency proceedings, rather than convincing them to do it."*

"Bankruptcy is the last bastion of the generalist."

Chapter 11 provides for a court-supervised restructuring and, crucially, protection from creditors, who are barred from seeking to retrieve their money until the company is restructured. A notable feature of Chapter 11 work is the growing prevalence of 'distressed M&A', which describes the selling of parts – or the whole – of the ailing company. Such sales are done under the provisions of Section 363 of the Bankruptcy Code and often referred to as '363 deals'. Deals can also take place outside of court, but it is less common; buyers often prefer the safety of court-sanctioned sales.

The number of parties involved in a restructuring can be vast. They come from all walks of a company's life and often have competing interests. Acting for the debtor is a challenge on its own, because *"everyone's problem is your problem. You have to deal with every creditor and ensure*

the pie is allocated fairly," **Davis Polk's** insolvency and restructuring practice **Don Bernstein** explains.

Representing creditors is often simply about trying to recover as much as you can from a debtor, but there are many different types of creditors to choose from. 'Secured' creditors include commercial and investment banks, insurance companies and hedge funds, while 'unsecured' creditors include bondholders and vendors, or 'trade creditors' (eg, auto parts suppliers). In Chapter 11, there are official committees of unsecured creditors and debtor in possession (DIP) lenders, while out-of-court proceedings will have bondholder committees.

Other parties involved may include strategic buyers and private equity firms and hedge funds interested in acquiring distressed assets. They engage in the purchase, sale and trading of debt claims. This has become one of the biggest administrative components of Chapter 11 cases. A special committee set up by the board to oversee the restructuring may also be involved and, in instances of 'gross mismanagement' by the company, a trustee is appointed to handle matters.

What lawyers do

Out-of-court restructuring for debtor

- Analyze the situation in order to determine the feasibility of staying out of bankruptcy. What's the problem? What caused it? How big is it? Will it result in a default that is uncontrollable? Who's in the creditor body? Are they secured or unsecured? What's the litigation status? What's the liquidity status? Are there sufficient funds to stay in business while being restructured?
- Look for 'red flags', such as jurisdiction. *"You need to know if the entity has international operations, how it operates, how it's interconnected,"* explains former **Weil, Gotshal & Manges** partner **Harvey Miller**.
- Work with financial advisers to create a model of how the crisis will be dealt with.
- Try to persuade creditors to *"just stand still"* and not pursue immediate payback. *"You need to focus on the nature of the debt in order to determine who you approach to get a standstill or moratorium,"* Miller says.
- Negotiate with creditors and try convincing them that the problem is best solved out of bankruptcy.
- If negotiations are successful, work out payment plans for each creditor.
- If not successful, file for Chapter 11.

Rankings in *Chambers USA*

Top Ranked

Akin Gump Strauss Hauer	Kirkland & Ellis
Alston & Bird	Milbank
Arnold & Porter	Mintz Levin Cohn Ferris
Davis Polk & Wardwell	Norton Rose Fulbright
Greenberg Traurig, PA	Paul, Weiss
Haynes and Boone	Perkins Coie
Hunton Andrews Kurth	Reed Smith
Jones Day	Vinson & Elkins
K&L Gates	Weil, Gotshal & Manges
King & Spalding	

Highly Recommended

Baker Botts	Mayer Brown
Bracewell	Morgan, Lewis & Bockius
Brown Rudnick	Morrison & Foerster
Choate Hall & Stewart	O'Melveny & Myers
Cleary Gottlieb Steen	Orrick
Debevoise & Plimpton	Paul Hastings
Dechert	Proskauer Rose
DLA Piper (US)	Ropes & Gray
Duane Morris	Schulte Roth & Zabel
Dykema Gossett PLLC	Sheppard, Mullin, Richter
Foley & Lardner	Sidley Austin
Fox Rothschild	Simpson Thacher & Bartlett
Gibbons P.C.	Skadden
Gibson, Dunn & Crutcher	Squire Patton Boggs
Goulston & Storrs	Stroock & Stroock & Lavan
Hangley Aronchick Segal	Thompson & Knight
Holland & Knight	Troutman Sanders
Hughes Hubbard & Reed	Vedder Price
Jackson Walker	Venable
Jenner & Block	White & Case
Kasowitz Benson Torres	Willkie Farr & Gallagher
Katten Muchin Rosenman	WilmerHale
Kramer Levin Naftalis	Winston & Strawn
Latham & Watkins	

For more detail on ranking tiers and locations, visit
www.chambersandpartners.com

Court-supervised restructuring for debtor

- Initiate a Chapter 11 case to pursue restructuring within the protective provisions of the Bankruptcy Code (usually known as 'filing for Chapter 11').
- Prevent stigmatization of employees and business operations. Create a detailed communication plan to include regulators, shareholders, employees, vendors and clients.
- Secure financing.

- Once liquidity is secured, work with the management team and financial advisers to decide what's core and non-core to the business. Establish the company's new vision.
- Build creditor consensus around the chosen exit strategy. This can be a lengthy process and require delicate negotiations.
- If creditors think they are being economically harmed, there could be extensive litigation.
- Document and effectuate the eventual agreement.

Realities of the job

- *"You need to be psychologically ready to handle the stress and strain inherent in being involved in a practice in which, by definition, there are huge amounts of failure,"* says **James Sprayregen** of **Kirkland & Ellis**.
- **Jonathan Henes** of Kirkland & Ellis sets out the skills needed by junior associates: *"In the early years the focus needs to be on strong writing skills and learning how to be a strong oral advocate whether in negotiations or in court. As you get more senior, you need to also focus on the commercial aspects of the restructuring and become a counselor to clients."*
- Henes highlights the attraction of the bankruptcy practice as being *"helping companies go from a place of trauma to a place of strength – that is a powerful thing."*
- This area is renowned for being particularly suited to those keen to get involved in the client side of things. Henes explains that you need *"good judgment to thrive because these are hard situations not just intellectually but emotionally. You need to be focused on the human aspect of it all."*
- The extent to which transactional work and litigation cross paths during a restructuring cannot be overstated. *"There is a transactional aspect even when in court. You litigate by day and negotiate by night,"* Don Bernstein describes.
- The nature of cases can vary enormously. Sprayregen adds: *"Our work involves dozens of industries and that really does give you the opportunity to learn a lot."*
- Debtors face innumerable difficulties. They have no political muscle, whereas creditors do – and flex it. Though bankruptcy laws are constantly amended, they continue to favor creditors.
- In order to lead such a diverse group of parties to a consensus, debtor attorneys must possess strategic, tactical and managerial skills.
- Steering clients clear of Chapter 11 through out-of-court restructuring often requires a creative and innovative approach.
- The current Chapter 11 was passed in 1978, but it comes from Chapter X, which was passed in the 1930s. *"The Bankruptcy Code has its roots in the Great Depression,"* Bernstein says.

- Chapter 15 is the provision for cross-border bankruptcies that dictates proceedings in the USA when the main proceeding is in another country. Designed to ensure that all creditors and debtors are treated fairly irrespective of jurisdiction, it may also involve Chapter 11 proceedings if the debtor's assets are sufficiently complex.
- Restructuring is a lengthy process that requires a considerable amount of work before an outcome can be reached. *"There are so many different stakeholders and other components, and you spend a lot of time on the process itself – which I didn't expect as a young associate,"* Sprayregen tells us.
- Bankruptcy and restructuring is considered a countercyclical practice. When the market is healthy, bankruptcy attorneys may find themselves working on more diverse corporate matters.
- Negotiating terms for debtors in possession is a complicated balancing act. Attorneys must assess liens or security interests, prioritize creditors, determine the value of secured properties and argue for or against continued possession of secured properties in order to remain operating to better pay off creditors.
- Sprayregen notes that, *"ultimately, the most successful cases will be the ones that are the least problematic. Those cases are less interesting from the media's perspective, but that's when you really see success."*
- **Ira Dizengoff** of **Akin Gump** describes how bankruptcy is a very fast-paced area of the law: *"The nature of the companies that undergo reorganizations means you will see more cross-border restructuring which adds to the complexity. You are at the cutting edge and it moves quickly – there is never a dull moment."*

"You need to be psychologically ready to handle the stress and strain inherent in being involved in a practice in which, by definition, there are huge amounts of failure."

Current issues

- While the recession brought about a significant rise in bankruptcy filings in the USA, this has since been decreasing. The United States Courts records business bankruptcies falling from 34,892 in 2013 to 23,109 in 2017.
- With e-commerce booming the woes of the retail industry look to continue. In 2017 more than 300 retailers filed for bankruptcy (a record) including giants like Toys R Us, and S&P Global Ratings suggests 2018 could see even more.
- According to Moody's Investor Service, a record $1 trillion of junk-rated corporate debt that will mature by 2020, putting companies in severe debt at extremely high risk.
- Oil and gas companies continue to give bankruptcy practitioners plenty of work. The industry hosted new fewer than 21% of 2017's 71 public company bankruptcies and four of the ten largest Chapter 11 filings in 2017.
- The Federal Reserve raised interest rates at both the start and end of 2017 and forecasted three additional three additional rate increases in 2018 and 2019. What does this mean? A higher interest rate environment leads of variable rates in loans and therefore to more bankruptcies and more restructuring.
- Bankruptcy can be an expensive and lengthy process and companies try to avoid it, but it's been getting steadily more costly. To give an example of what this can look like at the top end, Kirkland & Ellis' lawyers were charging Toys R Us as much as $1,745 an hour during the company's bankruptcy proceedings – though this was 25% more than the highest rate in ten of 2017's largest bankruptcies.
- In February 2018 the Trump administration announced proposals for a new 'Chapter 14' bankruptcy process. Ostensibly to prevent taxpayer-funded bailouts, the new process was suggested by the Treasury as a 'resolution method of first resort'. Details on what this would entail in practice, and whether or not it will actually be implemented, remain sketchy at the time of writing so keep an eye on how this develops.
- After nearly a decade in recession, the US territory of Puerto Rico filed for what amounted to a federal bankruptcy in May 2017. The island owed $74 billion in debts and more than $53 billion in unfunded pensions; by March 2018 law, accounting and consulting firms had charged it $75 million in fees as a result of debt reorganization proceedings.

Tax

In a nutshell

"Tax touches virtually every aspect of the economy," says **Les Samuels**, senior counsel at **Cleary Gottlieb**. Accordingly, tax law encompasses a variety of activities, from transactional support and structuring to tax planning and tax controversy.

Working alongside corporate lawyers, tax attorneys ensure that transactions are as tax-efficient as possible, be they centered on public or private M&A, capital markets, investment funds (private equity, REITs and mutual funds), joint ventures or partnerships. Tax planning advice requires familiarity with all relevant domestic and international laws, and it is essential to have an understanding of clients' overall objectives and the structuring of their businesses.

Tax controversy is more of an independent category, covering a range of contentious tax issues. These include tax-based litigation, IRS examinations and tax shelter investigations. Disputes are usually resolved at the administrative level. Transfer pricing is also grouped with tax controversy.

We've previously included wealth management and private client work alongside tax – that's now got its own summary on page 213.

What lawyers do

- Advise clients on the tax elements of transactions.
- Analyze cases and regulations to develop a real understanding of the tax implications of transaction structures. Findings are summarized as memoranda or given through direct counseling.
- Negotiate terms dealing with the tax aspects of transactions.
- Draft agreements, especially for M&A and joint ventures, which are particularly tax-intensive. An important element is the drafting of tax disclosures.
- Liaise with other non-tax lawyers and clients to ensure the smooth running of transactions.
- If working in tax controversy, negotiate with the IRS, respond to IRS questions, and draft memoranda and briefs.

Realities of the job

- Tax lawyers need to keep up with all new developments in both the law and the economy as a whole. This is especially important for a young lawyer, who needs to build expertise. The law is always changing.
- By keeping up to date, tax lawyers can become real experts and even innovators within the legal landscape. With experience, they may be able to offer a solution to a tax issue that has previously been unsolvable. For example, the tax lawyer will produce a new financial instrument that becomes accepted by the market. This will sometimes prompt the government to review its regulations.
- It's vital to have an affinity for reading case law and regulations, as this is how juniors will spend some of their time. They must be able to rationalize their findings and summarize them accurately.
- Tax lawyers must have full confidence in their advice. The research must be methodical and complete.
- In order to ensure that commercial transactions are as tax-efficient as possible, tax practices work closely with corporate departments and understand the non-tax issues that drive transactions. A successful tax department can be a useful marketing tool for firms looking to attract new clients.
- Tax lawyers need to express themselves clearly and concisely. Solid technical knowledge is essential, as is the ability to explain technical information to non-experts.
- Excellent interpersonal skills are a must. Tax controversy can sometimes involve liaising with the IRS, and it is important that lawyers be upfront and straight-talking. They may also work with international clients, so cultural awareness is important.
- Lawyers have the chance to work on a variety of matters, including charity and pro bono. They are expected to comment on proposed regulations and may also give tutorials to colleagues and clients.
- Tax lawyers sometimes break up their career by spending time working for the government, notably the IRS.

Current issues

- The Trump administration has made tax reform a key policy. In 2017 the President signed the US Tax Cuts and Jobs Act bill, cutting corporate tax from 35% to 21%. The measures were intended as a means to encourage the market and stimulate the economy, though the bill has attracted critics on both side of the aisle and the changes are expected to add more than $1.5 trillion to public debt over the next decade.

Practice Areas

Rankings in *Chambers USA*

Top Ranked

Alston & Bird	Kirkland & Ellis
Baker Botts	Latham & Watkins
Baker McKenzie	Mayer Brown
Cleary Gottlieb Steen	McDermott Will & Emery
Cravath, Swaine & Moore	Morgan, Lewis & Bockius
Davis Polk & Wardwell	Ropes & Gray
Dechert	Simpson Thacher & Bartlett
Gibson, Dunn & Crutcher	Skadden
Greenberg Traurig, PA	Sullivan & Cromwell
Holland & Knight	Vinson & Elkins
King & Spalding	

Highly Recommended

Akin Gump Strauss Hauer	Morrison & Foerster
Arnold & Porter Kaye	Munger, Tolles & Olson
Bracewell	Norton Rose Fulbright
Cadwalader, Wickersham	O'Melveny & Myers
Cahill Gordon & Reindel	Paul Hastings
Choate Hall & Stewart	Paul, Weiss
Clifford Chance US	Pillsbury Winthrop Shaw
Debevoise & Plimpton	Proskauer Rose
DLA Piper (US)	Reed Smith
Duane Morris	Schulte Roth & Zabel
Fried, Frank, Harris	Shearman & Sterling
Haynes and Boone	Sidley Austin
Hunton Andrews Kurth	Thompson & Knight
Irell & Manella	Weil, Gotshal & Manges
Jenner & Block	White & Case
Jones Day	Willkie Farr & Gallagher
Katten Muchin Rosenman	WilmerHale
Kramer Levin Naftalis	Wilson Sonsini Goodrich
Milbank	Winston & Strawn

For more detail on ranking tiers and locations, visit www.chambersandpartners.com

- Oil giant BP expects a one-off $1.5 billion charge as a result of tax reforms, which will affect its liabilities and deferred assets. Like many multinational companies, BP expects the new tax regime to be positive for its balance sheet in the long-run.
- Globally, there has been more cooperation regarding tax havens and information exchange to address the role of businesses in eroding countries' tax bases. So far, 113 jurisdictions have Foreign Account Tax Compliance Act agreements with the IRS to some degree, which has helped create greater lines of communication between the IRS and foreign financial firms. The IRS's offshore voluntary disclosure program allows overseas account holders to rectify any tax shortcomings, thus warding off the threat of penalty action.

- International transfer pricing has given some of the world's biggest companies a headache recently, as high-profile cases involving Amazon, Apple and Facebook have demonstrated. The movement of goods and currency across borders throws up various tax issues that authorities have been getting stricter on.
- Following the Supreme Court's approval of same-sex marriage in June 2015, gay and lesbian married couples may now file joint tax returns at state and federal levels.
- Heads up, readers, this one could affect you: effective as of the 2016 fiscal year, students who wish to qualify for tax breaks on educational expenses must now file a copy of the 1098-T Tuition Statement form before applying.
- The US is the only major economy not to have a value-added tax (VAT) system. However, there is a belief among some experts that a federal VAT system could be introduced in future.

What top tax lawyers advise

Leslie Samuels, senior counsel, **Cleary Gottlieb:**

"It's important to keep your eyes and ears open to make sure you understand everything about the transaction so your advice is the most effective it can be."

"You don't have to be a math genius to be a very successful tax lawyer. You're dealing more with concepts. We don't prepare tax returns, and we certainly don't get busy before the tax filing dates."

"To the extent that tax lawyers think they're just servicing the corporate lawyers, it's a total mistake. The work is so much broader than that."

"Keeping up with developments is exciting and demanding. There's so much you have to keep up with every day! But that's how you become an expert, which is one of the attractive aspects to practicing tax law. You really can become the go-to person who knows everything about topic X."

Basil Zirinis, partner, **Sullivan & Cromwell:**

"Students should definitely take as many tax courses as they can in law school – including corporate tax. The more of a background they have in tax, the more helpful it will be."

"The broader the courses you take, the better off you'll be. We do everything from corporate law to litigation in our practice – so the broadest possible academic experience is important."

"An international perspective on the world in general is helpful, especially because the explosion of wealth is global. It's not US and Europe any more. It's increasingly mobile – China, Latin America, etc. That's where the most interesting work will ultimately be for young lawyers, so languages are extremely important."

Practice Areas

Energy Infrastructure and Real Estate

"I always tell candidates to consider how their experiences demonstrate passion, initiative, leadership and commitment. Last year I interviewed a woman who loved competitive mountain biking – it was so different and she was so passionate, talking about why it really fitted her and why she loved it. It also wasn't at all consistent with the other things on her resume, so it was particularly interesting. I've also spent a 20-minute interview talking about podcasts, and that allowed me to understand what made that person tick and gave us something to connect on. Above all, we're looking for people who can develop relationships, stand up in front of courts, clients and boardrooms, and be articulate and relate to them."

– firm-wide hiring partner
Sharyl Reisman,
Jones Day

Energy & projects

In a nutshell

Energy and projects are two distinct but overlapping areas of law. When combined, they focus on the development, construction and financing of major natural resource (oil/gas, mining), power and infrastructure projects. The construction of pipelines, refineries, mines, power plants and petrochemical plants is a massive business, with high stakes and massive dollar values. Emerging economies are frequently the hungriest for infrastructural improvements, meaning a lawyer's work increasingly takes on an international flavor.

In addition, the projects component of an energy practice consists of both transactional and regulatory work (with regulatory work more prevalent in US domestic projects). There is a clear demarcation between transactional and regulatory work, and lawyers usually specialize in one of the two.

Non-energy projects are all about infrastructure. Typical examples might be road, airports, rail, shipping, telecoms and, most glamorously, sewage and water systems. The work would also include the construction of major multi-investor public buildings such as jails and stadiums.

What lawyers do

Energy – transactional & regulatory

- Transactional work can cover anything across M&A, joint ventures, capital markets, private equity, venture capital and project development and finance work.
- Energy lawyers deal with three types of clients: upstream, midstream and downstream. **Upstream** businesses deal with getting energy out of the ground – oil, gas, coal, sometimes geothermal. This includes mining and minerals companies. **Midstream** clients are in the refining, treating and transportation of resources industry and its offshoots. **Downstream** clients are energy distributors: gas stations, electricity providers, gas companies.
- Lawyers advise clients on negotiating and drafting agreements related to things like energy projects, the sale of power companies, investment in and development of upstream resources and the financing of various energy investments.
- Certain states, such as Texas, have a very particular regulatory structure, so lawyers are often called upon to provide clients that are new to the state with regulatory advice on purchases and sales, contracts between companies and users, public authority requirements and licensing.

- Many firms' energy work focuses either on infrastructure and construction projects or on representations in front of the Federal Energy Regulatory Commission (FERC). FERC is a US government regulatory agency. It regulates electricity sales, electric rates, hydropower projects, natural gas pricing and oil pipeline rates. Its decisions can be reviewed by federal courts.
- *"I like that it involves public policy. I find that very interesting. I like that what I do will have an effect on a wide variety of people and also that there is a lot of variety in what I do from one day to the next. I can do individual client counseling, I can contest cases and I can be involved in rule-making where policy issues are heavily debated all in one day. I find it interesting to have variety,"* says **Catherine Webking**, partner at **Scott Douglas & McConnico**.

Projects

- Projects lawyers have three or four types of clients: sponsors/developers who put together the project; financiers (banks, international development agencies, foreign export credit agencies); the provider or contractor (who supplies raw materials or undertakes construction); and sometimes the 'offtaker' who purchases the products produced by the project. The most significant roles for lawyers are representing either the sponsors/developers or the financiers.
- **Keith Martin**, partner and co-head of projects at **Norton Rose Fulbright**, says *"project finance transactions are complicated exercises in risk allocation that take a lot of time and generate lots of paper. The complexity is increased by the involvement of different countries and the number of people in different roles – sponsors, senior and subordinated lenders, tax and true equity investors, landowners, offtakers. These are interesting puzzles to put together – they take an ability to listen carefully, spot common ground and solve problems."*
- The overwhelming majority of international work for projects lawyers is handled in New York – which remains the 'money center' for transactions in Latin America. The Energy Policy Act of 2005 created a host of new regulations by which companies in the industry are required to abide. These include loan guarantees for technologies that avoid greenhouse gases, subsidies for alternative energy producers and incentives to drill for oil in the Gulf of Mexico.

Practice Areas

Rankings in *Chambers USA*

Top Ranked

Baker Botts	Shearman & Sterling
Bracewell	Skadden, Arps, Slate
King & Spalding	Sullivan & Cromwell
Latham & Watkins	Thompson & Knight
Mayer Brown	Troutman Sanders
Milbank, Tweed, Hadley	Vinson & Elkins
Morgan, Lewis & Bockius	White & Case
Norton Rose Fulbright	Winston & Strawn
Orrick	

Highly Recommended

Akin Gump	Jackson Walker
Allen & Overy	K&L Gates
Alston & Bird	Kirkland & Ellis
Cadwalader, Wickersham	Morrison & Foerster
Cleary Gottlieb Steen	Munger, Tolles & Olson
Clifford Chance US	O'Melveny & Myers
Crowell & Moring	Paul, Weiss
Debevoise & Plimpton	Pillsbury Winthrop Shaw
Foley & Lardner	Sidley Austin
Gibson, Dunn & Crutcher	Simpson Thacher & Bartlett
Greenberg Traurig	Venable
Haynes and Boone	Wilson Sonsini Goodrich
Hunton Andrews Kurth	

For more detail on ranking tiers and locations, visit www.chambersandpartners.com

Realities of the job

- This area of law is not widely publicized on legal courses. However, it can be a highly rewarding area of law to work in, as Catherine Webking explains: *"It is certainly not an intuitive area to go into from law school. But what is interesting is that the utility business is ultimately affecting everyone in the States so it is an area that really has a broad impact but is not well-known from law school."*
- Texas is *"the land of opportunity"* for energy lawyers focused on US-based projects and its law schools – most notably the University of Texas – are some of the only ones in the country to provide energy classes. In Texas the energy industry is regulated by the Railroad Commission of Texas. Alaska is the country's second oil state, but with the recent explosion of natural gas (and oil) shale development many other states have seen increases in energy activity.
- Work is often international or related to projects overseas because of hyperactive development of infrastructure and the energy sector in many emerging economies. *"Just look at where development is roaring to find out where we work: China, India, Brazil, Mexico, Indonesia, Peru, the Gulf states. There are giant infrastructure developments there – things are moving much faster than in the developed world."*
- The international nature of work means lawyers often have to deal with *"shaky jurisdictions. Structuring a deal to take into account political risk is very much a part of being an international projects lawyer. And that's not just in less developed countries – there could be similar issues surrounding a mining deal in California."*
- Working hours can vary greatly across the spectrum of work. While regulatory lawyers often work long hours, their schedule is often more predictable and manageable than that of transactional lawyers.
- In regulatory and advisory work, new recruits are often placed on contentious cases, as the hands-on approach is considered by many firms to be the best introduction to gaining expertise within the practice area.
- Energy transactional schedules are far less stable and this area of work may not be ideal for those with responsibilities or hobbies outside the work environment. Litigation work, on the other hand, is more predictable even when working long hours.
- Transactions can typically last anywhere between six months and three years. In a typical transaction, the partner's role is to manage the workflow and relationship with clients while other team members do the necessary groundwork and work in parallel to ensure the various elements of a deal fall into place.
- An excellent sense of organization is a must across all areas of energy and projects. It is also important to be comfortable with general administration law, and have good litigation and transactional skills. Eventually, an attorney can specialize in the types of cases they find the most rewarding.
- **Thomas Eastment,** former head of the energy regulatory group at **Baker Botts,** tells us *"a nice broad understanding of the key areas of law is crucial. This would include classic energy law but also environmental, finance and general commercial law. The issues we grapple with span all these, so you need to be nimble. The answer is not simply taking an energy course."*
- Another important skill is being able to handle numbers and technical issues. Catherine Webking says: *"I have an engineering undergraduate degree, which was very useful. There is a lot of number crunching to be done and our clients are engineers or accountants so being comfortable with numbers is important."* Webking also tells us that the variety of work on offer can be simultaneously stimulating and challenging. There is little repetition and the day will not be monotonous, but gaining an in-depth knowledge in a specific area will take longer: *"It is an ever-changing landscape in terms of corporate structures, there is a lot of activity related to companies acquiring other companies or merging with other companies so the clients themselves change quite often."*
- As it is a relatively small practice area, an attorney in this area will often be co-operating with the same small groups of people. Consequently, your opponent on one

Practice Areas

deal may become your ally on the next, and so it is important to maintain a professional attitude at all times.

- Particularly on the transactional side, it is important to be able to gauge what level of detail is sufficient. As **Todd Alexander**, partner at **Norton Rose Fulbright** explains: *"Unlike being in school where there is no cost to seeking perfection and you can research for as long as you like to write the best article you can, in a firm time is money. You may stop at 90% of the way there, thinking this is efficient, because the extra time doubles the price of the services provided. For half the price you get 90% certainty and sometime juniors struggle with that because they are used to being measured by having gotten the right answer. Perfection is not always what you're looking for."*

- Thomas Eastment says that *"with so much evolution in the market and government, flexibility is required to solve problems. You can't just look at the last deal or memo for answers to new questions that a client poses. Energy law isn't for someone who wants to feel like, 'I've got all this mastered, now I can use my cookie cutter'."* He advises that *"a nice broad understanding of the key areas of law is crucial. This would include classic energy law but also environmental, finance and general commercial law. The issues we grapple with span all these, so you need to be nimble. The answer is not simply taking an energy course."*

- **Jonathan Green**, partner and cochair of the project finance group at **Milbank**, says *"projects lawyers get the opportunity to do many different transactions without a whole lot of repetition. For young lawyers I think that presents benefits and challenges. The work tends to be extremely varied for many years, even for partners, and that keeps the learning curve very steep for a good part of your career. The challenge is that you don't have the opportunity to repeat transactions and hone your expertise early on, as you might in other areas. It takes longer to become an expert."*

Current issues

- Todd Alexander sees solar energy as a major area of growth in the future as *"solar installation costs continue to decline and are now competitive in many markets. Looking forward, solar energy is going to be leading the charge."* However many have expressed concern that President Trump's decision to place a 30% tariff on foreign-made solar cells and modules could damage one of the fast-growing segments of the US economy.

- Alexander also explains that battery storage is likely to become a significant subject: *"The problem with renewable energy is that it is intermittent in nature and not dispatchable. You can't ask for it on demand. There have been continuous improvements in battery storage which would allow all renewable energy to be generated when available and dispatched as needed."* Making headway in this field, Elon Musk's Tesla completed construction of the Hornsdale Power Reserve in December 2017, South Australia adjacent to a 99 turbine wind farm. Promoted as the world's largest lithium-ion battery, the battery system uses the same storage system found in Tesla's cars to store energy from the nearby wind farm.

- Proponents of the delayed Keystone XL pipeline received good news when President Trump approved the $8 billion project. Doubts persist about the plan's financial viability amid volatile oil prices and concerns about energy dependence; alarm bells rang after the pipeline leaked 210,000 gallons of oil in South Dakota in November 2017, further undermining the project's green credentials.

- Recent drilling and fracking developments, in conjunction with the lift of the ban on oil exports in 2015, mean the USA is set to become a net oil exporter within the decade – a forecast very much in line with President Trump's 'America First' energy agenda.

- Internationally, Brazil, East Africa, Australia and the North Sea are attracting increasing attention. Chinese and Indian companies especially are investing heavily in infrastructure and exploration in these new areas, as well as existing markets. South Africa looks ripe to become a key player in shale gas exploration.

- Estimates by BP predict that global energy demands will have increased by 35% by 2035. The report predicts that oil demand will continue to grow albeit at a slower pace, while natural gas will meet a much larger percentage of our demands.

- China, one of the world's biggest consumers of fossil fuels, is now leading the way in the realm of renewable energy. A report by the Institute for Energy Economics and Financial Analysis (IEEFA) estimates that in 2017, China's total investment in clean energy projects was $44 billion, a $12 billion increase from 2016.

- The Belt and Road Initiative, first unveiled by China in 2013, is set to be one of the largest infrastructure projects in history – the aim being to create a modern day Silk Road connecting Asia with rest of the world. Estimates indicate that projects in Asia alone will require investments of $1.7 trillion a year through to 2030. The Chinese government expects trade with countries along BRI routes to exceed $2.5 trillion a year within the next decade.

- In July 2017, France's Total signed a deal with Tehran to develop phase 11 of Iran's South Pars, the world's largest gas field. This marks the first major Western energy investment in the Iranian market since UN sanctions on the country were lifted.

Practice Areas

Project finance – Milbank

From desert-based solar projects you can see from space to the world's largest cheese factory – yes, Milbank's globe-trotting lawyers advise on the financing of it all. So if you're thinking of becoming a project finance lawyer, you should know that keeping a suitcase packed for impromptu meetings overseas is always a good idea...

Chambers Associate: What is project finance law?

Dan Michalchuk, partner: Project finance involves the development and financing of infrastructure, and spans many different and diverse industries and countries around the world. It focuses on the financing of a specific asset (it could be a solar power plant or a wind farm, a petrochemical facility, a pipeline, or any number of different assets) in which lenders or investors look principally to the revenues generated by that asset for the repayment of the loans that are provided by banks or other financial institutions for the asset's development. This type of structured finance is deployed most commonly in the development of large infrastructure projects and the exploitation of power, energy and natural resources.

Our clients are a mix of established institutions such as The Export-Import Bank of the United States, Google, GE, Citibank, Vale, Credit Suisse, Goldman Sachs, and First Solar, as well as newer start-up developers.

CA: What do associates do?

Genevieve Fox, associate: Junior associates are often tasked with preparing and maintaining closing checklists, which are used to track each component of the deal that needs to be completed in order to reach the financial closing. Junior associates also sit in on conference calls, coordinate and consult with local counsel, specialists and technical experts (such as engineers or insurance specialists) as necessary throughout the transaction, and prepare and review schedules and exhibits to documents and ancillary documents. Mid-levels and senior associates are often responsible for drafting and negotiating the financing and security documents, leading calls, and reviewing junior associates' work. Project finance associates also conduct diligence for each transaction and prepare diligence reports for our clients that flag key issues and advise on mitigating material risks.

Fernando Capellão, associate: At a high level, the work in our practice involves understanding how the businesses that we work with operate and their goals and the risks inherent to them. This allows us to structure transactions that, on the lending side, adequately protect financiers' interests and on the sponsor side, ensure that the business will be able to be managed efficiently and without having to resort to frequent waiver/consent requests.

"In the morning, I may be working on a construction financing of a wind farm in Texas and, in the afternoon, I may be working on a mining deal in Latin America."

DM: Given the cross-border nature of our practice, associates will be involved in not only the negotiation and drafting of the New York law governed documentation, but will also be expected to review and comment upon the documentation being drafted by attorneys located in each other jurisdiction applicable to the transaction. We don't just deal in paper, however. We are also advocates, even though we're not litigators. In-person meetings are a common feature of our deals as, even in a world where video-conferencing is a widely used tool, our clients often prefer to get together to hash out deals. Associates might find themselves in a large conference room in many different locations around the world assisting in that process.

CA: What do partners do?

DM: Partners usually lead a team involving a senior and/ or mid-level associate, and a junior. Our partners are typically hands-on, but delegate responsibility to associates depending on the associates' skill level. Partners are also entrepreneurial in our practice group, and often lead the charge on client development – whether it's putting together pitches for new work or socializing or meeting with clients outside the office.

CA: What are the highs and lows of working in this practice area?

Timothy Fitzpatrick, associate: One of the highs is that every day is different. In the morning, I may be working on a construction financing of a wind farm in Texas and, in the afternoon, I may be working on a mining deal in Latin America. You are always learning something new and, if you can handle it, you are given greater responsibility.

GF: What I like best about the practice is that it is tremendously dynamic – every deal offers something novel, and given the scope of our work – there are always new challenges and room for personal and professional growth. I also enjoy the tangible nature of our work, knowing that the work we do contributes to the development of a project that will ultimately bring something – be it cheaper and cleaner sources of energy, new infrastructure, or jobs – to other peoples' lives. Because the projects we work on are complex, when it comes to closing a deal, the process is often quite demanding, with a large volume of documents and questions being sent between the various legal and commercial teams as everyone works together to get everything into final form.

"...commodities are rising again, and the mining, LNG and petrochemical markets are back, causing a significant build-out in those assets."

CA: What factors are driving the sector?

DM: There are many different factors that affect our work. The first factor is the price of commodities. For example, when prices for natural resources such as gold, copper, silver or other commodities are high, we usually see an influx of mining projects around the world. Conversely, when the price of natural gas is low, we see larger numbers of projects that need cheap natural gas, such as gas-fired power plants, petrochemical facilities and liquefied natural gas export terminals, where natural gas is super-cooled to allow it to be loaded onto massive ships and sent around the world. Currently, after many years of downturn, commodities are rising again, and the mining, LNG and petrochemical markets are back, causing a significant build-out in those assets.

Legislation also shapes our practice. Due to government incentives over the past ten years, there has been an explosion of renewable energy projects, and we have developed one of the most prominent renewable energy practices in the world, from massive utility-scale solar projects in the desert that are so large that they can be seen from space, to domestic roof-top solar projects.

TF: One interesting development is the diversity of capital sources funding projects. While commercial bank debt was traditionally the main source of financing in this market (and continues to play a major role), we are seeing the increased involvement of institutional investors seeking long-term, low risk, fixed income products to match the long-term nature of their liabilities. Private equity has also recently raised significant funds to invest in the power and energy sector.

"A project finance attorney trains on the job, and the learning curve is steep but exhilarating."

CA: How is the increase in renewable and clean energy affecting the projects market?

TF: It is a very exciting time to be a projects lawyer practicing in renewable energy. Technological innovation, tax subsidies, consumer demand and evolving clean energy standards have been major drivers in the market. While tax reform has created head-winds for the renewables sector in the past, it is likely the sector will adapt most quickly to any future changes in tax law by developing new financing structures that will support the industry's substantial capital requirements.

CA: How can students and junior associates keep up-to-date with the market and industry trends?

FC: There are a number of specialized publications and project finance-focused events and conferences. As an associate, the opportunity to join client meetings and business development efforts, including pitches, also allows you to be exposed to the 'behind the scenes' discussions about future business trends and areas of concern.

"We once were even involved in the construction and financing of the world's largest cheese factory!"

GF: There are a lot of great resources for this. To name a couple: Latin Finance is a great resource for those interested in learning about or staying up-to-date with what is happening in the Latin American project finance space, and SparkSpread puts out daily blasts that highlight some of the bigger deals and players in energy finance.

Practice Areas

CA: Where can new associates expect to be in five years?

DM: Although law school helps to teach a young lawyer how to think, a project finance attorney trains on the job, and the learning curve is steep but exhilarating. From starting fresh as a first year, an associate will gain knowledge, responsibility and expertise quickly, and by the fifth year will be leading major transactions and regularly interacting with clients and opposing counsel (although this direct interaction starts almost immediately). Our teams are lean at Milbank – a structure that lends itself to everyone having responsibility for a piece of the puzzle that is a transaction, and quick learning.

GF: Associates who find themselves wanting to move out of Big Law after a handful of years practicing project finance have a range of options to choose from. A number of my colleagues have found fantastic opportunities working at private equity firms and banks, and others have gone in-house at solar and other energy-development companies. Project finance also cuts across various legal fields – touching on fields as diverse as environmental and regulatory law, to bankruptcy, mergers and acquisitions, and other forms of finance – and can thus be a great launching off point for other legal jobs as well.

CA: What opportunities are unique to Milbank?

DM: We are a very diverse practice group and in order to stay nimble and flexible – regardless of what the economy is doing – we practice in a wide variety of industries. These range from power projects powered by conventional means, like natural gas, to a cutting-edge renewables practice where we regularly work on a wide range of wind, solar and biomass power plants.Occasionally, we also are asked to apply project finance principles to other industries such as the construction of new satellite constellations. We once were even involved in the construction and financing of the world's largest cheese factory!

The international part of project finance is another reason why it's such an interesting discipline. We regularly work on infrastructure projects around the world, and often in less developed economies, as those are often the places where additional infrastructure is most needed. As a result of our international projects, there is often travel involved – associates never know when they may need to travel to Brazil, Chile, Colombia or somewhere else for last-minute meetings!

GF: Beginning in their fourth-year, Milbank associates spend a week at Harvard for an intensive training program that focuses on developing skills that cut across law, business and finance. It is a program that is unique to Milbank, and one that associates consistently praise for not just what they learn but also the fun they have.

> ## "Associates never know when they may need to travel to Brazil, Chile, Colombia or somewhere else for last-minute meetings!"

CA: What is your advice to students interested in this area?

DM: In law school the only relevant course for our practice (probably) is secured transactions, so you should take that, but otherwise in your search for firms make sure you are looking at the firms with top project finance practices, but also ones with a diverse practice just in case you find out that your interests are elsewhere. Project finance attracts people who are interested in international work, who may have some language skills (although I don't!), and who have some interest also in infrastructure, development and energy – these are things to stress when you are interviewing.

GF: I recommend that students read up on industry trends and check law firm websites to see what transactions firms are working on. There is no better way to learn project finance than by practicing it, and first-year associates are not expected to have a working knowledge of the field before joining the group. What makes junior associates stand out is often attention to detail, a drive to learn, a good attitude and the ability to take ownership over discrete tasks.

Authors

Dan Michalchuk
Partner

Genevieve Fox
Associate

Fernando Capellão
Associate

Timothy Fitzpatrick
Associate

Milbank

Climate change and renewable energy

In a nutshell

Climate change attorneys advise on four core aspects of law. Transactional advice is the most common aspect, and mainly involves negotiating carbon-related deals (such as carbon credits or projects to reduce carbon emissions, most of which have international dimensions). Second is litigation; it involves challenging climate change rules, regulations and laws, as well as defining the boundaries of the law. Regulatory advice is a growing area, due to the increasing number of climate change regulations being issued. Companies are therefore relying on lawyers more than ever to ensure that their activities are compliant with the latest regulations. Failure to comply leads us to the final aspect, enforcement, which is also rising in prominence as the body of regulations expands.

"You have a role to play in solving some of the world's most important problems. A lot of the industry focuses on making sure developing parts of the country and the world provide people with reliable and affordable energy in as clean a way as possible."

What lawyers do

- Climate change and renewable energy practices attract a broad client base that can be split into three categories: environmental groups, government groups, and corporations.
- Companies seek advice on reducing their carbon footprint, as well as broader issues such as employment, IP and finance. As a result, it's also important to have a good working knowledge of other legal areas such as general corporate law, M&A and tax.
- What lawyers focus on depends on their location: Washington, DC, for example, is at the heart of federal climate change regulation, so lawyers here are most likely to be involved in policy drafting. A practitioner in Texas, on the other hand, is more likely to spend their time advising fossil fuel companies on regulatory compliance. Renewable energy work, meanwhile, is mostly concentrated around large cities such as New York, DC, Chicago and San Francisco.

- Geographical connections also play a part in determining the scope of matters. For example, a lawyer based in California is more likely to be working with Asia on international deals than one in New York. Head to a regional firm if the scope you're after is smaller and more localized: firms in cities like Oklahoma City attract energy work but aren't known as 'practice area hubs' in the same way San Francisco and DC are.
- Associates tend to do a lot of hands-on work to gain expertise in areas that are still developing. **Roger Martella**, former environment practice head and climate change expert at **Sidley Austin**, explains that *"this is a rapidly growing practice and constantly evolving, so my associates are becoming experts in areas that will become more mainstream within a few years. We are preparing them for what we see as an inevitability on these issues."*

Realities of the job

- Climate change is a niche area, so it's unlikely that you'll be able to specialize full-time in it. Many lawyers specialize in a broader practice area – such as energy, environment, international law or litigation – and then work on climate change matters as part of their portfolio.
- Advising environmental organizations and government bodies may be your ultimate goal, but the reality is that most of the work involves assisting corporations with climate change compliance.
- As the body of climate change law is comparatively small, knowledge can be built up quite quickly. However, it is also important to be have some technical knowledge, so science and engineering degrees can be particularly useful in this respect.
- In terms of approach, being able to adapt to a client's style is important, as **Todd Alexander** of **Norton Rose Fulbright** explains: *"Some clients like a harsh, direct and pushy person, while others prefer someone conciliatory and facilitating. It depends on the client and situation."*
- One of the most rewarding aspects of the work is that it affects a large number of people, says Martella. *"You have a role to play in solving some the world's important problems. A lot of the industry focuses on making sure developing parts of country and the world provide people with reliable and affordable energy in as clean energy as possible. There is a social justice aspect to this."*

Rankings in *Chambers USA*

Top Ranked

Hunton Andrews Kurth	Latham & Watkins

Highly Recommended

Baker Botts	Paul Hastings
Baker McKenzie	Sidley Austin
Bracewell	Troutman Sanders
Crowell & Moring	Vinson & Elkins

For more detail on ranking tiers and locations, visit
www.chambersandpartners.com

- On the transactional side, no deal is like the last. Alexander reveals *"it is hard to create standardization because every deal is so unique. It is interesting and challenging, as you have no form to follow on a daily basis; each deal requires separate analysis and negotiation, so intellectually it is very rewarding as you are constantly challenged and learning."*
- This strand of work often involves international deals and a lot of travel. Although that may sound glamorous, the reality is that extensive travel is exhausting, and you may need to get used to working while jet lagged. As is the nature of transactional work, schedules can be unpredictable and demanding, so Alexander tells us that it's important to have a passion for the area: *"If you try to force yourself to go into this and you are not happy to make the sacrifices needed it won't be worth it. You have to find what the right balance is for you."*
- Climate change is also a highly controversial practice area, as new regulations are likely to be challenged both by those who think they go too far and by those who think they do not go far enough. Martella explains that as a litigator in the field it's important to detach oneself emotionally from the issues at hand. *"This is perhaps one of the most emotional and passionate areas of the law,"* he says. *"On both sides people have very strong views which create clashes outside of the courtroom. The impact goes beyond just legal issues; there is a strong nexus between climate change law and controversies."* A litigator must act in their client's interest, even if that goes against their personal views or ethics.

"This is perhaps one of the most emotional and passionate areas of the law."

Current issues

- Climate change remains the subject of intensive political debate, and the legislation surrounding it has become increasingly complex. The recent focus has been on enacting measures with the energy sector, which has become increasingly intertwined with climate change from a regulatory perspective.
- The improvement in electric vehicles in recent years is likely to make them as increasingly prominent part of climate change discourse and action. Global sales of Tesla electric cars broke the 250,000 unit mark in September 2017.
- In a drastic departure from the Obama administration's Clean Power Plan, President Donald Trump made the controversial decision to withdraw from the Paris Agreement in June 2017. By December climate change had been removed from the NSS (national security strategy) list of global threats. It's unclear so far how this will impact the legal landscape, as these decisions faced opposition from political and corporate figures; in any case, the earliest the US could formally withdraw from the Paris Agreement is November 2020.
- Despite the Trump administration's policy changes, the renewables market has continued to grow year-on-year. Solar energy is seen as the leader of the pack thanks to steadily decreasing solar installation costs, which have made it a highly competitive area of the market.
- The development of battery storage helps to tackle the difficulties posed by energy which has been produced from renewable sources. In early 2018 the FERC (Federal Energy Regulatory Commission) announced that it would let energy storage enter into wholesale markets and the bulk power grid, which it is hoped will reduce consumer costs and allow energy to come from cleaner sources.
- The current and future construction of transmission lines is important, as they will ensure that renewable energy plants are reliably connected to the grid and contribute to the power supply consistently.
- Global corporations such as Apple and Amazon are becoming increasingly interested in using and promoting renewable energy. They are now entering into purchasing contracts to buy energy directly from renewable energy producers, thereby helping these producers to operate more profitably.
- In January 2018 New York City officials announced that it was to divest $5 billion of fossil fuel-linked money from the city's pension fund. Mayor Bill de Blasio also announced that the city will be suing several of the world's biggest oil and gas companies for their role in global warming.
- Although it is yet to fully develop its presence on the market, China is seen as an emerging player in the world of renewable energy: the Institute for Energy Economics and Financial Analysis estimates that China is on track to lead global investment in the sector in years to come.

Real estate – Adam Leitman Bailey

It's the law of the land, which means there's a lot to learn for anyone considering becoming a lawyer in this area. ALBPC's dedicated real estate attorneys tell us about the challenge of keeping up with ever-evolving laws; how the bustle of New York City presents all kinds of litigious and transactional opportunities; and why it's vital to channel your inner bulldog when negotiating...

Chambers Associate: What does real estate law cover?
Danny Ramrattan, associate: Simply put, it is all about the land. Real estate law falls into two general categories – litigation and transactional. Each category has numerous subsets. Litigation attorneys handle disputes among people, such as between a landlord-tenant, mortgagor-mortgagee, and neighbors. Transactional attorneys complete deals – an example would be the purchasing of a house or condominium unit.

CA: What does a junior associate do?

Rachel Sigmund, associate: Adam Leitman Bailey, P.C. does not formally differentiate between 'junior' and 'senior' associates (there are just 'associates' without any official distinction for level). Associates are expected to handle all aspects of a client's account in consultation with the assigned partner, if applicable. This includes legal research and analysis; strategy preparation to achieve clients' goals and objectives; managing client expectations along the way; modifying strategies as necessary throughout representation to suit changing facts and/or new information received from clients; drafting letters, emails and litigation documents; going on meetings and attending site visits and inspections etc...

"Associates are expected to handle all aspects of a client's account in consultation with the assigned partner, if applicable."

Jackie Weinstein, partner: All attorneys at the firm, regardless of their level of experience, contribute with intake and strategy on every file. Newer associates, however, do the bulk of any legal research needed for a file, as our firm uses the lowest billing attorney to complete work whenever possible for our clients.

CA: What does a senior associate do?

JW: More experienced associates, depending on the file, can control his or her own cases, using paralegals and newer associates for ministerial work and any case law research needed. This can include strategy, drafting, court appearances, depositions, and client reporting.

CA: What does a partner do?

RS: The same as associates except, generally speaking, partners will delegate due diligence and investigative (time consuming, research based) type work to associates, in order to focus more on analyzing associates' findings and recommendations and communicating with clients of his or her department.

JW: It is the responsibility of the partner to make sure that any strategy is flawless and that the timeline of the case is on track. Partners also review and edit all litigation documents before filing, and, of course, keep the clients timely informed of all movement. Partners take on more of an oversight role in addition to doing papers and whatnot. They have more of a leadership role as far as the practices go.

CA: What is the best and worst thing about practicing real estate law?

DR: The best part of working in real estate law is the challenge of it. You will have to be able to navigate between the evolution of certain laws but also be able to go back historically and try to uncover a hidden gem to win a case for a client. This leads into the worst part of practicing in real estate law, which is trying to stay current and up-to-date on such a large body of law; it is dynamic and ever-evolving. This could be especially telling if you are at oral arguments and your adversary springs a new decision on you that came out the day before. However, if you are able to stay on top of the law, and are able to achieve a favorable result, you will feel accomplished knowing that you helped a client in such a challenging arena.

RS: For me, the best aspect is working in New York City which is world-renowned for its real estate market and the opportunities associated with it. With opportunities come legal disputes and the need for lawyers. Consequently, ALBPC's clients' issues range from 'typical' (for instance, the representation of buyers and sellers of residential condo and co-op apartments, mortgage foreclosure actions, commercial leasing, landlord-tenant representation, insurance defense litigation etc...) to the particularly unique: for instance, the representation of a tenants group in the rehabilitation and development of their 'squat' building in Manhattan's Lower East Side to a beautiful newly converted co-op building wherein the existing tenants group had the opportunity to become the owners of their apartments, which they formerly lived in as illegal 'squatters'. All of this comes with being located in New York City. The worst aspect is that client expectations are always extremely high and oftentimes not reasonable in the circumstances. The idea of 'managing client expectations' seems to take on a new meaning with New York City based clients.

"If you are able to stay on top of the law, and are able to achieve a favorable result, you will feel accomplished knowing that you helped a client in such a challenging arena."

JW: The best and worst thing about practicing in real estate is, ironically, the same thing: it can get personal.

CA: Which qualities make a good real estate lawyer?

DR: I think a good real estate litigation attorney needs to be diligent and aggressive. If you are diligent and well-prepared you will have a good grasp of the law and be able to argue your point. You also need to be aggressive in making sure you get your point across. These two qualities are essential together because if you lack one then you lack both. You may be aggressive and get your point across, but if you are not diligent in learning that area of law then your point may not be accurate. If you diligently know the law, but are unable to get your point across in court, then your knowledge of the law is useless.

RS: Quick thinking; easily adaptable to changing expectations and needs of clients; advanced interpersonal skills; confidence; hard working; diligent in keeping up with new trends and changes in the industry; being able to empathize with clients' feelings more so than other areas of law because the subject matter typically involves

the client's home and thus becomes very personal to them.

"Being a bulldog is a must for a real estate attorney. It is often about money, and the side with the stronger negotiator for counsel generally prevails."

Joanna Peck, associate: I think that you have to have really good interpersonal skills, good client management skills and be able to deal with people. If you are not good with people it's not going to work out.

JW: Being a bulldog is a must for a real estate attorney. It is often about money, and the side with the stronger negotiator for counsel generally prevails.

CA: What are the current issues in real estate that law students interested in the area should be aware of?

RS: They should be aware of the new tax law changes and how they are changing the market, pertaining, but not limited to, development trends, investment, and sales activities. Also, they should pay attention to the efforts of local government and officials to sustain (and increase) the amount of affordable housing options available throughout New York City to lower and middle income individuals and families.

JP: I think in NYC an important issue is adjacent property disputes, whether they're over construction or noise or neighborly things. In NYC everyone is living on top of each other so the disputes you see are generally between adjoining owners.

JW: As the head of the Foreclosure Litigation Department at our firm, we are seeing big changes of late with respect to how the New York courts are handling these matters.

CA: On that note what does the future hold for the real estate market?

JP: We only focus on NYC so I can't speak to the rest of the country but I think it is going to continue to flourish and expand, and with that we will see more adjacent property disputes.

"In NYC everyone is living on top of each other so the disputes you see are generally between adjoining owners."

DR: The real estate market may take a hit from time to time, but it is always on an upward trajectory.

RS: There will be a continued decrease in prices for luxury apartments over the next year due to (among other things) the federal tax law changes affecting New Yorkers. In addition, we can expect to see higher competition for homes under $1 million.

CA: And the legal market in relation to it?

DR: Land is the only thing that they are not making more of – the legal market for real estate attorneys will continue to grow.

RS: I think there will be increased transactional opportunities and potentially litigation as people try to rescind purchase agreements.

CA: How can law students brush up on their knowledge of the real estate market? Are there any books/publications that you would recommend?

DR: *Finding the Uncommon Deal* [written by Adam Leitman Bailey] is a great book to read in order to learn about real estate transactions. Most people don't truly understand things such as title insurance, and the book does a great job of deciphering those misunderstood concepts.

> ## "The real estate market may take a hit from time to time, but it is always on an upward trajectory."

JP: Real estate has a physical element, so it's not just about reading up on something – it's about going to see it and understanding why something is really important to a client. You have to go out and see what is going on with your clients and observe it.

CA: What experience could somebody gain in order to figure out whether they might be suited to working as a real estate lawyer?

JW: The best experience, of course, comes from working at a law firm and learning by hands on experience. Other than summering or interning at a firm, though, working for a title company can also give a student valuable experience to bring to later work as counsel.

CA: Describe the opportunities unique to ALBPC.

RS: I would say the responsibility that you get for all aspects of your clients' accounts, which means that you gain tremendous experience in not only the 'law' itself but also with regards to interpersonal, client interaction and customer service related skills. You develop accountability for your decisions at every level; you learn how to prioritize certain issues and client needs over others; and you hone your ability to manage client expectations. Essentially, at ALBPC associates (and not just partners) are able to serve as their own bosses much of the time because there is no 'true' hierarchical structure, which translates into a level of autonomy for associates that does not exist at other firms.

JP: It's extremely entrepreneurial here. If you want a 'white shoe' law firm – where people give you direction and you don't have to think – then this is not the place for you. You have to be on your feet, be entrepreneurial and not afraid to vocalize your opinions on what you think of a particular matter and where you see the opportunities. It takes a lot of common sense and strategic thinking.

JW: Our firm is the best in New York for everything real estate. Our attorneys are proud to be a part of the firm and, equally as important, are proud of the work product that our firm puts out. The firm is a family that works together to get results for its clients.

Practice Areas

Authors

Danny Ramrattan
Associate

Jackie Weinstein
Partner

Joanna Peck
Associate

Rachel Sigmund
Associate

ADAM LEITMAN BAILEY, P.C.

Real estate

In a nutshell

Real estate has multiple branches. Certainly, the practice no longer simply involves the sale of property by A to B; it now encompasses acquisitions and disposals, financing, leasing, development, joint ventures and funds.

Financing is a significant component of most transactions, and can involve sophisticated structuring, capital markets transactions, mortgage and mezzanine loans, debt restructurings, private placements, sale and lease-back financings, governmental incentives and tax aspects.

Another branch of real estate is land use, which requires attorneys to advise on state and local laws, such as zoning regulations, which affect the behavior and development of the real estate market. There are also aspects of real estate work that sometimes require advice on tax, litigation, restructuring and bankruptcy, and environmental law.

What lawyers do

- Draft a letter of intent, which sets forth the basic parameters of a transaction.
- Conduct due diligence. Make sure what the client is purchasing or underwriting holds no unwelcome surprises.
- Obtain municipal and/or state approval, where needed. Negotiate the contract, which allocates responsibilities among the parties.
- Negotiate financing documentation.
- Close the contract, joint venture and/or financing.

Realities of the job

- According to **Sullivan & Cromwell** chairman **Joseph Shenker**, there are three aspects to every deal: *"Of course you have the legal element, but on top of that there are the business and psychological elements to take into account."*
- Typical clients include developers, owners, institutional investors, lenders, tenants, underwriters, pension funds, insurance companies, private equity and hedge funds.
- Working in real estate requires sensitivity to each client's needs and expectations. While private clients are motivated by profit margins, the public ones are driven by policy and politics. Lenders tend to be cautious in their approach, while developers are bold and visionary. Harmonizing parties' competing goals can be tricky.
- Real estate is cyclical by nature. When the economy is bad, the real estate sector is often adversely affected. This means that *"if you have skills to put a deal together,*

you should also have the skills to take it apart - if and when it gets into trouble," says **Dechert** partner **Laura Ciabarra**.

- A transaction is truly a team-oriented affair; there will always be more than one attorney working on the deal. As such, having the ability to collaborate well with others is a must, in addition to coping with the stress of deadlines.
- *"In the week or so leading up to the completion of a deal, you'll probably find yourself in the office every day working until midnight,"* Ciabarra explains. *"I don't think I've ever worked on a transaction without there being that final week or two of craziness."* However, she describes real estate lawyers as *"deal junkies"* who thrive hectic nature of the closing stages, with everyone pulling together to reach a successful conclusion.
- Real estate lawyers tend to have a variety of projects in hand at any one time, which requires exceptional organizational skills.
- The work is often highly tax-driven. When it comes to the more complex transactions, understanding the relevant tax goals and limitations is particularly useful.
- Unlike corporate lawyers, who may have no more than a compute file to mark the end of a deal, real estate lawyers have a physical result that can be seen, touched, visited, lived and worked in.

Current issues

- *We're seeing a volatile market at the moment,"* says Shenker. *"The debt markets have not fully recovered from the global financial crisis and we are still dealing with overleveraged properties which need to be refinanced."*
- Despite this, there has arguably been more of a recovery than many expected – especially in the commercial market. According to a 2017 study by the Federal Reserve Bank of Richmond, lending to commercial real estate projects has passed pre-recession levels.
- The housing market has stayed buoyant, but growth is slowing down over time. In 2015 6.3% more homes were sold compared to the previous year; there was a further 3.8% increase in 2016, then 2.7% in 2017. The National Association of Realtors expects this growth to plateau and prices to remain flat or even fall in 2018.
- *"There's been an unusually large inflow of non-US capital into US real estate – particularly from Asia – so we're beginning to witness again the investment thesis that the US is a sanctuary for foreign capital,"* Shenker tells us. This is particularly true in Manhattan - where foreign buyers have been snapping up iconic buildings - and Boston, which has become the third most popular US city for foreign investors after New York and Los Angeles.

Rankings in *Chambers USA*

Top Ranked

Alston & Bird	Jackson Walker
Arnold & Porter	Katten Muchin Rosenman
Baker Botts	King & Spalding
Cadwalader, Wickersham	Kirkland & Ellis
Cleary Gottlieb Steen	Latham & Watkins
Cooley	Paul Hastings
DLA Piper (US)	Perkins Coie
Foley & Lardner	Simpson Thacher & Bartlett
Fried, Frank, Harris, Shriver	Skadden, Arps, Slate
Gibson, Dunn & Crutcher	Snell & Wilmer
Goulston & Storrs	Sullivan & Cromwell
Greenberg Traurig	Thompson & Knight
Haynes and Boone	Troutman Sanders
Holland & Knight	Venable
Hunton Andrews Kurth	Waller

Highly Recommended

Bracewell	Morgan, Lewis & Bockius
Brown Rudnick	Morrison & Foerster
Clifford Chance US	Munger, Tolles & Olson
Cozen O'Connor	Nutter McClennen & Fish
Debevoise & Plimpton	Orrick
Dechert	Patterson Belknap Webb
Duane Morris	Paul, Weiss, Rifkind
Dykema Gossett	Proskauer Rose
Fox Rothschild	Reed Smith
Gibbons.	Ropes & Gray
Hangley Aronchick Segal	Schulte Roth & Zabel
Jenner & Block	Shearman & Sterling
Jones Day	Sidley Austin
K&L Gates	Stroock & Stroock & Lavan
Kasowitz Benson Torres	Vinson & Elkins
Kramer Levin Naftalis	Weil, Gotshal & Manges
Mayer Brown	White & Case
Milbank	Willkie Farr & Gallagher
Mintz Levin Cohn Ferris	WilmerHale

For more detail on ranking tiers and locations, visit
www.chambersandpartners.com

- Recent disasters like Hurricane Harvey have made people focus a lot more on their leases. *"There are a number of clauses, such as casualty and interruption of services provisions, that some may not have paid sufficient attention to before – both in terms of the language used and what the insurance provides,"* explains **Jon Mechanic**, real estate department chairman at **Fried Frank**.

- *"The financing world is bifurcated right now,"* Ciabarra says. *"You have these high-end, well-maintained assets and the market continues to be very good for them. Then you have these secondary and tertiary assets that are struggling quite a bit – and will continue to do so for the next few years – so the gulf between the stronger and weaker assets has really grown."*

- The number of banks involved in construction loans has lessened recently, paving the way for other investment options. Mechanic confirms: *"A lot of opportunity funds in particular have been created, which highlights the fact that we're seeing many other forms of capital coming in to fill this void."*

- 'Secondary' cities are hot property in the current climate. Investors and developers are beginning to turn away from so called primary markets like NYC and San Francisco, which are highly competitive, and are snapping up deals in alternative markets like Seattle, Austin and Salt Lake City.

- The sweeping changes to the US tax code introduced in the Tax Cuts and Jobs Act of 2017 will likely have major implications for the real estate sector. This is particularly true of REITs (real estate investment trusts), for which 20% of dividends can now be exempted from tax under certain circumstances.

- Our online shopping habits and impatient desire for speedy deliveries may well influence how industrial spaces are both designed and situated: ideally as close to densely populated urban areas as possible, to guarantee that promise of a swift same-day delivery.

- Back in 2016 there was widespread fear that stricter lending requirements would deter banks from issuing commercial mortgage-backed securities (CMBS), an industry staple. The peak of uncertainty has now passed, however, and the number of such loans issued jumped from zero in January 2017 to 335 that August.

- One real estate sub-sector that's not been faring so well is retail. Major retailers including Toys R Us, Aerosoles, Alfred Angelo, and Vitamin World have declared bankruptcies while Sears, Kmart, J.C. Penney and others closed stores across the country. According to Cushman & Wakefield this trend is unlikely to stop, with the number of US stores closing to rise 33% in 2018.

- The Federal Reserve raised interest rates at both the start and end of 2017, and forecasts three additional additional rate increases over 2018 and 2019. If the hikes are small, or if inflation accelerates and there's no hike at all, the cost of borrowing and value of properties should remain stable. If interest rates grow significantly then borrowing will become a lot more expensive and real estate firms will find it more difficult to finance their projects.

Practice Areas

Environment – Allen & Overy

We are more aware of our impact on the environment than ever before, and lawyers play a key role in determining how their clients treat it. A&O's lawyers reveal the ins and outs of this practice and what becoming a lawyer here entails...

Chambers Associate: Can you give a brief description of what the environment group at Allen & Overy does?

Ken Rivlin, partner: Our Global Environmental Law Group includes more than 60 specialist lawyers in Europe, Asia Pacific and the Americas. Our partners and lawyers across the jurisdictions work together on a daily basis, providing integrated, cross-jurisdictional advice on a broad range of issues, including: due diligence and risk allocation in cross-border transactions, advice on product responsibility requirements (such as EU REACH, EU WEEE and RoHS and "copycat" rules in China, South America, the U.S. and elsewhere, managing product compliance issues, ensuring appropriate transfer of carbon credits, managing contaminated land clean-up issues, advising on domestic and international environmental marine liability and shipping issues, addressing oil & gas and minerals mining, extraction and distribution issues, and many other matters.

Felise Cooper, senior counsel: We advise clients on environmental risk and negotiate environmental issues in all kinds of transactions and on a stand-alone basis. We are known for our multi-jurisdictional practice and often undertake large-scale projects that require comparative analysis of environmental laws across many geographies.

Nick Ognibene, associate: The environmental group focuses on a mix of compliance advice and transactional support. We assist clients in compliance with American and international environmental regulations, and help our clients manage environmental liabilities arising from a wide variety of transactions, as well as those that emerge 'off-deal.'

"We are known for our multi-jurisdictional practice and often undertake large-scale projects that require comparative analysis of environmental laws across many geographies."

CA: What do associates do?

NO: Associates are responsible for a very wide array of tasks, from researching and drafting compliance advice to clients to facilitating environmental risk management through due diligence and contract drafting/negotiation. Associates are given significant responsibilities early.

FC: Associates draft environmental language for contracts; research environmental rules and requirements; draft advice memos; review environmental investigation reports, permits and compliance materials; draft environmental due diligence reports; and represent our clients in negotiations with counterparties. The day-to-day work is almost always varied, with an associate typically working on several different matters every day. Our practice touches all kinds of industry sectors, from products manufacturing to real estate to energy projects to shipping.

KR: Associates are involved in every aspect of our work, including, among other things, drafting and negotiating agreements, assessing environmental risk and evaluating complex sources of exposure (including but not limited contaminated land, impacts of climate change, product sustainability, water use and safety, human rights and worker safety) and explaining potential outcomes and alternatives to clients and colleagues. From day one, our associates speak directly to clients and learn to handle complex issues and situations. They see virtually every industry sector in every part of the world. In one day, they may work on a desalination plant in Chile, a wind farm in Canada, a mining operation in Africa, and a global industrial and aircraft turbine manufacturer. They also frequently work on exciting pro bono matters: recent matters have included several asylum cases, a survey of international laws governing waste contamination for the United Nations, and compliance and governance advice for a major US NGO. Most matters involve working with lawyers (environmental and otherwise) in other parts of the Firm throughout the world. The pace is quick and the work is challenging, but it's also a lot of fun.

CA: What are the highs of the practice?

FC: Juggling many matters and subjects can be a boon, because it keeps the work interesting and allows for opportunities to work with many different colleagues and practice groups in the firm. Another high is the opportunity to work with an outstanding and congenial group of colleagues across the world.

KR: The best highs involve helping a client solve a difficult problem, get a deal over the line, or position itself strategically for a new opportunity. It can be incredibly exciting and rewarding to complete a long, high-stakes negotiation with a signed agreement that meets the client's needs. The best and most rewarding part is when that client calls again for his or her next big matter – long-term relationships of trust with both clients and colleagues are what really make this job special.

Another great high is the international aspect of our work. We work with clients and colleagues across the world on a daily basis. At our last off-site (May 2018), which we held in Lisbon, our 60+ lawyer group (with lawyers from the US, Europe and Asia) spent two days together discussing global legal trends and refining our group's global strategy. We also sampled some great Portuguese wine!

NO: The highs are consistently engaging in substantive and interesting work, and being able to engage in high-level firm-based legal work while having a positive environmental impact (we do not engage in environmental litigation/defense).

"Our practice touches all kinds of industry sectors, from products manufacturing to real estate to energy projects to shipping."

CA: And the lows?

NO: When multiple deals and/or client needs come in at the same time; the practice does involve its fair share of busy times and it can sometimes be stressful to manage everything.

FC: Some people don't enjoy detailed analysis and would prefer to focus on the big-picture only; in this practice, you need to focus on both.

KR: I can't think of too many lows. We can get quite busy, and at the end of the day it is a job. But unless I could play shortstop for the NY Mets I can't think of too many other jobs I'd trade this for.

CA: What factors are currently driving environmental work?

KR: Our corporate and financial institution clients are increasingly focused on environmental compliance and sustainability. When I first began doing environmental policy work in the late 1980s (just before law school), the field was still reasonably new. The pace of Superfund (contaminated land) litigation, including related insurance coverage claims) was really picking up, asbestos and other "toxic tort" litigation was on the rise, the USEPA and other state actors, to varying degrees, were making enforcement a priority. As fines and trial awards piled up, banks and companies began taking notice.

Fast forward to today, banks and corporations have a much more sophisticated understanding of environmental risk. They also better understand how environmental and sustainability issues can impact not only share values and access to capital but also their brands and reputations. Added into this mix, environmental legal regimes have evolved substantially outside the US, leading to more regulation and enforcement globally. The impact of these trends has been multiplied by the accelerated globalization that has characterized the world's economy over the past thirty years. Some companies get it right. And in my experience, most do try. Those that don't usually do (and should) pay the price.

So what does this mean for our work? We are expecting to see increasing amounts of work advising on alternative energy, supply chain compliance and sustainability, and environmental and safety compliance, particularly in manufacturing, oil & gas and mining. Climate change mitigation is also increasingly a focus, as is improved compliance training and systems to better manage risk. There is increasingly broad recognition (notwithstanding some positions taken by the now not-so-new US administration) that sustainability must be a priority, and this is driving new work for us in countless ways. Clearly, protecting and preserving the environment is one of the greatest challenges the world faces – this is an incredibly exciting time to be doing what we are doing.

FC: Some factors include a global drive for increased corporate transparency on issues like environmental policy, supply chains, human rights, and business 'footprints;' continued globalization of business; changes in political agenda (e.g. Brexit, Trump administration); climate change developments; environmental disasters; and changes in government enforcement practices.

Practice Areas

"...a global drive for increased corporate transparency on issues like environmental policy, supply chains, human rights, and business 'footprints.'"

NO: Firms are always concerned about potential environmental liabilities associated with mergers and acquisitions, as well as financings. Many sectors that involve significant environmental, health & safety (EHS) risks are very active. Plus, in today's highly connected world, clients are especially eager to avoid reputational harm associated with environmental issues.

CA: How can students and associates keep up-to-date with these trends?

KR: Read. Read. Read. Everything. We have access to so much more information now than ever before. There is no excuse to be uninformed. I try not to limit myself to any one source. I read a rotating collection of daily papers (*NY Times, Wall St. Journal, FT, Washington Post*), receive updates from the EPA and EU Commission websites and various NGOs, and scan a few daily and weekly blogs. I switch between CNN and Fox just to be sure I am being exposed to various viewpoints. And of course I get my dose of Colbert and SNL Weekend Update when I can.

FC: Reading the news and specialist publications, discussions with colleagues and clients, and day-to-day work.

CA: What opportunities in environmental work are unique to Allen & Overy?

KR: The most unique aspect of Allen & Overy is our global reach. Our global environmental group has over 60 lawyers from 14 countries working together across a broad range of issues. Working at A&O, we need to be experts in comparative law, with a broad understanding of how key issues, such as owner or operator liability for contaminated land, veil piercing and successor liability are handled in different jurisdictions. We've had exciting engagements advising on the salability / viability of emission reduction credits under various trading systems. We frequently advise companies on how best to implement global compliance policies that assure compliance wherever they are located. And we recently did a global survey of community involvement in environmental policy-making for a Chinese-government sponsored project that looked at making Chinese environmental policy more open.

NO: Probably the most unique and best thing about the environmental practice at A&O is that it involves compliance and transactional work but *not* environmental liti-

gation/defense. Most environmental practices at larger firms involve varying degrees of environmental litigation and defense, which inevitably results in defending firms facing suits or investigations arising from environmental malfeasance on their part. So it can be difficult to engage in environmental work at a firm while consistently contributing to sustainability and not undermining it. A&O's environmental practice provides just such a (rare) opportunity.

CA: What advice do you have for students interested in this area?

KR: Learn as much as you can. Balance expertise with versatility, so that you can adapt. The world, including the legal world, is in a state of constant, accelerating change. Embrace that.

Also, look for mentors / examples. Find people who are five, ten, 15 years ahead of you on their career paths, and find a way to get to know them. Each person may have a quality or an experience that you can emulate and learn from (or avoid!). Think about what you want to do, see what others have done to be successful, and try to learn from that.

And, importantly, try to have as much fun as you can along the way.

NO: I do wish that I had taken more environmental law classes in law school, and would probably recommend the same for students interested in this field. That said, quality of professors and so forth is equally or more important. And stay true to your beliefs.

"In today's highly connected world, clients are especially eager to avoid reputational harm associated with environmental issues."

FC: Being a specialist increases your control over your schedule and your career. You can call the shots if you are not interchangeable with someone else. If you are unsure, you can get some broader experience before transitioning to this area; it is easier to go from generalist to specialist than the other way around.

CA: Where can new junior associates expect to be in five years?

FC: A mid-level or senior associate at A&O (in the U.S. or abroad) or another firm; an in-house environmental or transactional lawyer at a bank or corporation; occupying a government position; or working as an independent consultant.

NO: Being singularly responsible for managing EHS components of major transactions and handling client environmental compliance queries. There is a lot of early responsibility and significant opportunities to develop and take ownership.

Authors

Felise Cooper
Senior counsel

Nick Ognibene
Associate

Ken Rivlin
Partner

ALLEN & OVERY

Practice Areas

Environment

Rankings in *Chambers USA*

Top Ranked

Arnold & Porter

Baker Botts

Bracewell

Cravath, Swaine & Moore

Davis Polk & Wardwell

Gibbons

Gibson, Dunn & Crutcher

Greenberg Trauri

Hunton Andrews Kurth

Jenner & Block

K&L Gates

King & Spalding

Latham & Watkins

Mintz Levin

Morgan, Lewis & Bockius

Perkins Coie

Sidley Austin

Simpson Thacher & Bartlett

Snell & Wilmer

Troutman Sanders

Waller

Highly Recommended

Allen & Overy

Alston & Bird

Brown Rudnick

Cahill Gordon & Reindel

Crowell & Moring

Debevoise & Plimpton

Fox Rothschild

Goulston & Storrs

Haynes and Boone

Holland & Knight

Jackson Walker

Katten Muchin Rosenman

Kirkland & Ellis

Mayer Brown

Morrison & Foerster

Nelson Mullins Riley

Norton Rose Fulbright

Nutter McClennen & Fish

O'Melveny & Myers

Paul Hastings

Pillsbury Winthrop Shaw

Shearman & Sterling

Sullivan & Cromwell

Thompson & Knight

Venable

Vinson & Elkins

Weil, Gotshal & Manges

White & Case

For more detail on ranking tiers and locations, visit
www.chambersandpartners.com

"We are expecting to see increasing amounts of work advising on alternative energy, supply chain compliance and sustainability, and environmental and safety compliance, particularly in manufacturing, oil & gas & mining. Climate change mitigation is also increasingly a focus, as is improved compliance training and systems to better manage risk. Clearly, protecting and preserving the environment is one of the greatest challenges the world faces – this is an incredibly exciting time to be doing what we are doing."

– Ken Rivlin, partner, Allen & Overy

Practice Areas

Finance

"It's clearly an industry that is rapidly changing. It's going to be much more competitive, and as a result of that, there will be more pressures placed on associates and partners making it a much more challenging profession. I was recently discussing the differences in medicine and law with a friend of mine who is a surgeon. He made the comparison that it would be like cutting into a patient and finding that the patient's organs are all in different places. The age of being able to know what's coming next is evaporating."

– Holland & Knight's managing partner
Steven Sonberg

Banking and finance – White & Case

The stakes are high and the window for negotiations narrow – the pressure is certainly on for banking and finance attorneys. If you're looking to become a lawyer in the field, you'll need stamina and a knowledge of several practice areas, say White & Case's experts...

Chambers Associate: Can you describe what the bank finance group at White & Case does? Are there any specialist areas of work or clients that the group is known for handling/representing?

Rob Morrison, partner: The bank finance group at White & Case largely focuses on a broad range of financial transactions, including leveraged buyouts, dividend recapitalizations, ABL financings, restructurings and debtor-in-possession financings. We represent large financial institutions such as Deutsche Bank, Morgan Stanley, Jefferies Finance and Credit Suisse and private equity companies such as Harvest Partners, CVC, Stone Point and Roarke Capital.

Jake Mincemoyer, partner: Our primary focus is the syndicated leveraged loan market – typically acting for lead lenders – but in recent years we have established a growing borrower-side practice as well (supporting the firm's private equity clients or large corporates). However, we also cover the investment grade loan market for lenders and borrowers and have a number of direct lending clients as well. We support our project finance practice and have worked on a number of "cross-over" term loan B financings backing infrastructure and oil and gas deals in recent years. Our core strength, in all of these areas, are cross-border financings due to the strong integration we have with our global network of offices – all of which have top market local bank finance practices.

CA: What do associates do? What kind of work is involved day-to day?

Demian von Poelnitz, associate: Banking associates do a variety of work, depending on the nature of the transaction and their level of experience. At a senior level, this includes drafting commitment papers, security documents and credit agreements. Junior and mid-level associates are expected to coordinate the closing process, draft ancillary documents, and make sure that all documentary conditions precedent are in good order before a closing. As such, the junior associate has an in-depth understanding of the status of each of the documents necessary to close the transaction, in most cases more so than

the partners. This includes managing legal assistants, junior associates and any local counsel (whether foreign or non-New York) on a deal. Every associate is responsible for making sure that a client's needs are being met.

> *"Associates are involved in all aspects of the financing documentation process, from negotiation of grids and term sheets to closing the transaction."*

Given the tight timeline on our deals – especially in the context of an acquisition – a junior associate will have the opportunity to draft a number of documents from day one, including exhibits and schedules to loan documents, closing checklists and payoff documentation. In addition, there is a significant amount of client contact, even as a junior associate.

There is no "typical" day for a banking associate. Some days will be devoted entirely to conference calls with clients; some to drafting a credit agreement or security agreement; some to reviewing a set of commitment papers; some to discussing a proposed amendment to, or refinancing of, a credit facility that closed a few months or years ago; and some to fielding various requests from clients. Most days involve juggling all of the above!

Samantha Wilson, associate: Associates are involved in all aspects of the financing documentation process, from negotiation of grids and term sheets to closing the transaction. Day-to-day work involves drafting key loan documents, liaising with clients and the other side, managing diligence, attending and assisting on negotiation calls, and generally "project managing" the financing process. Associates are given a lot of free reign and client contact, so partners expect us to be able to drive the process forward in an efficient and timely manner.

JM: Our associates do as much as they can – we really focus on letting our associates stretch. We have a few third-year associates that effectively run deals on their own. Our associates will work on everything involved in a deal through the course of their careers – from due diligence and managing closing deliverables to negotiating intercreditor agreements. We like to staff our deals thinly, so that one or two associates will have full ownership of the deal, which we find helps them to get up the learning curve much faster.

CA: What are the highs of working in this practice?

JM: The highs are closing some of the largest and most complicated deals in the market for appreciative clients.

DvP: Our deals have relatively short timelines, so associates have opportunities to work for a number of partners and clients over the course of a year. The stakes for our clients – especially with respect to a syndicated facility or an exit financing – can be very high, and therefore very exciting. Moreover, this is a challenging practice area, i.e., you get to use your brain. For example, a typical deal requires an associate to have a working knowledge of several practice areas, such as real estate, intellectual property, anti-corruption, sanctions, environmental, labor and employment and tax, just to name a few.

"The stakes for our clients – especially with respect to a syndicated facility or an exit financing – can be very high, and therefore very exciting."

SW: The high is definitely working with some of the smartest and driven people, both colleagues and clients, in a fast-paced and collaborative environment. The broad and international nature of our practice also makes our work particularly challenging and interesting.

CA: And the lows?

JM: The lows are managing a constant barrage of deals when the market is hot (and being anxious for the next one when the market is slow). Timing of deals has also continued to shrink, so a deal that we would have worked on for four months when I was a junior associate may be completed now in four to six weeks, which can lead to a greater level of excitement, but also definitely increases the stress levels.

SW: The low would probably have to be the time pressure – getting a lot done in a short amount of time is inherent to most of our work, and while there is a certain rush to getting a deal done, it often means long hours, little sleep, a lot of stress and missing out on personal and family time. But being part of a supportive team makes this manageable.

"Often there are only a few days to review a set of commitment papers and revise them after discussions with your client."

DvP: Two things come to mind. First, the window for negotiating commitment papers continues to contract, while the length of the term sheets attached to the commitment papers continues to expand. Often there are only a few days to review a set of commitment papers and revise them after discussions with your client. Many associates find the learning curve to be a steep one. Second, the flow of work in acquisition finance is not steady throughout the year but instead ebbs and flows. For several months, it can be extremely busy and then all of a sudden it can be quiet for a number of weeks. It is an unpredictable practice area.

CA: What factors are currently driving the banking and finance market?

RM: There is a lot of available capital that both private equity companies and lenders are looking to put to work quickly, especially in the face of a somewhat unclear regulatory landscape under the current administration. The availability of capital has made for higher purchase prices for acquisition targets by fostering competition among bidders – those bidders are then able to create competition among lenders vying to provide the financing for those purchases.

JM: The primary driver at the moment is the "hunt for yield" by investors. A number of investors have record levels of cash to invest and leveraged loans pay an attractive yield, while currently having historically low default rates, which has attracted a lot of capital looking to invest in the leveraged loan market. At the same time, there has been little increase in the size of the leveraged loan market as most new deals have involved companies that were already issuers of leveraged loans. This has led to a classic supply/demand imbalance which has allowed leveraged borrowers to complete a number of opportunistic financings to extend maturities, pay dividends, loosen covenants and lower margins – all leading to a very busy market for leveraged finance lawyers.

DvP: Factors also include the rise of non-traditional lending sources, as well as financial sponsors asking for, and receiving, increasingly more borrower-friendly terms.

"A number of investors have record levels of cash to invest and leveraged loans pay an attractive yield."

CA: How can students and associates keep up-to-date with the banking and finance market and industry trends?

JM: For associates, working on deals and talking to their peers is the best way to stay up on trends. *Debtwire* and *Bloomberg* also provide very good reporting on the leveraged loan market and the *Wall Street Journal* should be required reading every morning for general finance trends.

SW: Read the business sections of the major newspapers to learn about what is happening to our clients and the economic events and policy changes that affect them. If you're not interested in reading this, then you probably won't be interested in the work that we do here.

DvP: Several publications and websites are often available free-of-charge to law students and associates, such as: the *Financial Times*, the *New York Times*, Practical Law Company, Practising Law Institute, and publications by the Loan Syndications and Trading Association. There are also many "continuing learning" seminars in most major cities that are often free or at a discounted rate for students.

CA: What do you think makes White & Case a unique place to practice in banking and finance?

RM: First, our associates get a lot of responsibility (and related training) from a junior level. We hire smart people and smart people need to be challenged to reach their full potential. Second, while many firms have offices in multiple countries, most of those firms don't work as a truly cohesive unit. At White & Case, we have a truly global presence and every office in the firm works seamlessly together on the cross-border deals for which White & Case is so well-known. This leads to our associates having a good experience with international finance transactions and also leads to the opportunity to travel and even spend significant periods working in one of our other offices.

> ## "Secured transactions and bankruptcy are fundamental areas that all bank finance lawyers need to understand, so students should definitely take these courses."

JM: There are a number of firms that are very strong in bank finance, but only a handful that offer a full lender and borrower side experience and even fewer still that offer a full cross border experience.

DvP: The most unique aspect for a White & Case banking associate is probably the opportunity to work on cutting-edge cross-border deals. We have a deep bench of partners who are some of the best attorneys in New York City for complex multi-jurisdictional financings. Further, associates work closely in tandem with our colleagues in other financial hubs around the world, such as London and Frankfurt.

CA: What advice do you have for students interested in this area?

JM: Bank finance is an area that is not well covered in law school. Secured transactions and bankruptcy are fundamental areas that all bank finance lawyers need to understand, so students should definitely take these courses, but they will do little to help students understand the day-to-day of being a bank finance lawyer. Any seminars or practical courses on M&A or other transactional topics would be useful as most of our deals are backing acquisitions, so these courses may give students a flavor of what "deal work" is like. But the best advice is to seek out a few bank finance assignments while summering at a firm and to speak with any alums, friends or family that work in the area.

RM: I would suggest taking a UCC Article 9 class and any class that their law school offers related to finance law and M&A. Also, don't be afraid to reach out to lawyers that practice in the field. I've gotten cold calls from law students before and I'm always happy to discuss what I do to give them a realistic picture of my practice and what my job really entails.

DvP: Law students interested in banking should do at least three things: (i) enroll in classes that reflect that interest, such as: Bankruptcy, Secured Transactions, Corporate Taxation, M&A, International Business Transactions and Accounting for Lawyers; (ii) seek out summer-employment opportunities with law firms that are market leaders in Banking, like White & Case; and (iii) take advantage of resources that are available at their law school to stay current on market trends in acquisition finance.

> ## "The fifth-year associate will be responsible for running the deal on a day-to-day basis."

CA: Where can new junior associates expect to be in five years' time?

SW: Being the point person for all aspects of a financing transaction and largely autonomous. By the fifth year, you should be able to negotiate key credit documents and

Practice Areas

pretty much run a standard financing process from start to finish on your own. Partners are obviously involved and on hand to supervise and lead negotiations, but there are many aspects of transactions you will be handling on your own. You will also be expected to assist with business development and maintaining client relationships.

RM: A fifth-year associate in the bank finance group will rarely have an associate above them on any deal. This means that the fifth-year associate will be responsible for running the deal on a day-to-day basis, which includes negotiating and drafting credit documentation and working directly with the partner on the deal. A fifth-year associate will also have a junior associate staffed underneath them and will be responsible for supervising that associate on a daily basis and helping to train them.

DvP: As a fifth year associate, you will begin to train and generally provide guidance to the junior associates on your teams. You will have developed close relationships with a handful of clients with whom you have successfully closed many deals, and you will continue to strengthen your business development skills.

Authors

Rob Morrison
Partner

Jake Mincemoyer
Partner

Demian von Poelnitz
Associate

Samantha Wilson
Associate

WHITE & CASE

Practice Areas

Banking and finance – the basics

In a nutshell

Banking and finance lawyers deal with the lending and borrowing of money, and the management of financial liabilities. Their task is to help structure their clients' transactions, to protect their clients' best legal and commercial interests, and to negotiate and document the contractual relationship between lenders and borrowers. It's a hugely technical, ever-evolving and jargon-heavy area of law. For anything banks do with capital raising or financial instruments, see Capital Markets.

> *"This area allows you to push yourself and increase the percentage of time spent doing things that are new, interesting, challenging and occasionally frightening."*

Straightforward bank lending: a bank or other financial institution lends money to a borrower on documented repayment terms. Bank loans may be bilateral (made by one bank to the borrower) or syndicated (arranged by one or more financial institutions and made by a group of lenders).

Acquisition finance: a loan made to a corporate borrower or private equity sponsor for the purpose of acquiring another company. This includes **leveraged finance**, where the borrower finances the cost of an acquisition by borrowing most of the purchase price without committing a lot of its own capital (as typically done in leveraged buyouts).

Real estate finance: a loan made to enable a borrower to acquire a property or finance the development of land, commonly secured by way of a mortgage on the acquired land/buildings.

Project finance: the financing of long-term infrastructure (eg roads or power plants) and public services projects (eg hospitals) where the amounts borrowed to complete the project are paid back with the cash flow generated by the project.

Asset finance: this enables the purchase and operation of large assets such as ships, aircraft and machinery. The lender normally takes security over the assets in question.

Islamic finance: Muslim borrowers, lenders and investors must abide by Shari'a law, which prohibits the collection and payment of interest on a loan. Islamic finance specialists ensure that finance deals are structured in a Shari'a-compliant manner.

Financial services regulation: lawyers advise financial and other businesses on everything that they might need to know about the legal limits of their financial and investment activities. They focus especially on new and complex federal and state regulations. Major clients are usually banks, hedge funds, private equity firms, broker-dealers and insurance firms. Post-recession there has been a multifold increase in the volume of legislation governing the financial sector.

What lawyers do
Bank lending

- Meet with clients to establish their specific requirements and the commercial context of a deal.
- Carry out due diligence – an investigation exercise to verify the accuracy of information passed from the borrower to the lender or from the underwriter of securities to potential investors. This can involve on-site meetings with the company's management, discussions with the company's auditors and outside counsel, and review of material agreements and other documents.
- Negotiate with the opposite party to agree the terms of the deal and record them accurately in the facility documentation. Lenders' lawyers usually produce initial documents (often based on a standard form or an agreed precedent) and borrowers' lawyers try to negotiate more favorable terms for their clients. Lawyers on both sides must know when to compromise and when to hold out.
- Assist with the structuring of complicated or groundbreaking financing models, and ensure innovative solutions comply with all relevant laws.
- Gather all parties to complete the transaction, ensuring all agreed terms are reflected in the loan documents, all documents have been properly signed and delivered and all conditions to closing have been met.
- In a secured loan (most bank loans to below investment-grade borrowers require collateral), ensure that the agreed-upon collateral has been properly granted and that all filings, registrations and other procedures necessary to 'perfect' the security have been or will be made.

Practice Areas

Rankings in *Chambers USA*

Top Ranked

Alston & Bird	Mintz Levin Cohn Ferris
Bracewell	Nutter McClennen & Fish
Cahill Gordon & Reindel	Proskauer Rose
Cravath, Swaine & Moore	Ropes & Gray
Davis Polk & Wardwell	Sidley Austin
Foley & Lardner	Simpson Thacher & Bartlett
Greenberg Traurig, PA	Skadden, Arps, Slate
Jones Day	Squire Patton Boggs
King & Spalding	Troutman Sanders
Kirkland & Ellis	Waller
Latham & Watkins	White & Case

Highly Recommended

Baker Botts	Morrison & Foerster
Choate Hall & Stewart	Norton Rose Fulbright
Cleary Gottlieb Steen	Orrick, Herrington & Sutcliffe
Debevoise & Plimpton	Paul Hastings
Duane Morris	Paul, Weiss, Rifkind
Fried, Frank, Harris, Shriver	Reed Smith
Gibson, Dunn & Crutcher	Shearman & Sterling
Goulston & Storrs	Sheppard, Mullin, Richter
Haynes and Boone	Thompson & Knight
Holland & Knight	Vedder Price
Hunton Andrews Kurth	Vinson & Elkins
Katten Muchin Rosenman	Weil, Gotshal & Manges
Mayer Brown	Willkie Farr & Gallagher
McDermott Will & Emery	WilmerHale
Milbank, Tweed, Hadley	Winston & Strawn
Morgan, Lewis & Bockius	

For more detail on ranking tiers and locations, visit
www.chambersandpartners.com

"We work at the intersection of law and markets, so lawyers in our field not only need an understanding of the law, but an inquisitive mind and an interest in real-world economic and political developments."

Financial services regulation

- Receive calls from banks and other financial institutions that seek guidance as to how business initiatives can be implemented most effectively in US markets, in full compliance with the letter and policy of US law.
- Sit down with the client – speaking to individuals at a very senior level – to find out what the client's business plan and intentions are.
- Analyze the implications of implementing that plan based on what current or future regulation looks like, or can be expected to look like, and what the legal, compliance, reputational, strategic, cross-border and related risks of that plan might be.
- Give advice on what changes may need to be made to the business initiative to achieve regulatory compliance and minimize risk.
- Regulatory lawyers are not just involved with compliance counseling: they also advise on enforcement and internal and external investigations; the restructuring and disposition of bank assets; the organization of bank units and subsidiaries; acquisitions, investments, strategic alliances and joint ventures; capital raising initiative and the creation and distribution of bank securities and deposit and other financial instruments; the structuring of 'living wills' and recovery and resolution plans; and the implementation and evaluation of bank marketing, cross-selling and similar initiatives.

Realities of the job

- Some firms act for investment or commercial banks on highly complex and often cross-border financings, whereas the work of others generally involves more mainstream domestic finance deals.
- A good working knowledge of the bankruptcy laws is critical for lawyers practicing in the area of leveraged finance. Banking lawyers advise for the worst-case scenario, which is often a bankruptcy filing by the borrower. Understanding how the rules change once that filing is made is critically important, even for lawyers who never expect to set foot in a bankruptcy courtroom.
- Lawyers need to appreciate the internal policies and sensitivities of their clients in order to deliver pertinent advice and warn of the legal (and reputational) risks involved in the transactions. Deals may involve the movement of money across borders and through different currencies and financial products. International deals have an additional layer of difficulty: political changes in transitional economies can render a previously sound investment risky.
- Banking clients are ultra-demanding and the hours can be long. On the plus side, clients will be smart and dynamic. It is possible to build up long-term relationships with investment bank clients, even as a junior associate.
- Working on deals can be exciting. The team and the other side are all working to a common goal, often under significant time and other pressures. Deal closings bring adrenalin highs and a sense of satisfaction.
- You need to become absorbed in the finance world. Start reading *The Wall Street Journal*, the various deal-related trade publications or other good business-oriented websites.

- Regulatory lawyers need to remain constantly aware of the latest political developments (potentially) affecting regulations. *"We are not management consultants, but our role involves a huge amount of market-based business analysis. Lawyers who want to work in this area need to become very knowledge-focused. Staying on top of the latest news in all the areas involved is a great ongoing challenge of the job,"* says **Robert Tortoriello**, senior counsel in **Cleary Gottlieb**'s financial institutions practice.
- Regulatory lawyers operate on shifting sands. *"Abnormal is the new normal,"* says Robert Tortoriello. *"It is a constantly evolving practice. At present lawyers are advising on the 'likely' implications of the 'likely' regulatory framework that will emerge from the ongoing legislative process, which has come forth from proposed regulations."*

Current issues

- Reforms to the Dodd-Frank Act remain a priority for the Trump administration. In 2017, Republicans passed the Financial Choice Act – pat of which would allow financial institutions to bypass the Dodd-Frank reform if they chose to be well-enough capitalized. It failed to get enough support in the Senate, but bipartisan legislation emerged in the form of The Economic Growth, Regulatory Relief and Consumer Protection Act. The bill cleared the Senate, 67 to 31. It is predicted to reduce the burden on smaller community and regional banks.
- Another major focus for the Trump administration is tax reform. In December 2017, Trump signed the Tax Cuts and Jobs Act which included lowering corporate income tax rate from 35% to 21%. Experts predict this will make the US more attractive for inbound M&A activity and may also increase the value of US-domiciled businesses. The changes will have a significant impact on deal-modeling, tax diligence and acquisition agreement negotiations.
- Following widespread cyberattacks on US financial institutions, the Department of Financial Services published requirements for financial services companies to boost their cybersecurity. Some of these rules came into effect late 2017, while others are expected to be introduced throughout 2018.
- Fintech may only make up a small share of the market but it's rapidly growing. While these start-ups can compete directly with banks in areas such as wealth management, loans or payment products, larger financial institutions are beginning to explore the opportunities fintech platforms can provide in areas such as mobile banking apps or services.

- Interest in blockchain (the database technology which underpins digital currency bitcoin) continues to increase. The security of the blockchain, its transparency – anyone using the system can view trades – and the irreversible nature of blockchain transactions have all proved attractive to financial institutions. Although the practice is yet to go mainstream, banks continue to experiment with how the tech can be applied to benefit their businesses. Seven large banks in Europe have partnered with IBM to introduce a blockchain for their cross-border transactions for smaller and medium-sized business clients.
- As Brexit continues to unfold down an unclear path, big US banks including Morgan Stanley, Citigroup and Bank of America, are drawing up plans to try to avoid moving hundreds of jobs out of London before the UK leaves the EU. The UK's exit could have major implications for overseas banks based in London if their access to the wider continent is cut off or the UK's banking industry undergoes a regulatory overhaul. Several US firms, particularly those with a base in London, have been quick to capitalize on the opportunity to provide financial regulatory advice to clients investing in both the UK and European Union. Some experts predict that Brexit could even allow US banks to extend their market share opportunity over their European counterparts.

Advice from the banking and finance gurus

Marc Hanrahan, partner and leader of the leveraged finance group, Milbank:

"It's a demanding area. People often work all night and into the next day."

"Since the economic troubles began, there's an increased emphasis on identifying and controlling risk. Issues that might not have been paid much attention five years ago are given tremendous focus now. Clients respect our contribution to transactions today. Lawyers are seen as less of an impediment and businesses know that they can't just disregard what we say."

James Florack, partner and co-head of the global credit group, Davis Polk:

"This area allows you to push yourself and increase the percentage of time spent doing things that are new, interesting, challenging and occasionally frightening. You'll be confronted with a puzzle, like a logic puzzle, and you have to find a way out of it that doesn't compromise your client – the bank – or indeed the bank's clients. You need an ability to solve problems creatively."

"It's important to realize that while we're running a business, the client is also running a business. If you solve a problem in a way that impacts negatively on the client's client – the borrower – you may end up reducing the usefulness of the financing and, as a result, corrode the overall relationship among the parties."

"Confidence in your intellectual ability, discipline and patience are necessary to work in this area. An even temperament is important because transactions aren't always negotiated in perfect conditions – they might be going on against the backdrop of a larger M&A transaction or under time constraints. You also need to recognize that the agreement you're putting into place needs to work for the client long-term. The banking lawyer has to have the discipline to calmly approach the problem and sort it. It's difficult because there's lots of pressure to get the thing done. Those who develop into the most respected lawyers complete the deal while taking into account the commercial objectives and context, and all the other abiding factors."

Jonathan Schaffzin, partner and member of the executive committee, Cahill:

"In this practice there are extraordinary opportunities for client contact and responsibility. Young lawyers have counterparts of the same age group at the financial institutions we deal with, so there's a unique opportunity to grow with clients and develop relationships that endure. Acquiring a knowledge of financial products and the client's business is a terrific part of the job. It's a very interdisciplinary practice where associates acquire knowledge of accounting and finance as well."

Robert Tortoriello, financial services senior counsel, Cleary Gottlieb:

"We work at the intersection of law and markets, so lawyers in our field not only need an understanding of the law, but an inquisitive mind and an interest in real-world economic and political developments. So if you aren't prepared to learn how to read a balance sheet, or work with care through the footnotes in a financial statement that describe a derivative, you will not be successful in this field."

"I believe that if you are interviewing and you feel that you can't be yourself, it probably isn't the right place for you."
– Alston & Bird's hiring partner Liz Price

Capital markets – Cahill

Intrigued by the thought of becoming a capital markets lawyer and want to know more? Cahill's pros in the area are on hand to shed light on their intricate and complex practice.

Chambers Associate: What is capital markets law?

Jennifer Ezring, partner: Capital markets, or securities, lawyers work on transactions where a company uses equity securities (stock, or other ownership shares of the business) or debt securities (representing an initial borrowing of money, with a specific amount to be repaid over time) to meet its financing needs. A capital markets attorney works either with a company (the "issuer" of a security) or an investment bank (the "underwriter" of the offering), but the goal on both sides of these collaborative transactions will be to ensure the issuer and the underwriters are in compliance with the securities regulations governing the capital markets, and to provide the company with adequate financing by structuring a security on terms that are palatable to investors.

CA: What kind of work can associates expect in this area?

Ani Ravi, associate: Junior associates work on:

- 'Due diligence,' which is about understanding an issuer's business at a detailed level to confirm, or help draft, the prospectus, and make sure that everything important about a client is being disclosed to potential investors. Due diligence involves reviewing contracts, doing research with third-party sources, speaking to company management, and sometimes doing on-site visits. Often the junior associates doing the due diligence know more about an issuer than anyone else on the team.
- Coordinating documents as a transaction is about to close – ensuring that funds are transferred, mortgages/security are granted, the right certifications, opinions and filings are made, and that all of the formalities necessary for a new stock or bond to be issued and trade have been completed.

Mid-level associates oversee some due diligence and also work on:

- Drafting a prospectus, which includes working with the company and investment bankers to describe a company's business, thinking about risks that might affect the company and drafting risk factors to include in a prospectus, and making sure that the prospectus complies with relevant securities laws.
- Negotiating contracts, including the Underwriting/Purchase Agreement, which is the contract between an issuer and one or more investment banks relating to underwriting a securities offering.

Senior associates, meanwhile:

- Oversee transactions on a day-to-day basis and serve as the primary client contact.
- Negotiate the more complex aspects of a transaction, such as the Description of Notes / Indenture, which (for bonds) describes the terms of a bond, including the "covenants", which are restrictions on an issuer's activities that are intended to prevent the issuer from weakening its credit quality. These covenants can be very complex and are highly negotiated.

CA: What do partners do in this area?

JE: Capital markets partners work with the issuer and the underwriters to decide what type of securities will best suit the company's needs, to understand the company's financial situation, to set the terms of those securities in order to ensure they will be saleable to the market at the time, and to structure the timing and mechanics of the actual offering to comply with all securities laws and regulations. The partners will work with the associates to negotiate final disclosure and offering documentation and the operative issuance documents.

CA: What are the highs and lows of the practice?

Sarah Walton, associate: Capital markets is an exciting practice. It is heavily market driven, so it is fast paced most of the time. Practicing capital markets exposes you to information about diverse domestic and international markets. Drafting disclosure requires an in-depth understanding of a company and the company's industry, so we are constantly learning new markets and industries.

Practice Areas

The low of practicing capital markets is the unpredictability of your hours. Given how much the market affects this practice, it is not uncommon for a timeline to get expedited due to favorable conditions. This can result in late nights and weekend work.

"Practicing capital markets exposes you to information about diverse domestic and international markets."

AR: High points include closing a deal, especially a high profile one – it's a nice feeling to see your hard work reflected in a newspaper article when your deal prices. Another high is navigating the various laws and regulations governing capital markets to allow your client to do a deal in a creative way.

Probably the biggest low is when a deal falls through at the last minute – often this can be days or even hours before you would have closed, and comes after weeks or months of work.

JE: On each new transaction we learn about a company from the inside out, working together with management, investment bankers, and often private equity sponsors, so the practice is always interesting and "fresh". The players are generally sophisticated and often have worked with each other before (including the "opposing" lawyers), which tends to bring a sense of camaraderie and collegiality. Because market forces are at work dictating when a certain security should be offered for sale, timing can be fast and pressure can be high when a transaction is in full swing, which makes the deal an exciting ride.

CA: How does your work interact with other practices?

JE: Capital markets associates act as the 'hub' of the transaction wheel, coordinating with attorneys in many other areas relevant to the transaction, including corporate attorneys who are focused on the issuer's overall practice and regulation, and verifying that the financing transaction will work within the framework of the company's other commitments and its organizational structure. A capital markets associate will confer with bankruptcy attorneys where there are questions of enforcement or protection in a 'worst-case' scenario; tax attorneys, who are involved in structuring the issuance on a cost-efficient basis; real estate and environmental attorneys where real property will be taken as collateral; and litigators, who evaluate various risks existing at an issuer or potentially created by a financing.

CA: How has this area changed since the recession?

AR: The recession brought in a number of new securities regulations, and there continue to be changes in the laws both in the US and abroad which affect what kinds of deals can get done. In addition, since the recession, banks have generally become more careful about risk, including being more careful in ensuring that prospectuses are accurate and not misleading, and that issuers do not have any regulatory issues. In particular, banks have become very concerned to ensure that issuers do not have any problems with sanctions, money-laundering, bribery, anti-terrorism, and similar areas.

JE: Any market disruption will affect securities work significantly. While the recession was a major market swing, even a smaller political event can cause rates to rise or fall rapidly, making one type of financing more or less palatable to issuers or investors. Given the amount of market sensitivity around an event as large as the recession, it has become increasingly important to be facile with all types of financing alternatives, and to be able to think creatively about what an issuer may be able to offer to investors.

"Private markets are the new public markets."

CA: What are the latest trends and developments in capital markets?

SW: There has been a continuing focus on sanctions and anti-corruption, and a recent focus on cybersecurity.

AR: There are a few major trends:

Increased ease of crowdfunding and other small-scale public offerings. It's now possible for small companies to raise relatively small amounts of money from the public without going through the full process required to go public.

- Private markets are the new public markets: companies of all sizes are finding that they don't need to be public to attract capital, whether it's large private companies like Uber (that are able to raise billions of dollars without going public) or companies of all sizes that issue bonds only to institutional investors.
- Lightly regulated or unregulated substitutes to traditional capital markets: these take many forms, from syndicated loans, the terms of which have become increasingly similar to bonds in some ways, and are often bought by the same investors and issued by the same clients, to crowdfunding and initial coin offerings which completely bypass traditional securities regulation.

CA: What personal qualities make a good capital markets lawyer?

JE: My top two answers to that question would be creativity and team play. Creativity is essential because each new transaction holds a puzzle that needs to be solved in a way that is mutually beneficial for all parties involved. Being able to work as part of a team is critical, because on each transaction you will find individuals with varied skill sets working together to create a product that meets a common goal—unlike some other areas of law, all parties need to embrace the result, even those technically "adverse" to each other.

AR: Being commercial: understanding the business and economic underpinnings of transactions. Being curious about businesses: the best capital markets lawyers understand how the businesses that they're representing work, whether that's a mine, a bank, a retail store or a hospital. Being able to multitask: each deal has multiple workstreams, and as associates become more senior, they are often on many deals at once, so the ability to switch gears quickly is essential. Being good at dealing with people: capital markets work involves dealing with many people with conflicting interests, and a good lawyer is able to satisfy all of the various parties that she/he has to deal with. Being resilient: sometimes a deal you've been working on for months just dies, and sometimes right after you close one, there are two more in line right behind it. Lastly, being good at managing – especially as associates become more senior, they have a management role on each of their transactions.

> ## "Creativity is essential because each new transaction holds a puzzle that needs to be solved in a way that is mutually beneficial for all parties involved."

CA: How can students brush up on their capital markets knowledge?

JE: While there are no prerequisites to becoming a capital markets attorney, students may find it helpful to have taken a basic accounting or finance course, preferably at the business school affiliated with their law school. The US securities laws, including SEC rules and guidelines and general disclosure issues, are central to the work we do, so courses in securities regulation and drafting will prove helpful after law school graduation. It definitely doesn't hurt to start reading some financial news on a regular basis as well.

SW: It is helpful to have a basic understanding of financial statements and general accounting.

AR: Law school courses that are very helpful include Securities Regulation, which provides an overview of the securities laws that govern capital markets transactions; Secured Transactions, which explains the rights of secured creditors; and a course in negotiation, offered by many law schools, which can be helpful as capital markets associates (particularly at Cahill) will be negotiating with their counterparts soon after they start practicing.

CA: What opportunities in the area are unique to Cahill?

AR: Cahill is the market leader in leverage finance and high-yield bonds – with over three times the market share of any of its competitors. This means that as an associate, you'll have the opportunity to work with a very diverse set of clients, and you won't be limited to one industry, or one geography, or one particular type of transaction. Because of the generalist philosophy and Cahill's strong market share, Cahill is often the go-to firm for many clients, and they rely on Cahill's advice in multiple practice areas – in particular, capital markets and leveraged lending. Many deals involve both a capital markets and secured loan component, or may switch from one to the other – because Cahill associates are generalists, they can advise clients on all aspects of a transaction.

JE: Cahill's market share and breadth of client base puts us in an excellent position to see and understand the latest technology and market terms at any given time. Because the capital markets are subject to significant fluctuation based on a number of factors, including everything from recent case law involving financings, collateral security, and bankruptcies, to the global political and regulatory environment – the 'best' answer for a client in a given scenario can change rapidly. Our associates are exposed to a broader segment of the market than those at our peer firms, which allows our attorneys to develop market knowledge right from the start of their careers and be seen by clients as a 'counselor' with valuable insight at an earlier stage.

Practice Areas

Authors

Jennifer Ezring
Partner

Ani Ravi
Associate

Sarah Walton
Associate

CAHILL

Derivatives and securitization – Allen & Overy

There's nothing derivative about the life of a lawyer in this multi-faceted area – becoming a legal hotshot here requires mastery of various asset classes and structures, so read on if you want to get the lowdown from sources at global outfit A&O...

Chambers Associate: Can you sum up what the derivatives and securitization teams at Allen & Overy do?
Natalie Murray, business development manager: The derivatives and securitization teams focus on transactional work for a range of financial products, and also provide regulatory advice on various security/commodity-related queries. The groups frequently work together as different transactions or projects will require insight into one of the team's specializations (for example, the derivatives team might require advice on risk retention from the securitization team; the securitization team might require advice on swap-related issues governed by Title VII of Dodd Frank etc.) The groups are known for their work with large investment and commercial banks, established funds and seasoned issuers (private, public and sovereign).

Daniel Resnick, law clerk: Our securitization team regularly advises arrangers, originators and trustees on transactions involving a wide variety of asset classes and structures. These include 'true sale' and synthetic securitizations, CLOs, CDOs and the establishment of securitization programs. In terms of derivatives, our work covers all the major product types (exchange-traded or centrally cleared, OTC and securities). Our securitization team works regularly with the derivatives team to ensure clients' transaction needs are met and complex structures can be successfully completed. Our group is known for our international innovation, which includes work on Greece's first private sector securitization; advising on the first auto loan securitization in the Middle East; and developing the first UK master trust structures.

Sandy Tapnack, associate: Our derivatives team advises on complex and bespoke derivatives and structured finance transactions for clients, and also advises on regulatory obligations relating to the same. Our securitization team, meanwhile, advises on note issuances backed by assets that produce cash flows. We advise a wide range of clients, including banks, financial institutions, corporates and funds. The teams work together when a deal requires the expertize of both strands (e.g. a securitization deal may involve a currency or interest rate swap).

"My day-to-day involves responding to client inquiries and balancing anywhere from two to eight projects at a time."

CA: What do associates do?

Zach Sinemus, associate: Associates have a lot of client interaction. My day-to-day involves responding to client inquiries and balancing anywhere from two to eight projects at a time.Some days I spend hours on the phone with other associates and/or partners and/or clients, and other days I am on my own at my computer for the entirety.

At the moment I have six billable projects and one pro bono project in play. Two of these projects involve dealing with clients and collateral custodians, three are memos to be sent to clients outlining the regulations applicable to products they are considering offering, and one is a diligence assignment concerning the novation of a swap as part of a corporate restructuring. Most of my day is my own to schedule.

NM: Associates collaborate on a daily basis with both junior and senior members of their respective teams – they get lots of direct partner contact and client involvement. This work involves a combination of transactional work (document drafting, client-facing interaction etc.); research projects; and memo drafting for internal and client use, as well as business development (for example, a presentation at the Tel Aviv Stock Exchange on the pressing subject of cryptocurrencies/ "initial coin offerings" and their potential regulation as a security vs. a commodity).

DR: Associates on the securitization team advise clients on regulations relating to securitization transactions, which include US risk retention rules, the Volcker rule and Regulation AB. Additionally, associates help draft transaction documents for companies that are looking to securitize their assets. Day-to-day work involves writing memos about securitization-related regulations and how they affect our clients; reviewing documents while checking for consistency and errors; drafting closing

Practice Areas

documents for transaction execution; and conducting research relating to updates in the field of securitization for both internal and client use.

"...a presentation at the Tel Aviv Stock Exchange on the pressing subject of cryptocurrencies/ "initial coin offerings" and their potential regulation as a security vs. a commodity."

CA: What are the high points of practicing in this area?

ZS: The highs are definitely the range of work we get to do and the number of jurisdictions our matters implicate. I am on matters at the moment with teams from Tokyo and London, and they really make me feel like I'm in a unique firm that offers multi-jurisdictional advice that other firms simply can't offer.

DR: Getting to work on exciting and cutting edge transactions, in addition to being able to work with more senior associates and partners routinely to gain hands-on experience and retain invaluable career advice.

ST: The highs are closing deals, anticipating clients' issues and solving them, and working with great colleagues.

CA: And the lows?

ZS: The lows recently have come from the degree to which our group has been focused on margin work. We cornered the market on sell-side margin regulation work (i.e. variation margin CSA negotiations, and initial margin CSA/CSD/CTA, ACA, and ECS negotiations) which has been both a blessing and a curse – it's been very exciting to be *the* firm to go to for margin work for some of the biggest swap dealers, but it has also been quite tiring to be so focused on a particular regulation.

"Most of the work that I do is focused on Dodd-Frank regulation, which is still relatively new to the market."

NM: It's hard to explain to your grandma what you do!

CA: Which factors are currently driving securitization work and the derivatives market?

ZS: There are constantly new regulations either being introduced or being phased-in, even under the new administration. Most of the work that I do is focused on

Dodd-Frank regulation, which is still relatively new to the market.

NM: Factors that drive the teams' work are the post-subprime mortgage crisis on a global scale; general regulatory updates with respect to securities/commodities and the market's reaction to Dodd-Frank; global regulation initiatives (such as MiFID II); and the impact of changes in the US political landscape on the market and regulation.

In the past 12 months particularly, global financial markets have increasingly explored blockchain and virtual currencies as potential solutions to many of the challenges and inefficiencies facing their participants today. This nascent technology is attracting interest from users, institutions, industry associations, governments and regulators who are excited by the promise of cost reduction and the potential for new possibilities and future growth. We are at the heart of the debate around ICOs, cryptocurrencies and blockchain/DLT, and are working with a number of clients on some exciting ventures.

"...the impact of changes in the US political landscape on the market and regulation."

DR: Some of the factors currently driving our work include: (1) concerns over the status of LIBOR and the ramifications that would arise if LIBOR ceases to exist, (2) a push to simplify the disclosure regimes surrounding asset-backed securities; and (3) risk retention and Volcker compliance.

CA: How can students and associates keep up-to-date with these trends?

DR: Students and associates can keep up-to-date with securitization trends by attending securitization and structured finance seminars, partaking in industry calls that discuss the latest securitization trends, conducting online research, reading external posts/updates/memos by Allen & Overy and on fellow BigLaw firms' websites and speaking with peers.

ZS: Everyone can follow press releases from the CFTC and SEC, which I would recommend doing if you are interested in following developments in the derivatives regulatory space. Law firms (A&O included) also regularly put out client alerts or publications aimed at identifying major developments in these spaces. I will also plug aosphere (an Allen & Overy affiliate), which provides "advanced delivery" (i.e. legal updates or overviews of regulatory regimes tailored so as to be digestible by non-lawyers).

Practice Areas

159

> *"Understanding the underlying products makes it easier to understand why regulations have been written the way they have been or why financings are structured the way they are."*

CA: What opportunities in derivatives and securitization are unique to Allen & Overy?

ZS: The opportunities unique to A&O come from our cross-border work. For instance, the US margin regime is only one of many margin regimes worldwide – our clients were able to come to us as a one-stop shop for all of their margin work, as we were able to coordinate amongst our offices so as to provide advice and transactional help to clients who are subject to multiple regulatory regimes.

NM: Our associates have the unique opportunity to learn about the securities/commodities markets on a global scale in both developed and emerging economies and to establish a truly global network of friends, colleagues and clients.

We have the largest global derivatives and securitization team of any international law firm. It has an intimate familiarity with the banking and securities laws and regulations and is regularly sought after by leading financial industry associations for advice and training. Our associates are also recognized as some of the best trained and talented associates in the field, frequently receiving offers to work at the world's best known financial institutions.

CA: What advice do you have for students interested in this area?

ZS: Take a securities or structured finance course in law school and do your best to understand the underlying projects and purpose of the products you wish to cover. It's possible to negotiate a CSA (Credit Support Annex)

or indenture in a vacuum, but it's much easier when you understand what the purpose of a hedge is, or the ways different products add risk to the market. Understanding the underlying products makes it easier to understand why regulations have been written the way they have been or why financings are structured the way they are, which in turn makes it easier to provide proper advice or identify relevant issues.

NM: This is a fast-paced and sophisticated area of law. It requires good commercial sense as well as a good understanding of the law, so staying abreast of market developments is key. General advice includes enrolling in accounting, corporate finance and securities classes in law school. Interning at a financial institution or regulator such as the SEC or CFTC would also provide good training.

DR: It is also helpful to speak with associates who are currently working in the field to gain more insight into what derivatives and securitization work involves.

CA: Where can new junior associates expect to be in five years' time?

DR: Junior associates can anticipate rising to more senior positions on their team, which will give them the opportunity to be in charge of transactions and work more hands-on with A&O clients. They can also anticipate getting to work at another A&O office or a client through secondment, or possibly getting an opportunity to work for the government (as a number of A&O attorneys have done recently).

ZS: Exit opportunities include going in-house to a bank or other financial institution, but we have had associates leave to go work for government agencies or for more specialized firms as well. We also have a number of international capital markets/derivatives & structured finance associates who have been with A&O for seven plus years, so it's also quite conceivable that junior associates will still be with A&O five plus years into their tenures.

ALLEN & OVERY

Authors

Natalie Murray
Business development manager

Daniel Resnick
Law clerk

Sandy Tapnack
Associate

Zach Sinemus
Associate

Capital markets – the basics

In a nutshell

Capital markets lawyers feel all the highs and lows of market forces more than any other practitioner, and when the Great Recession hit the practice went under too. However, the vast sums exchanged and the technicality of the transactions mean that it will always remain an important area for BigLaw firms. Essentially, the world's capital markets are trading floors (either real or virtual) on which cash-hungry businesses obtain funding by selling a share of their business (equity) or receiving a loan (debt) from lenders.

These 'markets' are used by companies with unique financing needs which traditional bank loans cannot satisfy. They offer more freedom to companies than obtaining cash via bank loans, which tie both parties into the term of the loan. Capital markets allow for companies to obtain massive sums with more flexibility; they also offer up limitless investment opportunities. Large financial institutions offer customized services to companies seeking funding on the capital markets. These services include advice on debt and equity offerings, on securitization and on the creation of derivatives. Debt (bonds), equity (stocks) and derivatives are all types of security, and capital markets law is sometimes referred to as 'securities law'.

"The range of capital raising companies pursue is almost endless, and is limited only by human creativity."

Attorneys advise companies ('issuers') and investment banks ('underwriters') on these complex capital markets transactions. Issuer and underwriter will both engage a separate law firm. The issuer's attorneys will sometimes help their client analyze which type of security to issue. This decision depends on the nature of the company, the desired duration of the loan, who the buyers are likely to be, and market demand. If an issuer is new to the market, they may begin by seeking their lawyers' advice on the processes involved, before approaching an underwriter.

Equity capital markets

Within equity, there are initial public offerings (IPOs) and follow-on offerings of common and preferred stock. An IPO is a transformational event for a company. *"The IPO is the 'ne plus ultra' of capital markets work,"* says **Josh Bonnie**, capital markets partner at **Simpson Thacher**. *"The decision of whether or not to become a public company is incredibly commercial and requires a great deal of*

strategy. It's unlikely the client will have IPO experience, so they will be reliant on their attorneys." The New York Stock Exchange and Nasdaq are the major exchanges in the US and most American public companies will be listed on one of them. Companies can list on multiple exchanges around the world.

Debt capital markets

This covers many types of debt instrument, but generally speaking it deals with a borrower raising capital by selling tradable bonds to investors, who expect the full amount lent to be paid back to them with interest. Bonds (also called 'notes') come in all shapes and sizes, from investment grade to high-yield ('junk') bonds. The terms of the bond – including the interest rate (or 'coupon') and maturity date – are decided on by the underwriter and issuer.

Why would a company issue bonds rather than take out a bank loan? As mentioned above, the terms of a bank loan can be restrictive to both parties: bank debt can prevent companies from making equity or debt issuances or from acquiring other companies until the loan is paid off. The terms of a bilateral loan tie both parties in, so a bank can't transfer risk or sell this debt with the same flexibility that the bonds market allows. Bonds are tradable; risk and its rewards can be sold on and spread across numerous lenders (bondholders), meaning that a company can raise much larger sums that can only be matched by arranging a syndicated loan (a group of banks chipping in on the principal), but without the same bank loan obligations that syndications entail. Plus bondholders can be anyone, not just a bank.

Structured finance and securitization

This can get gloriously complex, but its aims are simple: to increase liquidity and structure risk, which in turn offers up extra funding for borrowers. Securitization is the core of the process, which takes a lowly untradable piece of debt, such as a mortgage, vehicle loan or a credit card receivable, bundles it together with debt of the same class, and sells the bundle of debt on to investors, such as pension funds, hungry for the cash flows that come with the debt.

To securitize debt a bank will first set up a special-purpose entity (SPE) to isolate the debt risk from the bank's main operations, and separate the legal rights to the debt, enabling it to be transferred to new holders. Within the SPE are the bundled loans which enable the SPE to issue bonds, where the interest on the bundled debt forms the cash flows or bond yields. Mortgage securities like

Rankings in *Chambers USA*

Top Ranked

Cadwalader, Wickersham	Morgan, Lewis & Bockius
Cahill Gordon & Reindel	Sidley Austin
Cleary Gottlieb Steen	Simpson Thacher & Bartlett
Cooley	Skadden, Arps, Slate
Cravath, Swaine & Moore	Sullivan & Cromwell
Davis Polk & Wardwell	Vinson & Elkins
Latham & Watkins	Wilson Sonsini Goodrich
Mayer Brown	

Highly Recommended

Akin Gump Strauss Hauer	Kramer Levin Naftalis
Allen & Overy	Milbank, Tweed, Hadley
Arnold & Porter	Morrison & Foerster
Baker Botts	O'Melveny & Myers
Bracewell	Orrick, Herrington & Sutcliffe
Clifford Chance US	Paul Hastings
Debevoise & Plimpton	Paul, Weiss, Rifkind
Dechert	Proskauer Rose
Fried, Frank, Harris, Shriver	Ropes & Gray
Gibson, Dunn & Crutcher	Schulte Roth & Zabel
Hunton Andrews Kurth	Shearman & Sterling
Jones Day	Weil, Gotshal & Manges
Katten Muchin Rosenman	White & Case
Kirkland & Ellis	

For more detail on ranking tiers and locations, visit www.chambersandpartners.com

residential mortgage-backed securities (RMBS) and commercial mortgage-backed securities (CMBS) are among the most common in the market, but *"the range of capital raising companies pursue is almost endless, and is limited only by human creativity,"* says Josh Bonnie of Simpson Thacher. Collateralized debt obligations (CDOs) are a unique structure in that they group a variety of types of debt and credit risk, where different classes are called 'tranches', and the higher the tranche's risk, the greater the yield.

Securitization shouldered much of the blame for the credit crunch and the ensuing global economic havoc. Complicated structures led to a murky tangle of debt obligations, grouping different debt classes and exploiting credit enhancement. All was rosy until the housing bubble burst, mortgages defaulted and the ugly truth emerged. Don't let this put you off; there still is and will be demand for structured finance lawyers, but the order of the day is caution. For a leisurely introduction to the topic, watch *The Big Short*.

Derivatives

At its most basic, a derivative is a financial instrument used by banks and businesses to hedge risks to which they are exposed due to factors outside of their control. They can also be used for speculative purposes by betting on the fluctuation of just about anything, from currency exchange rates to the number of sunny days in a particular region. The value of a derivative at any given time is derived from the value of an underlying asset, security or index. Futures, forwards, options and swaps are the most common types of derivatives. **Forwards** are agreements between two parties that one will buy a certain product from the other for a fixed price at a fixed date in the future. Hedging against future price risks and speculation over the price movement of the underlying assets are the big attractions. **Futures** are standardized forwards, which can be traded on the futures market. Options are optional futures, where a buyer has the right but not the obligation to purchase or sell a product at a certain date in the future for a certain price. **Swaps** are agreements between two parties to exchange assets at a fixed rate, for example to protect against fluctuations in currency exchange rates.

What lawyers do

IPO or other equity offering

- Work with the client and its accounting firm to prepare and file a registration statement with the Securities and Exchange Commission (SEC).
- Do due diligence on the issuer company and draft a prospectus (as part of the registration statement) that provides a welter of information about the company and its finances, as well as past financial statements.
- Help the accountants draft a comfort letter, assuring the financial soundness of the issuer.
- File with the SEC and wait 30 days before getting initial comments from them.
- Undergo multiple rounds of commentary back and forth with the SEC. This can take one or two months.
- Negotiate approval of a listing on the stock exchange. This involves the submission of documentation, certifications and letters that prove the client satisfies the listing requirements.
- Finalize the underwriting agreement and other documentation.

Debt offering

- Plan out the deal with issuer and underwriter. A timeline is drawn up and tasks are allocated between the different parties.
- Draft a prospectus for SEC registration or a Rule 144A offering memorandum.
- Conduct due diligence on the issuer to examine its creditworthiness, make the disclosure accurate and highlight any associated risks.
- Deliver to the underwriters at closing a legal opinion and a disclosure letter on the offering based on due diligence.

- Draft the indenture: a document describing the bond's interest rate, maturity date, convertibility and so on.
- Draft the purchase (or 'underwriting') agreement.

Securitization

- Work with the underwriter and issuer to draw up the structure of a security, and help the parties negotiate the terms of that structure. *"We will literally sit down with all the parties and draw boxes, charts and arrows on a whiteboard in order to come up with new ideas,"* explains **John Arnholz**, structured finance transactions partner at **Morgan, Lewis & Bockius**.
- Draft the disclosure document and the prospectus or private placement memorandum. *"It is a descriptive piece – almost like a magazine article,"* says John Arnholz. *"It covers all the risks and other characteristics of owning a security."*
- Draft the purchase agreement documenting the transaction. *"This involves a lot of negotiation back and forth between issuer, underwriter, trustees, service providers and insurers,"* says John Arnholz.

Derivatives

- Be approached by a financial institution client (eg, a hedge fund) with an idea to create a new derivatives product.
- Communicate back and forth with the client discussing legal issues and risks related to various possible structures for the product.
- Home in on a specific structure for the product.
- Prepare a memo explaining the problems, issues and legal risks associated with the derivative's agreed-upon structure, as well as suggesting ways to resolve or mitigate those problems and issues.
- If all has gone well, and if the new structure has sufficient prospects for legal and commercial success, lawyers will draft new documentation describing the make-up of the derivative.

Realities of the job

- Notwithstanding the differences mentioned in the descriptions above, there are big similarities between the work of lawyers on debt, equity and other securities transactions.
- The nature of lawyers' involvement in a capital markets transaction depends on its novelty. *"If someone is doing a securitization or designing a derivatives product they must address those issues which are novel,"* says **Josh Cohn**, head of US derivatives and structured products at **Mayer Brown**. *"If you are working on a product based on a preexisting structure, you may be asked to look at certain details like new swaps arrangements."*

- Junior lawyers usually practice in all areas of capital markets law, sometimes combining this with other corporate work too. Some top firms have specialist departments for each capital markets subgroup. Partners often specialize in debt, equity, securitization or derivatives work, but they may continue to dabble in other areas too. *"I would advise junior associates to get involved with as many different types of transactions as possible,"* says **Robert Gross**, capital markets partner at **Clifford Chance**. *"You'll end up getting more to do that way, and it will be more burdensome, but you will get a ton of experience."*
- Clients in the world of finance are incredibly demanding and attorneys usually work very long hours. On the plus side, clients are also smart, sophisticated and dynamic. Large law firms usually have strong and close relationships with investment bank clients, meaning that juniors can get frequent client contact. *"I love working with companies' management teams and with bankers,"* says **Arthur Robinson**, head of the capital markets practice at **Simpson Thacher**. *"On each deal I do I 'meet' a new company and learn about the business from the inside from the CEO and CFO. It may sound odd, but companies do have their own personality, so it's akin to meeting a new person each time."*
- The content and organization of prospectuses tends to be fairly standard, but lawyers consider working on them a rewarding exercise because a good deal of creative writing is required to communicate a company's narrative.
- The purchase agreement is a lengthy contract in which the underwriter agrees to buy the securities and resell them to investors.
- As soon as a company undergoes an IPO, it will be subject to all the rules and requirements of a public company, so the necessary organizational structure must be in place before the IPO.
- Follow-on offerings of common equity are much simpler than an IPO because most of the basic disclosure has already been drafted and will only need to be updated.
- Underwriter's counsel draft most documents related to a bond issue. An issuer's lawyers will comment on them and negotiate changes.
- Due diligence is conducted by both underwriter's and issuer's counsel, but is most important to the underwriter. A due diligence investigation may help in establishing a 'due diligence defense' in any future investor lawsuits claiming a violation of securities laws.
- A debt offering can be registered with the SEC or unregistered under Rule 144A of the 1933 Securities Act. In the latter case bonds can only be bought by certain large registered institutional buyers.

Practice Areas

- Issuer's and underwriter's counsel work together with a team of bankers, accountants, insurers and an issuer's management to get securities issued. *"There is a very collaborative atmosphere,"* says **Bill Whelan**, corporate partner at **Cravath, Swaine & Moore**. *"The team has the common goal of getting the deal done. There are moments when we have disagreements, but rarely does it get acrimonious."* If teams get on particularly well, deals may end with a closing dinner or drinks event.

- The bond market is huge and influential. It is generally considered to have a large influence on the health of the US and global economy.

- Market conditions are very important to the success of capital market deals – more important even than the willingness of the parties to get the deal done. *"The one negative in this area of practice is that the markets are always unpredictable,"* says Bill Whelan. *"You can invest a lot of time in getting a deal organized, but market conditions can mean it falls through."*

- Practitioners recommend that those interested in the field should take law school classes in securities regulation, corporate finance and the Uniform Commercial Code (UCC). Knowledge of bankruptcy, property and tax law is useful too, as is gaining an understanding of the basic principles of accounting. Reading the financial press – starting with *The Wall Street Journal* – is a must.

Current issues

- A report by EY in late 2017 revealed that the year was the most active one for IPOs globally since 2007. All in all, there were 1,974 IPOs, and together they raised $338.4 billion. Activity levels were predicted to be stronger in the last quarter of 2017, but uncertainties in the Asia-Pacific region – which included alterations to listing rules in Hong Kong – meant that those expectations were not met. However, the Asia-Pacific exchanges still shone globally, and accounted for almost 60% of the deals recorded that year.

- In addition, EY's report tells us that the US exchanges were also performing better than the previous year, with both deals and proceeds shooting up – indicating a return of investor confidence. 24% of the US' IPOs were cross-border in nature. Hot areas for the US included energy, healthcare and technology. Activity in the latter sector continued into 2018, as streaming service Spotify made its direct listing on the New York Stock Exchange in April.

- The Dow Jones Industrial Average rose by 31% during Trump's first year as president. This performance has been attributed by some to Trump's loosening of regulations and series of tax cuts, but others aren't quite so keen to give Trump a pat on the back, and instead highlight an improving global economy as the catalyst behind this domestic boom.

- The US Federal Reserve raised interest rates by 0.25% in December 2017 – the third time it raised rates in that year. A further three increases are anticipated in 2018, off the back of improved economic forecasts in the US. Interest rates are predicted to be set above 2%.

- *"Securities law is changing dramatically,"* John Arnholz of Morgan, Lewis & Bockius comments. *"In the old days, rules about securities weren't written down. They were based on lore. Many regulations in the industry are new. That means old hands like me have a smaller advantage over new people entering the field than we used to. Industrious young associates can learn about new regulations and outsmart the partners!"*

- John Arnholz adds that *"for young associates eager to get client contact, no practice area provides more of an opportunity to work directly with clients."*

- A big development in Europe, meanwhile, is the European Commission's proposed 'Capital Markets Union' (CMU) – which aims to remove barriers to investment in Europe. The UK's Brexit has put a spanner in the works somewhat, although the CMU appears to be going ahead.

- The Goldman Sachs Outlook Report for 2018 predicts that global GDP in 2018 will grow by 4.0% – in 2017 the forecast was set at 3.7%.

Financial services – Dechert

Cardi B may well have made a splash with her money moves of late, but nobody moves it quite like financial services lawyers, who advise on a whole host of investments, funds and regulations surrounding one of the biggest industries in the world. We chatted to Dechert's financial services experts to find out more about becoming a lawyer in this dynamic practice.

Chambers Associate: What is financial services law?

Allison Fumai, partner: The Financial Services Group at Dechert focuses on the representation of financial institutions in the investment funds space, otherwise known as investment management.

My practice focuses on the representation of registered investment companies and their investment advisers. I regularly advise mutual funds, closed-end funds and exchange-traded funds and their investment advisers on issues relating to the development and launch of new funds, ongoing compliance and regulatory matters, mergers, liquidations and restructuring of funds.

Christine Ayako Schleppegrell, associate: Financial services law is a transactional practice that exists at the intersection of regulatory, corporate, and business law. Depending on regulatory and market trends, the practice can consist of 40% corporate and 60% regulatory work. We help clients navigate state, federal and international regulatory frameworks so that they can conduct their businesses, sell innovative products, and provide services to institutional and individual investors. Also, we collaborate with our clients' business teams to solve complex problems.

CA: What challenges come with the practice?

Jessica Lees, associate: The financial services industry is governed by a nuanced and constantly changing legal and regulatory landscape. The work is also fast paced and dynamic. We regularly advise clients regarding both U.S. and international legal and regulatory developments, many of which have a profound influence on our clients' daily business. While it takes strong organization, diligent research, and deep expertise, the financial services practice offers a unique opportunity to be involved in the daily activities of the financial services industry.

"The financial services industry is governed by a nuanced and constantly changing legal and regulatory landscape."

AF: One of the most challenging aspects of my practice is helping clients launch novel products in a highly regulated atmosphere. My clients often have great investment ideas or products that do not fit within the current regulatory framework.

Andrew Schaffer, associate: This is not an area of law that is taught to any great extent in law school and there is a lot to learn. Fortunately, senior associates and partners are generally very interested in teaching and mentoring associates.

CA: What are the highs and lows?

AS: I've greatly enjoyed working on new projects and taking the lead, particularly with respect to digital assets. The lows are that some projects are less interesting; overall it's a great mix of different things.

JL: Both the highs and lows of the financial services practice stem from the legal and regulatory landscape. The highs include researching and providing answers to difficult and challenging questions, which provide us with the unique opportunity to advise on real world matters directly impacting our clients' daily business. The lows include a significant amount of document and disclosure review. However, even the lows offer the opportunity to advise our clients on matters that directly impact their day to day operations.

CAS: One of the many 'highs' of this practice area is that there are great opportunities to become an expert in a specific area while also acting as a generalist in a high-demand field. Due to ever evolving rules and regulations, even junior associates have the chance to read a proposed rule, follow it through to the final version, and serve as

Practice Areas

the point person for client questions through the implementation stage and beyond.

There are few 'lows', but one may be adapting to meet client demands on short timelines. However, I have often found that projects with a quick turnaround frequently involve some of the most interesting questions and afford the greatest learning experiences.

"One of the many 'highs' of this practice area is that there are great opportunities to become an expert in a specific area while also acting as a generalist in a high-demand field."

CA: What is a partner's typical role in matters?

AF: One of the best things about my practice is that I get to work on a variety of matters and there is no 'typical' role that I play. I believe I have a unique perspective having started my career as an associate and risen through the ranks to partner. I have an appreciation for working closely with and managing associates on the more day-to-day and routine aspects of matters, while also working directly with and advising clients on the more a-typical issues that arise. I also spend a significant amount of time making sure I am educated on the latest regulatory developments and trends in the industry.

CA: What do associates do?

CAS: Senior associates coordinate with partners and work directly with clients to identify issues that are important to their businesses as well as those that a regulator may focus on. We also scope out and staff projects, deliver great work product, and answer clients' follow up questions. If a client has a specific question that requires a deep dive into a particular topic, we put the client in touch with subject matter experts at the firm, including those in other practice groups. Finally, senior associates train and mentor junior associates.

CA: What's the typical experience like for a junior?

JL: Given the breadth of the financial services practice and the number of regulatory and legal developments in this area, junior associates have the opportunity to be substantively involved in a variety of aspects of the practice from the beginning. Junior associates will primarily be involved in reviewing and drafting legal disclosure documents, which are then filed with the appropriate regulator and provided directly to our client's shareholders and/or potential investors. Junior associates may also

have the opportunity to be involved in researching legal issues, liaising with local counsel in various jurisdictions on international matters, undertaking the first review of various contracts and agreements, and drafting client memoranda.

"Junior associates will primarily be involved in reviewing and drafting legal disclosure documents, which are then filed with the appropriate regulator."

AS: Roles tend to increase as you grow in seniority; however, even first years can expect to have significant client contact and work directly with partners on some matters.

CA: Where can new associates expect to be in five years?

CAS: They can expect to have had great training in various aspects of financial services law including registered fund, private fund, investment adviser, and broker-dealer work as well as international financial products. In addition, they will likely be working toward becoming a subject matter expert on a certain topic or area of the law.

CA: How does your work overlap with that conducted in other practice groups?

JL: Given the nature of the financial industry, a given matter may implicate many different practice groups and areas. Accordingly, when we receive a question from a client, we consider all angles of the inquiry, which may include tax, employee benefits, general corporate and securities, and even litigation issues. We regularly work with attorneys outside of the financial services practice group to ensure that we consider all of the nuances of a particular client's business and needs.

CAS: The Financial Services group at Dechert works closely with several other practice groups including the Corporate, Employee Benefits, Tax, and Leveraged Finance groups. For example, our clients often have questions about the sale of financial products to retirement investors, which can implicate the Employee Retirement Income Security Act. Since our Employee Benefits attorneys are experts on this and other topics, we rely on them to provide comprehensive client service, especially when regulatory developments in these other fields impact our clients' businesses.

AF: Clients look to us for support across the entire fund life cycle, from development and formation, to marketing, operations and transactions. We provide advice re-

Practice Areas

lated to fund management and governance, as well as assist with the full range of regulatory and compliance issues. Our firm also assists with investigations and litigations involving regulatory entities around the world.

CA: What qualities make for good financial services lawyers?

AF: I would say good financial services lawyers exhibit similar qualities to good lawyers in general: thought leadership, excellent oral and written communication skills, responsiveness and the ability to put themselves in the client's shoes.

JL: A good financial services lawyer is practical, innovative and client focused. The financial services practice requires adapting to legal and regulatory developments and an awareness and application of many different practice areas. A good financial services lawyer is also one who is deeply invested in understanding client needs and expectations and is tenacious in his or her pursuit of each client's best interests.

"Clients look to us for support across the entire fund life cycle, from development and formation, to marketing, operations and transactions."

CAS: Attorneys should be curious about financial regulation and its downstream effects, all the way from large corporations to individual investors. Also, those who are interested in tackling the task of tailoring a general rule (intended to apply to all business types) to a client's specific model are often successful in this practice.

CA: What distinguishes the Dechert team from its peers?

CAS: Dechert has a robust training program for our junior associates so that they are well-positioned to take on challenging client work at an early stage. In addition, the firm has support at every level: mid-level associates can look to senior associates and junior partners for guidance, and senior associates can look to junior and senior partners for mentorship.

JL: Dechert truly practices a 'one firm' policy where its domestic and international teams regularly work together to solve client inquiries by combining deep, on-the-ground expertise with long-term experience in financial services matters.

AF: Dechert's financial services practice is among the largest in the industry, and we've been innovating in this area for more than 40 years. I'd also point to our global platform. We are the first (and leading) law firm with lawyers in all four of the EU's leading centers for international investment funds: Dublin, Frankfurt, London and Luxembourg.

CA: How do you see the market evolving in the future?

AF: Some of the issues we are seeing coming to the forefront are related to exchange-traded fund reform and the regulation of financial technologies and digital assets such as cryptocurrencies, Bitcoin and blockchain.

CAS: I anticipate increasing challenges for our clients as multiple entities attempt to regulate the same business activities and financial products. An example is the recent proliferation of fiduciary and best interest standards at the state and federal level, in response to the Department of Labor fiduciary rule. In terms of the legal market and demand for financial services, I think (and hope) that our clients will continue to ask the hard questions, which we welcome.

"...visiting any financial regulator's website (such as the SEC or FIN-RA) would be helpful."

CA: How can students get a head-start if they're interested in financial services law?

JL: If students are interested in financial services law, they should consider taking courses including Securities Regulation and/or Mutual Funds. Additionally, it is beneficial to keep up with the financial industry newspapers, blogs and various legal publications.

CAS: Students interested in this field should read the finance section of any newspaper and see if the issues discussed are of interest. While these are high-level summaries of the more nuanced issues we deal with every day, seeing what new issues are of concern is a solid starting place. Also, visiting any financial regulator's website (such as the SEC or FINRA) would be helpful.

AS: It helps to follow financial news because many of the financial companies that appear daily in the *Wall Street Journal* and other financial publications are our clients. Also, reach out to someone working in the practice to understand what we do on a day-to-day basis.

AF: Dechert's website is a great resource as well since our lawyers are thought leaders on many of the important issues that have defined the financial services industry over the years. Many law schools also offer courses on securities regulation, banking regulation and investment company regulation which would also be helpful.

Authors

Allison Fumai
Partner

Christine Ayako
Schleppegrell
Associate

Andrew Schaffer
Associate

Jessica Lees
Associate

Dechert LLP

To learn more about becoming a lawyer at Dechert, turn to p.314.

Practice Areas

Practice Areas

Intellectual Property

"The world we live in has accelerated. The internet has changed everything about life and certainly the practice of law. Things are much faster; it's easier to collaborate with colleagues around the world, and it's much easier to communicate with clients 24/7. I'm not saying that when I started it was a quiet and lazy time, but things certainly moved at a different pace. Today with communication platforms we're able to reach out immediately. Research has changed as well – back then we relied on classic libraries for the most part. We still have more than our share of hard books at the firm, but now people can have access to the entire universe of knowledge. That has broad implications on how lawyers practice and how efficient they can be."

– Gibson Dunn's chairman Ken Doran

Intellectual property

In a nutshell

There are four different types of intellectual property: patents, trademarks, copyright and trade secrets. Patents are issued by the US Patent & Trademark Office (USPTO) to the creators of new inventions or processes. They're practically a monopoly on the manufacture and sale of the patented invention, but they only last for 14-20 years depending on the patent type. Trademarks can potentially last forever, but only protect the words, symbols or phrases used to distinguish the brand or identity of a good or service.

Somewhere in between is copyright, which protects works of authorship such as books, movies, music and plays. Copyright is a complicated system of restrictions on copying, performing and otherwise profiting from protected works, and lasts for the life of the author plus seventy years. Finally, trade secret law protects the holders of proprietary information from having their information stolen or disclosed to the public in certain circumstances. Think Coke's secret formula, or the Colonel's recipe for KFC.

Companies big and small rely on IP to give them an edge over their competitors, and in 2016 IP-intensive industries directly or indirectly accounted for at least 45.5 million US jobs, and contributed $6.6 trillion to the economy. Clients can vary from a tech startup looking to patent the latest gizmo, to a film distributor trying to stop its content from being pirated. As well as being financially rewarding, IP law also offers some fascinating ethical questions, including:

- Do pharmaceutical patents give life-sciences companies an incentive to invest in creating life-saving drugs, or do they just keep their prices high?
- Should people named 'McDonald' be able to name their restaurants after themselves?
- And is your *Happy Potter* fanfiction copyright infringement, fair use, or just weird?

What lawyers do

- Engage in written correspondence to see if the alleged infringement can be resolved through a license and royalty agreement or other amicable resolution.
- If not resolved, attorneys representing the rights-holder file an infringement claim. Defense attorneys then respond with a counterclaim stating that either their client has not infringed or that the IP is invalid and unenforceable.
- Engage in discovery. Examine public records held in the USPTO that document the correspondence between the patent holder and the USPTO. Prepare interrogatories, requests for admission, and document requests seeking more information about the other side's positions. On average, discovery will take three years.
- Engage in the summary judgment motion phase. Engage in a Markman hearing, during which the judge interprets the language of the claims, ruling on any disagreements between parties on their interpretation. Markman hearings can take place any time before the case goes to the jury, but usually occur before trial.
- Go to trial, normally in front of a jury. This normally takes between four and ten days.
- Perform IP due diligence – review a third party's IP portfolio prior to your client entering into a transaction with them. Assess the strengths and weaknesses of the portfolio so that the client can understand the risks of doing business with the rights-holder.
- Draft commercial agreements between owners of IP rights and those who want to use the protected invention, design or artistic work. The most common agreements will either transfer ownership or grant a license.

Realities of the job

- In order to become a member of the patent Bar, you must pass an exam administered by the USPTO, which requires you to have completed a minimum number of technical or scientific courses in college or university. You don't actually need to be a member of the patent Bar to appear in federal district court on a patent case. Membership of the patent Bar is only necessary for attorneys who want to do patent prosecution work. **Paul Parker**, firmwide chair of **Perkins Coie**'s medical device industry sector, affirms that science qualifications are not a prerequisite for trademark and trade secrets work.
- Patent owners can file claims in any district court they want; some districts are considered more patent-friendly and are therefore more popular than others. The most notable of these is the Eastern District of Texas, based in Marshall, TX (population 24,000). Critics say its unorthodox rules and conservative jury pool favor patent-owners, while its supporters cite the court's efficiency. Overseas companies and inventors generally view the USA as a prime venue for patent litigation.

Rankings in *Chambers USA*

Top Ranked

Alston & Bird	Jones Day
Baker Botts	Kirkland & Ellis
Debevoise & Plimpton	Latham & Watkins
Finnegan, Henderson	Perkins Coie
Fish & Richardson	Sidley Austin
Foley & Lardner	Sterne, Kessler, Goldstein
Hunton Andrews Kurth	Troutman Sanders
Irell & Manella	WilmerHale

Highly Recommended

Akin Gump Strauss Hauer	Mayer Brown
Arnold & Porter	McDermott Will & Emery
Baker McKenzie	Morgan, Lewis & Bockius
Bracewell	Morrison & Foerster
Brownstein Hyatt Farber	Norton Rose Fulbright
Choate Hall & Stewart	O'Melveny & Myers
Cooley	Orrick, Herrington
Cozen O'Connor	Patterson Belknap Webb
Cravath, Swaine & Moore	Paul Hastings
Crowell & Moring	Paul, Weiss, Rifkind
Dechert	Pillsbury Winthrop Shaw
DLA Piper (US)	Proskauer Rose
Duane Morris	Ropes & Gray
Fitzpatrick, Cella, Harper	Schiff Hardin
Fox Rothschild	Skadden
Gibbons	Thompson & Knight
Gibson, Dunn & Crutcher	Venable
Greenberg Traurig	Vinson & Elkins
Haynes and Boone	Weil, Gotshal & Manges
Jenner & Block	White & Case
K&L Gates	Wilson Sonsini Goodrich
Katten Muchin Rosenman	Winston & Strawn
King & Spalding	

For more detail on ranking tiers and locations, visit
www.chambersandpartners.com

- As a result of globalization, the current manufacturing and importation process has become enormously complicated. This creates considerable challenges for patent wners seeking royalties or compensation at any level of the manufacturing and distribution chain.
- An IP portfolio can be the most valuable of a business's assets, particularly in the pharmaceutical sector. This means that IP lawyers need to form part of the deal team from an early stage.
- Every patent infringement appeal is filed with the US Court of Appeals for the Federal Circuit. If parties don't like the result there, the only option is to file a petition for certiorari with the Supreme Court, which has taken more patent cases in the last decade.

- Patent cases bring great risk to Fortune 500 companies, which can incur enormous damages dating back up to six years from the filing of the complaint. This explains the rise of non-practicing entities or patent trolls, which buy up portfolios of patents and make their money threatening to sue other businesses for patent infringement. Faced with such stiff penalties, and without the resources to fight the case in court, smaller companies and inventors pay the patent trolls hefty license fees.
- Different types of IP work means differing workloads, explains **Professor Tim Holbrook** of **Emory University**. *"Patent prosecutors tend to work more independently, as it's often just you and the PTO,"* he explains. *"Patent litigation often goes on for years, and requires long term thinking,"* he adds, *"while trademark litigation is all about speed. Cases are decided off a preliminary injunction, so if something's happening, it's happening now."*
- IP candidates who can demonstrate that they have business expertise will fare well. *"I think it's very helpful to hire people who have been in industry for a couple of years or more"* says Paul Parker, who also notes that *"unlike in a lot of areas where law is a cost center, in patent prosecution, as opposed to litigation, you are an asset creator – you create value for companies."* **Dale Cendali** of **Kirkland & Ellis** remarks that lawyers *"must stay nimble because what we think the world is today is likely to not be the case in ten years."*
- Good communication skills are a must, particularly in transactional IP and IP litigation. Lawyers need to be able to simplify and explain complex technical matters to lay judges, juries and clients.
- What do our expert lawyers enjoy most about their profession? Cendali likes *"the theater of trials and depositions and court hearings,"* adding: *"I really like working with my team."* Paul Parker enthuses: *"Being in IP law is a continual learning process about science and the world around us."*
- **Trent Webb** of **Shook, Hardy & Bacon** tells us: *"Being competitive and having a drive to win is very important, because every case involves trying to beat the other side. Creativity is also essential; we strive to find unique approaches to solving problems. You also need to be able to simplify and explain very complicated technical issues to lay juries. Communicating effectively to your audience is extremely important."*
- What challenges might an associate face? Paul Parker suggests *"for mid-level associates there is a period of time when there seems to be a lot of basic preparation and prosecution. It's a threshold you have to get through before operating at a much more strategic level with clients."*
- Dale Cendali advises budding IP lawyers *"to dig a little deeper to figure out the nature of the IP practice at different firms. What is it they do? How many associates are working in that group? What are the potential opportunities to make partner?"*

Practice Areas

Current issues

- The Apple-Samsung patent wars came to a head in 2017, after the US Supreme Court dismissed Samsung's final appeal and ordered it to pay $119.6 million in damages to Apple over the slide-to-unlock technology. At the time of writing both companies were set for another court showdown in a May 2018 trial.

- There is an ongoing debate about 'patent-eligible subject matter'. The 1980s days of patents for 'anything under the sun that is made by man' are long gone, with patents becoming increasingly difficult to obtain. *Alice Corp. v. CLS Bank* was a landmark case in the software industry (notwithstanding the fact that software was not explicitly discussed in the case), as the Supreme Court ruled in 2014 that Alice's patents were based on an abstract idea and were, therefore, invalid. Software giants including Microsoft and Google announced their respective stances in the legal wrangle, filing amicus curiae briefs.

- Following a lengthy assessment of US copyright law, the House Judiciary Committee announced its first subsequent policy proposal in December 2016. The Committee aims to establish advisory committees to facilitate communication with federal agencies about marketplace developments and new policies.

- The Lanham Act has been the subject of fierce debate in the past few years. In 2017, the Supreme Court ruled in *Matal v. Tam* that the provision of the Lanham Act that allows the refusal of scandalous or immoral trademarks is unconstitutional, as it breaches the Free Speech Clause of the First Amendment. This is a boost for the Washington Redskins – in October 2016 the Supreme Court refused to validate trademarks on its name, but following this latest ruling the Fourth Circuit vacated the original decision and the case was sent back to lower court.

- The Defend Trade Secrets Act became law in May 2016. According to Dale Cendali *"it's certainly true that trade secrets theft is becoming a growing issue relating to intellectual property."* As a result, trade secrets are now governed by federal law. The act notably allows employers to claim damages in trade secret cases, and stops whistleblowers from falling victim to retaliatory accusations of trade secret misappropriation.

- As the restaurant industry grows year on year, so does the competition. IP experts say this has lead to an increased interest in protecting recipes and restaurant brands as intellectual property: Dominique Ansell led by example in 2014 with the trademarking of the Cronut (with a capital C), so while there have been plenty of copycats since the pastry treat went viral no one else can sell their baked goods by that name.

- There's no getting away from blockchain as it gathers speed alongside the rise of cryptocurrencies. Experts speculate that the technology could provide a means for content creators to ensure they're compensated for their intellectual property, relevant to industries ranging from music to pharmaceuticals.

"Being competitive and having a drive to win is very important, because every case involves trying to beat the other side. Creativity is also essential; we strive to find unique approaches to solving problems. You also need to be able to simplify and explain very complicated technical issues to lay juries. Communicating effectively to your audience is extremely important."

– Trent Webb of Shook, Hardy & Bacon

Technology – Goodwin

Mid-level associates at Goodwin share their views on what it's like to become a technology lawyer and trends on the tech sector.

Chambers Associate: Which practice areas fall within the technology sector?

Emma Mann-Meginniss: The technology sector spans a number of different practice areas, from general corporate and securities work to mergers and acquisitions, labor and employment, intellectual property law, litigation, and capital markets.

Jesse Nevarez: At Goodwin, this would mean venture capital, M&A, capital markets (including IPOs and follow-on offerings) and a variety of intellectual property matters. Of course, depending upon the company or matter, we will leverage our labor, employment and tax expertise as well.

CA: Does Goodwin have a particular specialism in any of these?

EMM: Goodwin is a full-service firm dedicated to meeting our clients' needs no matter what stage they're in. We pride ourselves on being able to grow along with our clients, from the one-person founding team to a company of thousands of employees and offices worldwide.

My practice focuses on companies that are in their early to mid-stage of their lifecycles. I work with clients from formation through acquisition or IPO. We have subunits within our larger tech group who are experts in public offerings, capital markets, sell-side M&A, buy-side M&A, tax, labor and employment, IP, etc. And of course we have an incredible private equity group that can assist our later-stage clients that make the jump from startup to PE.

JN: Goodwin is one of the leading firms in this practice area with a particular focus on guiding new and emerging growth technology companies through a variety of life-cycle transactional events. We also have great expertise in guiding investors that wish to invest in or lead the funding in these types of transactions.

"The technology sector spans a number of different practice areas."

CA: What are the differences between non-contentious and litigious work for the technology sector?

EMM: One of the main differences is in the outlook of the attorneys involved. From the company's perspective, at a high level, there aren't many differences – in both areas, the company is focused on protecting the business. From the attorney's side, there are some significant differences, a lot of which are about the relationship with the client. I started my career as a litigator, and one of the things I used to hear from my clients a lot was something along the lines of 'This has been great, but I hope I never have to see you again.' On the corporate (or non-contentious) side, my role is more as advisor – someone my clients want to consult from the beginning, and not someone they call as a last resort.

JN: On the one hand, you can be part of an IPO process, where all sides to the deal (company, underwriters and their respective legal teams) are looking to present a unified story of the company that will draw great interest from investors. This presents a great incentive to work together. On the other hand, you can find yourself negotiating back and forth on the reps and warranties in an M&A deal, where each side has to consider a worst case scenario where the parties are arguing in court over the breach of these provisions. In this case, both sides have an increased incentive to draw harder lines during negotiations.

John Casnocha: On the corporate side we are focused on building companies, helping clients raise capital, complete acquisitions of complementary businesses and gain liquidity through initial public offerings or mergers. We are also drafting the contracts that could eventually be the basis for litigation so part of the job is protect our clients from future claims. In litigation, typically the alleged wrong act has already been done thus the work is really to resolve or settle the dispute. At that point, opposing counsel is an adversary rather than a partner and thus interactions are often contentious rather than productive.

CA: Which future technologies do you anticipate will be most lucrative for the legal sector?

EMM: If I could predict what would be the most lucrative, I might go into investing and skip the law altogether! A large part of the legal side of tech work really doesn't change from company to company, regardless of what kind of product or service they've created. That said, we're seeing a growing number of companies in the artificial intelligence space, and of course in bitcoin/cryptocurrency – that's been a huge area of growth for our firm in the past year, and it's touching many different groups within Goodwin. We have more and more companies interested in doing token offerings and venture capital clients considering investing in companies that are planning to do an initial coin offering.

JN: I definitely see the health and wellness technology space continuing to grow (with a particular emphasis on wearable technologies). People are increasingly focused on getting enough exercise, eating the right foods and having a way to keep track of all of this, and I believe that we have just scratched the surface of this sector.

JC: Cryptocurrency and autonomous vehicles.

Aaron Berman: I anticipate cryptocurrency as a growth area in terms of industry, and a lot of activity in cybersecurity. In Boston, we are also seeing advanced manufacturing capabilities, such as 3D printing, taking off.

> ## "We're seeing a growing number of companies in the artificial intelligence space, and of course in bitcoin/cryptocurrency – that's been a huge area of growth for our firm in the past year."

CA: How is Goodwin keeping apace with changes in technology?

EMM: Our group is really focused on making sure we have our finger on the pulse of what's happening with our clients. Part of that is researching and developing expertise in burgeoning areas within the technology sector (from a legal perspective). In the last year, there has been an increasing focus on cryptocurrency. In prior years, we've seen heavy interest in artificial intelligence, or employment/contractor misclassification issues having to do with companies like Uber or Lyft. We do what we can to get out in front of these issues, but some part of what we do is experiential – and that's where the sheer volume of clients really helps. We see the same issues arise on a regular basis and that helps us counsel our clients on both the potential solutions that work from a legal perspective and a business perspective.

AB: One example is that we have been quick to adopt and build strong relationships with new capitalization table management programs, including Carta and Shoobx, that allow companies to reduce the cost of managing relationships with investors and employees and model financing rounds and exit scenarios.

CA: How may working with technology clients differ from those in corporate or finance, for example?

EMM: The easiest way to understand the difference between a typical tech client and a client in corporate or finance is to think about the difference between a startup in Silicon Valley and an investment bank based in New York. The Silicon Valley startup is founded by a small team looking to raise early capital, hire the right people, figure out exactly how to put their great idea into practice, and grow quickly. The New York based investment bank is responding to market conditions, has a team of hundreds of thousands of people, is in the public eye, and is focused on sustaining shareholder returns. The startup responds quickly to market indications that something is working (or not) and doubles down (or cuts the fat and iterates) – which means that their needs, from a legal perspective, are highly dynamic. The bank is making more deliberate choices, evaluating market data over longer periods of time, and likely not moving as quickly.

JN: It can differ because the number of employees may be smaller. What this means is that almost every conversation that you have will be with a decision maker at your client, which in certain cases can speed up the process of a matter.

> ## "The easiest way to understand the difference between a typical tech client and a client in corporate or finance is to think about the difference between a startup in Silicon Valley and an investment bank based in New York."

JC: On average, founder clients are younger than banking or finance clients. Many times this is a founder's first time analysing the legal issues that we are discussing and so they are (i) more receptive and (ii) more appreciative of your work than other clients might be. In addition, clients reach out for more than just legal advice and understand that Goodwin has strong insight into what is market in Silicon Valley from a business perspective as

Practice Areas

well. We have helped shepherd other clients in similar industries and markets from incorporation to IPO or successful exits and thus they rely on us for business and strategy advice as well, and not just legal terms. Not surprisingly, founders are incredibly passionate about the company and their business and thus I find it helpful to take a real interest in the technology that my clients are offering and the problems that they are solving – clients appreciate it when you understand what they are doing and the purpose behind it.

AB: We see many personality types, which drives the way they do business in a more significant manner than in a large organization. Businesses are often smaller and change rapidly. You come across a wider range of sophistication, ranging from college students starting their first business to well-seasoned entrepreneurs who have been down this path many times before.

CA: What are you favorite cases to work on? What is the hardest part of your role?

EMM: I really enjoy working with early to mid-stage startup clients, as well as venture funds that invest in those companies. The entrepreneurs are passionate about what they want to do, and the questions they ask are critical to the development of the company from the early stages. There's often some mix of business and law in the services we're providing, whether it's counsel on the market for compensation packages for a particular level of hire or the terms they can expect in a venture financing.

JN: My favorite deals are the ones where everyone from the client to the investors and the legal teams are fully engaged in the matter. It always makes for a much smoother process and everyone walks away happy with the outcome. The hardest part of my role in those deals is that I have to bring it all together and make sure that every opinion is considered.

JC: I think working with founders is the most fun – especially when their companies are gaining steam and go from nothing more than an idea to a high valuation and profitable business. Founders typically look at you, even as a junior or mid-level associate, as a trusted advisor whose advice they really respect and take. That makes it fun. The hard part is that you do not always know the right answer and for many of these startups you are helping them make really critical decisions on how to raise money, entity structure, and licensing deals that could really help make or break them. Therefore, the key is sometimes knowing what you don't know, and then bringing in the right specialist or partner who has specific expertise on the area.

> **"Working with founders is the most fun – especially when their companies are gaining steam and go from nothing more than an idea to a high valuation and profitable business."**

CA: What was your role on the latest deal/case you worked on?

EMM: I usually have anywhere between ten and 15 active deals at any given time, so that's a tough one! I just closed a large, later-stage financing for a startup company that I helped form. My role on that deal was consistent with my role in other similar deals: I was the primary point of contact for the company, from the term sheet stage through drafting the definitive documents. Along with the partner on the client team, I counselled the client through the proposed changes and terms the lead investor put forth, and also managed the other more junior associates and paralegals on the team. In this case, there were some interesting business issues that arose during the deal that necessitated some more difficult, but interesting, conversations with the founders, and some research into typical market expectations for a company like this one. Ultimately, the investors closed on the deal on terms that were favourable to the company.

JC: My role really depends on the type of deal I am doing but largely I am my client's initial point of contact – who they first go to with questions. For deal work, I am typically leading the execution of the deals with oversight/guidance from the partners.

AB: My latest deal involved helping a company go through an IPO on a very tight timeline. We had to keep the business running and we were able to meet the very aggressive timeline, which resulted in a positive outcome for the client. My role was drafting the S-1 SEC filing, responding to SEC comments, negotiating agreements with the underwriters, and importantly, acting as the quarterback to ensure everyone was on the same page and moving towards meeting the deadline.

CA: How important is a scientific background to your work? Is there a type of person that would not thrive in this area?

EMM: Not at all. I think a technical background can be helpful if you want to do patent prosecution or have a specific desire to work on IP agreements, but even then, it's more important to have a deep understanding of a company's business and how it use its technology than a particular degree. As a general corporate lawyer in the

Practice Areas

technology sector, I don't think I'm hindered in the least for not having a technical background.

JN: It's not important at all. However, if you find yourself not understanding a concept, you have to be willing to do the research to be in the position to better advocate for your client.

AB: For tech there is no need for a scientific background. Someone who thrives is someone who can work on multiple deals at the same time and handle lots of interaction with clients from an early stage in their career.

Authors

Emma Mann-
Meginniss
Associate

Jesse Nevarez
Associate

John Casnocha
Associate

Aaron Berman
Associate

GOODWIN

To learn more about becoming a lawyer at Goodwin, turn to p.364.

Privacy and data security

In a nutshell

The issue of privacy and data security is one of the most pressing and controversial in our digital age – so naturally it's a growth area for lawyers. The law in this area is relatively new, but there's still a struggle to keep up with rapid technological advances. Multinational companies, developers of products and public bodies are all under pressure to comply to ever-changing regulation that protects the consumer. Lawyers advise clients on the collection, use and transfer of personal information.

Attorneys might focus on compliance and take a proactive approach, ensuring clients adhere to their obligations to protect personal information either from outside attack or from misuse by employees. Alternatively, lawyers might assume a more reactive role and deal with data breaches, as well as contentious matters and investigations conducted by data protection authorities. This part of the practice is also known as the enforcement side.

The rise of social media companies, smart technology and data transmission means that lawyers in this field are increasingly relevant. A growing awareness of what's being shared between organizations has prompted the need to protect not only personal data but intellectual property too. *"Cybersecurity is going to be a hot button issue,"* according to ex-head and founder of **Jenner & Block**'s privacy team **Mary Ellen Callahan**,*"there is more interest than ever in keeping information protected."*

What lawyers do

- Advise companies on data transfer and storage, and risk factors that make them vulnerable to cyber attacks.
- Negotiate settlements for clients accused of neglecting their legal obligations.
- Litigate on behalf of clients whose data has been breached.
- Are sometimes employed on a 'just in case' basis to take action in tricky situations.
- Work with engineers and developers to ensure that software adheres to regulatory obligations.

Realities of the job

- Given that this area affects all types of businesses, attorneys will have the chance to work with a wide variety of clients which can encompass anything from media personalities to military divisions and government organizations, sometimes all in the same day.
- The pressure can be high on the reactive side of the practice. *"The matters that arise are a really big deal for the client; it's like heart surgery,"* says **Doug Meal** of **Ropes & Gray**. *"Dealing with a major security breach feels truly life threatening for the client so it's really rewarding when, first of all, you get engaged by a client who needs help in this scary and stressful situation."* However, this can also *"put significant stress on you; the clients are really counting on you and you feel tremendous responsibility for them."*
- This burgeoning area of law provides plenty of hands on experience for young lawyers. Different members of teams might tackle completely different areas, then meet to discuss issues relevant to both, while also finding time for client calls. Reactive cases come with a faster pace.
- With new territory comes the need for creativity. *"This body of law barely existed ten years ago,"* says Meal, *"on every matter you're dealing with legal issues that have never been dealt with before. There are not enough prior decisions out there to really decide for you what the answer will be to an issue that arises. As a lawyer you have an opportunity as you're not bound by a whole body of established law. You have the ability to argue and have a role in making the law."*
- Although a technical background demonstrates skills relevant to data security law and can be helpful, it's not a prerequisite. Meal confirms that *"prior experience in computer technology is valuable but certainly not essential."*
- He also explains that variety is keen in the early-going: *"I would want the opportunity to do both compliance and enforcement for some period of time. I would be looking hard for a law firm that would give you a chance to do this in the area – it's quite important."*

Practice Areas

"This body of law barely existed ten years ago."

Rankings in *Chambers USA*

Top Ranked

Morrison & Foerster

Highly Recommended

Alston & Bird	Ropes & Gray
Arnold & Porter	Sidley Austin
Cooley	Venable
DLA Piper (US)	Wiley Rein
Hunton Andrews Kurth	WilmerHale
McDermott Will & Emery	Wilson Sonsini
Perkins Coie	

For more detail on ranking tiers and locations, visit www.chambersandpartners.com

Current issues

- The Trump administration could affect the Federal Communications Commission's (FCC) scope. *"The FCC was under Democratic control for the last eight years, and during that time it has dramatically expanded its regulatory reach in privacy and data security,"* explains Meal. *"The FCC is now under Republican control, so you could see a significant rollback of what was previously put in place."*
- One example is proposed changes to US net neutrality laws, which come with data privacy implications. It's possible that internet providers could charge additional fees for consumers to keep their browsing private, and monitor internet users more closely to calculate what other products they'd be interested in.
- The alleged Russian hacking of the Democratic National Committee highlighted new priorities for lawyers in the cybersecurity field. *"Good data governance and hygiene"* will become increasingly important factors, says Callahan. *"It's very sobering,"* she adds, pointing to the rising stakes of cyber attacks: *"CEOs have been fired over breaches that occurred due a lack of data security."*

- Following the allegations brought against Cambridge Analytica (the analytics firm was accused of harvesting Facebook users' personal information to target them with political ads), social media sites' data privacy measures have been called into question. In April 2018 Facebook founder Mark Zuckerberg testified on the subject before the United States Senate Committee on Commerce, Science, and Transportation.
- The Federal Trade Secrets Act may produce some interesting cases brought by companies whose trade secrets have been stolen. On a related note, lawyers will see an uptick in *"drafting employment contracts to comply"* to ensure employees don't pass information on to competitors, according to **Lori Lesser** of **Simpson Thacher & Bartlett**.
- The advance of technology – especially 'smart' devices – has already caused a number of privacy concerns. For example: the potential to track the movement of an electric car; to monitor the activity of smart technology; to reach private spaces with drones; and to watch a user through their own webcam are all possibilities which the law will need to keep up with.
- Mobile apps make personal information more accessible to companies than ever before. Many ask the user to input details about themselves; most neglect to read the small print and remain unaware of the extent to which their information could be stored and shared with third parties.
- Biometric identification (BI) is becoming more commonplace, and used increasingly as a security measure in mobile phones. The technology's coming on fast and improving all the time: the chance of somebody breaking into your phone because of a rogue Apple Touch ID match is 1 in 50,000, while in the newer Face ID it's just 1 in 1,000,000.
- As artificial intelligence (AI) gathers pace, so does its threat to cyber security. According to a Webroot report 91% of security professionals believe that hackers could launch more sophisticated cyber attacks than previously by using AI.

Technology – the basics

In a nutshell

Technology lawyers are experts on the rapidly changing laws and regulations surrounding complex communication technologies. Their classification as an attorney can vary – some fall under the IP umbrella, while others work within corporate or trial departments – but tech lawyers are united in their specialized industry expertise. Many narrow their focus to the telecommunications field, which deals with media such as telephones, cable, radio and the internet; others focus on information technology – which involves software, e-commerce and data privacy issues – or outsourcing, which oversees the provision of third-party services.

Whatever their specialty, a tech lawyer's primary role is to help clients abide by the complicated policies that pertain to certain technologies. In the US, such policies are by and large enforced by the Federal Communications Commission (FCC). Typical matters range from working on behalf of the government to promote fair market competition, to overseeing disputes between telecom corporations, to advising merging companies on contract negotiations.

Rapid advances in technology mean each generation of tech lawyers faces a shifting workload – attorneys today regularly contend with smartphone and internet-related matters, while their 20th century counterparts mainly dealt with telephone line technology, and attorneys in the 19th century grappled with the telegraph and other disruptive innovations.

What lawyers do

- Advise companies on commercial transactions, including mergers, acquisitions, investments and the purchase of services, particularly those with antitrust issues.
- Negotiate contract terms for companies acquiring new technologies or enhancing existing ones.
- Handle diligence and draft transaction documents.
- Assist with dispute resolution, often between telecom companies. Many disputes are cross-border and often fall under the IP bracket – for example, patent infringement cases.
- Represent clients at trial, usually in the State Court.
- Counsel communications companies, such as cable or internet providers, on their regulatory obligations.
- Help companies learn how to protect their IT and web-based assets and defend themselves against cybersquatting and other data protection issues.
- Represent clients seeking the provision of IT services through a third party.

- Assist the government to promote competition between telecom and other technology companies, and ensure services don't interfere with national security.

Realities of the job

- Technology transactions often require attorneys to work as part of a multidisciplinary team that incorporates lawyers from multiple fields, including IP, tax and corporate. *"My role is like that of a quarterback,"* **Baker Botts'** technology sector chair **John Martin** tells us. *"I coordinate lawyers from other practice areas and disciplines to develop and implement an integrated solution and to address the client's many issues. It's a multifaceted approach."*
- Technology is the perfect field for those wanting to experience ingenuity. *"It is energizing and exciting to be around creative and inventive people,"* says **Lori Lesser** of **Simpson Thatcher & Bartlett**. *"These people are changing the world, saving the world and affecting how we work, how we get to work and run our lives online. It's a real privilege to work with these people."*
- The field is constantly changing thanks to developments in technology, which means *"every deal is different and every transaction has its own challenges,"* Martin says. *"There's no cookie-cutter matter out there; each deal is unique, which makes this a challenging and intellectually stimulating field. Nothing is rote or routine, and the learning curve never plateaus."* This shifting workload also means *"practitioners should be comfortable with ambiguity,"* **Cherie Kiser** of **Cahill Gordon & Reindel** advises. *"The law surrounding communications issues is constantly changing because the technology is dynamic. Developments are happening in real time in this sector, and lawyers are called upon by their clients to help shape and influence those laws. One should be comfortable with that lack of stability."*
- Because technology lawyers are specialists, they typically *"handle the majority of matters themselves rather than delegating projects or issues completely,"* Kiser says. This means even top-level partners are obliged to contend with grunt work like diligence at times. *"Fortunately, matters are interesting!"* she adds. Technology and telecom matters have *"a language of their own that's highly technical and full of acronyms,"* Kiser warns. As such, attaining a good grasp of the relevant jargon – accessible through industry trade journals and magazines – is a crucial aspect of the job.

Practice Areas

Rankings in *Chambers USA*

Top Ranked

DLA Piper (US)	Mayer Brown
Gibson, Dunn & Crutcher	McDermott Will & Emery
Harris, Wiltshire & Grannis	Morrison & Foerster
Jenner & Block	Pillsbury Winthrop Shaw
Latham & Watkins	

Highly Recommended

Akin Gump Strauss Hauer	Proskauer Rose
Arnold & Porter	Shearman & Sterling
Baker Botts	Sidley Austin
Bracewell	Simpson Thacher & Bartlett
Choate Hall & Stewart	Skadden
Cooley	Venable
Haynes and Boone	Vinson & Elkins
Hunton Andrews Kurth	Weil, Gotshal & Manges
K&L Gates	White & Case
Kirkland & Ellis	Wiley Rein
Morgan, Lewis & Bockius	Willkie Farr & Gallagher
Norton Rose Fulbright	WilmerHale
Perkins Coie	Wilson Sonsini

For more detail on ranking tiers and locations, visit www.chambersandpartners.com

- Although a strong interest in technology is essential, a related degree is not necessarily a prerequisite. *"You don't need to have a technology background from university,"* says Lesser. *"You need to have the self confidence to know that you can be educated."*
- The area is a very good place for a lawyer who wants to hit the ground running. *"It is an emerging field; it's very easy to make a name for yourself early,"* says Lesser. *"It's not a field with people with decades of expertise. The law is brand new and every time there is a law on trade secrets, patent law enforcement or EU law, everyone starts on day one. If you're eager to learn, inhale as much knowledge as you can you will quickly be as experienced as someone older."* **Michael Steinig** of **Eversheds Sutherland** backs this up: *"Associates get more client interaction. They are negotiating what needs to go into documents very early in their career. One pro is the learning curve the associate goes on to advance."*
- When working on the transactional side, building good client relations is at least as important as the outcomes of certain cases. *"You can do a good job for your client and they say thank you but you don't win,"* says Michael Steinig. *"You don't have that high and low that you have in some other areas of law."*

- A job as a tech lawyer isn't limited to a BigLaw firm, though an increasing number of matters are now handled by teams at private firms, thanks to the manpower and other resources such establishments have at their disposal. Options outside of BigLaw include serving as legal counsel for the FCC and going in-house with a telecom firm.

Current issues

- The rapid rise of cloud computing has made it a *"very hot topic"* in the sector, Baker Botts' John Martin tells us. *"It's at an active and evolving stage, which lends itself to many interesting issues in terms of stability of service and allocation of risk. Think about your mobile device and all the data it contains – that's now being stored in the cloud rather than the device itself, which means you as a consumer will require on-demand services and updated info from the technology provider."* On top of that, data protection itself has become an area of huge expansion for many law firms. For example, if a New York-based official in a multinational company accesses HR data for staff based in Frankfurt, they may be in breach of the Data Protection regulations as EU regulations are much stricter than those in the US.
- Cybersecurity is therefore a concern of both law firms and their clients. Having large troves of confidential customer/client information stolen despite promising to keep it safe is highly damaging. On 3 January it emerged that most microprocessors were vulnerable to two types of attack named 'Meltdown' and 'Spectre.' While moves have been made to address the issues, companies such as Intel have already been hit by by at least three class-action lawsuits over these vulnerabilities. Companies who employ cloud technology are among those most at risk.
- The sector used to center around the US regulatory landscape exclusively; however, thanks to an increasingly global market, most technology and telecoms companies have expanded their business internationally, *"which in turn requires us to broaden our capability as legal advisers by collaborating with foreign counsel to apply our US-based knowledge transnationally."*
- As content-sharing technology becomes increasingly dominant, companies need to be as inventive as possible to protect their intellectual property and remain profitable: *"As we have more and more devices we change how people view content and make money off content and there are winners and losers,"* says Lori Lesser.
- Competition, influence and regulation concerns have been raised over tech platforms such as Google, Facebook and Amazon. By some estimates, Amazon captures over 40% of online shopping in America; in some countries Google processes more that 90% of web searches, while Facebook boasts the world's largest pool of personal data from its two billion monthly users.

Practice Areas

- Content on social media has also had seismic affects on the real world. Recent political decisions have arguably been affected and badly predicted by the patterns in which people share content, as well as the perceived rise in 'fake news' the use of these platforms by the media as well as the provider's responsibility to keep their service 'clean' will undoubtedly be hot topics as they continue to expand. In January, Facebook announced that it is altering its newsfeed algorithm so that users will see less content from sensation-seeking publishers and websites.

- From delivering pizza, to filming, to helping to find lost mountaineers, the potential civilian and commercial uses of unmanned aerial vehicles (more commonly known as drones) have proliferated. Clients are increasingly keen to discover how best to utilize these flying machines, and that means navigating a host of legal and regulatory issues. With all these unmanned aircraft whizzing about the sky, safety is a prime concern, but considering that drones were developed for intelligence purposes, so is privacy. Law firms have been setting up practice groups to help their clients navigate this spaghetti-esque tangle of regulations.

- 3D printers have also created quite a stir, particularly in the IP and product liability worlds. All that is needed to 3D-print something is an electronic schematic and a 3D printer, and the technology is already capable of producing prosthetics, aircraft parts and even rudimentary firearms. 3D printers are becoming more affordable and accessible, which raises the specter of their being used to produce unauthorized copies of patented inventions.

- The continuing development of self-driving cars will bring with it numerous ethical issues concerning with whom the culpability would lie in the case of an accident and whether the technology will protect the itself, the operator or other road users.

- With a main focus on making our lives easier, technology has the power to simplify outsourcing deals. *"Large outsourcing deals usually take nine months with several people working on it. Cloud deals are a lot less work and a lot quicker; they are more of a commodity. The power of that technology is able to replace the larger service agreements,"* says Michael Steinig. *"You don't need a 20-page establishment document, just click a button. The volume of the deal increases, but not so much the complexity."*

- An exponential increase in the availability of digital data and computing power alongside the development of more sophisticated algorithms is continuing to push the boundaries of AI. Many warn of the dangers of AI's presence in the workplace, warfare and its legal ramifications. Others also highlight the problem of companies such as Alphabet, Google and Microsoft monopolizing AI talent and expertise. By one estimate, companies globally have completed around $21.3 billion in M&A related to AI last year – 26 times more than in 2015.

- Law firms are already beginning to take advantage of the practical uses available for AI, from using computers to tackle grunt work such as document analysis to employing machine learning to predict outcomes of cases based on past analysis, previous court decisions and human reactions.

- New laws and policies are being invented as space travel becomes cheaper and commercially viable. In the US, The Space Resource Exploration and Utilization Act of 2015 for example allowed the president to 'promote the right of US commercial entities to explore outer space and utilize space resources, in accordance with such obligations, free from harmful interference, and to transfer and sell such resources.' Similarly, Luxembourg's deputy prime minister, Etienne Schenider, recently announced that *"Luxembourg is the first adopter in Europe of a legal and regulatory framework recognizing that space resources are capable of being owned by private companies."*

- With 2,569 deals struck, the technology sector hit its highest annual deal count since 2001, as investors looked toward the latest developments in the industry such as autonomous vehicles and blockchain technology.

Sports, media, entertainment and advertising

In a nutshell

Media and entertainment, advertising and sports are distinct yet overlapping areas of the law. Some aspects of their practice are common to them all – contracts law, for example – but ensuring a '100% beef burger' abides by the rules set by the Federal Trade Commission (FTC) is clearly a matter for an advertising specialist.

Whichever strand you practice, one thing is for certain: the work is incredibly varied. None of these specialisms has its own distinct branch of law. Rather, they involve piecing together elements of a broad range of legal disciplines and applying them to one particular industry sector.

Media and entertainment

Media and entertainment lawyers provide legal advice and representation to those working in the entertainment industries, including the fields of theater, television, music, publishing, gambling, film and digital media. The practice has a major fault-line down the middle, with most lawyers falling on either the transactional or the contentious side. Many entertainment lawyers hone one particular specialism – the music industry, for example – while others remain generalists.

Advertising

Advertising lawyers advise on every aspect of brand promotion, from drawing up contracts and deploying 'viral' campaigns to settling false advertising disputes. Again, the role of 'advertising lawyer' is somewhat of a misnomer as its attorneys tend to fall into subspecialisms – generally using their expertise to advise on regulatory, transactional or false advertising matters.

Sports

Split between transactional and litigation work, sports lawyers help out individuals and companies involved in the sports industry. That involves anything from drawing up player signing contracts, purchasing and selling stadiums and negotiating branding agreements to litigating licensing issues.

What lawyers do

Media and entertainment

- Draft and negotiate record, publishing, producer, management, distribution, touring, merchandising, corporate sponsorship, licensing and internet agreements.

- Consult with artists, record companies and publishers regarding their financing, entertainment and internet strategies, plus the protection of their IP rights.
- Advise media and entertainment companies on their M&A and merger activities.
- Provide pre-publication content advice to broadcasters and publishers.
- Litigate matters including contractual, copyright and trademark, employment, and payment disputes.
- First Amendment law is a substantial specialism in itself – advising on issues of free speech, censorship and defamation, among other contentious issues.

Advertising

- Advise advertisers on playing by the rules according to advertising watchdogs including the FTC, and legislation such as the Children's Online Privacy Protection Act.
- Counsel manufacturers on all facets of food and drug labeling, marketing and advertising requirements.
- Advise on sweepstakes and other commercial promotions.
- Litigate false advertising claims, from single party to consumer class actions – particularly those falling under the Lanham Act, the federal false advertising statute.
- Provide copyright advice on advertising issues.
- Negotiate advertising-based content licensing agreements, for a whole range of different media.

Sports

- Advise broadcasters and other sports bodies on audiovisual media piracy issues.
- Sports-related litigation – anything from athlete contractual disputes to stadium construction and copyright issues.
- Advise professional sports leagues, club owners, investors and other financial institutions on sports-related licensing agreements, project finance, securitizations, and security offerings.
- Involved in M&A transactions involving sports-related bodies, and in the purchase and sale of sports teams.
- Advise sports administrators, commercial bodies and municipal authorities on hosting major sporting events.
- Manage IP portfolios for sports brands.

Practice Areas

Rankings in *Chambers USA*

Top Ranked

Cahill Gordon & Reindel	Patterson Belknap Webb
Cravath, Swaine & Moore	Paul, Weiss, Rifkind
Debevoise & Plimpton	Proskauer Rose
Gibson, Dunn & Crutcher	Skadden
Jenner & Block	Weil, Gotshal & Manges
Kramer Levin Naftalis	Wiley Rein
Latham & Watkins	Winston & Strawn
Munger, Tolles & Olson	

Highly Recommended

Akin Gump Strauss Hauer	Katten Muchin Rosenman
Arnold & Porter Kaye	Kirkland & Ellis
Cooley	Morgan, Lewis & Bockius
Davis Polk & Wardwell	O'Melveny & Myers
DLA Piper (US)	Paul Hastings
Foley & Lardner	Reed Smith
Greenberg Glusker Fields	Sheppard, Mullin, Richter
Greenberg Traurig	Sidley Austin
Holland & Knight	Venable
Hughes Hubbard & Reed	Waller
Irell & Manella	WilmerHale

For more detail on ranking tiers and locations, visit www.chambersandpartners.com

Realities of the job

- You need to be prepared that being an entertainment lawyer is not going to be all that different from the job of any other lawyer. *"The day would be the same as that of a junior associate working on a matter in any industry: reading, drafting, spending a long time on the phone with clients. It's no different than work for any similar transactional or litigation practice group,"* confesses **Ruth Fisher**, a co-chair of **Gibson Dunn**'s media, entertainment and technology practice group. You will be expected, however, to understand very industry specific requirements, such as *"where the rights are owned and how they are owned."*

- *"If you could visualize it, you have to think about it as a wheel, where there's IP, advertising, data content, and technology – all of those are interrelated,"* illustrates **James D. Taylor** of **Loeb & Loeb.** You will need to master many different disciplines whether you are sports or media lawyer, and excel at those. Although it means more work, he stresses that *"the value and benefit of this is that you develop a holistic approach."*

- Work in the fun sector is far from being just fun! There is an awful lot to learn as you go: *"It takes a great deal of hard work to stay current. Projects move very quickly,"* warns **Kenneth Florin**, co-chair of advanced media and technology and chair of digital and social media at Loeb & Loeb.

- The fast pace and an ever-changing nature of the job is what actually makes it so exciting and special: *"I think what's of particular interest to younger attorneys is that the legal landscape is changing fairly dramatically because of technology,"* says James D. Taylor. *"What's unique is that what we are doing hasn't existed before: we are at the very beginning of digital revolution with things continuing to accelerate."* On the other hand, some elements of work do not change, so you can expect some continuity: *"Whether it is a talented director creating a new movie, or an artist creating a new recording, you have issues around that. Disputes arise between actors and studios. Those existed 30 years ago and stay the same"* reveals **Glenn D. Pomerantz**, litigation partner in the Los Angeles office of **Munger, Tolles & Olson**.

- *"I have wonderful clients,"* enthuses Pomerantz, *"but the entertainment industry tends to attract more volatile, eccentric people than other industries, not only as business people but as lawyers too."* If the idea of working with eccentric people scares you away, you may find some consolation in the fact that you do not need to change yourself or your style to fit the industry: *"I think so many types of lawyers that other industries need, this industry needs too, so there is wide room for lawyers with different styles."*

- *"In some ways it's high profile. When you go to a dinner party most people have understanding of issues you work on,"* says Pomerantz. However, he goes on to add: *"Much of what you do is what you'd do in other industries, it's just that it tends to be of more interest to wider community."* Ruth Fisher has a strong view on this: *"The point I'm trying to make is that it's a wonderful practice intellectually but it's not all about the glamor. We don't meet the stars!"* You should be prepared instead to meet studios, people dealing with large studios and distributors, remembering that *"clients are all the same: they expect you to do excellent work instantly."*

- With tough competition and few jobs, the path to becoming a lawyer in this discipline may be a long and arduous one, so it is for the patient. It's important not to overestimate one's chances just because of some experience at an entertainment company: *"No one should think they have an in because they have worked for an entertainment company. Half of students have experience in media companies."* Glenn suggests you pick a firm that does some entertainment work so you have a chance to practice it, but *"if not, do general work and that will give you experience relevant for industry."* It may sound a little obvious, but all sources agree that the rule number one is simply to be a first-rate lawyer.

Current issues

- Probably the most significant trend affecting the media industry today is the massive displacement across the sector caused by new technologies. Lawyers must be aware of the potential new opportunities and challenges to their practice as a result of technological innovations. Ruth Fisher sees *"a lot of opportunities now in helping clients navigate new distribution methods and finding ways for the ever-increasing number of channels to get to audiences."* Glenn Pomerantz says that dramatic changes in the music business brought about by rampant piracy in the early 2000s led to legitimate businesses launching their own music services including Apple's iTunes, Spotify and Amazon Prime: *"A lot of companies turned towards streaming services, and lawyers are affected by that… deals, issues, disputes."*

- New technology presents new threats to the media industry in terms of IP infringement. To take new-real time piracy as an example, we can expect to see more copyright holders litigating for copyright infringement. However, the owners of live-streaming platforms may find an easy escape considering that current US law is still not firm on this point. Another option for copyright holders is to harness new technology to their own advantage to protect themselves from piracy. *"Every company is thinking of how to take advantage of this great opportunity while at the same time trying to combat illegal distribution of their crown jewels,"* explains Glenn Pomerantz.

- Digital forms of advertising are clearly overtaking the traditional channels. America's TV ad-revenues are expected to slow down, whereas Internet advertising is forecast to expand considerably. It's estimated that online advertisers will outspend their TV counterparts by $40 billion in 2018.

- Amazon and Hulu presented further challenges to traditional TV players when they launched live streaming services in 2017. This will have an impact that spans beyond just advertising, as media and entertainment partner **Matt Thompson** at **Sidley Austin** tells us: *"Broadcast TV has been a declining for a long time – apart from sports and awards shows. At some point, an entity like Amazon is going to buy the broadcast rights for the NFL. When something like that happens, the future of broadcast TV will be uncertain."*

- Sporting regulation is facing changes and challenges in gender equality cases such as Harrison Browne's – a transgender man who plays for the National Women's Hockey League. In 2017 Browne was left with no choice but to announce his retirement from the NWHL in order to begin hormone replacement therapy. However, after winning the prestigious Isobel Cup, he decided to delay his transition and return to the NWHL. Sporting regulation means that transgender athletes like Browne are left in a tough spot both legally and personally – either leave the sport altogether to transition, or stay and delay.

- Since the 1992 Professional and Amateur Sports Protection Act of 1992, the operation of sports betting has been (mostly) illegal in all states except Nevada. There have of course been various ways around this, including fantasy sports contests, but soon there may not need to be – recent statements by the Supreme Court suggest the federal ban may be declared unconstitutional in the near future.

Advice from the gurus

Bruce Wilson, a senior corporate lawyer at **Covington & Burling** with expertise in sports law:

"Probably the most important thing I've learned is that in this transactional area, there's industry expertise but not sports law per se – it's not a separate branch of the law. There are very unique issues in antitrust law and competition, but the most important thing to remember is that a transactional sports practice requires you to draw on so many different areas of corporate work. It's M&A, financing, IP, media, and competition all rolled into one and you have to be comfortable in each of those areas."

"Challenges are the rules of the game. In order for sports to be interesting, someone else must be doing the same thing. You can't have a football game or test match with just one team turning up. It's a competitive universe, with people competing in terms of sport, attention and ticket sales. But competitors on the pitch need to be business colleagues off the pitch."

Scott Edelman, a litigation partner and co-chair of **Gibson Dunn**'s media, entertainment and technology group:

"From my perspective, I don't think entertainment law is inherently 'sexy'. I don't work with celebrities – I work with studios, networks and music companies, which are corporate enterprises just like Bank of America, General Motors and the Shell Oil Company. Even for those working at boutique firms who represent the talent, it isn't necessarily easy. Some celebrity clients can be demanding, and frequently need to be pampered. Competition to do entertainment work is intense, and nobody should get into entertainment law thinking it is easy."

"My general advice is don't load up on entertainment classes at law school – maybe just take a couple of basic classes like copyright or IP. If you want to get into entertainment law, use law school as a time to cover basic solid subjects including securities, commercial law and antitrust. There will be plenty of time to focus on entertainment later."

Faiza Saeed is presiding partner at **Cravath**, working in M&A primarily with media and entertainment clients:

"The clients are less accustomed to full-blown long-form agreements, and some of the dynamics that go into being more precise in describing a transaction and what the restrictions will be on two companies going forward. It's often helpful to speak their language, and understand how they do deals in their own business, so you can do a better job of counseling."

"I think that students have to make a decision as to which side of the business they're interested in. Are they deal-oriented, in terms of being a corporate transactional lawyer, or more on the entertainment side – dealing more with talent? They're very different career paths that lead to working at very different firms, and many are fuzzy as to which side they want to be on."

Larry Weinstein, co-head of **Proskauer Rose**'s false advertising and trademark group in New York:

"It sounds almost stupid to say as it's so obvious, but if you want to be a good advertising lawyer you need to find advertising interesting. If you're a sports lawyer, you have to like sport. If you're an entertainment lawyer, you have to like the music or the movie business, for example."

"When students are searching for law firms to apply for, they should try and get beyond the generalities they see on the firm websites. We do this kind of work 24/7, and there's a big difference between practicing advertising law at a firm like ours compared to other firms who only do false advertising work on rare occasions."

"When people interview at firms, they should take the time to explain why the firm is of interest to them. We are interested in investing in people who have a genuine interest in us."
– Arnold & Porter's chairman Richard Alexander

Media and entertainment – Sidley Austin

Becoming a media and entertainment specialist is a popular and therefore competitive undertaking. Sidley's media maestros tell us how they broke into the area and explore the trends that are the shaping the work conducted in it.

Chambers Associate: What is covered by media and entertainment law?

Rollin Ransom, partner: "Media and entertainment law" is really a misnomer. It can refer to legal issues of any type – finance, intellectual property, litigation, contract, etc. – as they affect participants in the media and entertainment industry, such as film and television studios, broadcasters, music companies, communications companies, and the like. It can also refer to substantive areas of the law, such as copyright, trademark, advertising, privacy, and communications law, that particularly affect participants in the media and entertainment industry.

Matt Thompson, partner: In the universe of entertainment law, like most areas of law, there's the litigation side and there's the transactional side. When people think of media and entertainment lawyers, they think of talent lawyers. Talent lawyers represent all the big bold names; big TV stars, internet stars – but that is not what I do at Sidley. I represent big studios, networks, cable companies and producers on the transactional side of the equation. Not individual actors, directors and producers – that's the talent side.

Aerin Snow, associate: Sidley's corporate media and entertainment practice is focused on assisting clients interested in navigating the ever-changing media landscape through mergers, acquisitions, recapitalizations, and other business transactions. We are M&A lawyers, with particular knowledge of and expertise in the media and entertainment field. Sidley also has a separate media and entertainment litigation practice.

> *"The media and entertainment world is tight-knit, so the partners' contacts are key to maintaining (and growing) deal flow."*

Chad Hummel, partner: I'm a litigator and I try cases in the media and entertainment space. Our clients are traditional media companies such as AT&T and DirecTV,

as well as studios in the city and some high profile individual talent too. I'd say that in the entertainment space, my litigation experience has been focused on three areas:

The first is criminal actions in entertainment. For example, the Anthony Pellicano case – a wire tapping case in the mid-2000s. I've also worked with Roman Polanski, Britney Spears, and other high profile celeb-types who get involved in criminal or civil law.

The second involves companies that get into litigation over a competitive position in the marketplace – especially with regards to advertising and marketing spaces.

Third, there's general litigation for entertainment companies that have significant internal or contract issues. Obviously sexual harassment has reared its ugly head in this space recently – I've been dealing with that kind of stuff for over 30 years.

CA: What do the partners do?

Luke Ashworth, associate: The partners are in constant communication with their clients and other industry folks. The media and entertainment world is tight-knit, so the partners' contacts are key to maintaining (and growing) deal flow. On deals, partners review major documents and manage the deal team to make sure the train stays on the track through closing.

Emily Zipperstein, associate: A partner will develop the transaction structure, advise on strategy and lead negotiations with opposing counsel on primary deal documents.

RR: In litigation, partners typically determine overarching strategy (in consultation with the client and the rest of the team) and are ultimately responsible for the litigation of the matter, including serving as lead trial counsel.

CA: What do the senior associates do?

AS: As a senior associate, I am responsible for overseeing every aspect of a transaction, from hammering out the details of a term sheet, to negotiating the primary transaction documents, to ensuring documents have been correctly signed by all parties. My role is to be the partner's right hand, managing the multitude of details so that a partner can focus on the big picture items that will make or break a deal.

CA: What do the junior associates do?

RR: In my experience, both senior and junior associates do whatever they demonstrate they are prepared to handle. For example, I have an upcoming jury trial in which the associate will examine at least one of the witnesses.

LA: Junior associates conduct due diligence (on the buy-side), draft/review disclosure schedules (on the sell-side), draft ancillary documents and certificates and maintain the signing/closing "checklists" which are incredibly helpful to keep everyone organized throughout the process.

"I started out as a general corporate lawyer – I jumped on media and entertainment as much as possible and a year later that was all I was doing."

CA: Describe an interesting matter you've worked on.

MT: On one transaction we were representing the buyer (a private equity fund) of the rights to revenue streams from a couple of very, *very* well known TV shows. We're talking two of the top ten US TV shows. It was around a $100 million deal.

CH: Following DirecTV's acquisition by AT&T in 2015, the Federal Trade Commission came after it for alleged false advertising practices and requested $4 billion dollars to settle the suit. This case involved defending the DirecTV business model, and it went very well – the judge suspended the trial and asked for briefing on judgment in DirecTV's favor.

CA: How hard is it to break into media and entertainment work?

MT: There's a very small group of lawyers doing what we're doing; in the entire US, the number of lawyers who do this day in day out on the transactional side is around two hundred. On the talent side, there are only small boutiques operating in the area. It's therefore very hard to get a job in media and entertainment directly out of law school – it happens, but it's really tough.

RR: Media and entertainment cases tend to be popular ones, because of the accessibility of the subject matter and the interesting nature of the legal issues presented.

CA: So just how do you go about getting staffed on media and entertainment matters?

MT: If you can't get a job directly within a firm's media and entertainment practice, try to get a job elsewhere at that firm. Come to Sidley and be a corporate lawyer – but make it known that you'd be interested in working on matters for the media and entertainment group.

If the opportunity arises, take it and do what you can to get into this area. I started out as a general corporate lawyer – I jumped on media and entertainment as much as possible and a year later that was all I was doing.

RR: Associates regularly express their interest in working on these matters, and subject to timing and their availability, I try to involve those associates in the cases – associates who take initiative and speak up for themselves are more likely to get the opportunities they desire.

CA: What are the highs and lows of working in media and entertainment?

EZ: Media and entertainment is a rigorous practice. The challenges of developing expertise across a broad range of practice areas are compounded by fast paced and high stakes deals. It involves many late nights, and is not as glamorous as one might expect.

That said, the work is incredibly rewarding, particularly for individuals with a deep interest in entertainment and media on a personal level. I have been fortunate to work with clients who are very passionate and personally invested in their work, which in turn has motivated me to challenge myself to identify creative solutions when negotiations appear to be at an impasse.

"As an avid film and television consumer, it is pretty great to have my work intersect with a favorite out-of-work pastime."

LA: Like all M&A practices, when we are busy, we are really really busy. In any event, it's virtually impossible to predict the busy times versus the slow times – the unpredictability is definitely the hardest part. However, we are constantly sharpening our skills by working on unique, complex transactions with very interesting and sophisticated clients.

AS: Almost all of the media and entertainment lawyers that I work with specialized because ultimately the product being produced by the industry they were representing brought them joy. And I am no different – as an avid film and television consumer, it is pretty great to have my work intersect with a favorite out-of-work pastime.

CA: What are the current trends affecting media and entertainment work? What does the future hold?

MT: The macro comment is that we're in the midst of a major disruption in this industry. Streaming services like Amazon, Hulu and Netflix have completely disrupted the industry. Broadcast TV has been a declining for a long time – apart from sports and awards shows. At some point, an entity like Amazon is going to buy the broadcast rights for the NFL. When something like that happens, the future of broadcast TV will be uncertain.

What is the future for theatrical film releases? Screening Room – a proposed platform that allows you to watch a movie at home on the same day that it's released at theaters – is a possibility which hasn't come to fruition yet, but will in the next year or three. It used to be that a movie would go to theatrical release and nowhere else for 90 days, and now it's 30 days. Under the Screening Room proposal, it's zero days. You could see *Star Wars* at home the same day it comes out.

What does all of this mean for entertainment lawyers? It's a fantastic time! It means there will be deals! We're all 24/7 consumers on any device. That's not going to change.We will seek out and pay for premium content. The people responsible for financing, producing, distributing, buying and selling that premium content are always going to have a job. And that's what we do – we facilitate the production and financing of content. So it's a great time to be a media and entertainment lawyer!

RR: I think there are many opportunities in this area. One aspect of the media and entertainment field that I enjoy is that the technology is always changing and evolving. That means that we have to be especially creative in thinking about how to apply existing (and even "old") legal principles to new technology. Rather than litigating the same issues over and over again, we are constantly faced with new issues – that keeps the practice of law fresh and engaging.

"Streaming services like Amazon, Hulu and Netflix have completely disrupted the industry."

CA: What is your top piece of advice for students interested in this area?

MT: People think that if they want to do media and entertainment, they should focus on those types of classes in law school. But there are other things that crop up all of the time in our practice – things that have nothing to do with entertainment, like corporate, tax, labor and employment, IP law etc. Those classes will all bleed into what we do, so it's important to enroll on them too.

Kelvin Le, associate: When I was preparing to transition into media and entertainment, I read 10-Ks from major studios, bought books on the business of entertainment, researched M&A trends in the industry and followed industry news from *Variety*, *The Hollywood Reporter* and *Deadline*.

CH: You don't learn how to be a litigator in law school. I recommend to anyone interested in the litigation side that they get a clerkship and obtain experience on their feet in a courtroom somehow. I never did it and I regret it. It's absolutely critical to learn litigation skills regardless of the industry you're focusing on. If you're in the litigating space it's all about understanding how to deal with juries and judges. That's the foundation – if you're a good lawyer and you can try cases, you can try them in any field!

RR: Pay attention to what is happening in the industry. There are articles every day – online, in magazines, in newspapers – about legal and business developments affecting media clients. As with any client, the more familiar you are with the business, the better you will be as a lawyer for clients in that field.

CA: What makes working in the field of media and entertainment unique?

KL: The industry and its business models are constantly changing, giving lawyers the opportunity to handle new challenges and advise on transactions that are at the forefront of where the industry is headed next. Plus, it's fun to work on deals where you truly enjoy the underlying assets – movies and television!

CH: The main differentiating factor is that there's press interest. So you need to understand the ethical rules in terms of dealing with the press – there's always a PR aspect with a high profile client.

CA: What makes Sidley stand out as a place to practice in the media and entertainment space?

RR: We have a broad-based transactional and litigation practice that reaches every area of media. We represent music companies, book publishers, television and film companies, Internet companies, communications companies – the clients run the gamut, and so do the opportunities.

EZ: Sidley associates have the opportunity to work directly with partners known as "dealmakers" throughout the industry whose work is making a significant impact.

KL: Furthermore, Sidley Austin's global reach and diverse client base give its media and entertainment lawyers another source of interesting deal flow, as many institutions, private equity firms and hedge funds have media and entertainment-related holdings.

Authors

Aerin Snow
Associate

Chad Hummel
Partner

Emily Zipperstein
Associate

Luke Ashworth
Associate

Matt Thompson
Partner

Rollin Ransom
Partner

Kelvin Le
Associate

SIDLEY

Practice Areas

Litigation and Dispute Resolution

Commercial litigation – Cleary Gottlieb

Much beloved TV shows like *Suits* and *The Good Wife/Fight* make it all look pretty exciting, but don't let your viewing habits inform your career choices – any serious aspiring litigator should consult the real experts first if they want to know what becoming a courtroom star involves. Hence why we've asked Cleary's litigators to tell you about the benefits of playing devil's advocate; why mastering the art of storytelling is crucial; and how a high degree of empathy can make all the difference.

Chambers Associate: How would you define litigation?

Jonathan Kolodner, partner: At Cleary Gottlieb, we define our litigation group broadly to cover a range of different practice areas, including civil litigation, arbitration, and white-collar criminal defense and enforcement. We are also a global disputes practice, meaning that we often work on matters across our 16 offices and handle litigation and investigations that involve multiple jurisdictions. And, of course, we have a significant *pro bono* litigation practice as well.

Alex 'Lenny' Leonard, associate: It is any formal process of dispute resolution that pits one side against another, and where there is a neutral party (e.g. a judge or jury) that will decide the outcome. Litigation can also cover regulatory and enforcement work, such as internal or governmental investigations, though at Cleary the enforcement work is viewed as somewhat distinct from the litigation work, even though the same lawyers tend to do both types and all are part of one litigation group.

Vanessa Richardson, associate: Litigation also includes strategic thinking before any proceedings begin to help parties anticipate potential risk, understand their options, and build a stronger case.

CA: What do the partners do?

JK: Litigation partners obviously have a range of responsibilities. Partners are responsible for advising clients and supervising litigation matters. Partners are also responsible for managing the practice generally, as well as marketing and business development. And critically, partners are responsible for training and mentoring associates, who are the future of the firm.

"It is any formal process of dispute resolution that pits one side against another, and where there is a neutral party (e.g. a judge or jury) that will decide the outcome."

CA: What do the senior associates do?

AL: Senior associates manage the team and make sure everything runs smoothly and important deadlines are met. They tend to participate in strategy planning with the partners and, sometimes, the client. They also serve as a resource to more junior associates and make sure they are aware of and are involved with the broader strategy. Senior associates will usually revise work product, such as briefs, that more junior associates draft before the draft goes to a partner for review.

CA: What do the junior associates do?

VR: Junior associates usually take the first crack at legal research, but junior associates also get opportunities to draft briefs, participate in interviews, and interact with the client. I took my first deposition as a third year associate!

Richard Freeman, associate: Junior associates have a range of experiences at Cleary. As a junior associate, I researched and drafted briefs, communicated the team's legal advice directly with clients, attended hearings, and managed sub-teams.

CA: What kind of work is involved in the day-to-day?

JK: Our daily work varies tremendously; that is one of the exciting parts of our practice. On some days, I will be actively engaged in an investigation, often across multiple jurisdictions, conducting interviews, reviewing key documents, or discussing strategy with the client or the global Cleary team. On other occasions, I will be having discussions with, or making presentations to, regulators and authorities. I also spend time meeting with clients, discussing their needs and concerns and providing guidance (as best I can) to help them.

AL: The litigation at Cleary also frequently involves travel as much of our work involves international companies, so you might spend time preparing for a trip to meet with key witnesses or to visit an important site. There is also frequently an effort to resolve cases through mediation or settlement discussions, so you might spend your day working on arguments about the merits of the case or potential liability to assist in those discussions.

"Winning is obviously a high – it feels pretty great when a judge grants your motion!"

For enforcement work, you might spend time working on a presentation to a regulator about the findings of an investigation or drafting an internal report to the client. You might also spend time meeting with a *pro bono* client or working on a brief or submission for his or her case.

CA: What are the highs and lows?

JK: It is always exciting to achieve a good result for a client in an investigation or a dispute, such as a civil litigation. But I also find it satisfying to help a client solve a difficult legal problem, to provide the answer to a question that a client has asked, and to help a client prepare for problems in advance, by giving them the benefit of our experience.

As you can imagine, as a litigator in the arena (to paraphrase Teddy Roosevelt), there are sometimes lows (and losses) as well.

AL: Put simply, the highest of highs are when you achieve the resolution that your client wants, and the lows are when you fall short in that effort. Specifically, if you spend months working on a brief and you win on the issue that you drafted the argument for, that is a big high – and a bonus if the judge writes an opinion specifically using your language.

"...a cartel bribed a few corrupt executives at the Company in order to secure favorable bids on projects."

VR: Winning is obviously a high – it feels pretty great when a judge grants your motion! But it is also a high

when you find a very helpful document, get someone to make a great admission in a deposition, or put the finishing touches on a strong brief. Our cases are challenging and exciting, and it is thrilling to read about your work in the paper.

Lows come when it feels like there is just too much to prepare and not enough time. The only way to get through those times is to have a laugh with your team and take it step by step.

CA: Describe your latest case: what was the client's problem? What was your role? How did you spend your time on it?

AL: My latest case was an enormous securities class action (*In re Petrobras Securities Litigation*) and related opt-out cases that we litigated for about three years before finally settling at the beginning of this year (it is still subject to final court approval). The client was accused of making material misstatements in its financial statements arising out of a multi-year corruption scheme where a cartel bribed a few corrupt executives at the company in order to secure favorable bids on projects.

As an associate on the case, I worked on everything from motions to dismiss, to opposing class certification (so document discovery), to preparing for, taking, and defending depositions, to working with experts, taking an expert deposition, and beginning preparation for trial. When we appealed class certification, I also worked on drafting the appeal to the Second Circuit and helped the partner prepare for oral argument.

"The fact that we were ready to march into court gave our client credibility to push for what they wanted in the negotiations."

VR: My latest case was an M&A related matter. Our corporate colleagues had negotiated a transaction, but the buyer was indicating that it might refuse to close. So we had to quickly learn the details of the transaction and analyze the strength of potential arguments. But because it takes some time to get papers ready, we were simultaneously drafting a complaint. We also prepared talking points for the client to use in negotiations, so we could build a favorable record. Fortunately, they worked out a business resolution, so we did not have to actually file the papers. But the fact that we were ready to march into court gave our client credibility to push for what they wanted in the negotiations.

I was the senior associate on the team. I supervised junior associates, drafted and revised the papers, conducted witness interviews, participated in strategy sessions with the corporate and litigation teams, prepared talking points for negotiations, consulted with local counsel, and so much more. It was a great opportunity to use a wide variety of legal skills.

RF: I have been working on an appeal for a sovereign client (after we won a motion to dismiss an investor's claims relating to the client's bonds). My role was to coordinate researching and drafting our briefs in the district court and in the court of appeals, to provide case updates to the client, and to help moot the partner arguing the case.

CA: What are the current trends in litigation?

JK: Whether we are talking about civil litigation or white-collar defense and enforcement, litigation continues to be very active. From my perspective as an enforcement litigator, one current (and significant) trend that I see is the continued growth of multi-jurisdictional investigations, as more non-U.S. authorities become active (for example, in connection with corruption investigations).

"Clients and judges have begun to push for more diverse teams."

There is related growth in civil litigation in the U.S. and elsewhere connected to these investigations. For example, a securities class action litigation in the U.S. can be based on the stock drop associated with a significant new enforcement investigation. Civil litigation has also changed over the last few years with the growth of third-party litigation funding, which aids plaintiffs in bringing (and funding) long-term litigation.

VR: One major trend affecting litigation right now is how much technology is revolutionizing the practice. It touches everything we do, and it is very important to keep up-to-date and to adapt to changes. Better technology also means that clients demand their litigators to be extremely responsive and as efficient as possible.

CA: What would you say the future of practicing litigation looks like?

JK: It's always difficult to predict the future, but for now, I think the litigation and enforcement practice will continue to grow. On the enforcement front, there is always a question with a new administration whether there will be a change in the government's approach. But so far at least, the U.S. authorities and regulators continue to be very active.

VR: I hope the future of litigation practice looks more diverse. Clients and judges have begun to push for more diverse teams, and Cleary has been extremely proactive

about recruiting and mentoring diverse associates. I am hopeful that those efforts will pay off.

"It helps to be good at playing devil's advocate."

CA: What personal qualities make for a good litigation lawyer?

AL: You have to be smart, driven, a hard worker, client-oriented, a good writer, a quick thinker, and have the ability to see things from multiple points of view. It helps to be good at playing devil's advocate.

VR: Empathy affects your work in so many ways. You need to take the time to really understand your client's goals, fears, and priorities because that will change your legal advice and recommendations. You need to think about what will be persuasive and compelling for the decision maker, be it a judge, jury, or arbitrator. And finally, you have to figure out the best way to motivate and inspire your colleagues because you need everyone on your team to be working together to deliver exceptional work product.

RF: Empathy, patience, perseverance, a healthy degree of skepticism, and an ability to imagine oneself in the shoes of a client, of an adversary, of a judge, and of a teammate.

CA: What can students do to prepare themselves for a career in litigation?

JK: There are certainly some important classes that students should take, such as evidence, that will be helpful to future litigators. More importantly, I think students should do everything they can to get real-world, on-their-feet experience, both for the experience itself and to get exposure to different areas of the practice. This might take the form of a law school clinic (such as for a legal services organization, or a U.S. Attorney's Office), or by volunteering for an organization.

"Read widely, and not just legal stuff. Litigation is about telling a compelling story, and there are lots of ways to do that."

Students can also look for opportunities to get similar experience during their first-year summer. I recommend taking trial practice (or moot court) classes as well – again, it's helpful to get as much of this kind of experience as possible!

Practice Areas

VR: Read widely, and not just legal stuff. Litigation is about telling a compelling story, and there are lots of ways to do that.

CA: Could you describe the opportunities unique to Cleary?

JK: Our matters are endlessly interesting and challenging. Many of our litigation matters are cross-border, and we work closely with our colleagues in Cleary's offices outside of the United States all of the time. In addition to offering all of our lawyers the opportunity to work on these global matters, our litigation group is also very flexible, and our associates get the opportunity to work in all areas of the practice depending on their interests.

VR: Litigation at Cleary is special because we get to be generalists, and we aren't expected to choose a major early in our career. That means junior associates can try lots of different things and work with lots of different people. I get to work on all kinds of cases and have had opportunities to develop a wide variety of legal skills.

Authors

Richard Freeman
Associate

Jonathan Kolodner
Partner

Alex Leonard
Associate

Vanessa Richardson
Associate

Practice Areas

CLEARY GOTTLIEB

Securities litigation – Milbank

Government investigations, civil lawsuits and a ton of regulations to get acquainted with – this is the complex brew of elements securities litigators have to skillfully navigate. If you're thinking of becoming a litigator in this subset then take note, as Milbank's lawyers lift the lid on what it's like to balance enforcement and civil work; the questions that need to be asked when developing case strategy; and why their practice is becoming "increasingly global."

Chambers Associate: What does securities litigation involve?

Grant Mainland, partner: Our securities litigation group handles a wide array of civil and criminal matters that arise under the federal securities laws. With the growth of our white collar practice, we have become particularly adept at handling parallel civil and governmental proceedings – for example, a DOJ or SEC investigation with companion class action lawsuits arising under Section 10(b) or other provisions of the securities laws. These days, the announcement of a regulatory or enforcement matter almost invariably results in class action filings. But government investigations and plaintiffs' class actions have fundamentally different dynamics.It's important to approach the enforcement side of the case with an eye to how it will affect the civil side, and vice versa.

In terms of the client base, while Milbank has particularly deep relationships with financial institutions, securities litigation often involves a diverse array of clients in various industries. For example, I'm currently working on a securities case against a South American company and another relating to a pharmaceutical concern.

"These days, the announcement of a regulatory or enforcement matter almost invariably results in class action filings."

CA: What do associates do?

Alexandra Paslawsky, associate: Every day is different, and associates are involved in every step of the process. Associates will do research, analyze documents, and prepare witnesses for interviews, depositions, and trials. I've played different roles on different teams, depending on what kind of case it is.

Anna Dimon, associate: The work day is largely driven by what stage of litigation a case is in; depending on the maturity of a case, more or less time will be devoted to reviewing documents and drafting briefs. Associates also complete as-needed research projects that come from clients on a rolling basis.

CA: What do partners do?

GM: Having just become a partner, I am increasingly focused on the overall strategy of the case. What are the themes we are trying to advance, whether through motion practice or mediation or otherwise? What kind of factual evidence do we need to obtain from the plaintiff or third parties or our own client? What kind of expert opinions or testimony will we need to defend against the claims? How will we handle any developments on the governmental side (if applicable)—say, a settlement or the announcement of an enforcement action?

In thinking through these issues, I work closely with the team of associates in developing our arguments; formulating and advancing our positions on discovery matters; liaising with experts, etc...

Daniel Perry, partner: Many of the class action cases that are brought don't have a lot of merit. In general, motions to dismiss are filed in these types of cases around 95% of the time, with an average of about 50% of those motions granted. Milbank's performance is a bit better than the market average. This work involves keeping up with the current law and being in the know, which is where a firm like ours really adds value – you may be in the middle of drafting a motion to dismiss when the Second Circuit hands down a decision. That's not at all uncommon, and our team excels at keeping up with these developments.

"What are the themes we are trying to advance, whether through motion practice or mediation or otherwise?"

CA: What are the highs and lows of the practice?

AP: These cases are filled with opportunities for young associates to get a lot of experience doing substantive work for major companies. There are a lot of opportunities for face time with partners and client contact.

The lows can be different depending on the case – sometimes you're working on an extremely tight timeline, so everything is expedited. Sometimes you may have a ton of documents to get through. But these are the things that can also make the case exciting and meaningful.

DP: This is a fun practice area because these are big cases, with big dollar values, and they get a lot of attention from the client. Cases are litigated in federal court, and the law is very well developed and interesting. One high of the practice is dealing with really sophisticated clients on these large, meaningful cases, with an opportunity to appear in federal district courts regularly.

As for the lows, the thing I find most tedious is the discovery that sometimes accompanies these cases. These can be large cases spanning many years, multiple business units, and large, complex companies, so the task of collecting, reviewing, and producing documents is substantial. It's also unlike other types of litigation, where you have an adversary on the other side that has similar production obligations, creating some balance where both sides are incentivized to cooperate and be reasonable in their demands. This is primarily a plaintiffs' lawyer-driven practice, so they can be somewhat unrestrained in what they ask for. One of the things we have to deal with is plaintiff firms over-reaching in discovery, purely because that's a strategy to draw this out and make the process so painful, unpleasant, and expensive that the company is incentivized to resolve the case. We are obviously experienced in dealing with that – but it doesn't make it any more fun!

"The intersection of civil securities lawsuits and government investigations – by the DOJ, SEC, state AGs, or other enforcement or regulatory bodies – is a critical dynamic."

CA: Which factors are driving the practice at the moment?

GM: The intersection of civil securities lawsuits and government investigations – by the DOJ, SEC, state AGs, or other enforcement or regulatory bodies – is a critical dynamic. In some cases, we handle both the government investigations and private suits. In others, we handle either the governmental or civil side only and coordinate with counsel handling the other piece of the case. In either event, attention to the broader picture is essential.

With more foreign companies listing shares on US exchanges, thereby subjecting themselves to the federal securities laws, there is an increasingly global aspect to the practice. This is especially so with respect to Foreign Corrupt Practices Act (FCPA) investigations involving corruption and anti-bribery issues.

"These cases are filled with opportunities for young associates to get a lot of experience doing substantive work for major companies."

CA: How can students keep up-to-date with the market and industry trends?

AP: I'd encourage students to attend talks by lawyers with experience in the industry. These are the people who have lived it, and I've found that their advice and insight can be invaluable.

DP: The nice part about this area of the law is that there's a lot of attention to it in the legal press, and you can fairly easily stay up-to-date by looking at journals that cover the securities litigation market. Cornerstone publishes a fantastic annual study on trends in the market. Of course, there's no substitute for reading the cutting-edge cases in the circuits and on occasion from the Supreme Court.

GM: There are many publications and blogs that closely follow recent developments in securities litigation – *The D&O Diary* is a very topical blog that comes to mind. Stanford Law School (working with Cornerstone Research, an economic consulting firm) also created the Securities Class Action Clearinghouse, which I find extremely helpful.

CA: Where can new associates expect to be in five years?

DP: Mid to senior-level associates in our group prepare and defend witnesses in deposition, and are often the primary drafters of motions to dismiss, motions opposing class certification, and for summary judgment. They also appear in court to argue discovery motions and the like. There are opportunities for substantive research, writing, drafting, and court appearances.

"This courtroom experience is something that I think really sets us apart – we feel strongly about getting our associates into court."

CA: What are the opportunities unique to Milbank?

DP: Beginning as summer associates, our aspiring litigators first get experience working on pro bono cases. In their first year, all Litigation associates begin taking part in Advocacy@Milbank, which is a multi-level training program tailored for our practice that spans their first six years at the firm. Part of this program is a partnership with the Office of the Appellate Defender in New York, where first-years team with more senior litigators to handle pro bono appeals, often arguing them in court.

This courtroom experience is something that I think really sets us apart – we feel strongly about getting our associates into court. In securities cases, whenever there are opportunities we try very hard to get our associates that experience. Our sense is that judges and clients are normally quite supportive – as are all of our partners – and what we've found is the associates do a really excellent job and rise to the occasion. That's just part of our culture as a litigation department.

Along with that, we're also committed to providing best-in-class training to all of our mid and senior-level associates through our Milbank@Harvard program. Each year, beginning in their third-year, classes of our associates from all of our practices around the world meet up for an intensive week of sessions up at Harvard, with Harvard Law and Business School professors. It's a totally unique program, and we hear from our associates that it really boosts their skills, their confidence, and their understanding of our clients' businesses.

CA: What advice do you have for students interested in this area?

AP: I'd tell students interested in securities litigation to demonstrate that interest! The best way to learn about the work and understand the practice is to ask people about it.

DP: Take all of the law school classes oriented toward securities and federal litigation, federal courts, evidence, securities regulation – make sure you have the building blocks your law school offers. Then, select a litigation department that regularly practices in this area. Once you're at the firm, those firms will invest a lot in training and educating and preparing you as a securities litigator.

Authors

Grant Mainland
Partner

Alexandra Paslawsky
Associate

Anna Dimon
Associate

Daniel Perry
Partner

Milbank

Practice Areas

White collar litigation – Cahill

In the fast-paced world of white collar litigation, junior associates get to utilize the skills of investigative reporters. We caught up with a few white collar litigators at Cahill to find out more about becoming a lawyer in their practice.

Chambers Associate: What is white collar law?

Brian Markley, partner: The representation of corporate clients and their officers, directors, employees, boards and board committees in cases and investigations, typically brought by government agencies, in the U.S. and abroad.

Helena Franceschi, associate: "White collar" law refers to the broad range of finance-related offenses that can be subject to regulatory investigations and enforcement actions. It covers a range of conduct and can implicate antitrust, the Foreign Corrupt Practices Act, anti-manipulation, and fraud statutes. Because white collar laws often concern the practices of global institutions, these investigations may involve cross-border proceedings before multiple regulators.

CA: What are the highs and lows?

Junine So, associate: The fast pace of some government investigations can translate to late nights and long hours, but also the highs of increased substantive learning opportunities, and an exciting and varied practice. There is also sometimes a large volume of document review, but synthesizing the results of your review into a story that is helpful for your client's legal arguments can be a satisfying and rewarding process.

HF: The work is sophisticated and often "above-the-fold" consequential. That is certainly one of the highs. Discovering the facts of any given case and piecing together the advocacy to support those facts – just as you would with any litigation – is also one of the highs.

Ivan Torres, associate: Whenever an investigation really gets moving the work typically gets very intense, but this is also when you start to see all your hard work pay off. This pay off can either be realizing patterns in the documents and financial records that you didn't appreciate at the beginning of an investigation, taking an interview where the interviewee's body language and reactions make it clear that they are surprised to see certain documents that you have shown them or surprised to hear certain questions, or being able to piece together the facts of a situation to explain what might look like misconduct on first glance was actually legitimate.

CA: What do associates do?

JS: Associates work on all aspects of an investigation including the fact development stage and the legal argument stage. The fact development stage involves reviewing documents, interviewing witnesses, and developing a timeline of key events. The legal argument stage involves conducting legal research and drafting memoranda, talking points, and presentations for clients and for regulators.

IT: I have been on investigation teams that were 20+ people where my primary role was to do second or third line review of documents and to build out chronologies based on those documents, but I also have worked on teams of less than five where I was visiting clients to conduct interviews, preparing and attending presentations to government regulators, and building out and executing our overall investigation plan. But as a general matter, the work on a white collar investigation usually includes a mix of document review with an eye towards building out the story of what happened, preparing for and taking interviews of key personnel, working with forensic accountants to follow the money trail, preparing presentations detailing your findings for the client (which typically include the general counsel, the board of directors, or independent board members), and sometimes interacting with the relevant government regulators to best protect the rights and interests of your client.

> *"Whenever an investigation really gets moving the work typically gets very intense, but this is also when you start to see all your hard work pay off."*

CA: What do partners do?

BM: Teach and mentor associates, provide guidance and direction for the case, serve as the primary client interface and take the lead in critical interviews, depositions and hearings.

JS: Like associates, partners also work on all aspects of an investigation, but they will generally have more visibility into and experience with clients' and regulators' thinking. Based on this experience, partners advise clients on the strengths and weaknesses of their cases, and make strategic decisions on how best to present them to regulators.

CA: How does your work interact with general litigation?

JS: The misconduct underlying a white collar investigation can often lead to civil suits by shareholders or other private parties. More generally, working on litigation and white collar matters requires much of the same skill set – attention to detail, sound judgment, and thoughtful critical thinking abilities.

BM: It's not uncommon for white collar investigations to have litigation components and lead to shareholder derivative suits, class actions, books and records demands and the like. Sometimes, those lawsuits are happening in parallel with our investigative work, which adds another layer of strategy to the matter.

CA: How soon should a litigator specialize?

BM: Knowing everything possible about a particular financial product or some other fact or issue at the center of a case or investigation is indispensable. With that said, at Cahill we also pride ourselves on being generalists capable of handling any sort of case or issue affecting our clients, whether it involves securities law, commercial litigation, contract disputes, insurance law, First Amendment matters, or anything else. So in short, the answer is that specialization is great but associates should also try to get a broad experience on an array of matters early in their careers.

HF: A litigator should make her own decision when to specialize, and in part the natural trajectory of a litigator's career will determine it. Some experience many matters as "generalist" for some time before affirmatively choosing to develop and refine a specific competency. On the other hand, others may inadvertently develop a competency through working with the same team over a period of time.

IT: At least at Cahill, there is no push to specialize early on. If anything, litigation associates are encouraged to maintain a diverse practice that includes both general litigation and investigations work. This diversity gives you a different perspective and helps you see the big picture

on matters better. For example, the typically less formal path investigations take lets associates get earlier experience with interviews that becomes helpful down the line when taking depositions. Likewise, having experience with the more adversarial environment of litigation is helpful as it makes you more critical in the way you approach an internal investigation.

"Like an investigative reporter, a white collar associate should be inquisitive above all else and have a desire to work hard, dig deep and gather and understand the facts of a case."

CA: Where can new associates expect to be in five years?

BM: It depends on the associate and his or her own individual goals and aspirations. If the associate wants to be partner, in their fifth year they should be thinking about running cases and investigations, directing junior associates, interacting daily with clients, taking depositions, dealing face-to-face with regulators and arguing motions in state and federal courts. Partnership isn't everyone's goal, however, so it may well be that five years in an associate is ready for some other opportunity. Cahill alumni are distinguished in so many areas. Some serve at high levels in government, are in-house counsel at corporate clients and financial institutions, or work in non-legal jobs in the art world, television and film. The point is that we give our associates an invaluable experience where they can take on as much responsibility as they want and can handle. That means they are well-trained and tested, making them ready for anything.

CA: What personal qualities make good white collar lawyers?

BM: Like an investigative reporter, a white collar associate should be inquisitive above all else and have a desire to work hard, dig deep and gather and understand the facts of a case. White collar work is deeply fact-intensive, so it's critical that we leave no stone unturned and understand all aspects of the case, inside and out.

IT: Curiosity and a willingness to learn and think on your feet. Often when you start an investigation you will have little background knowledge on the workings of a particular industry. To understand the motivations of the people who work at the company you have to really understand the work they do.

CA: What are the trends and big stories in the white collar market?

BM: A continued focus by the DOJ and SEC on FCPA and financial products investigations.

HF: Coming out of the financial crisis, we have seen regulators focus on benchmark rigging (e.g., LIBOR, foreign exchange, and others) as well as fraud more generally with respect to certain complex assets (e.g., RMBS). As algorithms and automated processes begin to play a bigger role in banks and other large institutions, we expect that regulatory authorities will continue focusing on allegedly predatory behavior in this area.

IT: Over the past few years there has been more of a push for companies to assist the government in investigating which individual executives were involved in alleged misconduct. In terms of big stories, over the last five years or so you have the interest rates-related investigations and prosecutions both here and in the UK, a number of anti-corruption investigations that focus on Latin America, including, for example, the Petrobras scandal and the fallout from the Mossack Fonseca leaks.

CA: How should students brush-up on their white collar knowledge?

IT: Following the news, including legal news and blogs related to white collar work are helpful because these resources give you pretty good insight into the trends going on. Law schools also often have great guest speakers who have either worked on these cases on the defense side or have prosecuted these cases.

JS: Keeping up with news stories about government investigations of individuals and institutions within the financial services industry, and developments in the regulatory environment.

CA: What are your tips for passing the interview process?

BM: The most successful interviewees are the ones who can speak passionately about their 1L summer experience, their interest in the law and being an associate at a firm like ours. Even if students don't have specific white collar experience – which is understandable as a rising 2L – they will be successful in the interview process if they show genuine excitement about starting a career at our firm, getting their hands dirty and learning how to be litigators and investigators working at the highest level on the most impactful cases.

HF: Demonstrate how you are self-motivated and able to multi-task with different projects and meet deadlines.

CA: Describe the opportunities unique to Cahill.

BM: Cahill, unlike any other firm I know, affords its associates the opportunity to take on as much responsibility as they want and can handle. We have a free market system that allows litigation or corporate associates to work on anything that interests them within those departments, whether it be securities law, commercial litigation, investigations, bonds deals, M&A, or whatever else is brewing at the time. I chose Cahill because I wanted to have some measure of control over my career and because I wanted the ability to choose the type of cases I worked on and the people with whom I worked. As a result, my practice is broader and more diverse than I ever could have imagined coming out of law school. Looking back, I know I made the right choice and I could never see myself at any other firm in the world.

IT: I have been able to work on a range of different projects including FCPA work, securities litigation, complex financial litigation, and First Amendment matters. By allowing associates to develop their own practice within litigation or corporate rather than having more rigid departments, Cahill allows associates more flexibility with the experiences they get and with partners and clients they get to work with. I have also found Cahill to be very willing to let associates take on work that typically would be reserved for more senior associates when they show an interest and an ability to take on greater responsibility.

Practice Areas

Authors

Brian Markley
Partner

Junine So
Associate

Ivan Torres
Associate

Helena Franceschi
Associate

Litigation

Rankings in *Chambers USA*

Top Ranked

Alston & Bird	McDermott Will & Emery
Cleary Gottlieb	Morgan, Lewis & Bockius
Cravath, Swaine & Moore	Munger, Tolles & Olson
Davis Polk & Wardwell	Nelson Mullins Riley
Debevoise & Plimpton	Paul, Weiss
Dechert	Perkins Coie
DLA Piper	Reed Smith
Foley & Lardner	Ropes & Gray
Gibbons	Sidley Austin
Gibson, Dunn & Crutcher	Simpson Thacher & Bartlett
Greenberg Traurig	Skadden
Hunton Andrews Kurth	Snell & Wilmer
Jenner & Block	Sullivan & Cromwell
Jones Day	Waller
K&L Gates	Willkie Farr & Gallagher
King & Spalding	WilmerHale
Kirkland & Ellis	Wilson Sonsini Goodrich
Latham & Watkins	

Highly Recommended

Akin Gump Strauss Hauer	Katten Muchin Rosenman
Allen & Overy	Kramer Levin Naftalis
Arnold & Porter	Mayer Brown
Axinn, Veltrop & Harkrider	Milbank, Tweed, Hadley
Baker Botts	Mintz Levin Cohn Ferris
Bracewell	Morrison & Foerster LLP
Cadwalader	Norton Rose Fulbright
Cahill Gordon & Reindel	Nutter McClennen & Fish
Choate Hall & Stewart	O'Melveny & Myers LLP
Clifford Chance US	Orrick
Cooley	Patterson Belknap
Cozen O'Connor	Paul Hastings
Crowell & Moring	Proskauer Rose
Duane Morris	Schulte Roth & Zabel
Dykema Gossett	Shearman & Sterling
Fox Rothschild	Sheppard, Mullin
Freshfields	Squire Patton Boggs
Fried, Frank	Thompson & Knight
Goulston & Storrs	Troutman Sanders
Hangley Aronchick Segal	Vedder Price
Haynes and Boone	Venable
Holland & Knight	Vinson & Elkins
Hughes Hubbard & Reed	Weil, Gotshal & Manges
Irell & Manella	White & Case
Jackson Walker	Winston & Strawn LLP
Kasowitz Benson Torres	

For more detail on ranking tiers and locations, visit
www.chambersandpartners.com

"Put simply, the highest of highs are when you achieve the resolution that your client wants, and the lows are when you fall short in that effort. Specifically, if you spend months working on a brief and you win on the issue that you drafted the argument for, that is a big high – and a bonus if the judge writes an opinion specifically using your language."

– Alex 'Lenny' Leonard,
associate, Cleary

"Empathy affects your work in so many ways. You need to take the time to really understand your client's goals, fears, and priorities because that will change your legal advice and recommendations. You need to think about what will be persuasive and compelling for the decision maker, be it a judge, jury, or arbitrator. And finally, you have to figure out the best way to motivate and inspire your colleagues because you need everyone on your team to be working together to deliver exceptional work product."

– Vanessa Richardson,
associate, Cleary

Practice Areas

International arbitration

In a nutshell

International arbitration addresses any case or potential dispute between parties – usually located in two different countries – and is the most common form of alternative dispute resolution (ADR). *"At the most basic level, international arbitration attorneys are international litigators in a transnational justice system,"* says **Donald Donovan** of **Debevoise & Plimpton**. *"It's a system that's validated by both national and international law, but not run directly by any given state."* Arbitrations often arise from clauses included by companies in their commercial contracts with one another. This means that, if a dispute arises between them, they are obliged to arbitrate their dispute rather than pursue traditional litigation.

Arbitration provides a binding solution to the dispute by way of an arbitral 'award'. The award can be enforced internationally through the provisions of the 1958 New York Convention on the Recognition and Enforcement of Arbitral Awards, which more than 140 states have ratified. *"Private parties often prefer international arbitration because it provides a neutral and relatively confidential forum, specialist arbitrators and greater ease of enforcement of the award in multiple jurisdictions. The New York Convention is unique in that there is no equivalent international treaty in force around the globe to ensure the international currency and enforcement of domestic court judgments,"* explains **David Lindsey**, partner and cofounder of international arbitration boutique **Chaffetz Lindsey** in New York.

The types of cases heard in international arbitration are typically cross-border commercial disputes that occur in situations like joint ventures or corporate transactions (including M&A). *"The types of disputes run the gamut, but they are all really linked to investment and transactions outside the home jurisdiction of the claimant,"* **Nigel Blackaby** of **Freshfields Bruckhaus Deringer** says. Disputes commonly originate in the oil and gas, telecom, privatized public utilities and construction industries.

One specific type of international arbitration is 'investment arbitration', where a claim is brought by a foreign investor directly against the host state of its investment. This arises from the likes of multinational ventures, such as energy projects, and can be instigated in two ways: investors and host states either consent in contracts to use international arbitration to resolve disputes, or investors make claims under bilateral (or multilateral) investment treaties (BITs). BigLaw firms – as well as specialist boutique firms in some instances – represent both claimants

and defendants in such cases, though they must be careful about conflicts.

The disputes are often considered under a foreign applicable law and resolved under the arbitration rules of the International Chamber of Commerce (**ICC**), the International Centre for Dispute Resolution of the American Arbitration Association (**ICDR**), the London Court of International Arbitration (**LCIA**), The World Bank's International Centre for Settlement of Investment Disputes (**ICSID**), or the United Nations Commission on International Trade Law (**UNCITRAL**). The nature of the dispute largely determines the relevance of each set of rules. Investor-state disputes, for example, are usually arbitrated under UNCITRAL or ICSID, while the LCIA and ICC rules are suitable for virtually all types of arbitration – though the latter is more appropriate for commercial disputes.

What lawyers do

- Receive instructions from the client, who thinks, for example, that their contract has been breached or that their rights under an applicable investment treaty have been infringed.
- Review the contract or treaty, solicit and review relevant documentation and speak to potential witnesses.
- Provide the client with a memo on the merits of the case. This may involve working with local counsel in the relevant jurisdiction.
- If a client wants to proceed, draft the necessary initiation papers – usually a 'Request for Arbitration' in accordance with the applicable arbitration rules, such as ICDR, ICC or ICSID – and submit to the relevant arbitral institution.
- The case is then registered and the request is communicated to the respondent, usually by the arbitral institution. The respondent answers, possibly with an objection to the jurisdiction and with a response to the case's merits. They name an arbitrator.
- In order to establish the tribunal, each party proposes an impartial and independent 'party-nominated' arbitrator. The party-nominated arbitrators then usually seek to agree on a 'president' or 'chair' of the tribunal, failing which, the president/chair will be nominated by the institution. Once constituted, the tribunal will invite parties to the first procedural hearing at the (usually neutral) seat of hearing (often jurisdictions with favorable arbitration laws and culture such as New York, London, Paris, Geneva and Singapore), where the cal-

Practice Areas

Rankings in *Chambers USA*

Top Ranked

Debevoise & Plimpton	White & Case
King & Spalding	

Highly Recommended

Arnold & Porter	Jenner & Block
Baker Botts	Norton Rose Fulbright
Cleary Gottlieb Steen	Reed Smith
Curtis, Mallet-Prevost, Colt	Shearman & Sterling
Dechert	Sidley Austin
Freshfields Bruckhaus	Skadden
Hughes Hubbard & Reed	WilmerHale

For more detail on ranking tiers and locations, visit www.chambersandpartners.com

endar and procedural order for the next steps will be established.

- In commercial arbitration, there is a period for exchanging documentary evidence, during which each side will produce the documents upon which it intends to rely. This does not typically include 'US-style' discovery, but a far more limited disclosure process.
- The next steps usually include a very detailed presentation of the facts and evidence by the claimant (including written witness/expert statements and all relevant documentation). This is called a 'Memorial'– it may also be included in a pre-hearing brief shortly before the hearing on the merits.
- Defense attorneys submit a 'Defense Memorial' or response brief with a similar presentation.
- There will often be a further round of 'Reply' and 'Rejoinder' memorials or briefs.
- Final hearing takes place, where witnesses are questioned and cross-examined before the tribunal, and oral argument is made. The written witness statements filed with the Memorials often take the place of direct testimony at the hearing.
- Submit final, post-hearing briefs. In complex cases, these can be lengthy.
- Tribunal determines award, which must be 'reasoned' (ie, the tribunal's reasoning for the award must be set out), in writing, and signed by the members of the tribunal. With a three-person tribunal, a majority determines the award.

Realities of the job

- *"The international context is fascinating because, regardless of whether it's a commercial or investor-state arbitration, you're always experiencing different cultures, countries, languages and personalities. It really is such a wonderful dynamic and mix,"* says **Carolyn Lamm** of **White & Case**.
- *"You can assist yourself greatly by having a real command of more than one language,"* Donovan explains. *"English is of course important, but having a command of other languages as well really helps."* Spanish, Chinese and Russian are three languages in demand. Portuguese is also increasingly valuable for international arbitrators, in conjunction with the growth of the Brazilian market in particular.
- *"International arbitration isn't entirely different from courtroom advocacy,"* according to Lamm. Compared to US litigation, however, international arbitration typically relies more on written, instead of oral, advocacy and on contemporaneous documents, rather than on witness testimony from parties. In final hearings, for example, written witness statements often take the place of oral direct testimony.
- *"In many ways the skills that make you successful in international arbitration are no different from the skills that make you successful in litigation,"* **Joe Profaizer** of **Paul Hastings** tells us. **Fried Frank** arbitration practice founder **Elliot Polebaum** concurs, elaborating: *"It's a good idea to have a grounding in disputes more generally. Working in the litigation department of a law firm is a good place to start, before getting specialized. There are opportunities to become enmeshed in the factual development of a case, learning and handling the disclosure process, including the deposition process in US litigations, and managing the documentation."*
- The job involves a lot of travel to identify relevant documents and interview witnesses. Depending on the circumstances, associates may also travel.
- It's important for international arbitration lawyers to build up their knowledge of economic and financial issues, as these form an important component of the work.
- *"Currently there is no overarching set of rules to account for all the various national backgrounds that lawyers in an international proceeding come from, so if you have lawyers from different legal systems they may not be conducting themselves in the same way,"* Lamm tells us. Despite this, the differences between European, US and Asian practices, and between civil law and common law, are not as great as they once were. Some say a more universal practice is developing; the International Bar Association's now widely used evidence rules are an example of this.
- In commercial arbitration, demands for documents from the other side are allowed, but not as much as in the discovery phases of US litigation. Depositions are rarely allowed, unless US parties are involved and the arbitration clause itself calls for them. (See the aforementioned IBA evidence rules for a good summary.)
- International arbitration has provided an effective platform for female practitioners to excel, which is demonstrated by organizations such as ArbitralWomen.
- David Lindsey says: *"Participants in the international*

arbitration Bar share a mutual respect and camaraderie that I have not witnessed in other areas of legal practice."

- International arbitration is generally a difficult profession to enter, and so it's typical for juniors to develop their skills as trial lawyers first. *"The bottom line is you must learn advocacy – how to present on your feet with care, thoroughness and confidence. You also need to know whether you love to do that, because some people just don't excel in that kind of situation,"* Lamm informs us.

Current issues

- New York, London, Paris and Geneva have traditionally been favored as the arbitrators' venue of choice, but Hong Kong and Singapore are quickly becoming popular alternatives. Don't expect newcomers to displace old favorites, commentators reckon the growth of Asian venues is thanks to a wider increase in international arbitration and a desire to emulate successful models found in the Europe and the USA.
- Arbitral decisions have been increasingly challenged over the last ten years; while most of these failed to overturn initial rulings, the last five years have seen a few succeed. Recently the world's largest arbitral settlement between the shareholders of Yukos Oil and Russia was challenged and defeated in a court in The Hague. This decision has been appealed by the former majority shareholders, who have abandoned their enforcement efforts in Belgium in order focus on preserving the arbitral award delivered by the original Hague ruling.
- **Jenner & Block**'s **Anton Valukas** tells us: *"Arbitration has become as complex as civil litigation. It's not unusual for arbitrations to involve extensive discovery, motion practice and protracted resolutions. As a result, arbitration may not continue to be the alternative choice for resolving matters."*
- Reacting to complaints that arbitration has become increasingly costly and slow, at the start of 2016 the International Chamber of Commerce (ICC) announced new time scale expectations for the submission of awards.
- Class arbitrations have been around in the USA for some time but thanks to some companies prohibiting customers from pursuing class arbitrations these actions are on the decline. Outside the USA it's a different story; although still infrequent, class arbitrations are increasingly springing up and commentators expect this to continue in the coming years.

- Though you might think the prospect of Brexit would have a big impact on the future of international arbitration in London, **Shearman & Sterling**'s **Mark McNeill** suggests that the city *"is in many ways the dispute resolution capital of the world, and it won't lose any of its major strengths post-Brexit. It will still attract many of the most important commercial cases, and what makes people choose it as an arbitration seat won't change overnight."*
- Alternative funding, such as third-party funding, will continue to finance arbitrations. Third-party financing sees external investors stump up the cash for companies to pursue arbitrations, on condition the investors pocket a proportion of any settlement awarded. Despite some hostility to arrangements in certain areas, some jurisdictions are warming up to the method; Hong Kong is set to review its restrictions on third-party funding.
- The number of investor-state disputes has increased considerably in recent years, with energy, oil, gas and mining companies leading the charge. As governments begin imposing limitations and conditions on investors' abilities to take on foreign governments, this incline in cases could soon start leveling off.
- According to Elliot Polebaum, *"international arbitration has become the dispute resolution mechanism of choice for international business. Big transactions involving important contracts can lead to significant and high-stakes disputes, and there has been an increasing number of such disputes in recent years."*
- Keep an eye on the dispute between ConocoPhillips and Venezuela over the illegal expropriation of oil investments to watch how another sovereign state attempts to push back against arbitral decision: Venezuela is currently trying to get the ruling overturned.
- India canceled investment treaties with more than 50 states in 2017 – a major step for one of the fastest-rising economies globally – due to fears that the existing treaties made it too simple for parties to bring international arbitration proceedings against the government. Negotiations are currently underway to formulate replacement treaties that will address these concerns.

Practice Areas

Appellate

In a nutshell

In simple terms, appellate law is a stage of dispute resolution. More specifically, it involves handling cases on appeal, but the best appellate practices think of it more broadly and consider sophisticated legal analysis, strategy and issue identification – even at the trial level – to be part of their core function.

Appellate lawyers, though all experts in appellate advocacy per se, often come to specialize in different areas. This includes the likes of antitrust, state and federal taxation, corporate law, punitive damages, telecommunications, labor and employment, environment and intellectual property. *"To be a good appellate lawyer is to have a set of skills that cross-cut substantive areas in the law,"* according to **Kathleen Sullivan** of **Quinn Emmanuel**.

They will also often have a court-specific focus, developing expertise in state appellate courts, federal courts of appeal, state supreme courts, or the US Supreme Court.

What lawyers do

- Evaluate the issues in the case.
- Review motions filed by lawyers in trial court, because they tend to identify the important issues.
- Read the trial transcript.
- Work with trial lawyers to understand the facts of the case.
- Conduct legal research to assess the strength of the issues raised at trial.
- Write an 'issues memo' after the research and analysis, and consult with the client and trial lawyers to identify the most promising issues.
- Write the brief. This process takes time.
- Share the brief with the client and trial counsel; incorporate their comments and reactions.
- Continue to refine the brief until it must be filed.
- Present the oral argument.
- Manage post-hearing steps.

Realities of the job

- Oral argument *"is an incredibly adrenalin-fueled experience,"* says **Evan Tager** of **Mayer Brown**. *"It adds spice to your ordinary research and writing routine."* Practicing appellate lawyers often note this as one their favorite parts of the job, with Kathleen Sullivan noting: *"There can be nothing more thrilling than distilling an entire appeal down to oral argument an appellate lawyer will make."*

- It is, however, a relatively small part of the case. The strength of the appeal rests on the shoulders of the brief, though most clients still hire appellate lawyers based on their oral argument capabilities. As Kathleen Sullivan notes, *"it can take longer to write a shorter brief. It is a skill to argue in a more succinct and attention-grabbing way,"* one which must be developed by aspiring appellate lawyers.

- Prior to an oral argument, appellate lawyers should go through one or more moot court sessions in preparation for the real thing. *"Appellate judges appreciate the extra preparation,"* explains **Stephen Shapiro** of **Mayer Brown**.

- *"The reality is that appellate work is far more people-centric than most assume,"* **Carter Phillips** of **Sidley Austin** says. *"You're going in as part of a much broader team, and if you're successful it's because you have the right skills to work effectively with others."*

- Appellate law is a highly intellectual area that involves cutting-edge legal issues. Phillips adds: *"Those who practice appellate law tend to have remarkably strong credentials coming out of law school."* According to **Kannon Shanmugam** of **Williams & Connolly**, the role of an appellate lawyers is to *"research legal questions, but also policy arguments. It is important to develop these skills early in your career."*

- Associates must enjoy spending countless hours doing research and crafting written statements. This work decreases with seniority.

- *"If you like to play with language, prose and sentence structure, if you consider writing to be an art, then appellate law is a great opportunity to immerse yourself in that,"* says Tager.

- There is no law stating that you have to do a clerkship in order to become an appellate lawyer, but *"it's much easier and a natural progression for those who have,"* Phillips tells us. Working in government in an appellate division can also be beneficial. Kannon Shanmugam elaborates: *"A clerkship is important, I don't think it's a requirement, but having done an appellate clerkship is useful to understand how appellate courts operate and their internal mechanisms and structures."*

- Courts around the country are constantly issuing decisions that appellate lawyers need to keep up with, though practitioners can generally limit their focus to decisions made in the courts or areas of law that apply to their practice.

Practice Areas

Rankings in *Chambers USA*

Top Ranked

Gibson, Dunn & Crutcher	Sidley Austin
Kirkland & Ellis	WilmerHale

Highly Recommended

Akin Gump Strauss Hauer	Latham & Watkins
Arnold & Porter	Mayer Brown
Jenner & Block	Morrison & Foerster
Jones Day	O'Melveny & Myers
King & Spalding	Orrick

For more detail on ranking tiers and locations, visit www.chambersandpartners.com

- *"It's useful to develop a wider array of litigation skills in the first year or two,"* according to Phillips. **Seth Waxman** of **WilmerHale** confirms: *"I could never have been the kind of appellate lawyer that I am without putting together cases from scratch, learning how to establish facts in a trial record and developing a facility for never doing the same kind of substantive case twice."*
- Another key difference between appellate law and litigation is the considerable shift toward answering questions as opposed to asking them. This is done by *"meeting the obvious questions head on in a brief, or being prepared to quickly and thoughtfully provide answers to questions that judges ask during oral advocacy,"* says Waxman.
- Judges are human. They have predispositions and find it difficult not to view a case through the lens of their biases, often frustrating even the best-laid plans – although this is less of an issue in the Supreme Court compared to the lower court levels.

Current issues

- Appellate lawyers are being brought onto cases at increasingly earlier stages such as immediately after jury verdicts or even when winning a case starts to look unlikely. Some clients are even requesting that an appellate lawyer be staffed from the get-go, with the purpose of keeping an eye on potential appeal strategies. Specialized appellate lawyers have also become increasingly common in recent years.
- Numerous new 'pro se' or 'pro bono' appellate programs have been developed throughout the country over recent years, to tackle the influx of self-represented civil litigants in appellate courts and to improve efficiency in this regard. Public Counsel operates two clinics to assist pro se litigants: the Appellate Self-Help Clinic and the Federal Pro Se Clinic.

- In Texas, a trend has been observed: the state's leaders are increasingly turning to appellate litigators to fill top government legal positions. Former Texas Assistant Solicitor General Jimmy Blacklock was appointed general counsel to the incoming governor, while another alum of the Texas Solicitor General's office, Brantley Starr, was appointed the new Deputy Attorney General for Legal Counsel. These big-shot appellate litigators were appointed because of their ability to handle the thorniest of legal issues: an ability which had been honed thanks to the complex issues generated within the Appellate Bar.
- Within the first year of his presidency, Donald Trump appointed 12 new federal appeals judges, a new record (for context, President Obama appointed three). If this trend continues, the stance taken by appellate courts may shift somewhat over the next few years to favor a more conservative approach.

*Editor's note: sample briefs and arguments are available at www.appellate.net

Advice from the appellate law gurus

Carter Phillips, partner and chair of the firm's executive committee, **Sidley Austin**:

"If you're coming out of law school, get a clerkship with an appellate judge because there's no better way to understand the process than to spend a year on that side of the ledger. After that, the critical mass of the practice is in Washington DC, so you should start out there if you really want to be an appellate lawyer."

"It's also good to spend time in government, as it's a great proving ground for developing appellate skills. And if you can land a spot in the Solicitor General's office, you will have the opportunity to argue before the US Supreme Court – and that's pretty heady stuff."

Stephen Shapiro, partner and founder of appellate group, **Mayer Brown**:

"The road to success in appellate law starts in law school, where interested students should work on a law review and take part in the moot court program. Most important, a neophyte appellate lawyer should read and listen to as many of the best briefs and oral arguments as possible."

"Young appellate lawyers learn a great deal from the edits of senior lawyers working on their draft briefs. They should keep those edited briefs in their files for future reference; I still have some edited drafts from my mentor, Judge Frank Easterbrook."

Practice Areas

Seth Waxman, chair of the appellate and Supreme Court litigation practice group, **WilmerHale**:

"You certainly need to have a real affinity for quiet solitary work. It's not the life of the academic, but some aspects are much more solitary than many other types of law practice. I always have my door open and I spend a lot of my day wandering in and out of colleagues' offices, as I tend to work better in a collegial setting. But at the end of the day, when you're talking about writing or preparing a brief, or preparing to argue a case, there is no substitute for spending a long time on your own with the door closed and focusing your mind in a concentrated way. To be fulfilled and successful as an appellate lawyer you have to have an appreciation for quite a different way of working."

"You should be excited and optimistic about becoming a lawyer. There's nothing better than being part of a team that's focused on helping clients solve complex issues to further strategic business objectives.

"You should also strive to achieve balance between your professional and personal lives. We work hard as lawyers. Each of us needs to make time to continue to pursue our interests and spend time with family and friends."
– Bracewell managing partner Greg Bopp

The Big Interview: Marc Kasowitz, veteran New York litigator and lawyer to the President

Marc Kasowitz (born 1952; JD Cornell Law School 1977) is one of New York's preeminent trial lawyers. He is currently a name partner at Kasowitz Benson Torres, a firm that he co-founded in 1993. Kasowitz has represented a number of high profile clients over the years, including television host Bill O'Reilly, the Port Authority of New York and New Jersey, tobacco giant Liggett Group, and – most famously – US President Donald Trump (who he has advised on various matters for over 15 years). Here Kasowitz reflects on his achievements, ambitions and role models, and explains what it really means to be an *'aggressive'* litigator.

Chambers Associate: What made you want to go into law?

Marc Kasowitz: I grew up in a middle-class family in New Haven, Connecticut, where my father owned a scrap metal business. I aspired to become someone to whom people turned when they faced significant challenges in their own lives or businesses, while remaining principled and steadfastly loyal to family, friends and clients. The lawyers were the wise ones in our community, and people regularly turned to them for advice. I also thought that being a lawyer would be intellectually challenging, which I found appealing.

CA: Who were your role models growing up?

MK: My father was my role model. He taught me that hard work and focus would always pay off in the long run. He was a natural leader, to whom honesty and fairness were essential. He had a strong moral compass, and always earned the trust of his customers.

CA: When did you get your big break?

MK: Twenty-five years ago, I got my big break when I and several others decided to leave the large law firm where we worked to form our own firm. We started with 18 lawyers and built our firm to more than 250 lawyers today. In the beginning, certain major clients decided to follow us to our new firm, and since then we've been successful in creating enormous value for our clients. I've never looked back.

"To us, aggressive means creative and strategic. We've found that thinking aggressively has enabled us to come up with angles, insights and approaches that other counsel either have not thought of, or, even if they have, they are not bold enough to have tried them."

CA: Did you always have the ambition to one day manage your own firm?

MK: Although I never really dreamed of running my own firm when I was young, as time passed and my practice grew, I, together with Dan Benson and Hector Torres, began to believe that we could do a better job ourselves, and decided to start our own firm.

CA: What is it about Kasowitz that enabled it to carve out its own space in the New York legal market?

MK: New York is the most competitive legal market in the world, and the most difficult to break into. We were able to come up with uniquely creative solutions to our clients' problems that ended up being extraordinarily successful. Those successes enabled us to carve out a highly visible and very positive profile for ourselves in a relatively short period of time.

CA: How do you feel about yourself – and the firm more widely – being labeled as aggressive?

MK: I like to think of our lawyers as thoughtfully aggressive, which I view as a great thing; we are not aggressive for the sake of being aggressive. We are passionate about the work we take on and the clients we serve, and we are committed to doing what it takes to obtain a positive result for our clients. Clients don't bring us easy problems – we often take on tough, out-of-the-box cases that other firms shy away from. In those instances, the clients are looking for lawyers who aren't afraid to take strong positions to deliver a favorable outcome. There is no "same old" routine litigation work at Kasowitz – we approach each of our cases with a fresh perspective to determine the best solution for our clients.

CA: What are the advantages of an aggressive approach to business?

MK: To us, aggressive means creative and strategic. We've found that thinking aggressively has enabled us to come up with angles, insights and approaches that other counsel either have not thought of, or, even if they have, they are not bold enough to have tried them.

CA: How did you first come into contact with President Trump?

MK: A long-standing client introduced me to President Trump 15 years ago, and I have been representing him ever since then.

CA: What has acting for Trump taught you about being a lawyer?

MK: Representing the President has confirmed for me many of the important lessons I've learned during 40 years of practice – the need for absolute discretion about the representation, the importance of zeal and passion for the client's position, and the obligation to render advice firmly and unwaveringly even under difficult circumstances. One of the most important lessons from representing the President has been the need to be cognizant of the extraordinarily intense media attention surrounding the President.

"Representing the President has confirmed for me many of the important lessons I've learned during 40 years of practice – the need for absolute discretion about the representation, the importance of zeal and passion for the client's position, and the obligation to render advice firmly and unwaveringly even under difficult circumstances."

CA: What effect has the Trump presidency had on the legal market?

MK: I don't think this Administration has had any particular effect on the legal market.

CA: What single achievement are you most proud of?

MK: My single greatest professional achievement has been founding and managing our law firm, which counts among its accomplishments some of the watershed cases in American legal history, such as the tobacco settlements. In handling these matters over the past 25 years, we have enabled generations of lawyers and professional staff to develop both professionally and personally, building their families and becoming active and contributing members of their communities.

CA: Which figures in law, politics or business do you hold in highest regard?

MK: In business, Prem Watsa, the visionary founder of Fairfax Financial; Bennett LeBow, chairman of the board of Vector Group; and Howard Lorber, president and CEO of Vector Group and chairman of Douglas Elliman. In politics, of course, President Trump, who defeated all odds in becoming President. My dear friend Senator Joseph Lieberman, who is senior counsel at our firm, is one of the truly great American politicians. And I have always considered Winston Churchill and Franklin Roosevelt to be two of the most important and heroic leaders in world history. In law, I am amazed at the accomplishments of firm leaders like Brad Karp at Paul Weiss, Norm Brownstein at Brownstein Hyatt Farber Schreck, and John Quinn at Quinn Emmanuel. All have built impressive firms, been close friends and have provided wise counsel to me. One of my closest friends, Vince DeBlasi of Sullivan & Cromwell, passed away recently; he was a giant in the New York bar and we will all feel his loss.

CA: What ambitions do you have for the firm over the next five years?

MK: My vision for the firm for the next five years is that it continues to obtain for our clients the same uniquely successful results it always has and, in the process, continues to attract lawyers and professional staff who are superbly talented and work extraordinarily well together in the closely knit and collaborative culture that we've worked so hard to build.

Practice Areas

Practice Areas
Personal Law

"I know it's hard to do, but selling yourself is important. Some people are overly shy and don't want to sound like they're bragging but you need to tell your story and be positive about the attributes that make you a great candidate, not in an abrasive way but in a confident, straightforward way. Talk about yourself the way your mom or dad would talk about your accomplishments, although I know this isn't 100% intuitive for people in their early twenties applying for their first jobs."

– hiring partner Mark Hayek, Fried Frank

Wealth management and offshore

In a nutshell

Private wealth lawyers advise wealthy families, individuals, trustees and fiduciaries on all aspects of estate planning. This can include asset management, tax planning, wills and trusts, charitable contributions and various types of estate litigation. Matters can be purely domestic or have an international element if, for example, a family has non-US resident members or has invested wealth overseas.

A great deal of private wealth work is tax-based, especially with regards to income and estate tax. However, specialists in this area also need to ensure their corporate tax knowledge is up to date, as it's not unusual for their family clients to have multimillion-dollar businesses to their names. As **Carol Harrington** of **McDermott, Will & Emery** highlights: *"In addition to the original family business, one client owns casinos, two major league sports teams and a charitable foundation – that's a similar situation for a lot of clients."*

"The ability to deal with numbers is important. You don't have to be a maths wizard, but you can't be afraid of spreadsheets."

Compliance is another important aspect of wealth management. Lawyers need to cultivate a lot of regulatory knowledge in order to advise their clients, who may have multiple requirements as shareholders of corporate entities, trustees of charitable foundations, charitable donors and recipients of trusts.

What lawyers do

- Structure assets to create tax-efficient structures for private individuals seeking to transfer assets to family members or executives of estates.
- Draft wills, trusts and estate documents.
- Regularly meet with clients.
- Aid families and wealthy individuals with their personal tax liabilities and solutions.
- Establish and structure charitable organizations, as well as charitable endowments and funds.
- Provide families with multi-jurisdictional advice pertaining to their international estates.
- Liaise with private wealth lawyers around the world.
- Represent trustees in litigation regarding their conduct when handling of an estate.
- Communicate and discuss strategy within a team.

"Any one of my clients could call me with something crucial to them: their dad's had a heart attack, so what do they do?"

Realities of the job

- **Basil Zirinis**, a leading wealth management partner at **Sullivan & Cromwell**, says: *"Our practice is a mix of drafting, meeting, advising and researching."*
- Wealth management tends to offer young lawyers more direct client contact than they'd typically get in a larger corporate or litigation department. *"If you're a strong associate and you show drive, there is always the opportunity to be very involved with families face-to-face,"* says Zirinis.
- Building relationships with clients is an important part of the job, as **Carlyn McCaffrey** of McDermott, Will & Emery explains: *"Many private client attorneys end up with hundreds of clients over their careers. They don't work for them all at the same time, but they don't finish with a client either. Estate planning is a lifetime enterprise. If you had a client 20 years ago that you did good work for, chances are you're still working with them today."*
- Harrington also drives home the importance of empathy and client-care skills as *"these are real life people-problems; sometimes kids aren't financially responsible, for instance, and sometimes families don't get on."* She adds: *"There's a crisis every minute and each client wants to be the only client you have. Any one of my clients could call me with something crucial to them: their dad's had a heart attack, so what do they do?"*
- Research forms a large part of the role. *"We're fortunate enough to have a practice where the questions are unusual and complex, and there are often no clear answers,"* Zirinis notes. *"We add value where the answer is unsettled, so the associates are doing research, but it's creative research. This makes it more challenging and more interesting."*
- Attention to detail is vital, especially when structuring assets for high net worth individuals (HNWIs). *"It's important that you understand the law; it's technical, complex and it can get pretty complicated,"* Harrington points out.
- Private wealth lawyers tend to juggle several matters at once. *"This element is a challenge, but at the same time it's a high point. There's so much variety and you never see the same thing over and over again. It's thrilling, exciting and fresh,"* Zirinis enthuses.

Rankings in *Chambers USA*

Top Ranked

Alston & Bird	Katten Muchin Rosenman
Baker Botts	McDermott Will & Emery
Choate Hall & Stewart	Milbank
Cooley	Norton Rose Fulbright
Cozen O'Connor	Perkins Coie
Foley & Lardner	Ropes & Gray
Goulston & Storrs	Snell & Wilmer
Greenberg Traurig	Waller
Holland & Knight	White & Case

Highly Recommended

Arnold & Porter	Nutter McClennen & Fish
Clifford Chance US	Paul, Weiss, Rifkind
Dykema Gossett	Proskauer Rose
Freshfields Bruckhaus	Schulte Roth & Zabel
Greenberg Glusker	Sheppard, Mullin, Richter
Hunton Andrews Kurth	Skadden
K&L Gates	Sullivan & Cromwell
Kirkland & Ellis	Venable
Morgan, Lewis & Bockius	Willkie Farr & Gallagher

For more detail on ranking tiers and locations, visit
www.chambersandpartners.com

- An interest in tax and a good feel for numbers is a must. McCaffrey says *"the ability to deal with numbers is important. You don't have to be a maths wizard, but you can't be afraid of spreadsheets."* Often clients will have business interests that need to be factored in, but the more complex sums are usually sent to the firm's corporate tax teams to figure out.

Current issues

- *"The global nature of wealth certainly has an impact on the practice,"* says **Amy Heller** of **Skadden**. *"It's increasingly common for wealthy families to have family members and assets in multiple jurisdictions, so it's important to have – at the very least – an awareness of other countries' laws and a sensitivity to other cultures."*
- The changing nature of the law means that lawyers must remain flexible in their drafting of wills, trusts and other documents; they require many additional clauses to ensure their smooth adaptation to shifting regulations.
- Privacy is integral to clients in the current climate. In 2017 the 'Paradise Papers' leak revealed details of massive offshore trusts held by the world's wealthiest individuals. Among these was American billionaire James Simons, who privately transferred $7 billion to Bermuda for tax purposes. The leak sparked widespread debate on the ethics of tax evasion versus tax avoidance.
- The Tax Cuts and Jobs Act of 2017 cut the corporate tax rate from 35% to 21%. It also served to benefit higher-income families thanks to the doubling of the estate tax threshold: tax now need only be paid on estates worth more than $11.2 million.
- According to the Financial Secrecy Index 2018, the US is second only to Switzerland when it comes to the secrecy and scale of offshore finances. Compiled by the Tax Justice Network, the US has a 4.09% FSI share, more than twice the share of Panama.
- According to a report by economist Edward N. Wolff, the top 0.1% of families in the US own more wealth than the bottom 90% combined – signaling levels of wealth inequality not witnessed since the Great Depression. On a global level, a 2016 Oxfam report found that just 62 people own as much as 50% of the world's population combined does. All of this, Carol Harrington believes, means that *"there is a lot of work to do. In the next ten to 20 years there is going to be the greatest transfer of wealth in the history of the world."*

> ## "When families are fighting they want you to help them settle it, but given the emotions and family history it can very difficult... there is often no clear or perfectly right answer."

Basil Zirinis' advice for aspiring wealth management lawyers:

- Hone your diplomacy skills: *"Because it's such a human area of the law, it can be extremely emotional. Do you leave assets outright? Do you trust your family? There is no right answer. When families are fighting they want you to help them settle it, but given the emotions and family history it can very difficult. It's not about 'right' or 'wrong' family members, it's just that there is often no clear or perfectly right answer."*
- Tax it up at law school: *"Students should definitely take as many tax courses as they can in law school – including corporate tax. The more of a background they have in tax, the more helpful it will be."*
- But still keep it broad: *"We do everything from corporate law to litigation in our practice – so the broadest possible academic experience is also important."*
- Expand your language skills: *"An international perspective on the world is helpful, especially because the explosion of wealth is global. It's not just the US and Europe anymore; it's China, Latin America and many other jurisdictions. That's where the most interesting work will ultimately be for young lawyers, so languages are extremely important."*

Practice Areas

Offshore uncovered

Haven is a place on Earth...

It's not all been piña coladas and snorkeling in the Caribbean lately. The Panama Papers and Paradise Papers leaks revealed the web of investments hidden in tax havens and sparked an inevitable witch-hunt in the press against the celebrities using them. The topic may come up in interview, and the critically-minded law student will want more than the sensationalism in the press; we spoke to Michael Rosen-Prinz, a private wealth partner at McDermott, Will & Emery, who explains that there's more to offshore law than avoiding taxes.

As with many areas of law, we'd advise not being seduced by the glamor. *"You might not be flying in on a jet at the last minute to close a deal,"* Rosen-Prinz laughed, *"but the real satisfaction comes from helping people solve their problems."* The challenge that lawyers often face is dealing with the complexity of problems that high net-worth clients tackle in their personal and professional lives, and *"their circumstances will often be novel and nobody will have ever dealt with it before. The answer won't be in any textbook."* Having bucket-loads of cash and a high profile means a higher-risk existence for a high net-worth family, which requires greater measures of protection. *"You meet people who have enough resources to do anything in the world,"* Rosen-Prinz explained, but they they might have to *"worry about finding a solution to protect their privacy and physical safety;"* this is a very different practice to commercial law.

"There's a lot of time for things to develop when you're asleep."

The confidential nature of private wealth means that *"working for a private family may not make a big headline in the same way as if you perform a huge merger,"* but the work is invariably international and fast-paced. *"There's a lot of time for things to develop overnight"* says Rosen-Prinz, which means the working day *"sometimes starts with some dread!"* Private wealth sees many areas of law coming into play. *"Tax is a big one, but substantive trust law and succession is probably a close second."* Often the clients will vary from *"entrepreneurs, private families and substantial family-held businesses,"* across multiple industries. A typical problem might be the family *"wanting to move their structures or themselves from one jurisdiction to another without adverse consequences."* The opportunity to advise celebrities is enticing, and indeed Rosen-Prinz confirms *"some clients are in the entertainment industry,"* but in these cases *"their business is themselves – that planning gets personal."* These don't always provide the meatiest cases for a lawyer. *"sometimes clients with the most boring sounding businesses can be the most interesting to work with,"* thinks Rosen-Prinz, *"like manufactures and commodities work, because of all of the exciting legal issues that come up in different jurisdictions."*

Private wealth is a flourishing area of the law. *"During the recession, private wealth was one of the few practices that boomed because many private clients weren't unduly affected when the commercial work dried up."* The number of self-made millionaires continues to rise across the globe; *"it's an exciting time,"* says Rosen-Prinz. This is an area of law well suited to students who are *"interested in learning about other cultures and feel comfortable working in an arena where you can never have all the answers."* The learning process is never-ending: *"even if you have memorized all of your own country's laws, you're never going to be as familiar with what, for example, Indonesian law and French law has to say on a particular matter."*

Following the Paradise and Panama leaks *"it seemed like a lot of people were shamed who shouldn't have been,"* believes Rosen-Prinz. Heads of state including Queen Elizabeth were left exposed, corporations like Nike and Apple were heavily criticized, the Icelandic prime minister had to step down, and Shakira, Justin Timberlake and Kiera Knightley all had their affairs scrutinized. The morality of tax avoidance is one question, but we've also learnt that personal security is a major concern to high net-worth individuals, and the structures offered by offshore investments provide anonymity. This was the argument Emma Watson gave after accusations of using an offshore fund to buy property in London. *"In the US,"* begins Rosen-Prinz, *"we believe it's your right and freedom to be able to buy your neighbour's house without them knowing you're the one making the offer so they can't jack up the price."*

To impress at interview you should *"show why you're committed to this area"* – this advice is universal, we'd add. While you're not expected (nor encouraged) to have close ties to Hollywood or Russian oligarchs, *"making connections by joining professional groups"* and *"getting to know people [working in the field] and hearing what they have to say"* will provide useful direction and insight.

Chambers HNW 2018

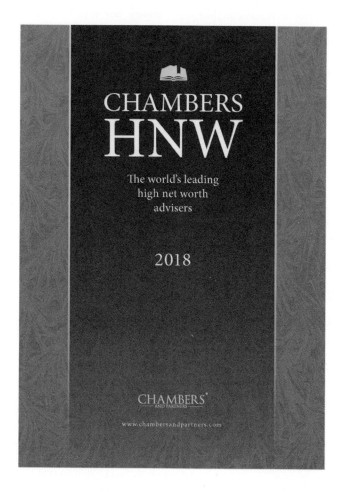

The world's leading high net worth advisers

Chambers' global reputation provides unique access to this notably difficult to reach audience. The guide is used by family offices and professional advisers to wealthy individuals, providing objective guidance on an international scale.

Practice Areas

Public Interest

"Keep your mind open. Don't come into this process with any preconceptions – you don't really know where the next opportunity is going to be. Take a broad view, and you might be surprised. When I came out of law school, I thought I would be an antitrust litigator. I went down a different path, so I would advise others to go into it with their eyes open and don't have preconceived notions about your future."

– US regional managing partner
Peter Lyons, Freshfields

Government

In a nutshell

Government contracts lawyers *"don't just sit at their desks reviewing contracts,"* says **Richard Rector**, chair of **DLA Piper**'s government contracts practice. *"Actually, what we do involves a broad range of legal skills, as over half of what we do is litigation."* Bid protests form the bulk of contentious work, along with disputes involving costs recovery or performance problems; lawyers also defend contractors accused of fraud or other misconduct. In addition, attorneys here help contractors to navigate the regulations and special rules tied to providing goods and services to federal government. Advising on subcontracts, scheduling and organizational conflicts are all common activities too.

"Law firms that lobby are not selling access, they are selling skills," says **Nick Allard**, current dean of Brooklyn Law School and former chair of **Squire Patton Boggs**' lobbying, political and election law practice. *"They are litigators serving as advocates in a broader array of arenas."* More specifically, government relations lawyers directly lobby the federal and state government on behalf of a variety of businesses – including healthcare, education and defense entities – on specific legislation or ongoing issues. They promote or oppose new initiatives to congress or the administration; attempt to persuade government to amend legislation; and try to convince courts to reinterpret laws. *"You get exposed to a wide range of industries,"* says Richard Rector, *"and so it never gets boring."*

Political law specialists advise on the organization and financing of election campaigns, which includes assisting corporations and other groups with election-related activities. On the litigation side, they help to challenge decisions made by electoral authorities, such as the Federal Election Commission.

"Law firms who lobby are not selling access, they are selling skills."

What lawyers do
Government contracts

- Virtually every government agency procures external services, but the Department of Defense is far and away the largest consumer. Other major areas are aerospace, construction, healthcare, homeland security, education and IT.

- When external services or goods are required, the government will issue a procurement solicitation (or 'Request for Proposal'). The process of procurement and contracting is run by a government official called the contracting officer.

- Lawyers help guide potential contractors through the solicitation procedures: pointing out the key risk issues; how the evaluation factors will influence the selection decision; and how this contract differs from previous ones. However, they do not advise clients on how to obtain a contract or how to market themselves.

- **Rand Allen** of **Wiley Rein** says: *"We advise a lot of companies on how to get into the government contracts arena without creating undue compliance risk, for instance by qualifying for a status which will minimize the intrusiveness of government in their business."*

- Government contracts tend to use 'boilerplates' or standardized terms and conditions. In contrast to a commercial setting, there isn't as much room to negotiate the requirements that form part of the contract. Lawyers also negotiate subcontracts and teaming agreements between contractors.

- After the formation of the contract, lawyers act for both plaintiffs (the disappointed bidders) and defendants (the awardees) during bid protests. A typical bid protest challenges the award of a contract at an administrative forum: the US Government Accountability Office (GAO) or the US Court of Federal Claims (CFC). These cases are usually resolved over three months, which means associates don't get bogged down by document review for prolonged periods. The GAO is required by statute to issue a ruling within 100 days. Plaintiffs have ten days to put together protest documents, and government agencies have 30 days to respond. CFC proceedings take about the same time, sometimes slightly longer. Associates prepare drafts of protest filings and identify applicable legal precedent. This involves close scrutiny of the original Request for Proposal; the government agency's award decision; and the proposals and negotiation responses submitted by both the awardee and the protester.

- Disputes also arise over the performance of existing contracts. Lawyers represent contractors in alternative dispute resolution or litigation in front of the Armed Services Board of Contract Appeals, the Civilian Board of Contract Appeals or the Court of Federal Claims.

- Lawyers defend contractors against allegations of fraud, as well as waste and misconduct under various federal criminal and civil statutes, including the False Claims Act.

Practice Areas

Rankings in *Chambers USA*

Top Ranked

Akin Gump Strauss Hauer	Perkins Coie
Arnold & Porter	Skadden
Crowell & Moring	Wiley Rein

Highly Recommended

Allen & Overy	King & Spalding
Alston & Bird	Mayer Brown
Cozen O'Connor	Morrison & Foerster
DLA Piper (US)	Pillsbury Winthrop Shaw
Fried, Frank, Harris, Shriver	Sheppard, Mullin, Richter
Gibson, Dunn & Crutcher	Squire Patton Boggs
Holland & Knight	Venable
Jones Day	Vinson & Elkins
K&L Gates	WilmerHale

For more detail on ranking tiers and locations, visit www.chambersandpartners.com

- Lawyers also act in disputes between prime contractors and subcontractors in federal and state courts.

"Lobbying involves so much more than this image people have of the glad-handing door-opener."

Government relations

- Government relations lawyers are approached by clients from all industries who believe a certain piece of legislation will benefit or harm their business, in order to get it promoted or changed.
- The service that government relations lawyers provide involves *"analyzing laws, writing memoranda to clients advising on legal provisions – telling them what their responsibilities are under new legislation – and preparing advocacy pieces for hearings,"* Allard tells us.
- Besides advocacy there's legal research into current statutes, drafting of proposed rules and legislation, and drafting of clients' comments on legislation.
- Government relations lawyers are a link between their clients and politicians and administrators. But Allard wants us to clear up a misunderstanding: *"Lobbying involves so much more than this image people have of the glad-handing door-opener. That is not interesting or high-end work. What we do is analyze, advise and advocate. We seek to understand our clients' business, their mission and what they want to accomplish."*

Realities of the job

- *"Government contracts is a very litigation-oriented area,"* explains **John Chierichella** of **Sheppard Mullin**. *"You don't just have the opportunity to litigate,*

though; you get to do so in relation to things that are incredibly interesting, whether it be a bid protest, debarment proceeding, False Claims Act case or subcontract dispute."

"If your eyes glaze over when reading a detailed technical or cost proposal, this is not the area for you."

- Bid protests are typically intense affairs, packed with information that must be absorbed in a short space of time. *"If your eyes glaze over when reading a detailed technical or cost proposal, this is not the area for you,"* says **Tom McGovern**, **Hogan Lovells**' government contracts practice area leader. Richard Rector of DLA Piper confirms that *"you have to have a very good analytical ability when reviewing a contract to understand how it applies to a particular industry. When we are interviewing, we look out for people who are detail-oriented and don't shy away from digging into the documents and enjoying the analysis and the investigation."*
- Associates working on a smaller bid protest may have the opportunity to actually lead the case. During a larger bid protest it's more likely that they'll work on a particular aspect of it.
- Cost issues can be daunting to analyze due to the vast body of regulations and complex wording to grapple with. However, Chierichella tells us that *"if you can understand that logic chain and overcome those concerns, there's a lot of benefit you can give to clients by working through cost issues to maximize the amount to be paid and the amount they will retain."*
- While most traditional law practices deal with questions pertaining to what the law *is*, political law mainly involves the question of what the law should *be*.
- Lobbyists' main clients include corporations, trade associations, universities, healthcare institutions, states and municipalities. Lawyers also do pro bono lobbying work on behalf of charities and other nonprofit organizations.
- *"One of the most important things to understand is that every company in the US is affected by the government's policies,"* **Tom Boyd** of **DLA Piper** tells us. *"Whether it's in the form of legislation, regulation or the exercise of executive power, it's going to impact the marketplace and every one of our clients."*
- Allard describes the public policy process as *"never-ending,"* adding that *"anything that is done can be undone."*
- It is usually easier to shoot down a planned bill than to get one passed.
- *"Whenever you're representing a corporation, part*

Practice Areas

of the picture will involve a high-profile public offi-cial," says **Ken Gross** of **Skadden**. *"So it's vital to under-stand how decisions will play out if they get picked up by the media."*

- The famous 'revolving door' relationship between the administration and lobbying shops provides lawyers at all levels with the opportunity to work in-house for the government.
- *"I think having some exposure to government service is very helpful in this practice,"* explains Gross. *"You're essentially seeing the picture from the inside, which cer-tainly helps when dealing with the regulation side of things."* **David Nadler** of **Blank Rome** confirms this: *"I would advise working for the government before a law firm, as it's rewarding in its own right, but it also paints a picture of what it's like to work on both sides of the table."*
- Government lawyers are also active at the state level. Smaller state-based firms – grouped together into the State Capital Global Law Firm Group – advise on busi-ness regulation, ethics codes, campaign finance and state government procurement.
- *"Clients come from all over the globe,"* Boyd says. *"So we're not only interested in the political issues concerning Washington, DC, but also the likes as they relate to client interests in London, Paris, Berlin and Brussels."*
- *"There is a relatively small Bar and you deal with the same people regularly on the other side,"* states Al-len. *"That generates more comity and less hostile behav-ior than some lawyers are used – to."*

Current Issues

- Contractors and government are always at odds as they attempt to achieve the best prices from their respec-tive positions. **Tom McGovern**, the government con-tracts practice area leader at **Hogan Lovells**, explains that *"contractors are consulting us for advice as to how to protect themselves from government budget cuts and austerity measures."*
- Government contractors are coming under increased scrutiny and pressure, particularly when it comes to al-leged violations of the False Claims Act (FCA), which imposes liability on people or companies that defraud the US government. Civil recoveries under the FCA reached $3.7 billion in 2017 according to the Depart-ment of Justice – the fourth highest annual recovery in the Act's history.
- A government shutdown occurred between January 20th and 22nd 2018 and more shutdowns may well happen throughout the year. Federal contractors can encounter a range of issues when these happen, includ-ing delays to new contract modifications and certain procurement processes.

- The government is interested in streamlining the pro-cess for acquiring and protesting government con-tracts. The 2017 National Defense Authorization Act (NDAA) made way for an e-commerce portal and the 2016 NDAA set up the snappily-named 'Section 809 Panel' to look into ways of improving the Department of Defense's (DoD) acquisition processes. The panel will be reporting its findings in early 2019. Keep an eye out for future developments.
- The budget cuts and reductions in overall government spending have made the competition for any govern-ment work all the more competitive. *"With tighter budgets come fewer contract awards, so contractors are more likely to seek redress through the bid protest process if they lose contracts they previously held,"* McGovern reports.
- That being said, Trump's 2019 budget proposal did con-tain a large increase in military spending. In addition, a two-year bipartisan agreement was reached in Febru-ary 2018 by Senate leaders, which raised spending caps on military and domestic initiatives by around $300 billion in total. Contractors operating in the defense or domestic arena may well find things easier, depending on what they're offering.
- Data security has become a significant area of activ-ity, especially in light of Edward Snowden's revelations about the activities of the security services. This affects all contractors who have access to government infor-mation, whether they store it on their own systems or are tasked with securing the government's own storage facilities.
- *"Contractors are concerned about mounting cybersecu-rity threats,"* emphasizes McGovern, *"both in relation to their own networks and those they maintain for govern-ment customers. The government is greatly concerned about the security of its own data entrusted to contrac-tors and expects contractors to adhere to strict informa-tion assurance guidelines and to cooperate and share data about cyber attacks in order to counter such threats. At the same time, there have been news reports of govern-ment intelligence agencies attempting to access data in commercial networks, including those operated by their own contractors, which is somewhat ironic."*
- Government contractors have been integral to the im-plementation of Obamacare. They have been *"at the forefront of setting up government websites, health in-surance exchanges and providing navigators to inform consumers of their various options,"* explains McGovern. *"This development is typical of this area of practice where the focus shifts depending on the government's priorities of the day."* Further shifts could be on the horizon if the current administration's efforts to repeal and replace the Affordable Care Act (Obamacare) are successful.

Practice Areas

Healthcare – Waller

Based in Nashville – which is known as the nation's healthcare capital – Waller is one of the leading firms in the U.S. for healthcare law. We caught up with a few of its seasoned attorneys to discover what it's like to become a lawyer in this broad and rapidly evolving area.

Chambers Associate: What is healthcare law?

Lanta Wang, associate: Healthcare law comprises the statutes and regulations that govern the healthcare industry, which includes a wide spectrum of branches of law from corporate governance to real estate to healthcare regulatory to tax law and many others. Legal assistance is crucial for these clients because the healthcare industry is one of the most heavily regulated industries in the United States and liability can be extremely burdensome if clients are not compliant.

J.D. Thomas, partner: Generally speaking, healthcare law covers the range of services that clients in the healthcare industry need which are specific or related to the unique business and regulatory issues of that industry. These include healthcare-related financial transactions, healthcare regulatory work, and litigation that involves healthcare rules and regulations.

John Haubenreich, partner: Practicing in healthcare law can mean anything from high-stakes litigation with the government; detailed analysis of real estate transactions; negotiating multi-million dollar mergers and acquisitions; conducting sensitive and confidential internal investigations; securing trademarks, patents, and copyrights; and more. Clients include hospitals, drug manufacturers, physician groups, insurance companies, individual doctors and other healthcare employees, products and software creators, and startups, among many others. The healthcare industry is so wide-ranging, and so highly regulated, that virtually any company or individual doing business will need legal advice and experienced representation, at many different points – and in many different contexts – during the course of their business.

"The healthcare industry is so wide-ranging, and so highly regulated, that virtually any company or individual doing business will need legal advice and experienced representation."

CA: What does a junior associate do in healthcare?

JDT: A junior associate can expect to be asked to support the firm's more senior lawyers. This can include researching and developing an understanding of the unique issues that affect healthcare clients, reviewing contracts and other documents as part of regulatory diligence, or supporting attorneys conducting witness interviews or internal investigations for healthcare clients in response to government inquiries and enforcement actions. Given the nature of Waller's healthcare practice, junior associates are exposed to the unique nature of healthcare law early and often.

JH: Junior associates can do anything from drafting contracts and agreements; conducting legal research and drafting opinions and memoranda for the client; working on discovery and legal briefs; helping interview witnesses and preparing investigation reports; and, in many cases, directly interacting with clients, opposing counsel, and – in the case of litigation – appearing in court.

CA: What does a senior associate do in healthcare?

JDT: Senior associates are expected to take on more of a leadership role in the matters they work on. For regulatory lawyers, this can include managing compliance issues related to specific corporate transactions or researching questions posed by clients about specific operations issues. For litigation associates, this can include managing an internal investigation; responding to a complaint; identifying and researching specific legal or regulatory issues; and developing overall themes or defensive strategies.

"The healthcare industry and healthcare law are fascinating and ever-changing, so there is never a dull moment."

CA: What does a partner do in healthcare?

JDT: In addition to managing the work done by senior and junior associates, partners in the healthcare group are expected to have their eye on the high level strategic issues their clients need to be aware of. This can include identifying issues that a client needs to consider when contemplating a particular corporate deal; advising a client on what daily operational issues may be of particular concern; or assessing the litigation or compliance risk of a particular event. In addition, partners are expected to keep abreast of changes in the healthcare regulatory landscape, and how that may affect their clients and the advice they give, whether it be with regard to a particular deal, a piece of litigation, or a government investigation.

CA: What are the highs and lows of practicing in your area?

LW: The healthcare industry and healthcare law are fascinating and ever-changing, so there is never a dull moment. However, on the M&A side, client demands and schedules can be unpredictable.

"Another fascinating element is the entrepreneurial nature of the industry. There are always new ideas and new clients who need legal advice."

JDT: The best part about the healthcare practice is that it is cutting edge and dynamic.It is always changing, and good lawyers have to keep pace with those changes to give their clients the best advice. Another fascinating element is the entrepreneurial nature of the industry. There are always new ideas and new clients who need legal advice. No day or issue is ever the same.

One of the hardest aspects of the practice is advising clients who have a significant regulatory issue that may have a material effect on their business and who didn't get good advice in the first instance. Sometimes there's very little you can do to help those clients and that can be particularly frustrating.

JH: Highs include some of the biggest litigation and deals in the legal system, particularly because the industry continues to grow at a rapid pace; interesting and challenging work given the tightly regulated environment; and the experience of being an expert in a sought-after field. Lows sometimes include frustration at the level of detail and roadblocks often encountered (given the number of laws and regulations involved) and the continually changing nature of the industry and the laws and regulations governing it.

"People who thrive in an environment filled with changes and challenges should consider being a healthcare lawyer, as well as those who are creative problem solvers."

CA: Which qualities make for a good healthcare lawyer?

LW: People who thrive in an environment filled with changes and challenges should consider being a healthcare lawyer, as well as those who are creative problem solvers. Also – and I say this lightheartedly – it helps to be resilient in dealing with physicians, particularly ER doctors.

JDT: A good healthcare lawyer is someone who has an inquisitive mind and really enjoys learning about what their clients do on a day-to-day basis, but is also a careful thinker and very detailed-oriented. The healthcare industry is subject to so many regulations and the application of those regulations is very fact specific. A good healthcare lawyer is going to know the regulations, know the law, and know what their client does, and be able to give advice based on an understanding of how all those things interact.

JH: A good healthcare lawyer will enjoy learning new things, will be analytical and attentive to detail, and will not be afraid of dealing with the government (or having to think about dealing with the government). If you can't see yourself working in a highly-regulated industry – or if the prospect just makes you too nervous – then you might consider looking at other opportunities.

CA: Do you find that the different specialisms attract different personalities?

JDT: In the healthcare field, I find that the most detail-oriented lawyers often do regulatory or operational work. They tend to be people who have an encyclopedic knowledge of the Code of Federal Regulations (CFR) that they can draw on in the advice they give. I think a lot of healthcare litigators are lawyers who are very rules-based (and thus comfortable with the regulations which may apply) but also strong advocates that enjoy being on their feet and arguing a position.

"Students need to pay attention to the overall shifts in the industry, such as changes to how healthcare is reimbursed and how it is delivered."

JH: Very much so – healthcare lawyers run the gamut from folks who would not be caught dead in court (for example, some corporate and regulatory attorneys) to lawyers who relish the chance to go to battle with opposing counsel and/or the government. Healthcare law is so broad, and encompasses so many different areas of law, that virtually every personality type that exists can find a niche in which to practice comfortably.

CA: What are the current issues in healthcare that law students should be aware of?

LW: There are many changes underway in the healthcare industry – which can be viewed as both opportunities and challenges. In addition to the constant change in healthcare regulations, the changes include: strategic partnershipsbetween players in the healthcare industry (research institutions, academic medical centers, community providers, speciality facilities, physician practices, etc.); the consolidation of providers; the uptick of specialty care providers; and the injection of private equity into the healthcare space.

JDT: On a macro level, I think students need to pay attention to the overall shifts in the industry, such as changes to how healthcare is reimbursed and how it is delivered. While they may have the same names, the clients that law students are going to be representing five years from now will be fundamentally different organizations than the ones we're dealing with today. On a more granular level, I think students should pick something that interests them and dive in. I do a lot of Anti-Kickback related work, so I am always paying attention to developments in that area. See what interests you, and become an expert.

"Technology could have a massive impact on the healthcare industry."

CA: What does the future of the sector look like?

JDT: The biggest issues on the horizon are the continued pressure on reimbursement and the changes to the way care is delivered. Companies are looking for faster and less expensive ways to deliver the same care. The biggest impediment to that is going to be regulations that don't keep pace. The law students of today will be asked by clients to help them create those new care models while still keeping an eye to regulatory requirements that may not have been written with those new models in mind.

JH: Depending on the regulatory developments, technology could have a massive impact on the healthcare industry. The model is moving towards more telehealth with the advent of advanced virtual reality/augmented reality, as well as advanced diagnosis via artificial intelligence (AI) and machine-learning systems. Combined

with the impact of medical records portability (e.g., the Apple initiative to keep at least some medical records on a person's phone), the healthcare sector could become much more competitive and fragmented than it is now. If changes in payors happen as well, the healthcare industry could look very different in ten to 15 years than it does now.

CA: How can law students brush up on their knowledge of the healthcare market?

JH: The American Health Lawyers Association (AHLA) publishes an excellent newsletter with healthcare news that I highly recommend; the AHLA also has law student memberships which are affordable and hosts great conferences. Same thing with the ABA Health Law Section, particularly its publication "The Health Lawyer," which is indispensable. In terms of reading about health law, I would recommend keeping up with technological developments via sites like Ars Technica, The Verge, and TechCrunch.

JDT: In addition, sources like Modern Healthcare, Law360 and Fierce Healthcare are all excellent places to keep apprised of developments and learn more about the industry as a whole.

CA: Alongside being a summer associate, what other experiences would you advise students interested in healthcare law to obtain?

LW: Go and talk to and/or shadow healthcare lawyers practicing in different specialties. It's also worth talking to healthcare administrators about the trends in the healthcare industry and the challenges they face in the current economy, reimbursement scheme and regulatory climate.

JDT: Read about and follow changes to the industry as a whole. Good healthcare lawyers know the industry. They know the macro issues as well as their specialty, and they know the lingo. The more of that you can pick up, the better the advice and counsel you'll be able to give.

JH: I would highly recommend getting some on-the-ground experience in the healthcare industry if at all possible, whether working or interning at a hospital, healthcare company, startup, or anything else connected with the industry. Seeing the business and patient care side of things is totally different from coming at it from a legal perspective, and getting that experience will be (1) invaluable later in a person's career and (2) make a person a more highly sought-after attorney.

Practice Areas

"Good healthcare lawyers know the industry. They know the macro issues as well as their specialty, and they know the lingo."

CA: Describe the opportunities unique to Waller.

JH: Waller's depth and breadth of experience in healthcare law is unmatched anywhere in the country. Nowhere else can you find the broad array of opportunities, including corporate and deal work; high-stakes litigation; government and internal investigations; finance, bankruptcy, and restructuring; real estate; labor and employment; intellectual property; and regulatory work. Nowhere else can you collaborate with the country's leading attorneys in any number of specialties, across hundreds of clients, from some of the biggest healthcare players in the world down to local physicians and startups that need a good lawyer. Finally, the history, structure, and culture of Waller rewards attorneys who want to take responsibility and develop their careers early, unlike most of the other law firms in this space; working here means real collaboration and chances to lead early in a person's career.

Authors

John Haubenreich
Partner

J.D. Thomas
Partner

Lanta Wang
Associate

Practice Areas

waller®

Healthcare – the basics

In a nutshell

Healthcare is an industry-specific practice area that encompasses a number of traditional law practices such as corporate and litigation. Because the industry is highly regulated, specialist healthcare lawyers are often needed to monitor and react to new regulations.

Typically, the matters that healthcare lawyers deal with encompass three different categories. First is the transactional element – essentially the buying or selling of healthcare businesses. Second is any litigation among healthcare companies, and third is advising on the regulatory sphere and in relation to any governmental legislative issues.

Healthcare is a massive part of the US economy. In 2015 healthcare spending was almost 18% of GDP, and by 2021 it is predicted to account for just under one-fifth of the country's economy. Many major firms have healthcare practices and there are many niche or boutique health firms, with many of them tied to specific states.

It is also a practice that continually evolves because of ever-changing laws. The passing of the Patient Protection and Affordable Care Act in March 2010 (aka Obamacare or the ACA), for example, remains a landmark moment. One thing is for certain: the nationwide demand for healthcare advice and representation has never been greater.

Clients include investment funds who are interested in investing in healthcare, and established providers, like hospitals.

What lawyers do
Healthcare: transactional

- Healthcare lawyers are sometimes brought in as troubleshooters at the same stage of a deal that tax and antitrust attorneys are brought in (see Corporate Law). This is often the case for smaller BigLaw health practices and local healthcare boutiques.
- At other times healthcare lawyers will run a deal from soup to nuts. This happens when there are numerous health industry clients or statutes involved, so lawyers who understand the regulatory context of a deal need to be involved from the outset. This happens more often in larger BigLaw healthcare practices and boutiques, but is increasingly common given the complexity of new healthcare reforms.

- Healthcare transactional work involves putting a deal together and doing the due diligence as normal. According to **Jeffrey Schneider** of **Hogan Lovells**, however, *"these are usually very complicated deals because of the regulatory constraints that exist, so you have to structure them in ways that you might not in other industries."*

Healthcare: litigation

- Litigation work – especially in relation to government investigations – is *"the high end of regulatory healthcare work for people who have been at it for a long time and are really good,"* **Doug Hastings** of **Epstein Becker & Green** says.
- Government-funded Medicare and Medicaid payments are a major source of litigation and government investigations. *"There is a whole set of rules on how you can get paid as a healthcare provider for Medicare and Medicaid services,"* explains Hastings. *"Anyone that provides healthcare – hospitals, physicians, hospices, home care providers – will have some Medicare patients. Not only are there questions surrounding the eligibility and amount of payment, but providers might face anything from a routine government audit to an investigation into healthcare fraud."*
- Healthcare and life sciences practices see a lot of qui tam litigation – cases in which someone who assists with a government prosecution can receive all or part of the penalty imposed.

Healthcare: advice

- Outside the times when healthcare lawyers are called in for litigation and transactions, they are constantly providing regulatory advice. Schneider says: *"It's about making sure clients comply with the vast array of regulations out there that limit a company's conduct, as well as helping clients think through problems and do things in the correct manner."*
- The advice covers more than just the regulatory side as there are also contractual issues to deal with, particularly with regards to physicians and medical staff relationships.
- Among the key pieces of legislation governing Medicare fraud and abuse are the antikickback law and the Stark Law. The latter governs physicians' referral of patients to medical facilities in which that physician has a financial interest.
- Federal antitrust laws and Food & Drug Administration regulations also form an important component of health lawyers' work.

Rankings in *Chambers USA*

Top Ranked

Akin Gump	King & Spalding
Alston & Bird	McDermott Will & Emery
Duane Morris	Norton Rose Fulbright
Epstein Becker & Green	Proskauer Rose
Jones Day	Ropes & Gray
K&L Gates	Waller

Highly Recommended

Arnold & Porter	Jackson Walker
Cadwalader, Wickersham	Katten Muchin Rosenman
Choate Hall & Stewart	Latham & Watkins
Cozen O'Connor	Mintz Levin
Crowell & Moring	Morgan, Lewis & Bockius
DLA Piper (US)	Nelson Mullins Riley
Foley & Lardner	Reed Smith
Fox Rothschild	Sheppard, Mullin
Gibbons	Sidley Austin
Greenberg Traurig	Skadden
Haynes and Boone	Thompson & Knight
Holland & Knight	Venable

For more detail on ranking tiers and locations, visit www.chambersandpartners.com

Realities of the job

- *"Like every lawyer you have to be able to listen and to communicate but I think particularly for health care law you have to be able to read the law and fully understand its nuances. It is a highly regulatory practice area so you cannot be afraid of diving into statutory text and regulatory text,"* says **Edward S. Kornreich** of **Proskauer Rose**.
- Kornreich continues: *"The joy I get from solving a problem for a client is what drives the practice. In healthcare, clients tend to be people who are interested in serving the public and by solving any issues you advance the public interest."*
- Kornreich adds that the type of person who would thrive in this area would be *"somebody who is a good communicator, thoughtful and has the ability to and enjoys reading, understanding and explaining the law, as well as applying it in various contexts. It is also useful to have someone who is orientated toward social welfare."*
- On working hours, Kornreich states: *"I think they are reasonable on average. This is generally because of the nature of people as they tend to be more willing to tolerate personal lives on the part of their employees."*
- *"I think what I like the most is I'm representing clients who are dedicated to making people better. It is a very human-orientated practice. It's not just about numbers or strategy or markets. The consumers really matter,"* says **Greg Luce** of **Skadden**.

- To succeed in this practice area Luce goes on to say: *"You have to have a thorough understanding of how this business and its sectors work. Every industry has its qualities but you need to understand how a healthcare provider or manufacturer operates to understand the implications of the legal regime. You really need to know your client."*
- Luce continues in offering general career advice for this practice area: *"I think you need to match your expectations to your interests. If you want to be a litigator and test yourself and you want to be in the cauldron of a court room then do. If you want to be in healthcare and get into the policy and regulations and interested in how industry is evolving, it is a great field. It is an area that offers a lot of opportunities for entrepreneurial thinkers."*
- *"You need to be solution-orientated and practical. There is a lot of gray area in the law because it is always developing so you have to review the facts and law carefully and provide a practical solution. It is a very complex practice area so you need to be able to take something complicated and explain it in a straight forward way for your clients,"* says **Jim Owens** of **McDermott Will & Emery**.
- Owens tell us his favorite aspect of working in healthcare: *"I love representing providers. Doctors and nurses and other healthcare professionals want to help people. They have good intentions and are very selfless – it makes me happy to work with those people. Everyone has healthcare in their life, it's a personal thing. To be able to work in an industry that is doing good is rewarding."*
- However, Owens warns against the trickier aspects of the practice area: *"The amount of change is difficult so you have to keep on top of it. You always have to check what the current law is as you deliver advice. There are so many aspects to what we do which makes it very complicated."*
- *"I would say that if you have an interest in healthcare or background in healthcare you should consider this field. In the US the population is ageing and the demand is rising. Because of this demand it will be a specialism in demand,"* Owens tell us.

Current issues

- **Edward Kornreich** says the Trump administration could mean *"ACA repeal, and its unknown replacement, if any. Uncertainty is enhanced by possible Medicare and Medicaid program changes. While there is the possibility of substantial regulatory reform, this is less certain in healthcare."*
- **Greg Luce** offers his opinion on the Trump administration: *"I think it will be very significant. It's hard to imagine a single sector that will be more affected than healthcare, with combined House and Senate interest in repealing and replacing Obamacare. It will make a sea of change in the way healthcare will be delivered. The*

main difference I think will be less of a role for federalist healthcare policy and increased private enterprise and state-directed healthcare."

- **Jim Owens** says: *"I think right now the general view is that it will be positive for most businesses and sort of the same with healthcare. Trump said he wants to repeal Obamacare, but Congress cannot do so successfully without coming up with a replacement law. If a replacement law is passed, it will provide a large amount of legal work for healthcare lawyers."*

- Although the Trump administration failed to repeal the ACA in July 2017, the act is not out of the woods yet. The Republican Party formulated their new tax bill (which passed Congress in December 2017 and was subsequently signed by Trump) to repeal the ACA's individual mandate – a clause that requires most Americans to have a certain level of healthcare coverage. The mandate will be formally repealed in 2019, but the intended effect of its loss has been questioned, as the majority of Americans will continue to secure healthcare coverage through their employers or public health programs. Those who gain their coverage from the private, individual insurance markets are likely to be the most affected by the change, with experts predicting that premiums could rise by 10%.

- The desire to dismantle Obamacare doesn't stop there though: as of February 2018 20 states (including Alabama, Georgia, Tennessee and Wisconsin) have collaborated on a lawsuit to repeal Obamacare entirely. Fuelled by the overturning of the individual mandate, the state attorneys involved are now questioning the overall constitutionality of the ACA.

- The Republicans in Congress are keen to follow-up their individual mandate repeal with reforms to Medicaid and Medicare. House speaker Paul Ryan is a dominant force behind such reforms, which could alter eligibility requirements and broaden the application of premiums.

- There is increasing consolidation among care providers and integration of hospitals with other facilities. There is an increasing focus on the social determinants of healthcare, where the discourse concentrates on how services are provided and finding preventative means to keep people out of hospital. According to a recent PwC report, 73% of provider executives and half of payer executives surveyed said that their organization has or is forming partnerships with local entities (like schools and churches) to better understand and tackle the social issues tied to healthcare.

- The ACA has also placed an emphasis on providing quality, value-for-money care; consequently hospitals are trying to maintain financial competitiveness while still providing excellent services. Mergers have become an increasingly popular method to try and boost savings (five major mergers in the sector were announced during just an eight-day span in December 2017). However, hospitals need to ensure they don't fall foul of antitrust laws or regulators in the process. Law firms will continue to see a range of healthcare clients seeking advice on mergers, and regulatory and antitrust matters.

- Broadening its sphere of influence, Amazon entered the healthcare market in 2017. With its well-established logistical expertise and the backing of several state pharmaceutical boards – which granted the company distribution licenses – Amazon now has a presence in the medical supply sector.

Life sciences – Goodwin

Four associates from Goodwin share their views on what it takes to become a successful life sciences lawyer.

Chambers Associate: Which practice areas fall within the life sciences sector?

Erini Svokos: On the corporate side, all areas of a corporate practice fall within the life sciences sector. Every life sciences company goes through the life cycle of any other company: formation, internal growth, external partnerships and either an exit or an IPO. I think the defining feature of the sector is the type of clients and the collaboration within the field. Because it's collaborative on the scientific side, it tends to be collaborative on the legal side. The bulk of my practice is working on relationships between our clients and their scientific partners, either academic institutions or other pharmaceutical/biotechnology companies, to develop technology.

Noelle Dubiansky: The life sciences sector crosses over many practice areas. Many of the commercial transactions that I work on are multidisciplinary and involve a multitude of issues. For example, if I'm working on a strategic collaboration between one of my biotech clients and a pharma company, I will routinely consult with colleagues in our corporate, FDA, intellectual property and antitrust practice groups.

James Xu: I focus on capital markets, IPOs, public offerings and public company reporting. Beyond the core of corporate work I just mentioned, FDA and regulatory work is very active and tends to be more prevalent in Boston and Washington, DC. We have a robust IP group and licensing experts who focus on patent prosecution in chemistry and biology. In recent years, securities class actions have also become a hot topic.

> *"Our clients are brilliant and are on the cutting edge of medicine. Often their goal is to develop therapies to address diseases."*

CA: Does Goodwin have a particular specialism in any of these?

JX: Goodwin has experts in each of these practice areas and we handle every stage of a life sciences company's business. Our clients are brilliant and are on the cutting edge of medicine. Often their goal is to develop therapies

to address diseases. It's wonderful we are contributors to that and the work can be challenging due to the nature of the industry. The FDA and their framework can often change quickly. As a firm, we have the depth of knowledge to create a cross-disciplinary group which allows us to work very well together.

CA: What do you enjoy least and most about your work?

ND: I really enjoy working with clients that are working on cutting edge technology and have the ability to make a substantial impact on patients' lives. One downside as outside counsel is that you work with many clients at one time and as a result you often don't see the incremental events that occur after the closing of a transaction.

CA: What are the differences between non-contentious and litigious life sciences work?

ES: The corporate side of the life sciences practice is more collaborative than the litigation side. Though things still can become contentious during an M&A transaction or a joint-venture negotiation, at the end of the day both sides are working toward the same goal of completing the transaction. On the litigation side, both sides are working for the opposite goal.

ND: On the transactional side, we are working with our clients and the other party to come to a mutual agreement on the terms that will govern the relationship between the parties and that will form the basis for future collaboration. It's not a win or lose situation that you often see in litigation.

> *"Usually most of my clients are in the discovery process of their first drug candidate or have just completed their early clinical trials for a drug candidate."*

CA: Can you give us an idea of the clients you work with and why they need lawyers?

ES: I work with mostly early stage biotechnology companies. Usually most of my clients are in the discovery process of their first drug candidate or have just completed their early clinical trials for a drug candidate. I've helped our very early stage life sciences clients work with academic institutions to license technology from a professor's laboratory to be used in the company's scientific development. Because it's such a collaborative field, a bulk of my practice is negotiating collaborations between our life sciences clients and either academic institutions or other biotechnology or pharmaceuticals to research new drug candidates or technologies. Our role is to help navigate those negotiations and alert clients to potential future risks regarding the terms of those transactions.

Sarah Ashfaq: We work with a broad range of life sciences companies, from early stage to mature public companies. Their legal needs vary and can include formation, corporation organization, structuring, assisting with employment-related issues, securing intellectual property, and executing financing transactions.

CA: How does the work differ from more traditional areas of law such as finance?

ES: The differentiating factor of the life sciences sector is that it is focused on discovery and scientific achievement. It's both risky and rewarding. A great scientific achievement or scientific failure can have an extreme effect on the success of a life sciences company. The work differs because the clients are beholden to the science.

ND: Life sciences work is very client specific and tailored to the client's technology. You need to take the time to understand the client's technology and products in order to be able to advise them properly.

CA: Where does the life sciences sector intercede with politics?

ES: Developing a drug requires significant financial investment. Therefore, many of the therapies or technologies our life sciences clients develop are expensive once commercialized and sold to patients. A lot of the intercession between the life sciences sector and politics centers around the price of drugs once they're being sold to patients.

ND: The life sciences sector is a regulated industry so it intercedes with politics in many ways. Depending on the administration and its focus, this can come into play because of the mandates that agencies such as the FDA, HHS and FTC focus on.

"There is a push to incentivize individuals to go into stem fields and encourage additional investment in hard science fields, which is a great thing."

CA: Are there anty political developments that have affected the sector recently? Are there any on the horizon?

ND: I don't think we can tell yet. We know that the current administration would like to narrow the Affordable Care Act but I think it's too early to see how this is going to play out and what the consequences will be. It will also be interesting to see how the recent tax reform will impact pharma, medical device and other life sciences companies, and in particular whether it will result in increased spending on new business and development activities.

JX: Government fund cuts impact basic investments and the actual science. There is a push to incentivize individuals to go into stem fields and encourage additional investment in hard science fields, which is a great thing. There are cuts in government funding which could be a negative for the industry we operate in and it's tough to gauge the net impact. Incentives by the government and allocation of resources to the Centers for Disease Control will have an effect on how much companies are able to do as well as investments in early stage life sciences companies.

CA: What was your role on the latest deal/case you worked on?

ES: On larger M&A and collaboration transactions, I typically work with the partners to draft the underlying contracts and assist in the negotiations. It's helpful for the associates on the transaction to have an in-depth understanding of the nuances of the terms of the contract.

ND: Recently I worked on a deal for a client that involved the out-license of a late stage asset from a pharmaceutical company. For this matter, I was the senior licensing attorney running the deal, including the negotiations, with support from a mid-level licensing associate and our corporate team on the equity portion of the deal.

JX: I am currently the lead associate on capital market offerings. I manage a team of associates and I touch on every aspect of a transaction, including, leading calls with clients and underwriters to drafting disclosures for filings.

*"It is a very exciting time in life sci-
ences with promising discoveries
and developments on the horizon!"*

**CA: What is the most interesting deal/case you have
worked on?**

ES: The most interesting deals I work on are collaborations between our biotechnology clients and pharmaceutical partners because each is unique. The terms
of the contract differ depending on the specifics of the
technology to be developed. Also, because the field is so
collaborative, most of the negotiations occur in person,
with all of the parties in the same room. The in-person
negotiations are the most interesting because it human-
izes the counter-party and I think leads to better deals
for both sides.

ND: I was one of two lead attorneys that worked on
Galapagos NV's global partnership with Gilead Sciences,
a strategic collaboration agreement which included an
upfront payment of $725 million. The deal was named
the Top Biopharmaceutical Licensing Deal of the 2016
Allicense Deals of the Year.

**CA: How important is a scientific background to your
work?**

JX: It's helpful, but not necessary for most practice areas
in our field. The exception would be patent prosecution.
What's more important is your work ethic and motivation to dig into a client's business.

SA: It certainly helps, but it is not critical. I don't have a
science background and I learn by doing. My knowledge
base has expanded tremendously since I joined Goodwin
and continues to grow as my clients' and their business
needs evolve. It is a very exciting time in life sciences with
promising discoveries and developments on the horizon!

Authors

Erini Svokos
Associate

Noelle Dubiansky
Associate

James Xu
Associate

Sarah Ashfaq
Associate

Practice Areas

GOODWIN

Life sciences – the basics

In a nutshell

Life sciences is an umbrella term that denotes all of the medical and scientific products and services that fall under the following areas: biotechnology, pharmaceuticals, medical devices, dietary supplements, foods, cosmetics and environmental agents.

For lawyers, the practice area is particularly diverse as it encompasses several areas of traditional practice including regulatory, criminal investigation, enforcement, compliance, competition, intellectual property and many more. Clients range from governments to major global pharmaceutical manufacturers to start-up companies that are inventing new medical drugs.

All of this variety is broken down into three core areas for lawyers: regulatory, intellectual property and corporate. Regulatory work encompasses the likes of market authorization of products, government affairs, competition matters and compliance work. Life on the intellectual property side is focused on protecting clients' patents, while corporate lawyers assist companies with both their everyday and transformative matters, from basic employment needs and governance issues to business-altering M&A deals.

What lawyers do

Regulatory

- Assist clients with getting their products to market in various jurisdictions.
- Liaise with the government when there are objections to clinical trials.
- Help companies to improve their manufacturing techniques.
- Advise clients on how to distribute their products in line with healthcare laws.

IP

- Represent clients during patent infringement proceedings.

Corporate

- Advise on complex contractual relationships like collaborations and alliances.
- Facilitate commercial transactions involving a life sciences element.
- Assist with M&A and venture capital work containing a life sciences element.
- Take the role of lead negotiator in business transactions.

Realities of the Job

- Working hours vary across the three core areas. Regulatory work offers the most flexibility, while the hours experienced by patent trial lawyers – especially as a case heats up – can be intense. Corporate hours, as you might expect, are dictated by the peaks and troughs of the deal cycle, so periods of late nights are followed by lulls of more standard hours.
- *"It is important to be a specialist but also to learn about other fields and how they impact on each other, e.g. how the area of product liability might influence regulatory advice,"* says **Scott Bass** of **Sidley Austin**. *"One of the main challenges is keeping up with fast-changing developments and staying informed."*
- This fast pace is at the same time one of the most exciting elements of the practice, Bass feels: *"The sector is constantly changing, so there's the opportunity to break new ground often. You get to help industry but also assist governments and consumers in a lot of what you do."*
- **Latham & Watkins' Judith Hasko** agrees: *"I think you have got to have a comfort level with an ever-changing legal and regulatory environment, and you have to be interested and comfortable with change. It is an exciting industry, but people who do well like change."*
- *"You also have to be commercially sophisticated and have an interest in the commercial drivers as to why a company wants to do something,"* Hasko continues. *"In my experience you need to work well with your client. They have critical information you need. You need the full input of your client and its your job to do that. It is also challenging to tailor advice so that it makes sense to them. You just need to fully understand their goals. What is also tricky is the ability to keep a lot of different elements in your head about the law and the client's business at the same time when you are negotiating."*
- *"There is a lot of opportunity in life sciences as the legal frameworks and government's policies are constantly changing,"* Hasko explains. *"This creates opportunities for lawyers. It is very exciting and rewarding to help to move products forward that will help people. It's not a practice for everyone as it can be very technical, but for those who have a connection with the industry I would say go for it."*
- On the corporate side, **Covington & Burling's John Hurvitz** tells us: *"You have an opportunity to be involved in all phases of the deal cycle from structuring to negotiating to implementation. Also, there is a lot of deal activity in the industry so you have an opportunity to work with clients over many years and multiple transactions. These deep and longstanding relationships are very rewarding, both professionally and personally."*
- Hurvitz adds: *"A scientific background is useful but not*

Rankings in *Chambers USA*

Top Ranked

Cooley	WilmerHale
Latham & Watkins	

Highly Recommended

Arnold & Porter	Mintz Levin Cohn Ferris
Dechert	Morgan, Lewis & Bockius
DLA Piper (US)	Morrison & Foerster
Finnegan, Henderson	Perkins Coie
Gibson, Dunn & Crutcher	Reed Smith
Irell & Manella	Ropes & Gray
Jones Day	Sidley Austin
Kirkland & Ellis	Wilson Sonsini
McDermott Will & Emery	

For more detail on ranking tiers and locations, visit www.chambersandpartners.com

necessary. It is more important to have an interest in the underlying science and technology, as there is ample opportunity to learn about the latest innovations and breakthroughs. The practice is multidisciplinary so to be successful you need to be comfortable working across a range of legal disciplines, such a IP, competition, corporate, and also to have a business mindset. The business issues and legal issues are inextricably intertwined in this practice."

- Life sciences collaborations are, Hurvitz tells us, *"very complex. In addition to working across legal disciplines, there are often multiple facets of the deal that have to be managed in parallel. It is like four or five dimensional chess at times. People who are smart, curious, have good memories and attention to detail will do well. You also need to be comfortable in making judgment calls. There are often so many business and legal issues at play in any given deal, that the clients typically look to the lawyers to offer practical guidance."*

- When it comes to regulatory work, *"the most challenging thing we face in our practice is the challenge faced by industry as a whole: it is an extremely difficult and long process from invention to product,"* says **Daniel Becker** of **Fenwick & West**. *"In a 25-year career only two or three inventions that I've worked on have become a marketed pharmaceutical product. We don't get instant or even near-term gratification."* However, *"every time I come to work it's nice knowing that the work I am doing makes a difference. Very few products I work on make it to market, but when they do and you see the positive benefits it is so thrilling."*

Current issues

- *"A key issue at the moment is how governments will regulate emerging technology such as diagnostics, wearables, and home testing kits,"* **Sidley Austin**'s **Scott Bass** explains. *"There is also an issue when it comes to the regulation of breakthrough drugs like biologics and genetically based drugs."*

- While the full effect of the Trump administration remains unclear, our interviewees made some predictions. Scott Bass takes a glass half-full approach: *"The prevailing view is that it will provide more incentives for companies to explore new areas with less government regulation."*

- In contrast, **Fenwick & West**'s **Daniel Becker** adopts a somewhat bleaker view: *"It's going to be a disaster. There will be many fewer individuals who have medical insurance; there will be an uninformed and unnuanced assault on drug pricing; and there will also be a chill on bringing in talent from other countries, as collaboration will become more difficult."*

- **Latham & Watkins' Judith Hasko** raises another Trump-related issue: *"What Trump is going to do is really unclear. He has made comments recently that he would impose some types of limits on drug prices or reimbursement for drugs, which would have a ripple effect across the industry. There are also some concerns that conservative government leaders may implement policies that could hinder certain types of scientific research."*

- On a positive note, the 21st Century Cures Act was enacted in 2016. $6.3 billion has been set aside for funding medical research, including former vice president Joe Biden's 'Cancer Moonshot' program. The law could speed up the approval process for prescriptions and medical devices, increasing activity in the sector.

- According to a report by Deloitte, global prescription drug sales are forecast to grow at an impressive rate of 6.5% over the next five years. Worldwide sales are expected to be $1.06 trillion in 2022. Worldwide pharmaceutical and biotech research and development is forecast to grow at 2.4% per year up to 2022 - slightly lower than the 2.5% annual growth between 2008 and 2016. Total R&D spend is expected to reach $181 billion in 2022, compared to $156.7 billion in 2016.

- The global personalized medicine market is forecast to reach $2.4 trillion in 2022 at an annual rate of 11.8%, more than double the projected 5.2% annual growth for the overall health care sector.

- Recent large-scale and innovative life science deals included Gilead Sciences acquiring Kite Pharma for $11.1 billion, Johnson & Johnson acquiring Swiss biotech firm Actelion for $30 billion and Thermo Fisher Scientific acquiring Patheon for $7.2 billion.

- 2017 was a breakthrough year in scientific achievements with drug approvals hitting a 21-year high. This will likely make it easier for drug manufacturers to eventually get their product to market.

Practice Areas

- 3D printing is being explored as a better way to manufacture cell and tissue products. Drugs and disease
  models can be tested on 3D-printed tissues instead of
  on animals or humans.

*"I think it's important for young, graduating law
students to be thinking not just in terms of their
substantive interests, but in terms of culture and
environment so they find a place they're comfortable in. I've found over the years that the primary
driver of success is creating the right environment for yourself. You enjoy the work more.*

*I think it's critical that students choose a place
where they really feel comfortable and respected,
and can have some degree of control over the
direction of their career."*
– Jonathan Schaffzin, member of Cahill's
executive committee.

The Inside View

The Inside View

As you will read in The Inside View, law firms can vary massively – all have their own quirks – but most share common features as businesses. Here's what JD grads should expect...

What firms have in common

- At most BigLaw firms juniors join a **single department** on their first day. Some firms allow rotations either within a broad practice area (like corporate) or across the whole firm.
- Usually entry-level associates begin life at a firm with low-level **'junior' tasks** – the grunt work like due diligence, document review, document production, collecting closing signatures and so on. You have to start somewhere, but things do get better: drafting, advising clients, negotiating with opposing counsel. How steep the learning curve is depends on the firm, but there are usually certain responsibilities that fall to individuals at each level. For instance, a BigLaw junior is unlikely to be taking depositions, but they may second-chair one. The higher the dollar value of a matter, the lower a junior's level of responsibility tends to be.
- If a firm is known for a certain area of practice, don't assume this is all it does (for example, there's a lot more to Weil Gotshal & Manges than just bankruptcy). Boutiques aside, at most BigLaw firms corporate and litigation are the two biggest departments. Either a **specialist department** – like IP or labor & employment – will exist alongside these, or specialities will be discernible in a firm's corporate or litigation work (for example, a focus on product liability or energy).
- Junior associates usually **have their own office**, although at the largest firms – especially in New York – juniors will share with another lawyer for their first one or two years.

- The most common cliché about BigLaw is true: lawyers do work some long hours. Client and partner demands can mean long days and all-nighters when the going gets tough. Where firms differ is in how often such 'firedrills' occur, how regularly you're expected to work weekends and late at night, and how frequently you end up canceling events in your private life for work.
- Many firms have a formal **billable target**. Others don't. But that doesn't mean lawyers work any less. All firms expect attorneys to work an amount which reflects how active their department is. If you're significantly below the average, that's bad news. Billing is the be all and end all of lawyer life.
- Law firms are increasingly relaxed about where lawyers do their work. Most juniors try to be in the office during **business hours**, but few partners expect juniors to be at their desks every day from 9am to 9pm. At the same time, many firms allow and expect flexibility from their juniors. This means that working from home in the evenings and on weekends is common. Associates are expected to check emails on their smartphones and be communicative outside office hours.
- Devoting a proportion of your time to **pro bono** is encouraged at most firms. Some allow a certain number to be counted as billable; at others this number is essentially unlimited. In practice, juniors are usually free to pursue pro bono projects provided they do not interfere with paid work. Only rarely do juniors devote more than 5–10% of their time to pro bono.

Adam Leitman Bailey, P.C.

Lawyers per state

25

Largest US office: New York
US offices: 1
International offices: 0
First-year salary: no lower than $150,000
Billable hours: requirement varies by associate
Summers 2018: 2
Revenue 2017: $20 million
Partners made in 2018: 0
Famous for: real estate work, especially condos and foreclosures

"We eat, breathe and sleep everything real estate" – this bold Manhattan boutique is on the hunt for self-starters with a thirst for litigation.

ADAM Leitman Bailey, the man, the firm, the brand, is a formidable force that seems somewhat larger than a 26-lawyer boutique that practices just one thing: real estate law in New York. Its focus – mainly contentious – is abundantly clear when you visit the website. So, too, is the firm's go-getting attitude: a squad of marching lawyers dressed for success with Adam at the center; 'The largest condominium settlement in New York history,' says one banner; 'Most New York real estate appellate victories,' says another; and 'WE GET RESULTS' is a permanent fixture.

This raises the question of what the results are, and who gets them? Well, back in 2011 the firm successfully sued Donald Trump into a settlement – this may not be a current story, but it's indicative of this small firm's skills, given the President's stated desire to never settle. It resulted in a 90% refund of the deposits that had been handed over by investors in Trump SoHo in response to their claims of fraud. Clients range from *"the home owner who has an issue with their neighbor to companies like Wells Fargo, Verizon and Fidelity National* [a real estate insurance giant]," said an associate. ALB promises victory in litigation: this is a bold firm on the hunt for gutsy associates. In return, the firm offers newbies plenty of opportunities in court, transactional juniors a lot of client

contact and all associates an environment where they can *"eat, breathe and sleep everything real estate."*

The Work

A lot of the firm's work comes through Bailey himself, after which he assigns it among the senior lawyers. In practice this means newbies have to *"go out and find it. At the beginning, it's harder to get work because you haven't been able to prove yourself,"* so work acquisition has to be about building relationships with senior members. Although the majority of what ALB does is contentious, there is also a transactional team *"that does bank closings, contracts and sales."* On both sides there are more specialist areas, with recent associates slotted into foreclosures, landlord/tenant, condominium/cooperative, title insurance, and commercial real estate.

"The partners really molded me into the lawyer I am today and I cannot be more grateful."

On the litigious side ALB often helps banks with foreclosures, which saw some juniors *"mainly writing and drafting; I could to go court but the type of work I do requires otherwise. But it's nice that they do give you that opportunity."* We spoke to some sources who were very frequently in court *"making oral arguments. We also have motions that need to be written and all kinds of documents that need to be reported and filed. It can be difficult as every county has their own rules and ways for each document."* Not that the challenge of the work was a problem:

On chambers-associate.com...

● Get hired at ALB: all the essential info

See firm profile on p.609

The Inside View

Rankings in *Chambers USA*

Real Estate

For detail on ranking tiers and ranking locations, visit
www.chambersandpartners.com

"I learned so much more than in law school just due to the hands-on experience. The partners really molded me into the lawyer I am today and I cannot be more grateful." Over on the transactional side, associates could be aiding condo boards and landlords by *"trying to cut deals; in practice I'm doing due diligence managing contracts, negotiation provisions and talking to my clients."*

The frequency and type of client contact associates got was mixed. Those doing contentious foreclosures mainly servicing banks found *"the partners handle the direct contact, which I am very happy with. I mean if I was a client and had something important being dealt with I would call my attorney and want them to be on the phone!"* However, insiders on the transactional side are constantly *"talking to clients, leading the calls and coming up with options. It's very, very rare that I am not spending at least three hours a day emailing them!"* The responsibility did pose an extra challenge, however, as it was not uncommon to have clients who are strong-willed and demanding – *"You end up saying 'that's what the building department requires, I am not making it up'. But they fight you on everything!"*

Culture & Hours

Our sources thought of themselves *"as typical New Yorkers,"* and there's an assumption that associates here *"are go-getters."* They *"take their work really seriously; we want to get and win the best cases,"* said an associate. Bailey himself has high standards on presentation and expects his team to look businesslike: *"We can't schlep into the office looking like we have not slept, which does mean I am doing my make up on the train some days."* Some sources put this down to the clients being *"very confident, professional people. Everybody has a sophistication to them and they are looking for sophisticated attorneys who have high expectations and want a certain kind of work."*

"We can't schlep into the office looking like we have not slept."

In any law firm, take a look at how revenue is generated and shared, and you have a better understanding of the culture. ALB's pay structure is relatively unique, and one that fosters a sense of ownership among all members: *"We share the common goal of trying to be the best lawyers we can."* All attorneys receive a base salary that varies depending on experience. However, there's plenty of opportunity to earn more at ALB: first, there's a 'revenue sharing program' that enables associates to earn a third

Recent work highlights

- Won a $40 million case in the Brooklyn Supreme Court which limited the degree to which successive condominium sponsors could be held liable for defects caused by the original sponsor
- Represented a Tenant Association in a $20 million dispute with their landlord, after the landlord's attempt to raise the rent and claim $2 million in costs
- Defended a restaurant during its eviction and the demolition of its premises after it was struck by a crane, in a $2.5 million suit
- Helped a defrauded commercial real estate broker claw back $550,000 that they had been owed

of their billable hours (that the firm collects and clients pay); second, there's a 'bonus possibility' scheme that allows each individual (regardless of level) to earn up to 20% of any new business that they bring in. Feelings were somewhat mixed toward the overall system. Some felt it's *"great as you get rewarded for how hard you work, which is the right way to do it."* Others felt it was *"a little bit frustrating"* that the calculation is not done on the total number of hours billed but rather on the revenue brought in, which left insiders *"taking the risk that clients are slow to pay."*

Bonus pay is determined by an attorney's billable rate, which is set by Bailey, and he has *"the authority to lower or raise them based on performance."* Billable hour targets can be anywhere between 1,600 and 2,000, but *"it's normally 1,860 to 2,000."* This translated into a starting time of around 9:30am and leaving at 7:30 to 8:30pm. These hours may appear on the more reasonable end of New York law, but one lawyer did mention that *"I only really have time to eat at my desk."* Late nights were not completely unheard of. Sources had been up till *"3:30am and then had to wake up three hours later to go to work. But that's not the norm."* Associates were happy that *"typically, we try not to work on the weekends, but with emails being what they are today, I am on 24/7."*

Pro bono hours
- For all attorneys: undisclosed
- Average per attorney: undisclosed

Office & Social Life

Although not unique to ALB, sources did note that maintaining a social life can be hard and involves *"a conscious effort to make time for friends."* But insiders did feel the office as a whole was *"very social. Adam likes to encourage us to feel we are all family. There are two holiday parties: one in the summer and one at Christmas. He basically requires that everybody go because he wants to make sure the firm keeps its family type of environment and everyone's*

See firm profile on p.609

The Inside View

Diversity	Partners (%)	Associates (%)
Women	22	40
White	-	-
Black/African American	-	-
Hispanic/Latin American	-	7
Asian	-	14
Mixed/Other	-	-
LGBT	13	-

face is seen. We also celebrate all members' birthdays and get their favorite cake, and have wine parties when people are hired, and when new associates pass the bar."

"Views of the Hudson river and the statue of liberty."

Reassuringly for these New York real estate connoisseurs, its Battery Park offices are *"a comfortable and beautiful space. They really take care of you! Each associate has their own office and there are beautiful conference rooms with views of the Hudson River and the Statue of Liberty."*

Training & Development

Like much at the firm, ALB's approach to training is pragmatic and one that fosters a lawyerly independence. Associates work directly with a senior lawyer who then reports on their progress to Bailey. Feedback and training mainly come in the form of getting *"told 'you did a hell of a job' or 'listen, we could do a better job next time'."* Experiences with this approach were mixed: some thought *"it's the one thing you will get the most complaints about. You are expected to be your own boss, do your own work and then ask for help if you need it."* Our sources were mainly comfortable with this style, though, and found that *"constructive feedback is given on a daily basis."* But views varied and some were effusive: *"So far they have been giving me the training to be the best attorney I can possibly be."*

"They have been giving me the training to be the best attorney I can possible be."

Diversity

Insiders felt ALB was *"very open to diversity, Adam is a proponent and would love to have even more."* As evidence they pointed to the firm's scholarship program, which offers underprivileged high school students a full ride to college along with mentoring and internships at the firm. One source also felt that the presence of *"two very strong female partners"* further demonstrated that there *"is definitely equality of opportunity."* In concrete terms diversity at the firm translated to a third of the firm's associates being female along with 20% of the partners, and a number of recent hires coming from minority backgrounds. But one area in which the firm notably diverges from the BigLaw norm is in educational backgrounds. ALB famously does not hire graduates from top-ranked schools (see Get Hired online for more), preferring instead to focus on high flyers in mid to low-ranked schools. Of the sources we interviewed, none had gone to the T14 and all were from local schools in New York State.

Strategy & Future

According to Bailey, *"ten years ago, we represented one Fortune 500 company and now we have just over 100 of them and represent just about every bank in the US."* This was done in part through cultivating clients entirely by referrals, relying upon the strength of their recommendations, and through a breakthrough with a huge condominium settlement: *"We found a way to use the Interstate Land Sales Full Disclosure Act (ISLA) to assist owners purchasing over 100 units in all newly constructed buildings to be able to terminate their contracts or receive a large discount off of the purchase price – that rocked America. In many ways, we were wreaking havoc on developers and now many of our former adversaries have hired us to represent them. It has become too dangerous for developers not to hire us even if only to conflict us out from suing them in the future."* Bailey insists he is intensely focused on the present: *"I know that in order for this law firm to excel in the long-term future, the only thing I must focus on is how we strive for greatness today. Today, if we have the best attorneys in New York in our office, the future of the firm should excel with this model of excellence. My motivation is excellence and not prestige and mega-profits for myself. Hence, the focus is on New York and real estate and the quality of our product."*

See firm profile on p.609

Akin Gump Strauss Hauer & Feld

Lawyers per state

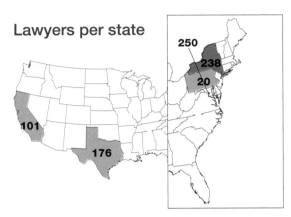

250
238
20
101
176

Largest US office: Washington, DC
US offices: 11
International offices: 9
First-year salary: $180,000
Billable hours: 1,950 soft bonus target
Summers 2018: 71 (13 1Ls, 54 2Ls, 4 SEOs)
Revenue 2017: $1.04 billion (+6.1%)
Partners made in 2018: 13
Famous for: global restructuring prowess; DC lobbying

Born in Texas, Akin Gump's biggest office is DC and management is based in New York. This is a firm with roots across the nation and growing international branches.

HUGELY influential in Washington, DC. Making a big impression on the international stage. Second name that rhymes with 'jump.' No, we're not talking about the 45th President: this is Akin Gump. *"We're well known as a DC-type firm even though we were founded in Texas,"* associates told us, *"especially given our ties to Robert Strauss."* The former US Middle East envoy, ambassador to the Soviet Union and Akin Gump founder gives his name to the firm's diversity scholarship.

Akin Gump earns tippy-top *Chambers USA* rankings for bankruptcy, government relations and Native American law nationwide. The firm also merits *Chambers Global* rankings for international trade and restructuring worldwide. *"I'm really proud to say we've doubled our international presence in terms of numbers of lawyers since 2012,"* chairperson Kim Koopersmith tells us. *"It's now at 20% in Asia and Europe, and almost half our offices are outside the US."*

The Work

Each office has its specialties – Philadelphia is an IP hub, for instance, and Houston has a sizable oil and gas practice – but everywhere that takes on juniors slots some into litigation. Staffing in the department is *"fairly organic,"* but *"there's now a practice area coordinator in DC. Partners aren't quite used to it yet."* Associates were happy to keep things loose, and generalists got to work on *"securities cases, restructurings and product liability. The latter involves more discovery and investigations – it's less intellectually rigorous but you get the nuts and bolts experience."* In contrast, securities work means *"a lot of interfacing with plaintiff counsel, as the partners are very hands-off."* DC litigators tend to focus on government contracts work, balancing False Claims Act cases with commercial matters. They found *"the more purely litigious matters are less predictable and more high-stakes, because you run the risk of missing court deadlines."* White-collar investigations work is also up for grabs.

Corporate is also common to almost every location, and is likewise shifting toward a more formal assignment system. *"It's better now,"* interviewees felt, *"as allocation is kept fair."* Rookies are general goods for two or three years, and can try their hand at debt finance, SEC filings and public or private M&A. M&A work comes with *"a lot of due diligence. Juniors organize all the specialists and draft small sections of ancillary agreements. Teams depend on you."* However, this does mean *"it can be tricky to take vacation."*

The Inside View

See firm profile on p.610

Rankings in *Chambers USA*

Appellate Law	International Trade
Bankruptcy/Restructuring	Investment Funds
Capital Markets	Labor & Employment
Corporate/M&A	Litigation
Energy & Natural	Media & Entertainment
Resources	Native American Law
Government	Projects
Healthcare	Tax
Intellectual Property	Telecommunications

For detail on ranking tiers and ranking locations, visit
www.chambersandpartners.com

"Juniors organize all the specialists and draft small sections of ancillary agreements."

The restructuring group is coordinated by an assigning partner in each office – a system which *"varies in how well it works. Sometimes everyone is busy so you'll get work even when you're feeling at capacity."* Akin Gump acts for both creditors and debtors, with one source estimating it splits *"70:30"* respectively. *"On debtor cases there's a lot more client contact as there are so many different things to do, so you build up more of a rapport."* Walking the tightrope between transactional and litigious-style work, restructuring juniors strike a balance between *"motion drafting, research, revising settlement sheets and implementing edits from seniors."* Given the firm's rock-solid restructuring reputation, it's no surprise sources were *"always busy. I'm a person who learns by doing and I've got just enough responsibility to feel challenged."*

The intellectual property team is about 50 lawyers strong nationwide, and the trickle-down work system left some *"feeling like there could be a little more structure and transparency."* The group primarily handles patent litigation defense for pharmaceutical and medical clients, but *"we don't say no to anything – if it involves patent litigation we'll take it."* Juniors saw some document review, but also more intellectual tasks including discrete pieces of research and preparing summaries of invalidity contentions. *"I'm happier than not,"* one source concluded.

The healthcare group also handles some IP as well as litigation, regulatory counseling and corporate work within the sector. Interviewees reported: *"We deal with issues across the practice and the firm makes sure juniors get fully involved."*

Recent work highlights

- Advised tech services company Novitex Holdings on its $2.8 billion merger with rivals SourceHOV and Quinpario
- Defended midstream partnership Regency Energy against multiple securities suits brought following an $11 billion transaction
- Represented EOG Resources in a $2.5 billion merger with Yates Petroleum and various related entities
- Helped cancer research foundation Smashing Walnuts to lobby Capitol Hill and secure $12.6 million in funding

Training & Development

Novices have a week of initial training covering the basics, followed by some practice-specific sessions. Following that there's *"not much formal training, though there are CLE opportunities to sign up to."* Some associates said training is *"something the firm could improve on,"* requesting *"more skills training."* But those who'd taken advantage of programs, including NITA deposition sessions and a *"two-day boot camp"* in restructuring, felt *"we get enough. A lot of learning comes on the job."*

The firm's Individual Development Plans review system has been *"retooled to be more open-ended, so you get more regular feedback from senior people you work with."* Sources were again split over the changes, but largely *"preferred the new way. Some partners don't take it as seriously as they should but it helps to keep us on the development path."* Juniors are also assigned both a partner and an associate mentor.

Offices

Several of the firm's offices are also going through changes and moving to new buildings in the next couple of years. And that's a good thing too – Akin's DC office has *"a great location, but the architectural style is definitely brutalist, with a lot of concrete. We're moving in mid-2019 and I'd imagine there will be a lot more glass."* The Dallas team are relocating in winter 2018 and are *"really excited about the super-modern new building."* One positive feature of both current locations is external offices for all – that's not the case in Houston, *"which kind of sucks, but that just comes down to the space we have."*

"The center of gravity is shifting toward New York."

Akin Gump New York spans the 41st to 46th floors of the Bank of America Tower and boasts *"spectacular views from the reception and conference rooms."* A recent lateral hiring spree means that *"starting in 2018 first to third years will be sharing offices."* The growth led some to suggest *"the center of gravity is shifting toward New York"* away from the official DC HQ. Management is indeed

See firm profile on p.610

Diversity	Partners (%)	Associates (%)
Women	20	43
White	87.8	79.8
Black/African American	1.85	3.8
Hispanic/Latin American	3.3	5.9
Asian	6.7	8.0
Mixed/Other	0.4	0.4
LGBT	2.2	2.8

based in NYC, but others clarified: *"There's still a lot happening outside of it, even if it is the hub."*

Culture

"There is a unifying culture that the firm tries to develop, though Texas lawyers are inevitably going to be different to New Yorkers," interviewees believed. Dallas juniors noted that *"the partners here are a young group and are very engaged with the associate experience,"* while a DC source said: *"I've worked in a number of dysfunctional offices, and this is nothing like that. Partners will pop into my office to chat about sports."* Associates applauded chairperson Kim Koopersmith for *"doing really well to establish firm values across all the offices. It seems like she's always everywhere!"* The firm's website identifies those values, in capital letters, as 'Collegiality, Commitment, Excellence, Integrity and Intensity.'

Each practice group has its own character, too. *"Litigation is more family friendly than corporate,"* sources revealed, *"and restructuring isn't all that social but other groups certainly are. People are generally friendly outside the office."* Summer is the busiest time in the social calendar, when attorneys often head to baseball games or the Kennedy Center in DC, but most offices also have biweekly happy hours and holiday parties. *"We're all very friendly together, but I don't have to spend a lot of time hanging out with coworkers if I don't want to."* However, associates agreed *"firm events are well attended,"* including those run by the active women's committee.

Diversity

In 2017, Akin brought in Michele Meyer-Shipp as its first ever chief diversity and inclusion officer, tasked with overseeing firm-wide diversity efforts. Hiring partner David Botter told us: *"We're really excited about her joining the firm. Our diversity efforts don't begin and end at OCIs – we work with law schools, affinity groups and other organizations throughout the year."* Implicit bias training has also been introduced, a program which *"originated with an affinity group and management took to heart."*

> *"The head of the firm and of the corporate group are both female role models."*

Statistically, Akin Gump is roughly average for gender diversity, but sources pointed out that *"the head of the firm and of the corporate group are both female role models."* Racial diversity *"has been a struggle across the firm, and going into recruiting season it's something we really focus on,"* insiders told us. *"I was expecting more diversity in terms of individuals' backgrounds,"* admitted one interviewee. As well as a national diversity committee, there are local groups in each office representing LGBT and ethnic minority attorneys.

Get Hired

"We're trying to retool the way we do interviews to be more effective," sources revealed, *"by asking questions that will indicate candidates' ability to succeed at the firm."* For more on this, visit chambers-associate.com

Pro Bono

Akin offers a Pro Bono Scholars Program, which sees seven to 11 students each year spend four weeks of their 1L summer at the firm doing pro bono before a (minimum) seven-week stint at a public interest organization of their choosing. It provides a good launchpad for associates who *"love pro bono and have got heavily involved,"* one source said. *"I try to do 100 to 200 hours a year."* Immigration, refugee and asylum matters are hot in the current political climate, but we also heard of cases like *"representing inmates in the federal prison system who've had their parole mishandled."*

Pro bono is counted wholly toward associates' bonus target, and sources *"hadn't experienced any discouragement to take it on. They do want you to do your billable work too, obviously!"* Interviewees also praised central management for maintaining a good flow of interesting cases and encouraging attorneys to get in cases of interest.

Pro bono hours

- For all attorneys across all US offices: 84,388
- Average per US attorney: 105

Hours & Compensation

Associates need to bill 1,950 hours to qualify for a bonus, and with all pro bono included most agreed *"it's very achievable if you stay diligent."* The target isn't formal and *"not reaching it probably wouldn't be a big problem."* Higher-level bonuses are available for workaholics – there's no official upper target but sources suggested

See firm profile on p.610

2,300 hours as a ballpark. *"Overall it's fair,"* most agreed, *"though it's interesting there are no stub bonuses for first-years."* The lack of first-year bonuses caused a stir in the legal press in late 2017, but in 2018 the firm announced it was introducing pro-rated bonuses for newbies.

"There aren't many people burning the candle at both ends; when they are they're doing it at home at least."

Facetime is *"important to an extent, but the firm is fine with flexible working and I've never felt like I can't go to a doctor's appointment or anything like that,"* associates agreed. That said, most found themselves heading home around 6:30 or 7pm, as *"everyone around here seems to do that. There aren't many people burning the candle at both ends; when they are they're doing it at home at least."* When pressed on how hot the candle can get, one source confirmed: *"When it's super-slammed I've been here until midnight, but that isn't frequent. I've never been here all night or anywhere close."* Attorneys get 20 days of vacation and interviewees had *"taken a ton of it. Things can come up but everybody else generally tries to pick up the slack if someone's away."*

Strategy & Future

Don't expect any dramatic policy shifts or major changes of pace at Akin Gump anytime soon: chairperson Kim Koopersmith suggests that *"what we'll do in the future is much the same as what we've been doing in the last dozen or so years – grow within the areas where the firm already does well."* Akin Gump knows what it's known for, it seems. Koopersmith summarizes this as *"energy, policy, international trade, restructuring, appellate law and disputes. I foresee continued expansion within all those areas, which may in some instances be geographic."* Associates noticed more laterals coming on board recently, but with *"so much work coming in"* they had no fears about the head count growing too quickly. To learn more about the future of the firm, read our full interview with Koopersmith at chambers-associate.com

The Inside View

Allen & Overy LLP

Lawyers per state

37

142

Largest US office: New York
US offices: 2
International offices: 42
First-year salary: $180,000
Billable hours: 2,000 target
Summers 2018: 22 (all 2Ls)
Revenue 2017: $1.98 billion (+0.5%)
Partners made in 2018: 0 (in the US)
Famous for: Cross-border work; British roots; magic circle prestige

Associates bring their A game to 'magic circler' A&O, where expansion plans are afoot and *"BigLaw resources"* are utilized in *"smaller, navigable offices."*

"IT'S in the DNA of the firm to do cross-border work, and my workflow has certainly reflected that," one happy junior summarized for us. Despite glowing reviews from associates year on year, Allen & Overy may not be the very first name that springs to mind when you think of BigLaw (unless you live in A&O's native London, or indeed any other global financial hub). However, with a slew of *Chambers USA* rankings in areas like antitrust, capital markets, litigation, and corporate/M&A, this magic circle member and its international reach merit attention. And while *"plenty of firms list a bunch of offices on their website, A&O is a firm that's actually fluently international,"* associates enthused. Their work had crossed borders into the Netherlands, India, Belgium, Libya, Germany, the UAE, Luxembourg, India and, of course, the UK.

"A&O is a firm that's actually fluently international."

Those lucky few who managed to land themselves an offer – class sizes typically consist of fewer than 20 associates – wanted A&O's magic combination: *"BigLaw resources and smaller, navigable offices."* The firm even won over summer associates who'd previously been on the

fence about BigLaw: *"Understanding complex problems that cover various jurisdictions is intellectually interesting. Getting a taste of that got me excited."*

Excitement is certainly in the air at A&O right now. Juniors are hopeful since *"head honcho"* partner Tim House relocated from London to *"make New York bigger, badder, and better"* as US and Latin America senior partner. An influx of new partners wasn't bad for morale either: *"Those partners could have gone anywhere. It's a vote of confidence."* On the finance and securities side, A&O strengthened its ranks with additions from Paul Hastings, Proskauer Rose and White & Case, while partners from Cadwalader and a white-collar defense boutique have bolstered the firm's litigation practice.

The Work

Incoming associates in New York have the option to sample two practice groups; if they decide to do so, they spend six months in each before choosing to focus on one permanently. If they are still unsure after these rotations, they also have the option to sample a third area. (In DC, things are different as the office is smaller: juniors here are assigned to a particular practice straight away, but still get to work on cross-practice matters that expose them to various areas). The main options are project finance, banking, international capital markets, corporate, leveraged finance, tax, restructuring and litigation. Across the groups work distribution involves *"an open dialogue"* with one or two partners, who are *"tasked with assigning according to business need and everyone's avail-*

On chambers-associate.com...

- Get hired at Allen & Overy
- Interviews with New York managing partner Dave Lewis and hiring partner Laura Hall

See firm profile on p.611

Rankings in *Chambers USA*

Capital Markets	Government
Corporate/M&A	Latin American
Environment	Investment
Financial Services	Litigation
Regulation	Projects

For detail on ranking tiers and ranking locations, visit
www.chambersandpartners.com

Recent work highlights

- Defended Samsung against allegations of participating in international price-fixing conspiracies
- Successfully filed a petition to obtain a €128 million arbitration award from Spain on behalf of equity fund manager EISER
- Acted for German healthcare company Fresenius Kabi during its $4.3 billion acquisition of Akorn, a Chicago-based manufacturer of pharmaceutical products
- Represented Credit Suisse as lead arranger of a series of loan facilities made for Linxens, a French manufacturer of connectors for smart cards

ability – it means you don't get people who are incredibly slammed while others are light on work."

A third of the associates on our list had ended up in litigation, which meant a *"50/50 split between civil litigation and investigations."* The former tends to be more domestic-focused while the latter is *"almost always international; when I got here I was placed on an enormous, multinational investigation into market collusion involving one of our big 'blockbuster' clients."* We spoke to associates who'd done foreign bribery cases *"representing either a European or US company being investigated by the government for potential corruption in Libya, Indonesia, India – any emerging market where you expect a high corruption risk."* That's undeniably interesting work, but how stuck in can you get as a junior? *"Your role is to be the one who's most familiar with the facts. Research is the junior bread and butter across investigations and disputes. Also fact-developing: reviewing documents and putting together a narrative of what's happened on a case."* One highlight was *"being able to take the lead during some witness interviews and getting those 'aha!' moments where you know you've got something significant."*

"Your role is to be the one who's most familiar with the facts."

"There's a focus on growing" the banking leveraged finance group, and *"it's exciting to be a part of it: at least half of the work is cross-border. We often work with private equity companies looking to purchase a company or make a strategic acquisition, and therefore negotiate credit agreements and commitment papers."* If a deal comes in, *"you'll spend time getting it launched, which involves a lot of drafting and client contact. Once it's submitted, you'll go back to maintaining the other deals you have on your plate, by doing typical administrative matters like schedules and deliverables."* On the whole, *"it's a very precedent-driven practice – you maintain and build up a database of precedent documents to use as a basis for drafting, but also shape documents according to the nuances of a particular deal."*

Corporate associates had worked on *"a couple of private M&A deals where you run the diligence process and work on the disclosure schedules that are tied to the purchasing*

agreement." Smaller deals saw them *"helping to mark up the purchase agreement and ancillary documents; setting up limited liability companies and handling one-off questions from clients where you research an issue and figure out an answer."*

Training & Development

"There are regular on-site CLEs tailored to your practice group," juniors reported. There are other formal programs to get stuck into: second-years take part in *"'make your mark' training, which gives you an introduction to how things operate and the firm's strategic focuses."* In addition, most practice groups run global 'universities,' which bring together associates from across the network for a couple of weeks' training in London: *"We learned about joint ventures, the diligence process, accounting – things that gave us a foundation and framework to refer back to."*

A&O recently switched to an 'ongoing feedback' system called 'Compass,' which sees associates meet with an assigned partner once every quarter to discuss their progress. *"It's basically formalized something that already happens a lot here – rolling feedback that's useful. If I didn't understand an assignment (or if my seniors felt I didn't understand it) then a partner puts time in the calendar to help me see where the disconnect was and how I can do better."* The firm has also recently launched an app which allows attorneys to submit regular feedback as well.

Diversity

"Gender diversity is a big priority," associates relayed, pointing to the firm's global initiative to boost the percentage of female partners to 20% by 2020. *"We're very close to hitting that figure in the US."* In New York, a new women's committee hosts quarterly events. *"The head of the entire firm spoke at the first women's cocktail hour, and the committee also held some training as part of the 'make your mark' series."*

See firm profile on p.611

The Inside View

Diversity	Partners (%)	Associates (%)
Women	18.2	44.1
White	90.9	72.1
Black/African American	0	2.9
Hispanic/Latin American	0	5.2
Asian	9.1	16.9
Mixed/Other	0	2.9
LGBT	11.4	4.4

Juniors also highlighted a *"fairly large contingent of LG-BTQ individuals. When I was in London there was an 'A&Out' event, and in New York there was a gala in the city and the firm paid for anyone who wanted to go."*

Hours & Compensation

Associates aim to hit 2,000 billable hours each year. *"During your first year they don't really expect you to hit it as it can take a bit of time to get ramped up."* Our sources mostly found the target achievable in subsequent years. If associates fall short of the 2,000 hours *"the firm generally doesn't penalize you for it, as long as you've been actively seeking out work when things have been slow."* Juniors didn't have *"the greatest clarity"* when it came to bonuses, but did say it was still possible to get one even if the 2,000 hour target isn't reached.

> *"...everyone has the time differences in the back of their mind."*

Juniors had this to say on dealing with multiple time zones: *"Everybody knows how to deal with other offices, so from the beginning everyone has the time differences in the back of their mind – if you know something is due in Europe, you'll know when it needs to get finished in New York."* But no amount of planning can completely combat potentially long hours – this is BigLaw, after all. Those in leveraged finance spoke of short bursts of being *"very, very busy for five days, where you're working round the clock,"* but also of *"not coming in before 10.30am"* during quieter periods. Busy times can mean up to 12 hours in the office, but in general the firm's stance on facetime was appreciated: *"You're allowed to work outside the office on an ad hoc basis as long as you can recreate the working environment."*

Culture & Offices

Just over two thirds of the associates on our list were based in A&O's New York digs. *"The office is really convenient – it's close to the Rockefeller concourse, so there's easy subway access and lots of places to grab lunch."* The rest of our sources were based in DC, not far from the White House. *"We have a vista of the Washington Monu-* ment – the rooms with the best views aren't partner offices, but client meeting rooms, and anyone can book them. I think that says a lot about our culture."*

And on the subject of that culture: *"It's never felt competitive, and any competition would be healthy competition, not 'this is my piece of the pie and no one else should touch it.'"* Others elaborated on this side of A&O: *"I wouldn't think twice about calling someone I didn't know in another office to ask a question. On my first assignment I just called someone in Germany and he walked me through the issue."* Associates who'd spent time in overseas offices noted: *"The culture isn't completely homogeneous but it's well integrated. People know all the other associates within their practice area, whether they're in London or Hong Kong."*

Being *"plugged into an international network"* doesn't mean associates forgo *"the benefits of a more intimate office environment."* A&O's US bases are still comparatively cosy next to some of the nation's domestic heavyweights, and at the time of our interviews, associates in New York were getting stuck into the fall spirit: *"Yesterday there was a trick or treat event for people's children, and someone brought in a fall-inspired cake. It's a warm and happy place to work."*

Strategy & Future

"This is a very exciting time for A&O," says senior partner Dave Lewis, who tells us that the firm's US strategy is focused on *"absolute growth. We are not nearly the size we need to be to complement our size, scope and breadth around the world. So we're looking to make our US offering considerably larger going forward."* For more from Lewis, visit chambers-associate.com.

Pro Bono

The number of pro bono hours that can count toward the billable target recently increased from 50 to 150 – a welcome jump, from our associates' perspective. Juniors can also devote 50 of those allotted hours to firm-sponsored community investment projects, like those conducted in association with the charity War Child. Another development saw *"a pro bono associate and partner appointed to spend a portion of time keeping track of who's doing pro bono and who the contacts are at organizations we work with, as well as sending out weekly emails that list opportunities."*

All associates are expected to reach a target of 50 pro bono hours each year, and many of our interviewees had devoted time to this noble pursuit. Examples included a contested divorce through Her Justice; an asylum matter tied to LGBT discrimination; an immigration case for

See firm profile on p.611

The Inside View

children seeking special juvenile status; and a brief composed for international organization Redress.

Pro bono hours
- For all (US) attorneys: 8,745.3
- Average per (US) attorney: 51.5

"We love to see people who have started their own businesses or those who are veterans – to me that shows a tremendous work ethic and a high degree of resilience. They are attributes that I have a lot of respect for. Let me give you an example: in our recent intake we had a person who noticed that their law school didn't have a domestic violence clinic. They got together with a couple of friends, founded one, went to the dean of the law school to get funding, and recruited students into it. Something like that shows real initiative and the ability to get stuff done, as well as a passion for an issue that matters to them."

– recruiting partner Carolyn Hoecker Luedtke, Munger

See firm profile on p.611

Alston & Bird LLP

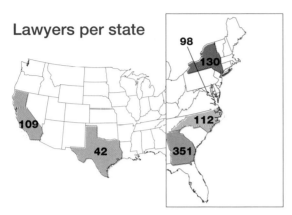

Lawyers per state

98
130
109
112
42
351

Largest US office: Atlanta
US offices: 9
International offices: 2
First-year salary: $155,000-$180,000
Billable hours: 1,950 target
Summers 2010: 55 (9 1Ls, 46 2Ls)
Revenue 2017: $781.8 million (+7%)
Partners made in 2018: 21
Famous for: High-flying status in Atlanta; good partner to associate ratio; emphasis on promoting home-grown talent

A&B juniors are keen to spread their wings – and this Georgian giant is just as keen to help them on their way.

"*WHEN you come to A&B you're not just a tool for billable hours, you're a future partner.*" No, that's not a marketing line lifted from Alston & Bird's website — that's the hope and ambition we often heard from the eager junior associates we interviewed here. Many of them were sold at the interview: "*I really did fall in love. I feel they're invested in my professional and personal growth, and how those two interact.*" As a legal market, Atlanta – where the firm's HQ is and the largest group of associates are based – certainly appealed to those "*looking for a little more work-life balance*" compared to what firms further up the east coast might offer. And when it came down to choosing A&B specifically, "*the prestige factor was number one: it has a reputation for being one of the top full-service firms in the city.*"

"home-grown talent – that permeates the culture."

A&B is indeed a weighty presence in the Peach State, where it picks up a number of top-tier *Chambers USA* rankings in areas like litigation, corporate/M&A, real estate, banking & finance and healthcare. Juniors enthused about a broad clientele that ranges from "*local big-names in Georgia to national and international clients,*" includ-

ing Coca-Cola, Nokia, UPS and Wells Fargo. Elsewhere, A&B also secures praise for its work within North Carolina, DC and California; the latter state became a point of focus in 2017, when the firm opened a new San Francisco office and expanded its offering in LA. However, in light of this growth associates were keen to flag that the focus is still very much on nurturing "*home-grown talent – that permeates the culture.*"

Strategy & Future

On the topic of the new Cali office, chairman Richard Hays tells us: "*We relocated a partner who's been with us for more than 20 years to the San Francisco office to help integrate new partners and others in the office. That has enabled us to serve our clients in the area, and has opened the door to new client opportunities – especially in areas like litigation and insurance.*"

Elsewhere, Hays explains that A&B's sector-based work in healthcare and with financial institutions continues to thrive. He adds that "*the economy is doing better, so we saw more M&A activity in 2017. Nobody has a crystal ball but we're expecting to see a continuation of that, along with some volatility. We also continue to see demand in the cybersecurity and data compliance area.*" For more from Hays, visit chambers-associate.com

The Work

At the end of the summer program, successful associates receive an offer to join a specific practice group – they

The Inside View

See firm profile on p.612

Rankings in *Chambers USA*

Antitrust	Government
Banking & Finance	Healthcare
Bankruptcy/Restructuring	Immigration
Construction	Intellectual Property
Corporate/M&A	International Trade
Employee Benefits &	Labor & Employment
Executive Compensation	Litigation
Energy & Natural	Privacy & Data Security
Resources	Real Estate
Environment	REITs
ERISA Litigation	Tax
Financial Services	
Regulation	

For detail on ranking tiers and ranking locations, visit
www.chambersandpartners.com

Recent work highlights

- Defended fast food chain Wendy's during a series of consumer class actions following a data breach of customer payment information
- Represented T-Mobile in multiple class actions and investigations relating to its alleged use of technology to monitor customer communications
- Served as counsel to the underwriters – including HSBC, Morgan Stanley and Wells Fargo Securities – of several public notes offerings made by Coca-Cola
- Acted for NBA basketball team Atlanta Hawks as it developed a first-of-its-kind training and sports medicine center

can make their preferences clear at the end of the summer. By far, most newcomers on our list ended up in the litigation & trial practice. IP litigation took the next largest chunk, while the rest were spread between transactional groups like corporate transactions & securities, real estate finance & investment, and financial services & products.

Across the groups, juniors get work in several ways. First, each junior is formally linked up with *"three people they can get work from – I have three partners but you could be grouped with senior associates too."* Second, there's a *"workflow management system"* that juniors fill out once a month to highlight whether they can take more work on or not: *"The practice group leader keeps an eye on how busy people are to spread the work around."* Third, there's the informal route of *"building relationships – it can just be a case of seeing someone in the hallway and asking if they have work. You gravitate to what you want and those people gravitate to you."*

The litigation & trial group practice covers *"a myriad of general commercial cases."* Among the most common strands encountered were antitrust, healthcare, white-collar defense, insurance and international arbitration matters. What juniors do *"totally depends on the size of the case: big clients may have a team of 30 people working for them, so we'll be doing doc review, but on a small case where you're working one-on-one with a partner we could be writing motions to dismiss and deposition outlines."* Other sources reported managing doc review teams and actually taking depositions during the discovery stages of cases. Some juniors in IP litigation had specialized in pharmaceutical matters, while others worked for *"a wide range of tech clients: I'm the lead associate on one case for a Georgia-based company and I'm heavily involved in the strategy."*

"...working one-on-one with a partner."

On the transactional side, juniors in the corporate transactions & securities practice are encouraged to work in both streams. Due diligence is *"pretty common,"* but sources also picked up ample experience *"handling signings and closings, doing research, and revising and drafting documents – I've put together ancillaries and produced the first draft of a simple purchase agreement."* Real estate sources had worked on a mix of public finance and development deals, and reported a good system for ensuring progress: *"We have a multipage checklist that covers the first three years in practice; it includes broad points like 'do a leasing deal' but also breaks them down into specific tasks."*

Hours & Compensation

Associates across the groups found the 1,950 billing target *"achievable – if you're billing regularly it's not so difficult."* Hitting those hours makes juniors bonus eligible, and there's more up for grabs if they bill more: *"At a minimum, you'll get 4% of your salary at 1,950, 8% at 2,050 and 12% at 2,150 – there's a discretionary amount for anything over that too."* Overall, sources felt *"well compensated,"* with Atlantans telling us *"our base salary is top of the market for the city, and while our bonus structure isn't, it is nonetheless competitive."*

"We're expected to have a life outside of work."

Work-life balance varied among groups. Those in the transactional practices were happier on this front, with one telling us that *"110% I've struck a balance, especially compared to other Atlanta firms."* Bear in mind that for some this still meant *"working maybe once every four weekends,"* and long days of ten hours and upwards were the norm. Litigators felt the balance *"isn't where it should be,"* but put this down to finding their feet in practice rather than the firm's stance on hours. *"One of the messages several associates got in our recent reviews was 'find a way to take vacation.' We're expected to have a life outside of work, and they realize the benefits of that, as you'll*

See firm profile on p.612

Diversity	Partners (%)	Associates (%)
Women	23.2	43.3
White	92.2	73
Black/African American	1.9	6.8
Hispanic/Latin American	1.6	5.7
Asian	3.5	11.7
Mixed/Other	0.8	2.8
LGBT	3	4.6

come back to the office and do better work!" We heard that "people with kids tend to leave by 5:30/6pm so they can have dinner with their families – if something comes up they can usually take care of it from home."

Training & Development

A&B's "pretty extensive" annual reviews combine a self-evaluation with critique from other attorneys, and culminate in "a meeting with your practice group leader and a partner on the associates' committee." Juniors found the whole process to be very worthwhile: "You get an email containing everyone's feedback the day before the meeting; they rank you in several categories and provide comments. I got constructive feedback and as a result of that put together a good action plan for my second year."

Practice-specific formal training is delivered through 'Alston & Bird University.' There are 'colleges' devoted to litigation, IP, corporate and tax, as well as more professional skills like business development and communication. IP litigators were particularly impressed, as their sessions were "focused on substantive areas of IP law – they're concentrated in the first year but continue beyond that." The firm's mentorship program also fared well: "When you start you get both a partner and a senior associate mentor for four years. They allocate a budget so you can take them to lunch and talk – they're there for you if you run into any issues or have questions." Some were especially happy with the scheme: "They really do invest in you and want you to stay for the long haul."

Culture

Associates repeatedly touched upon A&B's "emphasis on home-grown talent" when discussing the firm's culture. "What differentiates us is that we retain a lot of associates – the partners know that and so tend to invest in developing your skills." This, juniors felt, promotes a "healthy, phenomenal" culture from the top down: "It's anti-A&B to be a yeller. From our managing partner Richard Hays to our paralegals to the folks making coffee and keeping the space beautiful – they know your name and face. It makes the long hours easier."

"...doing the same work as the traditional 'white-shoe' firms, but with more of a smile on our faces."

Many linked this more amiable vibe to the firm's Atlanta roots. "It's an easy cop-out to say, 'we're a Southern firm so we have this Southern charm,' but I think there is some truth in it," thought juniors. "We pride ourselves on doing the same work as the traditional 'white-shoe' firms, but with more of a smile on our faces." At the same time, associates emphasized that "we're still a big firm, and a lot is demanded of us, but the people you're working for make it known how appreciative they are, and to the extent it's possible they are with you in the trenches. I had a major doc review project and the partner said: 'I'll take 100 docs, the mid-level can take 100 and the junior can take 100.' That level of pitching in tends to be the norm here."

Offices

A&B's Atlanta HQ is based in midtown in "the tallest building in the city." The office was renovated in 2014 and juniors raved about the improvements made: "When I've brought pro bono clients and my family here they've all been blown away. There's lots of marble and glass, every associate has their own office, and there are great resources in the building like a dry cleaners, a florist, and a gym in the basement." What's more, the area is fast becoming "a hub for Atlanta business. Looking out my window now I can see nine or ten cranes putting up new high-rises." The city itself is "super affordable – tons of people, especially juniors, are buying homes here. Plenty of us live within walking distance of the office."

The firm's New York office housed the second largest group of juniors on our list. Its Park Avenue address means it's a convenient "two blocks from Grand Central station." Renovations are also underway here: "We have four floors and we're working on them one by one – we've got clean carpets, nice furniture and a Starbucks on the first floor." The remaining juniors were fairly evenly spread between the DC, LA and Charlotte offices, with just one or two joining bases in Dallas, Durham and Silicon Valley. "They make a pretty concerted effort to keep everybody linked between offices," sources told us, highlighting a lot of cross-staffing on matters and "a travel budget that allows you to attend training sessions in other offices. Many people work from other offices too, if they're visiting family in a certain city, for example."

Diversity

Among A&B's diversity efforts, associates especially approved of "a confidential suggestion box," which resulted in the implementation of a "breast milk shipping program for women who are traveling for work – the firm pays to

See firm profile on p.612

The Inside View

have the milk refrigerated and shipped back home. After someone proposed it the program was in place within a month." Some associates felt the firm should do more to address unconscious bias in the workplace: *"White men tend to give work to other white men, so you have to be more of an advocate for yourself as a woman or a minority."* However, they felt confident that A&B's women's initiative and wider diversity committee would tackle this and other issues: *"They plan panels, mentoring programs, lunches and dinners. They also have a budget to send people to certain diversity CLEs."* The firm also told us that unconscious bias training is rolled out on an annual basis across all offices.

Pro Bono

Associates had made full use of the 150 pro bono hours that can count toward the billing target: *"I maxed that out and even went over. The experience you gain is transferable to the billable side."* In Atlanta, there's *"a full-time pro bono partner with tons of ties in the community. She helps to organize and distribute opportunities for all kinds of cases – landlord and tenant, domestic violence, appellate, asylum. You could go to her and say, 'I'm interested in saving the rainforest in a far flung country,' and she will get you involved."* Associates outside of Atlanta had no trouble getting work either: *"We get weekly emails from various organizations, and if we want we can develop our own projects – the firm's happy and willing to guide us through that."*

Pro bono hours
- For all US attorneys: 55,778
- Average per US attorney: 63

See firm profile on p.612

Arnold & Porter

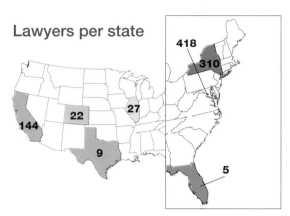

Lawyers per state

418
310
27
22
144
9
5

Largest US office: Washington, DC
US offices: 9
International offices: 4
First-year salary: $180,000
Billable hours: 2,000 target
Summers 2018: 8 1Ls, 57 2Ls
Revenue 2017: $951.5 million (+0.7%)
Partners made in 2018: 8
Famous for: life sciences expertise; commendable pro bono track record

As the dust settles on its 2017 merger, A&P is focused on further consolidation and expansion outside of its strongholds in New York and DC.

KICKING off 2017 with a bang, DC-headquartered Arnold & Porter officially tied the knot with New Yorkers Kaye Scholer on New Year's Day. The joining of these two *AmLaw 100* firms created a legal hotshot with over 1,000 lawyers, 13 offices worldwide and more than 30 practice areas. Juniors who'd originally applied to either A&P or KS suddenly found themselves part of something bigger, but any concerns that they'd ended up somewhere completely different were quickly dissipated. *"I'm happy with my decision to come here,"* one reflected. *"I think the firms have came together really well."* Another source revealed that *"people joke about how even the separate office buildings themselves seem very similar – they have the same materials and decor."* Further indicating a happy honeymoon period is the firm's recent name change (for marketing and branding purposes), from the rather convoluted 'Arnold & Porter Kaye Scholer' to the much smoother 'Arnold & Porter.'

"...we're keen to carry forward that momentum across all of our offices."

Our interviewees reflected the views of those at the very top: chairman Richard Alexander tells us: *"The two firms*

would not have combined if we hadn't had confidence that there was a cultural fit." There were also beneficial practice area and industry synergies, as Alexander explains: *"The combination puts us in an elite position in the life sciences industry because we have the core expertise for the range of issues: regulatory, litigation, counseling, antitrust, etc."* He adds: *"Real estate finance and finance more generally are areas of great strength to the firm. Then we have a very strong regulatory practice among other areas, like the government contracts, environmental, banking, securities and white-collar spaces."* Most of these areas pick up accolades in *Chambers USA*, and other practices of note include antitrust, general commercial litigation and IP, as well as corporate/M&A & private equity.

Strategy & Future

"We will continue our ongoing efforts to cross-sell our strengthened expertise as a combined firm and differentiate ourselves in the marketplace," Alexander adds. *"We want to continue to make sure the marketplace is aware of what we think is a unique a platform. We are focused on building on what we have done – and we're keen to carry forward that momentum across all of our offices."*

Does A&P have its eye on expansion into new markets? *"We're always looking for opportunistic expansions, but there's no particular market in mind at the moment,"* Alexander explains. *"We are also focused on the lateral market – we're really pleased that Bill Baer and Debbie Feinstein, two prominent antitrust practitioners in the US, returned to the firm. We will continue to invest in the practice areas*

On chambers-associate.com...

- Recruitment advice from members of A&P's hiring committee
- Interview with chairman Richard Alexander
- More on A&P's government contracts work

See firm profile on p.613

Rankings in *Chambers USA*

Antitrust	International Arbitration
Appellate Law	International Trade
Bankruptcy/Restructuring	IT & Outsourcing
Capital Markets	Leisure & Hospitality
Corporate Crime &	Life Sciences
Investigations	Litigation
Corporate/M&A	Media & Entertainment
Environment	Privacy & Data Security
Financial Services	Products Liability
Regulation	Real Estate
Government	Securities
Healthcare	Tax
Intellectual Property	Telecommunications

For detail on ranking tiers and ranking locations, visit
www.chambersandpartners.com

Recent work highlights

- Represented Samsung during a consumer class action that arose out of the recall of its Galaxy Note 7 phone due to issues with its lithium ion battery
- Advised LoanCore Capital on several real estate finance deals worth over $1 billion in total, including the $70 million acquisition financing of candy manufacturer Necco's headquarters in Boston
- Acted for manufacturer GE Healthcare as it secured a licensing agreement with medical imaging specialist Lantheus for the continued development and commercialization of an agent that could improve the diagnosis of coronary artery disease
- Represented Google and Motorola Mobility during a series of related cases involving nine patents tied to the use of digital rights management technology

in which we are well known and will work to grow all of our offices given our strengthened balance sheet." Go online to read our full interview with Richard Alexander.

The Work

Half of the junior associates on our list were working within A&P's expansive general litigation department. The firm's real estate, IP & technology, and corporate & finance practices took on a fair number of the remaining half, while groups like life sciences, government contracts and antitrust only took on a few each. In the larger practices, juniors are assigned work through an assignment coordinating committee, which is made up of both assigning partners and non-attorney practice managers. Associates can still get their work more organically, however: *"A natural part of BigLaw is developing relationships with partners, so you can end up working with them outside of the assigning system."* Others in smaller offices or teams reported a more informal approach to assignment overall: *"It would be nice if someone knew how much was on my plate before calling me, but I like that I can pick and choose which relationships I want to build."*

The umbrella of general litigation covers areas including intellectual property, employment, product liability, white-collar defense, and securities enforcement. *"As a fairly junior lawyer, I wanted the opportunity to try out different areas, and I've been able to do just that."* Large product liability trials could *"go on for many years,"* so sources opted to balance these out with smaller white-collar cases (*"on some of those it's just been me and a partner."*) Interviewees praised the *"substantive experience"* they'd been able to build, even on those larger cases where *"you're not necessarily in the courtroom but still contributing to case strategy."* Smaller matters saw juniors *"setting up client calls and traveling to attend client meetings,"* and there's plenty of *"brief writing and motion drafting"* up for

grabs too. *"You're busy, but not often overwhelmed – if I ever feel that things are piling up too quickly the teams are very understanding."*

"I like that I can pick and choose which relationships I want to build."

Real estate covers both real estate finance (mostly in New York), and more general transactions, like acquisitions and developments. Associates here had tried their hand at *"drafting contracts, coordinating with clients and third parties, and dealing with closing logistics. You can also take on discrete drafting assignments outside of the main deals you're working on."* On the finance side, a lot of clients are lenders, though a portion of the work does involve representing borrowers. Over in IP & technology, sources had encountered companies from the *"electronics, telecom and life sciences spheres."* Some had been honing their skills on medical device cases which exposed them to *"drafting, research and fact-finding assignments during the discovery stage."* Visit chambers-associate.com to find out more about A&P's top-tier government contracts work.

Training & Development

All associates complete a few days of orientation training when they join, *"which tells you all about how the firm operates and how to use the available technology to be efficient."* There's also a 'new associate retreat,' which lasts for two days and brings together all newbies from across the offices (*"even the international ones"*). It has been held in both the DC and New York offices in the past, and covers sessions on things like what is expected of associates, client service, networking skills, and the firm's core values. From then on, *"there are constant training sessions offered,"* which are tailored to associates' practice and year group. DC residents told us about some trial

See firm profile on p.613

The Inside View

Diversity	Partners (%)	Associates (%)
Women	21.4	51.4
White	88.3	75
Black/African American	2.7	6
Hispanic/Latin American	2	3.9
Asian	5.7	12.2
Mixed/Other	1.3	3
LGBT	3.3	4.9

sessions that were currently being held, as well as a writing group *"which meets monthly – it's fun and therapeutic, and teaches you how to make your writing stronger."*

"It's fun and therapeutic, and teaches you how to make your writing stronger."

Despite the wealth of formal sessions on offer, sources across the board agreed that *"the best learning comes from working on assignments and having good attorneys as your supervisors."* Interviewees were similarly relaxed about formal reviews (*"they'll come by and go over what people have said about me – hopefully it'll all be good"*), and were positive about the extent of feedback they were receiving on the job: *"You get it simultaneously as you work, even if it's quick comments from partners to say they liked your work."*

Culture

A&P was deemed especially *"supportive of family-friendly policies and work-life balance,"* with the DC office boasting a *"huge daycare center in the building where lots of attorneys send their kids."* Many sources agreed that *"supervising attorneys are very understanding about people needing flexible schedules to coordinate other responsibilities. People are expected to get their work done, but we're given leeway when we need it."*

"The firm is full of genuinely kind, smart, hard-working people."

"I really haven't noticed a difference since the merger," one interviewee told us, capturing the consensus view on the topic. Another added: *"The merger was a great fit. In New York Kaye Scholer had the larger office, so we didn't have a huge number of people come over, but we've made sure we've reached out, introduced ourselves socially and cross-staffed opportunities."* It was a similar story over in DC, where Arnold & Porter had the larger office, a source said: *"We had a small group come over from Kaye Scholer, but it's been a seamless transition."* Overall, sources felt that both legacy firms *"weren't over the top or flashy, in the way that some New York firms can be. Instead we're*

maybe a bit more reserved but welcoming, and the firm is full of genuinely kind, smart, hard-working people."

On the social scene, the New York office has combined the best of both worlds from the legacy firms: Arnold & Porter's Thursday night staple of pizza and beer, and Kaye Scholer's Friday night tradition of cocktails and canapés. In DC, however, *"the firm puts on a happy hour every day at 6pm. It's held in our garden room on the tenth floor, and while people don't attend every day, you can always find a crowd of people to sit and talk to."* The smaller offices usually host weekly drinks, and in Silicon Valley there's also a weekly yoga session which *"does make people seem more human!"*

Get Hired

"Make sure that you pay attention to where the practices actually are," juniors advised. *"Some are concentrated in a certain office, like regulatory in DC, for example."* For more advice from A&P's hiring committee, visit chambers-associate.com

Offices

New York and DC were where most of the juniors on our list resided (70% combined). Over in DC there's a lot of litigation and regulatory work available, and the office itself is *"fantastic: it's only two years old and everything is clean, open and full of light."* In New York, litigation is the biggest group, but there's also a hefty corporate and finance offering. Juniors here share an office for the first two years before graduating to their own space in the third year.

Smaller bases include the recently renovated Silicon Valley office. It houses a prominent intellectual property department, as well as life sciences and corporate groups. The San Francisco office, meanwhile, is located in the financial district of the city, and has views of *"Market Street, which is a bit like the Champs-Élysées of the city – okay, I'm exaggerating a bit but it is a beautiful city!"* Here there's a good representation of the main practices, as well as specialist areas like attorney liability. *"It's a mid-sized office in the network, but we don't feel like the ugly stepsister – we definitely feel like we have a presence here."*

Diversity

A&P has several active affinity groups that come complete with helpful acronyms: VALOR (Veterans and Affiliates Leadership Organization); ACCORD (Attorney Community Championing Our Racial Diversity); and WISE (Women's Initiative for Success and Empowerment). There's also a Pride group and a parents' network.

See firm profile on p.613

These groups generally meet on a monthly basis, and a retreat recently brought all diverse attorneys together: *"It was the first one hosted by the new firm, and hopefully it will become an annual thing."* Praise went out to A&P's recruitment efforts, especially in San Francisco, where *"we host special events at local law schools in the Bay Area – it's a separate channel to the OCI process."* We heard that the firm's other offices also host similar events at local law schools.

Hours & Compensation

Associates become bonus eligible if they reach the firm's 2,000-hour billing target – 200 hours of which can be made up from pro bono and business development-related activities. Our interviewees agreed that reaching 1,800 hours of client billable work was *"certainly achievable – most people are happy with that."* Daily starting and finishing times varied across the board, *"but spending ten hours in the office standard."* Litigators found their schedules *"more predictable than those in the transactional groups – you can maintain a fairly typical 9am to 7pm day."* Transactional attorneys *"usually work from home in the evening or on the weekend if there's more work to do,"* but did highlight that their weekends were mostly free – the case was the same for litigators.

"Everything seems to follow the market" when it comes to salaries and bonuses, and while some said that they would *"give it up to work fewer hours,"* others felt well remunerated for the work they did. There's no formal vacation policy at A&P – *"the idea is that we're all adults and can take vacation whenever we want, as long as we tell our teams we're going away and we're not leaving them in the lurch."* Juniors reckoned that *"as long as you're smart about taking leave, no one cares and there's no push back."*

Pro Bono

Many highlighted how *"highly committed"* A&P is to pro bono work, as *"people treat it the same as any other matter in terms of importance."* Legacy A&P was well known for its commitment to pro bono, and today the combined firm has a number of longstanding partnerships with organizations including Planned Parenthood and Whitman-Walker Health, as well as various groups that deal with immigration issues under the new administration. Our sources had got involved with prisoners' rights, fraud, death row and asylum cases.

The only grumble came from those who'd capped out on pro bono too early: *"It feels a bit crappy sometimes when you see the absolutely amazing pro bono work the firm does, but feel you can't do it because you've hit the billable limit."* However, attorneys can go over the 200-hour mark if they want, with one source telling us that *"yes, there's a cut off to how many hours you can use to be bonus eligible, but I'm well over the cut off and I still would take on more pro bono work."*

Pro bono hours
- For all US attorneys: 101,438
- Average per US attorney: 117

See firm profile on p.613

Axinn Veltop & Harkrider LLP

Lawyers per state

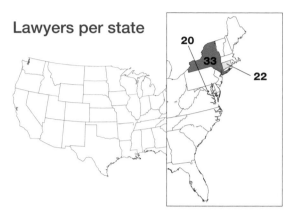

20
33
22

Largest US office: New York
US offices: 3
International offices: 0
First-year salary: $180,000 (NY/DC), $170,000 (CT)
Billable hours: 2,000 target
Summers 2018: 0 (0 2Ls)
Revenue 2017: undisclosed
Partners made in 2018: 2
Famous for: antitrust and IP; being a millennial

This boutique with a *"startup"* vibe is a firm to put your antitrust in.

BORN in the 90s, this millennial boutique has a special interest in antitrust and intellectual property. Co-hiring partner Jeremy Lowe describes the firm as being *"very much like a startup company. Everyone's excited about the growth and direction of the firm."* Head count has grown steadily in recent years, from under 60 attorneys in 2015 to over 70 in 2018. Associates describe Axinn as *"a very small firm that works on very large matters"* in the specialist areas it operates in. In New York, matter value tends to be in the range of a few 100 million dollars, or just over a billion at most. *Chambers USA* ranks Axinn for antitrust work in both DC and New York and commercial litigation in Connecticut.

Antitrust and IP are the firm's twin specialties: the former practice is home to around 45 attorneys, the latter to around 30. One area of expansion for Axinn is biotech. Outgoing managing partner Jim Veltrop tells us that *"Northern California is a major biotech hub,"* so don't be surprised if the firm opens a new office here in the near future. Lowe elaborates: *"The West Coast provides us with a great opportunity to grow in up-and-coming areas of litigation."*

The Work

Axinn's antitrust and IP groups take on the bulk of new starters, but the general litigation practice takes on a handful each year too. However, co-hiring partner Dan-

iel Bitton tells us: *"The division is not as crystalline as it may seem. The groups are very integrated and there's a lot of cross-pollination."* Juniors' work is allocated formally via an assigning partner *"who makes sure we get to work with a good variety of people."*

"It has a David vs Goliath feel to it."

In the antitrust department, *"we do all kinds of antitrust work – deals, litigation and providing counsel. A lot of people are either focused on deals or litigation but everyone gets a little experience of everything."* The work is predominantly litigious. Cases cover *"a number of industries: pharmaceutical, healthcare, insurance, manufacturing..."* The client list includes diverse and well-known national names like Google, Airbus and Stanley Black & Decker. A junior told us of their work: *"On one case I was primarily responsible for the initial draft and formulation of an argument."* Another added: *"On a day-to-day basis I manage contract attorneys handling doc review, speak to clients and make sure we meet discovery deadlines – I'm making sure all the trains leave the station at the right time!"* Associates also tend to be *"responsible for working with experts and putting the advocacy together."* The work can make forays into strategy on some cases. *"You can have a crack at the first draft of FDA white papers and presentations,"* a source reported.

The IP team works on patent litigation: *"In the overwhelming majority of cases we are representing generic drug companies, challenging other producers to get generic versions of pharmaceuticals on the market."* On such cases, associates *"draft pleadings, look over documents, and get the opportunity to depose witnesses and prepare experts*

The Inside View

See firm profile on p.614

Rankings in *Chambers USA*

Antitrust
Litigation

For detail on ranking tiers and ranking locations, visit
www.chambersandpartners.com

Recent work highlights

- Served as lead counsel to Stanley Black & Decker in its $900 million purchase of the Craftsman brand
- Represented Google before the Federal Trade Commission in litigation against contact lens company 1-800 Contacts
- Represented law firm Reed Smith in litigation over its alleged mishandling of pretrial preparations in a sex tape lawsuit against its former client, rapper 50 Cent
- Won a case for Par Pharmaceutical and Apotex against AstraZeneca, preventing it from blocking FDA approval of generic versions of its cholesterol drug Crestor

for depositions." Juniors enjoyed working on something that has *"a real-world impact. If you end up winning, that company can make lower price drugs for consumers. It has a David vs Goliath feel to it!"*

Pro Bono

Up to 100 pro bono hours can count toward associates' billable target. However, many of our junior interviewees had exceeded that amount. Regular emails are sent out listing opportunities, which range from veterans' rights affairs to housing discrimination matters to asylum cases through the International Rescue Committee. Attorneys in New York had worked for Volunteer Lawyers for the Arts, which involves representing *"low-income artists in copyright and trademark cases involving creative work."*

Associates heralded Axinn's pro bono as providing them with *"a lot of autonomy."* For example, one told us: *"I got to conduct a deposition. There was a partner who was overseeing it, but I did all the client calls, initial drafting and drafting of the agreement."* One source observed: *"There's never been a time when a partner said we were spending too much time on pro bono."*

Pro bono hours

- For all US attorneys: 3,113.2
- Average per US attorney: 35.4

Training & Feedback

Rookies have a few days of orientation when they start at the firm. *"It covers what you need to function here – technology, software, the helpdesk, memos, working at Axinn in general."* After this, *"you're basically put straight on a case and you learn by doing. There's a steep learning curve and you're expected to catch up as you go."* Associates agreed that *"it definitely was scary and intimidating at first – that's the idea, as it helps instill a fire in you. People won't be hard on you if you have trouble at the beginning, but if there are candidates who want hand-holding, they might not be a good fit here!"*

There *is* a firm-wide training program, however. Jim Veltrop tells us: *"We have a two-year cycle to cover each aspect of litigation. We have a week-long trial workshop – everyone puts their pencils down and works on their trial skills in a comfortable environment."* Associates found the

training beneficial: *"We drafted openings and closings, did cross-examinations of witnesses and also got to play the witnesses! We had one-on-one feedback, so it was as helpful as it was interesting."*

Culture & Offices

Jim Veltrop describes Axinn's culture as *"the kind you see at a lot of startups outside the law. We're really trying to instill openness: for example, we have an intranet with features like a Facebook-type page where people can talk to each other."* An associate said: *"I like that we're small, a growing enterprise. We're a really close-knit bunch."* However, when it comes to the working environment, *"it's very intense, very serious. There's not much time for small talk."*

There is time to relax with colleagues outside of work though. The whole firm went on a 20th anniversary celebration trip in 2017 – *"we went to Mohonk Mountain House for the weekend. It has a huge spa and hiking trails right out the door. There was no business side to the trip whatsoever!"* More regular social events on offer include barbecues, theater trips and basketball games. An interviewee reflected: *"Your relationships run deeper when you've sat next to someone at a ball game, rather than just saying 'hi' in the office every morning."*

"They're doing a good job keeping everyone sociable as we grow."

The New York HQ is in a prime location. *"We've got Times Square on one side and the Rockefeller Center on the other,"* observed one source. The office itself is *"minimalist – it has lots of monochromatic artwork and modern photography."* In the nation's capital the office is near Chinatown, with the interior being *"admittedly a little bare. It reflects the somewhat relaxed environment round here!"* DC associates also praised *"the best receptionist in the world, Angela. She's super friendly and always great with clients and guests. The best!"* As for Hartford, associates dubbed the city *"rather sleepy – it's a great place to raise kids, but not a place with great nightlife!"* This is reflected

The Inside View

Diversity	Partners (%)	Associates (%)
Women	16	35
White	96.0	65.0
Black/African American	-	-
Hispanic/Latin American	-	-
Asian	4.0	30.0
Mixed/Other	-	5.0
LGBT	8	8

in the building's *"more traditional feel – a dark-wood, older aesthetic."*

Associates revealed that the atmosphere differs between offices. *"We all work equally hard but relative to New York, Hartford and DC are more casual and even-paced."* Although there are three offices, many associates pointed out that *"because it's a small firm you really get to know everyone."* Despite expansion, we didn't hear of any growing pains. Sources said that the firm is *"doing a good job keeping everyone sociable as we grow."*

Hours & Compensation

Associates need to bill 2,000 hours to be eligible for a full bonus, and 1,800 for a smaller portion, though *"the firm hasn't been 100% transparent – it's not entirely clear to me how it works."* However, associates agreed that they *"don't feel a lot of outside pressure to hit the target."*

DC and New York associates typically get in around 9am or 10am, with Hartford attorneys coming in earlier at around 8am – *"I receive emails from them when I'm still in bed!"* a New Yorker joked. Hartford and DC associates tend to leave around 6pm or 7pm, while New Yorkers typically stay till later. However, across the offices many *"tend to log back on at home and work until about 9pm or 10pm."*

We heard that sometimes there are some more extreme working patterns. *"I had two months during which I was working from waking up till going to bed,"* one source reported. *"But then there were two months when I wasn't doing much at all. By the time you think 'oh my god, can I really do this?', it slows down again!"* The hours pressure is helped by *"a new formal policy whereby you can work from home two days a month, without question."* Are people making use of the new policy? Yes, we hear, *"but the office hasn't become a ghost town yet!"*

Diversity

"The majority of my office is white and male," one associate said bluntly. *"I only recently heard that we even have a diversity committee!"* The diversity committee has historically been small, but has recently more than doubled in size. We heard that it's *"becoming more active and working to become visible inside the firm and outside. We're meeting more regularly, trying to go to more events about diversity and trying to reach more diverse candidates."*

"The firm is heading toward a more diverse future."

Hiring partner Jeremy Lowe is also the chair of the diversity committee. *"We have a number of diversity initiatives,"* he tells us. *"The next summer class is the most diverse we've ever had and this year we've joined the Minority Corporate Counsel Association and their law firm affiliate network."* The firm attends events such as the National Black Law Students Association career fair and the Lambda Law Diversity Networking Reception at George Washington Law School.

In a relatively small firms like this, small changes can be significant. In the most recent promotions round before our research, all three individuals promoted to partner or counsel were women and one was Asian American. *"It's really had an impact on us,"* reflected one source. *"It gives us hope and makes me think the firm is heading toward a more diverse future."*

The Inside View

Baker Botts LLP

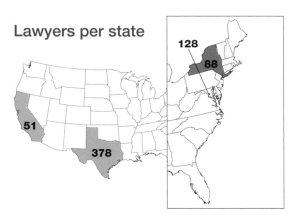

Lawyers per state

128

88

51

378

Largest US office: Houston
US offices: 7
International offices: 7
First-year salary: $180,000
Billable hours: 2,000 target
Summers 2018: 103 (32 1Ls, 71 2Ls)
Revenue 2017: $731.8 million (-13.5%)
Partners made in 2018: 11
Famous for: attributes-based 'level system'; Texas heritage; emphasis on energy and technology sectors

Sticking to what it's good at is utmost on Baker's agenda, so if you're interested in energy and technology this seasoned Texan should be on your radar.

"WE have a real focus on energy and technology," Baker's partner in charge of recruiting & development, John Martin, tells us. *"We have such a breadth and depth when it comes to our offering in those two industry sectors."* The firm's roots in Houston (where it maintains its HQ) have given Baker an edge in the energy space, while its expansion west into Palo Alto and San Francisco has bolstered its access to the tech sphere. Closer to home, a base in Austin – dubbed 'Silicon Hills' – has also added to Baker's capabilities in this ever-evolving sector.

"We don't aspire to plant a flag in every US city and European capital."

Despite a volatile oil industry in recent years, Baker's twin focuses appear to have paid off. *"From a financial perspective we're as strong as we could be,"* says Martin. *"We've had three years of record financial performance and we're having another strong year over 2017/2018."* Practice area-wise, Martin labels Baker's IP, antitrust and corporate groups as *"extremely active,"* and encourages students to keep an eye on the firm's presence in California: *"Our growth in California has been notable – over the last five years, we are the fastest-growing law firm in the combined markets of San Francisco and Silicon Valley."* On a nation-

wide scale, *Chambers USA* identifies Baker's projects expertise in the oil & gas and liquefied natural gas spaces as its pièce de résistance, while in Texas the firm picks up a raft of high rankings in areas like corporate/M&A, general commercial litigation, technology, real estate and tax.

The majority of Baker's juniors are based in its Texas offices (in Houston, Austin and Dallas), and for them Baker's standing in the state was a key pull factor: *"The historical aspect of the firm is appealing. It was founded in 1840 and has maintained its reputation for quality over a long time. That attracted me more than its potential competitors, many of whom are new arrivals on the Texas scene."*

Strategy & Future

"We're not a firm that aspires to be everywhere," John Martin continues. *"We don't aspire to plant a flag in every US city and European capital. We are a firm that believes we need to stick to our strengths and strategic plan."* Readers who anticipate joining Baker's ranks in a few years' time can therefore expect it to look largely the same as it is today – both geographically and in terms of its focus on energy and tech. That isn't to say that Baker doesn't have plans to enhance its expertise and reputation though, as Martin tells us: *"We will continue to defend our home markets in Texas and we will continue to grow in California, on the East Coast and in London – our energies are quite focused on those geographies."*

On chambers-associate.com...

- Advice on getting hired by Baker Botts
- More on Baker's offices

See firm profile on p.615

Rankings in *Chambers USA*

Antitrust	Intellectual Property
Banking & Finance	International Arbitration
Bankruptcy/Restructuring	Latin American Investment
Capital Markets	Litigation
Climate Change	Products Liability
Corporate/M&A	Projects
Energy & Natural Resources	Real Estate
	Tax
Environment	Technology

For detail on ranking tiers and ranking locations, visit
www.chambersandpartners.com

Recent work highlights

- Achieved a win for client Fujifilm after it brought a case against Sony for infringing its patents protecting its advanced storage technology
- Represented Liberty Media Corporation during its $8 billion acquisition of Formula One
- Defended Samsung Electronics against a lawsuit which targeted the company's use of virtual reality technology in its Gear VR headset
- Advised Chesapeake Energy on the disposition of various upstream oil and gas assets worth over $2.5 billion

The Work

Baker's litigation department scooped up the largest group of juniors on our list, followed closely by IP and corporate. A few had joined the firm's global projects and tax groups. All departments pair newbies up with a mentor to help get them started, before letting them source matters in a more free-market way. *"We get the best of both worlds,"* said litigators, who enjoyed the freedom to source their own work and take advantage of the more formal safety nets in place: *"We send out weekly reports, so everyone has a good idea of how busy you are."*

"I start with a blank page and write the whole thing."

Oil & gas clients regularly call upon the IP department, but this group is also known for its work in the electronics and life sciences industries. *"Our clients range from small sole-inventor types to giant technology companies,"* juniors revealed. The work itself is split between the filing and securing of patents (prosecution), and contentious work for clients who feel their IP rights have been breached (enforcement). Our sources had been able to get work from both sides of the department. *"I've worked on litigation cases where I'm the main attorney, so I do all of the initial discovery requests and handle all the motion filings. On larger cases I'll take on discrete parts of the litigation, so I might be looking into certain terms within a broader claim construction."* On the prosecution side *"you have a docket of patent and trademark work, so you're in charge of filing the initial applications, monitoring requests for responses and following up with the client if more information is needed."*

"It covers really general civil litigation," juniors in Baker's dedicated litigation department told us. The mix of matters depended on location, with those in Austin encountering a lot of appellate and class action cases, while their counterparts in Dallas had sampled securities and aviation disputes. *"We're a trial-focused group and we take matters to trial from start to finish,"* sources reported. This enabled them to do *"a lot of discovery work, which is not necessarily doc review, but more preparation for discovery motions and depositions."* Others praised the group for steering them away from doc review to *"more complex"* matters: *"Two-thirds of my work involves brief writing. I start with a blank page and write the whole thing after doing the research for it. The rest of my time is taken up with research projects for other folks, as well as some motion practice."*

Baker's *"very generalist"* corporate department spans M&A, securities, venture capital, private equity and commercial work. Interviewees here were busy *"marking up a lot of commercial agreements for clients, as well as putting together due diligence checklists and drafting resolutions."* Sources especially liked transactional work *"because everyone is focused on a common goal. There's also scope for creativity because you're identifying risks or issues and solving them in the documents you draft."* The firm's global projects group, meanwhile, is *"mostly focused on energy work; there are subgroups focused on upstream oil & gas matters; projects involving the likes of liquefied natural gas and refinery facilities; and regulatory issues involving public utilities."*

Training & Development

Come review time, Baker's 'Associate Attributes Model' comes into play. *"It breaks down the core attributes that you should be striving to develop at each stage. When senior attorneys and partners submit their feedback on our work, they'll be commenting on not just the substance of our work, but how it reflects our progress in relation to those core attributes."* Juniors were happy with this system, as it *"allows you to set goals for yourself, and is also useful for explaining to clients the value that you add."*

"...they bring judges in to assess us."

After a week of *"regular orientation training,"* which gathers all new starters in the Houston office, juniors embark on their practice-specific trainings. Sources credited Baker for having *"a pretty robust program"* that *"has become much better over the last year or so."* Those in IP

The Inside View

See firm profile on p.615

Diversity	Partners (%)	Associates (%)
Women	20	43
White	88	74
Black/African American	3	2
Hispanic/Latin American	4	6
Asian	4	13
Mixed/Other	1	5
LGBT	3	4

attended *"monthly 'fundamentals' sessions that are incredibly helpful. They've recently started doing practical skills workshops on depositions, where they bring in judges to assess us."* Corporate juniors were positive about their *"101 basics"* sessions, while litigators told us that *"there are in-house opportunities to improve your knowledge; we bring in people from the National Institute for Trial Advocacy to help us gain more practical experience. In addition, if an associate hasn't done a deposition by the point that they're expected to, the firm will go out of its way to make sure that happens."*

Hours & Compensation

Juniors work to meet a 2,000-hour billable target each year, *"which generally means you'll be aiming to bill eight hours a day, but you won't always be able to do that!"* Those in IP and litigation tended to be in the office between 8am and 6pm, but juniors in both groups reported spells of longer hours: *"When there's trial prep I might start at 10am and leave late at night – sometimes the wee hours of the morning."* A similar level of unpredictability was reported in the corporate and global projects groups; those in the latter could go from leaving at *"3:30pm one day to 11pm the next,"* and corporate juniors revealed that *"things often blow up after noon, which can mean I'm working until 10pm."*

If juniors hit the targeted 2,000 hours then the word on the street is that *"you become eligible for a New York market-rate bonus."* However, bonuses are affected by Baker's 'Associate Attributes Model.' Sources admitted that *"it's a bit complicated,"* but in essence it works like this: the firm has four 'levels' which are distinguished by certain attributes. Each level covers experiences and skills tied totwo to three associate year-groups, and comes with a range of potential bonus payouts depending on mastery of those specified attributes. *"The firm tries to be transparent about what each of those levels looks like, but it can be a bit of a black box when it comes to how the system applies to each person."* Sources were nonetheless enthusiastic about the potential to earn more money based on their skills rather than their class year. Base salaries, meanwhile, are fixed at each level.

Culture

"Our firm has a reputation for being a little more buttoned-up, which is incorrect," thought sources. They did, however, highlight that Baker *"attracts hard-working people – you get so much to do here, so you have to be efficient and dedicated to your tasks."* Others echoed these sentiments: *"We're a grounded group of lawyers who are a little more serious about what they want and how they would like their careers to progress. We're people who prioritize professionalism, but a relaxed and approachable type of professionalism."*

"We're people who prioritize professionalism."

"Most people here want to work hard and then go home to their families," so Baker isn't like *"some firms that are more party-oriented."* Interviewees added that *"most folks have kiddos, which means that it's a family-friendly environment, but not one with lots of happy hours after work."* That's not to say that Baker lawyers don't make time for socializing: we heard of holiday parties, women's initiative events, informal practice group happy hours, and Thanksgiving pot lunches that *"definitely make the firm feel like a community instead of just a workplace."* Insiders also wanted to reassure future joiners that *"if you want a more social experience you can find it here – it does exist! The junior associates tend to socialize outside of work, and tomorrow I'm going to dinner with four of my colleagues. We've had a hard week and want to de-stress!"*

Pro Bono

"Our pro bono program is amazing!" associates happily relayed. *"Every hour you bill counts toward our billing requirement."* Some of our sources had even racked up 350 pro bono hours in the space of a year. *"As long as you're getting your mandatory day-to-day billable work done you can take on pro bono in whatever capacity you want."* Those who bill 30 hours in a year become the proud recipients of *"a glass award – most people get the little glass thing!"*

"Every hour you bill counts toward our billing target."

Interviewees found it easy to get staffed on matters via local organizations and volunteer centers, but also picked up pro bono via firm lunches (*"where they talk about what kind of needs there are"*), via networking events, and by pitching projects to partners. *"People take on what they're passionate about,"* and we heard of a broad range of matters covering asylum and immigration issues, divorces and custody battles, prisoners rights' appeals, contract negotiations for local artists and inventors, tax advice for

See firm profile on p.615

small businesses, and participation in efforts to assist in the aftermath of Hurricane Harvey.

Pro bono hours
- For all US attorneys: 34,842
- Average per US attorney: 52.2

Get Hired

"Being on a journal helps to demonstrate your writing skills and sets you apart, but grades are really important – if you're coming in from one of our pipeline schools you need to be in the top 25 of your class." For more advice from Baker's juniors, visit chambers-associate.com.

Diversity

As with many firms, sources highlighted that Baker *"isn't doing so well at the partner level,"* but with regards to gender thought that progress was being made: *"We have a relatively new primary and secondary caregiver leave policy which is very generous – obviously that's not the only thing we need to do but it will go some way to help."* At the time of our calls associates highlighted the recent departure of Baker's diversity champion and coordinator as an issue: *"That was the most convincing part of the firm's policy and they haven't replaced her yet. She did a ton, and I hope they build a new position."* The firm did confirm to us that they are currently searching for a replacement and hope to have a new diversity champion and coordinator in the near future.

See firm profile on p.615

Bracewell LLP

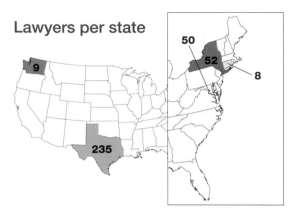

Lawyers per state

50
52
8
9
235

Largest US office: Houston
US offices: 8
International offices: 2
First-year salary: $180,000
Billable hours: 2,000 target (or 1,800 reduced compensation track)
Summers 2018: 39 (11 1Ls, 28 2Ls)
Revenue 2017: $278.7 million (+0.6%)
Partners made in 2018: 8
Famous for: three-sector focus on energy, finance and technology; highly regarded oil and gas expertise; healthy long-term career prospects

Energy work isn't all that's powering this Texan dynamo – finance and technology also fuel the firm's fire.

CONTRARY to popular belief, not *everything* is bigger in Texas. Houston-born Bracewell is a relative pocket rocket compared to many of the global juggernauts in *Chambers Associate*, and newcomers *"really liked that Bracewell was smaller; the partner/associate ratio is closer than it is at a lot of larger firms, so you're not just a number. It's a place where people stay and grow."* There's also plenty of power under the Bracewell hood – the firm packs a nationwide punch in *Chambers USA* for its energy work, especially when it comes to oil and gas expertise in the regulatory and litigation spheres. In its home state it's especially well regarded for its environment, banking & finance and technology practices.

These practices slot into Bracewell's broader picture, which managing partner Greg Bopp tells us more about: *"Our vision is to continue to be a global leader in the energy, finance and technology industries, as well as a powerhouse in strategic practice areas such as litigation and government relations."* The headline-grabbing hire of Crowell & Moring's former chair, Angela Styles, in DC has recently boosted Bracewell's government contracts clout, but Bopp tells us that he expects all of the areas mentioned above to grow. At the moment, Bracewell has eight domestic offices (four are in Texas, while the rest are in New York, DC, Connecticut and Seattle) and two

overseas bases (in London and Dubai), but that number could go up…

Strategy & Future

"We're always open to exploring new locations that allow us to better serve our clients' needs," Bopp reveals. *"We will strategically grow each of Bracewell's ten offices by deepening relationships with current clients and continuing to recruit top talent."* For the full interview, visit www.chambers-associate.com

The Work

The Houston HQ houses the biggest group of newbies, followed by the New York and Dallas offices respectively (only a few were based in Bracewell's Seattle and DC bases). Most associates fall into either the litigation or business & regulatory groups, but the odd outlier fits into a smaller niche like labor or technology. Business juniors dive into a relatively informal pooling system, while litigators are assigned a supervising partner *"who's responsible for making sure we have all the work we need, but not too much."* How much work comes from the supervisor themselves *"depends on how busy they are,"* but on average junior litigators felt that *"around half of it comes from them, and the remaining half comes from other partners."*

Bracewell's business & regulatory unit spans corporate, government contracts/relations, projects, real estate and more. The energy sector is *"a big focus"* no matter which

On chambers-associate.com...

- Get hired: interview info and more
- Interview with managing partner Greg Bopp

See firm profile on p.616

The Inside View

Rankings in *Chambers USA*

Banking & Finance	Intellectual Property
Bankruptcy/Restructuring	Labor & Employment
Capital Markets	Litigation
Climate Change	Projects
Corporate/M&A	Real Estate
Energy & Natural	Tax
Resources	Technology
Environment	

For detail on ranking tiers and ranking locations, visit www.chambersandpartners.com

Recent work highlights

- Acted as US counsel to Canadian oil and gas pipeline operator Pembina during its CAD9.7 billion acquisition of energy company Veresen
- Defended oil and gas company Apache against $1.1 billion-plus litigation brought by three energy rivals
- Represented Yuhuang Chemical as it acquired an $800 million loan facility to fund the construction of a methanol plant
- Structured and negotiated an outsourcing agreement for one of the world's largest oilfield services companies, which secured IT infrastructure services from IBM

office you're staffed in; juniors in the unit informed us that *"a lot of the clients we work with are energy funds and utilities."* They'd also picked up a lot of work on the M&A side of the practice, typically on the buyer side of the transaction. *"Because we're so leanly staffed I've managed to get a broad junior experience,"* one deal-doer said, before explaining: *"I'll do the typical due diligence and contract reviews, but also write up LLC formation resolutions and take the first turn at production sharing agreements and asset purchase agreements."* Going into the third year, associates *"get a lot more experience of midlevel work. During the busy periods you learn a lot."*

"I like being involved in the whole case rather than just being part of the production line."

Fledgling litigators were able to dabble in a mix of complex commercial, real estate, technology, IP and tort litigation, and were *"really pleased to have built up a broad practice."* The Texan offices – you guessed it – have a *"heavy energy focus,"* but work from that sector is less omnipresent in New York and other bases. *"As a junior we're involved with writing pretty much every motion in a case,"* sources explained. *"Most matters are done with just one or two associates and the partner. I like being involved in the whole case rather than just being part of the production line."* Document review and discovery are part of the junior associate experience, *"but not to an overwhelming extent as the firm trusts us to try our hand at things – and they're supportive if you don't get it right straight away!"*

Get Hired

"Initiative is the key word – rather than just doing what's assigned to you, we're looking for people with a strong work ethic who'll follow through to the next step." Brace yourself well for a Bracewell interview by checking out www.chambers-associate.com

Training & Development

Two days of 'new associate orientation' brings all fresh-faced juniors together in Houston and takes them through everything from IT to confidentiality. Corporate juniors then begin a *"great"* weekly boot camp program that consists of weekly videoconferences. There isn't a litigation equivalent, but most in the department *"haven't panicked about a lack of training. Partners do a lot of hands-on training, so it's not lacking at all!"* Juniors get reviewed every six months, and begin the process with a self-evaluation: *"The associate answers ten questions, then meets with the evaluation committee and their supervisor to get feedback."* Some found the process *"less helpful than informal and ongoing feedback, which senior associates are especially good at providing."*

Culture & Offices

Associate classes *"tend to be pretty close; we hang out outside the office and the partners sponsor us to socialize sometimes. We're pretty good at finding ways to organize that!"* Summer is the peak of the social calendar, but each office also has a Christmas holiday party and a spring service project that *"helps the local community. I've loved getting to do that, as it gives you a different perception of your colleagues."* Juniors reported high levels of communal energy across the offices, with one insider commenting: *"You need to be social here! Everybody works hard and plays hard."*

Bracewell's Houston, Dallas and New York offices have all been recently remodeled in line with *"a very contemporary design."* Houstonians in particular appreciated the *"new breakout rooms, as we have a designated space for team working,"* as well as new electric standing desks. Up in New York there are *"amazing views of Central Park and the Hudson River. Everyone has their own office and you get a lot of room even as a first year."* The recently introduced 'One Bracewell' mantra has led to increasing cross-office collaboration, though New Yorkers reported less of this than their Texan colleagues.

The Inside View

See firm profile on p.616

Diversity	Partners (%)	Associates (%)
Women	22	44.4
White	91.7	84.2
Black/African American	3.2	3.0
Hispanic/Latin American	2.5	5.1
Asian	1.9	5.1
Mixed/Other	0.6	3.1
LGBT	-	-

"We all know each other, each other's spouses, and each other's dogs."

"The whole is only as good as the sum of its parts, and Bracewell does a great job building strong teams that invest in one another," an associate said of the firm's overarching culture. *"We all know each other, each other's spouses, and each other's dogs."* Each Monday at 8:30am Central Time, all attorneys at the firm (pets sadly aren't invited) participate in a videoconference called the Monday Morning Meeting; *"you get to see people in every office every week."* Sources firm-wide noted a *"Southern culture permeating the atmosphere,"* with New Yorkers telling us that *"the partners know what the associates do – they ask me how my soccer games went, for example. It's more of a community than a hierarchy – less formal and rigid than other firms."*

While some Big Apple associates grumbled that *"transparency isn't one of Bracewell's strong points,"* those in other offices believed *"they've been very forthright with us. People here feel like they're able to ask management direct questions."* They were particularly complimentary of the firm's willingness to involve juniors during the recruitment process and get their views on potential new arrivals. *"By submitting our views, we can help to decide what type of firm Bracewell will be in the future,"* they reasoned. The management committee also meets with associates annually to talk through the firm's priorities and goals going forward.

Hours & Pro Bono

There's also a meeting at the beginning of each February to explain the bonus structure for the coming year. Currently, bonuses are dished out to those who hit the 2,000-hour mark. This can vary slightly by office: in NY and DC, for example, 1,900 hours makes you eligible for a 50% bonus. Associates had mixed reactions to this figure: some worried that *"2,000 hours has become a requirement rather than a target – it's a big point of contention,"* while

others argued: *"It's a goal, not a hard target. I don't fear for my job if I'm not going to reach it."* In the Texan offices, 2,000 hours was deemed *"very achievable; first years may find it more difficult but the work is there if you want it."* Other sources – particularly those in New York, where work peaks and troughs were more common – were less confident.

Regardless of the bonus arrangements in any given year, Bracewell allows its attorneys to bill 100 hours of pro bono and diversity-related work toward their 2,000-hour goal. Housing and landlord/tenant cases were felt to be the most common, followed by immigration and asylum matters. *"In the first year I had a pro bono matter that took up a lot of time over twelve months,"* a junior recalled, *"and I worked on some additional matters with the client too and the firm was very supportive throughout."* Many enjoyed *"getting to be the primary attorney and take the lead on the case. It can be more difficult to find matters that suit transactional lawyers, but those assignments do exist."*

Pro bono hours
- For all attorneys across all US offices: undisclosed
- Average per US attorney: undisclosed

"Late nights are very infrequent and I've never once stayed up all night working."

While there's *"no average day,"* Bracewellians generally did pretty well on the hours front. *"I try to get in at 8am and leave at 6pm – that typically means I don't have to work at home,"* one representative source explained. *"Late nights are very infrequent and I've never once stayed up all night working."* Colleagues agreed that *"busy periods can require you to work well into the night, but they're rare."*

Diversity

On the gender front, interviewees flagged that *"there are a ton of female partners who are extremely intelligent and wonderful mentors."* Half of the firm's practice groups are led by women, but, disappointingly, only one attorney within the nine-strong 2018 partnership promotion round was female. Smaller offices like Dallas are *"a little less diverse"* than Houston, while *"New York is lacking in minority partners. We interview a lot of diverse candidates but when you walk in the door it's hard if there aren't examples to follow."* In a bid to address issues at the pipeline level, Bracewell currently offers a 'Diversity and Inclusion Fellowship' in several of its US offices.

See firm profile on p.616

Brown Rudnick LLP

Lawyers per state

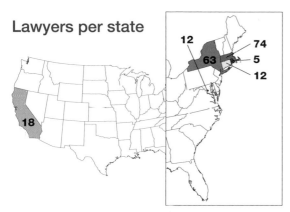

Largest US office: Boston
US offices: 6
International offices: 2
First-year salary: $180,000
Billable hours: 1,950 target
Summers 2018: 11 (1 1L, 10 2Ls)
Revenue 2017: $192.2 million (+0.6%)
Partners made in 2018: 4
Famous for: bankruptcy expertise

Brown Rudnick may be smaller than its competitors, but this sporty Boston outfit wins big in bankruptcy and restructuring.

"DEMAND for legal services really isn't growing as it has previously – competition is more intense," says Brown Rudnick CEO Joe Ryan. But that hasn't got this Bostonian down. *"Clients now pick and choose more, rather than using one firm for everything. We've benefited from that."* That's because – in the hectic heat of a Chapter 11 scenario – the firm's bankruptcy and restructuring expertise makes it a wise choice.

And *Chambers USA* recognizes this: Brown Rudnick gets top marks for bankruptcy in its native Massachusetts, plus further kudos in New York and nationwide, beating a number of legal heavyweights to the punch. Associates were sure of their choice too: *"Even though it's a smaller firm they still handle some of the biggest cases in the country. As an associate you get a balance between lean staffing and having a lot of experience at a junior level."*

The Work

Associates are split pretty evenly between the New York and Boston offices, although a few are scattered between the DC, Orange County and Hartford bases. At the time of our calls, two-thirds of juniors were in litigation & restructuring. The remainder slotted into the corporate & capital markets practice, which covers subgroups like finance, real estate and intellectual property. Work is initially assigned through a manager, *"but after a few months partners start asking to work with you – it develops organically."* In general, associates felt *"this is definitely a place where they throw you in at the deep end. In other places you can hang out in the background but here you have to step up very early on."*

> *"This is definitely a place where they throw you in at the deep end."*

Restructuring associates courteously explained that *"bankruptcy is split between litigation and transactional work. On the transactional side you're doing deals, bond exchanges and workouts, while on the litigation side you're involved in an array of pleadings, motions and objections – pretty much the type of thing you would expect in traditional litigious work."* The litigation aspect is more common, and Brown Rudnick specializes in helping distressed investors, working frequently with unsecured creditors and equity committees. Associates found that *"there's a lot of research involved, so you're drafting research memos or briefs. But even as a first year you will be drafting motions that are filed in court."* Associates had also drafted pleadings, and on *"small creditor committee cases it can be just you and a partner. I was essentially running the case."* However, less thrilling admin tasks cropped up on larger cases, where juniors *"felt like a much smaller part."*

> *"Even as a first year I was drafting motions that were filed in court."*

On chambers-associate.com...

- We spoke with co-hiring partner Jeff Jonas to find out what it takes to get hired at Brown Rudnick
- Read the full interview with CEO Joe Ryan

See firm profile on p.617

The Inside View

Rankings in *Chambers USA*

Bankruptcy/Restructuring	Real Estate
Environment	

For detail on ranking tiers and ranking locations, visit www.chambersandpartners.com

Those in commercial litigation told us: "*Bankruptcy accounts for 50-60% of the work, and the rest is on various things including IP, real estate and breaches of contract. Because we're a smaller firm, any litigation matter will come through our group – it changes things up.*" One associate weighed this up: "*It keeps things interesting and fresh, but sometimes it feels like you don't get enough focus on one thing.*" Again, juniors had "*drafted motions that were filed in court. People say you'll be doing 12 hours of document review a day but it's actually only come up a few times.*" Instead, associates happily reported "*getting a ton of writing experience. It's been my favorite thing. I've been involved in discovery on civil litigation cases: writing letters, listening in on meetings, writing amicus briefs and drafting initial disclosures and answers.*"

Training & Development

Trainees usually head to Boston for a week of training when they start their time at Brown Rudnick, where partners and senior associates present on a variety of topics. However, we heard that there are plans in the works to reduce that to three days and provide more office-specific training. Once they reach spring, associates will begin a program of lunch hour training sessions. In addition, associates told us that "*last year people asked for more training on the finance side of things, and they're beginning to do that now. There will be an accounting course for midlevel associates and juniors starting soon.*"

Associates receive an annual feedback review where "*the firm generates a list of attorneys you've worked with for 20 hours or more – they then fill out a form to feed back. After that there's a meeting with the professional development staff and you get assessed in seven categories.*" This went down well with interviewees, who found it to be "*really detailed – you get a lot of information about what to improve or continue doing.*" Nevertheless, while "*the majority of feedback is given through the annual review, if something arises the appropriate people will sit you down and talk it through with you.*" The importance of this hadn't escaped the firm, with associates reporting "*a push for more real-time feedback recently.*" One area juniors did flag up for improvement, however, was upward feedback. "*There used to be a process where juniors would provide anonymous feedback to partners and management, which I think is really important.*" Fortunately we heard from the firm that this process will be reinstated.

Recent work highlights

- Represented the term loan agent Wilmington Saving Funds Society with regard to the bankruptcy of the sports retailer Sports Authority
- Led by a partner in the London office, attorneys in Boston acted for Science Group (a UK-based company) on its acquisition of US consultancy business Technology Sciences Group, which was owned by law firm Dentons
- Arguing that his cooperation deserved a lesser sentence, the firm represented Paul Robson, a former Rabobank interest rate swaps trader accused of Libor fixing. He escaped jail time

Get Hired

"*One of the most important qualities we're looking for is a willingness to go outside your comfort zone,*" co-hiring partner Jeff Jonas tells us. "*You also need to be willing to speak up and make yourself heard.*" To learn more about getting hired at Brown Rudnick head to chambers-associate.com

Culture

As in previous years, associates emphasized the differences in culture between the New York office and the rest of the firm. "*The New York office is definitely a more challenging environment, with more stereotypical New York lawyers.*" Another added: "*I prefer the culture in Boston but if you're going to be a global law firm you need a New York office and you need that kind of personality. Nobody goes into it with their eyes closed.*" True as that may be, we did hear that "*the firm has been very open about making a major effort to improve morale.*" That's ongoing (we reported this last year too), and it's having material effects. A recent initiative changed the firm's policy on marketing hours, so that marketing is now included in attorneys' billable hours targets. "*It's definitely made reaching billable targets more achievable and less stressful,*" associates said.

While it's important to be aware of these points, associates' responses still described an environment where "*you can joke and have fun with everyone.*" On the social side of things, the New York office had get-togethers every other week, while Boston met up once a week. We also heard about reinvigorated quarterly socials: "*The firm gives associates a budget to go and hang out and destress a little bit.*" Another added: "*The firm's just started giving out a $50 gift card to associates every month to go have fun.*" Associates' social calendars get a little busier when summer associates are at the firm, but on the whole the Brown Rudnick social scene was reported as being fairly relaxed.

See firm profile on p.617

Diversity	Partners (%)	Associates (%)
Women	18	45
White	90	78
Black/African American	0	4
Hispanic/Latin American	5	10
Asian	1	5
Mixed/Other	4	3
LGBT	0	1

Hours & Compensation

The change in policy regarding marketing seemed to have alleviated associates' concerns about meeting their targets. Juniors' workloads *"ebbed and flowed"* – at busier times, 12-hour days could be a regular occurrence. *"The inconsistency can be challenging, but overall I feel pretty good about my workload,"* said one, while another commented: *"I've had a fair amount of Sunday work, but the fluctuating hours actually help with work-life balance."* The minimum number of hours to achieve bonus is 1,950, drawing the opinion from one relieved interviewee that *"if marketing and pro bono hours weren't included it would be life-breaking!"*

Offices

"You're always in contact with other offices," said associates. That's especially true *"in bankruptcy as the practices in the New York and Boston offices are very close."* Beyond frequent emails and phone calls, we're told that *"if you're working closely with other offices people will go for a few days to get some face time,"* though it's a more common occurrence for seniors. Juniors had also been in contact with the firm's international bases: *"If I need to call London it's still a four-digit number."* When it comes to the office interiors, we were slightly alarmed to hear about *"a uniquely designed black, red and white theme in Boston,"* but a quick image search reassured us of its aesthetic merits. One associate less in favor of futuristic interiors remarked that *"the New York offices are very beautiful, but it's all glass so there's nowhere to hide. I prefer my solid door in Boston!"* However, we did hear that associates can request a 'privacy wall' if the transparency gets too much.

Pro Bono

"If there's one thing I can't fault the firm on it's their commitment to pro bono. There's no cap on billable hours, and the fact that they give that freedom goes a long way toward encouraging people. You never feel like you have to conserve your hours." Juniors had been involved with *"a lot of Chapter 7 individual bankruptcies, including a couple of student loan cases – it's normally impossible to discharge a student loan!"* The firm *"works closely with local projects in Boston, so a lot of pro bono comes through them."* The firm is partnered with Volunteer Lawyers for the Arts of Massachusetts, and interviewees had also worked with Kids in Need of Defense on immigration cases. *"It's a great way to get experience because 99% of the work is down to the associate. It's on a smaller scale but you get experience going in front of a judge and going through probate proceedings."*

Pro bono hours
- For all US attorneys: 9,517
- Average per US attorney: 36

Diversity

"We've redoubled our efforts when it comes to our equality, inclusion and diversity initiative," says CEO Joe Ryan, and last year Brown Rudnick introduced a director of equity, inclusion and diversity in New York, Ari Joseph, and a diversity partner, Sunni Beville. *"Diversity is something the firm's very cognizant of,"* associates said. *"At associate level it's pretty even between men and women, but at partner level men far and away outnumber women,"* they explained. We were also told that the firm has adopted a new interview method which tackles implicit bias in an effort to improve diversity in recruiting. *"It's pretty homogeneous right now, so we'll see how things change."*

Strategy & Future

CEO Joe Ryan tells us: *"The firm continues to have much more of an international focus. Our team in New York is doing a lot of work for Latin American clients, for example."* Exporting the firm's model of stateside collaboration, *"more global initiatives have led to a lot of crossover between practice groups and offices, from Paris to California."* Also worth noting is the firm's attempts to diversify its work. Ryan tell us that *"IP, as a practice, is certainly a growth area."* Visit chambers-associate.com for more insight from Ryan.

"You're always in contact with other offices."

See firm profile on p.617

Cadwalader, Wickersham & Taft LLP

Lawyers per state

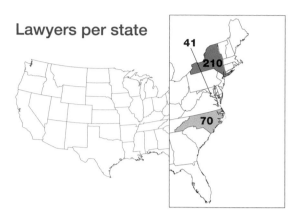

41
210
70

Largest US office: New York
US offices: 3
International offices: 2
First-year salary: $180,000
Billable hours: 1,800 plus 200 non-billables
Summers 2018: 37 (35 2Ls, 2 SEOs)
Revenue 2017: $408 million (-9.7%)
Partners made in 2018: 7
Famous for: all things finance; founded during George Washington's presidency

Born just three years after the Constitution came into force, Cadwalader may be a monolith of Wall Street, but it has not stood still.

IT'S hard to imagine a New York without a Statue of Liberty. But for nearly a century before Liberty rocked up with her torch, Cadwalader was already standing tall in the city shining its own light. And, as if embodying the spirit of the statue as it greets new arrivals to America's shores, Pat Quinn, Cadwalader's managing partner, muses: *"If you come here, you're part of something bigger than just a job. Who wouldn't want to be part of that history, and of the next chapter of that institution?"*

The firm shake-up we reported on last year has left our sources unmoved. This firm was, they rationalized, founded in 1792 and is made of sturdy stuff. Our interviewees insisted that it was *"all positive: we have more events, it's a little smaller and you feel more comfortable walking around getting to know everyone."* The effect, from what we can tell, is a more loyal associate cohort: *"I am the biggest cheerleader of Cadwalader – three years later I'm happy with my job and my choice."* Wall Street old-timers might remember this firm's reputation for ruthlessness, but post-2008 crash the firm's leaders have sought to create a different, more supportive, collaborative atmosphere – associates attest to this every time we interview them.

Cadwalader has, for centuries now, done things very well. Its most successful practice area is capital markets, with

the derivatives and securitization departments taking top rankings in *Chambers USA*, plus many rankings in real estate, corporate, energy, financial services, healthcare, litigation, tax and more.

The Work

At the time of our calls, 43 of 66 juniors were based in Manhattan, with the rest in DC and Charlotte. The firm also boasts offices in London and Brussels, though junior travel opportunities *"are quite limited,"* with international work mainly conducted out of New York. Head office associates are most likely to work in either capital markets or corporate, but there are also junior associates in litigation, IP, financial services, restructuring and tax. DC claimed seven associates, spread between the office's main areas of practice: capital markets, white collar defense & investigations, and antitrust. Charlotte's associates were split between capital markets and finance. Each team has a professional development manager who can dish out work, but there's also an *"informal approach where a partner who has worked with an associate before says 'can you help out on another case?'"*

"I feel like it's been a really natural progression."

It came as no surprise that New Yorkers in capital markets were comfortably busy: *"There's one associate who's on eight separate matters. I mean, it's great but that's not humanly possible!"* Associates in this department commonly get involved in creating investment vehicles from

See firm profile on p.618

Rankings in *Chambers USA*

Capital Markets	Financial Services
Corporate/M&A	Regulation
Employee Benefits &	Healthcare
Executive Compensation	Litigation
Energy & Natural	Real Estate
Resources	Tax

For detail on ranking tiers and ranking locations, visit
www.chambersandpartners.com

Recent work highlights

- Advised BNP Paribas on a $3.25 billion committed senior secured working capital facility
- Represented Assured Guaranty in connection with Puerto Rico's $73 billion debt, the largest ever US municipal debt restructuring and the first bankruptcy of a US territory
- Served as counsel to Oppenheimer & Co and Morgan Stanley on the $400 million notes offering by Aeropuertos Argentina 2000
- Acted as international counsel in the €1.3 billion restructuring of fashion company Camaïeu

various debt and asset classes. Sources were mainly doing commercial backed securities – *"I often do sales of securities and assets that are not cash."* In DC, recent capital markets work has included advising *"a company that operates all airports in Argentina. We assisted them with a bond offering. I got to review and draft all the documents. It was the best thing about the second year."*

A real estate insider told us: *"We typically represent finance for the letting side of commercial real estate."* A highlight was *"going from drafting to working directly with the client and answering their questions – I feel like it's been a really natural progression."* A Charlotte finance insider told us: *"Responsibility differs, but often I'm in charge of turning credit agreements, which is a great learning experience."*

The litigation group has gone through a rebranding in recent years. *"When I started we were 'corporate litigation'; now we're 'corporate and financial services litigation and regulation.'"* But be assured this is *"just a long name for litigation!"* As you might expect, the firm's penchant for finance dictates the theme of much of this litigation team's work, which, associates felt, is often *"litigation work for the other departments."* But associates didn't find this restrictive: *"If you balance it right you can do a lot of different types of work."* In litigation, responsibilities might take the form of *"shareholder disputes, antitrust, white-collar, breach of contract, and IP matters."* Sources were keen to mention: *"We don't have many midlevels, so I've had a fair amount of important drafting experience and being in client meetings."*

Training & Development

Associates *"have weekly training in various relevant areas."* As one capital markets associate said, *"they take the time and treat us as an investment."* Incoming classes can also look forward to a Cadwalader iPhone app complete with all necessary resources. MP Pat Quinn says: *"We're proud of our focus on technology – we're constantly looking at the way the next generation of lawyers will practice."*

> *"We're very focused on the way the next generation of lawyers will practice."*

There's a mentorship program, which matches juniors with a junior mentor. Each pair is given a budget, and they do things like *"see great Broadway shows."* One pair saw a show on *"the night it was filmed, and now you can see them in the audience on Netflix!"* Additionally, new associates are given a partner mentor; one associate revealed: *"My partner mentor is the nicest person in America."* Aside from formal training, one junior said: *"The best training comes when you're actually working on a deal and they sit down and explain things line by line."* Many prefer this informal training and note it encompasses peer-to-peer learning too. *"By the second year, we don't interact a ton with the partners. We're like border collies, we train each other!"* First years have biannual reviews, and everyone else gets an annual review.

Diversity

Though the firm-wide diversity figures are typical for BigLaw, our sources were optimistic about the newest classes of associates and the prospects for minorities, women and LGBT lawyers: *"Cadwalader's definitely responding to culture as it shifts,"* an associate thought. One associate involved in hiring told us: *"Our dedicated committees have made recruiting diverse candidates the number one focus, and that's shown so much."* This ground-up approach continues with the start of a training program that sponsors talented candidates from diverse backgrounds at different points in their careers. Pat Quinn tells us: *"It is important that the next generation of leaders at our firm include our increasingly diverse legal team. There's a place for everybody here."*

Cadwalader's affinity groups put on events throughout the year, and *"they're heavily attended and have a lot of support from the administration."* In Charlotte, the women's affinity group's community-engaged events include *"Girls in Finance, where we invited girls from local high schools to come and get ideas about jobs in finance."* Other

See firm profile on p.618

Diversity	Partners (%)	Associates (%)
Women	21	40
White	89	75
Black/African American	1	4
Hispanic/Latin American	1	4
Asian	3	15
Mixed/Other	6	2
LGBT	5	4

affinity events are more social: *"We'll have Chinese calligraphy night where we have classes and drinks."* Many associates pointed out: *"It's reflected in our pro bono immigration work that they're really supporting diversity."*

Pro Bono

A NY litigation associate told us: *"Pro bono is heavily encouraged in the firm as a whole. In our department, everyone is involved with at least one pro bono case."* Not everyone we spoke to in New York could partake, though: *"I haven't done any – the hours are long enough!"* This doesn't seem to be the case in DC, however: *"It doesn't affect anyone's work at all. Everyone has done pro bono."*

Many work in *"an immigration law clinic that was opened by a second-year associate a few years ago. A lot of litigators take on pro bono cases there."* Immigration is popular pro bono work in DC as well, with one associate *"working on an immigration case for a kid that's nine years old."* Associates got a buzz from this kind of work: *"We're primarily a transactional firm – it's nice to break away from that and serve the local community."*

Pro bono hours
- For all US attorneys: 6,314
- Average per US attorney: 20

Hours & Compensation

Typical reports of regular hours were *"during busy times, eight-to-nine billables each day, and when it slows down seven billables each day."* However, one capital markets associate noted: *"The most I've billed in a day is 19 hours. It's like, why even bother going home when I can just shower at the gym?"*

The hours put in were as demanding as you might expect from this sector of the market, but flexibility and a practical attitude was noted across the board: *"My assignments*

allow me to structure my time as I want to, which I appreciate." Associates in New York reported doing some work remotely, but we detected that in DC there's more freedom to do it: *"People regularly work from home when they're not needed in the office."*

Associates get the bonus if they bill 1,800 hours plus 200 'quality non-billables.' Additionally, associates were keen to tell us: *"If you supersede that and get 2,200 hours, you get a 120% bonus that we call the 'super bonus.'"*

Cadwalader has 'unlimited vacation,' which apparently associates translate as *"take what you dare."* Luckily, it seems a lot less scary in numbers: *"I took 20 days off as a first year. It's around 14 to 20 on average, maybe more, maybe less."*

Culture & Offices

Associates felt Cadwalader has come some distance since its reputed 'shark tank' days pre-2008 crash. We heard that some partners can be *"very loud, but their bark is worse than their bite."* Another associate reassured us: *"No one's ever been rude or made me feel that I'm not part of the team."* And *"the strongest aspect of life here is how supportive associates are of each other; we all have each other's backs."*

Associates in Charlotte said: *"Here we only have about 60 attorneys, so people know each other on a far more personal basis."* DC juniors similarly told us: *"Our office is smaller, so everyone loves to talk. We often get emails just inviting everyone out to lunch."*

Manhattan associates joked about their Liberty Street offices: *"We call it 50 shades of beige, I think the decor could use some help…"* Though the panoramic views left associates without a sarcastic quip: *"I have a view of the Statue of Liberty and the Hudson, it's beautiful."* Over at DC there's *"a lot of wood. It's a very traditional, classic office with lots of frosted glass."* What DC lacks in uniqueness, it makes up for in substance: *"They cleared a few offices to make a lounge with a TV. Some spent Superbowl Sunday there watching the football during their breaks."* The similarly beige Charlotte office is on the rise: *"We just expanded our office at the beginning of this year to another floor to accommodate more attorneys."* New Yorkers have to wait until their second year to get their own office, but DC and Charlotte associates get them immediately.

"I have a view of the Statue of Liberty and the Hudson, it's beautiful."

See firm profile on p.618

Cahill Gordon & Reindel LLP

Lawyers per state

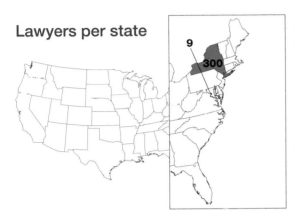

9

300

Largest US office: New York
US offices: 2
International offices: 1
First-year salary: $180,000
Billable hours: no requirement
Summers 2018: 44 2Ls
Revenue 2017: $387.7 million (+ 1.3%)
Partners made in 2018: 2
Famous for: First Amendment practice; extra bonuses; the free-market system

This New Yorker's famous free-market system allows juniors to define their careers, fostering independence and a culture of *"mutual respect."* Big bonuses are also part of the deal.

"I HAVE control over what I am doing. I knew I wouldn't get trapped doing something I wasn't interested in for several years." Every year, the associates we interview speak highly of the firm's free-market assignment system. Its effect is something akin to Spider-Man's favorite motto: empowered junior associates take charge of their careers, with very positive results. The opportunity to not be pigeonholed or spoon-fed was a prime reason why our sources chose the firm, a choice that was made easier by *"the firm's number of vibrant practices that seemed to match areas of growth in different industries."*

Many were familiar with the firm's First Amendment practice, headed by the renowned Floyd Abrams, but for the majority of interviewees it was the amount of work for banking clients and financial institutions that stood out. Cahill's expertise in areas such as banking and finance, capital markets and insurance dispute resolution is recognized in *Chambers USA* with top-tier rankings nationwide. Other areas including the First Amendment practice, environment, general commercial litigation and white-collar litigation are also recognized with impressive marks in Cahill's home state, New York.

Over the years we've noted that this rather unique firm attracts pragmatic types: *"I think the people are very authentic and down to earth. People aren't overly formal with each other, which makes it a lot easier."* The firm's reputation for paying above the odds in bonuses was also another pull factor, which we'll get on to later...

The Work

"I really enjoy the free-market system," juniors reflected on work assignment. *"If you're proactive enough, it gives associates the ability to get different types of matters from different attorneys across the firm. I'm never bored!"* As previously mentioned, for many sources its reputation preceded it: *"I heard a lot about the free-market system during the recruiting process – I liked the idea that you're trusted to handle your own projects and matters once you'd demonstrated yourself to be ready."* Although independence is undeniably a large part of the system, juniors recognized that *"you are also expected to reach out for help if and when you need it."*

"It can be a bit intimidating at first, but people are so kind and accessible."

Many admitted *"it can be a bit intimidating at first, but people are so kind and accessible."* The only grumble was the disparity in hours that could potentially occur as a result: *"The bonus structure means it's 'all for one, one for all,' so it's not based on billing more hours – we'll take home the same. Some people can fly under the radar and*

See firm profile on p.619

Rankings in *Chambers USA*

Banking & Finance	Litigation
Capital Markets	Media & Entertainment
Environment	Tax
Insurance	

For detail on ranking tiers and ranking locations, visit www.chambersandpartners.com

Recent work highlights

- Represented J.P. Morgan, Wells Fargo Securities, Morgan Stanley, RBC Capital Markets, and Merrill Lynch, Pierce Fenner & Smith as initial purchasers in a $1.5 billion notes offering for Restaurant Brands International
- Represented the underwriters in a $1 billion public offering by Xerox
- Represented Morgan Stanley as initial purchaser in a $2.3 billion notes offering for DAE Funding
- Secured a dismissal of a multibillion-dollar shareholder class action regarding securities fraud claims against Deutsche Bank

get away with not pulling their weight before it's noticed. I partly wish there was someone to check that work went to people who clearly weren't doing enough." Having said that, sources liked that *"it allows the teams to form organically"* and *"not having to get approval to turn work down if you've got a lot going on."*

Juniors are split pretty evenly between litigation and corporate. Both sides maintain *"there aren't strict divisions or particular sub-practices. It's pretty generalist."* Litigators experienced a range of matters, from complex civil litigation or class actions to government or internal investigations matters. *"Within that, a lot is centered on the finance industry. There's securities law and regulation, general commercial, antitrust and some insurance."* Juniors noted: *"We're a big firm, but a little smaller with our class sizes, which means matters are pretty leanly staffed. I've been able to help draft motions and appellate briefings, and have got involved with deposition prep."* Naturally, there were also some *"typical first-year assignments like doc review"* but juniors reckoned it was *"a pretty healthy mix."* Some litigators can choose to take a year out to do a judicial clerkship if they can source the opportunity to do so. The firm supports you and writes a recommendation when needed.

Corporate juniors get involved in a lot of *"lender work, loan work or bond work."* Many sources we spoke to focused on capital markets: *"I would say the majority of deals are high-yield bond deals, then there's also a lot of credit agreements."* Juniors noted: *"We only really represent banks, and it comes down to representing them as underwriters in the capital markets sense of them issuing bonds or as a lender"*– this shows in the group's client list: J.P. Morgan, Deutsche Bank, Merrill Lynch, etc. Some sources also mentioned the work they did in acquisition and leveraged finance. Overall, juniors described the work as *"process-oriented, even at higher levels."* Sources highlighted *"helping out with the general process – a lot of emails and communications. We coordinate the different processes that are required either internally or with the company's counsel."* Others mentioned being *"the key person on due diligence, which isn't particularly substantive but is important."* Many also got involved in drafting various documents, including indentures for bond deals, credit agreement amendments and ancillary documents.

"When people trust you here, you're given good levels of responsibility. There's no work they won't let you do."

Culture

The common theme from our sources is that the firm is *"very relaxed on a personal level, but very professional on a work level."* Interviewees felt there was a culture of *"mutual respect"* through the way *"flexibility is afforded to associates – there's no face-time requirement and you're not micromanaged. You're respected, and therefore expected to get your work done and handle your own things."* Others praised how *"at firm events, everyone from partners down is great to talk to and everyone is fun."*

"...really great party informally called the Cahill prom."

Alongside the unwavering professionalism, sources felt Cahill is *"a very social firm."* A famous tradition is the annual fishing trip for summer associates. *"Cahill goes on a fishing trip in a boat on Long Island, and it's always a big hit. They catch fluke and other things."* The busy summer also sees attorneys go out to Broadway shows and dinner, watch Mets games, and play shuffleboard which sources found *"weirdly fun."* There's also lots of cocktail receptions as well as volunteering events: *"During my summer, we volunteered at a soup kitchen."* Outside of the summer months, interviewees also mentioned a *"really great party informally called the Cahill prom"* which happens every few years. *"It's at the Natural History Museum and it's a really fun black tie event. You get to socialize and see everyone all dressed up."* The firm also hosts monthly happy hours, and diversity groups set up various events throughout the year.

Hours & Compensation

The respectful culture permeates the firm's attitude to hours as well: there is no official billing target and *"they stress that there isn't actually any number that your salary or bonus is tied to."* The overall idea is that *"as long as*

See firm profile on p.619

Diversity	Partners (%)	Associates (%)
Women	21	42
White	89	81
Black/African American	3	5
Hispanic/Latin American	0	5
Asian	6	9
Mixed/Other	2	0
LGBT	6	5

you get your work done, they're less concerned with where and when." An average day might see an associate turn up around 9:30am and head home for 7ish, maybe with a couple of hours work at home. Busier periods however mean associates might not leave until 10-11pm, occasionally finishing in the early hours: *"We work late – not every night, but it does happen."* As a result, sources found making time for their private lives could be somewhat challenging. Juniors reckoned: *"You have to make sure you are conscious of that and carve that time out for yourself. People are usually receptive and understanding about it."*

"...they want us to share in the wealth of the firm."

But associates' hard work doesn't go unrewarded: attorneys get market salary and the standard market bonus, but on top of that, there's usually an additional bonus too. *"We work harder than other firms, but we get paid more,"* reckoned one associate. *"It's nice that our hard work is acknowledged and they want us to share in the wealth of the firm."* Plus it's not discretionary – *"it's not only for people who bill over 2,200 hours or something. If they're giving it out, it'll go to everybody."*

Pro Bono

"The firm is definitely committed to pro bono matters. It makes it less stressful that pro bono hours count the same as hours for clients, so you never have to feel guilty about doing pro bono." Cahill has partnerships with several nonprofit organizations such as Sanctuary for Families and The Door, and also does significant work for the Legal Aid Society. Juniors in the past have worked on criminal appeals, helping veterans to start up businesses, divorce matters, asylum matters and housing eviction matters among many others. Sources felt *"the firm does a really wonderful job of identifying different areas of pro bono work stemming from all sorts of fields. They also do a great job of explaining how the opportunities can improve upon different skills."* Corporate juniors admitted *"having time to really dedicate to pro bono can be difficult. Even if we're not busy, the work is quite unpredictable. You're afraid you'll be busy and won't be able to dedicate the time*

required." That said, *"it's something everyone strives for, and the firm encourages it."*

Pro bono hours
- For all US attorneys: 10,912
- Average per US attorney: 34.8

Training & Development

To prepare juniors for the hard work that will come their way, first years start their time at Cahill with a weeklong training program. It was described as *"a true overview of most of the resources at the firm, then some specific things you might need to know for your practice."* Sources receive *"a large stack of material for reference which you keep – I still have mine with me."* There's also a large focus on IT and using the firm's systems. *"They told us you're not going to be absorbing everything they tell you. It's more of an introduction and they provide resources to help you learn on the job."* After the intro, there are periodic practice-specific trainings.

"If something is wrong, they won't wait until the end of the year to tell you."

There are formal reviews once a year in January, as well as regular informal feedback sessions, which are *"conducted by the senior people you work with."* For the latter, *"messages are only relayed to associates if there's a recurring issue. If something is wrong, they won't wait until the end of the year to tell you."* Frequency of feedback is dependent on the particular partner mentor.

Offices

A New Yorker remarked: *"It's not the nicest building ever, and we kind of get teased for it being a little boring."* That said, it meant juniors felt more *"laid back coming into work because it's not all glass or marble."* Overall, associates didn't really mind the office look: *"We like to make a point of not spending our money on things like marble in the office or decorations, but use it to pay for extra associate bonuses."* The downtown location was praised by many, who felt *"the financial district is a little bit quieter and less hectic than midtown."* The DC office is much smaller, which meant that unlike first years in NY who share their office with a fellow junior, DC first years get their own offices.

"We like to make a point of not spending our money on things like marble."

See firm profile on p.619

Diversity

"When I came here as a summer, one thing I noticed was that we didn't seem to have much diversity in the summer class or among associates, in terms of race and ethnicity. I think the firm took those comments to heart, and in the past two years, they've really increased their diversity efforts. They're really making progress, and I'm glad they've taken those concerns seriously." Juniors admitted "every firm can always do more" on the diversity front, "but at the same time I think we're doing fairly well now." Sources also felt "they make a good effort in terms of affinity groups. Those events have pretty decent turnouts – for instance, there was an event last night hosted by the women's initiative." However, some felt they'd "like to see more diverse partners and diverse people in positions of authority."

Strategy & Future

"We're happy with the size and culture of the firm. Part of the reason it attracted me was knowing we were very financially stable with no crazy plans," juniors reflected. Executive committee member Jonathan Schaffzin weighs in, saying: "We have no master plans. We try to respond to our clients' needs with strong, attentive and high-quality legal services and pay attention to the ever changing marketplace, but we don't try to guess what will be going on in the world in ten to 20 years' time. We don't have plans to expand into new geographic areas or practices that we aren't strong in to begin with. We're not significant risk takers, and we want our lawyers to be nimble and adaptive." Go online for our full interview with Jonathan Schaffzin.

"I've found over the years that the primary driver of success is creating the right environment for yourself."

– Jonathan Schaffzin, Cahill executive committee member

See firm profile on p.619

Choate Hall & Stewart LLP

Lawyers per state

181

Largest US office: Boston
US offices: 1
International offices: 0
First-year salary: $180,000
Billable hours: 2,000 to be bonus eligible
Summers 2018: 15 (2 1Ls, 13 2Ls)
Revenue 2017: $236.3 million (+8.1%)
Partners made in 2018: 2
Famous for: Bostonian brand; one-office model

One of Boston's finest, Choate offers juniors plenty of responsibility in the city of the Red Socks and Sam Adams.

ACCORDING to associates, this 120 year old Bostonian offers two things. First, it's *"a firm where nice people work."* So far, so unremarkable. But insiders put this down to Choate's 'under one roof' business model – the conscious decision by management to operate out of just one office to encourage people to mingle and get on. *"At Choate everybody knows each other and asks about families and weekends,"* one junior observed. Another added: *"The one-office model and the fact there is some good continuity of people here are probably self-reinforcing aspects of the firm."*

Second, juniors felt that the fact the firm staffs *"a little bit more leanly than others means juniors get to do more on each deal. When you combine that with seeing the same people on the same team constantly you're responsibility grows much faster."* The firm's single site has not stopped it from growing (modestly), from a lawyer head count of 165 to 181 in the past five years. Gross revenue, meanwhile, has more than doubled since 2004, and in 2017 it increased by 8.1% to $236.3 million. Chairman John Nadas feels a proprietary sense of pride in the firm: *"We consider ourselves to be the custodians of a great institution and we intend to make it even stronger and then pass it on to future generations."*

Did you know?

Choate Hall & Stewart rose to fame in 1919 when name partner Charles Choate defended distiller US Industrial Alcohol in the class action lawsuit brought against it over the Great Molasses Flood. This bizarre disaster was caused by the bursting of a huge molasses tank owned by the distiller and killed 21 people in downtown Boston.

Chambers USA ranks the firm in Massachusetts across its main practice areas, including corporate, litigation, insurance, antitrust, banking & finance and IP. The rankings are mostly in *Chambers USA*'s second and third tiers, but across the board Choate is usually the highest-ranked firm with *only* an office in Boston, and it ranks alongside the Boston offices of major national firms like Weil and Morgan Lewis.

The Work

At the time of our research, most junior associates were in either the litigation or business departments, split evenly between the two. There were also solitary juniors to be found in private wealth, IP litigation and real estate. Work is initially managed by an assigning partner though over time *"you build relationships and gradually shape you own way."* Insiders generally liked this system as it *"means you have an advocate to help you get the kind of work you want to get. The partners have their favorites but the assigning partner means you get a chance to work*

On chambers-associate.com...

- Get hired at Choate
- Interview with chairman John Nadas and recruiting head Elaine Bortman

See firm profile on p.620

Rankings in *Chambers USA*

Antitrust	Intellectual Property
Banking & Finance	Litigation
Bankruptcy/Restructuring	Private Equity
Corporate/M&A	Tax
Healthcare	Technology
Insurance	

For detail on ranking tiers and ranking locations, visit www.chambersandpartners.com

Recent work highlights

- Represented tech company Thinkalogical when it was acquired in a deal worth $160 million
- Helped crime writer Patricia Cornwell settle a long-running dispute with her financial advisers
- Helped GeNO, a healthcare company, secure funding worth $45 million
- Defended insurer Travelers against claims by Amerisource-Bergen, a pharmaceutical company, that their insurance coverage should extend to claims made by the state of West Virginia that they fueled opioid addiction in the state

for more people. It also helps us not to get completely smashed and overwhelmed."

Business is a broad umbrella department that covers various subgroups, including finance & restructuring, life sciences, business & technology, sport & retail, healthcare, tax and private equity. Associates can keep things broad and sample work from all these areas but the juniors we spoke to had gravitated toward private equity work, advising private equity funds on venture capital and *"representing startups from a corporate perspective."* Clients include Massachusetts video-screen producer Seachange International, Wells Fargo, JPMorgan Chase and Boston-headquartered private equity firm Summit Partners. *"One of my emerging technology clients will be in tomorrow, so I am currently prepping for that meeting,"* a junior told us. *"We're doing a deal for them that's closing at the end of the month – a private equity firm is taking a minority stake in the company – so most of the meeting will be focused on that. I also had two deals close recently so there are post-closing matters to handle."* Sources found that *"on a lot of deals it's just you and a partner, so you get more things like drafting purchase agreements to do rather than just sticking with diligence. With one client I have gotten to a point where I am running and closing the deal."*

Choate's litigation clients include pharma companies Merck & Co and Shire, tech outfits HP and Dell, and financial services firm Fidelity Investments. Litigators cover insurance, IP, labor & employment, government enforcement and appellate work, and juniors work across these areas. *"There's always something to do,"* one source said, *"meeting deadlines for motions and doing the entry-level junior associate work like document review, plus doing legal research, getting things filed with the court, drafting pleadings and helping to prepare depositions."* Another interviewee reported that a typical day might consist of *"case research into the rights of our clients, writing up a 'cheat sheet' for a partner, drafting a motion to dismiss and brief writing."* We also heard that one junior had *"participated in presentations to the government to convince them not to pursue a case against a client."*

Culture

Choate's one-office model means *"it's pretty rare to not be able to put a face to the name."* Juniors also noted: *"Most people in the firm are from or went to college in New England, so they like it here in Boston."* It also seemed to us that many Choate juniors had previous careers, were a bit older and/or had families. One source felt this created a somewhat less frenetic social atmosphere than at other firms. *"I have friends at big New York firms and they seem to have a younger 'go get drinks and party at the weekend' crowd. Choate is more 'come in, work hard and go home to your family.'"*

"Choate is more 'come in, work hard and go home to your family.'"

This isn't to say there's a complete dearth of social events. *"The business group has a lot of client events, for example,"* we heard. The firm also runs both a holiday and summer party, hosts speakers and there's a *"monthly pizza night where everybody can catch up and hang out."* In the summer juniors can join summers on a sailing trip and a day at a country club with *"golf, tennis and yoga."*

Diversity

Juniors were positive about LGBT and gender diversity at the firm (over half of associates are women), but noted the firm is *"predominantly white."* There was recently an 'open forum' on diversity which *"gave everyone an open space for dialogue about how we can get better."* The firm also has a diversity hiring scheme for summer associates and organized a lecture series on *"topics including implicit bias and women in the workplace."*

Pro Bono

Opportunities include education advocacy (*"you help students who are being denied some educational service"*), legal clinics at homeless shelters, asylum cases and for one insider *"a hearing before an administrative law judge on a social security disability case."* Pro bono is mostly litigious but the firm has been trying to *"find more corporate*

See firm profile on p.620

The Inside View

Diversity	Partners (%)	Associates (%)
Women	21	49
White	93	84
Black/African American	2	2
Hispanic/Latin American	3	5
Asian	2	7
Mixed/Other	0	2
LGBT	6	3

opportunities. I helped set up an LLC for an entrepreneur." There's no cap on the pro bono hours that juniors can count toward their bonus target, though they need to hit 1,900 to count pro bono toward the target. One junior pointed out: "If you were doing 100 hours of pro bono per month that would not be acceptable."

Pro bono hours
- For all attorneys: 5,289
- Average per attorney: 27

Hours & Compensation

At the time of our calls the firm's bonus policy was causing some frustration among our interviewees; associates were not guaranteed a bonus for hitting the 2,000 hours target. Instead, this target made them bonus eligible, and the professional development committee and managing partner made the final decision on the amount awarded. One source grumbled: "We don't get paid market bonuses and it's not clear to us how or why we get a certain amount." Another put things more bluntly: "I think compensation has been the biggest negative about being here." On the plus side, most sources said they didn't have much difficulty hitting the 2,000 threshold. In addition, there's even more good news: before we went to press the firm told us that it had changed its policy, so that market-rate bonuses are guaranteed for all associates who hit the 2,000-hour target; above market-rate bonuses are paid out to those who perform particularly well.

"There is a lot of fluctuation."

During quiet periods litigation juniors work 9am to 7pm, while busier times see them exiting around 10pm. We even heard of one associate operating on less than four hours' sleep, "but that was in the middle of a trial – things like that are very atypical." Those in business & technology "are beholden to clients so there is a lot of fluctuation." Most days start at 9am or 10am with juniors leaving at 6pm when it's quiet, 7pm to 8:30pm when things start to heat up and midnight when it comes to crunch time.

Office

Renovated three years ago, Choate's office has "lots of glass, which takes some time getting used to." On the plus side the location near Boston Harbor means "you have beautiful views no matter where you are" and keeping things see-through has encouraged juniors out of their internal offices to "get talking to people a bit more." One source did, however, think that "everything is a little bit smaller than before and the soundproofing is not as good. You have to shut your door to keep the noise out sometimes."

Training & Development

After initial training, juniors said, "once a month a partner comes in and gives a presentation, which could be on document review or a junior's role on a trial team." A transactional junior told us about "an annual retreat where everyone in the private equity department gathers for a weekend to take apart a transaction document. That really helped my understanding of larger deals."

"A lot of mentoring also happens outside of that structure."

The firm's mentoring program has been formalized recently with monthly lunches set up by mentors and regular mentor/mentee meetings. Sources were generally happy with the firm's efforts, and one said: "I see my mentor quite often, though a lot of mentoring also happens outside of that structure."

Choate is pushing for feedback to be given contemporaneously. While some associates said they "had not noticed a huge shift," insiders did like the change. "Feedback might not be as effective or productive if you didn't get it until the end of your work," one believed. A few insiders felt the quality and effectiveness of feedback varies "from partner to partner but some have really taken to giving it." In addition to all this, anonymous surveys and open forums with the managing partner allow juniors to give their thoughts on seniors and Choate more generally.

Strategy & Future

"Boston is so strongly embedded in the history of the firm that I don't see us opening up an office elsewhere," one junior believed. "It's the distinguishing feature that makes Choate unique." Chairman John Nadas agrees: "Choate is built different than other leading law firms. We conduct our highly focused national and international practice from one office in Boston, giving our lawyers the best of both worlds: high-stakes work in a close-knit environment, where partners truly care about associates' long-term development and work every day to help them improve."

The Inside View

See firm profile on p.620

Cleary Gottlieb Steen & Hamilton

Lawyers per state

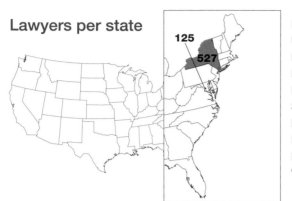

125
527

Largest US office: New York
US offices: 2
International offices: 14
First-year salary: $180,000
Billable hours: no requirement
Summers 2018: 119 (4 1Ls (DC), 108 2Ls, 7 SEO)
Revenue 2017: undisclosed
Partners made in 2018: 2 (in the US)
Famous for: international reach; top antitrust practice; overseas investment know-how

Despite Cleary's natural superiority on the global stage, new associates happily reported that *"there's no air of superiority."*

"THIS may sound silly," said one slightly bashful interviewee, *"but what mattered to me when choosing this firm was that it was less formal – not just in dress code but in the way people interacted with each other; it's more laid back and there's no air of superiority."* The majority of our sources also cited Cleary's culture as one of its key selling points (and we'll explore it in more detail shortly), but while its dress code may well be more relaxed, there's nothing casual about Cleary's work: *Chambers USA* rates it as top dog in the States for a range of practices, including antitrust, capital markets, financial services regulation, securities, and tax. Its New York HQ is especially known for its white-collar, real estate and Latin America investment capabilities, while its remaining domestic office in DC rules the roost when it comes to antitrust work.

"It was Cleary's international presence that stood out."

But Cleary's prowess extends far beyond the borders of the US; its practice is heavily weighted overseas, with a total of 14 international offices supporting its two domestic bases. These can be found across Europe, the Middle East, Asia and Latin America, forming an expansive international reach that proved equally attractive to incoming junior associates. *"I wanted to do work with an international focus, and while I was doing interviews it was Cleary's international presence that stood out,"* one junior relayed, echoing the motivation of many others. *"The thing that associates have in common is international experiences and/or backgrounds,"* another source pointed out. *"Alongside good law schools and grades, we have very similar backgrounds in that respect."*

Offices

Most interviewees had worked with the firm's international offices, and opportunities to do so had started early: *"The fact that summers can potentially work in a foreign office was really attractive,"* recalled juniors. *"In addition there's a formal program where you can spend several years at a foreign office; a lot of partners have done that."* Associates also get the chance to earn some air miles: *"If matters are really busy associates have been able to go to Brussels or London for a few months – I also know people who are going to Frankfurt and Buenos Aires."* In the Latin American practice there are plenty of opportunities to work in Brazil or Argentina: *"As a third year you're encouraged to consider going for a season."*

The majority of Cleary's juniors were based in its New York office, which is located downtown in the financial district: *"It's not as crazy as Times Square, and the opening of the new World Trade Center complex has given the area a breath of fresh air – it's up-and-coming."* The office itself *"may be from the 60s, but it still feels airy and associ-*

On chambers-associate.com...

- Get hired
- Interview with hiring partner Liza Lenas and director of legal recruiting Donna Harris

See firm profile on p.621

The Inside View

Rankings in *Chambers USA*

Antitrust	Financial Services
Banking & Finance	Regulation
Bankruptcy/Restructuring	International Arbitration
Capital Markets	Investment Funds
Corporate Crime &	Latin American Investment
Investigations	Litigation
Corporate/M&A	Private Equity
Employee Benefits	Real Estate
& Executive Compensation	Securities
Energy & Natural	Tax
Resources	

For detail on ranking tiers and ranking locations, visit
www.chambersandpartners.com

Recent work highlights

- Served as global antitrust counsel to Dow Chemical during its $130 billion 'merger of equals' with DuPont
- Represented Credit Suisse, J.P. Morgan, Santander, BTG Pactual and Goldman Sachs as initial purchasers during leading Mexican energy company IEnova's $1.45 billion follow-on equity offering
- Acted for Brazilian energy company Petrobras and both its current and former execs during securities fraud litigation brought in New York and Pennsylvania
- Advised Japanese pharma company Takeda on its $5.2 billion acquisition of ARIAD Pharmaceuticals

ates (for the most part) have big windows in their offices. I have an unobstructed view of the Statue of Liberty." Juniors share an office for their first year, "which is generally awesome – it's nice to have company on those late nights!" A more congenial atmosphere is also fostered by a mixed seating plan: "People aren't separated by practice area. In my corner there's a litigator, a tax attorney and a private equity specialist. It's nice to interact with people outside of your group."

The Work

In New York Cleary's litigation/arbitration, M&A, capital markets, private funds and real estate groups housed the most associates. Those in DC were mostly able to take on a mix of antitrust, litigation and corporate work. "*You're not bucketed into a specific area, so I've done everything from advisory work to litigation and enforcement matters,*" revealed one source in the capital (take note that most juniors tend to stick with either transactional or litigious work, but some do both). In general, "*Cleary likes its associates to rotate through a variety of different things,*" so even in New York sources had picked up a decent mix of work within their respective departments.

Juniors pick up this varied workload within "*a regulated free-market system: it's free-market in that you voice your preferences, but regulated in that we have an assignment coordination function that helps to allocate us the matters we want.*" Some sources had bypassed the coordinators completely ("*I just shoot an email to the people I want to work with saying that I'm interested*"), while others very much encouraged their use: "*People can and should feel comfortable letting the staffers know if there's something they're interested in trying out. The staffers remember stuff like that and keep your goals in mind.*"

"... best described as a renaissance lawyer."

In litigation, New Yorkers had sampled a range of fraud, IP, securities, bankruptcy and white-collar crime cases. On a "*massively complex international cross-border bankruptcy dispute*" juniors had been able to "*attend a Second Circuit argument in the very first week – we've been very involved in litigation before the court of appeals and bankruptcy court.*" Elsewhere, responsibility came in droves, as sources recounted "*second-chairing depositions in the first year*" and "*working on an amicus brief that got filed before the Supreme Court – they let me have my name on it!*"

Those in DC had picked up plenty of antitrust work – the office's star practice. "*On that side all of the clients we've worked with have been international, and you get to work with the Brussels office a lot.*" Sources had spent their first year focused on merger notifications and government investigations, before progressing onto more contentious work, "*which is great for your development.*" They were "*incredibly impressed*" by the work on offer: "*I've worked on presentations to the Department of Justice, attended two depositions, overseen filings in other countries, responded to government questions and turned data analysis into exhibits.*"

On the transactional side, M&A juniors had worked with "*a mix of financial institutions, private companies and strategic buyers,*" and noted a clear line of progression "*from a lot of due diligence in the first year to much more drafting in the second year – I'll take a first crack at the ancillaries and organizational documents.*" The strength of Cleary's Latin America practice was highlighted by capital markets juniors, who told us that "*in general Lat Am-focused lawyers are expected to be more generalist. I think of myself as a finance lawyer that does capital markets work.*" Those who'd veered toward Latin American work had also taken on "*some complicated project finance deals with bank and public debt components, as well as M&A deals and sovereign entities work.*" As a result they felt their role was "*best described as a renaissance lawyer: every day there's a different problem and the clients really look to you for everything.*"

See firm profile on p.621

Diversity	Partners (%)	Associates (%)
Women	19	49
White	88	66
Black/African American	4	7
Hispanic/Latin American	4	9
Asian	4	12
Mixed/Other	1	4
LGBT	5	6

Strategy & Future

On the capital markets side, sources felt that Cleary was doing a good job of *"staying ahead of the game"* when it came to *"the big political changes that have taken place in Latin America, in countries like Brazil and Argentina."* Hiring partner Liza Lenas tells us: *"We're continuing to focus on client service and we believe that our antitrust, M&A and litigation/arbitration practices will continue to grow."* As for new offices, Lenas says there are no plans in the offing, but: *"Of course, we're Cleary, so we're always looking for opportunities to expand into new geographies, but consistency and the cohesion of our lawyers is our first priority, so we approach expansion fairly conservatively."* For more from Lenas and director of legal recruiting Donna Harris, go to chambers-associate.com

Training & Development

Training at Cleary kicks off with a two-week mini MBA program that gathers all new associates in its New York HQ: *"You get an introduction to the firm, its practice areas, its core values, its financial statements... we even got training on our personal finances!"* juniors enthused. *"The best bit was actually the Excel training from someone whose job it is to read spreadsheets. They somehow made something really boring seem really exciting!"*

"They somehow made something really boring seem really exciting!"

Following this, transactional juniors attend 'Corporate College,' which *"usually consists of training sessions in the morning, but we sometimes host pizza nights where we discuss topics – a week ago we had one on registration rights agreements and what to consider when drafting them, for example."* Cleary's 'Litigation Academy,' meanwhile, scoops up all contentious-focused newbies in New York for *"an intensive weekend of deposition training."* On top of these formal programs are *"a ton of CLEs geared toward different practice areas – some are mandatory and some are just really helpful to attend!"*

Culture & Compensation

Associates sang Cleary's praises when it came to the culture of the firm, and many cited the lockstep compensation system and absence of billable requirements as the reason for such glowing reviews. *"Everyone gets compensated the same according to their year, and the same goes for partners, which is why you see partners from different groups seeking help from one another – no one's worried about dividing the pie."* The positive effects of sharing out the pie are clear, as *"there are certainly fewer sharp elbows here than at other New York firms. People tend to not take themselves too seriously, and that's what's cool about our culture. Everyone's doing really challenging work but they maintain a down-to-earth, human approach and are willing to teach you along the way."*

"...no one's worried about dividing the pie."

Sources also detected another common attribute among Cleary's attorneys: *"When I was considering firms as a student I got the impression that people at Cleary were generally more intellectually curious, and I've definitely found that to be true now that I'm here."* Without the pressure of reaching a billable requirement, juniors felt they had time to pursue more stimulating work and focus on what's important: *"When I speak to my friends at other firms it seems like their hours are more of a concern. I prefer getting everything done to the standard the firm expects rather than just counting hours."*

Hours & Social Life

How this overarching approach translates into actual working hours depends on the practice. Litigators and antitrust associates reported steady 9am to 6pm days with some additional evening work from home (*"it's generally pretty manageable"*), while transactional sources told us that *"it's so unpredictable."* A capital markets junior said that *"if it's crazy then you can expect to have a few 2am finishes,"* while those in M&A revealed that *"you can have two months where you're slow and then two where you're really busy and working every day except Sunday."* However, associates were grateful for the opportunity to work remotely (first years can do so one day a month, but after a year the allowance is bumped up to two days

See firm profile on p.621

per month), and told us that Cleary takes a humane view when it comes to working hours: *"They care about us not burning out and want to retain talent. During my first year the staffing people reached out and encouraged me to take a vacation; they said they thought it was important and would explain to my team that that's part of the deal. They want people to be happy."*

"Nobody judges you if you see this as just a job, but at the same time there is a social life." In DC there's a monthly happy hour, as well as *"regular cross-practice lunch meetings and holiday and Halloween parties."* Over in New York weekly wine and cheese evenings keep things social, but the juniors in general *"get together throughout the year – there's a good amount of people being friends with each other!"*

Pro Bono

With no billable requirement comes no limit on how much pro bono work associates can take on. *"All teams take into account that people are going to be pulled in different directions,"* insiders told us, *"so it's okay to take on pro bono and partners don't view it as lesser work. They accommodate it as though it were billable, although of course if there are deadlines you sometimes have to prioritize."* Interviewees we spoke to had worked on a wide variety of cases including federal clemency projects, asylum issues, prisoner re-sentencing matters and state election challenges. *"I'm on the pro bono reserve list so I see all the opportunities and there's a lot going on,"* said one junior. *"The pro bono coordinators send regular emails asking for assistance."*

"They accommodate it as though it were billable."

Pro bono hours
- For all US attorneys: 84,269
- Average per US attorney: 115

Diversity

Quite a few sources highlighted Cleary's track record in this respect: *"A couple of years ago there was a lot of pushback when only one female partner was made up, and a lot of people were concerned about a lack of equality at the firm."* However, most interviewees agreed that *"the firm has been responsive and is committed to trying to improve. There have been a few town hall meetings and executive committee discussions; they keep us looped in about how to increase the number of diverse candidates accepting our offers, and they compare our success rates year after year. Looking at the more recent rounds of promotions I think you can see results."* Small changes had made a big impact: *"On the MBA all of the partners automatically referred to judges and clients using female pronouns. It really impressed me. People are very mindful here of hierarchy and inclusive language."*

"When I was considering firms as a student I got the impression that people at Cleary were generally more intellectually curious, and I've definitely found that to be true now that I'm here."

See firm profile on p.621

Clifford Chance US LLP

Lawyers per state

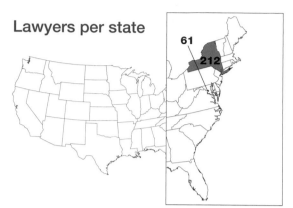

61

212

Largest US office: New York
US offices: 2
International offices: 30
First-year salary: $180,000
Billable hours: no requirement
Summers 2018: 20 (1 1L, 18 2Ls, 1 SEO)
Revenue 2017: $1.99 billion (-3.4%)
Partners made in 2018: 1 (in US)
Famous for: magic circle prestige; reigning champion of Chambers Global

'Truly international' is much more than a moniker for this magic circle member.

ON numbers alone, Clifford Chance has a lot going for it. Its global revenue continues to hover around the $2 billion mark, while its worldwide ambitions have translated into 31 offices strategically dotted across five continents. However, CC's associates were adamant that there's far more to the firm's scope than just the numbers: "*We really are global in the sense that we talk to colleagues in each country on a daily basis.*" Those searching for "*a firm that could hold its own*" across regions had good reason to prioritize CC, as regional managing partner Evan Cohen explains: "*Once I moved to Clifford Chance and became part of a nearly 200-attorney office, I was immediately aware of the magnitude of the CC global network and the benefit it provided our clients. For students interested in the very best global opportunities, there really is no better place.*" On top of its foothold in no fewer than 20 countries, the firm also boasts more top-tier *Chambers Global* rankings than any other law firm, and is a world leader in areas including banking & finance, capital markets, corporate/M&A, insurance, private equity, projects & energy and tax. And it came in at number two on the *Chambers Global* Top 30 – higher than any of its magic circle companions.

It's always been a more conservative picture in the US, but healthy figures suggest they're moving in the right direction – revenue grew to $263 million in 2017, and that same year CC's managing partner Matthew Layton expressed his desire to increase US revenues in the medium term so that they account for over 20% of the firm's total turnover. With just the two offices in New York and DC, the US practice is just one part of the Clifford Chance machine, but that's not to say the work is any less interesting than bigger US players. What appealed to CC initiates were the firm's "*huge deals you read about in big journals – that was very exciting to me.*"

The Work & Offices

One aspect of Clifford Chance's international scope associates liked best was "*the ability to call one of our foreign offices rather than going and talking to the client about hiring local counsel, which would mean asking for bids and submitting a proposal to the client. Instead, there are so many scenarios I can just reach out to a local Clifford Chance office.*" In the US, the New York and DC offices make up just one part of the Clifford Chance machine. And that was the appeal for many: "*the combination of an extremely large, international firm with the much smaller feel of the relatively small US offices.*"

By default, all US incomers go to CC's transactional associate pool, unless they express interest in litigation right off the bat. Juniors stay in the pool for two and a half years. Up to that point of specializing, an associate coordinator ("*she's amazing*") dishes out work from three

On chambers-associate.com...

- More on getting hired at Clifford Chance
- Interview with regional managing partner Evan Cohen

See firm profile on p.622

The Inside View

Rankings in *Chambers USA*

Capital Markets	Projects
Corporate/M&A	REITs
Insurance	Tax
Latin American Investment	Transportation
Litigation	

For detail on ranking tiers and ranking locations, visit www.chambersandpartners.com

Recent work highlights

- Advised Coca-Cola in its $580 million acquisition of South American beverage company AdeS Alimentos de Soja
- Represented Goldman Sachs and a syndicate of banks in a $390 million loan for a Colombian toll road project
- Advised a committee of bondholders in the restructuring of renewable energy company Abengoa, worth approximately €20 billion
- Acted for Chinese telecom equipment company ZTE Corp in a US investigation of unauthorized exports to Iran

broad areas: capital markets, banking and finance, and corporate. CC associates liked getting exposure to different types of work, but advised it might not work for people who know exactly what type of work they want to pursue. Overall though, they appreciated being free from practice group constraints: *"With rotations you could either get slammed, or the opposite and have a slow couple of months. This way you can pick up the slack in other groups."*

"There's a US aspect to many deals but you're also working with teams across the globe."

Associates said the banking and finance group was *"a little bit giant. It's a lot of teamwork because there are so many moving pieces. A number of associates get staffed on a matter and we all split the work depending on availability."* Most deals were *"generally led by another office, but the client happens to have assets in the US – that's always pretty cool."* Not only was it common to work with international offices, but associates interacted with a range of places: *"I'd say maybe 50% of my international work is focused on London and Europe, and then I've done a solid chunk with Latin America and a smaller slice with Asia."* We heard about a lot of interesting cross-border matters including *"a number of bank bond deals for toll roads in Colombia. It's really big and there are so many players. We'll have a loan component and a bond component. The loan has been under local law so you have all these local lenders getting involved in negotiating docs, while at the same time getting ready for bond issuing."* When it comes to the nitty-gritty of the everyday, *"I do everything from negotiating contracts to sending dial-ins for calls."*

Juniors in corporate told us about M&A deals with *"a bunch of US investors investing in a foreign company, so there's a US aspect to many deals but you're also working with teams across the globe."* Highlights for current juniors included one deal in which *"we don't have a lot of resources, so it's up to me, my research and any precedents I can dig up to be able to navigate the different issues that come up, which is really cool."* Associates outlined that initially, *"you're going to be tasked with a lot of diligence, but after my first deal I was put in a position to actually lead diligence in a smaller acquisition and liaise with other*

specialist groups in our firm, which was interesting." In the structured debt practice within corporate, associates got a *"fair amount of repeat work. Really big M&A projects don't come to us as often so there's not as much heavy diligence. Initially tasks tend to be running document checklists and gathering signature pages."*

Globally, the firm is huge in all areas of capital markets and the New York office's derivatives and securitization practices attract particular acclaim. *"I've worked with a lot of REITs – we're very heavy-handed in that area,"* one junior told us, while another had also *"worked with several aircraft financing companies such as LATAM Airlines"* and handled *"several high-yield debt offerings."* That entailed *"lots of drafting – I would draft the risk factors, the business section, the bulk of the offering memorandum and underwriting agreements."*

One area that accounted for a lot of juniors' time was the firm's *"robust"* aircraft practice. *"First years are involved in a lot of aircraft deals. For each aircraft there has to be a transfer of assets into a special purpose vehicle, and juniors tend to take the lead on that because although it's not a huge closing, it still needs to occur. It's the first time a junior would take a meeting deal and run the closing checklist, and seek advice from local experts – that's one of the things you learn as a junior."*

Associates in Clifford Chance's smaller litigation and dispute resolution group still enjoyed a similar level of cross-border work: *"Everything has some international flavor, whether the client is abroad or the facts occurred abroad."* The work entailed *"some due diligence, looking at specific transactions and writing memos, going through DOJ documents, doc review, and some broad outlines of witness prep."*

Get Hired

If you're *"willing to embrace the international aspect,"* go to chambers-associate.com to find out how to impress at interview.

The Inside View

See firm profile on p.622

Diversity	Partners (%)	Associates (%)
Women	13	44
White	85	63
Black/African American	0	1
Hispanic/Latin American	3	9
Asian	3	17
Mixed/Other	10	10
LGBT	1	2

Training & Development

All first years are assigned a Career Development Partner (CDP), but it can be changed: "*I didn't develop a relationship with mine at all, and then a different partner offered to be mine.*" The CDP is one of the partners present at associates' formal annual reviews. Juniors get an informal 'check-in' at the six-month mark too, and "*the firm reviews vertically, so I review partners as well.*"

"I've done double my CLE requirements in the first few months!"

Associates attend "*mandatory overviews of each major group and subgroup. It feels like every week. I think I've done double my CLE requirements in the first few months!*" After feedback, the firm "*has been trying to spread training out more rather than frontloading.*" As this training falls away, juniors transition into the Clifford Chance Academy, the firm-wide training program – "*that's a couple of times a year.*"

Hours & Compensation

In the DC office, associates felt the 2,000-hour billing target was "*more of a conversation in New York.*" We'd say that was true, but it wasn't a difficult chat: "*It breaks down to 40 hours in a work week, which is a regular working week for any person, so I don't think it's unreasonable.*" Rationalizing aside, associates admitted: "*I'd be lying if I said the hours weren't long. On a crazy day I could be in the office until any time. But on a normal day I probably sneak out around eight or nine.*" And working internationally inevitably entailed some weekend work: "*We had a deal with Japan and our Sunday was their Monday, so by nature of the time difference I was working.*"

"Our Sunday was their Monday, so by nature of the time difference I was working."

Associates enjoyed more flexibility to work remotely though, after the firm introduced a tech stipend: "*That's been a huge positive development.*" The perks of being a British firm shows in the 20 vacation days. "*A coordinator makes sure everyone is covered during their time off. I disappeared to the other side of the world and when I came back all my work had been done!*"

Culture

Although its US practice isn't enormous, associates emphasized that the CC culture very much depended on the group: "*Personalities are very different. Some are more distant, and seniors generally aren't very communicative. Others are more friendly, it's not uncommon for them to take people out to lunch.*" Some associates felt attorneys were "*more colleagues than friends. People are pretty serious about work.*" Others, while agreeing with the latter, were committed to having fun at the same time: "*We had a rough Thanksgiving because we had a ton of work, but we still got together and cooked a couple of turkeys. People brought friends along, so in the end we had this fun Thanksgiving which all started because we knew we were gonna have to work a bunch.*"

"Everyone seems to be working together to survive – it can be hard at a law firm!"

Overall, associates were happy among their peers: "*We're competitive in the sense that we want the firm to succeed but we don't compete against each other. Everyone seems to be working together to survive – it can be hard at a law firm!*" As much as they valued each other, that's not to say juniors didn't appreciate their seniors. One commonality we noted in associate feedback was a "*great emphasis on teaching – I was given the opportunity to team up with a senior and a partner on drafting articles for client alerts and various publications. I've found it valuable to be encouraged to develop my knowledge of my practice area.*"

Diversity

From its London nerve center, the firm radiates progressive vibes. CC is one of a handful of leaders in diversity in the UK, and on both sides of the Atlantic, juniors commend the firm's commitment to eliminating bias in recruiting. Clifford Chance's diversity committee has various arms including groups for Asian American, Latino and black attorneys. Associates at the junior level did find a lack of women at the top discouraging, but the firm has adopted the Mansfield Rule, so at least one candidate considered for leadership roles will be a woman. And associates felt the firm was open to plans and initiatives brought by the diversity committee: "*The diversity committee is in charge of an art exhibition on our main floor, and liaises with the art curator once a month. We had special exhibits for Black History Month.*"

See firm profile on p.622

Pro Bono

Pro bono hours were unlimited, but *"the firm encourages that all pro bono is done by two associates so we don't run into time restraint issues. It is nice to be able to lean on each other."* Some felt pro bono wasn't as much a *"natural part"* of CC life as it could be, though associates did get *"weekly opportunities"* from the firm. Associates had been involved in *"helping high school kids prepare for a worldwide competition in The Hague."*

Pro bono hours

- For all (US) attorneys: undisclosed
- Average per (US) attorney: undisclosed (50 hours minimum encouraged)

Strategy & Future

From global associate updates, juniors were encouraged by the firm *"emphasizing a focus on building the Americas practice further. They're consistently increasing junior and lateral recruitment. That measured approach makes us feel good. We're not going to be overextended and will continue to grow and improve."* Go to chambers-associate.com to read our interview with regional managing partner Evan Cohen and discover how technology will be shaping Clifford Chance's practice in years to come.

Clifford Chance took 2nd place in our 2018 associate satisfaction survey.

See firm profile on p.622

The Inside View

Cooley LLP

Lawyers per state

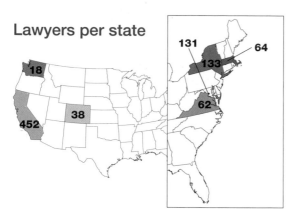

131 · 64 · 133 · 18 · 38 · 62 · 452

Largest US office: Palo Alto
US offices: 10
International offices: 3
First-year salary: $180,000
Billable hours: 1,950 target
Summers 2018: 61 (8 1Ls, 51 2Ls, 2 others)
Revenue 2017: $1.07 billion (+9.8%)
Partners made in 2018: 18
Famous for: emerging companies; cool California vibes

Associates describe Cooley as *"a firm on a meteoric rise."* Juniors get a decent variety of work with cutting-edge clients, together with a *"West Coast vibe."*

COOLEY sits among the top firms in the country for its venture capital, startup and life sciences work. The firm's strengths and character owe much to its Bay Area roots – it's *"right next door to all the players."* The firm's client roster is teeming with startups on the ones-to-watch list, but it also has industry giants such as Facebook, Google and Uber on its books. Some of the more exotic clients drawn to its doors include Elon Musk's SpaceX, which plans to colonize Mars, as well as Thalmic Labs, who are basically turning people into cyborgs. *"We work with clients through their whole life-cycle,"* juniors explained, *"from their growth stage all the way until when they are fully established."* CEO Joe Conroy expands upon this, explaining that *"tech companies come out of a garage and within two years are major consumers of legal services. We benefit from that shrinking time span. It gives us a competitive advantage."*

> *"We work with clients through their whole life-cycle."*

Chambers USA attests to this firm's full-service credentials across the network; however, providing cutting-edge clients with all their corporate, IP, regulatory and conten-

tious needs has proved to be the true recipe for success in Cooley's *"meteoric rise."* This year's cohort was attracted by the growth phase at the firm. Turnover in 2017 increased by 9.8%, marking the firm's grand entry into the billion-dollar revenue club. In the third quarter of 2017 alone, Cooley claims to have handled deals representing more than $5.3 billion in invested capital. The firm also elected 18 new partners in January 2018. Credit for this success is spread across its 12 offices. The biggest two are the firm's Palo Alto and Washington bases, followed up by a *"rapidly expanding"* post in New York. Elsewhere the firm has bases in Seattle, San Francisco, San Diego, Reston, Boston, LA and Colorado. Internationally Cooley has, so far, planted flags in London and Shanghai.

Offices & Strategy

Associates were clear that the firm's growth was very visible among its network of offices. In Palo Alto, *"we are running out of space,"* sources explained, adding that *"for the first time first years have been allocated internal offices."* Juniors in New York similarly remarked: *"We are growing very quickly – our current space can't handle our capacity. We have recently added a whole arbitration and debt financing group as part of the firm's plan to build out the office as a new hub, balancing its presence on the West Coast and serving as an access point to the rest of the world."* To accommodate the growth, Cooley is one of a number of firms planning to relocate its NY base to the redeveloped Hudson Yards area in early 2019.

On chambers-associate.com...

- More about getting hired at Cooley
- Interview with Cooley CEO Joe Conroy
- A few Silicon Valley facts

See firm profile on p.623

The Inside View

Rankings in *Chambers USA*

Antitrust	Media & Entertainment
Capital Markets	Privacy & Data Security
Corporate/Commercial	Private Equity
Corporate/M&A	Real Estate
Intellectual Property	Startups & Emerging
Investment Funds	Companies
IT & Outsourcing	Technology
Life Sciences	Telecommunications
Litigation	Venture Capital

For detail on ranking tiers and ranking locations, visit
www.chambersandpartners.com

Recent work highlights

- Advised DraftKings in its merger with FanDuel. DraftKings and FanDuel are the nation's two dominant daily fantasy sports websites
- Represented venture capital firm Menlo Ventures on the closing of its fourteenth fund with investor commitments of $450 million
- Acted for Otsuka Pharmaceutical on its collaboration and license agreement with Akebia Therapeutics in the US for Vadadustat, a product candidate in development for the treatment of anemia associated with chronic kidney disease

"We are growing very quickly."

Over in San Francisco and the pattern continues: *"We've been very busy hiring people. We have just had an influx of people from Wilson Sonsini but we are locked into our lease and are running out of room!"* While the firm's growth is impressive, juniors insisted that *"growth is very well managed. We are not looking to be a mega global firm that serves everybody and everything."* Conroy affirms that he is *"dismissive of growing to a number"* and explains that Cooley's future growth rate is *"bound more by what position we want to take in each market."* New York was flagged as a key area, as was the Bay Area.

The Work

The 'business' (corporate) practice takes just under two-thirds of juniors, with litigation taking up the rest. Traditionally starting as generalists within their designated group, newbies are free to explore different areas. For litigators this means a mix of antitrust, commercial disputes, IP and white-collar crime cases, whereas transactional hopefuls keep busy in subgroups like corporate/M&A, emerging or public companies, technology, and venture capital. Assignment coordinators are in place to *"have conversations about workloads, time constraints of projects and preferences,"* but otherwise it's *"a free market,"* juniors explained. *"You are free to approach any partners you want to work with and if you want to totally avoid one type of work, you can."*

"It's both very intellectually satisfying and exhausting!"

Cooley litigators had sampled a range of work including IP, trade secrets, employment and contract disputes. *"We've done a lot of inter partes review cases recently,"* one junior of the Palo Alto team observed. *"It's all about providing submissions to the board to invalidate patents against our clients – it's all very technical. When I first started, I was just reviewing the submissions and doing overall checks, but now I'm actively drafting them."* Other sources described their preference for cases that are *"more people-related and fact-sensitive. I enjoy digging around in trade secret cases, seeing what things were disclosed, finding out which companies have a background with each other, and looking at where a licensing may have gone wrong."* Whatever the case, litigators emphasized Cooley is a place *"where they give you as much responsibility as you can handle."* We heard of sources drafting summary judgment briefings, arguing in court, drafting interviewing outlines, drafting expert reports, and participating in expert depositions.

Newbies in the 'business' group start out broad, doing a mix of work which could range from startups and venture capital funding to M&A and IPOs. *"Not all the deals are super high value but just because they're not in the billions doesn't mean we sacrifice on quality,"* one junior explained. *"I've had great experiences getting a feel for M&A work, from profiling targets and drafting corporate profiles to putting together schedules and merger agreements."* Another regaled their experience of *"holding an entire auction process for a potential merger. I was in regular contact with the CEO, having to walk them through the all disclosure obligations under the agreement."* In life sciences, juniors are busy doing IP licensing for biotech and pharmaceutical companies as well as *"partnering products at a clinical stage with someone who wants to take it further down the line and commercialize it. As a junior I review everything from two-page confidentiality agreements to 100-page collaboration agreements. The way I describe it is we are putting together a puzzle and designing the puzzle pieces – it's both very intellectually satisfying and exhausting!"*

Culture & Hours

The volume of work generated from startups opens up a somewhat unique opportunity for Cooley associates: *"Working with an early-stage client is different from working with big, established clients who only want to interact with partners,"* sources mused. *"I'm a second year and I'm already getting phone calls and emails from CEOs on a*

See firm profile on p.623

The Inside View

Diversity	Partners (%)	Associates (%)
Women	23	53
White	86	76
Black/African American	1	2
Hispanic/Latin American	3	3
Asian	7	13
Mixed/Other	3	6
LGBT	2	3

regular basis. It's exciting working with founders so intimately to achieve their visions, many of whom have put everything on the line."

While associates appreciated this provided a *"great opportunity to learn and grow,"* they also acknowledged it as a *"double-edged sword,"* highlighting the *"stresses of coordinating directly with CEOs when you don't want to make yourself or the firm look stupid."* A certain pragmatism is required: many startups are *"used to being dynamic, and prone to frequently changing their direction overnight. Sometimes it feels like they are creating fire drills for no reason,"* although sources observed this was more pronounced on the corporate side.

"...a vibe that is professional, but without a certain formality."

"Cooley advertises that it is somehow different from other firms," thought associates, and this is true in many respects. But take a look at the hours and there is no mistake this is BigLaw. *"I think the reputation of Cooley as a great place to work gives people a false sense of a great work-life balance,"* one source reflected. Others told us they rarely had problems hitting their 1,950 hours target. As with previous years, associates explain the firm's culture as a result of its *"West Coast roots."* But, taking a more realistic view, a source this year spoke of *"a vibe that is professional, but without a certain formality."* As one junior elaborated: *"I'm not a very formal person and I didn't want to have to work somewhere where I would have to look like a fancy lady every day – I appreciate that I can be myself and casual here."*

A less buttoned-up culture also translated into a liberal approach to remote working. *"As juniors, we are treated as adults – we are not expected to be chained to our desk all day."* Those in the firm's New York office observed that *"a lot of people leave the office before 6pm and are able to eat dinner with their families before hopping back online later."* Others reported on the added bonus of *"working a lot of Fridays from home."* Finally, while juniors acknowledged that *"there is a knack to picking when to take time off,"* sources were happy to report that their vacations were

"true vacations," without the stress of trying to draft a disclosure on a beach in the Bahamas.

Training & Development

Training gets under way with a week of Cooley College: a five-day series of events, some of which are for all new associates, and some are specific to corporate and litigation. On the corporate track, for example, juniors receive lectures *"breaking down all the stages of an M&A transaction"* and are provided with *"annotated versions of key documents you will encounter."* They also provide basic finance and accounting training for both sides to better improve financial literacy. *"It is a bit like drinking from the fire hose but it's helpful to refer back to the binder of materials you are provided with later on,"* juniors surmised. The firm also does a good job with on-the-go feedback. *"In the early stages of a transaction I will always draft up a proposed response email to a CEO and shoot it by a couple of people on the team before sending,"* one source explained, adding that *"having their guidance helps manage the challenge of being in the driver's seat."*

"It is a bit like drinking from the fire hose."

Juniors appreciated the firm's efforts to make juniors *"feel like part of the business. We are always kept in the loop on the firm's financials, the average amount of hours billed and our biggest clients; and each partner gives a brief summary of what they see in the pipeline and future deals."*

Pro Bono

An unlimited number of pro bono can count toward billable. Associates were involved in a range of cases including immigration and asylum, work for KIND (Kids In Need of Defense), clemency projects that address sentencing disparities, and domestic abuse cases. Sources also highlighted that the *"firm has been very active in response to specific situations. We have recently had some really terrible fires in the Wine County so the firm has been teaming up with local organizations to help people with their insurance claims process. The firm puts all its support staff at our disposal for pro bono cases."*

Pro bono hours
- For all US attorneys: 44,486
- Average per US attorney: 56.5

Diversity

"Our CEO is very committed to diversity," one source declared, offering an interesting theory as to why: *"In my head it stems from the fact that he was a single father and so is therefore very sympathetic to the challenge of single*

See firm profile on p.623

parenting, which tends to be laid on the mother." We were reluctant to pry too much into his personal life but Conroy did have this to say: *"It is something I have been actively proselytizing about for some time. A big part of my push, culturally, is to make this industry more diverse and inclusive – at all levels. It is not just about ticking things off a checklist; it is that you consider the goal of being substantially more diverse and inclusive in all of your decision-making processes."* The head of the women's program in New York was described as *"incredible: if I were having issues about taking time off or transitioning back to work from parental leave, she would bend over backward to help."* Those in San Diego gave equal praise to *"the powerful partners who champion us,"* adding that *"one of the partners mentoring an associate recently got them an introduction to a judge for a clerkship."*

"...the powerful partners who champion us."

Offering more concrete evidence, sources pointed to the various programs in place to improve diversity. Recipients of the firm's diversity fellowship program for example can spend their 1L and 2L summers with the firm and receive a total of $30,000 toward law school tuition (the third and final $10,000 installment is paid when they join as an associate).

Get Hired

"The students who really stand out are those who look for opportunities to cultivate relationships with us prior to the start of Interviewing season," Cooley's chief legal talent officer Carrie Wagner tell us.

"Pursue the profession with passion and look for an area of law that you find challenging and enjoyable, as opposed to what you think is going to be the next hot practice to be involved in. If you're not cut out for it, you won't enjoy it, and if you don't enjoy it, you won't last. Look for an area that challenges you and gets you stimulated."

– Dykema CEO Peter Kellett

The Inside View

See firm profile on p.623

Cozen O'Connor

Lawyers per state

65
32
96
20
274
51
1
8
8
12
8
50
34
7
40

Largest US office: Philadelphia
US offices: 24
International offices: 3
First-year salary: $130,000 – $165,000
Billable hours: 1,600 – 2,000 target (varies by practice area)
Summers 2018: 6 1Ls, 23 2Ls
Revenue 2017: $416 million (+10.6%)
Partners made in 2018: undisclosed
Famous for: insurance and subrogation; lateral hiring

Approaching its 50th birthday, Cozen's fire for growth still burns bright as its size catches up with BigLaw's senior citizens.

FOUNDED in 1970 as a four-attorney insurance and commercial litigation boutique, Cozen has grown to over 700 lawyers in 27 offices in the US, the UK and Canada. Sources found the firm to be *"a young, energetic, creative law firm that cares about developing its young lawyers and investing in them."* Its headcount grew by an estimated 14% in 2017 alone, with a recent spate of lateral hires bulking out the private client, litigation and project finance practices. Clients come chiefly from middle-market industries.

> *"...a young, energetic, creative law firm that cares about developing its young lawyers."*

In *Chambers USA*, Cozen wins most of its rankings in its home state of Pennsylvania, for areas including construction, corporate/M&A, healthcare, insurance, labor & employment, litigation and real estate. Nationwide, the firm gets kudos for its insurance disputes, government relations and transportation practices. But Cozen doesn't just do nicely on paper – juniors were also attracted to the people they met. *"When you talk to lawyers they can be a bit rough around the edges or have high opinions*

of themselves, but I didn't get that sense at Cozen,"* one source said. *"They're just normal people who like a joke like anyone else."*

The Work

At the time of our research around half of Cozen's juniors could be found in the firm's 'litigation pool.' The other half are scattered across transactional teams like real estate, tax, IP, corporate and transportation. Sources reckoned *"the firm is branching out, and is dedicated to growing its transactional practice,"* having historically been known best for insurance and commercial litigation. There were several juniors in real estate at the time of our research. *"I do zoning work, property acquisitions, sales, leases and financing,"* a source here told us. *"I've also dealt with a contract between the owners of an office park and different vendors that they're working with to run their operation."* We heard that deals *"range in size – some are worth hundreds of millions of dollars, some are smaller."* In Pennsylvania the firm recently advised on the acquisition of the Wanamaker Building and counts the City of Philadelphia as a client.

> *"They remember what it was like to be in my shoes."*

Juniors in the litigation pool can sample insurance, environmental, labor & employment and general commercial work. They can also try *"both plaintiff and defense work"* which many found *"invaluable."* Sources described the pool as *"a very formal system that works like a well-oiled*

On chambers-associate.com...

- Get hired: interview with hiring partners Lezlie Madden and Dan Luccaro
- Interview with managing partner Vince McGuinness

See firm profile on p.624

The Inside View

Rankings in *Chambers USA*

Construction	Intellectual Property
Corporate/M&A	Labor & Employment
Government	Litigation
Healthcare	Real Estate
Insurance	Transportation

For detail on ranking tiers and ranking locations, visit
www.chambersandpartners.com

Recent work highlights

- Represented BRK Brands, a smoke and carbon monoxide alarm manufacturer, in a product liability and wrongful death suit
- Helped Wills Eye Hospital gain enrollment in Medicare following the government's determination that Wills Eye is not a 'hospital' because its focus is on outpatient rather than inpatient care
- Advised the Commonwealth Medical College on its integration with Geisinger Health System
- Represented Utz Quality Foods, the largest independent privately held snack company, on its acquisition of Inventure Foods for $165 million

machine." Everyone in the pool has someone assigning and managing their work, and that coordinator *"makes sure everyone has enough work or redistributes work if someone has too much. They also look out for work you're interested in."* Once associates finish their time in the pool and join a subgroup (after about a year or so), work assignment becomes more free market, although most tend to work for a couple of specific partners – *"that's definitely an organic process."* The biggest litigation subgroups are commercial litigation, insurance and subrogation. Across the groups juniors handle *"complaints and answers, motions to dismiss, motions for summary judgments, client updates"* and more. Do responsibilities change after you leave the pool and enter a subgroup? *"On bigger cases I do similar work to when I was in the pool,"* one junior reflected, *"but on smaller cases the partner lets me handle everything and monitors my updates – I'm the one going to court and calling the client."* At times, this could be overwhelming, but juniors added: *"I can't speak highly enough about the associates here. They remember what it was like to be in my shoes, so no one is going to turn you away."*

Training & Development

Training kicks off with an orientation in Philadelphia: all new entry-level associates are flown in for a three-day period. Juniors found this training to be *"admin-focused: things like billing, and how to handle yourself in a law firm."* Litigators have specific training programs called CODEP (the Cozen O'Connor Deposition Program) and COTA (the Cozen O'Connor Trial Academy), which sources found *"very hands-on"* and *"the kind of training you can use day to day."* Transactional interviewees found *"the firm emphasizes feedback from partners, which is where you get the most training. They make you feel like they really care about your development."* Outside of that, there are classic CLEs and *"opportunities to participate in video conferences and webinars with firm leadership."*

Hours & Compensation

Billable targets differ by practice area, ranging from 1,600 to 2,000 hours, and associates found that to be reasonable. *"One thing I appreciate is that the firm doesn't use a universal number across practices,"* said one interviewee.

"They understand the nuances of billing." Bonuses at Cozen are *"completely discretionary,"* associates said, though our sources guessed that *"it's a holistic process – they look at your reviews, the hours you've billed, and your overall contribution to the firm."* In addition, for the past two years Cozen has rewarded its associates' hard work with a year-end bonus, which is allocated based on the firm's profits.

"I think it's a good trade-off."

On a regular day juniors are in the office for around 8:30am to about 6pm. When things get busier, this could extend to an 8pm finish, followed by *"logging in at home."* Juniors appreciated the flexibility offered by teleworking and emphasized that *"there's no one going around seeing who's here or not."*

Historically Cozen's salaries have been below market, though one associate noted: *"They've increased salaries three times since I started!"* Salary doesn't match the Cravath scale, but juniors found: *"When you balance that out with what's asked of us, I think it's a good trade-off."*

Culture

"The Cozen culture is awesome," one source beamed. *"I would describe us as having a very Philly culture – laid back, and not cutthroat at all. Everyone is supportive of each other and willing to help anyone out regardless of expertise."* On top of its Philadelphia roots, juniors reckoned the firm's relative youthfulness also had a bearing on the culture. *"They like to use the word 'entrepreneurial,'"* we heard, *"which I interpret as meaning young and fresh. Cozen is more open-minded than other firms – if you have a vision or goal, they're going to support you."* Many agreed that *"while the firm has resources comparable to big firms, it maintains a small-firm togetherness."*

"a very Philly culture"

See firm profile on p.624

Diversity	Partners (%)	Associates (%)
Women	23	47
White	94	81
Black/African American	2	4
Hispanic/Latin American	2	6
Asian	1	6
Mixed/Other	1	3
LGBT	1	3

But with all Cozen's growth and expansion, how is it going to maintain its culture? In 2017 we heard from DC that new arrivals had stirred things up and toughened up the culture a bit. This year a source in DC described the culture as *"work hard, play hard"* and said that Cozen is *"a firm willing to take risks other firms aren't willing to. It always seems to be looking for the next opportunity and whether to acquire laterals."* Meanwhile a source in Philly had this to say about the culture: *"People are keeping an eye on it, but so far it's stayed exactly the same. Management is pretty mindful and selective of which firms and which people they're adding."* Another junior added: *"The culture trickles down from the partners. The ones I've worked with have always taken an interest in my personal life, as well as understanding my career goals."*

The culture is reinforced by a number of social activities. *"Last year we had an associate symposium where we all went to Philadelphia for the weekend,"* a source reported. *"It was a mix of work and play, which was nice."* The firm also has an associate committee – *"each office has a rep who is in charge of local events like happy hours or grabbing lunch."* Such events include anything from sports games to informal drinks after work.

Pro Bono

"The firm has really ramped up what it does for pro bono," associates agreed. *"When I got here it was like the Wild West with no real system. Then midway through my first year, they hired Melinda deLisle [as pro bono director], who over the course of a year totally unwound that Wild West system and put in place a smart, centralized pro bono database."* Every junior we spoke to sang deLisle's praises, especially when it came to *"advocating for people who have had pro bono cases with long hours to get all the credit they deserve."* Attorneys get automatic credit for up to 75 hours, and they can submit a request to count hours above that. Juniors can get involved in a variety of pro bono, including civil rights litigation, asylum cases, homeless advocacy projects and veterans' matters.

Pro bono hours
- For all US attorneys: 21,372
- Average per US attorney: 31

Diversity

"I think Cozen is in a good place when it comes to women, but I think we could do better in terms of other areas of diversity," one source commented. *"I would love to see more diverse faces."* The firm has a Women's Initiative that is *"giving female associates a sounding board."* A diversity committee meets regularly to *"discuss how to increase diversity in terms of recruitment, but also how to retain diverse attorneys."* Cozen also has a number of affinity groups for diverse attorneys to get involved in.

Offices

Cozen is headquartered in Philadelphia, in *"an awesome office with an ideal location."* The HQ recently moved digs to One Liberty Place, just two blocks from City Hall. *"I don't know what the old building was like, but this one is definitely fancy,"* said one happy junior. Other offices also praised the HQ: the office in Pittsburgh is reportedly set for a move and one interviewee enthused: *"I don't care what they do with it, I just want to get what the Philadelphia folks have as quickly as possible. Their office is gorgeous."* Currently, Cozen has two offices in the Big Apple – one in Midtown and one in Downtown. A source explained: *"Traditionally, one has been more litigation-focused, and the other has been more transactional. That said, I think the goal is to eventually merge the two offices."*

Strategy & Future

Cozen has been expanding rapidly in recent years, and managing partner Vince McGuinness says it has *"a very active lateral integration program"* so new hires can get to know their colleagues. The firm recently passed the 700-attorney mark, and one source reported: *"Firm management have said they won't shy away from 900 attorneys."* McGuinness says the plan is for growth across all practice areas: *"We want to continue to be conservatively managed, and represent the middle market in terms of industries, which is something we do well. Then in terms of geographies, we will continue to grow as we have in DC and New York, then in other markets where we're gaining good traction like LA, Chicago and Miami."* For more from McGuinness, go to chambers-associate.com

See firm profile on p.624

Cravath, Swaine & Moore LLP

Lawyers per state

505

Largest US office: New York

US offices: 1

International offices: 1

First-year salary: $180,000

Billable hours: no requirement

Summers 2018: 89 (5 1Ls, 82 2Ls, 2 SEOs)

Revenue 2017: $706.7 million (-4.2%)

Partners made in 2018: 6

Famous for: its influential business model; formidable presence in the fields of M&A, capital markets, banking, securities and tax

New Yorker Cravath holds its perch as BigLaw's principal trendsetter.

PERHAPS more so than any other firm in our guide, Cravath comes with labels attached and a mythology in tow. It's a New York firm with an iconic business model, compact footprint, and a long list of enviable achievements in the world of BigLaw – taken together, that formula has held the attention of the legal market in a mighty grip. The aforementioned business model is called 'The Cravath System', and it sets out a firm philosophy that's focused on enduring success instead of rapid profit and growth. It has shaped Cravath's systems for hiring, training and compensating its attorneys, and you'll notice most firms borrowing from it in some way. A prime example: when Cravath took the decision to raise its first-year salary to $180,000 in 2016, the majority of BigLaw's players followed suit.

The firm's philosophy on growth is demonstrated by its size: it has only one international office – in London – to accompany its sole domestic base in New York, which houses just over 500 attorneys. It's a striking contrast to many of the flag-planting imperialists in BigLaw, but Cravath's ability to tackle stratospheric deals shows that what it lacks in physical size it can more than make up for in coveted expertise (see its recent work on British American Tobacco's jaw-dropping $97 billion acquisition of Reynolds for another perfect example). *Chambers*

USA therefore places Cravath among the very best in the nation for its M&A, capital markets, securities, banking and tax work, while in New York it also snares top rankings for its media & entertainment, environment, and general commercial litigation practices.

The Work

Joining Cravath means embracing its rotation system, which requires associates to switch between groups every 12 to 18 months – those in litigation tend to do the longer stints. It doesn't just apply to juniors: attorneys rotate around the houses until they settle down and make partner (some even continue beyond that point). *"The rotation system was a big reason for joining the firm,"* one associate told us. *"It keeps things interesting, and it's not like you're in and out of groups, as multiple practices interact – it's all very interrelated."* The benefits of such a system soon become clear, as this source revealed: *"When I interact with corporate attorneys on the other side, their eyes glaze over when it comes to things like financing – in comparison, we are fluent in all aspects of the deal."* While the first month in a new group can be *"difficult"* as associates get up to speed, juniors didn't feel *"left alone in the wilderness: everyone's helpful, and the partners are very aware – they give you direction."*

Out of the second and third-year juniors on our list, almost 50% were rotating in Cravath's corporate practice, while around 40% were doing so in litigation; the rest were split between the tax; trusts and estates; and executive compensation and benefits groups.

"You can effectively run deals."

On chambers-associate.com...

- Insight from associates on getting hired
- Interview with Michael Paskin, Litigation Hiring Partner, and Scott Bennett, Corporate Hiring Partner

See firm profile on p.625

The Inside View

Rankings in *Chambers USA*

Antitrust	Environment
Banking & Finance	FCPA
Capital Markets	Intellectual Property
Corporate Crime &	Litigation
Investigations	Media & Entertainment
Corporate/M&A	Securities
Employee Benefits &	Tax
Executive Compensation	

For detail on ranking tiers and ranking locations, visit
www.chambersandpartners.com

Recent work highlights

- Representing Time Warner during its pending $108.7 billion sale to AT&T
- Advised British American Tobacco on its $97 billion acquisition of Reynolds
- Acting for pharmaceutical manufacturer AKORN throughout an SEC investigation into accounting restatements
- Representing Qualcomm after it filed a breach of contract suit against four iPhone manufacturers for alleged failure to pay royalties on their licensing agreements
- Defended Avon against a class action lawsuit that alleged the cosmetics giant had falsely marketed its 'Anew' anti-aging skincare products

Stellar M&A work is the firm's corporate headliner – but that doesn't mean associates working in that department are relegated to a minor role. Sources reported working in small teams on big deals, and highlighted *"complete visibility: I was on all of the calls."* Our interviewees quickly progressed beyond due diligence. *"As I began to wrap up my rotation I was given ancillary documents, like services agreements, and by the end I was given more significant operative documents to work on. You can effectively run deals, though the most senior person on the deal holds the pen on the main transaction document."* Other groups to sample in Cravath's corporate practice include private equity; capital markets; syndicated lending and restructuring.

Over in litigation, juniors also gave their responsibility levels the thumbs-up. *"With every case there's been client interaction: from emailing to speaking with them in person. I've written more briefs than I can count, plus I've led conference calls and prepared witnesses for depositions. I don't know anyone at another firm who has done that."* However, associates reminded us that *"it doesn't mean there's an absence of hierarchy. If you're the most junior person on a case you will still be doing some of the more administrative work."* Associates mentioned interesting work on cases related to benchmark-rate litigation and residential mortgage-backed securities claims.

Culture

With Cravath's identity wrapped up in its titular 'system,' associates drew lines between their day-to-day experiences and the firm's central tenets. With competition between partners quashed via lockstep bonuses, associates found that *"you'll walk into a partner's office and half the time there will be another partner in there talking with them. Because our partners work together, it encourages associates to do the same – it's a tight-knit place."* The rotation system produces a similarly cohesive effect. *"With associates rotating through groups at different times, the sheer number of people you work with is really high."* The subsequent bonds formed prompted associates to say that *"there's very much a small-firm feel."*

Much like the smallest of small towns, Cravath prefers its own people. Associates are never hired laterally, and law school recruitment is meticulously selective. *"Everyone knows how we work here: we're completely available when we're working to a deadline and we put absolutely everything into that first draft – everything is very polished. When you deal with folks at other firms, that same drive isn't there. There's something nice about working at a firm that emits a consistent level of quality, competence and dedication to the job."* To sustain this approach, one interviewee affectionately admitted that attorneys tend to be *"law nerds, who geek out about the exciting and unique elements of what we work on."* High-level matters mean that *"people take their work seriously,"* and a businesslike feel extends beyond the clean-cut suits that attorneys wear every day: *"People are direct. If they don't like your work product, they will tell you."*

"There's something nice about working at a firm that emits a consistent level of quality."

To reward that dedication, Cravath puts on some grand social events for its attorneys to enjoy. There's an annual party at Central Park Zoo, which lawyers can bring their families to, and every other year there's the legendary Cravath Prom. *"It's like the fanciest wedding you've ever been to!"* one associate enthused, while listing previous venues that have included The American Museum of Natural History and a fancy spot on Ellis Island. Themed monthly happy hours in the office provide a more regular opportunity for mingling – as ever the firm sets the benchmark high, bringing in fancy catering from local restaurants for their office drinks. But, given the firm's famous work ethic, we weren't shocked to hear that *"this is not the kind of place where people go for a drink every week after work."*

See firm profile on p.625

The Inside View

Diversity	Partners (%)	Associates (%)
Women	22	39
White	94	73
Black/African American	0	4
Hispanic/Latin American	2	4
Asian	4	16
Mixed/Other	0	3
LGBT	4	5

Hours & Compensation

"I encountered resistance to talk about hours during interviews at some peer firms, but people were candid at Cravath. Not everybody will thrive here – they want people who can self-select." Yes, long hours are on the cards for all of Cravath's associates, but the well-publicized lack of a billing target brings some benefits. "I didn't realize how big of a deal it was until I saw how much anxiety it produces at other firms. I was slow this summer for a couple of weeks: it was great. I read to the end of The New York Times every day and watched every CLE I could. Because of the rotation system – where your work comes from partners rather than a central coordinator – you never have to look for work."

However, there are also peaks as well as troughs, which are exacerbated because "this is not a traditional setting where they can throw another first-year on a deal. You are responsible." Throw in the short-term needs of some demanding clients and our associate sources struggled to define a normal day, but a representative associate told us: "I tend to get in around 9.30am, and will generally leave around 9.30pm." There is no average, though, and associates' hours fluctuated based on the stage of the case. All associates had a handful of all-nighters and forfeited weekends to their name, but didn't question the need to do it – Cravath is, after all, a natural environment for high-achievers. One recalled "a trial that lasted two and a half weeks; everybody was at their desks around 9am, and we wouldn't step away until 4am. Many teams have a healthy and sensible view on what hours we should be working – with others that is less true." Saving graces include "a concierge service for associates, which can drop off your dry cleaning or pick you up a coffee when you're closing a deal." And with these demands, there's clearly no need for a face-time culture. Associates also noted an accommodating attitude toward vacation.

Offices

All Cravath attorneys share an office until their third year, and tradition dictates that whoever is the more senior occupant has the window desk. Sources told us the firm has recently given up one of the floors it occupies in the building, so "things are getting a little more cramped." However, Cravath's home still has a rather palatial feel.

"We're in a landmark building (Worldwide Plaza) and the interior has its own style. It's not unattractive or ugly, but it's not the modern style you would see in most offices either. If you picture a law firm from an old movie – all dark wood and beige tones – that's it. It has its own charm." In the cafeteria, the movie theme continues as hungry associates are greeted by "some fun artwork: there are posters of films like Edward Scissorhands and Beetlejuice." With its scarily subsidized prices, sources were pleased to tell us that "the cafeteria is great. Everyone gets on with the cafeteria staff and they put a lot of effort into the food. They do a pasta with stuffed peppers... I so need that recipe!"

Training & Development

New skills have to be learned each time an associate rotates between groups and partners. However, Cravath doesn't weigh down its roaming attorneys with tons of formal training. "Nobody has the time to hit pause and take a month-long seminar in banking," said time-pressed juniors. "There are plenty of resources online – like precedents and fantastic CLE videos – but actually finding a moment to review them can be tough. You pick it up here and there." Most learning therefore occurs on the job, and associates found themselves "calling on other people who – since they rotate in a different sequence – have the benefit of experience. That gets you through your first deal. It encourages collegiality and I now have a network of friends and colleagues to ask advice from."

Pro Bono

"If you want to get involved in pro bono then it is there for you," juniors reported. "There are newsletters that list available matters, including one that's devoted to corporate assignments, which is key given that a lot of pro bono is litigation-heavy." Sources had also picked up pro bono work directly through the relationships they'd cultivated with partners. However, the general opinion among associates was that "pro bono isn't emphasized as much as it is at other firms. You have to go after it a bit if you want to be involved." That said, sources still found Cravath to be "respectful of pro bono when you're working on it – the firm won't object to you getting involved."

The firm works with organizations like the Innocence Project, the Montefiore Children's Hospital and Her Justice. We also heard of juniors working on "immigration cases tied to Trump's executive order and reform to the DREAM Act," plus an interesting 'fair use' matter involving an artist who had lifted and exhibited other people's photos from Instagram.

Pro bono hours
- For all US attorneys: 25,838
- Average per US attorney: 51

See firm profile on p.625

Diversity

Interviewees felt that steps were being taken in the right direction on this front. *"We have Faiza Saeed, who is our presiding partner now. Having Faiza at the helm is comforting for female associates."* However, our female sources in corporate were particularly keen to see an improvement in gender diversity, with some reporting that they'd *"never worked with a woman partner"* and were *"oftentimes the only woman on the team."* In contrast, those in antitrust said that *"the team is mostly female, so I've been lucky to work a lot with other women."*

"Having Faiza at the helm is comforting for female associates."

Those involved in interviewing *"saw candidates of all backgrounds coming through; I hope that we'll continue to see that level of diversity in our incoming classes and that it's maintained as those classes progress at the firm."* Sources also acknowledged that *"we get the standard diversity and sensitivity training, which challenges us to address inherent biases."*

Get Hired

"The partner said we'd talk half about work, half about life. We talked for an hour about music and I really learned a lot about him." To find out more about Cravath's recruiting process, go to chambers-associate.com.

Strategy & Future

Though the firm tends not to hire partners laterally, *"when it sees fit it won't sleep on opportunities,"* associates revealed. There have been very rare partner hires in the past, and at times Cravath has brought in lawyers as counsel instead. One recent example is Evan Norris, who previously served as director of the DOJ's task force that investigated claims of corruption and bribery at FIFA (the international soccer governing body). Despite this strong preference for its own associates joining the partner ranks, sources felt that *"most people don't come in eyeing the partnership."* A common target among interviewees was the fifth or sixth-year mark, and with Cravath's prestige, many looked forward to *"the excellent exit opportunities."*

"We know what we're good at."

Associates are kept up-to-date at regular town hall meetings, but when it comes to strategy sources reiterated to us that *"the core aspects of the firm don't change much."* Corporate hiring partner Scott Bennett confirms: *"We know what we're good at. We don't venture too far afield. If we move into something new, it's more of an evolution; it will be an extension of a product we currently offer."*

See firm profile on p.625

The Inside View

Crowell & Moring LLP

Lawyers per state

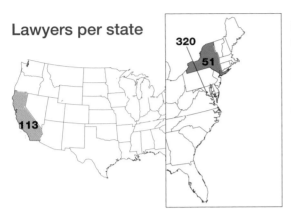

320
51
113

Largest US office: Washington, DC
US offices: 5
International offices: 2
First-year salary: $180,000
Billable hours: 2,000
Summers 2018: 21 (1 1L, 20 2Ls)
Revenue 2017: $418.7 million (-3.6%)
Partners made in 2018: 7
Famous for: DC powerhouse; rubber ducks; amenable culture

Practically a next-door neighbor to the White House, this quirky midsizer is well suited to handling all things government.

"WE'RE weird." That's how one Crowell & Moring associate likes to put it. *"Quirkiness is a virtue"* at this midsized international firm. *"They want to be seen as a firm that evolves with the times,"* one associate said; several of our interviewees gave a sense that they were put off by other *"traditional, more macho"* firms, and enticed by Crowell's career development prospects, and the *"freedom to contribute meaningfully to cases."* There's been *"a lot of lateral recruiting efforts"* this year – associate and partner – across all five of Crowell's domestic offices. New hires have come from the Department of Justice, the Department of Health and Human Services, and Homeland Security – in case you hadn't clicked, DC-based Crowell is known for its government contracts work, and has been scooping top rankings in government work from *Chambers USA* for years now. Firm chair Phil Inglima tells us: *"We continue to work very consciously to hold on to our core identity of a firm that faces government, works with and against the government, draws talent from the government and gives back to the government."* Although merger talks with Herrick Feinstein fell through, chatter of changes to come persists on the Crowell grapevine. Phil Inglima hints at what the future may hold: *"Growth continues to be an important strategy for us in New York, and we're going to have to be looking beyond our walls to do that."*

DC's influence can be seen in the firm's best recognized strengths – healthcare, IP, environmental law, climate change, International trade, antitrust, white-collar crime – but its commercial offering is also broad, with well-regarded corporate, private equity and commercial litigation practices. Anyone serious about Crowell's specialist areas should take a look at the blogs and podcasts it produces on its website, covering areas like whistle-blowing, trade secrets, and health law. One podcast 'Trump: The First Year' follows regulatory changes under the new administration. While *that* Donald continues to divide opinion, one Donald who wouldn't have any trouble fitting in at Crowell is Donald Duck – in DC, the office is famous for its foyer fountain full of rubber ducks.

The Work

Crowell juniors are assigned to two departments *"normally within their top three choices."* More senior attorneys approach juniors with work through an online system that logs their hours and availability, but associates also have the *"freedom to chase their own work."* With *"low walls"* between practice areas, associates here emphasized the approach here is not at all *"one size fits all"* but that they had *"the agency to shape their own strategy."* One associate appreciated *"the book wasn't written for me."*

Crowell's well-established government contracts group drew in the current crop of associates for being *"one of if not the best."* A lot of the team *"studied government contracts at school and knew exactly what they wanted to*

On chambers-associate.com...

- Get hired at Crowell

The Inside View

See firm profile on p.626

Rankings in *Chambers USA*

Antitrust	Government
Climate Change	Healthcare
Corporate/M&A	Insurance
Energy & Natural	Intellectual Property
Resources	International Trade
Environment	Litigation

For detail on ranking tiers and ranking locations, visit
www.chambersandpartners.com

Recent work highlights

- Acted for hotel chain Hyatt facing damages of over $11 million in a fraud allegation
- Handled all government contract matters during the $8.5 billion Hewlett Packard Enterprise merger
- Obtained a $1 billion contract for Enterprise Recovery Systems (now AllTran) in an unprecedented decision from the US Court of Appeals
- Represented AT&T in an $85 billion merger with Time Warner

do, but there's something for everyone." The team divides its time between bid protests, claims recovery, internal investigations, ethics and compliance issues, appellate work, litigation, transactions, procurement protests, brief writing, and *"research assignments on some obscure issues."* One *"self-proclaimed dork"* particularly enjoyed the scope for administrative law research. Associates in this department enjoy *"a sense of ownership"* in their practice, and appreciate *"a lot of client interaction"* and *"being able to answer their questions."*

"It was just how I'd pictured it at law school."

Several antitrust and litigation associates got the chance to work on the proposed $34 billion Aetna/Humana merger (*"the largest-value merger of its kind at the time that had ever been litigated to a judicial decision"*). Juniors were on trial prep, mock cross-examinations, economic research, drafting questionnaires, preparing trial exhibits and *"everything else that goes with preparing for trial and being part of a big team."* The *"crazy, hectic hours"* went hand in hand with this one, and law school premonitions were realized: *"It was just how I'd pictured it – eating Chinese food with people around a table, trying to figure it out."* Aspiring litigators also do a fair bit of motion drafting, brief writing and some doc review.

Opportunities are pretty *"forthcoming"* at Crowell. One associate was put on a United Airlines antitrust litigation *"before the end of orientation week,"* and getting to work with *"the partners I wanted to be when I grew up."* During a mock deposition, one associate got to *"pretend to be a Department of Justice lawyer grilling the senior executive. That was intimidating and incredible."*

Associates described the healthcare lawyers as *"a funny bunch"* – we'll take that to mean they're hilarious. Here there's an *"unofficial split"* between litigation and regulatory. They handle contract disputes, class actions, fraud and abuse work, and general compliance issues, *"helping hospitals comply with government programs where they can receive additional funding."* They deal with clients' compliance questions, providing them with *"a risk assessment, basically."*

Cybersecurity is a growing area for the firm. *"It was a working group"* when one junior started, and has since become its own fully-fledged practice group. Other juniors are sprinkled among other departments like IP, international trade, corporate, insurance, environment, and white-collar, among others.

Training & Development

There's *"a ton"* of training at Crowell. Each group *"has its own benchmark and tells you what you should be achieving,"* and partner mentors *"encourage monthly lunches or coffees to check in."* This year associates enjoyed *"pretty regular training retreats"* and white-collar associates got stuck into *"role-playing"* how they'd respond to a call from *"a client being raided by the FBI."*

"Hardcore trial training."

Crowell takes part in the Loaned Lawyer Program, sending voluntary associates on six-month secondments to the Legal Aid Society's housing unit. There, they can get *"totally immersed"* in work such as *"eviction defenses"* with a full salary, so they *"don't have to stress over finances."* One associate who'd completed the program gushed, *"It's a great way for associates to get on-your-feet experience in court."* Then there's the invite-only week-long trial academy, where 12 to 16 lucky invitees endure *"hardcore trial training"* with guest speakers and a *"big mock trial in the federal district court."*

Offices & Culture

Just *"a few blocks from the White House"* you'll find Crowell's HQ, which is now starting to resemble something *"like an Apple store"* thanks to *"sleek"* upgrades that haven't quite yet reached every corner. One hopeful junior angling for some of the refurb action said, *"My office is kind of 'meh.' I wouldn't take pictures of it and brag."* They have an otherwise *"high morale"* in DC, with a weekly 'Cheap Booze' night, which was *"the brainchild of one of the partners."* It takes place in the cafeteria, which received rave reviews. *"I sit dangerously close to that cafeteria,"* one associate said.

See firm profile on p.626

The Inside View

Diversity	Partners (%)	Associates (%)
Women	23.3	54
White	87.83	61.18
Black/African American	3.7	8.55
Hispanic/Latin American	3.17	7.24
Asian	3.7	18.42
Mixed/Other	1.59	4.61
LGBT	3.2	4.6

A "*family-friendly*" atmosphere "*permeates through the office*" in LA, and New York is said to have a similar "*homey*" feel. The "*active*" San Francisco team has run a few relay marathons, and after last year's they "*went back to a partner's house for brunch.*" Some associates would prefer "*more geographical options*" within the firm, and there has been "*a big push to make smaller offices more relevant.*" Crowell also has an Orange County office, and overseas ones in London and Brussels.

"We're the firm with a bunch of rubber ducks."

"*Yes, we're the firm with a bunch of rubber ducks,*" one associate acknowledged. The unconventional mascot evolved after firm founder Took Crowell placed a plain old rubber duck in a "*pretentious, eyeroll-inducing*" fountain in the DC office's lobby. A few more found their way in there, and despite a couple of attempts to distance themselves from the image, the firm eventually decided it didn't give a duck, and embraced their aquatic motif. Forty years on, rubber ducks are to be found "*lining the desks*" of well-respected Crowell attorneys, and there are "*thematic*" ducks for every occasion including a Fourth of July duck, a superhero duck, and a poker duck for the summer program casino night. A bemused associate admitted, "*I didn't know there were so many kinds of rubber duck.*"

Hours & Compensation

Last year's salary bump made associates pretty happy, as well as the switch to a lockstep bonus system – everyone is guaranteed if they hit their billing target. A 100-hour jump put that up to 2,000. A government contracts associate was confident speaking for their group: "*We're so incredibly busy that people aren't struggling to meet it,*" but for associates elsewhere, "*it can be quite stressful.*" Another had "*less time for vacation.*"

"It can be quite stressful."

At the time of our research, there were "*murmurings*" of change still to come. "*I think they're going to change our compensation,*" one junior speculated. In late 2017 the

firm formally announced that 70% of the bonus associates receive will be based on hitting the 2,000 hours target and 30% on quality of work.

"*Hours are long*" across departments, with many juniors spending over nine hours in the office each day, and one remembered a 15-hour day during trial. "*There isn't a huge face-time requirement*" though, which was a big plus for associates: "*They treat us like adults.*"

Diversity

Crowell & Moring has had two female leaders in the past decade, which is a rarity in the profession. However, associates point out that "*the partnership isn't 50:50 for sure. It would make you feel better about your prospects if we knew both perspectives were being taken into account.*"

"A work in process."

The firm held its first diversity retreat in DC this year, which turned up ideas that Crowell is "*in the process of implementing.*" Partners have taken "*bias training*" and heard from an "*expert who used walk-through scenarios to show how biases may play out in the workplace, and how to mitigate that.*" Despite the "*significant steps*" Crowell's taken this year, it's "*still a work in process,*" one minority associate said, "*but they're doing everything I'd expect a big firm to be doing.*"

Pro Bono

Public service partner Susie "*amazing*" Hoffman assigns projects across offices, but the firm also "*gives you the keys and lets you run with it,*" one associate said. "*Lambda Legal asked if I could handle a brief regarding the misgendering of a trans student at school, and now we've had two cases in the LGBT civil rights movement, solely because the partner fully supported me when I went to her.*" Pro bono opportunities arise "*after every major disaster, like the Orlando shooting.*" One recent opportunity is with the Texas Access to Justice Foundation, helping to ensure immigrants in Houston won't be deported when seeking help in the wake of Hurricane Harvey.

"It was fun seeing celebration emails go around the firm."

Other cases associates were keen to talk about included an asylum case for a woman from Burkina Faso, who was "*ostracized for not undergoing FGM,*" and a clemency petition for an inmate under Obama's clemency project. One associate billed 250 hours on a petition that "*challenged a life sentence for crimes committed as a juvenile,*" which a federal judge eventually granted. "*It was fun seeing celebration emails go around the firm after that.*" Pro

See firm profile on p.626

bono hours currently "*count 100% toward the billable target,*" but some sources were sceptical this "*might change in the near future.*" However, management assured us it has no intention of changing the policy.

Pro bono hours
- For US attorneys: 45,530
- Average per US attorney: 81

Strategy & Future

After rapid expansion in the 2000s (three mergers and three office openings), it might look as if the pace has slowed down over this decade. Two offices closed their doors in 2016 (Anchorage and Cheyenne), and a merger with Herrick Feinstein was called off earlier this year.

Phil Inglima replaced Angela Styles as firm chair in late 2017. Inglima says: "*We don't anticipate any major shift in direction. We've really been focused in the past few years doubling down on our strengths and continuing to expand and increase our offerings in ways we think meet the growing client needs. In our view we've always had a strong regulatory core, we've been reinvesting in that strength in the past year, and we've also been growing our litigation strength over time.*"

"The best thing I think you can do in your 1L summer is take a position in some sort of legal field. It doesn't necessarily have to be a law firm – clerking for a judge is great too, or working for organizations where you're demonstrating legal skills. If you know what office you're interested in, it's great if you have a connection to that particular area in your 1L summer too."

– Dykema hiring partner Lisa Brown

See firm profile on p.626

Curtis, Mallet-Prevost, Colt & Mosle

Lawyers per state

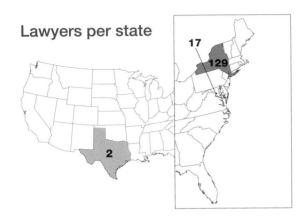

17

129

2

Largest US office: New York
US offices: 3
International offices: 14
First-year salary: $180,000
Billable hours: 2,000 target
Summers 2018: 10 (2Ls 10)
Revenue 2017: $155 million (-12.4%)
Partners made in 2018: 2
Famous for: expertise in international arbitration work

Associates in Curtis's small intake are likely to meet *"a barrage of international experience."*

EVERY relationship has its blips, everyone has the occasional spat, sovereign nations and international corporations included. And when the fists do start flying, this 187-year-old New Yorker is often called on to wipe away the rather costly tears. Curtis specializes in international arbitration – a slightly more discreet approach to dispute resolution – but what makes it so qualified internationally? Despite being on the smaller side in the US, Curtis has a disproportionately international footprint. Fourteen offices are situated abroad, from perches in commercial centers like Dubai, to far-flung outposts in locations like Kazakhstan.

The firm's cross-border focus is further emphasized by its international workforce, and the breadth of rankings *Chambers USA* lavishes upon it. Curtis snags recognition for its dispute resolution work in Oman and Africa, corporate and commercial work in the UAE, M&A in Italy, plus, of course, international arbitration in the USA.

However, those desiring a prized spot in international arbitration should note: *"It's rare that they have summer associates and it's not something just anyone can get into right off the bat."* For more detail on Curtis's international arbitration work, head online.

On chambers-associate.com...

- Get hired at Curtis: insider tips and tricks
- More on Curtis' fascinating international arbitration work for nation states

Most associates head into either the corporate/international or litigation groups, while restructuring takes a few, leaving only a few rare spots within the international arbitration team. That's not to diminish the international opportunities in other practices, however. There's a small international trade team, and one corporate insider found *"an international aspect touching every deal in some way; for example, helping American clients sell investments in their company to foreign investors."*

The Work

Both corporate and litigation have an assigning partner *"who keeps track of everything so that nobody is getting hit with work from all sides. Personally I think its good; without this system I can foresee people getting overworked. Lawyers don't like to say no."* Corporate associates however, found they could still *"go door-to-door and ask for specific work, so really there is a bit of a free-market system."*

While the litigation group takes on some international work, a large amount of its caseload is domestic. On offer is *"a bit of everything,"* including antitrust, bankruptcy and commercial litigation, with some arbitration added in for good measure. Our sources highlighted an increase in *"cybersecurity-related cases, given the greater prevalence of data breaches."* Their days were filled with *"a fair bit of document review, research, writing of memos, plus work on sections of briefs. That got me fired up: getting to see your work appear in a final draft of something is one of the highlights."*

The Inside View

See firm profile on p.627

Rankings in *Chambers USA*

International Arbitration	International Trade

For detail on ranking tiers and ranking locations, visit www.chambersandpartners.com

Those who join corporate can be involved in M&A, private equity, securities offerings, corporate governance and regulatory issues. And therefore, a typical day starts *"witha bunch of emails to answer, followed by legal research, drafting – maybe a section of a share purchase agreement – andsometimes due diligence. I also get to be on high-level conference calls, with the FCC for example, although I'm only taking notes."* Others could be less passive: *"I'm not leading the client meetings, but I'll speak to provide perspective on certain issues."* As with many corporate departments, *"you can be very, very busy for an extended period of time. At a bigger firm there might be more support available across the transaction, but I've gained great experience each time it has been that busy. I guess that's the double-edged sword of being at a smaller firm."*

Get Hired

Some form of worldly knowledge is extremely common among associates, whether through travel or speaking a second language. For more information on recruitment from the firm's hiring partners, go to chambers-associate.com

Training & Development

Formal feedback on associates' performance is provided once a year by a single reviewer who gathers information from senior lawyers the junior has worked with. A year is a long time to wait for feedback, and some judged these formal reviews *"not particularly informative,"* so we were pleased to hear that *"day-to-day feedback comes from the more senior associates you are working with."* However, this informal feedback varied from partner to partner. *"A lot of the time you have to divine criticism from their revisions,"* said one associate, but others reported: *"I'vebeen sat down and gone through memos line by line, having where I could improve highlighted."* Associates were also sat with older colleagues – *"without that I would have been a deer in the headlights."* Ultimately, *"the culture is one where you feel able to ask whether you did a good job or not."*

An introductory training program covers *"the computer system, legal research and writing, and basic deal functions."* From there litigators receive *"monthly breakfast presentations on areas of law we should be more familiar with."* One-off CLEs are also provided for all teams, *"on accountancy, or LexisNexis might cover research methods."*

Recent work highlights

- Defended Venezuela against a $30 billion damages claim brought by subsidiaries of oil and gas company Conoco-Phillips. The firm managed to cut the claim by a third
- Represented India in a dispute worth $2.6 billion with Vodafone
- Defended mining company Glencore against a $125 million indemnity claim by global defense contractor Lockheed Martin
- Represented GAL Manufacturing in its sale to private equity firm Golden Gate Capital

Corporate also had a lunch seminar touching on *"the art of the deal,"* though we're (almost) certain it had nothing to do with Trump's book.

Pro Bono

"Curtis redeveloped their pro bono committee in the last year. It's been strengthened and streamlined so we now have nonprofits come in every week to talk about their cases." As a sign of the times, many sources had been involved in representing those in immigration detention, but work is also available through a partnership with Her Justice (who offer services to underprivileged women in NY). Associates could alsocome up with their own ideas – *"some people have done trademark and copyright disputes"* – or reach out to partners involved in less common cases. So, the opportunities are there, and all pro bono hours count toward the billable total, but are people participating? One source judged that *"most, if not all, associates havedone a case at some point."* Others were more cautious: *"There's a mix of attitudes, but we lean toward being engaged in it. The reasons for that range from being able to really help people in need, to getting time with clients and in front of a judge."*

Pro bono hours

- For all US attorneys: 5,750
- Average per US attorney: 38

Diversity

Although most sources feltthat *"Curtis has a strong inclination toward diversity,"* associates were not convinced the firm was doing a successful job of promoting it. Sources spoke of recent training on implicit bias, which the whole firm had to attend – a fairly impressive move – but beyond this, insiders were *"not aware of any specific efforts to improve diversity."* Not so impressive. One associate reported: *"There isn't a huge amount of diversity in litigation, white people are the majority. There aren't any African American associates."* On the flipside, sources noted that the corporate group had a relatively high number of Latino and Asian American attorneys. *"We*

See firm profile on p.627

The Inside View

Diversity	Partners (%)	Associates (%)
Women	13	36
White	79	75
Black/African American	4	1
Hispanic/Latin American	13	13
Asian	2	8
Mixed/Other	2	3
LGBT	4	3

have so much work from Latin America and Central Asia you get people from all over the world. Most lawyers here speak at least two languages and the number of Spanish speakers is huge."

Culture & Offices

Curtis has offices in New York, DC and Texas, though New York housed all but two associates. *"It's a little anti-quated. It's in a famous old building at 101 Park Avenue, very close to Grand Central, which makes it easy to commute to – plus there are a lot of good lunch spots."* Curtis claims three and a half floors in total, so associates typically share offices until their third or fourth year.Not that sources minded much: *"I like that you get somebody who you can share all the idiosyncrasies of the workplace with."*

Owing to its relatively small size, sources appreciated the possibility of knowing large portions of the firm. *"You aren't just another face in the crowd."* Associates are however, just another suit among… lots of suits. *"Curtis is a very traditional environment. Our casual Fridays only involve not wearing a tie."* Beyond being *"cordial,"* descriptions of the culture came back to two adjectives: international and traditional, and a more traditional interpretation of junior-senior hierarchy by a few cropped up. *"The majority of partners are great to work with, but I'd describe others as shouty. You have to remind yourself that they do it because they care about the cases and are excited. It's not necessarily that you did something terribly wrong."* Conversely, teams were typically described as *"close-knit,"* and tension was released in more positive ways: *"We had pizza parties when we were staying up late to file something and we'd have a bottle of champagne when we sent away the documents."*

Curtis likes its social occasions jolly and 60 minutes long. *"There are happy hours when a crop of associates join the firm, when a partner leaves, when we have charitable events and when associates informally get together outside the office."* Some are associate-only: *"It's nice to have a break from the partners, get together, share what everyone's working on and not worry."* And uniquely *"litigation has a tradition of surprise birthday parties, though it's not that much of a surprise anymore!"*

Hours & Compensation

Associates typically started around 9:30am, departing between 6:30 and 7:30 pm. Busy times delivered weekend work, and *"3am finishes, but it's extremely rare. A late night is typically 10-11pm and those happen a few times a month."* Expectations seemed clear for associates, who noticed that *"everyone comes in five days a week – there's not a lot of working from home."* Nevertheless, we heard that *"as long as you get your work done, I've never had a problem telling a partner I'm going skiing this weekend and need to leave at noon on Friday."*

When it comes to bonuses *"everyone tries to hit the 2,000 billable hour requirement. In litigation it's generally not a problem but in corporate it's a bit harder."* One corporate source felt that *"hitting it really depends on how well the firm is doing,"* though both pro bono and business development hours can count toward it. Sources also spoke about how compensation *"starts at the market rate for the first four years and then drops off. It's something that you have to accept – Curtis isn't one of the largest firms in the top 200."*

Strategy & Future

Managing partner Joe Pizzurro is bullish: *"We punch above our weight in many of our practices and are well known. Most of the firms on the other side of the table are multiple times our size."* A sweeping provision of services isn't the be-all and end-all. *"The firm will continue to play to its strengths. Those strengths I would classify as being in the contentious area domestically, as well as international arbitration."*

See firm profile on p.627

Davis Polk & Wardwell LLP

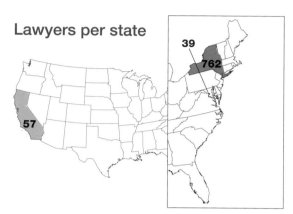

Lawyers per state

39

762

57

Largest US office: New York
US offices: 3
International offices: 7
First-year salary: $180,000
Billable hours: no requirement
Summers 2018: 175 (7 1Ls, 159 2Ls, 9 other)
Revenue 2017: $1.24 billion (+5.1%)
Partners made in 2018: 8
Famous for: New York heritage; polite culture; capital markets and M&A prowess

The nice folk at Davis Polk keep their cool in the heat of the corporate-law crucible.

"OBVIOUSLY the firm is extremely prestigious..." Associates at Davis Polk – one of the oldest and most revered law firms in New York – often skipped over this fact as they rushed to chat about other aspects of the firm, but it deserves a little more consideration. After all, the 'white-shoe' origins of the firm make it what it is today: a global powerhouse, with top-notch restructuring, M&A, credit, financial services regulatory and capital markets practices that serve a who's-who of international players. Put simply, DP is a world-beater. Managing partner Tom Reid is more than aware that he sits *"at the head of an institution that has been around since the 19th century, and has been at the top of its game for all of that time."* Fortunately, the firm has just notched up another vintage year: Reid tells us that *"2017 has been phenomenal, especially for our M&A practice – it's powered the firm forward again this year."*

Interviewees could feel the positive imprint of the firm's history: a polite, well-mannered approach that still very much exists today. *"I always pictured lawyers being aggressive and in-your-face. That's not what Davis Polk is about,"* one source told us, and that point was critical for our interviewees, who found themselves picking between firms with the highest of expectations: *"In the end*

On chambers-associate.com...

- The full interview with managing partner Tom Reid
- Recruitment insight from associates and hiring partner Dana Seshens

I asked myself: where would I want to be working late into the night? The answer was Davis Polk. The people are calm, collected, collaborative and friendly."

The Work

During the summer program, new starters have the option to sample work across DP's corporate, litigation and tax departments. Around 60% of the juniors on our list had gone on to join the corporate department, which is split into subgroups including capital markets; financial institutions; M&A; credit transactions; insolvency and restructuring; and executive compensation. Thanks to a six-month rotation system, corporate juniors can try two different areas before finally settling down (the daring among them can even opt to join a group they've not yet tried). *"The system gives you a good mix of exposure and opportunity to work on things at a meaningful level,"* commented one corporate associate.

Rookies in the M&A team find themselves serving clients in the private, public, blue-chip and private equity spheres, on *"a range of deals that stretch from the blockbuster DreamWorks/Comcast-style matters to the more modest $500 million transactions – but almost everything has an international element."* Sources in this group were candid: *"I'm not going to tell you there isn't the aspect of being a first-year, which means diligence and the less glamorous work. However, I found that responsibilities escalate from the basic things quickly. You can graduate from that type of work in six months."* After progressing, associates found themselves *"running the diligence process and*

See firm profile on p.628

Rankings in *Chambers USA*

Antitrust

Banking & Finance

Bankruptcy/Restructuring

Capital Markets

Corporate Crime &
  Investigations

Corporate/M&A

Employee Benefits &
  Executive Compensation

Environment

FCPA

Financial Services
  Regulation

International Trade

Investment Funds

Latin American Investment

Litigation

Media & Entertainment

Private Equity

Securities

Tax

For detail on ranking tiers and ranking locations, visit
www.chambersandpartners.com

Recent work highlights

- Acted for big-time oil and gas player Baker Hughes during its $25 billion combination with General Electric's oil and gas business
- Advised hospitality giant Hilton on three secondary offerings of stock which totaled $2.63 billion
- Following the restructuring of the Global Development Bank of Puerto Rico, DP is representing a group of bondholders who hold $1.1 billion in bonds issued by the bank

assisting on things through to closing. By the time you're two years in you're assuming a more holistic role and co-ordinating teams that are implicated in the deal." There's plenty more on offer than M&A, as one source told us: "I really wanted to do complicated and nuanced corporate work, and this is the place to do it. DP's not only good at M&A and capital markets, but also derivatives and insolvencies." The financial institutions subgroup (FIG) also got associates excited: "They're always thinking about new markets and brainstorming products that they could roll out."

"I really wanted to do complicated and nuanced corporate work, and this is the place to do it."

Beyond corporate, around 25% of beginners enter DP's litigation department – a bigger single portion than any of the corporate subgroups. Intrepid litigators can sample commercial litigation (which is broad, but associates did frequently mention financial disputes), bankruptcy and white-collar crime. One source opined that "the responsibility can vary by team. Some people are inherently willing to trust juniors with higher-quality work; sometimes I've been stretched and challenged, while at other times I haven't – it's not all first-level doc review though." Indeed, our interviewees quickly got a taste of the more interesting aspects. "I've definitely been able to write more than I expected I'd be able to," said one. "I've written large portions of briefs and outlines for depositions – I've also attended several interviews in investigations." Juniors even got their sleuth on by "listening to audio calls between relevant parties."

Offices

Davis Polk has US offices in New York, DC and Menlo Park, California. The Big Apple HQ provides some lucky attorneys with views of the Chrysler and Empire State buildings, and "has something of a grand entrance, since

it sits on top of the US post office. You ride up to the eighth floor and it's the classic Davis Polk style: caramel-colored wood, with lots of gold and gleaming white everywhere." New Yorkers gleefully reported that "we all have floor-to-ceiling windows in our offices and there are standing desks available. Another great thing about being at a large firm is that we have a pretty big legal assistance department. It means you can be a lawyer without worrying about the other stuff."

New York takes in the vast majority of new joiners, while the smaller Menlo Park base absorbs a handful and the DC office only brings in one or two each year. Between DC (which maintains a strong governmental/regulatory focus) and New York there is "quite a bit of contact: if not daily then several times a week. It feels pretty fluid." Further afield, the firm has offices in Beijing, Hong Kong, London, Madrid, Paris, São Paulo and Tokyo.

Training & Development

Associates were realistic about their chances of making partner. "From a sheer numbers perspective, there is a real pyramid structure: a lot of associates, fewer partners." But the firm's prestige meant associates had seen many of their predecessors take the leap away from private practice, regularly moving into government roles. "I'm always amazed at the opportunities people get as they complete their fourth or fifth year." For those looking to make partner, they can take solace in the fact that "the firm prides itself on minimizing lateral hiring."

Long before these considerations are made, new starters begin by congregating in the Big Apple for Lawyering 101: a week of orientation which covers the office essentials such as computer training, document management and billing. "One part they do focus on is health and well-being. A partner comes in and describes how they were previously overworked, and encourages you not to go down that route." After that week comes specific practice area training. "When I joined leveraged finance I knew nothing about it," confided one interviewee, "but we had about 20 hours of training within the first couple of weeks, which soon brought me up to speed." Lawyering 101 is followed every second year by Lawyering 301 and Law-

See firm profile on p.628

Diversity	Partners (%)	Associates (%)
Women	20	45
White	90	69
Black/African American	1	6
Hispanic/Latin American	2	3
Asian	7	20
Mixed/Other	0	2
LGBT	3	6

yering 501. Corporate juniors on rotation receive six-monthly reviews, while those in their permanent groups attend annual checkups.

"One part they do focus on is health and well-being."

For more immediate guidance, associates found that *"you have to initiate the feedback loop. People always say 'thank you,' but if you want something more tailored and detailed you have to drive it yourself."* The general opinion was that *"mid-levels are more than willing to invest in junior associates,"* but a couple of interviewees did note that *"while some mid-levels are good at bringing first years in on the meat of the matter, others aren't so good."* Some felt an upward review process would fine-tune this relationship.

Pro Bono

Interviewees informed us that *"a group of DP attorneys went to JFK airport in response to Trump's travel ban. Some even stayed overnight. Most people here have a sense that they should be giving back."* Without a billable hours target, *"there is ample opportunity to do pro bono, and there is always a ton of it around – but the firm doesn't pressure you to do it."* We therefore found something of a divide. On one side: primed-and-ready pro bono participants with over 100 hours clocked in a year. On the other: associates too busy to take on much, or any. When associates start, however, *"you fill out a survey for the pro bono coordinators so they can work with you to figure out where your interests lie."* Among the opportunities on offer, we heard about *"family law matters; criminal appeals or even trials; 'elder law' tasks (like drafting wills, setting up trusts); drafting contracts for non-profits; and election protection issues."* Clemency work also featured: *"That provided me with my most rewarding moment so far,"* a humbled junior revealed, *"as in the end someone with a life sentence was able to go home."*

Pro bono hours
- For all US attorneys: 54,859
- Average per US attorney: 62

Culture

"When I joined I was worried about being just one person in a very large firm," a source recalled. *"It's not crazy to feel that way when you have to walk through the doors of a huge skyscraper. But when you get here, between informal mentors, formal mentors and staffing coordinators, you end up being really well taken care of."* Associates couldn't help but paint a rosy picture of the internal relationships at DP. *"In a way it does feel like the old guard (this is not a Silicon Valley firm, after all), but people have been remarkably open and patient about helping each other: they've shared tips, answered questions, and not tried to get ahead of each other."* On an even more basic level: *"People will say 'hi' to you in the halls, even if you've never formally met. It's not a place where everyone's heads are down."*

So, attorneys at DP are polite people – that's a good place to start – but they're also talented, which they need to be, because *"the expectations around quality of work, attention to detail and not making mistakes are pretty high."* One associate remarked that *"you always feel that you're not the smartest in the room – but that means you're in the right room. It can be intimidating, but it's good to know you're constantly being challenged."* Sources also observed that attorneys *"put great stock in their work,"* and were adept at managing stress. *"Even when things get busy or complicated, our partners and associates remain excellent people to work with. They let you know when the pressure is on, but they don't take it out on you."* Those in need of a release should take note of this associate's proclamation on the social life: *"I would call it a 'design your own' adventure. If you want a work setting where you go out and get drinks, there are definitely people who will do that."* Happy hours occur regularly, and there's also a well-attended Christmas party that's held in the office.

Get hired

"The callback interview focuses on culture. The firm places a high value on maintaining an ultra-respectful environment." For more insight on the firm's recruitment process from associates and hiring partner Dana Seshens, go to chambers-associate.com

Diversity

"Men will let you go first when you get in and out of the elevator," one female interviewee commented. *"They'll also hold doors open for women. Good manners are just part of the culture here."* But other female sources stressed that this approach *"comes across as considerate and polite; as a woman I am not made to feel that I stand out as though it were the 1950s. I feel empowered and respected as an equal."* We're happy to report that the firm's approach to diversity has little of the 50s about it either. *"It's making*

The Inside View

strides when you look at the pipeline of people we're bringing in. The third and fourth years are diverse – now we'll have to see if they make partnership." Associates also told us about affinity groups that "have frequent events; these are well attended, and not only by those from the group being represented." With the upper echelons in mind, the firm has started an initiative – called 'Davis Polk Revisited' – to bring back women attorneys who have left. Interviewees did feel that "more of the focus needs to be on associate development and retention."

"I feel empowered and respected as an equal."

Hours & Compensation

The firm's compensation structure (no billing target, accompanied by lockstep base salaries and bonuses) "takes the pressure off," and dampens down competition. However, associates told us they were "very busy: the unpredictability can be frustrating, but it's not at a level that is inconsistent with what we were expecting." Ten-hour days were felt to be quite average, though most sources expected to fit in a couple more hours at home. More demanding spells, however, were common. "I can get in at 9:30am and be working until one, two or three in the morning. One-offs are fine (they happen), but doing that for a whole week or longer, plus lots of weekend work – that's unsustainable." Fortunately, DP has controls in place: "If you have long periods of working into the evening you will be on people's radar and you may get a call from the staffing coordinator. Those hours should be temporary." In addition, associates' hard work is appreciated. "Partners send emails saying 'thanks for putting the time in.' They also host team drinks after a big brief or something similar. It's not the craziest gesture but it's nice to know they are aware."

Strategy & Future

Davis Polk isn't one for surprises. "We are a long-term business," says managing partner Tom Reid. "Our growth comes from partner promotions, and they take eight or more years. Our growth is therefore dictated by how the class of arriving associates develops. We hire lateral partners on a limited basis." At the same time, the firm is reactive to change. Reid believes the Trump administration means "potentially significant reform. That has allowed us to do what we do best: to be thought leaders. When there is a moment in Washington where policy seems up for grabs we excel by having knowledgeable lawyers who can explain potential scenarios for clients." To read the full interview with Reid, go to chambers-associate.com

"When things get busy or complicated, our partners and associates remain excellent people to work with."

See firm profile on p.628

The Inside View

Debevoise & Plimpton LLP

Lawyers per state

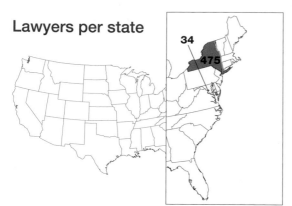

34

475

Largest US office: New York
US offices: 2
International offices: 7
First-year salary: $180,000
Billable hours: no requirement
Summers 2018: 95
Revenue 2017: $822 million (+11.8%)
Partners made in 2018: 7
Famous for: respectful culture; mega-achievement; diversity efforts

The extraordinarily genteel men and women of Debevoise & Plimpton sit pretty at the top of New York's legal scene.

IF you're looking for a law firm that values sharp minds over sharp elbows, you've probably hit the jackpot with Debevoise & Plimpton. With a reputation for polite partners and prestigious practices, you'd be forgiven for thinking of Debevoise as 'white-shoe'. They're putting their best foot forward when it comes to broadening their horizons, however, and the firm opened a new office in Tokyo in 2016. This established New York firm has a history dating back to the thrifty 30s, when it was founded by graduates from Harvard Law School and Oxford University. The firm now has some impressive alumni of its own including the 31st chair of the Securities and Exchange Commission Mary Jo White and former Attorney General Michael Mukasey.

Debevoise gets top marks from *Chambers USA* for the private equity practice on which it was built, and it also has top-ranking white-collar crime, intellectual property, insurance, arbitration and media & entertainment practices. While Debevoise has seven international offices and a small base in DC, New York is by far the largest office, home to two-thirds of the firm's lawyers.

On chambers-associate.com...

- Get hired at Debevoise
- Interview with director of legal recruiting Sandra Herbst and hiring partner Nicole Mesard

The Work

Most first-years head to the firm's New York office, although a handful go to DC each year. Most are in either corporate or litigation, with a few in tax & employee benefits. There are staffing coordinators who look at associates' individual hours and assign work accordingly. "*I really appreciate the staffing coordinators,*" one associate told us. "*It's nice to know there's someone watching out for you.*"

"It was great to be able to take advantage of our offices in Frankfurt, London and Tokyo."

Corporate associates rotate between two different subgroups and then have to decide at the start of their third year whether they want to stick with one of the two they've tried or move into a new one. There are 20 practices to choose from, and options include M&A, real estate, capital markets, leveraged finance, private equity, investment funds and insurance. One corporate rookie told us: "*As a junior a lot of what I do is due diligence. I've also assisted with plenty of main documents like purchase agreements as well as ancillary documents.*" Another junior said: "*I've been working on drafting a private placement memorandum as well as reviewing subscription materials for fund maintenance.*" Others mentioned the international element of some of the work in corporate: "*On one matter we were dealing with local counsel in over 20 jurisdictions.*" The same source added: "*When you're dealing with different antitrust laws and national legislation it's important to have good local counsel. It was great*

See firm profile on p.629

Rankings in *Chambers USA*

Banking & Finance
Bankruptcy/Restructuring
Capital Markets
Corporate Crime &
    Investigations
Corporate/M&A
    Employee Benefits &
Executive Compensation
Environment
FCPA
Financial Services
    Regulation
Insurance

Intellectual Property
International Arbitration
Investment Funds
Latin American Investment
Litigation
Media & Entertainment
Private Equity
Projects
Real Estate
Securities
Tax
Transportation

For detail on ranking tiers and ranking locations, visit
www.chambersandpartners.com

Recent work highlights

- Represented Verizon during its $3.1 billion acquisition of Straight Path Communications
- Advised the City of New York on responding to inquiries into Mayor Bill de Blasio's campaign fundraising practices
- Advised Discovery Communications on its $14.6 billion acquisition of rival Scripps Networks Interactive
- Acted for Envision Healthcare Holdings during its merger with surgery center AMSURG to create a $10 billion business

Training & Development

Associates' first three weeks at Debevoise are spent in New York attending a mini-MBA course which features teaching by lecturers brought in from Columbia Business School. "*It's good to get that foundation and insight into the bigger picture,*" a junior reflected. "*You also get to learn business accounting and administration skills.*" While some juniors said that they found the initial training "*a bit general,*" most were pleased to tell us that the day-to-day feedback system had seen improvement. "*Recently the system's been formalized more,*" one junior reported, "*although I've noticed during rotations that some groups are better than others.*" Another source added: "*Recently associates requested mid-level training in tax and they're doing that now.*"

"*People definitely don't shy away from giving feedback, but it's always in true Debevoise fashion,*" smiled one junior. "*The meanest thing anyone will say is that something could have been done better.*" As a result, some said, "*occasionally things can feel passive aggressive because people are so eager to avoid confrontation.*" But sources agreed: "*On balance I definitely appreciate that that's the culture here, rather than the place being full of yellers.*" Associates also get access to a partner and an associate mentor.

"*The firm's really committed to developing its junior associates into great attorneys,*" associates agreed. "*This is definitely somewhere that lets you build your own career.*"

Culture

When it comes to culture, associates sang Debevoise's praises. "*When I was researching the difference between high-ranking law firms it really came down to culture,*" one Debevoise junior said. "*I knew I wanted to be somewhere that had earned a great reputation without being cut-throat.*"

"There's a culture of saying 'thank you' for research."

In keeping with the firm's reputation for impeccable manners, one junior said: "*I've been here for two years*

---

to be able to take advantage of our offices in Frankfurt, London and Tokyo.*"

Most of the juniors we spoke to said that client contact gradually increases as time passes and usually takes the form of emails, which are initially proofread by someone more senior before they're sent. "*They don't give you more responsibility than you can handle,*" asserted one interviewee. "*I've run a few negotiations myself and I've been able to run pitch meetings for new work. Partners call you out if you don't speak up on a call, so you're always encouraged to get involved.*"

In litigation the first few assignments come from a staffing coordinator, but "*there's also a free-market approach if you want to reach out and look for work yourself.*" A rookie litigator told us: "*I've done some of the dreaded document review but I've mostly done research and drafted motions, letters and court and filings, and attended depositions and witness interviews.*" Juniors also prepare presentations, draft temporary restraining orders, compose motions for summary judgment and email clients.

Over in tax, newbies told us: "*Even though we just do tax you get to work on a variety of matters. People basically come to us for anything involving numbers. We specialize in funds and private equity bodies, and I've worked on both the sponsor and the investor side.*" Another said: "*We really cover all areas, from disclosures and partnership agreements to side letters. I've also worked on a bunch of M&A deals, insurance matters and capital markets transactions, as well as general financing and credit agreements.*" Basically, juniors said, "*tax attorneys are in charge of making sure waterfall and economic provisions actually work.*"

See firm profile on p.629

Diversity	Partners (%)	Associates (%)
Women	21.9	53.6
White	86.7	64.3
Black/African American	1	7
Hispanic/Latin American	3.8	9.3
Asian	7.6	16.2
Mixed/Other	1	3.2
LGBT	3.8	6.7

and I still haven't found a single mean person. Everyone's nerdy – in a good way – and I've never been left without help. The partners are all really passionate about what they do." Another added: "I like coming to work every day; people are always grateful for the work you put in and there's a culture of saying 'thank you' for research, which goes a long way when you're a junior."

"I work with people beyond my practice group on a daily basis," associates told us. "Our culture is based on collaboration, and clients are definitely paying for the firm as a whole when they choose us." When it comes to getting the firm together outside of work juniors told us: "There are a lot of firm-wide events: diversity speaker series and guest judge talks which everyone's invited to attend. You're also kept in the loop with emails and messages from the presiding partner." There's also an annual summer party at Central Park Zoo, and lawyers are encouraged to bring their families and plus-ones along.

Aside from the more formal events, we heard about bi-monthly happy hours and monthly lunches for individual groups. "Most of the time they're well attended but it's really up to you," a junior said. "You're able to pick and choose events without ever feeling pressured. You're definitely allowed to maintain a life outside work."

Get Hired

Associates told us: *"Debevoise is looking for smart, decent people who are genuinely interested in the work they're doing."* Pay attention law nerds! *"You're more likely to hear people here talking about the latest Supreme Court case than the football game at the weekend,"* we heard. Creativity and efficiency are also high on the list of desirable qualities for a Debevoise lawyer. For more on getting hired and the full interview with hiring partner Nicole Mesard and director of recruiting Sandra Herbst, go to chambers-associate.com

Hours & Compensation

"There's a soft billing target of around 2,000 hours, but nobody's going to be upset if you don't meet that," juniors said. They praised the staffing system for associates again when it came to cutting stress levels at work: "Ultimately it's the firms' job to bring in billable work, so if there are slow times it's generally down to the state of the market. Nobody is under the impression that it's their job to create work out of nowhere."

"The time management you learn to do is kind of scary."

When asked about hours, juniors said: "When you work for a BigLaw firm you know what you've signed up for, and there have definitely been some busy times." One source told us: "You have to work to maintain balance in the hours you do. You learn little tricks to maximize the time you have for yourself – the time management you learn to do is kind of scary." Associates did feel that because the bonus is lockstep there's less pressure to rack up the hours. "The firm makes a solid effort to respect people's personal schedules and vacations."

Pro Bono

Debevoise counts pro bono work as part of billable hours, and in 2016, 98% of US associates did pro bono. "The firm helped me to bring in some work I was passionate about," one associate told us. "I thought there would be a lot more red tape involved in getting into my field of interest, so getting to work with the client I wanted was really fantastic."

"The firm helped me to bring in some work I was passionate about."

The firm recommends attorneys do 50 hours of pro bono a year, but most associates we spoke to had totaled more. A junior noted: "It's generally harder to get corporate than litigation pro bono but the firm makes a big effort to get me relevant work." Associates can get involved in immigration cases, funds-related work for non-profits and civil rights matters, among other things.

Pro bono hours
- For all US attorneys: 51,788
- Average per US attorney: 102

Diversity

In addition to the regular mentor program at Debevoise, members of under-represented groups like ethnic minorities and LGBTQ+ individuals get a mentor on the diversity committee. "They check you're getting the work you want as well as the training you need, and they make sure you're getting challenged enough," we heard.

See firm profile on p.629

The Inside View

There's also a Women's Resource Group. "*It's really fantastic,*" a junior said. "*There are 'Ask a partner anything' lunches and events – we also go to SoulCycle together and hang out regularly.*" Other sources told us: "*For diversity more generally we have all sorts of initiatives across the firm. There are speakers at least once a month and other programs. It's clear the firm takes a lot of pride in it.*"

Offices

Juniors in New York told us that the midtown office is coming up to the end of its current lease, but said: "*I honestly can't see us moving. The thought of moving all that paperwork makes me anxious!*" As a junior you get to choose between having your own internal office or sharing with a buddy in an office with a window. "*The views are amazing and the offices are very spacious with closets for spare shoes and things,*" juniors reported. They added: "*The firm recently upgraded the office tech, plus you get a $1,500 allowance for things like phones and iPads every couple of years.*" Interviewees said that the firm was undergoing a general push "*to be at the cutting edge of technology.*" There's also "*a ton*" of secretarial and paralegal support available, and associates praised the proofreading service which is available 24 hours a day, 365 days a year. Each corporate group has its own assistant and document production office, and litigators have help with technical filings.

None of our interviewees had been on client secondments or international placements, but we were told that spells in the firm's London and Tokyo offices are possible, particularly in corporate, and we heard about some associates jetting off to Moscow. Juniors in tax told us: "*We have weekly conference calls with tax departments around the world to keep everybody up to date.*"

> *"The firm recently upgraded the office tech."*

Strategy & Future

Associates told us: "*Although we are constantly adapting and becoming more flexible, the core of who we are remains the same.*" Others said: "*We're very well positioned in the market. Job security isn't something to worry about here.*" Juniors also mentioned the forays that the firm's been taking into new technologies, for example its growing interest in blockchain and fintech. "*We're pushing to make sure we're on top of the latest developments,*" interviewees told us.

See firm profile on p.629

Dechert LLP

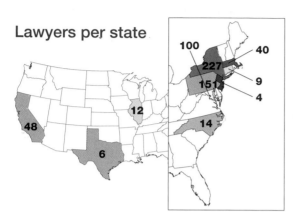

Lawyers per state

100
40
227
151
9
4
12
48
14
6

Largest US office: New York
US offices: 13
International offices: 14
First-year salary: $180,000
Billable hours: 1,950 target
Summers 2018: 43 (6 1Ls, 37 2Ls)
Revenue 2017: $978 million (+7.3%)
Partners made in 2018: 6
Famous for: 'global specialist' approach; top-tier in Philly

Mirror mirror on the wall, which Philly firm is the most global of all?

ON top of their legal talents, it seems Dechert attorneys might also be psychic. In our last edition CEO Henry Nassau predicted the firm would *"surprise in how successfully we build up our biggest offices,"* including New York and London. Twelve months later, the former has brought in four new corporate laterals, and the latter has taken in multiple partners in corporate, tax, litigation and finance.

We don't need a crystal ball to tell you Dechert's spread of *Chambers USA* rankings includes a top prize for investment funds nationwide, as well as for antitrust, litigation and tax in Pennsylvania. Firm-wide revenue is steadily nearing the $1 billion mark. Beyond its *"really strong global presence"* (Dechert has more offices outside the US than in it),interviewees felt the firm's chief appeal was that *"people here are friends, rather than just colleagues. Everyone actually enjoys working together."*

The Work

Summer associates have the freedom to sample as many different practice areas as they'd like, before committing to one upon joining the firm as a junior. The majority of new arrivals head into the corporate & securities; finance & real estate; financial services; or trial, investigations &

securities groups. Other teams – including antitrust, intellectual property and international arbitration – take a handful of newbies each year.

> *"As a first-year you're at least in on most calls even if you're not saying much."*

Each department has its own work assignment system. In corporate, a workflow coordinator distributes tasks to associates, who submit weekly availability reports and can request work from a specific area. M&A, securities, capital markets and private equity work is all up for grabs. *"Everyone's so busy that we have to take a lot of responsibility,"* happy associates told us. *"I'm working on first and revised drafts of documents as well as research."* There's no barrier to client contact, either. *"As a first-year you're at least in on most calls even if you're not saying much,"* an interviewee told us. *"I've got to the point that I'm regularly calling and emailing clients, sometimes even a CEO! You get to know clients on a quite informal basis."*

Dechert's general commercial and white-collar litigation groups have recently fused to form one trial department, within which juniors can sample a range of sub-sections including securities, employment and contract disputes. Those we spoke to had taken full advantage, tackling *"cases ranging from big corporate suits to small discrimination claims."* Document review and research are common in the early going, but juniors also get to put pen to paper (metaphorically). One reported: *"On pretty much every case, I've been offered a section of the brief or motion to write. Partners and senior associates definitely value my input and take my suggestions seriously."*

On chambers-associate.com...

- Get hired: tips for OCIs and callbacks
- Interviews with CEO Henry Nassau and hiring partner Jim Lebovitz
- More on Dechert's overseas offices

See firm profile on p.630

Rankings in *Chambers USA*

Antitrust	Investment Funds
Bankruptcy/Restructuring	Life Sciences
Capital Markets	Litigation
Corporate/M&A	Private Equity
Financial Services	Real Estate
Regulation	Securities
Intellectual Property	Tax
International Arbitration	

For detail on ranking tiers and ranking locations, visit
www.chambersandpartners.com

Recent work highlights

- Represented numerous financial advisers in Section 36(b) cases worth over $100 million, arguing they hadn't charged excessive fees
- Advised industrial and construction equipment dealership H&E on its proposed $1.2 billion acquisition of competitor Neff
- Defended Endo Pharmaceuticals in a reverse payment litigation challenge brought by the Federal Trade Commission
- Acted for financial holding company CIT Group on its $1.5 billion sale of European rail leasing business NACCO

"On pretty much every case, I've been offered a section of the brief or motion to write."

Litigators and finance & real estate associates can get tasks both from a workflow coordinator and directly from partners. The finance & real estate team handles both loan origination and securitization, which often involves collateralized loan obligations. *"When you first start you're in charge of running checklists and the due diligence,"* sources said. *"Then you begin to take on a more active role: talking on the phone to clients and drafting ancillary documents and comments."* Across practice groups juniors have a sizable workload. One told us: *"It's been a very busy year – it's stressful but fun because the work is so interesting."*

Financial services associates are each staffed on a number of client teams. Many of these are dedicated to the firm's asset management clients like ECN Capital, CION Investments and CIFC. *"We represent mutual funds and independent trustees,"* a junior informed us. *"There's also a good deal of broker/dealer work and international matters."* Juniors spend their days reviewing client documents, researching discrete points and assisting with board materials; some get the chance to draft short memos. As a general rule of thumb, the smaller the office the greater the early responsibility. In larger bases like Philadelphia and New York, smaller matters provide some opportunity for rookies to push themselves more than usual.

Several associates we spoke to said they'd worked with colleagues abroad, for example in the Middle East. *"I've worked with London, Hong Kong, Beijing and Dubai,"* one interviewee reported. We also heard of associates *"representing Chinese and French nationals and US nationals abroad."*

Offices & Culture

Either Philly or the Big Apple could be considered Dechert's beating heart – both offices house the firm's art collection, collected by *"a former chairman who was very devoted to bringing in cool pieces. It's easy to take for granted, but the collection is incredible."* Other locations may not boast any avant-garde masterpieces, but share the same modern, white-and-glass aesthetic. Dechert DC already occupies the top two floors of its K Street building and is taking over a third, while the Boston base is *"in the heart of the financial district, on the 41st floor of a high rise. I got my own window office from the start."* Healthy inter-office collaboration is *"one of Dechert's big selling points. The firm is very good at letting you travel, and when you do every office feels the same."*

Insiders suggest Dechert *"definitely strives for a one-firm feel,"* but were torn about how successful this policy has been. A New Yorker reported that *"having spent some time in Philly I'd say it's a little stiffer there, perhaps because Dechert is one of the very top firms in the market. It wasn't anything negative, just a different vibe."* Over in DC, the atmosphere is *"more casual, people have quite quirky personalities."* Some suggested *"the culture is very practice-group based: all have their own flavor and way of doing things."* The common denominator we picked up firm-wide is that *"people work hard, there's a good team environment and people form close relationships."* Such friendships can even cross the partner-associate divide, which most juniors felt wasn't too broad to bridge: *"Partners are very conscious about making everyone feel part of one team."*

"Everyone in the office goes for a chat – hopefully not about work."

After-work socializing is commonplace throughout the firm, particularly in the larger bases. New York hosts Thursday evening dinner and drinks, and *"it's always a lot of fun as everyone in the office goes for a chat – hopefully not about work."* Up the coast in Boston, the office recently celebrated its 30th anniversary with an office party, while the DC office *"always tries to put on associate-only events so we can get to know each other."* There are also gatherings for everybody across the network including Christmas festivities, Halloween costume contests

The Inside View

See firm profile on p.630

315

Diversity	Partners (%)	Associates (%)
Women	16	45.4
White	89.8	73.7
Black/African American	1.9	3.2
Hispanic/Latin American	4.9	3.2
Asian	2.9	18
Mixed/Other	0.5	1.9
LGBT	2.9	3.2

and ugly sweater parties. This stacked events calendar suggests that Dechert's attorneys are pretty tight-knit.

Training & Development

If this touchy-feely warmth isn't enough, the firm encourages seniors to look after newbies with cold, hard cash: via the Exceptional Teachers Reward mentors can win $10,000. The monthly Critical Skills Institute associate program is designed to develop communication, leadership, client relation and management skills, and there's practice group-specific training on top of that. *"The firm does a great job with training and it seems very important to them,"* associates said, *"though there's only so much you can learn in theory before actually doing it."*

Formal reviews take place twice a year: associates fill out forms that highlight what matters they've worked on for more than 15 hours, and who with. The midyear is *"very informal"* and largely oral, but the year-end evaluation is *"a much more involved process with more detail. It's extensive and very helpful."* Aside from a few grumblers, associates were also largely happy with the real-time feedback they received. One reported: *"Everyone I've worked with is very good at talking things through with you. Normally by the time you go into evaluations you have an idea of what will be said."*

Get Hired

"You have to be someone willing to put in the hours to produce good work, but even more than that Dechert focuses a lot on community so it's important you can demonstrate a commitment to that." For more tips on getting through Dechert's OCIs and callbacks visit www.chambers-associate.com

Pro Bono

All attorneys are required to devote at least 25 hours a year to pro bono, and juniors can count up to 200 hours toward their billing target. After that permission is required to count more, but one interviewee told us: *"I don't know of any requests ever getting turned down. I've* gone well over 200 hours after taking some big cases."* Far from being discouraged from taking too much, associates reported that *"pro bono is one of the big missions of the firm. Clients like the fact that we do so much."* On top of the pride that comes with using your legal powers for good, going past 50 hours wins you a small recognition award. The firm's pro bono managers send out weekly emails with opportunities, and interviewees said they'd taken on *"domestic violence cases, immigration matters and landlord/tenant disputes."* Corporate associates often struggle to match litigators in the pro bono stakes, but our corporate sources at Dechert had access to plenty of transactional pro bono.

"I've gone well over 200 hours."

Pro bono hours
- For all attorneys across all US offices: 63,390
- Average per US attorney: 104.1

Hours & Compensation

Reaching the yearly billing target of 1,950 hours makes associates bonus eligible, with a higher bonus on offer for those who bill more. Our interviewees considered the target *"very achievable – most people don't have trouble hitting it."* Some did add that *"as a first-year it's a little bit more difficult because you start slowly."*

"When I do take vacation there's a tremendous effort to allow me to really have time off."

Associates said they typically wrap up their working day *"some time between 7pm and 9pm,"* getting in at 9:30am in New York and earlier elsewhere. A New Yorker told us what their hours get like at the extreme: *"I've definitely had nights when I've been here till 1am or 4am. And there's been at least one night when I didn't go home, but that was abnormal and happened because of a very tight deadline."* However, juniors said they *"definitely"* have *"time for a private life, but it can be difficult to schedule things as you never know when an emergency will come up."*

Associates can take up to 20 vacation days a year. One source confided: *"I went away for a weekend at one point, and something major came up so I ended up spending most of it working."* Another told us, contrastingly: *"When I do take vacation there's a tremendous effort to allow me to really have time off."*

Diversity

Dechert historically isn't the strongest performer on the diversity front – only 16% of partners are female, for example – and associates agreed: *"We could definitely*

See firm profile on p.630

The Inside View

do better, and the firm is making a concerted effort to improve." The latest promotions to partner have been around the 50% mark. In some offices, attorneys are taking things into their own hands, with ethnically diverse associates *"getting together for monthly lunches and inviting people across the firm to share their experiences. The firm has been very receptive to the initiative and encouraged it."* Dechert has an array of official affinity groups that include Asian, Black, Latino and LGBT associations, and most visibly the Global Women's Initiative. The firm also hosts a yearly diversity summit in New York, and recently appointed Satra Sampson-Arokium as new director of diversity and inclusion. *"I'd give Dechert middling grades for achievement, but high marks for trying,"* one source concluded.

Strategy & Future

An associate told us that the firm *"tries to give the impression of transparency"* regarding its future plans and strategy, with *"quarterly meetings with the CEO on our financials."* The firm promotes itself as a 'global specialist' on its website. We wondered what this meant. *"We specialize in particular practice areas,"* CEO Henry Nassau informed us: *"Real estate securitization, M&A, funds work, white-collar investigations, international arbitration, IP and commercial litigation."* As for future strategy, Nassau tells us a recent spate of lateral hires is *"absolutely"* indicative of what's to come. *"In 2017 we've hired six lateral partners and seven lateral associates in New York, and five partners and 12 associates in London. The greatest opportunities for potential future growth are in New York, London and Washington, DC, but our other smaller offices with specialized practice areas remain quite strong too."* To read the full interview with Nassau, head to www.chambers-associate.com

"Students will need to familiarize themselves with different firms and get to know them through as many events and opportunities as possible, but obviously not at the expense of their academic achievement. Many students benefit from mock interview programs, and we do participate in those at various law schools. The key is to know your narrative and that means being prepared to discuss anything on your resume. It's also important to come armed with questions you have about the firm that will help you decide whether the firm is right for you."
– national hiring partner Emily Rapalino, Goodwin

See firm profile on p.630

DLA Piper LLP (US)

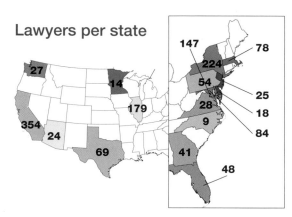

Lawyers per state

147
78
224
27
14
54
25
179
28
18
9
354
24
84
69
41
48

Largest US office: New York
US offices: 28
International offices: 67 (plus 20 affiliates)
First-year salary: $180,000 in major markets; $160,000 elsewhere
Billable hours: 2,000 target
Summers 2018: 65 (15 1Ls, 50 2Ls)
Revenue 2017: $2.63 (+6.5%)
Partners made in 2018: 19
Famous for: global expansion; massive mergers

'Gee, Brain, what do you want to do tonight?' 'The same thing we do every night, Pinky – try to take over the world!'

AFTER Destiny's Child released their fourth and final album in 2004, the world was ready for another powerful trio to seek global domination. Fortunately, three law firms based in San Diego, Baltimore and London were hatching a plan. In January 2005 their destiny was fulfilled, and through the largest merger in legal history the catchily named DLA Piper Rudnick Gray Cary was born. Now named DLA Piper, this firm has proved itself to be a real survivor. It's currently one of the world's largest by head count, with over 4,000 attorneys in 40 different countries around the world, and 28 offices in the US alone.

"...the resources of a large firm and the culture of a smaller one."

DLA tops the charts in a menagerie of practices, with number one hits including franchising, corporate & commercial and real estate in *Chambers USA*. The firm is ranked in 16 US states across a wide range of practices, from corporate in California to technology in Texas. We all know size isn't everything, but try telling that to DLA's latest recruits: "*I knew I wanted to work for a big firm, and well, they're one of the biggest.*" It wasn't just the firm's

On chambers-associate.com...

- Interview with managing partner for the Americas Stasia Kelly
- Interview with hiring partner Tina Martini
- Get hired at DLA Piper

global reach that attracted associates, however. DLA's local expertise across multiple locations coupled with its friendly reputation drew juniors, who told us: "*I wanted to work somewhere with the resources of a large firm and the culture of a smaller one.*"

The Work

DLA's main practice areas are corporate, employment, finance, IP & technology, government affairs, litigation, real estate, restructuring and tax. The majority of the second and third-year associates on our list were split between litigation and corporate, but the firm's real estate group also took on a significant number. The associates all meet for a two-day orientation (most of this years' interviewees had headed off to Chicago for theirs), and as of fall 2017 many associates will join the 'First Year Associate Practice,' which enables entry-level juniors to get work from across the firm's different practices during their first year. At the end of this period they join a specific practice group. Hiring partner Tina Martini tells us: "*We piloted it in our Chicago office, and it met with tremendous success so we are rolling it out on a more national basis this fall. It helps attorneys to ensure that when they move into a new practice area, it's in an area in which they are interested. It also ensures that the attorneys in various groups have had the opportunity to get to know associates by the time they are second years.*"

In litigation, typical tasks include document review, drafting motions and interview outlines, drafting letters to bodies like the FCC and FCPA, and court filings. One

See firm profile on p.631

Rankings in *Chambers USA*

Bankruptcy/Restructuring	Litigation
Chancery	Outsourcing
Construction	Privacy & Data Security
Corporate/Commercial	Products Liability
Corporate/M&A	Real Estate
Franchising	REITs
Government	Retail
Healthcare	Sports Law
Insurance	Startups & Emerging
Intellectual Property	Companies
International Trade	Tax
IT & Outsourcing	Technology
Leisure & Hospitality	Telecommunications
Life Sciences	Venture Capital

For detail on ranking tiers and ranking locations, visit
www.chambersandpartners.com

Recent work highlights

- Acted as counsel for food sector client Dannon on domestic intellectual property matters
- Working with Lululemon Athletica to expand its IP holdings and protection of its designs and products
- Representing Fox in three high-profile lawsuits alleging claims of race discrimination as well as one claim of pregnancy discrimination
- Represents 30+ hotels including Hilton, Marriott and Starwood regarding the taxation of bookings made through online companies such as Expedia. These cases are largely run from California, where the tax problems are at their most volatile

associate told us: "*I had a meeting with a partner and a client in the first few weeks and more recently I've been visiting client offices and reviewing potential witnesses.*" Others said: "*On a more local level I've been directly involved with attorneys of record, which is great because I've been able to get experience arguing in front of a judge while the partner sat next-door.*" While some associates appreciated getting a wide range of experience, others felt like they didn't have time to get comfortable: "*One complaint I have is that I feel like I'm doing everything for the first time.*" They added: "*No associate's ever going to say they've had enough court experience but when I look at my peers at other firms I've had much more. You don't have to steamroll your way into it but if you don't ask you won't get it.*"

"You get real substantive work right away."

Over in corporate, juniors told us: "*It's pretty standard for first-years to take on a large role in the diligence process as well as ancillary documents.*" Others added: "*I think the team is great at mentoring and giving us good experience drafting things for clients.*" Other typical tasks include preparing consents for transactions and assisting managing main agreements as well as managing smaller operative documents. Teams in the firm's smaller offices benefited from the leaner teams, saying it meant that "*you get real substantive work right away,*" whereas those in larger offices like New York felt: "*you have less of a clear and defined role as a junior.*" Another associate said that responsibility can vary from client to client: "*With startups in particular you get to manage those relationships in a ton of ways, from client meetings to unsupervised emails.*" Clients range from local businesses to international companies, so there is often interaction with DLA's other US offices, and juniors said that they had experience working

with clients and authorities in multiple jurisdictions: "*I'm in contact with people in Europe and Asia very regularly.*"

Culture & Offices

Most juniors are split between DLA's Chicago, New York, Washington DC, San Francisco and Palo Alto offices, with the rest dotted between the firm's many other domestic bases including Boston, LA, Miami and Houston. The Chicago office recently relocated to a swanky riverside building, and New York is currently in the middle of major renovations. Associates emphasized the differences between locations, telling us: "*Each office has its own culture and personality.*"

"It would be ludicrous to impose a single culture."

"*Because DLA is the result of multiple mergers, often the core cultures of offices are from legacy firms.*" Lawyers in Boston said that more people worked from home than in New York, for example, and the dress code varies from office to office. In Baltimore the office is in a much more suburban location than some of its counterparts: "*It's very bucolic, just outside the city limit and overlooking a forest.*" Juniors in Washington told us: "*Our motto is that our reach is global and we have the resources of a global firm, but our partners all have local expertise.*" Managing partner for the Americas Stasia Kelly told us: "*We have the maturity to recognize and promote differences in culture while being collaborative across our global platform.*"

Juniors in New York told us: "*We're sort of going through a cultural transition because we've just moved floors. Before we were segregated between separate floors but there's already a totally different energy now that everybody's closer together.*" Because of the number of laterals DLA brings in regularly, many associates told us that the firm is a melting pot of firm cultures. However, they also said that "*the firm by virtue of interaction encourages people*

See firm profile on p.631

The Inside View

Diversity	Partners (%)	Associates (%)
Women	21.7	43.5
White	83.6	75.1
Black/African American	2.4	3.9
Hispanic/Latin American	2.7	2.3
Asian	5.8	11.6
Mixed/Other	2.4	5.7
LGBT	1.1	1.8

to get to know each other. I've got to know senior partners through social events."

"I've been thrilled with the amount I've laughed here."

"I've been thrilled with the amount I've laughed here," one first-year told us. "The firm has a culture of collaboration and a friendly and open atmosphere." Another added: "Everybody has the expectation of doing great work but there's also willingness to support you outside of office life." We heard about a wide range of social events, from dragon boat races and 5K runs for charity to cocktail evenings and dinners.

Training & Development

"There's the expectation from the get-go that partners are always there to talk to you, which is outstanding," one source told us. "They make a serious effort to inject learning opportunities into your day-to-day practice," they continued. The firm has recently set up a shadowing program so that associates can sit in on meetings and calls and attend trials, without the hours being billable to the clients – juniors can, however, pick up billable credit for these hours (up to 30 hours for first and second years).

There are three levels of associate academies that juniors undertake in their first three years. The first of these, the aptly-titled 'New Associate Academy,' gathers all newbies in one location and provides them with a series of training sessions over three days; the sessions are designed to help incoming juniors bridge the gap between law school and practice, and external consultants are brought in to help equip these fledgling lawyers with the skills they'll need. Back in their home offices, juniors can take advantage of in-house training programs. "They're usually one-hour training sessions where lunch or breakfast is served. They tend to be broadcast from Southern offices. I've found them very useful." When associates log 100 hours, relevant partners are automatically prompted to provide feedback. Associates commented, however, that "oftentimes the feedback system's not fully utilized, so I think we could definitely use more constructive criticism."

Diversity

This year saw the introduction of a new diversity and inclusion initiative at DLA which included the implementation of the Mansfield rule, which dictates that 30% of those being considered for leadership roles must be women or minorities. The firm has also hired a professor from NYU for mandatory firm-wide training on D&I, with associates and partners being sent to New York. "It's really important that people become aware of their unconscious biases," associates agreed.

"DLA really values a global outlook."

Juniors also told us: "There's a diversity retreat every other year which is really cool. Last year's was in Texas and included the Puerto Rico office. Instead of talking about the lack of diversity they taught us about working on skills development and on retention, which was a really interesting way of approaching the issue." There are also affinity groups in individual offices. Finally, associates told us: "DLA really values a global outlook and has a strong commitment to diversity because of the international nature of the firm."

Hours & Compensation

The billing target at DLA is 2,000 hours. "It's pretty industry standard, but I think DLA could be better at allowing non-billable work to count toward targets." Most associates told us that their hours were pretty steady, with the occasional late night or weekend spent working: "My wife might not agree but I'd say I have an acceptable work-life balance." Another added: "Most weekends I don't open my computer except to check my emails. Partners think ahead about prioritizing matters rather than putting something on your desk at 8pm."

"My wife might not agree but I'd say I have an acceptable work-life balance."

The salary at DLA is market (varying slightly between offices), and bonuses are based on hours and performance ratings. "I would like more transparency when it comes to bonuses," one associate told us. "They use a formula but we don't have any visibility on it." There is no formal vacation policy but the majority of people we interviewed said that they preferred the system, adding: "People respect your vacation times and social commitments."

Pro Bono

According to one enthusiastic associate, DLA Piper is "astonishing" when it comes to pro bono. "The firm is a lot more supportive of pro bono work than some of its peers, and you get the opportunity to do a ton in your first year." Juniors are expected to complete a minimum of 60

See firm profile on p.631

The Inside View

pro bono hours, and up to 100 can be counted as billable, although extensions can be requested. When associates first join they're put on the pro bono helpline. Juniors in Baltimore told us that they work with parents and families from disadvantaged schools in the area. "*The issues range from criminal problems to bankruptcy, and junior associates are the first port of call.*"

Interviewees also mentioned the new project in which attorneys are sent abroad to teach law students. Some of this year's recruits were headed to Ethiopia, we were told. We also heard about work in food banks, doing advocacy on asylum cases, representing people in guardianship cases, writing briefs at the Supreme Courts and working on a prisoner civil rights investigation. "*It's really invaluable to have all the firm's resources at my disposal. There was a much faster turnaround than the state would have had because I had teams of secretaries and paralegals.*"

Pro bono hours
- For all US attorneys: 117,000
- Average per US attorney: 74

Strategy & Future

With another flurry of mergers in 2017, DLA shows no sign of complacency. Managing partner for the Americas Stasia Kelly tells us: "*Everything we do is in an effort to position ourselves as a firm that is a trusted adviser in the boardroom and can provide support to our clients wherever they are or are doing business.*" She continues: "*There's a lot of commoditization going on at peer firms, but we're positioning ourselves as advisers on a more sophisticated level. We will also continue to innovate as we increasingly position ourselves as a global legal enterprise that is on the cutting edge of the practice and business of law.*"

Get Hired

"*We use behavioral interviewing techniques where we talk about the spirit of the firm and who we are and ask questions to try and get a sense of what makes candidates tick and whether they have a 'fire in the belly,'*" says hiring partner Tina Martini. Read more about getting hired at chambers-associate.com

See firm profile on p.631

Duane Morris LLP

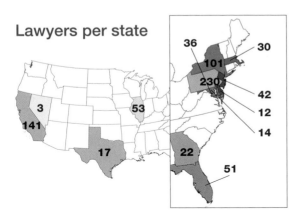

Lawyers per state

36
30
101
230
42
12
14
3
53
141
17
22
51

Largest US office: Philadelphia
US offices: 21
International offices: 8
First-year salary: $165,000 (Baltimore, New York, Philadelphia, DC and Chicago); $150,000 (San Diego); $140,000 (Miami, Cherry Hill)
Billable hours: 1,950 target
Summers 2018: 21 (1 1L, 20 2Ls)
Revenue 2017: $466 million (+2.6%)
Partners made in 2018: 9
Famous for: uniform decor; deep Philly history

Its eye may be on new opportunities both at home and abroad, but strong Philly roots keep this expanding firm grounded.

DUANE Morris is so rooted in Philadelphia that one of its founders, Russell Duane, was a descendant of Benjamin Franklin. This rich heritage in the City of Brotherly Love still shapes the firm today: *"They funnel a lot out of the Philly HQ, and that sets the tone for the culture at large."* But while Philadelphia plays an important role, it's important to flag this firm's capacious dimensions: it has 21 domestic offices covering legal hotspots across the country, as well as eight international offices, which are mostly concentrated in Asia but include bases in London and Oman. The firm's most recent openings including a post in Taiwan and one in the 'Silicon Hills' of Austin: *"It's a hi-tech community, and we want the office to function as an extension of our IP, transactional and litigation practices,"* chairman emeritus John Soroko tells us.

With a broad spread of offices comes a wide array of practices. *"They span everything from Wall Street to Main Street!"* Soroko explains. *"Our four largest practice groups are – in descending order – trial, corporate, IP and employment."* In *Chambers USA,* the firm picks up its heftiest clutch of rankings on its home turf of Pennsylvania, but on a broader level particular strengths include healthcare, construction, insurance, IP and immigration.

Strategy & Future

Alongside new offices, the other big news coming out of DM is a change in leadership. After ten years at the top, Soroko passed the chairman torch to Matthew Taylor in January 2018. Reflecting on his tenure, Soroko is proud to have strengthened the firm's presence in emerging markets: *"It's an excellent strategy given where the world is heading. We started in locations like Myanmar and Vietnam, and more recently established alliances in Sri Lanka and Mexico."*

"Success in today's legal climate requires a great deal of flexibility and innovation."

So what does the future hold under Taylor's stewardship? *"Our core practices, values and culture will remain very much in place,"* Soroko affirms. However, that doesn't mean that DM is reluctant to change in other respects: *"We continue to understand that success in today's legal climate requires a great deal of flexibility and innovation, so we're constantly looking for new opportunities."*

Offices

At the time of our calls, Philadelphia housed the most second and third-year juniors (11), while New York claimed six and San Diego three. A further seven were split between Chicago, Baltimore, DC, Boston and Miami. Despite DM's geographic diversity, associates highlighted how familiar each office across the network feels: *"They're all absolutely identical! You walk into Philly, you*

On chambers-associate.com...

• More on getting hired at Duane Morris

See firm profile on p.632

Rankings in *Chambers USA*

Banking & Finance	Insurance
Bankruptcy/Restructuring	Intellectual Property
Construction	Labor & Employment
Corporate/M&A	Litigation
Healthcare	Real Estate
Immigration	Tax

For detail on ranking tiers and ranking locations, visit
www.chambersandpartners.com

Recent work highlights

- Defended a group of telecom companies, including Time Warner Cable and Bright House Networks, against a patent infringement complaint filed by Mobile Telecommunications Technologies
- Advised the CEO of a multibillion-dollar energy company during an internal investigation into alleged conflicts of interest, breaches of fiduciary duties and violations of securities laws
- Represented Hill International as it divested its $140 million construction claims business via a sale to British private equity buyer Bridgepoint Development Capital
- Acted for Canadian bank CIBC as it put together a $35 million technology financing for a venture capital-backed company

walk into DC, and you won't feel like you're in a different office. It's like you're in an extension of where you do most of your work!" The similarities extend to *"the color scheme, the same really nice paintings and even great views."* Soroko tells us this uniformity *"sends a message to all of our lawyers that our offices outside of Philadelphia are not just 'satellite' or 'branch' offices, but core offices with core legal teams."*

Culture

Associates agreed that this decorative tactic helps to maintain a *"one-firm, 'we're all in this together' environment. We're one team."* But this isn't the only unifying trick up DM's sleeve: every associate we spoke to was keen to mention the firm's annual fall conference, which brings together every lawyer from across the entire network. Its location alternates between Philadelphia and Boca Raton, and *"for new associates this gathering is, like, the greatest thing EVER!"* Weekend activities include *"a tennis tournament, golf, a spa day and a beach visit,"* while serious business covers *"firm-wide meetings, practice group dinners and team building exercises."*

"They say 'if you're not happy, we can change something.'"

Back in their respective offices, associates pretty much unanimously agreed that the partners promote a positive atmosphere. *"They say 'if you're not happy, we can change something, just let us know!'"* A healthy dollop of socializing helps to keep work relationships strong; in New York, for example, juniors told of happy hours where *"the managing partner and the partners who have kids and other commitments show up – the partner/associate divide isn't that strong."* Meanwhile in Philly much of the socializing comes with food-based perks, courtesy of a top local chef: *"We have wine and cheese nights, as well as a monthly associate lunch. Yesterday we had pork tenderloin, sage chicken and rum and banana bread pudding. I'm thrilled I ended up working here!"*

The Work

Of course, associates do have to fit in work around all of these tasty treats. The majority of the juniors on our list (14) had joined DM's trial group, while corporate took six and IP three; lone associates could be found in the firm's employment, business reorganization and financial restructuring, real estate, and wealth planning groups. Assignment across the board is fairly free market and associates are given a few years to find their niche within their group.

"The trial group generally handles EVERYTHING," litigators emphasized. Indeed it does: cases cover the likes of antitrust law, professional liability, insurance, construction, aviation, securities and much more. Our sources had encountered *"complex mortgage foreclosures, class actions, banking disputes, white-collar defense matters and some government investigations."* Sources appreciated the opportunity to sample, and one had *"worked with 17 different people. You get to see a lot of different styles of lawyering."* At the junior level, *"it's about laying the groundwork: we're conducting legal research, getting guidance from partners on what to argue, reviewing facts in documents and having a first crack of drafting everything – pleadings, motions etc…"*

"Everything from Wall Street to Main Street!"

DM's corporate practice is similarly broad, with areas of expertise including M&A, private equity, investment funds, capital markets and tax. Juniors here tend to find their niche quicker than their counterparts in trial. One who'd developed a tax focus told us: *"My favorite thing about it is research, but I also review contracts and recently drafted a highly complex partnership agreement, which was really cool."* Another interviewee explained that M&A work involves *"a fair amount of responsibility; I'm coordinating the delivery of documents with clients, re-*

See firm profile on p.632

Diversity	Partners (%)	Associates (%)
Women	22.4	39
White	89.02	81.92
Black/African American	2.5	2.82
Hispanic/Latin American	2.99	3.95
Asian	4.98	7.34
Mixed/Other	0.5	3.38
LGBT	1.25	1.13

viewing those documents and researching certain markets. I haven't drafted any of the larger documents, but I have done the ancillaries, which is appropriate for my degree of knowledge."

IP associates told us the work is split between *"securing new patents or trademarks and handling disputes over existing ones."* The former strand gave juniors a chance to *"meet and interview inventors, and then spend a week or so writing up a patent application."* The litigation side, on the other hand, *"is different because of the amount of money at stake in the case. I'm given scope to figure out what needs to be done, but I'm more directly managed and it's more of a team effort."*

Hours & Compensation
Salaries vary depending on location, but all of them fall below the prevailing benchmark that is the 'Cravath scale.' Not that this bothered our interviewees: *"Whatever the difference is between a Cravath and a Duane salary it is so worth your sanity!"*

"It is so worth your sanity!"

A superior work-life balance spurred on these positive comments. *"I've only worked until the early hours of the morning twice since being here, and they were both extraordinary circumstances – that's almost unheard of for any associate at the firm that I know and talk to."* On the whole, juniors *"still put in the hours."* Trial associates typically worked from 9am until 7:30/8pm (*"with the occasional dreaded 11:30pm filing"*), while corporate sources clocked up nine-hour days on average, but could *"rack up 14 hours if we're approaching a closing."* A firm-wide billable target of 1,950 hours was deemed reasonable.

Pro Bono
Juniors can count up to 100 hours toward their annual billing target. *"It's encouraged and you get credit for it, so you know it's not just lip service,"* associates happily

reported. The firm hosts *"pro bono appreciation events; we invite pro bono clients to celebrate the work that's been done – it shows we have a genuine interest in the community."*

Our sources had worked on trademark requests, veteran healthcare matters, *"an appeal for a juvenile sentenced to life without parole,"* and an asylum case *"on behalf of a transgender woman seeking to stay in the US; it's quite something to switch gears from a corporate bank case to one where you're helping to save someone's life."* Sources had no trouble securing work: *"There are local pro bono coordinators – from the day I started they put me on cases!"*

Pro bono hours
- For all US attorneys: 36,797
- Average per US attorney: 49.2

Training & Development
First, all new recruits get sent to Philly for *"two days of really extensive training on all the IT systems and firm programs."* Next comes a first-year professional development program that sees newbies attend monthly sessions on the likes of *"public speaking, business development and marketing, how to get work, how to prepare for your first review, etc..."* Monthly CLEs are *"open to everyone and hosted by both people from the firm and outside consultants: DM is good at providing these opportunities and you don't have to go searching!"*

Many praised the partner support they'd received: *"At reviews they ask if you're happy, how morale is and what work you want to be doing."* One associate added: *"I'm very lucky to work with talented partners – they want you to get better as an attorney."*

Diversity
Location tended to govern views on diversity. New Yorkers, for example, gave positive accounts: *"The partner I work for was praised by the chairman for always assembling a diverse team – I think it's the New York state of mind."* In a smaller office, however, one source was less impressed: *"There are a lot of white males."*

National initiatives include an annual diversity and inclusion retreat *"where diverse lawyers attend meetings and have discussions with the firm's leadership."* Local inclusion committees also exist, and we heard especially good things about the one in Baltimore: *"They plan monthly happy hours and discussions, and these aren't just limited to lawyers – everyone's included, so staff, legal assistants, etc..."*

See firm profile on p.632

Dykema Gossett PLLC

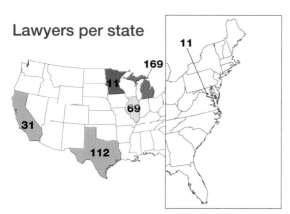

Lawyers per state

11
169
11
69
31
112

Largest US office: San Antonio
US offices: 13
International offices: 0
First-year salary: $120,000-$150,000
Billable hours: 1,950 target
Summers 2018: 12
Revenue 2017: $212 million (3.2%)
Partners made in 2018: 12
Famous for: Michigan might with a strong national presence

It's a mighty legal brand in the Midwest, but recent expansion in Texas has given Dykema a taste for further national growth.

"DYKEMA has really strong credibility in this state," a Michigan-based associate enthused, "but it also has a better national presence than other local firms." Indeed: while five of the firm's offices can be found in The Great Lake State, it also has a further eight spread across Texas, California, DC, Illinois and Minnesota. Detroit is still very much the firm's beating heart though, and retains its status as the firm's official headquarters despite the San Antonio office housing the most attorneys in the network.

Since successfully exiting its bankruptcy in 2014, Detroit has witnessed "a lot of development, and Dykema has been a part of it," associates proudly revealed, flagging the firm's work on the city's new public transport system. Famously, the automotive industry is prominent in Detroit, through good times and bad. Unsurprisingly, Dykema has been involved in many automotive-related matters, and is now steering its focus towards what the future holds: "New mobility services within the automotive industry – what some refer to as autonomous vehicles – is an area we've targeted for us to grow in and be a player in," CEO Peter Kellett explains.

"We want to continue expanding our geographic reach."

He adds: "We've had continued growth and success in our recent expansion in Texas, and continue to do well there." Kellett is referring to Dykema's 2015 merger with Texas-based firm Cox Smith, which added bases in San Antonio and Dallas, and doubled the firm's number of lawyers in Austin. Beyond that, Kellett also highlights that Dykema has had "a number of new client matters in different areas, affirming our focus on our key sectors." These include the automotive, energy, financial, insurance, food & beverage, and dental industries. Michigan is still considered the firm's stronghold in *Chambers USA*, where it picks up high rankings in areas like corporate/M&A, real estate and general commercial litigation. Dykema also scores praise for its real estate work in Illinois and its bankruptcy/restructuring expertise in Texas.

Strategy & Future

"We want to continue to grow our geographic reach," Kellett adds. "We're having ongoing conversations with other groups and firms about combining and growing the footprint of our firm geographically." Where does Kellett see the firm growing? "We're very much mindful of the fact that we have opportunities here in the middle region of the country to expand. There are places where we're not already – generally the Midwest is a place where we have some presence but it's not uniform. It's a logical place for us to look." Visit chambers-associate.com to read our full interview with Peter Kellett.

On chambers-associate.com...

- Get hired at Dykema
- Interviews with CEO Peter Kellett and hiring partner Lisa Brown
- More on Dykema's social life

The Inside View

See firm profile on p.633

Rankings in *Chambers USA*

Banking & Finance
Bankruptcy/Restructuring
Corporate/M&A
Employee Benefits &
   Executive Compensation

Labor & Employment
Litigation
Real Estate

For detail on ranking tiers and ranking locations, visit
www.chambersandpartners.com

Recent work highlights

- Defended Toyota during a class action tied to the automaker's use of Takata's airbags
- Secured a victory for State Farm Mutual Automobile Insurance Co. in the Michigan Supreme Court, which impacted the application of the state's 'no-fault' insurance law
- Represented Cedarbrook Senior Living during its acquisition, development and financing of a continuing care retirement community in Rochester, Michigan
- Acted for payment processing specialist NRT Technologies during its acquisition of Las Vegas-based company VisuaLimits

The Work

Half of the second and third-year juniors on our list were based in Dykema's litigation department, which is divided into subgroups like commercial; financial services; labor & employment; and products, class actions & professional liability. The remaining half were split between the firm's business services (which includes corporate finance and taxation & estates practices) real estate & environment, regulated industries and intellectual property departments. Across every department there's a *"free market system where you develop relationships with certain partners and develop a niche for yourself."* Sources liked *"being able to try out different types of law to get a good idea of what you like."* They also had this advice: *"When you start, treat the partners like clients and build the relationship so they feel comfortable assigning work to you."* If juniors get stuck *"you can go to the practice group leader and they will help you."*

> *"You get a feel of how courtrooms work and how to interact with judges and opposing counsel."*

Litigators are *"encouraged to work with any subgroup regardless of which one you're initially placed in."* In commercial litigation, sources had encountered a lot of breach of contract cases for *"clients ranging from small local entities to large Fortune 500 companies."* Financial services matters enabled sources to work with *"banks and mortgage providers,"* while product liability cases exposed them to *"big automotive clients – we've recently had a case where an automotive company sued their parts supplier."* Tasks included *"creating deposition exhibit binders and outlines, then going to the depositions with partners to provide support."* One mentioned being *"sent to status hearings really early on. You get courtroom experience in a non-threatening way. You don't start off arguing motions, but you get a feel of how courtrooms work and how to interact with judges and opposing counsel."*

In the business services department, our corporate finance sources had experienced many commercial lending deals. *"We work with a lot of midmarket clients in many different industries,"* our interviewees revealed. Some had worked with energy clients, while others told of deals involving *"pet food companies and dental service organizations."* Associates had done the classic junior tasks of conducting due diligence and drafting ancillary documents, but had also tried their hand at *"doing the first draft of a loan agreement."* Overall, business services sources felt that *"they do give us a lot of responsibility and expect us to know our stuff – the partners rely on us to provide them with the correct information."*

The real estate department covers both finance and development work, and attracts a lot of clients in the telecom industry. On the lending side, our interviewees had been *"drafting loan documents – they're often construction or acquisition loans."* Telecom work saw sources hone their skills on *"leases, easements and some fee deals, as well as a bit of buying and selling work – I work with some clients just on my own!"* Others had ventured into broader commercial leasing matters, as well as contentious condemnation cases: *"It's my third year and I'm still experimenting with things."* National work *"is definitely a significant proportion of what we do – a lot of the lending work is Michigan-based, but you also end of working on sub-leases in California and Nevada, for example."*

Training & Development

An initial two-day orientation program clues new starters up *"on things like the phone and IT systems, how documents are saved – everything you need to give you a solid foundation at the firm."* A month and a half later, all newbies congregate in Detroit for the 'New Associates Retreat,' which takes them through the firm's evaluation and advancement processes, as well as the firm's history and pro bono opportunities. There's also a set of 'New Associate Programming' sessions for juniors, which run on a weekly basis for the first two and half months that they're at the firm; topics covered here include time management and professionalism. In addition, litigators attend bi-monthly training sessions for their first six months, which are delivered through the Dykema Litigation Institute. *"They're good, focused on important topics and pretty intensive. However, at times you don't get a sense*

See firm profile on p.633

Diversity	Partners (%)	Associates (%)
Women	24	52
White	90	72
Black/African American	3	11
Hispanic/Latin American	5	4
Asian	2	9
Mixed/Other	0	4
LGBT	1	1.1

of what you're applying them to as you haven't built up enough experience yet." Juniors in other departments told us that "on the job training" is more common.

Annual reviews provide juniors with feedback on the substantive work they've done. As part of the process, an appointed person from the professional personnel committee "represents you to the broader committee, which listens to the feedback and subsequently decides what your bonus will be. The one critique I have is that the person representing you might not have worked with you at all that year."

Hours & Compensation

Associates have a 1,950-hour billable target, which sources found be to "tough, but not impossible." Optimism varied depending on the practice group: those in corporate finance, for instance, said they were "on pace to hit 2,000 hours," while their counterparts in business litigation said "I'm not going to hit the target – I'm not close." Overall interviewees felt that it's "challenging as a younger associate, as you have to build up your reputation with attorneys to get work." Hitting 1,950 hours officially makes juniors eligible for a merit-based bonus, but we did hear that Dykema also has an alternative bonus formula: "If you're not hitting your hours but are still profitable to the firm, you can still get a bonus."

"It's quite common to work remotely at some point."

Most juniors reported being in the office between 9am and 7pm on average, though unsurprisingly this varied across practices. Litigators told us that when "giant cases come up you can have a wonky schedule and be working from 8am to anywhere between 6pm and 11pm." Most sources rarely worked at the weekend, but some in the transactional groups did find themselves "working for a bit every other weekend – I can still do things outside of work, I just need to plan around it." Others added that "if you need to work from home, that's not an issue. It's quite common to work remotely at some point."

Pro Bono

"I would give the firm an A+ for pro bono!" one junior exclaimed. Up to 100 hours can potentially count toward the billing target (subject to approval), and it's compulsory to rack up 30 hours – those who fail to reach this donate $500 to a charity of their choosing. Many interviewees had accrued over 100 hours, and sources reassured us that "getting approval has never been an issue – I went way over 100 and the firm is giving me credit for that." One minor grumble came from those outside of Michigan, who explained that "the pro bono coordinator is based in Michigan, so a lot of opportunities and connections are based there too. They could improve on broadening the scope a bit." Our interviewees had nonetheless got involved in various matters, such as immigration and asylum; prisoner and civil rights; and human trafficking cases.

Pro bono hours
- For all attorneys: undisclosed
- Average per attorney: undisclosed

Diversity

Dykema's diversity committee "is not only trying to recruit more diverse candidates, but looking into retention to address root causes for minorities not staying." One diverse junior praised the firm's efforts: "When there's a diversity event in a different office, they will fly you out so you can attend if you're interested. They sort the hotel out and everything." As a result, sources felt "the firm is really putting its money where its mouth is." Dykema has partnered up with the Universities of Michigan and Illinois to offer diversity scholarships, and also participates in initiatives like the Wolverine Bar Association's summer clerkship program for diverse 1Ls.

Offices

The juniors on our list were based in Dykema's Detroit, Bloomfield Hills, Chicago, San Antonio, Lansing and Los Angeles offices. Because Dykema is registered as a Detroit-headquartered business, it goes into a "smaller pool of preferential service providers in the city." And the city has a growing need for them, as sources agreed that "Detroit is undergoing a renaissance – it's really coming around." Appropriately, the firm's headquarters is located in the Renaissance Center – "currently the tallest building in Detroit!" – which is also the world headquarters for General Motors, one of the firm's big clients.

"Detroit is undergoing a renaissance."

The Chicago office has its quirks, as it's the product of a few mergers between firms in the market; one junior explained that "people hold onto some of the rituals and rules from their legacy firms – Rooks Pitts attorneys, for exam-

See firm profile on p.633

ple, had a rule where if there was a conversation between two or more people, another person could come in and completely change the topic of conversation by claiming Rooks Pitts rule." Over in Texas, one San Antonio resident told us that *"we're right in the heart of downtown. In the office we have lots of cool artwork, including a sculpture of a bear made from shoes!"*

Culture

"People come to Dykema and they seem to stay here because of the overall culture – there's a real sense of camaraderie between our lawyers." This sense of camaraderie came up on multiple occasions during our interviews, with sources emphasizing Dykema's *"very collaborative culture"* and good relationships between associates and partners: *"The partners are easy to talk to and go to for advice – they all know we're on the same team."* One reflected: *"Initially I had a fear about law firms being cutthroat, but I didn't see anything like that here. That's a big reason I stayed after the summer."*

"We project a friendly, Midwest culture."

Although this was the consensus across all offices, our sources also noted slight differences between Dykema's bases. Those in the Michigan offices told us that while *"the firm has put things in place to push for a modernized feel, on the whole it feels more traditional due to its longstanding presence, clients and partners."* This is reflected in Detroit's dress code, which was said to be *"a lot more formal"* than it is in the firm's other offices. Sources here nonetheless felt that *"we project a friendly, Midwest culture,"* in which *"it's not uncommon to hear partners say, 'Hey, it's four-thirty, and my son's got a hockey game – I gotta make it.'"* The Chicago and San Antonio offices were described as *"more homey"* than the Detroit stronghold, while the smaller LA and DC bases were seen as *"smaller and tight-knit."*

Get Hired

"I definitely like to see someone with a lot of personality, who doesn't take themselves too seriously but at the same time is very driven." For more recruitment advice from Dykema's associates and hiring partner Lisa Brown, visit chambers-associate.com

Epstein Becker & Green PC

Lawyers per state

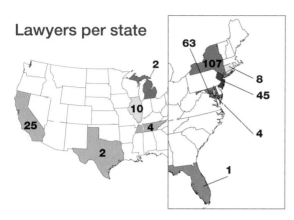

Largest US office: New York
US offices: 14
International offices: 0
First-year salary: varies by practice and location
Billable hours: 1,950 requirement
Summers 2018: 10 (2 1Ls, 8 2Ls)
Revenue 2017: undisclosed
Partners made in 2018: 4
Famous for: labor & employment law; healthcare law

Working at Epstein is a labor of love for lovers of labor law, and a hearty home for those with a hankering for healthcare.

"AT the moment there is a lot of uncertainty about healthcare in politics in Washington DC," observed one Epstein associate. "And where there's lots of uncertainty, we see ourselves as here to help." Healthcare law is one of Epstein's twin focuses – the other is labor and employment. The firm has over 40 years of experience in these areas and uses a mantra of 'focused excellence' to promote its expertise. *Chambers USA* ranks Epstein for both health and labor law in New York and New Jersey, and for health law nationwide and in DC. Labor and healthcare each make up 40% of the firm's practice, with the remaining 20% being employee benefits and immigration.

> "The reason clients come to us is that we think deeply about emerging problems in the healthcare market and in the workplace."

The associates we interviewed appreciated the exposure to interesting work provided by the firm's focus on the always-changing areas of health and labor law. "You often get the opportunity to work on matters that you'll hear about on the news," one told us. Firm chair Mark Lutes added: "We think the reason clients come to us is that we

think deeply about emerging problems in the healthcare market and in the workplace." Those clients include Johns Hopkins Hospital and Bain Capital on the healthcare side and Honeywell, Home Depot and AXA Investment Managers in labor and employment.

Epstein has 14 offices across the US, though several of those only have a couple of lawyers. The most recent addition to the network is a Nashville office, which opened in 2017. New York, Washington DC and Newark are the three largest outposts and this is where the firm regularly recruits junior associates.

Strategy & Future

In recent years Epstein has been active advising clients on issues related to the Affordable Care Act, such as physician reimbursements, as well as on new developments like telehealth. In addition, the sector is experiencing a significant trends toward consolidation (ie mergers between healthcare providers), another area where Epstein lawyers are active.

As for the future, the firm says the election of President Trump provides its clients withboth opportunities and challenges. While the President is yet to enact his pledge to 'repeal and replace' the Affordable Care Act, Epstein is committed to guiding its clients through whatever bumps along the road that the political landscape throws up for the healthcare sector.

On chambers-associate.com...

- Chairman Mark Lutes on trends affecting healthcare and labor lawyers
- Get hired at Epstein

See firm profile on p.634

The Inside View

329

Rankings in *Chambers USA*

Healthcare   Labor & Employment
Immigration

For detail on ranking tiers and ranking locations, visit
www.chambersandpartners.com

On the labor law side, issues around cybersecurity and artificial intelligence are keeping lawyers busy. Go to our website to hear more from firm chair Mark Lutes on trends affecting health and labor law.

The Work

Most associates join the Washington DC or New York offices, with a handful going to Newark. Two-thirds of juniors join the health & life sciences practice and one-third the labor practice; DC only recruits healthcare juniors. Associates say you need to be a bit of a self-starter to rustle up work in the first few months. While some projects are lined up by departments, it's mostly up to associates to build contacts and seek out opportunities within the firm. "*Sometimes it's hard to go out and find work as a first year,*" one associate said, "*but after six months I had built up enough relationships that others came to me with work.*" The upside is that "*you get to shape your own workload and decide who you want to work with.*" We also heard that new starters can turn to mentors and other staffing resources if they are having any trouble finding work.

Healthcare work is split between regulatory matters – for example, consulting on federal and state Medicare and Medicaid policies – and transactional work, where an influx of cash from private investors means there's plenty of deal work. Clients in DC range from "*major hospital systems and household names to startup companies.*" The team has been kept busy lately by ongoing privacy and security issues like data breaches, and it's also been advising clients that are negotiating service contracts with national health insurance companies. Juniors said their work consists of "*reviewing government documents, crafting responses, putting together schedules for agreements and answering questions on regulatory issues.*" There's a public service ethos to being a healthcare lawyer, we were told, as clients are "*constantly trying to figure out how to make the healthcare system more efficient and serve people better.*"

"I've had the opportunity to work on motions in limine during federal cases."

Juniors in the labor practice usually take a litigation or an advisory track. We heard of a couple of interviewees administering subpoenas and writing up documents like bonus certificates, memos and offer letters. A chunk of associates' time is taken up revising company policies,

Recent work highlights

- Advised Los Angeles hospital owner Prospect Medical Holdings on the acquisition of three hospitals in Connecticut on the same day
- Acted for health tech provider Altegra in a Medicare-related False Claims Act case in Texas related to allegedly fraudulent risk adjustment data
- Represented BT Americas in a wage and hour collective action related to alleged failure to pay overtime, off-the-clock violations and the misclassification of workers in its global call center in Chesapeake, Virginia
- Defended a top New York law firm in a race discrimination lawsuit filed by a Hispanic employee who claimed white employees were paid more and given better promotion opportunities and performance reviews

handbooks, training materials and payroll procedures. On litigious matters juniors prepare depositions and organize evidence. "*I was drafting discovery documents and preparing exhibits,*" one source told us. "*As the case progressed I was helping to sort through and draft letters and summary judgment motions.*" During trials juniors prepare witness examinations and exhibit binders. "*I've become very familiar with disparate impact analysis, and I've had the opportunity to work on motions in limine during federal cases,*" a junior reported.

Bridging healthcare and labor at Epstein are the firm's employee benefits and immigration practices. Changes at the state and federal level under the Trump administration have meant that lawyers at Epstein have had to keep clients in the know about how they might be impacted by immigration changes. For example, workers in employment under DACA may no longer be protected from deportation under revised rules. Changes have also been proposed to the H-1B visa program, which allows employers to hire foreign workers in specialty occupations.

Culture & Training

"*You have to be entrepreneurial to get ahead here,*" associates agreed. "*And staying on top of current trends is down to you as an associate.*" Because of the firm's relatively small size, "*you can connect with everyone and contribute to the organization as a whole.*" Such connections were encouraged by a three-day retreat in Philadelphia for associates in 2017. "*It gave us the opportunity to meet people from other offices and we were told about things like strategy and recent developments within the firm,*" a source said. Associates also get the chance to go to lunch with the firm chair annually for a one-on-one discussion about where the firm is headed.

"The majority of training happens when you're on the job."

See firm profile on p.634

The Inside View

Diversity	Partners (%)	Associates (%)
Women	30	59
White	88	79
Black/African American	2	5
Hispanic/Latin American	3	4
Asian	5	9
Mixed/Other	2	3
LGBT	2	2

Summer associates take part in the EBG Academy, which first years are also invited to attend and which "*covers the basics of how to be a first-year associate.*" There is introductory training for first-years covering drafting, billing and using paralegals and secretaries in the first couple of weeks, but "*the majority of training happens when you're on the job.*" When it comes to assessment and appraisals, "*every partner always gives feedback and there are also self-assessments, which help you grow and address issues.*" For all juniors there's a new shadowing program to help with training which means associates can attend trials even if their time isn't being billed to the client. "*I was able to attend a trial that I wouldn't have been able to otherwise,*" an interviewee said.

Get Hired

A proven commitment to Epstein's two main focuses is a must for would-be applicants. "*I would say that generally candidates need prior experience in healthcare or labor law,*" says director of legal recruitment Amy Simmons, "*either from coursework or lived experience.*" For more on getting hired, head to chambers-associate.com

"Given the billable requirement I'm fine with it: it's a trade-off."

Hours & Compensation

Epstein's salary falls below the market rate and varies between practice and location. While some associates felt that the current model for pay was "not sustainable in terms of retention," others said: "Given the billable requirement I'm fine with it: it's a trade-off." Associates we spoke to said that the 1,950-hour billing target is "totally achievable" and praised the "fantastic support and flexibility" of the firm when it came to working from home and visiting other offices. The average junior's working day lasts ten to 11 hours; for instance 9am to 8pm or 8am to 6pm. While there are "some long hours when there are deadlines," it's "always manageable" juniors agreed.

Associates get four weeks' vacation, although most hadn't taken that much during their first couple of years, and said that they still expected the odd phone call during their time off. As for the bonus target, insiders said: "*I wish there was more transparency. I feel like the firm needs to work on incentivizing people so they'll stay on at the firm.*"

Offices

The DC office, just one block from Georgetown, was recently refurbished and is "*really beautiful,*" according to associates. While Epstein's New York branch might not be as up to date, all associates get their own office and everybody was happy with the facilities across the DC, New York and Newark offices. A junior in Newark told us: "*I can reserve an office in New York if I want to.*" Others said that they had worked at the firms' other locations too, including Boston. Epstein also has offices in Baltimore, Chicago, Detroit, Houston, LA, Nashville, Princeton, San Diego, San Francisco and Stamford.

Pro Bono

Epstein's policy on pro bono changed in 2017: up to 100 hours can now be counted toward associates' billing target (hours spent on the firm's new shadowing program can also count toward this allowance). "*There's been a real enthusiasm and a push for pro bono lately, and most partners are really encouraging it,*" said one junior. Another added: "*I've worked on a couple of successful pro bono appeals and it's been really rewarding to be able to make a difference.*" Juniors may do pro bono related to the firm's specialties, like drafting an employment handbook for a small business or handling a social security disability discrimination claim.

Pro bono hours
- For all US attorneys: 4,657
- Average per US attorney: 17.1

Diversity

Epstein recently hired a new diversity manager to help with the firm's initiatives. Associates told us of an active women's group, as well as a variety of events during Black History Month 2017. Others mentioned that they had been allowed to go to conferences on diversity issues in business. Juniors agreed: "*There are a strong number of women who have made partner as well as a ton of female associates. It's very encouraging to work with so many women.*"

See firm profile on p.634

Finnegan, Henderson, Farabow, Garrett & Dunner

Lawyers per state

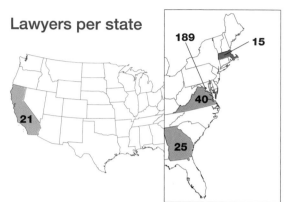

189

15

40

21

25

Largest US office: Washington, DC
US offices: 5
International offices: 5
First-year salary: $180,000
Billable hours: 2,000 target (or 1,900 plus 100 pro bono hours)
Summers 2018: 32 (3 1Ls, 29 2Ls)
Revenue 2017: $309.1 million (-0.3%)
Partners made in 2018: 10
Famous for: IP, patents are really their thing

DC-based Finnegan is onto a win again with its IP practice and global reach.

"I KNEW Finnegan was one of the best IP firms in the country," associates told us when explaining why they joined. Founded as an IP firm in 1965, Finnegan has expanded its reach (and its name) but not its focus. This DC-born outfit has five offices in the states, four in Asia and one in London. In the firm's own words, it offers *"full-service IP legal and technical experience in virtually every industry and technology."* Finnegan gets top rankings in *Chambers USA* for IP in Northern Virginia, the District of Columbia, Georgia, and Massachusetts as well as nationwide recognition for areas including patent prosecution, life sciences, trademark, copyright and trade secrets. Over 75 of its attorneys hold PhDs and more than 230 are registered to practice before the US Patent and Trademark Office (USPTO). *"The firm has a great reputation for both patent prosecution and litigation so you can move around within IP more easily,"* an associate reflected.

The firm scored highly in our 2018 survey for associate satisfaction. Unlike the chemical compounds these lawyers grapple with, the formula for their own happiness remains very simple: *"interesting work and people I like*

working with"* is all it really takes, associates decided. *"Partners understand that we're people and not cogs in machines"* – see Culture, below, for more on this.

The Work

Most associates are based in DC, with the rest dotted around the firm's Atlanta, Reston, Palo Alto and Boston offices. Newbies are divided into one of the following practice groups: electrical, chemical, mechanical, biotechnology & pharmaceutical, or trademark and copyright, depending on their academic and technical backgrounds. *"There's kind of a free market approach to work assignment,"* associates told us. *"If you want to work on something you have to reach out. There's plenty of work to go around so you just need to let people know the kind of work you're interested in."*

Depending on which groups they get involved with, Finnegan's associates can expect to work on matters relating to the following: electronics, computers, industrial manufacturing, consumer products, medical devices, biotechnology, pharmaceutical, chemicals, or alternative energy. Within each practice, juniors take on a mix of both patent prosecution and IP litigation work.

"You get to see some amazing technology on the brink of its field."

Most of the associates we spoke to had spent the majority of their time doing litigation, and told us that their

On chambers-associate.com...

- We learn about recruitment and training at Finnegan with recruitment manager Laurie Taylor and chief recruitment & professional development officer Tim Henderson.
- Interview with managing partner Mark Sweet

See firm profile on p.635

The Inside View

Rankings in *Chambers USA*

Intellectual Property   Life Sciences
International Trade

For detail on ranking tiers and ranking locations, visit
www.chambersandpartners.com

clients were usually Fortune 500 companies. They added, however: "*Sometimes it's a smaller company I'm not familiar with, but you get to see some amazing technology on the brink of its field.*" Others enthused: "*I've worked with start-up companies to develop patent strategies from scratch, which was really fun.*" Juniors revealed: "*I've seen cases in various stages, from early complaints to looking at witnesses and infringement positions.*" When reeling off their varied caseloads, juniors also said: "*I've looked at a lot of PTAB IPRs* [that's intellectual property matters going to the Patent Trial and Appeal Board] *and I've had experience drafting construction briefings, developing initial positions, preparing experts for deposition and managing document reviews.*"

On the prosecution side, insiders said: "*I've had a lot of client contact. I've conducted examiner interviews, written patent applications and I've done some portfolio analysis as well.*" Another added: "*Some of my PTAB matters had hearings so I attended those and got to second chair, which was a great experience.*" Finally, juniors told us: "*When working on copyright and trademark issues I've mainly done pre-infringement analysis – telling the client what the legal landscape is and whether they'll have any issues going forward.*"

"*Sometimes the workload can be quite heavy, but if you have too much on your plate the firm is good at reallocating work or getting the help you need to keep your life in balance.*" Juniors agreed: "*People who are much more senior than you take your ideas seriously, which is really gratifying as a young attorney.*" When we asked associates about their responsibility levels they said: "*As a junior you're able to strike the balance between supervision and being allowed to lead. For example, when I was working on depositions I prepared the outline and chose which documents to review with the witness and then got to lead an actual preparation session.*"

Training & Development
Associates all head to DC for a week of orientation that includes a "*patent prosecution boot camp.*" When it comes to training they said: "*I think they do a really good job of marking things out instead of just talking at you.*" They added: "*The firm also pays for you to do extra CLEs if you want to seek them out in a particular area.*" One thing that stood out for all the associates we spoke to was the legal writing program, which continues throughout the year

Recent work highlights

- Obtained an injunction for sports company Under Armour against a Chinese Company called 'Uncle Martian', which had copied their logo and designs in a high-profile fashion show.
- Firm client FedEx was accused of patent infringement on two counts, and Finnegan successfully filed an inter partes reexamination on one patent and an inter partes review on the other at the US Patent and Trademark Office.
- Working with BrainCo, a company specializing in Brain Machine Interface (BMI) wearables, to develop its intellectual property strategy. Some of this technology will allow users to directly interact with devices using only brain signals.
- The District Court in Delaware ruled in favor of Finnegan client Forest Laboratories in a litigation against defendant Mylan involving Savella, which is a medicine used to treat fibromyalgia.

and "*dives deep into grammar and writing style to make sure everybody's up to speed.*" Additionally, we heard that there's ongoing training throughout the program: "*Pretty much every week there's some kind of prosecution or litigation training. Typically there's a different theme every month.*"

"*They're always looking to improve.*"

Managing partner Mark Sweet highlighted the firm's longer-term training investment: "*Our LEAP program (Learn, Enrich, Achieve, Progress) allows associates to gain great experience as they move up the ladder. The training and focus changes over time and includes business development training and coaching, helping our attorneys to maintain and establish client relations.*"

"*One thing I think the firm does really well is ask for feedback on training; they're always looking to improve,*" we heard from an associate. "*We also have an associate advisory committee, where a couple of people from each practice group meet with management once a month and go over anonymous feedback.*" Associates have reviews every six months during their first two years: "*There's a mentor partner who collects reviews from everyone you've worked with and they sit you down and tell you how you can improve based on that feedback.*"

Get Hired

"*We're looking for someone who wants to grow with the firm – it's less up and out than others.*" Learn how to get in from associates and the heads of recruitment on chambers-associate.com

See firm profile on p.635

The Inside View

Diversity	Partners (%)	Associates (%)
Women	28	38
White	85	68
Black/African American	3	6
Hispanic/Latin American	1	3
Asian	10	22
Mixed/Other	1	1
LGBT	2	2

Culture

A sense of innovation and never standing still was palpable in most of our interviews. "*It's nice to work with people who are shaping the legal landscape,*" one interviewee articulated. Associates found the working culture at Finnegan to be undoubtedly collaborative. Recruitment manager Laurie Taylor posits that this "*stems back to our original partners' philosophy of having firm clients rather than individual clients.*" And juniors "*really appreciate this. It means that you have the resources of the whole firm and you get to work as part of a team with different partners.*"

"We get bagels every Wednesday."

Although work at this level will inevitably involve some pressure, "*it's not a stressful environment to work in, and everyone's respectful and easy to talk to,*" thought associates, who were upbeat about the work-life balance. They added: "*I think partners understand that we're people and not cogs in machines, and we're more productive if there's a social atmosphere.*" They do indeed – over to Mark Sweet: "*We want great performers of course, but we also want friendly and personable people who you could go and enjoy an adult beverage with.*"

And finding an adult beverage is not hard: "*There are a lot of events here: there's an all-attorney reception every month, happy hours, and we get bagels every Wednesday in my office. I'd say we're pretty social for an engineering firm!*" There's also an annual retreat for attorneys: this year's was on the coast just off Maryland: "*There were a lot of social and group-building activities, and we also went over the health of the firm and strategy with managing partners.*"

Offices

"*It definitely feels like there's a one-firm culture here,*" associates told us. "*I don't think people in Palo Alto feel isolated; there aren't any standalone offices as such.*" Associates had also been in touch with the firm's international bases: "*On the prosecution side I work a lot with the London office so that we can draft applications for prosecution in Europe and the US simultaneously.*"

Those in the firm's satellite offices said that they were "*very close knit: maybe more so than in DC just because there are fewer attorneys.*" Juniors in DC told us: "*They've just remodeled the office here and there are a lot more collaboration spaces now. All associates get a window office and there's a really nice cafeteria as well.*" Finally, we heard: "*The facilities have been great in all the offices I've been to; anything I need the firm provides.*"

Diversity

"The firm has done a really good job of hiring female attorneys with engineering backgrounds."

The firm's diversity initiatives were mentioned as a draw when applying: "*I could tell that it was committed to diversity, which I really liked.*" Others said: "*I think the firm has done a really good job of hiring female attorneys with engineering backgrounds.*" Other juniors added: "*We have a women's forum that organizes various events and panels, and I really like that the firm recognizes that women have unique issues in the workplace. It's nice to have that support system.*" Finally, associates who had been involved in hiring told us: "*The firm really makes an effort to recruit from a diverse pool of candidates.*" The firm has had a diversity scholarship in place since 2003. Chief recruitment & professional development officer Tim Henderson goes into more detail on diversity and training online.

Pro Bono

"*As a firm we're devoted to pro bono,*" associates said. Juniors are allowed to count 100 hours toward their billable target, although some said that in special circumstances exceptions have been made. We heard about a wide range of pro bono work, from children's law and immigration to work with veteran appeals, which is something the firm specializes in. "*The firm was really great with helping me get to DC for my pro bono case,*" one East Coast associate told us. "*I've never felt unprepared when it comes to pro bono. The firm makes a real effort to train you and keep you ahead in terms of legal knowledge so you're ready for things like attending criminal court.*"

Pro bono hours
- For all US attorneys: 11,271.2
- Average per US attorney: undisclosed

Hours & Compensation

"*I usually arrive at 8.30am,*" was common from the associates we spoke to, and most claimed leaving at a time that gave them an actual evening. Although some juniors said: "*There's more of a roller coaster aspect to hours when*

See firm profile on p.635

you're on litigation, but you have a bit more leeway on prosecution so it balances out." There's a bonus system in place for every 100 hours hit after 2,000: *"If you end up in the middle of one bracket they roll over so that they count the next year."* Most agreed: *"I find it pretty easy to hit the 2,200 area without needing to take too much work home, and I can still have a personal life."*

"What I tell people is cast a wide net. Talk to people, talk to other lawyers at other firms, to friends, friends of friends and your professors. There's a whole host of resources available to law students to help them make a decision. If diversity is your issue, ask to speak to diverse attorneys. If you're hoping to start a family, talk to lawyers with kids.
Take your time. Identify what's important to you. Firms should be more than happy to do it; we're certainly more than happy to do it. I never begrudge a person taking time – it's a big decision, take your time, put in a plan."

– Hughes Hubbard hiring partner
George Tsougarakis

The Inside View

See firm profile on p.635

Fish & Richardson PC

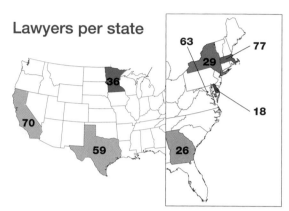

Lawyers per state

63 77
29
36
18
70
59 26

Largest US office: Boston
US offices: 11
International offices: 1
First-year salary: $180,000
Billable hours: 1,900 required
Summers 2018: 25 (10 1Ls, 15 2Ls)
Revenue 2017: $416.8 million (+2.2%)
Partners made in 2018: 21
Famous for: top-notch IP work; increasing presence at the International Trade Commission

This Boston-headquartered specialist is a big fish in the world of intellectual property law.

"THE thing that makes us distinct is that we're a pure IP firm – we've been around since the Wright brothers patented the airplane!" Yes, Fish associates were quick to tell us about their firm's rich heritage (which dates back to 1878) and scope of expertise tied to all things IP: *"If you want high-stakes litigation and cutting-edge patent law, landing a spot here will be your dream job."* Fish is among only five firms to pick up a top nationwide *Chambers USA* ranking for IP; it's also highly regarded for handling disputes before the International Trade Commission. Peter Devlin, Fish's president, tells us: *"We are a leader in that field, which has been growing in importance as the global economy changes and in light of increased competition from China."* Life at Fish isn't just about litigation though, as Devlin explains: *"One of the hallmarks of our firm is its balance between litigation and patent and trademark prosecution – that balance is absolutely crucial to our success."*

With such a hefty reputation to maintain, Fish is looking for candidates with a superior level of expertise to fill its 11 domestic bases. A look at Fish's 'current legal openings' webpage will give you a clear indication of what this firm is after: 'strong backgrounds in computer science,' 'advanced chemistry degrees,' and 'talented engineers' are the backbone of Fish's attorney base. *"Name a scientific*

background and we have it," sources declared, with many boasting PhDs in everything from physics to bio-chemical engineering. With a wealth of expertise to draw upon, Fish is able to service clients across a range of sectors, including aerospace & defense, financial services, digital health, energy, life sciences and transportation.

Strategy & Future

"We have really focused on developing our commercial litigation practice this year," firm president Peter Devlin tell us, *"but in areas that mesh well with our ability to solve technical issues – product liability and mass tort cases, for example."* Devlin also wants to continue to grow the firm's pharma litigation capabilities: *"Ten years ago we didn't have a pharma lit practice and now we have one that's among the best in the country – we are very proud of that. We want it to balance the tech side of the work that we do, so there's more of a 50:50 split between the two."* Fish will also be casting its net further in the future: *"I see us growing our business from other countries. China is a key target for us, and we're looking to grow our client base there."*

Offices

Associates were confident that each of the firm's offices could offer newcomers a good spread of work, but also highlighted their regional specialties. *"The pharmaceutical and bio group is mostly done out of the Delaware office because that's where most of ANDA (Abbreviated New Drug Application) is handled,"* a Boston-based junior pointed out. *"Boston is more focused on software and*

On chambers-associate.com...

● Get hired
● Interview with president and CEO Peter Devlin

See firm profile on p.636

The Inside View

Rankings in *Chambers USA*

Intellectual Property	International Trade

For detail on ranking tiers and ranking locations, visit
www.chambersandpartners.com

Recent work highlights

- Defended Microsoft after Parallel Networks filed a lawsuit alleging that the tech giant had infringed two of its patents covering the creation and management of custom websites
- Represented medical device company Smith & Nephew during litigation against a competitor involving a patent for 'orthopedic suture anchors,' which are implants used to reattach soft tissue to bone
- Secured two trial wins at the International Trade Commission for client Nautilus Hyosung – the largest provider of ATMs in the US – after competitor Diebold alleged patent infringement and requested an exclusion order to bar Nautilus Hyosung products from being imported into the US
- Registered Seattle-based outfitter Filson's iconic 'peanut-shaped' tab design after proving that it had acquired enough distinctiveness to be recognized as a protectable trade dress

mechanical engineering, but still has a big life sciences practice too." Down south, the firm's Houston office lends itself naturally to the energy sector, while the San Diego base offers *"an even split between life sciences and electrical engineering work."*

Boston serves as the firm's HQ and offers associates their own *"fully decked out"* offices from the get-go. *"The entire office is made of big glass windows, which overlook the city on the one side and the ocean on the other,"* associates beamed. However, competition for the best office is heating up, as sources in the *"hi-tech and electrical-focused"* DC office revealed: *"We moved into a brand new building in spring 2018 in the redeveloped 'Wharf' area, which is right on the waterfront – there's going to be a water taxi service available!"* Boston and DC housed the majority of juniors on our list, while a further eight bases (including San Diego, Atlanta, New York and Houston) each took in a few as well.

Culture

Now you might think that large groups of people with multiple scientific degrees working side by side would make for a more 'geeky' working environment – and you'd be absolutely right! *"We definitely are a little bit nerdy,"* one source confessed, *"but in a good way! We have the social skills to be outgoing and fun to hang out with – although our conversations sometimes tend to run towards technology, video games and science."*

"Name a scientific background and we have it."

Still, for those craving a rowdy, happy-hour-every-night kind of firm, Fish probably isn't the one for you – we were told that the average junior associate is a tad older than those at other firms, particularly on the patent prosecution side where *"the focus is on hiring PhDs; they're often in their mid-thirties and have families, so they tend to come to work and then just head home afterward."* Juniors also drew attention to *"the fact that we're all individually very competent but still team-oriented. We need to be collaborative as we often have to pick up the phone to ask one another about certain types of tech or a particular field of science."*

The Work

New starters join either patent litigation or prosecution, then later divide into smaller subgroups based on their interests. The vast majority of associates – 32 of the 36 second and third-year juniors on our list – were working in the patent litigation group.

Sources felt that a 'free-market' description of Fish's work assignment process was *"accurate: there's no centralized process, but the group leaders do receive a list of every associate's hours each month, so they know who's busy and who's got some room in their schedules."* It's therefore a case of *"going out and finding work, by individually interacting with the partners you want to develop relationships with: people tend to gravitate naturally toward the areas they are familiar with but you aren't pushed to go anywhere. The best part of the job is learning about new science and technology."*

"China is a key target for us."

Associates quickly put their degrees to good use: *"I have used my physics degree in pretty much all of my cases,"* one junior told us, with others explaining how they'd use their expertise on matters involving *"aerodynamic golf balls, as well as hearing aids and medical devices."* Sources explained that on a *"typical case involving multiple patents, you'll probably take on responsibility for a couple of them. That involves going through the file history to identify anything that may affect the claim; supervising a 'tech specialist' [a science expert with no law degree]; and launching into the claims construction process, by developing and drafting an argument."*

Providing juniors with portions of the overall case to manage is all part of the firm's *"divide and conquer strat-*

See firm profile on p.636

Diversity	Partners (%)	Associates (%)
Women	20.3	33.3
White	86.8	69.1
Black/African American	0.5	5.6
Hispanic/Latin American	1.6	1.9
Asian	8.8	18.5
Mixed/Other	2.2	4.9
LGBT	1.6	4.9

egy," which ensures that *"we utilize the maximum amount of our technical knowledge and get exposure to a broad range of tasks."* Inter partes review (IPR) cases were flagged as a particular highlight: *"IPRs give people a way of challenging a patent in an administrative setting instead of a court proceeding. They tend to be smaller in magnitude and provide great opportunities for juniors to take on substantive work early on – I was preparing depositions within a month of starting here."*

Pro Bono

Juniors can officially put up to 200 hours of pro bono work towards their billable hours target, but can apply for more to count in special circumstances. Our sources were grateful for the opportunity, *"as we know so much about patent law – it's nice to have an alternative stream of work to pursue."* Some juniors had taken on IP-related cases in the trademark space, but we heard of many others connected to civil rights, bankruptcy, asylum and sexual discrimination matters. Pro bono principals are on hand to assign work in each office, and most locations are *"partnered up with referral agencies that send work through – my office has links to immigration and LGBT-focused ones."*

Pro bono hours
- For all US attorneys: 20,662
- Average per US attorney: 56

Diversity

Sources explained that Fish has to contend with the lack of diversity within both scientific academia and the legal industry. *"There aren't a lot of female engineers across the US, for example,"* one junior highlighted, before pointing to the firm's gender statistics: women make up 33.3% of the associate ranks and 20.3% of the partnership. The firm's ENPOWER women's initiative was established to drive those numbers up. It offers forums and mentoring circles within the firm's offices, and our female interviewees emphasized the presence of *"strong women attorneys who have been great mentors."* Meanwhile Fish's 1L Diver-

sity Fellowship Program aims to boost ethnic diversity by offering each fellow a paid summer associate position, plus mentoring opportunities and a scholarship of up to $10,000. In addition, the firm has five active affinity groups.

Training & Development

All new starters complete a program of *"intensive training"* when they start, which is called 'Fish-FYI' and runs for *"the first few months while you're getting ramped up on matters."* After that, the firm does offer periodic three-day workshops on topics such as *"conducting depositions,"* which are run by external groups: *"They normally occur every two to three months but are only offered to around ten to 15 associates, and you apply to attend."* We also heard about a 'patent boot camp,' which is held over two and a half days and covers the likes of patent application drafting and inventor interviews for the firm's junior patent prosecutors. These training programs are supplemented by weekly webinars presented by Fish's partners on more *"narrow issues such as how to write a summary judgment brief or draft a discovery response. They're presented by stellar attorneys so their advice is very valuable, but it feels more like pointers than formal training,"* some sources felt.

Hours & Compensation

Litigators agreed that the firm's billing requirement of 1,900 hours is achievable, though in the past we've heard that it can be a bit more of a challenge for patent prosecutors. *"1,900 is the true minimum,"* juniors emphasized. *"It's totally acceptable to be at 1,901 hours, and there's no unspoken target of 1,950 or 2,000 hours."* In the vast majority of cases, bonuses kick in at 1,900 and rise in increments depending on hours billed and other factors like the feedback received during reviews and commitment to 'firm-building' activities like business development. At 2,100 hours associates can expect to receive a Cravath-level bonus. Overall, juniors felt that there *"needs to be a lot more transparency on how bonuses are earned."*

An average day in the office ran from 9am to 6:30pm/7pm, but juniors were eager to tell us how flexible Fish is on working from home: *"I usually do that once or twice a week,"* one Bostonian revealed, *"and so do a lot of people – there's a seamless transition between work and home, and the firm is respectful of everyone's families and home life."* While litigation can involve *"an ebb and flow in caseload,"* sources were pleased to tell us that they haven't *"stayed late in the office once this year."* Some juniors did log back on for a few hours when they got home though.

See firm profile on p.636

Fitzpatrick, Cella, Harper & Scinto

Lawyers per state

Largest US office: New York
US offices: 3
International offices: 0
First-year salary: $180,000
Billable hours: 2,160 target
Summers 2018: 9 2Ls
Revenue 2017: not disclosed
Partners made in 2018: 2
Famous for: IP prowess

For all problems IP, there's no pick like Fitzpatrick.

THE firm's minimalist motto 'We Are IP' leaves no one pondering what it is that this brainy bunch do. And just in case it still wasn't obvious enough, *Chambers USA* gives the firm impressive marks for its IP work both in New York and nationwide. Unsurprisingly, that particular focus tends to attract a particular kind of person: *"Most people here are engineers or scientists of some kind so we all tend to be a bit nerdy!"* sources admitted. This went down a treat as it meant associates *"instantly had something in common."*

Although Fitzpatrick's expertise focuses on intellectual property, within that sphere the firm spans every industry you could possibly patent. We're talking pharmaceutical, electronics, life sciences, energy, telecommunications and automotive, just to name a few. *"The firm made a name for itself in doing branded companies versus generic companies litigation, though we have branched out a bit now. We certainly still do a lot in that field, but we've diversified a bit."* Famously, Fitzpatrick was involved in the first ever Hatch-Waxman case for Merck & Co back in the 80s, and the area remains a strength for the firm. That said, the firm's client roster has certainly expanded on from pharma companies, and now includes big names such as Canon, American Express, Calvin Klein and IBM.

The Work

Newbies almost exclusively begin in the Big Apple, while DC traditionally takes one or two a year. New York has more of a focus on patent litigation, and DC patent prosecution, though litigators have occasionally been found in DC and vice versa. Litigators have assigning partners and a weekly survey to *"let the partners know what you're working on, if you need more work, and how much time you think you'll have available."* However, many also found they could get work more informally *"from partners you've already worked with."* Patent prosecutors have a docket for work distribution and are supervised by one partner.

"As a junior, you're not just relegated to menial tasks."

Litigators still do a hefty amount of work on Hatch-Waxman lawsuits for pharma companies (representing the branded side), though the range of clients has expanded to include biomedical device companies and electronics companies like Phillips and Canon. Tasks have included *"drafting discovery requests and responses, drafting briefs and letters to opposing counsel, legal research, and of course doc review which is always fun..."* Sources also had experience writing expert reports and deposition outlines. *"As a junior, you're not just relegated to menial tasks. You'll have to do some, but generally they let you be very involved."* Recently, there's also been an uptick in due diligence work: *"If, say, a big company is looking to acquire a smaller company, we'll do the due diligence on the IP side and give our opinion on the strength of the portfolio before the purchase."* The due diligence teams are usually small, so client contact is pretty common.

On chambers-associate.com...

- Get hired at Fitzpatrick
- Interview with partner Mike Sandonato

The Inside View

See firm profile on p.637

Rankings in *Chambers USA*

Intellectual Property

For detail on ranking tiers and ranking locations, visit
www.chambersandpartners.com

On the prosecution side, juniors saw a higher portion of mechanical and electronics clients – *"there's been work regarding fire protection systems, sprinkler systems, printers and fixing devices for printers."* Sources mentioned that *"we get a lot of applications that have been filed in foreign countries, so either we file them in the US Patent and Trademark Office, or work with clients to draft the applications so they originate in the USPTO."* Tasks involve everything from drafting the application *"all the way to issuance and enforcement against competitors."* Some also tackled inter partes review (IPR), which operates under faster timeframes than traditional litigation. Juniors here felt their responsibility was *"relatively high for someone at my experience level."*

On chambers-associate.com...

"Be prepared to work hard, and be prepared to get comfortable working outside of your comfort zone" – partner Mike Sandonato. Go online to learn from juniors and management about how to get hired.

Training & Development

"For new first years they do a two-week boot camp with a bunch of trainings," followed by periodic training on various things like motion practice, collecting evidence and writing. Juniors found the annual training program through NITA (the National Institute of Trial Advocacy) to be *"very helpful"* as it tends to go through *"all aspects of a trial, so you get to practice getting facts from witnesses, taking depositions, writing motions – the whole gamut."* Other than that, juniors found *"hands-down learning, hitting the ground and just doing it"* to be an effective way to learn. Annual reviews provide formal feedback, usually around November time. These also *"give you a chance to raise any concerns you have about your own development."*

Culture

"It's very close-knit," said juniors about the culture. *"Since it's a smaller firm and everyone has similar backgrounds, there's a lot more of a sense of community."* Some initially presumed that *"a bunch of people with scientific backgrounds who are also lawyers wouldn't be a great mix,"* but then found that *"the people here are really great. Everyone is friendly and you can have a conversation about normal topics with people, not just limited to work."* Every year as-

Recent work highlights

- Secured a victory for Canon in a trial against Color Imaging, a toner company, and General Plastic Industrial, a plastic manufacturer, stating that the two defendants willingly infringed a Canon patent on toner bottle technology
- Represented Novartis before the PTAB, successfully arguing for the dismissal of Par Pharmaceutical's petition for the initiation of an IPR to challenge Novartis's patent

sociates mention the *"nerdy vibe,"* but in a way that makes colleagues endearing and interesting. This isn't exclusive to Fitzpatrick; sociable nerds seem to find their natural habitat in patent law.

> *"You can have a conversation about normal topics with people, not just limited to work."*

The firm goes to some effort to give its lawyers a break from the patents. There's the Fitzpatrick Olympics (*"we break into teams and do things like rock climbing, basketball, bowling..."*), and we also heard of attorneys *"going to see Jerry Seinfeld doing standup, a private tour of the Guggenheim, and cooking classes."* The bulk of events happen in the summer, but *"associates have impromptu happy hours and do stuff on the weekends sometimes."*

Diversity

"When you look at the firm or the website, it's not the most diverse firm in New York, but every year there are more and more women and minorities in the summer classes." The firm is aware that *"engineering and science tend to be more male-dominated,"* so *"they're certainly making an effort there."* For instance, one source highlighted that *"the last first-year class was all women, and one guy."* Fitzpatrick has an active diversity committee, and a Women's Initiative Program.

Hours & Compensation

The firm doesn't set a hard target for hours, though it is *"encouraged to do around 180 a month."* Juniors noted that *"there will be months when you're under and it's not like you'll get in trouble for that."* Associates appreciated a certain flexibility over day-to-day hours, though most added they'll *"stay as long as it takes to get the work done."* That said, *"there's no one patrolling the halls to see if you're in at 9am."* When we asked our sources about their hours, most mentioned getting in at 9am and leaving at a time that allows them to see the family and take the dog out – between 6 and 7, unless there's a trial coming to a head. *"During the week it's obviously more difficult, but for the most part, on weekends I have time to go out and do my own thing."*

See firm profile on p.637

The Inside View

Diversity	Partners (%)	Associates (%)
Women	14	47
White	92	69
Black/African American	0	0
Hispanic/Latin American	0	2
Asian	6	22
Mixed/Other	2	7
LGBT	1	1

"There's no one patrolling the halls to see if you're in at 9am."

After last year's salary uncertainty, this year associates were pleased to report Fitzpatrick had matched the market raise. Bonuses were still a source of some uncertainty: *"They say bonuses are discretionary, but it's not the most transparent process."* Some speculated that factors such as hours, quality of work, and how the business is doing might affect an attorney's bonus. Sources added: *"A few years ago they started the initiative of combat pay – if you've done substantially more hours than others, you'll be rewarded, but we're still not entirely sure how that works."* The firm tells us that everybody gets a discretionary bonus, even if they don't hit the hours target.

Pro Bono

Every pro bono hour counts toward billables, though *"it is up to the individual attorney as to how committed they want to be to pro bono."* The firm send out a plethora of opportunities, but *"also allows the associates to branch out and find their own opportunities if they want."* Fitzpatrick partners with organizations such as the Legal Aid Society, and Catholic Charities in DC. Matters have included immigration and asylum cases, housing matters, disability matters, and domestic abuse cases, with some IP and copyright-related matters being on offer too.

Pro bono hours
- For all US attorneys: 2,219
- Average per US attorney: 19.2

Offices

Sandwiched between MoMA and Radio City Music Hall, the firm's midtown location has everything on its doorstep and is *"easy to get to from anywhere."* Many praised the *"fully stocked fridges with different kinds of free soda,"* as well as the *"private outdoor terrace where we can have lunch, and where the happy hours are held."* The DC office is also in a well-connected, central location – *"you can get to it without having to drive."* It's near *"a wealth of restaurants, shops and historical sites."* The office itself has been recently renovated, which associates felt has *"really spruced up the place."*

"Private outdoor terrace where we can have lunch, and where the happy hours are held."

Strategy & Future

Many felt management were *"not really forthcoming"* about the firm's strategy for the future. Some speculated that *"competition is up, as now every firm has a patent litigation practice, whereas before it was a more niche practice."* That said, *"most people here are still comfortable."* Every source we spoke to admitted that *"management could be slightly more transparent."*

Partner Mike Sandonato tells us: *"As always, we're looking to increase the pool of our talent by hiring excellent entry level candidates as well as lateral candidates,"* but in terms of other investment, *"we have no immediate plans to open a new office – we're very happy with the national footprint that we have now."* He estimates that the split between the firm's main practices is *"about 75-80% litigation and about 20-25% patent prosecution."* Looking ahead, Sandonato adds that *"we have a large number of trials coming up, and we're excited about the future of both our life sciences and technology practice areas."*

On chambers-associate.com...

"By choosing patent litigation or prosecution you're choosing an intellectually stimulating profession that will keep you challenged throughout your entire career." Read our full interview with Mike Sandonato online.

See firm profile on p.637

Foley & Lardner LLP

Lawyers per state

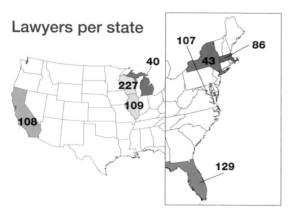

107
86
40
43
227
109
108
129

Largest US office: Milwaukee
US offices: 21
International offices: 3
First-year salary: $140,000-$180,000
Billable hours: 1,900 required
Summers 2018: 81 (21 1Ls, 60 2Ls)
Revenue 2017: $686.2 million (+2.3%); $830 million post-merger
Partners made in 2018: 17
Famous for: friendly, down-to-earth atmosphere and being Wisconsin's oldest and largest firm

This Milwaukee-born firm proves it's the cream of the crop in the Dairy State and beyond.

TO celebrate its 175th birthday, Foley went wild in typical law-firm style... and merged with Texan firm Gardere Wynne Sewell. The two firms had a history of working together, and the move opens up Foley's access to Texas, as well as a base in Mexico, bringing a stream of Latin American opportunities. The firm is a leader in its native Wisconsin, but now has 21 offices across the US and three international bases. Its Badger State practice picks up the most acclaim in *Chambers USA*; its corporate, IP, litigation, real estate and banking & finance practices all get top marks. Foley also gets significant mentions in Massachusetts, Illinois and DC for practice areas including healthcare, patent prosecution and insurance. Associates told us: "*I wanted to be at a large firm with lots of resources and good training, and when I summered here the people made it a no-brainer.*"

The Work

Associates are split between three main practice areas: litigation, intellectual property and business law. At the time of our research the majority of the group were pretty evenly split between litigation and business law (transactional), but the IP practice housed a fair num-

ber too. Most interviewees told us that work assignment was mostly done on a free-market basis, although some in transactional groups had help from a coordinator to manage work flow. "*When I first started I was borderline harassing people asking for projects,*" recounted one source. "*But now I don't think I've had to ask for work for two years.*"

Those in litigation felt that "*cases are very leanly staffed. Usually it's just me, a mid-level associate and a partner, and often it's just me and a partner so you get a lot of real work very quickly.*" We heard about a wide variety of work including insurance litigation, trade secrets cases and administrative appeals. Our sources also described work with pharmaceutical companies relating to Medicare and Medicaid as well as the False Claims Act. Juniors went on: "*Often I'll be managing the baseline things such as drafting motions, attending hearings and management conferences and coordinating with local counsel.*" Others said: "*There have been a handful of cases where I've worked under a more senior associate writing discrete motions and editing briefs; mostly it's legal writing and research. You're not stuck doing document review for 30 hours a week.*"

> "*You're not stuck doing document review for 30 hours a week.*"

One business lawyer told us: "*Here in Milwaukee the biggest thing our group is known for is Midwest manufacturers and public companies. If you named a large company I would be surprised if we didn't represent them in some capacity.*" Associates told us: "*I've been pleasantly surprised*

On chambers-associate.com...

- Get hired
- Interview with CEO Jay Rothman
- Interview with director of legal recruiting Rebecca Bradley and hiring partner Bob Scher

See firm profile on p.638

Rankings in *Chambers USA*

Banking & Finance	IT & Outsourcing
Bankruptcy/Restructuring	Labor & Employment
Corporate/M&A	Leisure & Hospitality
Environment	Litigation
Franchising	Natural Resources
Healthcare	Projects
Insurance	Real Estate
Intellectual Property	Sports Law

For detail on ranking tiers and ranking locations, visit
www.chambersandpartners.com

Recent work highlights

- Foley advised Pentair, a multinational industrial company, on the $3.15 billion sale of its Valves & Control business to Emerson Electric
- The intellectual property team at Foley won on a motion on behalf of Rockwell Automation in a multi-patent litigation concerning motion control technology for a Fortune 500 company, in a matter worth $10 million
- Foley continues to counsel Harley-Davidson on a variety of corporate and finance matters. The firm recently completed an asset-backed securitization, and has been working on a major renovation of the company's corporate headquarters in Milwaukee
- Represented Cummins in a truck transmission joint venture with Eaton Corp., in a deal worth $1.24 billion

at the level of autonomy I've had. On a couple of the smaller deals I got to take the first crack at a purchase agreement and felt very lucky to have those opportunities." There's work on both the buyer and lender side, and on the latter juniors can expect to "*draft ancillary documents, officer certificates, resolutions and scheduling documents.*" Others told us: "*40% of my work is based around securitizations, and they're pretty easy because the deals are often similar. The rest of my work is mostly managing and making sure everything is signed off on time, so in that sense it's often more management than legal skills.*" They added: "*I feel like Foley gives a good amount of responsibility. I get the feeling that my peers at other firms are more micromanaged than I am.*"

The IP department is split into IP litigators, IP transactional and patent prosecutors. Prosecutors are split into chemical, biotech & pharma, mechanical & electromechanical technology, or electronics. We heard: "*There's a lot of emphasis on IP here. A lot of the attorneys I work for are in Detroit, Chicago and Milwaukee so there's a bit of flexibility.*" Litigators told us: "*Mostly you'll be doing onboarding, document reviews, complaint drafting and a bit of work involving interference and PTO work.*" On the prosecution side, associates told us: "*From a tech perspective we have everything from bathroom fixtures to automotive clients, alternative energy and defense contractors. We also have relationships with universities and inventors looking for attorneys to partner up with.*" They continued: "*In terms of work you'll be doing preparation and prosecution applications, due diligence and patentability agreements. It's a real mix.*" Some IP litigation cases can get gloriously technical, such as one this year on behalf of Rockwell Automation regarding motion-control technology.

Culture

Most interviewees praised the firm's inherently Midwestern culture, saying: "*It doesn't feel as buttoned up here as you would expect a law firm to be.*" On that subject, something interviewees were also keen to flag was the firm's "*casual dress code. It's nice not to have to wear a*

suit every day." Others added: "*People here are very down to earth. When I first walked in here it didn't feel stiff or sterile, and I felt like people enjoy each other's company.*" Some, however, told us: "*Because of the firm's Midwestern values it can feel a little more conservative in terms of running a business, which can be frustrating at times.*" They reasoned, however: "*I think in general people are willing to tolerate those things because we know the financials of the firm are focused on its long-term health so we don't have to worry about job stability.*"

"When I first walked in here it didn't feel stiff or sterile."

Plenty of interviewees mentioned the all-attorney retreat that takes place every other year. "*It had a really positive vibe. They put a lot of resources into doing it and it really showed. There was some programming but outside of that it was a lot of fun; it didn't feel like a work event.*" Back at the office associates told us: "*We have lunches every Friday which are well attended, as well as a softball league and happy hours.*"

Training & Development

Associates all get a short orientation period where they're taught about the technical aspects of office life. Following this there is more specific training on a regular basis, including CLEs which are often included in investment hours and also feature a free lunch, according to interviewees.

"*Often it's hard to get immediate feedback on your own work,*" sources told us. "*But there's a substantive performance review every six months which is very helpful.*" Others added: "*The firm tries to push the mentor thing but I'm not how sure how much of that is lip service as I haven't seen mine much.*" If you ask for feedback you'll get

See firm profile on p.638

Diversity	Partners (%)	Associates (%)
Women	22.4	43.2
White	90	78.4
Black/African American	1.7	3.7
Hispanic/Latin American	3.2	5.7
Asian	4.2	9.3
Mixed/Other	0	2.2
LGBT	1	5.1

it, most agreed, and they all appreciated the transparency of "*an associate committee which gives feedback upward.*"

Offices

The firm has 21 offices in the US, as well as bases in Brussels, Mexico City and Tokyo. Most associates are based in Milwaukee, Boston, Chicago and DC. In Milwaukee juniors told us: "*We're in a US bank building and it's the tallest in the city. There's a new gym in the basement and they've made significant improvements on the food court in the past two years.*" Others said: "*They're not as sleek as DC or New York, but they're still perfectly nice.*" Some, meanwhile, were less enthused: "*The offices are severely outdated. They've been talking for years about getting a new layout and new furniture but it's looking like it won't be until 2021.*"

"I've been told it looks like a hotel here."

Those in Boston said: "*I've been told it looks like a hotel here. It has very warm, welcoming decor and it's in Back Bay near where the marathon finishes.*" DC, as previously mentioned, boasts the most modern offices and is decked out in glass and white interiors. Associates told us: "*We're told it's mandatory to work with other offices, which is definitely a good thing. The more people you work with the better a lawyer you become.*"

Diversity

"*I would say the success rate here hasn't been as high as we would like when it comes to diversity, but it's not for lack of effort,*" one junior told us. "*Management unveiled a Diversity and Inclusion plan a couple of months ago. It needs a bit of fleshing out to be meaningful but it's good that the message is there.*" Another added: "*The CEO Jay Rothman is enthusiastic about diversity, and partners are very vocal and are doing more in concrete ways.*" We heard about LGBT, African American and Hispanic-American affinity groups (the membership of the African-American group has doubled of late), as well as efforts to improve diversity in recruiting. Associates added: "*Based on my class and the two or three classes since there has been a*

better ratio of male to female and non-Caucasians, but in general it's still majority white males, especially in certain groups.*"

Pro Bono

The firm awards 100 hours of pro bono to go toward billables, and associates told us that most requests for extensions were approved. "*It's very rewarding to spend my professional time working on a case I feel personally invested in and get billable credit for it. I basically got to run a case by myself with only nominal supervision.*" A Business Law junior told us: "*I assumed I'd have no pro bono opportunities but I've hit around 100 hours both years. I've worked on a couple of nonprofit cases and the firm's been really supportive.*" Others added: "*There's more freedom to pick up the phone and interact on pro bono because there's no bills to worry about so there's less red tape.*" We also heard: "*Any time I've gotten into a jam, partners and senior associates are always willing to take the time to help me figure it out. I'm also starting to be able to delegate which is a new and exciting skill.*"

"It's very rewarding to spend my professional time working on a case I feel personally invested in."

Those on litigation told us that there were occasions where they ran up hours unexpectedly and struggled to get approval if they went significantly over their 100 hours: "*There could be a little more transparency when things get blown out of proportion on a case.*" Examples of pro bono work we heard about included asylum and discrimination cases, as well as those in IP working with inventors to get patents approved. "*There's an understanding that if you haven't done 20 hours a senior attorney will come and knock on your door and ask you if there's anything they can interest you in doing.*"

Pro bono hours
- For all US attorneys: 45,778.1
- Average per US attorney: 55

Hours & Compensation

Associates told us that the firm's billable requirement was raised from 1,850 to 1,900 in 2016 to coordinate with a salary increase. They added: "*There's also a 150-hour investment time requirement so your total commitment is at least 2,050. I try to bill eight hours a day but that only gets me to 2,000.*"

"There are times when something will come up at the eleventh hour."

See firm profile on p.638

The Inside View

Business law juniors on the transactional side told us: "*The hours can be unpredictable. There are times when something will come up at the eleventh hour and you'll have to stay well past midnight, but that's what we're paid to do.*" Meanwhile, on the finance side we heard: "*I feel like my schedule is more balanced than some of my peers. I enjoy having the regular 9am-6pm working day.*" Juniors in IP told us: "*There isn't a typical day. There's a lot of seesawing in terms of workload. If you're with someone on a deadline you'll be here until midnight but if things are slow there's no need for you to be in the office.*" While some said that it was fine to work from home, others told us. "*There are partners who want you to be there physically, it depends on the person.*" Finally, when asked about vacation interviewees told us: "*If you go away you definitely need to be available. You're expected to answer emails and know what's going on.*"

Strategy & Future

"*Every year CEO Jay Rothman holds a town hall meeting and gives an annual summary on things like earnings, budgets and projections, and answers questions.*" Associates added: "*When issues arise there's an associate committee, so you can speak to a representative and the committee will present it to management.*" Others said: "*The process can be a little slow and murky, but it doesn't lurch from one thing to another so even if change is slow you have stability.*" Finally, associates said: "*When things have been passed up it seems like it's received pretty well. I'd say they do a fairly good job of keeping things transparent.*" To read our full interview with CEO Jay Rothman, go to chambers-associate.com

Get Hired

"If I was talking to myself back then I'd say it's funny how little the rank matters when you're in the daily grind." More wisdom from associates who passed interview can be found online.

See firm profile on p.638

Fox Rothschild LLP

Lawyers per state

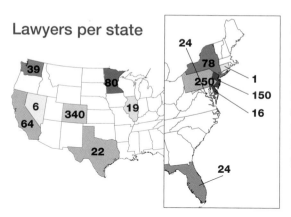

Largest US office: Philadelphia
US offices: 21
International offices: 0
First-year salary: $115,000-$160,000
Billable hours: 1,850 required (1,900 litigation)
Summers 2018: 33 (7 1Ls, 26 2Ls,)
Revenue 2017: $449 million (+7.9%)
Partners made in 2018: 17
Famous for: national presence; chutzpah

An *"entrepreneurial spirit"* permeates this full-service, Philly-born firm.

'HARD-working,' 'client-oriented,' 'commercial' – these words are emblazoned across law firm advertising the world over, and this branding homogeneity causes problems for students who just want to get to know the firms. But Fox Rothschild's marketing plumps for something more individual – 'chutzpah,' 'moxie,' 'grit' – and it tells you a lot about the firm. *"Fox was on my radar because of their marketing materials and their fresher look,"* an associate thought. *"I liked the fact they had full-body photos of their lawyers on their website rather than the usual mug shots. It reflected the fact that while Fox is obviously a serious place to work, the people here are less stern."* Our sources decided these first impressions had substance, agreeing there was a real *"entrepreneurial spirit,"* and explained that *"Fox doesn't just represent huge corporate clients – we are happy to take any business."* The firm caters mainly to the midmarket, and while it has a presence across the nation, associates mused that the firm is *"definitely more well known in Philly and the Northeast corridor than other parts of the country."* Philadelphia is the biggest office with around 100 lawyers, followed by Minneapolis (80 attorneys), New York (78) and Princeton (69). At the time of our research there were juniors based in 17 of the firm's 22 offices.

Sources were drawn to the variety of practice areas on offer at Fox – a hefty 67 according to the firm's website. The usual suspects such as litigation, corporate, real estate and labor & employment sit alongside more specialist areas such as drone law, zoning & land use, and cannabis law. The firm is recognized by *Chambers USA* for its work across four states, with rankings for areas including corporate M&A, litigation, healthcare and labor & employment. Fox also earns a top-tier nationwide ranking for gaming & licensing law – work done, unsurprisingly, chiefly out of the Atlantic City office.

Culture & Offices

Consistent with its entrepreneurial spirit, Fox is a place which *"appreciates creativity"* and where *"associates are never inhibited from making suggestions about the work. It's often two or three people on the team bouncing ideas off each other. The firm makes efforts to include everyone including paralegals and juniors."* All Fox associates are given an annual marketing budget of $500 on joining, which they are *"encouraged to use to build up a book of business from the beginning."* With the exception of the odd *"irrational partner,"* associates also emphasized that the firm is *"good at making sure associates and partners are in the trenches together,"* exemplifying some of that 'moxie' and 'grit' we were talking about earlier. Monthly associate meetings keep associates in the loop on any major changes afoot, which ensures *"that everybody knows the score – it helps us to understand the firm's expectations of us and how to meet those expectations."*

"Fox has grown by acquiring smaller firms."

Associates did however identify discernible differences between the offices and even a bit of tension. *"Fox has*

On chambers-associate.com...

- Interview with managing partner Mark Morris
- More on getting hired

See firm profile on p.639

The Inside View

Rankings in *Chambers USA*

Bankruptcy/Restructuring	Intellectual Property
Corporate/M&A	Labor & Employment
Environment	Litigation
Gaming & Licensing	Real Estate
Healthcare	

For detail on ranking tiers and ranking locations, visit
www.chambersandpartners.com

Recent work highlights

- Acted for Pennsylvania pharmaceutical manufacturer Lannett in a securities fraud case over an alleged conspiracy to fix generic drug prices
- Arranged for the buyout of a deceased business partner's interest in a national hotel management company with 30 hotels under contract
- Marketed the public offering of $2.5 million of shares for the Spokane-based Red Lion Hotels Corporation
- Defended DIRECTV and DirectSat in 16 cases across the US, worth $150 million, challenging the businesses' pay structure as joint employers

grown by acquiring smaller firms, some of which still have a core of 30 attorneys who are now under the leadership of Fox in Philly," sources explained. As such, those in some of the smaller outposts such as Atlantic City felt that their offices *"didn't have any of that big-firm mentality that can make things uncomfortable,"* and took issue with things being so *"Philly centralized: they are not familiar with the working habits and culture of other offices so sometimes the decisions made are not correct. Everything just trickles down."* However, the firm's executive committee is made up of managing partners from each of the firm's offices, who do have influence over any decisions being made.

The Work

At the time of our calls, the largest cohorts of juniors were in Philly, New York, Princeton, Atlantic City and Minneapolis, with others spread across Philadelphia's Chester, Bucks and Montgomery counties as well as Pittsburgh, Wilmington, Morristown, Washington DC, Dallas, Denver, West Palm Beach, San Francisco and LA. At the end of their summer with the firm, juniors rank their top three preferences for practice areas they'd like to join, and were happy to report that *"rarely does the firm not honor your top choice."* The corporate and litigation groups take on most juniors, followed by labor & employment. We heard that *"work assignment is meant to be run through the head of each office and allocated evenly,"* but that for most juniors the reality is that you *"receive work more informally from the people you naturally gravitate toward."*

The labor & employment team mainly sticks to management defense and draws in *"a good mix of national and regional clients"* such as Pennsylvania recruitment agency McGrath Systems and the Holland America Group cruise line. Associates start with *"piecemeal assignments, doing research for different cases without seeing a case from the beginning,"* but are able to advance to *"take ownership of cases"* and gain experience drafting discovery requests, answering complaints *"and doing any other grunt work behind the scenes."* One junior relished the *"divide and conquer"* approach in their group, involving *"regular scheduled collaborations and swapping of work between juniors and seniors."*

Over in litigation sources were happy to report that *"you're not doing doc review: you're practicing law."* One source boasted of *"handling all my own matters: I have unsupervised contact with the court and opposing council; I'm the primary contact for clients; and I am able to attend depositions and hearings outside the office. The cases I handle tend to be commercial, mid-level damages claims in the couple of hundreds of thousands range."* For those perhaps uncomfortable being *"thrown to the wolves"* like this, sources assured us that *"you have control over getting as much responsibility as you want."*

In the corporate team attorneys tackle a range of business transactions: operating agreements, licensing, purchases and sales, contract formations, corporate governance and securities deals. Partners each specialize in different areas and clients include technology, pharmaceutical and consumer services companies. We heard of one associate who *"recently assisted with a hospital merger, handling the research aspects, looking into the certificate of need, then drafting a memo."*

Training & Development

Training kicks off with an initial orientation in Philly that lasts for around three days and covers basic skills like billing, IT and general admin. Following this, transactional associates and litigators have their own practice-specific training program, and they can count up to 25 hours from their programs toward their billable total. The *"very structured"* litigation program continues for associates' first four years and covers areas such as *"working with experts and developing a litigation budget."* This is supplemented by weekend training on areas such as trials and depositions. *"They try to create a whole trial experience and bring in people off the street to be the jury,"* sources revealed.

"They try to create a whole trial experience."

See firm profile on p.639

Diversity	Partners (%)	Associates (%)
Women	28.5	50.6
White	92.8	83.8
Black/African American	1.2	3.7
Hispanic/Latin American	1.8	1.7
Asian	3	7.1
Mixed/Other	1.8	2.5
LGBT	0.4	3.3

As for less formal training, first and second-year associates can count 50 hours of time spent with their mentor or *"observing a more experienced attorney on another case"* toward their billing target. Sources believed this commitment to training is indicative of *"the firm's investment in you as an associate – they're not just grinding you to crank out hours."*

Juniors were confident about their future at the firm, highlighting that *"one of the firm's selling points is the higher percentage of associates making partner compared to at other AmLaw 100 firms."* One concluded: *"I do think that if you put in the time and effort you can make partner in eight to ten years."*

Hours & Compensation

"Most people come to Fox knowing they are paid below market because of the work-life balance on offer," juniors reasoned. Litigators have a billing requirement of 1,900 hours, while it's 1,850 for everyone else. Most found that hitting the target *"had never been an issue,"* consistently billing eight to ten hours a day anywhere between 8am and 8pm. However, we also heard reports of associates working closer to 12 hours a day, as well as the odd weekend. Some sources reflected that the quality of your work/life balance *"depends on the partner you are working with. There are some who want work done straight away on the weekend even though it could wait until the working week, which can be frustrating."*

Moreover, despite *"the leadership's reasoning that slightly lower billable rates justify lower salaries,"* the below-market pay and discrepancies between offices were the source of some dissatisfaction among associates. First-years in New York, LA, San Francisco and DC start on $160,000, while at the bottom end of the scale new starters in Denver and Las Vegas are paid $115,000. *"My sense is that Fox has lost a few good associates because of the salary issue,"* one source reflected. Associates did however praise the policy that gives associates 10% of any business they bring in over $10,000. One junior remarked: *"I've brought in a few clients already and I'm only a second-year."*

Diversity

Overall, 28.5% of partners are women and interviewees commented that *"the firm does a lot to unify women throughout the firm."* The Women's Initiative comprises three subcommittees including a leadership, connectivity and associate steering committee. The group's designated budget has been put to good use, seeing juniors sent off to attend the Pennsylvania Women's Conference – headlined by Michelle Obama in 2017 – and in other places used to sponsor fundraisers for local nonprofit women's charities. Sources were more muted in their review of ethnic diversity at the firm, reflecting that *"women versus men isn't a problem as much as ethnic diversity."*

Pro Bono

Associates can count up to 50 hours of pro bono toward their billable hours target. However, juniors were disappointed to report that there is *"not much excitement about or even acknowledgment of pro bono,"* adding that *"any work is done off your own bat – it would be nice to have a fixed system."* Interviewees acknowledged that *"some partners are more excited about it than others,"* but otherwise conceded that it's *"not on the firm's radar."* We also heard that the firm has recently appointed two partners to breathe life back into the pro bono committee; they will be working with partners in each office to implement a more formal structure and boost participation in pro bono.

Pro bono hours
- For all attorneys: 8,755
- Average per attorney: 9.5

This is reflected in the stats, as the average annual number of pro bono hours recorded per attorney at Fox comes to just under ten. Sources felt that this was slightly compensated by *"the emphasis placed on going to fundraisers on behalf of the firm,"* which sees juniors heading off to *"lots of different events,"* including a recent lunch with the Governor of Pennsylvania.

Strategy & Future

"First, we feel we are well poised to fill out some of the offices we have," says managing partner Mark Morris. *"After laying down some solid foundations, we are looking to make use of the infrastructure we have created. In offices such as Chicago, Dallas and Miami we want to grow beyond 20 to 30 lawyers to 70."* Morris adds: *"We have opened a new office in Seattle as a result of our merger with Riddell Williams, which has expanded our geographic footprint and resulted in some good cross-referrals for our clients."* To find out more about Fox's future, head to chambers-associate.com to read our full interview with Morris.

See firm profile on p.639

Freshfields Bruckhaus Deringer LLP

Lawyers per state

53
145

Largest US office: New York
US offices: 2
International offices: 25
First-year salary: $180,000
Billable hours: no requirement
Summers 2018: 16 (2 1Ls, 12 2Ls, 1 SEO)
Revenue 2017: $1.8 billion/£1.330 billion (+0.2%)
Partners made in 2018: 12
Famous for: top British firm; international reach

With an already flourishing global garden, Freshfields is now focusing on growing its US crops.

"THE atmosphere here is so energetic," juniors enthused, adding: "The global focus of the firm is on our US presence right now – the place is really growing." Freshfields' global nature has long been an attraction to associates all over the world, but right now a focus on US growth is where the excitement's at. The New York branch of this elite globetrotter opened its doors in 1977, followed by DC in 1998. Compared to the firm's long European history (it was founded 30 years before the Declaration of Independence), the US presence is still fairly fresh, so to speak. With that in mind, the firm achieves respectable recognition in *Chambers USA* for its international arbitration, commercial litigation, white-collar disputes, antitrust, corporate M&A and capital markets work.

> ### "Freshfields endeavors to be a global firm with united teams across different countries."

The 'magic circle' firm's international reach still remains "the big Freshfields draw" for many. US managing partner Peter Lyons tells us: "We don't have a dominant national culture: it's an international place. When you work here, you don't go a day without talking to somebody elsewhere around the world, whether that's a client or someone in another office. If you're a person who only feels comfortable

talking to other Americans, this is not the place for you." During the summer program, associates go on secondment to a foreign office for two weeks, which juniors felt was "reflective of how Freshfields endeavors to be a global firm with united teams across different countries."

The Work

New York juniors are stationed in capital markets, finance, corporate or dispute resolution, while DC juniors also have the option of joining the ACT (antitrust, competition and trade) team. Disputes takes the largest chunk of juniors, and covers international arbitration, investigations and civil litigation. M&A follows in numbers, then ACT, then capital markets and finance.

Assignment works differently in the two US offices: for DC juniors, the system is somewhere "in between an informal assignment system and a more formal system." Some groups have "a partner who manages everyone's workloads – you email them when you have capacity and want to be staffed on something new." In other groups juniors generally "manage our own workloads, then pipe up if there is a lull." In the bigger New York office, most groups have assigning partners. A source reported: "Every week we hand in a sheet of estimates of what we think our time commitments will be for the week. Partners are then responsible for allocating work to those who have time, or when someone comes to them and asks." If a new matter comes in from a client whom a junior has worked with previously, "you're often asked to jump back onto a matter as the firm likes to show clients the same faces."

See firm profile on p.640

The Inside View

Rankings in *Chambers USA*

Antitrust	International Arbitration
Corporate/M&A	Litigation

For detail on ranking tiers and ranking locations, visit
www.chambersandpartners.com

"You're constantly coordinating with other offices around the globe."

International arbitration is a popular branch of the disputes group. *"It does mostly investment arbitration,"* one source explained, *"but there is a growing practice of commercial arbitration too."* Interviewees reported that the practice is rife with cross-staffing across Freshfields' international network. A junior told us: *"I have colleagues who have worked with the Rome office, the London office and been on secondment abroad."* Day to day, the drafting of claim memorials takes up a fair bit of associate time as *"they can be quite lengthy – anywhere from 100 to 300 pages."* Other junior-level tasks include *"preparing outlines for examinations of witnesses and experts"* and *"getting to run a couple of witness meetings."* The investigations side of the practice deals with *"litigation and internal investigations for large banks"* and other Fortune 500 companies.

The corporate practice has a pretty broad remit: it covers capital markets, finance, M&A and IP. Attorneys work across several industries from pharmaceutical and entertainment to construction and mining. M&A juniors do *"a mix of public and private M&A and a lot of private equity work."* Sources admitted that *"of course there's due diligence – every corporate junior at every firm does some due diligence."* There's also the chance to get drafting – *"not only ancillary documents, but core legal agreements like share purchase agreements."* Here too, interviewees noted the highly international nature of the work: *"You're constantly coordinating with other offices around the globe."*

The antitrust group is based in DC, though *"it's an entirely international practice."* A lot of the group's work revolves around merger control and clearances – *"taking deals through the regulatory process with agencies like the DOJ and SEC."* There's also some cartel and criminal conduct work. Juniors said they were able to *"draft and analyze advocacy pieces"* and *"prep clients for agency meetings."* Junior tasks also include doc review and legal research. One source acknowledged: *"There is always going to be a learning curve, especially with specialized knowledge, which can be a bit terrifying. But I've had a steady increase in responsibility which coincides with my level of comfort."*

Freshfields' international outlook means there's the opportunity for international travel to clients or firm offices. *"I've been to the UK at least six times in three years,"*

Recent work highlights

- Advised European communications satellite operator SES and its subsidiary O3b Networks on the procurement structure for the construction of seven satellites
- Advised Italian airline Alitalia on its US restructuring, as the company sought Chapter 15 bankruptcy protection
- Secured $1.2 billion in damages for Canadian mining company Crystallex against the Venezuelan government for the latter's expropriation of the Las Cristinas gold mine
- Defended Raoul Weil, former CEO of UBS's wealth management division, in a federal jury trial investigating Swiss banks and bankers for allegedly helping US taxpayers evade billions of dollars of tax on assets secretly held in Switzerland

a third-year associate told us. Longer-term secondments are also available, though associates need to make a business case for them. One reported: *"If you want to go to a particular office, you can argue what would make you a good candidate to spend a year there."* And associates don't even have to leave the US to notice the firm's internationalism: we heard that *"when working within the US, there are plenty of people here seconded from foreign offices."*

Culture

Every source unanimously agreed that the firm's international reach influenced the overall culture. *"The type of people that work here are people who are comfortable working with people from very different backgrounds,"* reflected one junior. This open-mindedness means *"every day you might meet someone new, and the way they think about a legal problem might be completely different to what you've considered."* Interviewees also agreed that attorneys at Freshfields have *"a good bit of ambition. People are always striving to secure the best work."*

"People who are comfortable working with people from very different backgrounds."

The social side of the firm is pretty lively: New York associates recently laced up their sneakers to run the half marathon. If running 21 km isn't up your alley, juniors also mentioned team barbecues, going to baseball and basketball games, and *"dinners at the hottest new restaurants in DC."* Juniors noted that *"people here are invited to big events in each other's lives,"* including birthdays, engagement parties and baby showers. In addition, *"every time a big case or deal closes, everyone goes out for drinks after."*

See firm profile on p.640

The Inside View

Diversity	Partners (%)	Associates (%)
Women	22.5	54
White	92.5	75
Black/African American	2.5	3
Hispanic/Latin American	5	6.8
Asian	0	13.6
Mixed/Other	0	1.6
LGBT	-	3

Diversity

Associates praised the firm's commitment to improving the gender balance – over half of US associates are women. Sources highlighted a *"women's mentoring program in which female juniors are matched with a partner, and they try to work out what needs women have in the workplace and what support is needed."* There are also women-centered business development events. Associates also noted that the LGBT affinity group Halo is very active. Although attorneys from numerous countries work at Freshfields, juniors agreed that *"a good bit of work could be done"* to improve the representation of minority groups.

Training & Development

"There are practice-specific trainings for different associate levels," we heard. *"There's a junior module, a mid-level module and then a senior module."* US juniors can also dial into training taking place in other offices to participate remotely. *"For example,"* said one source, *"the London office does big capital markets training sessions."* Formal training aside, many found they *"prefer to learn on the job in some situations."*

Practice groups also have annual global conferences in different exciting locations each year. For example, disputes lawyers from around the world all jetted to Italy in 2017. Alongside training and team bonding exercises, the conference has *"an extremely social side to it – it's a great opportunity to meet everyone you've been working with in the other offices."*

> *"The London offices does big capital markets training sessions."*

Formal appraisals take place annually, though first-years have an extra one after six months. Juniors approach senior associates and partners they've worked with and ask them to submit a short appraisal. *"Two partners then meet with each associate to discuss your work. The formal process is a nice way to recall the informal feedback you receive throughout the year. It's nice to be able to sit down and reflect on what you've done and where there's room for improvement."*

Offices

In the Big Apple, Freshfields is based in the Citigroup Center on Lexington Avenue. The offices boast *"amazing"* views of Central Park, the Empire State Building and the Chrysler Building – *"it's one of the best things about the office."* Associates usually share with another attorney until their third year, though some younger associates mentioned already having their own office.

DC associates do all have their own office as soon as they start. The office *"still feels very new as we only moved here in 2014. It was designed from scratch and has a very sleek look."* Juniors also mentioned a gym in the building and noted its convenient location right by Metro Center.

Hours & Compensation

There's no hours requirement, though most associates aimed for around 2,000 a year. That said, *"it's not tied at all to your bonus. They expect that there will be years when you bill under and years when you bill over, depending on the work you get."* Salaries and bonuses are both lockstep, and the firm matched the Cravath raise in 2016. Vacation is a pretty standard 20 days. *"Generally you need to be reachable, but people have been good about trying to leave me off email chains when on vacation."* The global nature of the firm means time differences can cause scheduling nightmares. *"If you're working with somewhere in Asia, you learn to take conference calls at 2am,"* one interviewee observed wryly.

> *"If you're working with somewhere in Asia, you learn to take conference calls at 2am."*

Working days for New Yorkers usually end at around 8pm, though some leave earlier as the firm is *"fine about people working from home in the evenings or at weekends."* The occasional late night in the office is inevitable, but it's *"the exception more than the rule."* DC juniors noted the introduction of a new policy that means attorneys can work remotely once a week, which *"everyone is excited about."*

Pro Bono

"The firm is extremely supportive of pro bono," one junior remarked. *"If anything, there are too many pro bono opportunities and not enough time to explore them all!"* One source recalled having a hearing for a pro bono client and was *"pleased with how my team took it, giving it the same importance as a paying matter."* Pro bono cases up for grabs include asylum and immigration matters, helping human trafficking victims and domestic violence matters. Corporate juniors reported getting involved in

See firm profile on p.640

setting up foundations and helping get 501(c) status for non-profits.

Pro bono hours
- For all US attorneys: 12,927
- Average per US attorney: 62

"The plan is to grow the US business from 200 to 300 lawyers by 2021."

Strategy & Future

"Growing in the US is a priority for the firm globally," an associate told us. *"I think with both New York and DC growing, people are feeling more excited,"* the same source continued. *"We're often viewed as an outpost, but we have a very strong set of practitioners and clients here in the US."* Managing partner Peter Lyons confirms: *"We're in growth mode here. The plan is to grow the US business from 200 to 300 lawyers by 2021."* Go to chambers-associate.com for our full interview with Lyons.

To view Freshfields' worldwide rankings at a glance, visit www.chambersandpartners.com

See firm profile on p.640

Fried, Frank, Harris, Shriver & Jacobson

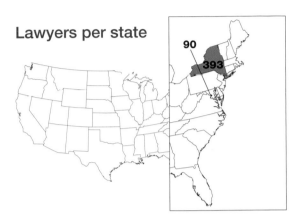

Lawyers per state

90
393

Largest US office: New York
US offices: 2
International offices: 2
First-year salary: $180,000
Billable hours: 2,000 target
Summers 2018: 73 (3 1Ls, 68 2Ls, 2 SEO)
Revenue 2017: $634.9 million (+14.1%)
Partners made in 2018: 7
Famous for: real estate, corporate and funds; New York roots

Juniors were frank about their reasons for joining this Manhattan maestro: big-ticket clientele; a robust corporate offering; and smaller teams that offer early responsibility.

"FISCAL year 2018 has been another strong year of growth for the Firm," chairman David Greenwald is pleased to tell us. From its two offices in the US – its HQ in New York and its DC base – Fried has been busy helping the likes of Bain Capital to establish a new $9.4 billion fund; Sinclair Broadcast Group to snap up the Tribune Media Company for a cool $3.9 billion; and a former Bank of America Merrill Lynch executive to settle securities violations claims.

These highlights show off some of Fried's core practices (asset management, M&A, private equity and litigation), but its others include capital markets, finance, tax and real estate. With regard to the latter, juniors told us that *"it's the best real estate department in New York City,"* and Greenwald is quick to sing its praises too: *"From counseling Related Companies on various aspects of the development at Hudson Yards, to our representation of Brook-*

field Asset Management in many of their transactions, our work in the real estate space continues to be transformational."

But do the *Chambers USA* rankings back all of this up? Nationwide, Fried's real estate expertise is certainly singled out as an area of strength, as are its investment funds and tax practices. In the Big Apple, its general commercial litigation and real estate lawyers come out on top, while over in DC its corporate/M&A, private equity and tax clout are of note. Further accolades in *Chambers Global* and *Chambers Europe* demonstrate Fried's international reach, which is focused on the key financial centers of London and Frankfurt.

The Work

The vast majority of the associates on our list were based in Fried's New York HQ, but a handful were toiling away in DC. Department-wise, most (almost 60%) had joined the firm's corporate practice, while Fried's litigation and real estate groups scooped up a large chunk of the remaining juniors. Only a few could be found in the firm's tax, restructuring & insolvency, and executive compensation & ERISA departments. All departments have a designated assignment coordinator to dole out the work, *"but like many firms the matters you get end up coming*

The Inside View

See firm profile on p.641

Rankings in *Chambers USA*

Banking & Finance	Investment Funds
Capital Markets	Litigation
Corporate/M&A	Private Equity
Employee Benefits &	Real Estate
Executive Compensation	Tax
Government	

For detail on ranking tiers and ranking locations, visit
www.chambersandpartners.com

Recent work highlights

- Counseled Knight Transportation during its merger with Swift Transportation Company, which had an enterprise value of $6 billion
- Secured a favorable outcome for portfolio manager Vanderbilt Capital Advisors, which was accused of mismanaging insurer Standard Life's $2 billion portfolio by investing in risky subprime securities
- Advised Bermuda-based Brookfield Property Partners on various aspects of its development of a 67-story office tower, One Manhattan West, including a lease to the National Hockey League for its new headquarters
- Acted for Goldman Sachs Merchant Banking Division as it formed its flagship corporate buyout fund – West Street Capital Partners VII – which raised an aggregate of $7 billion upon closing

through a mixture of the formal process and then just the people who you gravitate to."

Corporate is split into seven subgroups: asset management; capital markets & corporate governance; corporate real estate; finance; M&A & private equity; environmental; and IP transactional. Associates are placed in a specific group when they start but do have the option to move around after six months if they want to. Quite a few of our sources had worked in the asset management subgroup, which *"represents both fund sponsors and investment managers – we advise on organizational matters, and also help funds to comply with regulations."* For juniors, this involved *"helping to renew subscription documents; negotiating with the other side during transactions; communicating with overseas parties; drafting agreements; and researching issues that come up."* Overall, interviewees felt that they'd *"received a large degree of responsibility – I've taken the lead on parts of the transaction and I've enjoyed that."*

"We work on some really flashy and notable developments, which is exciting!"

Litigators reported taking on *"an interesting array of work,"* which spanned the likes of *"class actions over car parts; shareholder disputes over mergers; bankruptcy cases; employment matters; and the more general contract-related fallouts. Fried likes to make you more of a generalist right off the bat, so you have knowledge of lots of things."* Workwise, sources relayed that *"on some cases you'll be doing first-year tasks – like doc review, research and drafting discovery documents – but on other cases you can do more advanced stuff like writing briefs, contributing to strategy and decision-making and second-chairing depositions, which is a lot of fun."* New Yorkers told us that *"the department here is relatively small compared to our peers, so we have leaner teams. You're not one of 50 first-years staffed on one case forever – that experience isn't possible here."*

The real estate department *"on the whole has a focus on New York, but works on transactions all over."* These deals cover matters from joint venture formations to acquisitions and dispositions. Insiders had been *"advising clients*

on zoning and other land-related matters, as well as seeking government approvals." They found that *"there's no upper limit when it comes to taking responsibility in this department; I have calls and meetings with clients, and I've drafted the application materials that are submitted to the government."* The best thing about the group? *"We work on some really flashy and notable developments, which is exciting!"*

Pro Bono

"I think pro bono is one area where the firm truly excels," juniors told us. *"The firm's dedication is, quite frankly, stellar. Up to 300 hours count toward our billable target, so the firm really does put its money where its mouth is."* All associates are also required to bill a minimum of 20 hours in order to qualify for a bonus. *"The firm seriously pushes it and expects it – our pro bono coordinator constantly sends out opportunities via email, but people also just get one another involved, which is cool."*

"The firm's dedication is, quite frankly, stellar."

The firm works with organizations like Her Justice, Planned Parenthood and Lambda Legal. Our sources had taken on a range of work; some had gone to the family court to appeal immigration rulings; others had delved into the stream of criminal cases overseen by the Southern District of New York; and a few had focused on more corporate matters by *"drafting contracts for small businesses that are starting to think big."*

Pro bono hours
- For all US attorneys: 33,291
- Average per US attorney: 68.2

See firm profile on p.641

Diversity	Partners (%)	Associates (%)
Women	15	42
White	96	73
Black/African American	0	7
Hispanic/Latin American	0.8	6
Asian	2.4	10
Mixed/Other	0.8	4
LGBT	1.6	5.4

Training & Development

All new associates complete a weeklong orientation in New York before joining their own practice groups. *"They call it Fried Frank University and you spend all day in different classes that cover topics like writing, how to work with a secretary, billing, professional responsibility and client/attorney relationships – everything you need to know as a first-year they cover in that first week!"* Monthly lunches and CLEs follow as part of the first-year attorney development series: *"These take you through things like public speaking, accounting, and working through generational differences. The firm's also really good about taking requests for CLEs and allowing you to attend external panels and conferences."*

"Everything you need to know as a first-year they cover in that first week!"

Culture

"It's a New York-headquartered law firm, so the pace is quicker and people do work hard, but they're kind too," thought one junior, whose sentiments were shared by many other insiders. *"We all share the goal of doing elite-level corporate and finance work, and everyone really cares about the end product, but there's a lack of formality for formality's sake. There's no culture of mean yelling; the environment is collaborative; and the hierarchy is fairly flat."* Regular meetings that keep associates in the loop bolster this sense of 'togetherness.' Fried's chairman, David Greenwald, hosts *"biannual meetings with associates, in which he lays out the firm's recent performance and its plans for improvement. He's very frank about how the firm's doing."*

Juniors also felt that having lots of different things to chat about helped to foster close bonds. *"Everyone here has interests that are not generic,"* summed up one interviewee. *"I know someone who's writing a fantasy novel, someone else who was a yoga teacher, someone else who was a speech writer for Hillary Clinton… People come from very different backgrounds and life experiences, and that makes things interesting."* This all bodes well for a fair amount of socializing at the firm, and we heard about *"monthly associate lunches; 'dessert Thursdays'; attorney cocktail parties; and a big summer blowout at Central Park Zoo."*

Hours & Compensation

If juniors bill 2,000 hours they become eligible for a full bonus. Our sources generally found this target manageable, especially as up to 300 hours of pro bono and 125 hours of qualified non-billable work (like marketing, recruitment and business development activities)can count toward it. *"The firm is good and really flexible with bonuses,"* interviewees explained. *"If you bill between 1,850 and 2,000 you qualify for a partial bonus; between 2,000 and 2,200 you get a full one; and between 2,200 and 2,400 you get an extra percentage; and beyond 2,450 you get a super bonus!"*

"The firm is good and really flexible with bonuses."

Does this bonus-related flexibility have any impact on the hours worked by juniors? In corporate, *"there is an expectation that you'll be responsive for most of the day, including outside of office hours, but that's not really specific to our firm."* Litigators, on the other hand, said they *"have worked on the weekends, but haven't been slammed – generally it's been very manageable,"* while real estaters had *"worked late nights and weekends, but there's no fake urgency; you work late only when something is really important."*

Strategy & Future

In order to boost its core practices, Fried Frank has been busy drawing laterals into its fold of late, as Greenwald reveals: "We have added six lateral partners, five lateral special counsel and 26 lateral associates this year, and welcomed an incoming associate class of 69 to further increase our capacity to serve our clients and to tackle new and exciting challenges." For more from Greenwald, visit chambers-associate.com

Offices

What are the firm's New York digs like? *"Totally nice,"* one source summed up casually, while another expanded: *"Our office is on the southern tip of Manhattan with a gorgeous view of the water. All the offices have huge windows and there's a lot of wood around so it's got a very old-world law firm feel."* Juniors were also keen to tell us about the associates lounge, which comes complete with *"snacks, a TV and a ping pong table. It's part of an initiative to create more collaborative spaces, and it's turned out to be a nice feature."*

See firm profile on p.641

Diversity

"There are ongoing and transparent conversations about how we're going to ensure we're a diverse firm, especially when it comes to the partnership and promotions," juniors revealed. On the whole, interviewees felt that Fried was making progress, and praised the efforts of the firm's diversity and inclusion director, as well as its *"numerous affinity groups, which are very active."* The focus is also on the make up of incoming classes; sources involved in recruitment told us: *"We recruit through our affinity groups at law schools and have summer 'buddy' programs to further encourage diversity."*

**Coming soon on chambers-associate.com...
Behind the scenes in funds and investment management, as told by lawyers at Fried, Frank.**

See firm profile on p.641

The Inside View

Gibbons P.C.

Lawyers per state

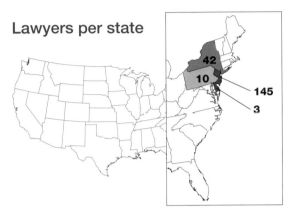

42
10
145
3

Largest US office: Newark
US offices: 5
International offices: 0
Second-year salary: $135,000 (plus clerkship bonus)
Billable hours: 1,980 target
Summers 2018: no summer program
Revenue 2017: $99.4 million (-2.9%)
Partners made in 2018: 1
Famous for: its focus on hiring judicial clerks; litigation prowess; emphasis on family

New Jersey stalwart Gibbons goes ape for judicial clerks who can hit the ground running.

JUST as fellow NJ native Bruce Springsteen said, you can't start a fire without a spark, and Gibbons' incoming litigators can't get hired without a clerk(ship). Yes, Gibbons is notable for recruiting seasoned judicial clerks into its litigation department. Hiring partner Peter Torcicollo tells us: *"It's beneficial to the firm in a couple of ways. First, our clerks join us having already forged really strong bonds with judges and staff – they've got the keys to the courthouse! Second, and importantly, they come to us with an extra year of development on their path to becoming fully-realized attorneys."*

"They've got the keys to the courthouse!"

Our associate interviewees told us that their clerkships *"were helpful in that they teach you how to conduct research efficiently and how to write as clearly as possible."* Armed with their newly acquired skills, juniors sought *"a higher caliber of firm"* and found exactly what they were looking for in Gibbons. *"As a result of the clerkship model, they put immediate trust into associates. I was never doubted – during my first week here I was asked 'well, what do you think?'"*

These eager newcomers flagged Gibbons' superb reputation for litigation work across a number of areas: *Cham-*

bers USA bestows high rankings on the firm's general commercial, product liability and white-collar/government investigations expertise in particular. Yet it's not all dramatic courtroom showdowns at Gibbons: the firm also boasts noncontentious expertise in its corporate, employment, IP, real estate and government affairs practices. And while most juniors join Gibbons Newark HQ, a few each year can be found in the firm's other domestic offices, in Trenton, New York, Philadelphia and Wilmington.

The Work

Of the nine second and third-year junior associates on our list, five were in Gibbons' commercial and criminal litigation (CCL) group, while the rest were split between government affairs, employment & labor law, real property, environmental, and intellectual property. Despite being allocated to a certain group, associates are nonetheless free to sample work from other departments if they'd like to. Each practice group has an appointed 'manager' who oversees staffing: *"You call them and let them know if you need any work, but as you progress at the firm partners will just come back to you and give you follow-on work. The partners are very accessible here – there's no fear of talking to them!"*

"CCL is a 'jack of all trades' practice group," associates told us. *"Matters here run the gamut: I've worked on environmental, breach of contract, corporate, criminal, IT, construction and pharmaceutical cases."* It's safe to say that *"there's always something new and interesting to learn*

The Inside View

See firm profile on p.642

Rankings in *Chambers USA*

Bankruptcy/Restructuring   Intellectual Property
Corporate/M&A   Labor & Employment
Environment   Litigation
Healthcare   Real Estate

For detail on ranking tiers and ranking locations, visit
www.chambersandpartners.com

Recent work highlights

- Defended Inovio Pharmaceuticals after it was sued by a former shareholder of its predecessor company, who alleged that he'd been prevented from exercising thousands of stock options
- Represented Swiss healthcare company Hoffmann-La Roche and Roche Laboratories during an ongoing matter involving 6,000 product liability cases tied to the alleged gastrointestinal effects of a drug called Accutane
- Acted for convenience store maestro 7-Eleven during state court litigation that contested operating hours limitations
- Advised real estate equity firm Lubert-Adler Partners as it invested in a developer that was looking to finance a $200 million mixed-use project on the St. George waterfront in Staten Island

about – you might be dealing with a dairy company one day, a fast food company the next, and a healthcare company the next."

"...as I demonstrated what I could do my responsibility grew."

So what do CCL juniors get up to? *"My daily tasks include overseeing the discovery process and keeping the partner looped in on that, as well as drafting motions – the writing element has been intensive,"* said one junior. Others agreed, and told of *"drafting third party complaints and counterclaims,"* as well as helping to prepare witnesses and taking depositions: *"In my first year here I took depositions, and as I demonstrated what I could do my responsibility grew – now I'm making important decisions in cases on my own."*

Then there are the smaller groups. Gibbons' IP group covers litigation, patent prosecution and transactional work, and draws in clients from the pharma, tech, retail and leisure industries. The criminal defense group covers the likes of internal investigations and appellate cases, while real estate attorneys deal exclusively with commercial matters across three areas: environmental, land use and development, and transactional. An associate in one of these practices commented: *"My group is small enough to allow me autonomy on many matters. I have direct client contact on a regular basis, and this week my boss said 'I think you should do the whole case' – he saw that I was running with it and doing well."*

Pro Bono

Gibbons allows its attorneys to count 50 hours of pro bono toward the firm's billing target. However, associates found they had plenty of encouragement to do more: *"The firm really impresses on us when we first join how important pro bono is – we're really expected to do at least 50 hours."* Juniors highlighted Gibbons' involvement in the Partners for Women and Justice program, which *"assists low income and abused women through matters like restraining orders and child custody cases – it's extremely rewarding and the firm really encourages it."* Other sources had taken on prisoner civil rights cases and volunteered at the firm's clinics devoted to *"expungement issues and*

small crimes – we take on matters and solve them there and then if we can."

Pro bono hours
- For all attorneys: 14,960
- Average per attorney: 81

Training & Feedback

A week-long orientation program welcomes juniors to the firm. *"It gives you varied training on the computer and billing systems, certain polices, and the pro bono program."* From then on *"the backbone of continuing legal education"* is The Gibbons Academy, which hosts monthly training sessions for newcomers. *"They get internal experts from various fields to deliver the courses, and sometimes they bring in external educators too."* The annual review process involves a designated attorney *"collecting all the feedback submitted by the partners you've worked for. You then sit with them and another attorney of your choosing to discuss it. It's a beneficial process that gives you an idea of how the firm thinks you're doing."*

Offices

New starters at the firm share an office with a more experienced associate, *"so you have that person there to ask really dumb questions and to get some informal training from."* This arrangement can also have social benefits: one junior told us their office mate *"invited me to social events and connected me to other attorneys, so I didn't get isolated."* Eventually juniors get their own office, *"but it's not clear how long it will take for that to happen. As nice as it is to make friends, it's much nicer to have your own office!"*

"Newark isn't the thriving metropolis Manhattan is," one junior sighed, *"but it's nice to be here and know that you're in Gibbons' hub."* Associates were also keen to point out that the office is *"linked to Newark Penn station by*

See firm profile on p.642

The Inside View

Diversity	Partners (%)	Associates (%)
Women	22	43
White	94	86
Black/African American	2	5
Hispanic/Latin American	4	3
Asian	0	5
Mixed/Other	0	1
LGBT	2	8

an overhead walkway," making for speedy access to the bright lights of New York City (FYI: associates can get to the New York office without even having to step outside, as Gibbons' Big Apple base is perched directly above New York Penn station). On the whole, juniors wouldn't *"characterize Gibbons' office space as architecturally remarkable, but it more than satisfies what you'd expect from a professional workspace!"*

Culture

Juniors told us of a *"fairly formal"* surface to life at Gibbons: *"There's a formal dress code – always suit and tie – for example, and also a formalized process for getting work as a new associate, which generally involves being called in to see the practice head, who then puts you in touch with a partner who needs you. It's a very professional place."* However, beneath this surface *"it's not so stuffy – people are for the most part approachable and a pleasure to be around. I basically like everyone I work with!"* Others flagged that *"you wouldn't describe Gibbons as a place that hosts regular social events during the days and evenings."* There's *"a bit of a disconnect between the groups, and people tend to mostly stick with their own."* The result is that the Newark office is *"very quiet and very focused – we all know what needs to be done, and everybody wants to do well."*

"It's a very professional place."

This doesn't mean that Gibbons' attorneys don't know how to slide into social mode at the appropriate time. We were told of annual inter-office events, including March Madness get-togethers and a full week of celebrations surrounding St. Patrick's Day: *"There was a limerick contest and lots of other little activities that each office puts on."* In addition, we heard of summer barbecues and an Independence Day celebration.

Diversity

"It's not incredibly diverse," sources told us, *"and we could hire more candidates of color in particular, but overall there's definitely an effort in the office to increase diversity."* Among those efforts is the firm's participation in the New Jersey Law and Education Empowerment Project: *"Over*

the summer we have local kids come in to do placements. We're making an effort to start earlier, to go into schools and get kids interested in the law."* Gibbons' Women's Initiative (which recently celebrated its 20th birthday) was also mentioned, as *"it looks at programming networking events and mentoring lunches: they have a dedicated interest in making sure female associates do well at the firm."*

Hours & Compensation

Associates aim to meet a 1,980 hours billing target, and reiterated to us that *"there's no unspoken rule that you have to meet this, which removes some stress – if you're not going to hit your billables they'll make sure you're not just sat around doing nothing and staff you on pro bono matters."* Salaries start at $135,000, which was deemed *"a decent amount for New Jersey – it's not as high as what you'd get in New York, but we don't have those insane expectations around billable hours. There's a tradeoff and it's worth it."* Bonuses are discretionary at Gibbons and aren't just tied to hours – *"they also take into account your pro bono work and whether you've been a good corporate citizen."*

Most interviewees preferred getting into the office early (before 9am) and would leave by 6.30pm. *"After that, you'll probably be the only person left on the floor."* Some associates do *"plug back in at home: sometimes I'll work for hours in the evening and sometimes I won't work at all – with litigation you go with the flow of the case."* The nature of litigation was, however, described as *"fairly reliable – cases have schedules so you can predict when you'll be busy."*

Strategy & Future

This junior mirrored many when they said: *"I would like some more transparency from the firm about its plans. There's no sense that the sky is falling, and I'm not overly aggravated by not knowing more, but I want to feed my own curiosity!"* Chairman and managing director Patrick Dunican Jr. tells us that juniors have a lot to look forward to: *"Over the next twelve months, I expect that Gibbons will continue to provide the tools our attorneys need to develop and advance professionally. We have high expectations for client service, skills enhancement, billable hours, pro bono commitment, and business development, but our more seasoned attorneys lead by example. Our newer attorneys can also rely on innovative platforms for leadership training, continuing legal education, and mentoring to help them advance their careers to partnership and beyond. In terms of results, we now have numerous non-equity partners with books of business of at least $1 million, and, in 2018, we plan to make several equity partners."*

See firm profile on p.642

Gibson, Dunn & Crutcher LLP

Lawyers per state

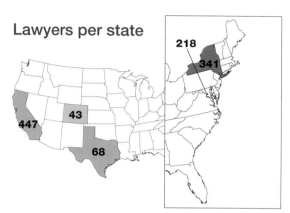

218
341
447
43
68

Largest US office: New York
US offices: 10
International offices: 10
First-year salary: $180,000
Billable hours: no requirement
Summers 2018: 137 (7 1Ls, 129 2Ls, 1 other)
Revenue 2017: $1.64 billion (+1.9%)
Partners made in 2018: 13
Famous for: helping to overturn Proposition 8; huge presence on East and West Coast

Life for juniors at Gibson Dunn is a bit *"like a Goosebumps choose-your-own-adventure book,"* one empowered employee emphasized.

"LITIGATION powerhouse" and corporate colossus Gibson Dunn needs no introduction, but here's one anyway. Founded over a century and a quarter ago in a small, dusty city with a population of 50,000 called Los Angeles, this BigLaw behemoth bulldozes the competition in its 20 office locations around the world – as numerous top-tier rankings in the various *Chambers* directories demonstrate. *Chambers USA* alone places the market leader in the very top tier for over 25 separate practice group categories, ranging from various different types of litigation (for which it is most famous) to corporate/M&A, retail, IT & outsourcing, environment, real estate, and tax. One associate justifiably bragged: *"It's just legal stars up and down the directory!"*

Most of Gibson's 1,100 or so lawyers in ten offices at home are in New York, California and DC, with the remainder in Texas and Colorado. The firm's ten overseas offices cover Asia, Europe, the Middle East and Latin America. Frankfurt became the latest international addition in 2016. Closer to home, Houston opened its doors in 2017, boosting the energy practice and becoming Gibson's second office in the Lone Star State after Dallas.

Gibson's free-market system is another famous selling point. Readers with *"outgoing"* personalities interested in *"charting their own course"* should read on.

The Work

Gibson Dunn's associates around the country told us the way they get work was a big draw when they joined. For their first couple of years, juniors can rotate through different practice areas every six months (though this is not compulsory). Furthermore, there's *"no formal assignment;"* instead, the free-market system allows juniors to *"reach out"* to senior associates and partners for work that interests them. This process is *"entirely word of mouth, whether through emails or face to face."* For one satisfied junior, *"it's like a Goosebumps Choose Your Own Adventure book."*

This set-up works well both for those who know right away what work they want to do and those who don't. *"I try to get my hands on anything and everything,"* one open-minded junior reported. The system *"empowers you to pick and choose how you want your career to look, without being constrained,"* a more focused associate told us. *"We get a sense of ownership."* Some interviewees had traveled down some surprising paths: *"I thought I'd be a litigator, but after doing one or two corporate assignments I decided to give corporate a shot."* Others liked that *"you aren't cornered into anything you don't want."* Someone who'd had enough of M&A deals keeping them in the office until the small hours found *"if you don't like something, you can just free market your way out of there."*

On chambers-associate.com...

- Get hired at Gibson Dunn
- Full interview with chairman Ken Doran

See firm profile on p.643

The Inside View

Rankings in *Chambers USA*

Antitrust	International Trade
Appellate Law	Investment Funds
Banking & Finance	IT & Outsourcing
Bankruptcy/Restructuring	Labor & Employment
Capital Markets	Leisure & Hospitality
Corporate Crime &	Life Sciences
Investigations	Litigation
Corporate/M&A	Media & Entertainment
Employee Benefits &	Outsourcing
Executive Compensation	Private Equity
Energy & Natural	Projects
Resources	Real Estate
Environment	Retail
ERISA Litigation	Securities
FCPA	Tax
Government	Technology
Insurance	Transportation
Intellectual Property	

For detail on ranking tiers and ranking locations, visit
www.chambersandpartners.com

"You need to develop the habit of knocking on partners' doors" when getting to grips with the system. The first few weeks can be *"a weird push and pull between wanting to get your hands dirty"* and thinking *"wow – how do I actually get work around here?"* A litigator felt that *"there's a sense you need to be savvy to get what you* want," and if you perform well, you might even find a partner knocking on your door. Some associates warned that less extroverted people might find the system tougher because *"you probably don't want to say no if you're working with partners."* Nevertheless, *"it was surprising how easy and necessary that became!"* A corporate associate admitted: *"Saying no is a nice option to have."*

"If you don't like something you can just free market your way out of there."

The vast majority of junior associates are in corporate and litigation, with a few in real estate and tax. Corporate newbies see a mix of M&A, capital markets, private equity, venture financing, funds, restructuring, insolvency, and securities work, among other things. *"My day-to-day is different every day,"* we heard a lot, and the size of the deal is *"the big variable."* Associates do a lot of drafting and reviewing letters, schedules and agreements, and touching base with clients. *"I started having client contact three or four months in, which was a little nerve-racking, but I jumped on board because it was needed at the time."*

Over in litigation, associates are involved in all sorts: white-collar matters, class actions, appellate work, government investigations and bankruptcy cases, among others. Junior tasks include legal research, creating out-

Recent work highlights

- Representing New Jersey in SCOTUS case to authorize sports betting
- Defending Uber against price-fixing allegations
- Advised Pepsi in series of class actions against several of its brands, including Tropicana and Quaker Oats
- Defended Fitbit against 150 claims of trade secrets misappropriation
- Achieved unanimous verdict for Hewlett-Packard in contract dispute, resulting in $3 billion in damages

---

lines for depositions, identifying documents and exhibits, and fact-checking. *"Most of what I do is brief writing,"* one reported, but *"I've also second-chaired depositions, and I've done a fair amount of deep research into client issues."* Having a second language was a bonus for one litigator, given *"a high level of responsibility early on"* on a case with foreign clients.

Support is in place if associates find themselves overwhelmed or, on the flip side, if they're struggling to find enough work. Only a few associates mentioned slower months; when seeking work, *"if I don't get it this time, there'll be another chance. That's the merit of the free system."* It is *"most tested"* during the busiest times, like when an enormous *"emergency litigation"* matter comes in. *"Those cases have a gravity that sucks people in, and they can eclipse the free market system because they require so much of the office's time and attention."*

Training & Development

Associates get a designated partner-mentor, who provides regular feedback in the lead-up to six-monthly reviews. *"They're there to let you know if there's any room for improvement before you hit that mark."* Sources also praised mentors they'd come to know *"organically"* through working with them. One Californian associate was pleased to discover *"the partners have been nothing but generous with their time."*

Training programs are provided across practice groups, and junior associates can drop in on whatever takes their fancy. These are usually live-streamed across offices, with a partner in the room to give their perspective on the topic.

"I sat down with lawyers from all over the world."

A training staple at Gibson is the New Lawyer Academy. Fresh recruits from across the Gibson globe are invited on a three-day retreat, held in La Quinta, California in 2018. While some reflected that they didn't find the training as *"useful"* for the corporate side, they all appre-

See firm profile on p.643

Diversity	Partners (%)	Associates (%)
Women	20.2	43.7
White	89.6	77.8
Black/African American	1	2.2
Hispanic/Latin American	1.9	5.2
Asian	6.3	10.9
Mixed/Other	1.3	3.9
LGBT	2.2	6.7

ciated meeting new colleagues: "*I sat down with lawyers from all over the world, and everyone was nice, smart and grounded. That was really gratifying.*" The new recruits also got stuck in to an array of team-building activities, with some even dabbling in a spot of karaoke – Gibson Dunn is not for the shy.

Offices & Culture

In terms of inter-office links, associates said they had "*no hesitation*" reaching out to other offices: "*It's less about who's in the office, and more about who has the right skill set.*" While the "*suits-style*" New York office is still one of the firm's "*more intense*" offices, its associates said the LA-founded firm isn't quite as "*buttoned up*" as some Big Apple firms. More than one interviewee praised how personal obligations are handled with a "*Californian generosity.*" Juniors spoke of a tight-knit feel here, with regular lunches, after work drinks, and weekend dinners. "*I think I'm happier than my friends at other BigLaw firms.*" Any negatives? "*There could be more snacks in the office.*"

"*I'm happier than my friends at other BigLaw firms.*"

Over in California, some LA associates hesitate to label the office 'laid back', opting instead for "*communal,*" "*upbeat,*" and "*accepting*" of life outside the office. A corporate associate revealed: "*If you've got someone coming to do a repair, you can work from home.*" Another added: "*90% of my floor doesn't eat dinner here,*" though it's quite common to take work home. "*Once people get to know you, it becomes much more flexible. As long as the work gets done, you can do what you need to do.*" The firm's global support teams sit here, which is "*convenient if you have a technical issue.*"

Perhaps unsurprisingly, Washington has a reputation for being "*the most culturally conservative,*" but a DC associate said their office "*prides itself on its work-life balance.*" One highlight for summer associates here is the poolside party at star lawyer Ted Olson's home. In the smaller offices, Dallas has a family-friendly feel to it: "*People know each other's families – the kids came along to the office Halloween party.*" Palo Alto doesn't miss out on the fun:

along with a fantasy football league, there's an attorney band who recently took to the stage at an informal work bash. "*They had a great sound! I think that is indicative of how we all get along in Palo Alto.*" Gibson Dunn also has offices in Denver, San Francisco, Orange County and Houston.

Pro Bono

Interviewees spoke glowingly about how the firm "*puts its money where its mouth is*" regarding pro bono work – for at least one, it was the reason they chose the firm. Others valued it for giving more responsibility than they usually get. The firm has a one-for-one credit policy on pro bono hours, with no cap – they're all billable. Associates are "*actively encouraged*" to take on cases via regular emails, with the implied caveat: "*Be reasonable, don't do 700 hours, we do need to keep the lights on!*"

"*The firm puts its money where its mouth is.*"

Conviction appeals and asylum cases – some "*a direct result of the travel ban*" President Trump imposed – have kept juniors busy recently. Other matters include working with Lawyers Without Borders on a women's rights case in Kenya, and research involving several offices into police brutality, training and reform.

Pro bono hours
- For all US attorneys: 159,093
- Average per US attorney: 126

Diversity

Around 20% of partners are now women (up from previous years), and associates pointed to female role models at the firm. Some would like to see more structure to the current women's group: a "*mentor group specifically for women, so women associates can engage with women partners and learn right off the bat.*"

"*A priority in the next generation.*"

Diversity, particularly among ethnic minorities, "*is something I think about,*" several admitted. "*It would be interesting to see minorities making it to partner in the smaller offices.*" Comparing the LA office's workforce to that city's ethnically diverse population, another noted "*there's work to be done.*" That said, "*the firm is doing good work in recruiting,*" and others agreed that "*it seems to be a priority for the next generation.*"

See firm profile on p.643

The Inside View

Hours & Compensation

Gibson Dunn doesn't impose a formal annual billable hours requirement: *"There's no real target,"* associates confirmed. Informally, the goal is 1,950 hours. Some we spoke to had no problem reaching that, while others had fallen a little short but experienced *"no real consequences, as long as they see that you've tried to push for work."* Another added: *"For the first few years, they're flexible."* One associate had heard of junior colleagues *"going south of 1,200 and still getting a full bonus,"* though we wouldn't recommend it.

It comes as no surprise that New York scoops the prize for most *"brutal hours"* among the offices, with some associates clocking out as late as four in the morning during their busiest months. The firm's 'unlimited' vacation policy hasn't *"culturally intimidated"* any of the juniors we interviewed, though some were unsure how well it works: *"Younger associates might feel scared to take vacation, so maybe a mandated rule would be better."*

Strategy & Future

"It's been a very exciting year for us," chairman Ken Doran tells us. The firm is now *"up and running"* in Houston, where lawyers *"handle a full range of oil and gas transactions; we have a great team there and they are a synergistic fit with our global energy practice."* Doran goes on to explain that the firm has no immediate plans to open more offices, but is interested in a particular jurisdiction: *"For years we've been hearing that India may open up for international firms – that's yet to happen but we will continue to watch that."*

"Our long-term strategy is simple," adds Doran. *"We focus on maintaining the quality of our people. I think our culture is what separates us from other firms, and our focus on it has kept us on a good path throughout a period of great turmoil in the world."* For more from Doran, visit chambers-associate.com

Get Hired

Chief recruiting officer Leslie Ripley emphasizes: *"Self-confidence is important, but not arrogance. Everything here is a team approach, and arrogance won't work."* She underlines the importance of *"well-rounded"* recruits, a quality echoed by several associates who participated in OCIs. According to a New Yorker, *"it's good for us to have complex individuals who bring ideas into the firm we didn't have before. The deadliest practice of law is someone who never had a job between college and law school, and has no pro bono passions in their corporate career."* For more advice on getting hired, go online.

In 6th position, Gibson Dunn was the best-performing of the US giants in our Associate satisfaction survey in 2018.

See firm profile on p.643

Goodwin

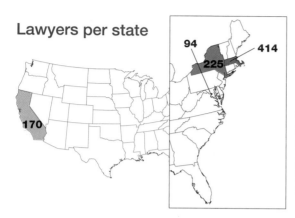

Lawyers per state

94
414
225
170

Largest US office: Boston
US offices: 6
International offices: 4
First-year salary: $180,000
Billable hours: 1,950 target
Summers 2018: 59 (1 1Ls, 58 2Ls)
Revenue 2017: $1.03 billion (+13.2%)
Partners made in 2018: 12 (in the US)
Famous for: respect for work/life balance; growing international scope; tech, life sciences and private equity work

A rebrand, expanding international reach and a sturdy reputation in areas like tech and life sciences make Goodwin an attractive place for litigators and deal-doers alike.

GOODWIN is one of Boston's powerhouse firms. Its junior associates knew they'd be joining a firm with a robust set of resources and practices, as well as a clear sense of direction: *"Goodwin is a firm that knows what it's good at and sticks to it."* But an examination of Goodwin's *Chambers USA* rankings show that it is in fact good at a variety of things, both litigious and transactional in nature: in its native Boston the firm excels in areas like banking & finance, IP, general commercial litigation, venture capital investment, and real estate. On the national stage, however, its corporate/M&A and REITs practices stand out, alongside high nods for financial litigation, fund formation and life sciences work. The latter is a key industry focus for Goodwin, as are the technology, real estate, financial and private equity sectors.

Favoring a policy of steady and careful growth, Goodwin has continued on its upward trajectory in recent years. In 2015 the firm debuted in mainland Europe by opening offices in Frankfurt and Paris within six months of each other, boosting its real estate, private equity and M&A capabilities. This expansion was followed a year later by a snazzy rebrand, which in the spirit of conciseness saw

the firm drop the 'Procter' part of its name; this aesthetic overhaul was bolstered by a physical move in Boston to brand new premises in the city's Seaport District. While most of Goodwin's juniors are based here, the firm's New York office also takes on a hefty chunk of new starters. Its remaining domestic bases (in DC, San Francisco, Silicon Valley and Los Angeles) hire a handful each year too. Sources in the Northern Cali offices told us that *"we're known for our tech and emerging companies work,"* but were also drawn to Goodwin because *"it felt more laid back."* As we'll see, this easygoing vibe is not just consigned to the West Coast offices at Goodwin. To top off this successful run, the firm recently posted a record year of revenue growth, which saw the amount push past the $1 billion mark for the first time.

The Work

Juniors elect to go down the litigation or business law path at the end of their summer, and subsequently start full-time associate life as generalists for their first two years. This gives newbies a chance *"to play around with all the subgroups and get a feel for what's on offer."* For litigators these groups cover the likes of product liability, IP, white-collar, securities and antitrust work, among many other strands. In the business law department, juniors had sampled everything from venture capital matters and M&A deals to real estate transactions and tax issues.

In the beginning, work is assigned in a simple way: *"Associate development managers [referred to as ADMs]*

On chambers-associate.com...

- Get hired, featuring an interview with national hiring partner Emily Rapalino
- Interview with partner and Boston office leader of the business law department Scott Webster

See firm profile on p.644

Rankings in *Chambers USA*

Banking & Finance	Labor & Employment
Capital Markets	Leisure & Hospitality
Corporate Crime &	Life Sciences
Investigations	Litigation
Corporate/M&A	Private Equity
Employee Benefits &	Products Liability
Executive Compensation	Real Estate
Environment	REITs
ERISA Litigation	Securities
Financial Services	Startups & Emerging
Regulation	Companies
Food & Beverages	Tax
Intellectual Property	Technology
Investment Funds	Venture Capital

For detail on ranking tiers and ranking locations, visit
www.chambersandpartners.com

Recent work highlights

- Advised life sciences consulting firm PAREXEL Internationalon its $5 billion agreement to be acquired by investment firm Pamplona Capital Management
- Represented global venture capital firm 83North as it established a $250 million fund that will direct its investments toward European and Israeli entrepreneurs who've started early-stage tech companies
- Acting for the Massachusetts Bay Transportation Authority (MBTA) during a multi-million dispute with freight railroad Pan Am Railways over whether MBTA is obliged to pay for a form of 'positive train control' on certain rail lines
- Representing Gillette (the subsidiary of consumer products giant Procter & Gamble) during a patent infringement case against competitor Dollar Shave Club

look at your hours and staff you on projects based on your schedules." Juniors estimated that around 50% of their assignments were staffed like this during their first year, but they tended to transition into *"more of a free-market system"* by their third year. Some juniors praised the ADMs for being *"an easy pathway to express your interests through – they do try to connect us, and they send round a monthly email asking us what we want to do."* However, others highlighted that *"there can be a perception that the assignments obtained directly from partners are better than those sourced through the ADMs."* In addition, assignments from the ADMs *"are not always in the practice groups that you want to work in – they try to steer you towards the areas where the resources are needed."*

"...we're known for our tech and emerging companies work."

Typical first-year tasks for business juniors include *"doing all of the back-up diligence on IPOs,"* as well as *"taking the first crack"* at stock certificates, signature packets and ancillary documents. *"As a first-year the firm tries to protect you as much as they can,"* one deal-doer explained, *"but in the second-year things really take off, especially with regards to direct client contact. It's been a drastic step up."* Running venture capital deals was flagged as a particular highlight for one source, who praised the level of client contact required when helping to form a company: *"As a second year I was running deals in the $2 million range but going into the third year it's more in the $4-5 million range. I'm taking a much bigger lead on M&A deals too."* One third year provided us with a breakdown of their average day: *"A third of my day is spent doing client management – things like answering one-off questions or collecting input on negotiations. Another third is spent internally coordinating with other team members, while the final third sees me drafting documents."*

Litigators follow a similar trajectory, with one source noting that *"most associates should be taking depositions by their third year."* This junior took us through their role throughout a typical a case: *"I start by fact-checking expert reports, and during the deposition phase I help to prep the partners. As we move into pretrial I draft orders and outlines of direct testimonies; by the time we get to trial I'm helping to prep the witnesses."* Some juniors enjoyed white-collar cases the most, as they're *"fact-intensive and fast-moving – especially when they're in the investigation stage and you're responding to queries from the DOJ."* Others preferred patent litigation cases, as they often come with good drafting opportunities and allow juniors to spend ample time liaising with experts.

Offices & Strategy

"THIS IS IMPORTANT," one source declared. *"Goodwin's policy of not making juniors specialize until their third year means that they encourage us to work with people from all of the offices. We do a lot of cross-staffing, which is wonderful; the team I'm currently on has members from across six offices."* Fortunately, our sources also liked the offices they were actually based in. The Boston HQ was dubbed by one interviewee as *"the best law firm office I've ever stepped foot in: we moved a year ago into a brand new building with lots of natural light and touches that were designed for a law firm in this millennium."* New York residents were also happy: *"We're in the New York Times Building, and we share a cafeteria with them. The location is ideal, as we're in something of a transit hub."*

"...the best law firm office I've ever stepped foot in."

The New York office has indeed benefited from its status as a hub in recent years. Sources had *"noticed a power shift from Boston to New York, especially as the firm has become more international. The head of litigation is here*

See firm profile on p.644

The Inside View

Diversity	Partners (%)	Associates (%)
Women	22	47
White	92	75
Black/African American	1	3
Hispanic/Latin American	2	4
Asian	4	15
Mixed/Other	1	3
LGBT	3	4

and a lot of the major cases are originated here. They're trying to grow out of the impression that we're a Boston-based firm, so that we're seen as a truly international entity." On the whole our interviewees were buoyed by the fact that "we're definitely growing, and it's visible. In San Francisco, for example, it's evident in the rising number of attorneys we have and the larger physical space we're occupying." Others flagged that "there is excitement about the firm's future; they're taking a reasoned and practical approach to growth – it's very organic."

Culture

Many of our interviewees were looking for a firm with a more "easygoing environment" at the time of their OCIs, so we were curious to know how their expectations matched up to the reality of life at Goodwin. "It's a go-getter culture but it's not cutthroat," one junior reflected. Another praised the firm for being a place that "encourages you to ask questions rather than make mistakes. I have messed up a few times and the partners have all been very nice about it – they understand that you learn from them." Sources felt that this level of interaction was facilitated, in part, by the fact that "the partners are generally younger than they are at most firms, which makes it easier to talk to, be candid with and even be friends with them."

"It's a go-getter culture but it's not cutthroat."

On a more obvious level, Goodwin's less buttoned-up vibe is evident in its dress code. "Three people have walked by my office wearing jeans in the last five minutes," one interviewee told us, adding that "there is one partner who turns up in Hawaiian shirts and Birkenstocks every day!" Of course, sources recommended that incomers still have a suit at hand for facing clients or attending court, but otherwise explained that "jeans Friday is creeping into every day." But it's not just the more relaxed dress code that shapes this "relaxed and laid back" vibe. "I think it's more about the hiring," one interviewee pondered. "They avoid pretentious people. Also, they don't try to change you – they're not looking to mold you into a particular type." Ultimately this more flexible atmosphere bodes well for a healthy social life from coast to coast. San Fran sources

told us that "a lot of my colleagues like to go out for a drink – we're just normal people who happen to work in the law," while Bostonians revealed that the firm hires out a gym each week "so we can go and play basketball. Around 20 to 30 of us go. Last night, I was working late on a deal and the partner encouraged me to finish early and go – they do a good job of trying to respect people's work-life balance."

Hours & Compensation

For one source, Goodwin's culture was evident "in the better-than-expected work-life balance that I've had here. The more I've been exposed to what my friends at other firms in New York are doing, the more I realize how good I have it. There's not a rigid face-time requirement and a lot of people work remotely every Friday." Associates aim to meet a 1,950 billable hours target from their second year onward; if they do, a bonus is granted, and we heard that "it's based on both your year and the quality of your reviews." Most of our interviewees found the target achievable, especially because a generous amount of pro bono can be put toward it [see below].

At the same time, sources did admit to working "some intense hours" as they approached trial and deal closings. So while a "normal day" might see juniors exiting around 6:30pm (and billing around eight to ten hours), a busy period could see associates finishing closer to the 10pm mark – in some cases for a couple of months. Juniors did, however, elaborate on some regional differences: "In New York it's more common to roll in later and leave later, but here in California most people get in before 8:30am and the office tends to be empty by six."

Training & Development

Formal training is divided into business and litigation tracks. The former favors "a lot more front-loaded training and covers anything you want," sources explained, "from using Excel to forming signature pages – I remember receiving more calendar invitations than I could accept!" Litigators, on the other hand, described a "lighter, more 'as you go'" approach to training."The more substantive sessions occur later on," juniors noted. "In the third year, you're taught how to prepare your own depositions and manage cases, and you're also given a breakdown of what the steps are to the partnership." Until then, "the emphasis is more on midlevel mentors walking first-years through things," and the quality of such tutelage is "dependent on the midlevel you are working with – I have such a good relationship with mine, for example. It's so easy to talk to each other!"

See firm profile on p.644

The Inside View

Pro Bono

All pro bono hours can be counted toward Goodwin's billable target. As a result, some juniors reported billing over 200 hours of pro bono each year. Our sources had worked on immigration, asylum and prisoners' rights matters, but also mentioned specific relationships with GLAAD, Kids in Need of Defense (KIND) and the Innocence Project. *"There's also a housing court you can attend once a month, to assist landlords and tenants who fall beneath our pro bono threshold."*

Some of our transactional sources grumbled that *"there tends to be more opportunities for people in litigation. The partner in Boston emails out around eight opportunities every other week, but there are hundreds of us jumping for them – they go really fast."* However, we also spoke to transactional associates who had no problem racking up over 100 hours of pro bono.

Pro bono hours
- For all US attorneys: 59,453
- Average per US attorney: 67

Diversity

The firm's affinity groups include a women's initiative, an LGBT group, and the Committee on Racial and Ethnic Diversity (CRED). Associates reflected that the groups are *"pretty active,"* and typically host monthly dinners and regular events. Bostonians agreed that their office *"doesn't feel as diverse compared to New York, as Boston is a less diverse city generally."* They did, however, mention that both 1L and 2L diversity fellowships are on offer; the latter provides students from under-represented backgrounds with a $15,000 award to help cover expenses during their third year of law school.

In New York, sources felt the women's initiative was the most visible: *"They have created an open forum where people can speak freely, form mentor relationships, elevate issues, meet others outside of their group, and generally create awareness."* Those in the Californian offices, meanwhile, told us that *"there's a good amount of room left for improvement,"* highlighting practice groups with no female partners and a recent dip in local women's initiative activity following a key figure's departure. The firm, however, tells us that things are back up and running on that front now.

On chambers-associate.com...
Goodwin's lawyers give us an inside view on their technology and life sciences practices.

See firm profile on p.644

Goulston & Storrs

Lawyers per state

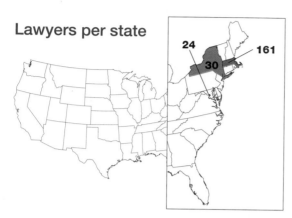

24   **161**
30

Largest US office: Boston
US offices: 3
International offices: 0
First-year salary: $180,000
Billable hours: no requirement
Summers 2018: 7 2Ls
Revenue 2017: $176 million
Partners made in 2018: 3
Famous for: real estate, especially in Boston and DC; offering transparency through monthly associate meetings; non-competitive culture

From its Boston stronghold Goulston offers top notch real estate work in a non-competitive atmosphere – but ambitions to grow its other domestic bases and practices show it's not standing still.

DESCRIBED as *"the premier real estate firm in Boston"* in our sister publication *Chambers USA*, Goulston earns a top ranking in Massachusetts for its expertise in this area of the law. It's a firm that draws in regional and national developers alike, as well as investors eying up the juiciest new projects. Its robust reputation also ended up drawing in many of our associate sources, who highlighted their interest in commercial real estate in particular: *"I was looking for a place where I could get sophisticated commercial experience on both transactions and permitting/development work – development is not something you can usually do at the big firms."*

While real estate may be a solid foundation for Goulston, it is building upon it a reputation for work in its many other practices, which include corporate, IP, tax and private client & trusts. In *Chambers USA*, other practices to get a nod in Massachusetts include banking & finance, bankruptcy/restructuring and general commercial litigation, while on a nationwide scale Goulston's industry expertise in retail and leisure & hospitality garners praise. For our associates, *"the fact that Goulston is a leading commercial real estate firm was just a factor and not a decision-maker."* So what swayed them in the end? Many

put it down to Goulston's *"small-firm feel"* that comes with attractive advancement opportunities: *"It's not uncommon to see people progressing from a summer associate to making partner, and I wanted to be at a firm that genuinely invests in people's futures."*

Offices

All of the juniors on our list were based in Goulston's Boston HQ, which is split across two buildings; the firm occupies one floor of an office on the waterfront, as well as an entire building next door: *"It's a converted factory, which is unconventional"* but universally adored thanks to its trendy brickwork and abundance of open spaces. Particular praise was bestowed on the firm's support staff: *"There's a legal assistant for every attorney, plus we have staff here all the time – even after hours. I've never found myself high and dry."* Goulston has two other domestic offices in New York and DC, and interviewees felt that there was a good amount of interaction with them. *"We're encouraged to stop by New York and DC if we're traveling,"* and the firm's work allocators also staff matters across all three locations, increasing collaboration. Overseas, a 'relationship building office' in Beijing was felt to have served its purpose and closed its doors, with a string of Chinese clients to its name.

"I've never found myself high and dry."

On chambers-associate.com...

- Get hired at Goulston
- Interview with chairman of the summer committee, Joshua Davis

See firm profile on p.645

The Inside View

Rankings in *Chambers USA*

Banking & Finance	Litigation
Bankruptcy/Restructuring	Real Estate
Environment	Retail
Leisure & Hospitality	

For detail on ranking tiers and ranking locations, visit
www.chambersandpartners.com

Strategy & Future

Associates were keen to tell us about Goulston's monthly associate meetings, which involve a presentation delivered by the firm's managing directors over lunch. *"Itkeeps us updated on the health of the firm and what's going on,"* sources revealed, praising the firm's transparency on *"partner pay, recruitment, trends, firm financials and expansion plans."* So what had sources learned from this *"open forum"*? *"We are going to continue expanding our New York and DC offices, and will grow our practice groups outside of real estate – we're trying to build up our size."*

The Work

Each group has two directors (partners are called directors at Goulston) who serve as work-allocators and manage associates' assignments. *"If directors think you'll be interested in a matter they'll contact an allocator,"* sources explained, highlighting that *"it's good to have a buffer so that if you're too busy they can go back and re-staff."* Overall, *"the system tracks what you're doing and who with to make sure that you become a well-rounded attorney with a good variety of skills."* Most associates land in the real estate group, but a few on our list were working in Goulston's litigation, corporate and private client & trusts departments.

The real estate group's *"bread and butter"* is commercial work, but juniors did speak of being able to do *"smaller residential deals on behalf of non-profit clients, as our pro bono work is sometimes integrated into the regular assignment system."* Areas covered within the group include development, finance, construction, international investment and condominium work. *"In some real estate practices you'll go into a specific subsection, but here they let you try out everything for the first couple of years, which gives you a more global picture."* One source emphasized that *"even though my focus is on development matters, they keep other transactions on my plate so that I don't lose skills tied to them."* The geographic scope varies depending on the type of work, interviewees explained. For example, land use matters are usually based in Massachusetts, while sales and purchases have more national dimensions. *"Leasings are all over the place – I'm often working on assignments occurring on the West Coast or in the Midwest."*

Recent work highlights

- Represented longtime client Boston Properties on various real estate projects, including the $660 million development of a new world headquarters for Marriott International and the $2.3 billion refinancing of the General Motors Building in New York City
- Acted for national multi-media company America's Test Kitchen during litigation brought against one of its founders and former CEO for alleged breach of fiduciary duties and misappropriation of confidential information
- Represented investment service Gordon Brothers in connection with the liquidation of Joyce Leslie – a regional women's clothing retail chain with an inventory worth $3.5 million
- Advised Pyramid Hotel Group on a range of matters tied to its portfolio, including its $200 million acquisition of a San Francisco-based hotel from an affiliate of Blackstone, and its ongoing acquisition of land owned by the Bank of America earmarked for a mixed-use hotel and retail condominium project

"...you often see projects you're working on posted in The Boston Globe."

One source described working with *"a lot of developers in Boston. I've been able to do waterfront work, which is very complicated, and I was able to work exclusively with a partner doing that."* On the whole, the group's clients were deemed *"very sophisticated – as is the work."* Associates enjoyed working on *"high-profile"* matters and enthused that *"you often see projects you're working on posted in* The Boston Globe." Transactional matters in particular gave juniors the opportunity to work on *"major financings involving foreign investors."* Typical associate tasks included due diligence, conducting zoning reviews, analyzing permits, and putting together first drafts of documents like contribution agreements, resolutions and certificates. *"The work is challenging but I don't feel scared to ask questions. Compared to my friends' experiences, I think I've been given responsibility that they wouldn't get until many years later,"* one interviewee concluded.

Training & Development

There's *"a little bit of an orientation"* to welcome juniors to the firm, plus a general training program provided via Goulston & Storrs University. However, sources agreed that training is *"meant to be very organic and managed through the projects that are given to you over time."* To supplement this more organic approach, we heard that partners in certain groups *"host weekly hour-long sessions over lunch to delve deeper into a topic and increase our knowledge of it."*

The Inside View

See firm profile on p.645

Diversity	Partners (%)	Associates (%)
Women	22	57
White	99	75
Black/African American	0	8
Hispanic/Latin American	0.5	6
Asian	0.5	11
Mixed/Other	-	-
LGBT	3	4

For their first few years at the firm, juniors get an official review every six months in which they sit down with two partners from outside their group, who provide feedback from partners they've worked with. By the fifth year, associates can expect to receive a more in-depth review which involves "*a self-reflective portion where you evaluate your skill-set and what you want to do with the next part of your career. They talk you through the opportunities that are available at the upper levels so that you're aware of your prospects.*"

Hours & Compensation

Everyone we spoke to at Goulston praised the work/life balance they'd experienced, with most describing an average day that lasted between 8.30am to around 7pm. There can be occasional late nights, while weekend work was deemed "*rare – when it does happen the director will also be working. It's not the type of place where working every weekend is necessary.*" Instead, "*there's a focus on a family culture here,*" which for our sources translated into a positive stance on flexible working: "*It's not like you have to stay until 6pm just because you have to – it's perfectly fine to leave and work remotely.*"

When it came to compensation we heard more good news: "*We're on the Cravath scale so I don't have any complaints there.*" Attorneys at Goulston don't receive bonuses, but interviewees made it clear that they viewed this in a positive light: "*The trade in for not having bonuses is a friendlier culture. It's a self-selecting decision and it makes me a happier attorney. At the end of the day we're compensated in other ways: I've always had the opportunity to take vacation, and the firm really does respect your time off.*"

Culture

"*I know everyone uses the word 'collegial,'*" one associate admitted, "*but everyone knows each other here, from the directors to the paralegals.*" Another source agreed: "*There's a camaraderie here, and people take an interest in your personal life to better understand where you're at with work.*" When pressed for reasons why Goulston promotes such an agreeable culture, some attributed it to the legacy of "*prior managing directors, who've passed down the message that your colleagues are so important. It means that everyone is so invested in their colleagues' success.*" Others put it down to the lack of official billing targets and bonus payouts: "*It doesn't encourage a competitive angle, so everyone is willing to help each other out. I can't count the amount of times I've gone into someone's office unannounced with a question and they've invited me in and talked me through it for an hour. It's a testament to the culture and it's a big thing that's kept me here.*"

> "*It means that everyone is so invested in their colleagues' success.*"

Sources also told of monthly associate socials, as well as happy hours and firm-wide events that celebrate the holidays: "*Goulston makes an effort to bring people up from DC and New York so that we can all meet.*"

Pro Bono

All pro bono hours count as billable at Goulston, which means "*there's not that hesitation to take on pro bono work. The firm really puts its money where its mouth is.*" Associates added: "*A lot of it tends to be included in your regular work allocation matters. Sometimes you're given a project and you don't know it's pro bono until you go to log your hours!*" The chair of the firm's pro bono committee is the firm's managing director, "*which gives you a sense of how highly valued pro bono is.*" One interviewee reflected: "*It's wonderful because you get to really dive into the material. I think it's a real selling point of the firm and it's provided me with some of the most gratifying work I've done here.*"

> "*It's wonderful because you get to really dive into the material.*"

Pro bono hours
- For all attorneys: 14,170
- Average per attorney: undisclosed

Diversity

"*It's a conscious goal of the firm,*" juniors declared, who were pleased to tell us that "*our numbers have steadily been increasing over the years – as time goes on there are more and more diverse attorneys here.*" Goulston's diversity committee helps to steer efforts when it comes to the recruitment and retention of minorities, and was praised for considering "*the whole gamut of people covered by the definition of diversity.*"

See firm profile on p.645

The Inside View

Greenberg Glusker Fields Claman & Machtinger LLP

Lawyers per state

92

Largest US office: LA
US offices: 1
International offices: 0
First-year salary: $160,000
Billable hours: 1,850
Summers 2018: 3 2Ls
Revenue 2017: undisclosed
Partners made in 2018: 3
Famous for: representing Hollywood A-listers and other showbiz titans

The spotlight rightly shines on Greenberg Glusker's showbiz successes, but that's not all folks: this La(w) La(w) Land starlet rolls out the red carpet for non-Hollywood clients too...

THERE may be no business like show business, but the law can get you closer to Tinsel Town's glitz and glamor than you might think. How many law firms can boast of being regularly mentioned in *Variety* and *The Hollywood Reporter*, as this one is? LA's small but influential Greenberg Glusker is famous in Hollywood circles for assisting the likes of Paramount, DreamWorks, Steven Spielberg, Tom Cruise, James Cameron, and that music-to-movie (and back again) chameleon, Madonna. Speaking of the music industry, over the years, GG has literally helped rock-star clients including The Beatles, Britney Spears, members of Guns N' Roses, plus the estates of Bob Marley and Ray Charles.

Chambers USA hands out the legal equivalent of Oscar nominations to the firm's media and entertainment litigators in California. Outside this industry, the directory also ranks GG's environmental practice and lists the real estate team as 'recognized practitioners.' Meanwhile, the new *Chambers High Net Worth* guide applauds Greenberg's full-service work for wealthy individuals. Entertainment, then, isn't the whole picture; this all-singing, all-dancing law firm also has a rich local pedigree in areas like corporate, finance, IP, bankruptcy, and general

litigation. Associates were drawn both by its *"great"* reputation in the City of Angels and the *"combination of high caliber work and lifestyle opportunities in a 90-lawyer firm where you can get to know everybody's name. Greenberg checked all those boxes."*

The Work

Litigation work comes from *"a mix of high net worth individuals, A-list entertainers, and companies both mid-market and* Fortune 500," a junior associate here explained. Newcomers typically get a taste of as many types of disputes as possible. Allocation is handled by the head of department, who discusses associates' availability with them via weekly emails before distributing tasks. Interviewees said *"they're excellent at making sure everyone always has something to do. I've learned so much from working with almost everyone in the team and I'm never worrying about hitting hours targets."* Cases span from copyright and contract breaches to employment, real estate litigation and even trespass matters. Given *"as much as responsibility as I feel comfortable taking without being left to flounder,"* sources had been in direct contact with clients *"literally right off the bat."* Motion writing, research, frequent court appearances and defending depositions formed a typical associate work diet.

"They do throw you in the fire a bit, in a good way."

On chambers-associate.com...

- Get hired at Greenberg Glusker
- Interview with hiring partner Brian Kang

The Inside View

See firm profile on p.646

Rankings in *Chambers USA*

Media & Entertainment

For detail on ranking tiers and ranking locations, visit
www.chambersandpartners.com

Recent work highlights

- Representing Amber Heard on her divorce from Johnny Depp
- Acted for DreamWorks to recover 7.4 million units of home video inventory held by a former distributor
- Advises Bob Marley's estate, including on recent licensing agreement for the formation of Marley Natural cannabis line
- Served as environmental counsel to Federal Realty Investment Trust on a $80 million upmarket shopping mall development in LA, The Point

Greenberg Glusker's smaller corporate team also has a work allocator, but we heard that it operates on a looser free market system in practice. Associates *"really like how it works. You can tailor your career to what you're interested in, and I haven't had to say no to too much work."* The practice's three main buckets are *"predominantly sell-side"* M&A, early-stage venture capital financing, and outside general counsel. Associates get stuck into *"everything from forming a company to selling it off,"* with clients including *"a lot of companies involved in entertainment or technology. We're not representing Google or Facebook, but doing more mid-market stuff worth up to $100 million."* Although we heard that *"they do throw you in the fire a bit, in a good way,"* on the plus-side *"the firm doesn't hide associates from anything."* A colleague agreed: *"One thing Greenberg is great about is getting juniors a lot of responsibility,"* including on *"heavily in-demand"* entertainment-related deals involving LA-based production companies.

Real estate associates also got a glimpse of the Tinseltown lights via *"working with individual entertainment clients on their property matters too."* Think lavish mansions in the Hollywood Hills, although the practice's more mainstream work is in the purchase and sale of commercial real estate. Institutional clients bring in a sizable chunk of business, and associates had worked on a range of deals spanning *"anything from a big insurance company acquiring $200 million of property to a couple buying a home."* Work allocation is again co-ordinated by the department's head, who interviewees felt is doing a good job: *"I am definitely happy with what I've got so far. You see the whole timeline of deals."* They suggested *"the workload ebbs and flows a lot"* but were generally busy reviewing titles, drafting agreements, preparing closing documents and taking the lead on smaller issues – once they'd got their foundations steady.

Training & Development

All associates get *"relatively informal"* twice-yearly reviews with their heads of department, who solicit feedback from across the firm as a whole in June and December. There are also informal assessments, *"in that when you turn something in, partners are good about saying what you could improve; everything's quite constructive. Some are also big on emailing the managing partner thanking everyone on the deal for their help."* Greenberg Glusker has also recently introduced an *"outstanding"* formal Associate Training and Development program, divided between firmwide logistics tutorials and practice group training on more discrete legal topics. *"It's a lot more structured than before; the firm is willing to invest a lot in training associates,"* the scheme's guinea pigs happily declared. *"There are always people there to ask questions without worrying you'll be laughed at."*

Office & Culture

Reassuringly, the Hollywood sign is visible from the firm's *"pretty typical"* sole office, located on Avenue of the Stars in Century City where there's *"more of a relaxed vibe than downtown LA: it's a lot less crowded."* The marble lobby and ocean views drew no complaints, though some were less impressed by the kitchen's *"burnt orange counter tops,"* leading most to conclude *"it's not the best office, but it is nice!"* Questionable color choices aside, the only other issues we heard about were *"the placement of the fruit bowls, and poor wifi keeping us from accessing Instagram."* Both problems, you'll be glad to hear, were brought to the associate committee and solved.

Several interviewees pointed out that having just one office means *"everyone you work with is in the building and you get to know everyone, even attorneys in different practice groups. It's small enough that there's a sense of community and common respect."* People felt that management is open about the firm's financials and future direction – the managing partner and associate committee meet every couple of months to run through recent developments. They also explained that a higher ratio of partners to associates than other firms means *"there's less hierarchy and more opportunities for people at different levels to interact, either in work or socially."*

"There aren't too many crazy 24-hour-working people here."

Summer is the peak social season, when the California sun is at its hottest and *"there's a festive atmosphere"* as summers and current associates alike partake in parties at partners' houses, associate dinners, and trips to the Hollywood Bowl. The firm also runs an annual ski trip, Christmas party, fantasy football league and social

See firm profile on p.646

Diversity	Partners (%)	Associates (%)
Women	22	43
White	90	90
Black/African American	-	-
Hispanic/Latin American	2	3
Asian	8	7
Mixed/Other	-	-
LGBT	-	-

retreat *"with no work component – it's all playing golf and getting massages."* Each week attorneys come together for lunch on Monday and 5pm Friday drinks, providing *"lots of opportunities to bond with people, and you do get the chance to as Greenberg respects work/life balance."* Sources revealed *"there aren't too many crazy 24-hour-working people here,"* but also appreciated *"not feeling pressured"* to dive headfirst into every social occasion.

Get Hired

"The three things the firm is looking for at interview are academic performance, emotional and intellectual maturity, and being able to speak well to clients." That's one associate's summary of the Greenberg Glusker creed, with the added proviso that *"they're really trying hard to consider diversity as well."* There are no set questions you can expect to come up at interview, as the process is geared more toward *"conversation and finding out if you'll fit the culture. There are no trick questions."* Come callback time, grades and qualifications will be a foregone conclusion – at that stage personality is key. Sources advised *"we're looking for people with decent social skills who won't put their foot in their mouth."*

"Greenberg is looking for people who could join a big national firm..."

Ties to California are basically essential, although the firm does dabble in out-of-state hiring for the right candidates. Commitment is key, as *"Greenberg is looking for people who could join a big national firm but appreciate what we're doing here and will stay,"* rather than using the firm as a stepping stone. *"Having an interesting background you can talk about"* will make your application stand out. Despite having nothing to do with law, necessarily, it *"came up in a lot of interviews and was a good jump off point for conversation."* Sports, art and theater are examples of useful interests to have.

Managing partner Bob Baradaran recommends that wannabe lawyers *"look at factors beyond firm size and compensation statistics"* when making their applications, as *"the people and culture at a firm are probably more important than anything else. A large contingent of our firm*

is very high-caliber former students who've spent a few years at other firms before realizing that's not where they'd like to build a career."* Associates agreed: *"Pay attention to who you're going to be working with. It makes a big difference to know who's going to supervise you and who you'll be forging relationships with."*

Diversity

"We're fairly good in terms of gender balance," both female and male associates agreed. *"There are more men than women overall but all firms have a problem with female representation at the top."* There were worries that *"there's less ethnic diversity, and we're maybe not reflective enough of Los Angeles in that sense."* Some even felt *"the firm talks about diversity a lot but that doesn't seem to be having much of an effect on the demographics."* Greenberg's diversity committee hosts Bar Association dinners and collaborates on external events. Hiring partner Brian Kang tells us: *"The firm actively participates in LA law schools' diversity fairs. Candidates' qualifications are what's most important, but we definitely take diversity into consideration."* Associates suggested some departments are doing better than others at diversity – those in real estate, for example, felt their team was *"very diverse"* but concluded that the firm (and profession as a whole) still has room for improvement.

Pro Bono

"Getting opportunities to do pro bono work all the time" via regular emails, associates were relieved to find *"it doesn't feel like a taboo, and I've never been told I'm doing too much. It's a great opportunity to get to run the strategy of a case."* The firm regularly collaborates with local nonprofits Bet Tzedek and the Los Angeles County Bar Association on small claims: our interviewees had taken on a range of eviction defenses, injunction requests, adoption cases and other small projects. 100% of pro bono counts toward the hours target for associates.

"It's a great opportunity to get to run the strategy of a case."

Pro bono hours
- For all attorneys: 1,541
- Average per attorney: 47

Hours & Compensation

1,850 represents a *"nominal"* billable hours target, but *"the firm is explicit not to worry too much about it as a first-year: they understand we're still getting our feet wet."* Most associates found this requirement *"pretty realistic"* anyway. With an average day running 9am to 6.30pm, and weekend work a rarity, all those we spoke to had plenty of

See firm profile on p.646

time to get out and enjoy the Cali sun. It's also important to note that *"discretionary"* bonuses are no longer tied to number of hours billed; they're now based on a range of factors including work quality. A $160,000 starting salary might not quite be A-list money, but associates felt *"the trade-off of having manageable hours makes it fair. We're not at the very top of the market but it's in line with firms of our size and it's a pretty generous wage."* The firm also provides 15 days of vacation a year.

Strategy & Future

Quizzed on Greenberg Glusker's place in the market, managing partner Bob Baradaran explains: *"Greenberg is uniquely situated as a 90-plus attorney single office firm, with the culture of a small firm and the quality and sophistication of work that you typically find at the top law firms in the country. Also, clients value the fact that our lawyers stay here long term and serve on client teams that learn and understand each client's business and objectives."* Entertainment is a particularly lucrative area, and *"around a quarter of the firm is somehow connected to that space;"* a proportion that's still growing.

"Clients value the fact that our lawyers stay here long term."

"Last year I was talking to someone who'd not had a lot of work experience but had had an internship as a 1L. They quickly realized they had an issue with organization. They weren't used to multitasking, which is a very different experience at law school than at a firm. It's having to take notes for three classes versus having five or six partners reaching out to you directly, and trying to figure out who you prioritize. Seeing how they acknowledged an area for improvement and the steps they took to improve/resolve that issue showed great judgment."
– McDermott hiring partner Eric Gilbert

See firm profile on p.646

Greenberg Traurig, PA

Lawyers per state

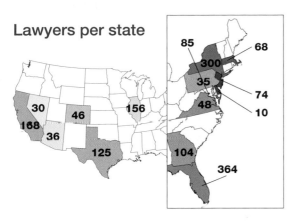

85   68
300
35
30   46   156
168
36
125   104
364
48   74
10

Largest US office: New York
US offices: 29
International offices: 9
First-year salary: $110,000-$180,000
Billable hours: no official target
Summers 2018: 34 (5 1Ls, 29 2Ls)
Revenue 2017: $1.48 billion (+7.2%)
Partners made in 2018: 33 in US
Famous for: megafirm with a flair for real estate

It's not easy being green, but this youthful Miami-born firm proves that hard work pays off.

FOUNDED in 1967, Greenberg Traurig has grown from a small South Florida firm specializing in real estate to a global giant with 38 offices in ten countries around the world. When we asked sources for the secret ingredient in the firm's recipe for success, they told us: *"You don't grow from a tiny Miami firm to one of the largest in the world without having an eye for entrepreneurial people who can attract and retain work."* Associates were drawn to GT's huge US network spanning 19 states: *"They have cutting-edge practitioners in pretty much every market, and I love being able to interact with other offices."*

"They have cutting-edge practitioners in pretty much every market."

These days GT's practice has gone well beyond real estate (although this remains the jewel in the crown if its *Chambers USA* rankings are anything to go by), with formidable rankings in Florida and New York for its corporate and litigation practices respectively. But the firm's offices across the US pick up rankings for all kinds of sectors – it pays to take a closer look at *Chambers USA.*

The Work

Of 113 associates, Greenberg's corporate and litigation practices claimed the majority: around 60%, while real estate housed another 25%. The firm's smaller offices adopt a work assignment system that is *"a little more organic,"* as opposed to the larger offices, where *"there's a coordinator for first and second years and someone who oversees it all."* New Yorkers in the corporate group revealed a new system whereby *"around once a week a partner will ask what your workload looks like as an extra way to monitor business."* A DC second-year told us: *"It's not 'eat what you kill'; it's based on developing personal relationships with shareholders."* (Here they call partners "shareholders".)

Sources in corporate said the group does *"a mix of every single type of work: private equity, M&A, capital markets, debt work. Name any practice area and you'll find someone here who does it."* We spoke to associates across a range of specialisms and offices, and most concurred: *"You have months where you're working on bigger deals, and then times when you're working on more discrete matters rather than balls to the wall M&A."* In terms of clients the majority, we were told, were often publicly-traded companies with a largely national scope. Enjoying the level of exposure they got, juniors said: *"Being able to understand how a transaction is run is a huge bonus."*

"Name any practice area and you'll find someone here who does it."

On chambers-associate.com...

- Interview with CEO Brian Duffy
- More on getting hired

See firm profile on p.647

The Inside View

375

Rankings in *Chambers USA*

Banking & Finance
Bankruptcy/Restructuring
Construction
Corporate/Commercial
Corporate/M&A
Energy & Natural
  Resources
Environment
Franchising
Gaming & Licensing
Healthcare
Immigration
Intellectual Property

Labor & Employment
Latin American Investment
Leisure & Hospitality
Litigation
Media & Entertainment
Native American Law
Natural Resources
Products Liability
REITs
Real Estate
Retail
Tax

For detail on ranking tiers and ranking locations, visit
www.chambersandpartners.com

Recent work highlights

- The real estate team in Miami secured a $36.8 million loan in 2018 to revamp two historic buildings on Miami Beach into a new hotel
- A multi-office team represented Loews Hotels in Orlando in forming a new hotel complex with Universal Parks and resorts
- The firm is representing Goldman Sachs in a 1 billion tender offer for 100% of shares in a leading Polish stock exchange listed developer
- The New York team represented Siris Capital, a private equity firm, in its acquisition of Intralinks, a leading technology provider for banking and capital markets providers

One DC recruit reflected: "*On a scale of one to ten I'd say my responsibility has been around an eight. I've heard about people at other firms who have been in diligence basements for their first year, but that hasn't been my experience.*" Associates had, nevertheless, been dealt a generous helping of due diligence, as well as drafting memos and ancillary documents, gathering feedback and coordinating closings. Finally, those in the firm's smaller offices felt "*you get more responsibility here than in New York because there's less of a hierarchy here.*"

In litigation, interviewees had sampled a variety of matters including labor and employment, securities and bankruptcy cases. "*I've been pleasantly surprised by my assignments,*" one Boston resident informed us. "*I got to attend over 20 hearings in my first year, which were mostly discovery but some dispositive motions too. I got to do twelve depositions and was heavily involved in everything surrounding them.*" Others concurred: "*As a junior you get to handle smaller claims in state court, so you get more autonomy.*" Sources had been involved in "*a ton of mediation and arbitration,*" and listed a range of tasks including "*preparing witnesses, pre-mediation memos, preparing outlines for depositions and exhibits as well as drafting motions for summary judgments.*"

Greenberg's esteemed real estate practice housed a quarter of this year's interviewees. The firm's huge national scope proved a hit with juniors: "*The wonderful thing about us is that we have national clients even though our offices are regional. We get to work on complex transactions at a very early stage.*" The range of work on offer ticked more boxes, and we heard about work involving affordable housing, public finance, developer transactions, buying dirt and construction lending. Sources explained that because of the national nature of the work "*you're constantly being challenged. There are always com-*

plex issues arising from the nuances of other states that sometimes even the shareholders haven't seen before."

"We get to work on complex transactions at a very early stage."

Newbies continued to praise the quick responsibility they'd experienced: "*I get more client contact every day and I'm always involved in the process. We're not just pushing paper.*" That's not to say diligence didn't come up, but sources reasoned: "*It's nice to have some work that you're comfortable with rather than spending 40 hours a week doing work that really makes you dig deep.*" Interviewees had drafted title reviews, negotiated purchase contracts and "*quarter-backed closings*" to name a few examples of their workload. Despite the challenges that come with the firm's "*lean staffing model*" we heard that supervision is still plentiful: "*Shareholders are very supportive. If I'm on a loan with elements I've never worked on before someone's always happy to go through it step by step.*" Finally, they enthused: "*The firm is so interconnected that if someone here doesn't know the answer there are 2,000 other people who might.*"

Offices

New York is the firm's largest office, but Miami is the birthplace of GT. "*It's beautiful. I interviewed at a lot of places and this was the best, design-wise.*" Sources across the board praised the "*incomparable*" resources, including 24/7 document services, tech help and office staff. Up in New York the office is located "*right in midtown, near Grand Central,*" although we heard rumors that the office may be moving. Compared to other BigLaw firms in the city, juniors felt "*our office has more of a community feel because it's a little smaller.*"

"Our office has more of a community feel."

See firm profile on p.647

The Inside View

Diversity	Partners (%)	Associates (%)
Women	22.5	47
White	86.6	77.4
Black/African American	-	-
Hispanic/Latin American	-	-
Asian	-	-
Mixed/Other	-	-
LGBT	-	-

With 29 offices in the US alone, it's no wonder how associates felt: "*Being the global behemoth that it is, I think GT needs to be pretty decentralized.*" While the culture varies between offices, all of our interviewees enjoyed GT's huge national and international footprint and subsequent wealth of resources. "*I don't feel disconnected here.It always surprises me when a shareholder knows exactly who to reach out to in each office. If we need a subpoena or local law advice in another state they always know a couple of people to choose from.*" Those in Fort Lauderdale agreed: "*The firm projects a culture of feeling small while being so huge and I've really found that to be true.*" When it came to working with other offices we heard "*I've worked with 15 of our 29 offices and the depth of speciality and local knowledge is unrivaled. I've also worked with Korea, Poland and Shanghai.*"

Culture

Sources reflected: "*When you like what you're doing and the people you're working with it just breeds success. I think that's something our clients really admire.*" Other reports chimed with this sentiment, with juniors describing the firm as "*fairly flat in structure*" and "*a well-oiled machine rather than a sweatshop.*" One Philly newbie felt that "*there's the expectation here that people stick around longer than at other firms. There's no point investing energy if people are going to leave anyway, so there's an interest in your career and making sure you're happy.*" The firm's relative youth added a sense of entrepreneurial spirit according to one source: "*If you're working at a high level it's recognized immediately. GT is only 50 years old and I don't know if you'd get the same opportunities as a junior if the firm was 200 years old.*" Florida recruits told us: "*GT had a nasty reputation here, but we're actually known for being one of the friendliest offices with the highest morale. We're all close, in and out of the office, and people are very understanding when it comes to having a personal life.*"

"When you like what you're doing and the people you're working with it just breeds success."

Many sources across offices praised the work-life balance at GT, describing a "*family-friendly*" culture. We heard

about monthly happy hours and holiday parties, but overall the social side of things was fairly casual. We did hear that a number of shareholders are involved in various charitable events, and that "*it's common for people to hang out outside of work. People are close enough to invite each other round their houses and so on.*"

Hours & Compensation

GT doesn't operate an official billable target, although juniors told us 1,800 hours was the minimum requirement to be eligible for a bonus. "*We're told it's based on quality over quantity, but no one really knows what the system is,*" sources revealed. "*It's definitely a source of frustration. If you get to the end of the year and have a great review you still don't know what to expect in terms of compensation.*" Others said: "*From my perspective it's not something the firm takes lightly. It's on a case-by-case basis and I'm fine with that.*" On the compensation, which matches Cravath in New York but varies elsewhere, associates felt: "*even making $5,000 less than someone over the street can be annoying. It's not a deal-breaker for me but it's something people should be aware of.*"

Most interviewees reported regularly leaving work between 6.30 and 8pm, with one enthusiastic associate lamenting the fact that "*the culture is less full-on than you'd expect from a BigLaw firm. The office is usually pretty dead by 7.*" Some New Yorkers in corporate said there were rare occasions where "*I haven't gone to bed until 4am and then had to go straight back into work that morning.*" Most associates agreed "*people usually go home and then work from there.*"

Get Hired

"If you're not geared toward building your own network you probably won't succeed here." Find out what Greenberg is looking for in future recruits at chambers-associate.com

Pro Bono

Greenberg has recently introduced a minimum pro bono requirement of 25 hours, and associates told us they frequently get "*robust newsletters*" advertising opportunities. Those who had done pro bono had worked on a variety of matters, including a free Estate Planning Clinic in Fort Lauderdale for Holocaust survivors, which was "*a truly great experience,*" according to interviewees. Boston sources told us about an initiative which helps juvenile immigrants gain asylum in the US, while those in Philadelphia had worked on a "*pretty cool*" project which aims to bring an affordable energy loan initiative from New York to Pennsylvania.

See firm profile on p.647

A number of sources, however, told us: "*I've been try-ing to get pro bono but I haven't been successful,*" while others simply said: "*I haven't had the time or the inclina-tion.*" These reports came mainly from sources in corpo-rate, who added: "*I'm not even sure how a transactional attorney can get pro bono work. Pretty much all of us in corporate were floored by the new requirement because we haven't heard about any opportunities.*" Others were more encouraged by the new initiative: "*I think it'll incentiv-ize people to do more by removing the perception that it's optional.*"

Pro bono hours
- For all US attorneys: 25,622
- Average per US attorney: 16

Training & Development
Following orientation, associates receive "*constant ongo-ing training, sometimes to an annoying extent.*" Litigators praised GT's "*amazing skills training series that's offered nationwide.*" They elaborated: "*Each year they host a few programs and 30 to 40 associates are invited from across the firm to take part. If you're training to do a deposition you get a packet of information and they hire real judges to enact it. It's a great program and great way to meet associ-ates and shareholders from other offices, but getting onto it is hard.*" On the transaction side there's a corporate boot camp, although some felt the training was "*a bit piece-meal.*" Many CLE's are available on the firm's intranet, "*which is a great way to tailor your own training, as well as identifying people who work in specific practice areas.*"

When it comes to feedback, associates get one formal evaluation per year, where there's also the opportunity to provide upward feedback. Some suggested: "*It might be better to have semiannual evaluations because informal feedback throughout the year can vary wildly from share-holder to shareholder.*" Those who had lateraled over from other firms felt: "*Here it's a little more transparent com-pared to other places where people sometimes brush you off and say everything's fine.*"

Diversity
Sources typically agreed that "*the firm does a pretty good job of making an effort. Looking around you can see people from different backgrounds.*" We didn't hear much about initiatives although corporate insiders assured us "*we're run by a bunch of women who have female leadership development training.*" When it came to recruiting, we heard: "*There's a good mix of men and women in our sum-mer group, although they could do a better job of hiring more African American people.*" In New York we heard: "*Our office is incredibly diverse and inclusive. Tradition-ally New York firms have had an issue but GT is really on the forefront of making sure that diversity is an important part of our firm's character.*"

"A truly great experience."

Strategy & Future
We heard: "*Due to the nature of being at such a big firm, when major decisions reach associate level it's already been in the pipeline for months.*" Despite this, sources described "*associate meetings where managing partners and shareholders go through numbers and their vision going forward,*" adding: "*We get given a lot of informa-tion I wouldn't expect, like financial statements and bill-ing hours. It's nice to get a peek behind the curtain.*" As-sociates across the firm revealed: "*Management has been pushing something called associate development training where you learn how to make a pitch and how they decide who makes partner.*" Finally, juniors in certain offices told us about all associate dinners that happen once a year, where "*we get the opportunity to voice any grievances we might have, and a lot of times these suggestions are imple-mented.*" Go to chambers-associate.com to read our full interview with CEO Brian Duffy.

See firm profile on p.647

The Inside View

Hangley Aronchick Segal Pudlin & Schiller

Lawyers per state

Largest US office: Philadelphia
US offices: 4
International offices: 0
First-year salary: $135,000
Billable hours: no requirement
Summers 2018: no summer program
Revenue 2017: undisclosed
Partners made in 2018: 2
Famous for: a life-sized model cow in the HQ; sense of humor; litigation chops

Bite-sized Hangley attracts expert litigators from far and wide.

SOMETIMES good things come in small packages. This lesson applies as much to law firms as it does that neatly wrapped Tiffany's box sitting under the Christmas tree. While some firms have summer classes consisting of well over 50 eager juniors, for young Hangley, this figure is closer to their total number of attorneys. But don't let its size fool you: this petite firm still packs a punch – especially when it comes to litigation and insurance. All-encompassing BigLaw clout isn't everything – it's more a case of selective nous for this crew. Named shareholders Hangley, Aronchick and Schiller are among the best litigators in Pennsylvania, and the firm scoops rankings from *Chambers USA* for insurance (recently representing Zurich), real estate, bankruptcy, and more general litigation in Pennsylvania.

If there were a ranking for a firm's sense of fun – a rare trait in the world of law – Hangley would surely secure one. Their website shows its *"quirky sense of humor"* placed front and center: you'll find a whole page dedicated to comical anecdotes about Hangley's lawyers, with one favorite featuring football tickets, potential acrobatics, and creative cheers (head online for an explanation). The survival of that oddball streak can be best explained by the firm's size: a defining feature all round. *"It's the kind of place where you could rapidly become a better*

lawyer, become more involved and engaged in client issues, and get more responsibility than at larger firms, while still getting the same quality of work." But take note – a small intake, plus the fame of its litigation excellence, means tough competition for a job. Read on for more detail.

The Work

Levity aside, associates chose the firm for its *"combination of interesting and challenging work,"* though they couldn't help but favor having a *"more hospitable environment in which to do that work."* Usually, the firm hires one or two associates a year, who typically join the populous ranks of litigators.

Juniors start as generalists, branching off later to one of the more specific groups if they desire. On top of the work coming from a general litigation group, associates dip their toe in *"a number of different areas which aren't technically general litigation, like insurance coverage, antitrust and environmental."* There's a staffing shareholder who *"periodically checks in with you and sees how busy you are. Generally if matters come in, they'll go to the assigning shareholder who will dole it out accordingly."* Sources found them to be *"very considerate of the experiences that people are looking for."*

General litigation covers *"a broad array of commercial disputes,"* whether that be *"inter-company or public affairs matters."* There's also a *"fair share of appellate work and patent litigation,"* and the group has represented *"large institutional clients and companies"* as well as municipali-

On chambers-associate.com...

- Interview with CEO and firm president David Pudlin
- Get hired at Hangley

See firm profile on p.648

The Inside View

Rankings in *Chambers USA*

| Bankruptcy/Restructuring | Litigation |
| Insurance | Real Estate |

For detail on ranking tiers and ranking locations, visit
www.chambersandpartners.com

Recent work highlights

- Representing a class of about 2,400 juveniles and their parents, in a class action arising out of a conspiracy involving two judges who were paid roughly $2.6 million to maximize the number of children committed to two private juvenile detention facilities
- Represented the City of Philadelphia in the defense of the extensively publicized Philadelphia Beverage Tax. The firm obtained the complete dismissal of a challenge to the tax
- Serving as real estate counsel to German-founded global supermarket Aldi, securing real estate holdings and advising as land use counsel on development projects
- Lead trial counsel for Comcast in a patent infringement dispute over telecommunications technology which pits a number of Comcast entities against several Sprint Communications entities

ties and states (including the City of Philadelphia). It's an extremely broad remit, and associates noticed a healthy amount of cross-staffing within the small firm, where *"sometimes we will bring in other people – when we need a bulldog litigator we'll get that person in, or if we need a nuanced transactional lawyer for some part. It's a small firm but there are a lot of good lawyers here with diverse experiences and bases of knowledge."*

"When we need a bulldog litigator we'll get that person in."

With more shareholders than associates, *"by necessity we have to staff leanly."* The default on a case is usually one shareholder and one associate – a far cry from the mythologized BigLaw sweatshop. As such, juniors felt they'd had *"a very valuable set of experiences,"* including attending trial, taking part in conference calls, writing all levels of briefs, drafting motions, legal research, and *"a fair amount of involvement with case management and logistics."* A couple of interviewees mentioned *"being second chair"* at various hearings and trials, and one junior talked about *"being encouraged to go out and develop contacts. It takes a long time to build a book of business, so why not start now?"* Interviewees agreed that *"it's been nice to have full ownership over certain things."*

Training & Development

Hangley does not currently have a summer program (see our 'Get Hired' section for more details). With associates entering the firm at a higher level of experience than the average newbie, sources admitted *"there's not really much formal training when you join; but I don't think that's necessarily a bad thing – the firm philosophy is about learning by doing."* We did hear mention of some *"formal trainings on different topics once in a while, whether that's practice tips or more substantive legal sessions."* But it's a fairly slimline offering overall – not that juniors were displeased about that set-up: *"A lot of the stuff is good to pick up on the go because you get context."* As for reviews,

these occur annually and *"it's up to associates to identify the shareholders from whom they'd like feedback. There's not much formal structure to the meeting itself, we just discuss any issues that come up. People are willing to go pretty in-depth into the evaluations."*

Culture

Due to its size, *"everyone knows everyone here. People feel more comfortable being themselves."* In line with the website antics, associates had experienced a firm with *"a jovial side"* where people have a *"sense of humor. That makes it a much easier place to work."* The ratio of shareholders to associates also meant that *"compared to other firms, it's much flatter in terms of hierarchy. It's a place where associates are valued and respected. There is a sense of camaraderie and trust, plus generally people just enjoy being around each other."*

"People feel more comfortable being themselves."

As we've mentioned, associates at Hangley are generally *"a little bit older and more experienced."* It makes sense then that the social side isn't as full-on: *"Most people have families at this point. It's not like a whole bunch of 26-year-olds with lots of money to throw around. We're social, but there's not something every week."* The firm still hosts *"periodic happy hours"* and *"other celebrations from time to time."* There's also Friday lunches *"for attorneys, paralegals, and staff"* which the firm pays for. Informally, people *"get together on an impromptu basis too."*

Hours & Compensation

There's no official billing requirement at Hangley, although billables are connected to the budget: associates are budgeted for 1,800 hours a year. *"Sometimes people*

See firm profile on p.648

Diversity	Partners (%)	Associates (%)
Women	31	50
White	-	-
Black/African American	-	-
Hispanic/Latin American	-	-
Asian	-	-
Mixed/Other	-	-
LGBT	-	-

bill below, sometimes people bill above, but it generally doesn't affect eligibility for bonuses. There's not a huge incentive to bill higher." Associates weren't entirely sure on the bonus structure, but asserted that *"if things go well for the firm, everyone takes some share in that."* Salary itself increases by a fixed amount each year.

"We don't have that intense focus on billing around the clock."

A typical day for most *"would be 9am to 6pm,"* but working on the level of litigation that they do, with the small teams they have, associates told us about *"times where you're incredibly overwhelmed, especially when you're working on multiple matters. Sometimes you have to be in two places at once, but that's not how it usually is. There are extremes at both ends of the spectrum occasionally, but usually the hours are fairly regular."* So there might be occasional midnight finishes, but weekend work was also seen as rare: *"My boss is very good about not working on weekends when it's not absolutely necessary."* Sources vouched for *"one thing that sets us apart: we don't have that intense focus on billing around the clock. Unless there's a trial it's a reasonable hours expectation."*

Offices

It's always sunny in Philadelphia (we can't verify this!), where Hangley's HQ can be found, but there are other offices. Neighboring Norristown hosts the family law practice, while Harrisburg has a number of antitrust attorneys. *"I'd say the vast majority of our lawyers are in Philadelphia,"* sources estimated. Some noticed that *"in the past we've made a push to expand our work into New Jersey, so the Cherry Hill office is our toehold there."* That office mainly consists of litigators and real estate attorneys. *"Often people who are based here but have cases in New Jersey can go and work there."* The Philly HQ is up on the 27th and 28th floors of its building, so boasts *"amazing views"* while also being conveniently located *"close to the train station."* Most important of all, however, because this is Hangley, it plays host to a life-sized fiberglass model of a cow.

Pro Bono

"If pro bono is something you want to pursue, the firm will support that. They do value it." Sources had been involved in prisoners' civil rights matters, fair housing issues, veterans cases, and child trafficking cases. Hangley also has strong connections with the Innocence Project and the ACLU (American Civil Liberties Union). *"The firm has a reputation for having a social consciousness, and to that end, encourages pro bono work."* That said, juniors *"certainly got the message not to overload yourself with pro bono."*

"The firm has a reputation for having a social consciousness."

Pro bono hours
- For all attorneys: undisclosed
- Average per attorney: undisclosed

Diversity

Interviewees reckoned that *"in terms of recent hiring decisions, you can see that the firm is making an effort to do better on diversity."* Gender diversity was felt to be the firm's strongest suite, with sources saying: *"There's good female representation in partnership, as well as at associate level."* As of 2018, Hangley had 31% female partners and 50% female associates. However, sources couldn't name any active diversity initiatives, though they maintained that *"although we're not as diverse as we would want to be, it's not for a lack of trying. As a whole, the profession could do better, but that's been acknowledged and is in the process of being addressed."*

Strategy & Future

Hangley associates felt relatively well informed about firm goings-on: *"We have an associate who is liaison to the board, who attends meetings and reports back on what's going on."* As CEO David Pudlin tells us, that benefits the firm in the long term. *"We have always tried to include our younger attorneys in firm management. They can then develop a proprietary feel for the place early on. By being inclusive and open, we have a far lower turnover rate."* As for the firm itself, Pudlin announces: *"2017 was financially our best year ever,"* although bankruptcy is *"not a growth area as of now. The economy is doing great – that practice usually grows when the economy isn't doing so well."* It's a steady ship at Hangley, targeting steady growth; those seeking a policy of aggressive expansionism should probably look elsewhere. Read our full interview with David Pudlin online.

The Inside View

See firm profile on p.648

Harris, Wiltshire & Grannis LLP

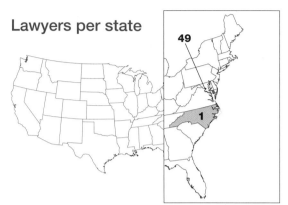

Lawyers per state

49

1

Largest US office: Washington, DC
US offices: 2
International offices: 0
First-year salary: $178,500
Billable hours: no requirement
Summers 2018: 3 2Ls
Revenue 2017: undisclosed
Partners made in 2018: 1
Famous for: telecom expertise; tight-knit boutique environment

This steadily diversifying telecom specialist reaps the cultural rewards of its slimline size.

AS HWG reaches its 20th birthday, it has plenty of reasons to celebrate. Cue the customary ringing of the firm's gong: a peculiar (but very real) ritual used to recognize firm successes, big and small. Attorneys must know its deafening clang well. Having cemented its position as one of the best telecom firms in DC – earning a top-notch *Chambers USA* ranking for its troubles – HWG has grown out of its boutique status, developing broader work in government investigations, criminal defense, civil litigation, appellate, privacy and energy.

What the firm lacks in size, it makes up for in quality. Its top telecom practice has big tech clients like Google, Microsoft and Facebook calling on HWG, and one associate described how, *"looking at partners' bios, everybody has such an impressive background. I'm almost in a state of awe!"* But beneath this rampant success lies a rarer triumph: a gong-worthy culture rid of hierarchy, but full of respect, inclusiveness and joviality. *"Partners here have figured out how to build a firm that lets people have more of a work-life balance,"* HWG's baby lawyers declared.

The Work

Telecom, which encompasses regulatory, litigious and transactional matters, provides the largest share of the

firm's work, but there's an increasing diversity on offer, of which associates get a fair mix. *"Transitioning between types of work is fairly seamless,"* they told us. *"Most juniors tend to do both telecom and wider litigation, and the assignment process is relatively organic, so you can steer your own path."* Newcomers get three or four initial assignments to kick off, then chat to partners or counsel to arrange follow-up matters. Sources explained that *"once you've worked with a partner, they'll come back to see if you're interested in other things."* As a last resort, assignments are floated on an email chain and associates decide among themselves who has enough time and interest in the project to take it on – a quite uniquely democratic process.

HWG's modest size also provides some unique opportunities. *"On my second day here I was in a meeting with the client and got asked a substantive question. I was a bit shocked, but it was amazing,"* one junior said. We heard of several similar experiences: *"I'd only just started and I was trusted to lead a client call – that's not something you'd get at a big firm."* Day to day, sources also kept busy with more typical legal research, finding themselves monitoring sector trends as well as drafting motions and oppositions. With sources in agreement that *"you get an unusual amount of responsibility,"* we wondered if juniors ever felt out of their depth? *"There are definitely times I've been nervous but I don't think anybody gives me tasks I'm not capable of,"* came the typical response. *"I'm confident partners will help if I fall flat on my face and they understand I'm still learning. If I were somewhere else it would take me a lot longer to get the opportunities I've had."*

On chambers-associate.com...

- Get hired at HWG
- Interview with managing partner Bill Wiltshire

See firm profile on p.649

Rankings in *Chambers USA*

Telecommunications

For detail on ranking tiers and ranking locations, visit
www.chambersandpartners.com

"I'd only just started and I was trusted to lead a client call – that's not something you'd get at a big firm."

Most newbies focus on litigation cases that are *"less technical and easier off the bat than FCC telecom matters."* Alongside representing huge telecom clients, the firm also backs prominent individuals and retail clients in disputes. *"Because we're a smaller firm, there's more diversity in the work between defense and plaintiff sides,"* said one source. *"In both criminal and civil work, it's pretty wide-ranging."* Legal ethics cases are also available in the early going – sources reported assisting lawyers from other firms over internal conflict issues and the rigmarole that arises when partners want to leave their firm. Juniors still get a shot at some *"really soft telecom work, with policy questions that don't require a lot of technical knowledge."* As they get a grip on the sector, associates can move towards more complex telecom projects.

Training & Development

A 'telecom 101' session giving first years a grounding in the practice area is one of the firm's monthly 'Nothing But Law' talks. These alternate with 'Anything But Law' presentations given by members of staff on their personal interests, offering a brief reprieve from the law. But beyond 'Nothing But Law,' *"there isn't much formal training,"* according to associates. *"I don't want to spend three days in a classroom, but a little more structure might be nice,"* said one. A more cogent annual review process was described as *"helpful for working out what skills you need to sharpen."*

Culture & Pro Bono

HWG placed in the top ten for benefits and lifestyle in our 2017 associate data survey – so what's the firm's secret? *"It's not nearly as hierarchical"* for one – *"there's really no differentiation between senior attorneys and juniors. When we meet in our communal space everyone sits at the same table and chats."* And with the firm's steady expansion has come a greater appreciation of what the firm stands to lose. *"There's a danger that the culture will change, but management are very aware of that. They definitely don't want HWG to turn into a BigLaw firm."*

"They definitely don't want HWG to turn into a BigLaw firm."

Recent work highlights

- Represented the Entertainment Software Association (a videogame trade association which includes Microsoft, Sony, Nintendo and others) in FCC rule-making on the Open Internet
- Successfully argued that based on past FFC precedent, Northstar Wireless was eligible for small-business bidding credits to be used in a wireless spectrum auction
- Worked for Floridian State Attorney Aramis Ayala in a suit brought against Governor Rick Scott. He had removed Ayala from 25 death penalty cases after she announced she would no longer pursue the death penalty
- Filed amicus briefs in the US Court of Appeals on behalf of a group of 138 organizations supporting the plaintiff in the transgender rights case *Gloucester County School Board v. G.G*

Monthly pizza lunches, bowling nights and karaoke are all fixtures on the calendar, while the *"defining characteristic"* of the social scene is a weekly Friday happy hour kickstarted by the ringing of *that* gong. *"Most people go – we usually have a keg, wine, soft drinks and an assortment of snacks."* But there's no pressure: *"There's no forced socializing. Most people here have families and are allowed to have other priorities outside work."* When they're not heading home to their families, lawyers have been known to bring their families to them. *"It's not uncommon for someone to email and let everybody know their kids will be hanging out in their office."* Offspring, spouses and significant others are likewise invited to an annual barbecue and picnic.

The firm also hit the top twenty in our survey for pro bono. Pro bono hours are treated the same as billables, and juniors recalled that *"during our orientation we were encouraged to either go and find our own opportunities or find something a partner is working on that we'd like to jump into."* Landlord/tenant cases are HWG's specialty: *"they're fun and easy, and you get good experience on your feet in court."* Disciplinary work for pro bono organizations is also on offer, as are child custody disputes. In one recent example *"the firm expected the case to be a quick demonstration where the CPS [Child Protective Services] would soon back down. It ended up going all the way to trial, and at no point did partners decide it would become too much work. That demonstrated a lot of commitment."*

Pro bono hours

- For all attorneys: 3,593
- Average per attorney: 108

Diversity

Associates also saw a strong commitment to diversity on HWG's part, if not such tangible results so far. *"As a*

See firm profile on p.649

Diversity	Partners (%)	Associates (%)
Women	23	64
White	83	57
Black/African American	3	0
Hispanic/Latin American	0	7
Asian	7	29
Mixed/Other	7	7
LGBT	10	7

smaller firm we're only bringing on two or three associates each year," sources pointed out. *"Diversity does factor into our hiring but we often struggle to find ethnically diverse candidates."* Things are looking rosier on the gender front: *"It's a great firm for women and we have less trouble retaining female attorneys than many peers. It's probably because HWG is so good with flexible working."* A 23% female partnership is indeed above the average for firms listed in *Chambers Associate*. *"Diversity is an area where the firm is demonstrating a lot of improvement,"* chipped in another source. *"Like all firms, most partners here are white men but there's a clear goal of hiring more diversely."* Commendably, HWG already smashes industry averages with a 10% LGBT partnership.

"It's a great firm for women and we have less trouble retaining female attorneys."

Office

Located in downtown DC, the current office building has been a telecom hub for a while – it used to belong to the FCC. *"The location is convenient, right at the heart of Washington,"* and while HWG *"doesn't have an in-house restaurant or anything like that, it's a perfectly attractive place to work. The firm has gone out of their way to put artwork on the walls and every attorney gets their own office."* Juniors reported that their fast-growing firm had *"stuffed the space almost to capacity."* It's a good problem to have, and at the time we went to press, HWG was preparing to take over an additional floor of the building to make sure everyone gets their personal space.

Hours & Compensation

Sticking with a straightforward attitude of *"doing the work that needs to be done,"* the firm doesn't set a billing target for its associates. Those we spoke to agreed that *"hitting a certain number of hours really isn't something anybody thinks about here – if anything, people are worried about working too much!"* Lawyers still have busy days of course, which can become busy nights. *"The latest I've worked until was 11pm,"* a source confirmed. *"That was on a tight timeline. During slower periods I'll only work a standard nine to five."* Another suggested that *"even staying until 8pm is pretty rare."*

"If anything, people are worried about working too much!"

The firm's bonus system bucks convention, allocating tracking points and paying out quarterly. Most *"really liked it. As with many things at HWG it's geared toward long-term planning."* Bonuses are calculated based on the firm's profitability each quarter, and management *"makes sure it gets feedback from associates on how the system is working. It's unconventional, but it makes you really feel part of the team. When we do well it's not just the partners profiting."* On top of that, associates also get *"technically unlimited"* vacation, which all felt encouraged to dip into.

Strategy & Future

The firm's telecom practice still produces about 50% of its workflow at present, but the percentage is steadily dropping. Managing partner Bill Wiltshire explains *"that's not because we're doing fewer telecom matters, but because of the growth in the number of projects in other areas."* Going forward, Wiltshire suggests HWG is *"looking to add complementary practices related to the federal government which add to our current core strengths in telecom, litigation, international trade, energy and ethics."* To read the full interview, check out HWG's Bonus Features on www.chambers-associate.com

Get Hired

"One thing that really differentiated HWG is that pretty much everybody who interviewed me had read at least some of my writing." Find out what else distinguishes the firm from others at www.chambers-associate.com

See firm profile on p.649

Haynes and Boone, LLP

Lawyers per state

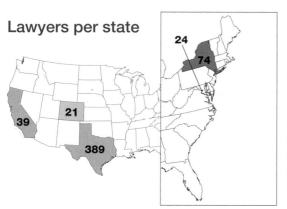

Largest US office: Dallas
US offices: 12
International offices: 3
First-year salary: $180,000
Billable hours: 2,000 target in Texas, 1,800 in New York
Summers 2018: 47 (18 1Ls, 29 2Ls)
Revenue 2017: $397.5 million (+6%)
Partners made in 2018: 9
Famous for: strength in the Texan market; ambition to expand

Juniors say it's definitely more 'hey' than 'boo' at this Texan powerhouse, which has serious plans to strengthen its scope both domestically and internationally.

"WE'RE projecting our revenue to hit $400 million for the first time in 2018," managing partner Tim Powers told us in late 2017. There isn't far to go: revenue reached $397.5 million in 2017. Powers continues: *"We feel good about that growth; some of which has been added by our new London office, but much has stemmed from a higher level of productivity across the firm overall."* London became the firm's third international base in 2016 (joining offices in Shanghai and Mexico City), and signaled Haynes' growing ambitions overseas: *"We're feeling strong about our offshore shipbuilding practice there, and have added strengths in financial services and corporate, which will bode well for the integration of US/UK activities."*

> *"Being focused on energy, technology, financial services and private equity is part of what makes us a Texas powerhouse."*

On the US side of the equation, *"we're still very much focused on our home bases in Texas,"* Powers emphasizes. Haynes and Boone traces its relatively young roots back to 1964, when name partner Richard Haynes opened up shop in Dallas. Since then the firm has established a further five bases in the Lone Star State, in Austin, Fort Worth, San Antonio, Houston and Richardson. *"Being focused on energy, technology, financial services and private equity is part of what makes us a Texas powerhouse; we believe these areas allow us to grow – initially in Texas and then further afield,"* says Powers. Out of state, Haynes and Boone has offices in New York, Chicago, Orange County, Palo Alto, DC and Denver. A look at *Chambers USA* reveals that the firm's strengths are indeed concentrated in its home state, where its high performers include real estate, energy, insurance, IP, bankruptcy and finance.

Strategy & Future

So what's on the agenda at the moment? *"In order to compete we need to be larger in New York and DC; we would like to double how many lawyers we have in the former in order to achieve substantial breadth and depth,"* says Powers. The firm will also continue to eye opportunities in California, as *"our tech drive allows us to be strong in that market."* Elsewhere, *"the only other domestic market we could look at is Charlotte, which would be driven off the back of financial services work. However, we won't make a move there without finding the perfect lawyers first – it's just a possibility at the moment."* Go online to view our full interview with Powers.

On chambers-associate.com...

- Interviews with managing partner Tim Powers and hiring partner Eric Williams
- Get hired: more tips on impressing at interview

See firm profile on p.650

The Inside View

Rankings in *Chambers USA*

Antitrust	Healthcare
Banking & Finance	Insurance
Bankruptcy/Restructuring	Intellectual Property
Corporate/M&A	Labor & Employment
Energy & Natural	Litigation
Resources	Real Estate
Environment	Tax
Franchising	Technology

For detail on ranking tiers and ranking locations, visit
www.chambersandpartners.com

Recent work highlights

- Won a $500 million judgment for media company ZeniMax against Facebook-owned virtual reality company Oculus for theft of intellectual property
- Represented Bank of America in its role as administrative agent during the allocation of a $430 million loan for the construction of a high-rise hotel in Seattle's business district
- Acted for independent oil and gas company Callon Petroleum during its underwritten public offering of 40 million shares worth over $630 million
- Advised Fort Worth-headquartered chemicals company KMG Chemicals on its $495 million acquisition of pipeline specialist Flowchem

The Work

Many departments have some form of formal assignment system that *"works in conjunction"* with the *"organic process"* of juniors knocking on doors and shooting out emails to those they want to work with. Haynes' business transactions section absorbed the most juniors on our list, followed by litigation and real estate. A few associates had joined the firm's finance, bankruptcy, IP and IP litigation sections.

In business transactions, practice groups include investment funds, healthcare, private equity, estate planning, energy and capital markets/securities. In private equity, juniors spent their time *"working with PE firms as they sold companies or purchased assets from other firms."* This involved *"doing diligence on our client's target assets and companies, as well as drafting the ancillaries attached to the larger purchase agreement. There's also a lot of organization work, where you keep a catalog of everything that's going on."* Over in capital markets there are a lot of public company offerings up for grabs, which see juniors *"running the IPO checklists and keeping on top of the hundreds of items we've got to get done. We also get to do more concrete things like drafting, editing and reviewing statements."*

"I don't know how it could be done better or shared more equally."

Litigation covers practice groups like labor and employment, insurance, appellate, white-collar defense, and business. On the white-collar side, our sources had taken on a lot of work tied to the healthcare sphere, where *"the government has made allegations against hospitals, or instances where individual physicians have had lawsuits filed against them. We work on matters where fraud and abuse are alleged to have taken place."* This translated into *"an equal share of legal research, drafting litigation-related docs like motions and orders, and doc review – the cases are staffed quite leanly, so it can be just me and a partner splitting the work between us. I don't know how it could be done better or shared more equally."*

Real estate associates were happy that their section acts *"as more of a standalone group: here we're 90% pure real estate deals and 10% supporting larger corporate deals."* Over the course of one year an associate had worked on *"hospitality, industrial and office projects, as well as alternative energy deals and 'dirt' work. I'd break it down into these three categories: sales and dispositions; financing; and entity formations and joint ventures."* In New York leasing is a big part of the work. On larger deals a junior's role is *"more organizational, but on smaller deals you work on the main operative agreements and coordinate a lot with the client to check which way they want to do things."*

Training & Feedback

A three-day spell on the introductory 'HayBoo U' program *"covers all the preliminary stuff you need to know, like how to use the legal tools and resources at our disposal, plus tips on writing effectively."* After that, there are *"regular CLEs and lecture-style sessions"* tailored to each practice area, and these cover *"a variety of topics, including recent news and cases that might impact our practice."*

"They take care of the people coming up after them."

Many associates praised the *"approachable and tactical manner"* in whichpartners delivered their day-to-day feedback, and said *"older partners are interested in teaching young associates – they take care of the people coming up after them."* Biannual formal reviews take place with a designated evaluator (usually a partner outside of an associate's practice group): *"The midyear ones aren't as comprehensive, but at the end of the year we get a written evaluation and the designated partner goes through all the reviews we've received from lawyers we've worked with for more than 25 hours."*

See firm profile on p.650

The Inside View

Diversity	Partners (%)	Associates (%)
Women	23	41
White	89	71
Black/African American	0.9	5
Hispanic/Latin American	6	6
Asian	4	16
Mixed/Other	0.4	0.9
LGBT	2	3

Pro Bono

There's always *"plenty of training"* available via the firm's *"endless"* pro bono opportunities and its connections to groups like the Human Rights Initiative. The firm's recent partnership with the Dallas-based Genesis Women's Shelter meant associates were *"walked through the basics of family law in the office,"* as the firm geared up to handle more domestic issues. Others had benefited from training on *"how to write a will"* through the Dallas Volunteer Attorney Program. Juniors can bill up to 100 hours of pro bono work, *"but possibly more if they see you're working hard on something."*

Pro bono hours
- For all US attorneys: 13,043
- Average per US attorney: 25.9

Hours & Compensation

Attorneys in Texas aim to bill 2,000 hours while their counterparts in the Big Apple shoot for 1,800. Across those locations juniors felt *"the firm's realistic about the expectations it sets"* and that the targets were achievable from the second-year onwards: *"In your first year everyone recognizes that you're not going to bill as much due to the ramp-up period in the first couple of months."* Hitting the target ensures that associates receive a 'high-base' bonus, while falling short means they still receive a 'low base' one: *"There's no minimum to remain in good standing to get a bonus. It's all individualized, based on hours, the type of work you're doing and your overall contribution to the firm in the form of business development and community involvement etc…"*

Standard working hours in the office did vary by practice group: those in litigation, for example, reported coming in at 9am and leaving by 7pm, while those in real estate regularly worked between 8am and 7:30pm. Juniors in the more transactional teams reported being *"crazy busy at times, so sometimes you won't leave until after midnight."* Most didn't *"work a lot on the weekend"* but had done so when matters required it.

Culture & Offices

Almost three quarters of the second and third-year associates on our list were based in Haynes and Boone's Texan offices; Dallas took on the majority of these, while a few called San Antonio, Houston and Richardson home. Of the non-Texan offices, New York took in the most juniors, while a few could be found in DC, Denver, Orange County and Palo Alto. The Dallas HQ was deemed *"beautiful – there are floor-to-ceiling windows that allow plenty of sunlight to come in."* The individual offices are *"designed to be a similar size regardless of the partner or associate occupying them,"* added juniors, highlighting the firm's egalitarian approach. Name partner Mike Boone *"often goes down to the cafeteria, sits at an empty table, and allows whoever to sit with him – the culture stems from the leadership."*

> ### *"I'm much more comfortable going to talk to a partner I accidentally hit in the face with a ping pong ball."*

Other Texans also emphasized how good partner/associate relationships are, and cited games of ping pong during breaks to demonstrate their point: *"I'm much more comfortable going to talk to a partner I accidentally hit in the face with a ping pong ball."* Another told us how much they appreciated receiving *"nice notes from partners saying 'we understand you're working hard, so let's go have a happy hour.'"* Overall those across the firm's offices felt that *"there are no internal rivalries – we see that in how the partners treat each other, and that approach in turn influences the associates. At other firms, people want to be the star, but there's none of that here. If I have a dumb question, I'll immediately call one of the other juniors, even if it's just 'where does the comma go?' It makes being new and doing a complex job so much easier."*

Diversity

"Relative to other firms it's pretty diverse, but compared to the general population it's not," was associates' verdict on the current balance at Haynes and Boone. They did, however, credit the firm for *"providing more opportunities than there were before – there's a dedicated committee of people raising and promoting diversity here."* Of the opportunities and initiatives now available, sources highlighted the firm's diversity retreat, which takes place once every two years: *"It's a really productive event. This year they invited someone to talk about implicit bias and female associates have noticed a marked difference in interactions."* The firm's pipeline efforts were also talked about enthusiastically, with juniors flagging the 1L scholars program and a Dallas-based *"partnership with a local school program, which aims to make students at every stage of education aware of the possibility of pursuing a legal career."*

See firm profile on p.650

Hogan Lovells

Lawyers per state

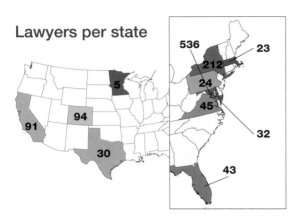

536
23
212
24
5
45
94
91
32
30
43

Largest US office: Washington, DC
US offices: 14
International offices: 36
First-year salary: $180,000 in most cities
Billable hours: 2,000 target
Summers 2018: 102 (17 1Ls, 85 2Ls, 2 SEO)
Revenue 2017: $2.036 billion (+5.5%)
Partners made in 2018: 12
Famous for: broad range of offices and practices; transatlantic heritage

England's 'lovely Lovells' formed one half of this transatlantic success story – but its international scope and sweep of practices show there's much more to HL than a reputation for being 'nice.'

TEA and scones, or fries and a soda? Transatlantic giant Hogan Lovells comes with flavors of both – an infusion borne out of the 2010 mega-merger between DC's Hogan & Hartson and London's Lovells. Today, HL's offices in both cities have 'headquarter' status, but the firm's reach extends far beyond them: even after closing an office in Mongolia in 2017, HL's name sits atop 50 locations across the world, and *Chambers Global* recognizes the firm as top of the market in 24 different practice areas spanning various jurisdictions.

In the US, thoroughbred HL is certainly no one-trick pony; it scoops up a healthy spread of top-tier *Chambers USA* rankings spanning corporate, litigation, healthcare, investment, international trade, private & data security, telecommunications and transportation. DC managing partner Eve Howard explains: *"Our internal focus on industry sectors has really gained traction and allowed us to bring all the different strands of our practices together. Something that makes us distinctive from other firms is the breadth and depth of industry focus we have."*

On chambers-associate.com...

- More on the Pathways program from DC managing partner Eve Howard
- Get hired: interview advice
- Interview with hiring partner Tim Lloyd

The Work & Pro Bono

Incoming juniors slide into one of five groups: corporate, government regulatory, and litigation, arbitration & employment (LAE) take the majority; the rest join finance or IP. In its flagship DC office new recruits have the chance to do four-month rotations in different practice areas (including a pro bono option). The aim is to settle into one within two years, though *"most people know where they want to go by their second rotation,"* sources said.

Each group in each office has a workflow coordinator, but interviewees got most of their work directly from partners on an ad hoc basis. Corporate is a particularly free-flowing group, with juniors typically dipping in and out of M&A, private equity, securities, life sciences and other subsections. Due diligence is a common thread throughout, but *"the level of responsibility can escalate pretty quickly. That said, they never let it go beyond what you can handle."* Higher level tasks include drafting commercial agreements, as well as board minutes and resolutions. Client contact is also common: *"I ended up as the primary connection for the CFO and general counsel,"* one source revealed, *"it was an incredible experience."* Others agreed that *"senior associates and partners are very good at keeping juniors in the loop of the deal."*

In government regulatory, some focus their practice on Food and Drug Administration work and can specialize in food or healthcare within that; others might home in

See firm profile on p.651

The Inside View

Rankings in *Chambers USA*

Antitrust	Intellectual Property
Appellate Law	International Arbitration
Corporate Crime &	International Trade
Investigations	Latin American Investment
Corporate/M&A	Leisure & Hospitality
Employee Benefits &	Life Sciences
Executive Compensation	Litigation
Energy & Natural	Media & Entertainment
Resources	Natural Resources
Environment	Privacy & Data Security
Food & Beverages	Real Estate
Government	REITs
Healthcare	Securities
Immigration	Telecommunications
Insurance	Transportation

For detail on ranking tiers and ranking locations, visit
www.chambersandpartners.com

on trade or cybersecurity and privacy matters. Each wing then splits into different feathers: for instance, cybersecurity and privacy encompasses transactional regulation, regulatory counseling and agency interaction. Wherever the wind takes you, diligence and document review are *"pretty standard"* along with initial drafts of motions. Investigation matters *"vary the most, as you see elements of fact-gathering, memo preparation, talking to clients and conducting interviews"* across the longer projects. Interviewees were *"pleased to be exposed to many different areas,"* and also found that *"partners are very willing to invest juniors with significant responsibility."*

"It's generally encouraged that you take on a broad mix of work as a junior."

LAE insiders had their own high-flying tales to tell, with one recalling: *"As a first year I was put on a trial team and ended up second-chairing two key witnesses."* Litigious strengths vary by office: DC is the white-collar hub; Denver houses an extensive environmental and energy practice; and Colorado Springs has a strong foundation in construction. Regardless of location, newbies aren't pigeonholed, as one New Yorker explained: *"It's generally encouraged that you take on a broad mix of work as a junior – you can do commercial litigation, internal investigations, arbitrations or bankruptcy cases."* Most groups afforded *"a fair bit of drafting"* on things like motions to dismiss and witness statements, as well as standard research and document review assignments (*"I'm not doing the sexiest work, but it's more than I expected"*). With white-collar work, *"the traditional model of juniors stuck on document review is thrown out of the window. As a second year I manage a lot of contract teams and prepare talking points for conferences and government presentations."*

Recent work highlights

- Acted for PwC Bermuda in a series of cases related to Bernie Madoff fraud, totaling more than $4 billion in value
- Advised Lockheed Martin in $4.6 billion combination of its Information Systems & Global Solutions subsidiary with tech firm Leidos
- Represented real estate investment trust JBG Companies in proposed $8.4 billion merger with Vornado Realty Trust
- Counseled numerous clients including Nissan and 21st Century Fox on recent tax reform proposals

DC first-years can do a four-month rotation devoted entirely to pro bono. *"It literally covers everything from individual representation of tenants facing eviction to Supreme Court amicus briefs."* On a broad level, associates get staffed on pro bono matters via partner T. Clark Weymouth and a full-time pro bono associate (who serves an 18-month term in the position). *"When you join you're asked to provide a list of what you might be interested in,"* juniors explained, *"and every time relevant cases pop up you get an email. It's an effective mechanism for sending through a steady stream of opportunities."*

Associates must dedicate 20 hours minimum to pro bono each year. Once they've logged 1,850 hours of paid work they can use pro bono to get them to their hours target (see below). There's also an option to apply for credit without reaching the 1,850 threshold if a matter goes on long enough: *"I had a case that took up over 300 hours and the firm granted me billable credit for it."*

Pro bono hours
- For all US attorneys: 102,539
- Average per US attorney: 91.1

Hours & Compensation

The billing target itself is 2,000 hours. *"Some make it and some don't,"* but sources agreed that *"the firm helps you get the work to reach it, and the pro bono allowance helps people out."* Associates tended to spend around ten hours in the office on an average day, before logging on for another hour or two after a home-cooked meal. *"I've been lucky not to have many crazy nights in my first year,"* one source reflected; *"here and there I've been up working until 1 or 2am, but the nice part of the agile working policy is people can start and leave when they want unless something urgent comes up."* Some preferred to bill a few hours at the weekend to keep late nights and long slogs to a minimum.

"The bonus policy has become much more transparent."

The Inside View

See firm profile on p.651

Diversity	Partners (%)	Associates (%)
Women	30	51
White	85	70
Black/African American	1.5	5.4
Hispanic/Latin American	6	5.25
Asian	3.4	11
Mixed/Other	4	8.4
LGBT	3	5.25

The first-year starting salary is $180,000 in all US offices except Miami, Minneapolis and Colorado Springs; the latter two don't normally take newcomers. *"The bonus policy has become much more transparent"* after some confusion in recent years – associates who hit the 2,000-hour mark automatically qualify for a market bonus, while going above and beyond can nab you extra. Most were happy with the arrangement, as *"it takes a lot of stress off people – there aren't tons of metrics to consider."* The unlimited vacation policy was similarly popular, though *"at first juniors aren't sure how to handle it; it's now clear the firm is good at respecting vacation time."*

Training & Development

"We all have one week of training when we first get here, which is focused on administrative things like how to keep time, as well as your expected work product in the law firm universe," associates revealed. After that there are both class-based and practice area-specific training. With regard to the latter we heard of *"quarterly M&A sessions"* and *"weekly lunches in white-collar,"* while the former was described as being *"focused on entrepreneurial qualities – they get us to think like clients."* In addition there are *"plenty of advertised PLI sessions and we can take online courses whenever we want."*

"They get us to think like clients."

With the associate review process itself being reviewed at the time of our research, some juniors felt a little lost at sea. *"It still feels like we're in a transition,"* they reflected;*"it's a matter of everyone being on the same page with the new system."* The backbone of the new Pathways program is bringing structure to everyday feedback, so it's *"less partner-heavy"* and more informal. Denver was the trial office for the scheme – guinea pigs there *"liked*

that it's more organic" andgave the new feedback model top marks. To learn more about pathways from DC managing partner Eve Howard visit www.chambers-associate.com

Diversity

Diversity initiatives include affinity groups for African Americans, Latin Americans, women and LGBT lawyers: a new scheme called Pride+ was launched in 2017 to provide more help for LGBT attorneys throughout their careers. Some fretted that *"Hogan doesn't feel particularly diverse, and race-wise it definitely comes up short,"* but acknowledged *"they're trying really hard and moving in the right direction."* Every year or two the firm hosts its 'Pathways to Success' conference: the firm's African American lawyers congregate in the capital, where they meet diverse law students and offer advice on their career paths.

Nationwide, female associates highlighted success in the promotion of *"strong female leadership"* – for example, the head of the DC regulatory group Alice Valder Curran and co-head of appellate Cate Stetson. Sources also enthused about *"the huge women's initiative that holds meetings on a regular basis, as well as larger events two or three times a year."* HL is aiming to have 30% of its firmwide partnership made up of women by 2022. In the US, that figure currently already stands at 30%!

Culture & Offices

Despite one source describing their colleagues as an *"eccentric family,"* others made it clear that HL's attorneys are rather more functional than the Simpsons or the Griffins: *"The leadership has very intentionally developed a culture that's high-performing but humane, and I have so many friends I spend time with outside work."* Another declared that *"there are lots of people here I could talk to about different non-work topics,"* and associates universally appreciated that while *"BigLaw is very intense, Hogan is very good at making life a bit more convenient."* Given the firm's broad reach, it's no surprise that different offices have unique characters. Sometimes this is reflected in the choice of clothing: in Silicon Valley, for example, you'll find *"shorts and flip flops,"* while in Denver *"the partners wear cowboy boots – that's just part of living here!"*

Denver's attorneys walked their boots over to new premises in 2016. The new office *"has glass doors, which produced a very mixed reception initially but everyone's embraced it now."* The LA and Silicon Valley bases are similarly new and hip, with the latter dating back to 2013, while team New York is *"in the process of moving to a new space near Grand Central; we'll be there by January 1, 2019. The current office is a bit too small but the firm is building out as we grow. It has more of a 24/7 feel, with*

See firm profile on p.651

people coming in later and working later." In DC, associates "sit in beautifully remodeled offices. The redesigned floors give every attorney the exact same-sized room and nobody has a corner office – they're now collaborative spaces." Most offices have a pet name for their common areas: in DC it's 'The Hive', while in Denver it's 'The Junction' and in Baltimore it's 'The Nest'.

"There are lots of people here I could talk to about different non-work topics."

Each office also organizes its own events. DC's rooftop deck is particularly popular and plays host to associate happy hours on Friday nights. Overall "there's a good amount of socializing, particularly during the summer when the firm sponsors events," but juniors also dug into their own pockets for "frequent lunches with colleagues." Being in a smaller office "can limit the social side, but it depends on what you're looking for. I didn't sign up to go out drinking every night." With a few exceptions, sources concurred that "people are good friends here and we're a much more social firm than others." They also felt that the sheer size of the firm ensures there's something of a partner/associate hierarchy, but "relationships vary depending on who you're working with." One summarized it like this: "I feel very comfortable knocking on a partner's door, but only after checking with their assistant that they're free!"

Strategy & Future

There's been some degree of upheaval at HL lately – in the US, the firm reduced its business services ranks, with around 40 members of staff accepting an offer of voluntary retirement. However, associates felt that "there's a lot of transparency" when it comes to where Hogan is headed. One associate committee member told us: "The firm is very forward-thinking and wants to make sure it's leading and innovating within the market." DC managing partner Eve Howard tells us "being fit for the future is in our minds equal parts strategy and culture: one without the other ultimately fails. We look at our culture in five different ways – being ambitious, committed, supportive, innovative and responsible – and there's a real focus from the leadership in making sure these attributes are consistent throughout our firm." The approach is clearly paying off – in 2018, HL broke the $2 billion revenue mark for the first time.

Hogan Lovells is a giant international firm. To fully grasp the firm's global accomplishments, visit www.chambersandpartners.com

See firm profile on p.651

Holland & Knight LLP

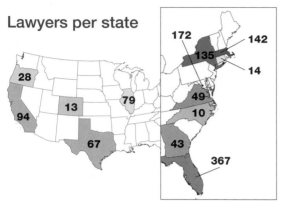

Lawyers per state

172
142
135
14
28
79
49
13
10
94
67
43
367

Holland & Knight LLP also has an office in Alaska with 10 attorneys

Largest US office: Washington, DC
US offices: 24
International offices: 3
First-year salary: $180,000 in major markets
Billable hours: 1,900 target
Summers 2018: 34 (3 1Ls, 31 2Ls,)
Revenue 2017: $848.2 million (+5.6%)
Partners made in 2018: 31
Famous for: Florida institution; multipolar firm

A full-service firm from the Sunshine State, H&K's reputation for conducting *"sophisticated work for big clients"* shines bright across 24 US offices.

IT was in 1968 that two smaller firms merged to form Holland & Knight. Its name partners were Spessard Holland – who served as both a US senator and governor of Florida – and Peter Knight, who was elected mayor of Fort Myers before he turned 21 and has an airport in Tampa named after him. Fast forward half a century, and associates rightly call this firm a *"Floridian powerhouse firm"* – it has a network of 27 offices (eight of them in Florida) and 1,250 lawyers. Five of the offices have opened in the past six years alone, reflecting H&K's upward trajectory toward becoming a billion-dollar firm – revenues reached $848.2 million in 2017. Managing partner Steven Sonberg is proud of the firm's sustained growth since 2009 but has no specific designs on hitting ten figures just yet. Our associate interviewees reflected that while *"having the specialties we do lends itself to charging high rates, our diversity of practice lends itself to greater stability through tougher economic times."* True enough: *Chambers USA* awards the firm an array of top marks across the country including gold stars for M&A in Northern Virginia, zoning and land use in California, litigation in Florida, and aviation nationwide.

Juniors were confident the firm's reputation is still strongest in the Sunshine State: *"There we are THE firm. Places* *like Miami may have a lot of big-name firms, but those are only satellite offices, whereas Holland & Knight has an established presence with a big-firm feel."* Elsewhere, sources felt that a presence in Boston and Washington, DC – which is actually the firm's largest office– secured H&K *"a very good reputation throughout the country."* However, they also acknowledged that in some of the firm's smaller outposts such as Chicago, *"if you weren't familiar with the legal scene, you might not have heard of us."*

Offices & Hours

Holland & Knight has no official headquarters. *"We are more a spread of disparate connections,"* associates believed. *"There is no Mecca of sorts that everybody goes to – we all have our own orientations."* The offices that are *"heavy hitters"* – Boston, Miami and Washington – *"have most of the influential partners,"* sources reflected, but they otherwise felt that *"even the tiny offices are treated as coequal,"* pointing to recent investments made into the smaller West Palm Beach office as evidence. When it comes to departmental structure, *"the firm is divided between business, litigation, real estate and government policy. As a junior, above me is my practice group leader, who is under the firm-wide practice leader for each of the four areas, who falls under the board of directors."*

While associates had frequent experiences of cross-staffing between offices, stressing that *"you're never going to feel like an alien from another planet if you visit another office."* Office moves are frequent, although some did re-

See firm profile on p.652

The Inside View

Rankings in *Chambers USA*

Banking & Finance	Leisure & Hospitality
Bankruptcy/Restructuring	Litigation
Construction	Media & Entertainment
Corporate/M&A	Native American Law
Environment	Products Liability
Food & Beverages	Real Estate
Government	Retail
Healthcare	Tax
Labor & Employment	Transportation
Latin American Investment	

For detail on ranking tiers and ranking locations, visit
www.chambersandpartners.com

Recent work highlights

- Advised government IT provider CRSA during its $235 million acquisition of consultancy firm Praxis Engineering
- Advised JPMorgan Chase and a group of 14 lenders on a $200 million syndicated unsecured loan to Colombian energy firms Promigas and Gases del Pacífico
- Acted as lead trial counsel to Bob's Discount Furniture - a national furniture retailer - during a class action filed in New Jersey state court involving alleged violations of New Jersey's Truth-in-Consumer Contract, Warranty and Notice Act
- Represented Aviation Capital Group as seller and servicer on the sale of a portfolio of 18 aircraft on lease to 17 airlines in 16 jurisdictions

port a bit of office politics in the event they wanted to transfer to another office. Associates also felt the firm could benefit from spelling out more *"uniform expectations of its associates."* The issue was especially acute in regards to hours where we heard reports of some juniors billing below the 1,900 target and others going as high as 2,400 hours. We also heard reports of some practice group leaders unofficially setting their own target at 2,000 hours.

Some felt the discrepancies could be put down to the work assignment system. While broadly a free-market system, where *"the onus is on associates to manage their workload,"* juniors revealed that *"what one group does in one office might be totally different to a group in another office."* For example, in Miami business juniors are required to submit a mandatory report every Friday detailing their availability for the following week, whereas New York litigators have more of an *"informal system of letting our practice group leader know what we are doing on a twice monthly basis."* Juniors believed it would be beneficial to *"have a bit more structure to oversee how busy associates are and keep us accountable for how much time we are spending on things."* This was especially true for first-years, some of whom admitted not *"feeling comfortable saying no to taking on more projects."*

Still, despite occasional reports of *"going to bed at 3am and waking up at 5am,"* and the odd working weekend, sources said H&K *"embraces a good work-life balance"* – or at least a *"semblance of work-life balance appropriate to working in BigLaw."* One junior told us: *"I've been able to pursue hobbies outside work that I never thought I would be able to."* Sources also appreciated the firm's liberal approach to vacations. *"I've booked a trip to Europe this weekend and I didn't ask anyone. As long as I'm available with a cell and laptop, they don't mind."* Another source told us that a *"partner threatened to disconnect my remote access when I was trying to work during a two-week vacation."*

Culture & Compensation

Work-life balance aside, sources identified *"longevity and a clear path to partnership"* as the defining feature of H&K's culture. *"A lot of people who I interviewed with have been here since they were associates, and a lot of senior associates have been here since they were summers,"* one newbie observed. We spoke to one fourth-year who was certain that *"partnership was on the horizon. I am strategically being given work that will help me become a partner and my practice group leader has involved me in a number of committees so that in four to five years' time I will be on upper management's radar."* Other mid-level associates detailed their involvement in marketing activities and participation in trade associations in preparation for partnership.

"A lot of the people I interviewed with have been here since they were juniors."

Sources felt the firm secures associates' loyalty through its *"very informal"* working environment. Though juniors acknowledged the presence of *"an old guard that is formal and wears suits,"* they stressed that *"they don't in any way expect that of everyone,"* adding that partners' presence is *"in no way dictatorial."* Even those based in the New York office felt it was far removed from *"the cutthroat and compulsive"* stereotype attached to BigLaw in the Big Apple. However, despite a low attrition rate at the junior level, sources felt a lack of transparency around compensation could lead to problems further down the line. *"It's an issue that has been raised every year at associate meetings,"* one source vented. *"The more you progress it becomes less and less clear because you have fallen so far off the Cravath scale,"* as the firm stops paying lockstep after two years. One insider disclosed: *"My current salary is $200,000 but going into next year I've been informed that it could be anywhere between $200,000 and $235,000."*

See firm profile on p.652

Diversity	Partners (%)	Associates (%)
Women	23	53
White	87.2	71.6
Black/African American	2.4	6.8
Hispanic/Latin American	7.8	11.9
Asian	1.8	8.2
Mixed/Other	0.8	1.5
LGBT	0.03	0.02

The Work

Work at H&K is split into four sections – business, litigation, real estate and government – which are then divided into different groups. The business section, with about 60% of new starters, is made up of the following groups: corporate, financial services, private wealth, structured finance and syndication. For those with commitment issues the firm *"is happy for people to change practice groups. I know five or six associates who started in litigation and changed to corporate after a few years."*

> ## "At first I was preparing witness outlines, researching questions of law and providing memos."

Highlighting the firm's high partner to associate ratio, many of our interviewees were well accustomed to being the only associate on deal-and-case teams. *"Partners are always looking to collaborate rather than delegate down,"* one litigator felt. *"At first I was preparing witness outlines, researching questions of law and providing memos, but before the first year was out I had met with clients directly. As a second-year I have attended court by myself in a landlord and tenant case and have taken my first deposition."* Another source, *"in the middle an arbitration that is set to have a hearing next month,"* reported: *"I've gotten experience preparing witnesses – including expert witnesses – for cross-examination."* Federal court cases were highlighted as a particular highlight by one junior: *"I think that's where you have the highest level of work. You get to draft sophisticated briefs and opposing counsel tend to be more respectful."*

Juniors in the corporate group get to work on different types of matters. *"Fifty percent of my workload has been securities and financial regulation, such as helping clients with compliance and annual reports,"* one first-year explained. *"The other half has been a mix of private equity, M&A, venture capital and restructuring deals. I have done due diligence, but I've also been writing initial drafts, liaising with clients and regularly handling management of deals."* One source in syndication described a similar management role: *"I was the first pair of eyes on everything that comes through. Recently I've been running conference calls involving 25 to 30 people."*

Pro Bono

All associates have an annual pro bono target of 50 hours. *"There is no cap on how much you can do, but you can get billable credit up to 100 hours,"* sources explained, adding: *"You have to get approval to get credit for the next 50 hours, anything above which is not credited."* Sources felt the firm is making good efforts to develop its *"reputation for contributing to communities,"* and some juniors identified *"a recent push to step up our efforts."* Associates reported working on immigration and family abuse cases as well as more region-specific work: in Florida juniors have been involved in cases surrounding Hurricane Irma, while those in Houston have been working on FEMA claims following Hurricane Harvey. Newbies can sign up to projects from emails sent out every week, but also highlighted that it is very easy to get approval for projects sourced independently.

Pro bono hours
- For all US attorneys: 72,742
- Average per US attorney: 60

Training & Development

All first-years are enrolled onto the professional development learning track upon joining the firm. What does that mean? Well, there is *"a list of online in-person conferences and tutorials that you have to complete in your first two years."* Newbies are required to complete general assignments on topics such as legal writing, client service and marketing, which go on to become practice-group specific. For business attorneys training sessions may include 'securities 101' or *"what corporate lawyers should know about tax issues."* Sources explained that *"some of the training is practical: they will set up a live chat with a professional and you will have homework to complete over a month."* Litigators similarly have mandatory sessions every other month on topics such as arguing a motion and preparing for a deposition. *"They are helpful, particularly if you do the preparation,"* sources reflected.

Juniors felt the fact the firm is *"partner-heavy"* enables them *"to grow faster than at other firms where there are lots of mid-level associates working between you. It's very easy to go to a partner and get constant feedback."* Newbies are also assigned partner and associate mentors during their first week, with female attorneys having the option of picking up an additional female mentor during their third year as part of the Women's Initiative.

Diversity

Juniors recounted a number of diversity initiatives in what they interpreted as *"a really big push by the firm."* These include African American, Asian American/Pacific Islander, LGBT, Hispanic and Native American af-

See firm profile on p.652

The Inside View

finity groups alongside a Women's Initiative, Rising Stars program and veterans' group. Sources pointed out that *"the affinity groups operate more on a firm-wide level and conduct quarterly multi-office video conferences where they often bring in guest speakers."* The Women's Initiative operates on a local land firm-wide level and meets monthly. *"We have monthly lunch meetings as well as a few bigger events throughout the year,"* one junior of the Miami office explained. This includes a spa day *"which is a networking event with local business clients in the community."* The Rising Star program, for fifth-years and up, offers *"high-level mentoring and an executive training program for a year."*

Strategy & Future

We spoke to associates who were confident about the future of the firm, remarking that *"firm-wide we have been doing incredibly well."* Managing partner Steven Sonberg gives us some extra perspective: *"2017 was a good year for us. We have had excellent years since 2009, and we are very proud of that. Over the last three years, our net income has increased 25% and our profitability per equity partner – which tends to be a benchmark in measuring how firms are doing – increased 19.8%."* He adds that H&K's *"corporate M&A and private equity practices have been very strong. They are some of the areas that we began investing heavily in around five years ago, and where we have had good fortune in bringing over lateral groups that have contributed significantly to our growth."* To read the full interview with Sonberg, go to chambers-associate.com

"Last year I was talking to someone who'd not had a lot of work experience but had had an internship as a 1L. They quickly realized they had an issue with organization. They weren't used to multitasking, which is a very different experience at law school than at a firm. It's having to take notes for three classes versus having five or six partners reaching out to you directly, and trying to figure out who you prioritize. Seeing how they acknowledged an area for improvement and the steps they took to improve/resolve that issue showed great judgment."
– McDermott hiring partner Eric Gilbert

See firm profile on p.652

Hughes Hubbard & Reed LLP

Lawyers per state

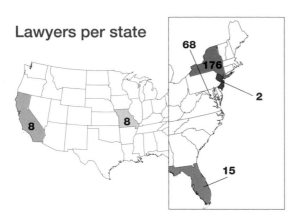

68
176
2
8
8
15

Largest US office: New York
US offices: 7
International offices: 2
First-year salary: $180,000
Billable hours: 1,950 target (1,750 billable)
Summers 2018: 19 (all 2Ls)
Revenue 2017: $322 million
Partners made in 2018: 3
Famous for: founderCharles Evans Hughes; diversity milestones; international dimensions

This midsizer is powered by international capabilities that take it far beyond its traditional stronghold in Manhattan.

"IT was just the right size, neither too big nor too small," Hughes Hubbard's juniors reflected. And so just (a bit…) like Goldilocks on her quest, our associate sources found their perfect fit in the form of this modestly proportioned Big Apple institution, which turned 130 years young in 2018. HH's ties to New York are significant: its founder, Charles Evans Hughes, had an illustrious career as Governor of New York, but also became a figure of nationwide significance when he served as US Secretary of State, a Supreme Court Chief Justice and even a Republican presidential candidate.

HH also expanded its reputation beyond the borders of the Empire State. It now has six domestic bases, which give the firm coverage on both coasts, as well as further inland in Kansas City, Missouri. But for our interviewees it was HH's broader dimensions that appealed: *"It's one of those firms with really active practices in international fields like arbitration and trade. I wanted to be involved in them."* Offices in Tokyo and Paris enhance HH's capabilities in this respect, and *Chambers Global* ranks the firm in both of the areas just mentioned. On its home turf, this litigation-heavy practice is recognized for its product liability and white-collar knowhow, while on the transactional side *Chambers USA* singles out the firm's aviation

finance, Latin American investment and corporate/M&A expertise as particular highlights.

The Work

Litigation is the main destination for newly-minted attorneys, but a scattering of juniors can also be found in corporate, tax, IP, international trade, and anti-corruption and internal investigations. The last two practices are based in the DC office, which takes on a fair number of incoming juniors, but the New York HQ takes on the most (Miami, meanwhile, usually hires just one newcomer a year).

In both New York and DC *"there are two work assignment systems that run in tandem."* Traffic managers collect availability reports from associates and distribute tasks to those who've selected a green light; at the same time *"you start to get work directly from partners. It's a good way to balance variety and working repeatedly with partners you get on well with."* HH's attorneys don't officially specialize until they reach mid-level status. This policy works for those who *"come into the firm without a concrete idea of what they want to do – it gives you a chance to try out different things."* While *"it's possible to informally pre-specialize by going back to get work from the same partners,"* it's worth noting that *"you may be staffed on other things if you're needed."*

Hungry litigators took full advantage of the disputes buffet on offer, piling their plates high with fraud, product liability, bankruptcy and general commercial matters,

On chambers-associate.com…

- Get hired: interview insight and more
- Interviews with hiring partner George Tsougarakis and DC managing partner Bill Stein

See firm profile on p.653

The Inside View

Rankings in *Chambers USA*

Bankruptcy/Restructuring	Litigation
Corporate/M&A	Media & Entertainment
International Arbitration	Products Liability
International Trade	Transportation
Latin American Investment	

For detail on ranking tiers and ranking locations, visit www.chambersandpartners.com

Recent work highlights

- Represented one of two former J.P. Morgan employees who faced SEC and criminal charges over the $6 billion 'London Whale' scandal
- Served as counsel to Madison Square Garden during its $181 million acquisition of a majority stake in restaurant and nightclub operator Tao Group
- Acts as primary litigation counsel for New York Blood Center, and has defended the blood bank in cases worth seven figures
- Secured a $1.4 billion award for Canadian mining company Crystallex after It brought a bilateral investment treaty claim against Venezuela

as well as internal investigations and international arbitration work. *"What I enjoy about the practice is that it doesn't have a limited industry focus,"* a source explained. *"I've dipped into energy, banking, aerospace and real estate matters."* As a result, *"no two days are the same,"* but common tasks include *"conducting legal research and providing opinions, plus helping to draft first versions of motions and, in some cases, entire briefs."* Do any specialties offer a shortcut to the juicy work? *"Product liability involves a lot of legal analysis upfront,"* we heard, *"while bankruptcy matters involve less complex legal work, but you're still in charge of drafting the motion. Overall there are moments when you can get in over your head, but those are the ones that provide great opportunities for growth."*

"Product liability involves a lot of legal analysis upfront."

HH's corporate team is smaller, so *"juniors tend to specialize more quickly."* Each office has its own flavor: New York has M&A, structured finance and funds teams; Miami deals *"mostly with Latin American clients"*;and DC's tighter focus is on aviation finance and compliance. A few newbies in the capital go into international trade and ply their own trade on *"a combination of litigation and regulatory matters."* The team *"advises clients on economic sanctions and customs laws, helps them to apply for licenses, and drafts government filings."* New arrivals *"got a primary drafting role from the very beginning"* alongside *"less demanding tasks, like preparing PowerPoints or materials for meetings."*

Training & Development

All incoming associates attend a weeklong program in New York, which has a rather splendid name: 'The Hughes Institute.' *"It's geared toward litigators and corporate juniors, and it's full of seminars that get you up to speed. I'm constantly revisiting the materials!"* After this, first-year litigators attend a trial advocacy workshop which lasts for a few days : *"A professor teaches us and there's a case simulation where we each do opening and closing statements and cross-examine an expert witness. It's a very good program."* Corporate juniors attend their own trainings, which are spread out over their first few months at HH. Beyond that, *"we're encouraged to take*

CLEs, which are either hosted at the firm or made available via an external provider."*

Annual reviews are held in late January/early February and goals for the year ahead are set. *"During the evaluation two to three partners will walk you through the feedback that's been collected on your performance, but if there's an issue people don't wait for the review to address it – they'll take you aside and explain how to fix it."*

Culture & Diversity

So what's the atmosphere like within HH's hallowed halls? *"It's a quirky environment full of brilliant attorneys,"* sources replied. *"It's a lot more casual than expected, which enables you to really build up personal relationships – the firm's size also lends itself to that."* Interviewees were quick to provide anecdotes to demonstrate their point.One fondly recalled that *"when I went into my callback interview someone down the hall sneezed, and my interviewer immediately called down to them and said 'bless you!'"* Another said that *"there's a partner who gets upset if you email him instead of just stopping by – he says that his door is open for a reason!"* Juniors therefore agreed that *"the people here genuinely seem to like each other, which you can't say about every law firm."*

"When the stars align and we all have the same night off we do go out."

HH's size means that *"everyone knows everyone and we celebrate each other's birthdays,"* so be prepared to donate to whip-rounds for cake. When not breaking out the candles for a sing-song, attorneys *"organize happy hours if they feel like it."* The firm also sponsors events including bowling nights and an annual trivia night, which *"are there if you want to attend them – a lot of people have families so it's understandable that they want to spend their evenings and weekends with them."* Juniors felt that *"people are often especially friendly with those from their summer class,"* and though the hustle and bustle of law means

See firm profile on p.653

Diversity	Partners (%)	Associates (%)
Women	21	51
White	90	66
Black/African American	2	9
Hispanic/Latin American	3	8
Asian	4	9
Mixed/Other	1	3
LGBT	2	5

"everybody has a busy schedule, when the stars align and we all have the same night off we do go out."

Affinity groups – for female, black, Latino, Asian and LGBT attorneys – provide another route for getting chummy with colleagues. *"We also have a diversity task force which sponsors a lot of events and gets speakers in,"* sources revealed. HH's historical diversity achievements make for impressive reading: it was the first Wall Street firm to hire a female associate in 1942, the first to appoint an African-American female partner in 1969, and the first major New York firm to promote a woman (Candace Beinecke) as chair – Beinecke serves as senior partner today. That's a hefty reputation to live up to, but associates had noticed that *"diversity has got a lot better recently thanks to the make-up of incoming and lateral associates."* Several pointed to New York as the best performer in the network, while those in DC noticed that *"we've got a lot more racially diverse lately – the women's committee here is also really active and hosts workshops and round table discussions."*

Pro Bono

Almost every source we spoke to had done some pro bono work. One described it as *"a significant part of associate life,"* and indeed all attorneys must bill at least 20 pro bono hours each year. *"There is an incentive to do a lot beyond the minimum: the policy is that if you reach 50 pro bono hours anything above that counts toward your billable bonus targets."* A maximum of 200 hours of pro bono can be counted as billable. Our sources told of working on International Human Rights Tribunals, Fourth Amendment housing disputes, uncontested divorces and collaborations with local institutions like the Beth Israel Medical Center.

Pro bono hours
- For all US attorneys: 32,725
- Average per US attorney: 123.5

Hours & Compensation

HH has a tiered bonus system, so there are a few numbers to remember. Associates must hit 1,950 hours to be eligible for a bonus at half the market rate; 2,100 gets them market; 2,300 hours lands them market and a half. Finally, the mega billers who reach 2,500 get a tasty double market bonus. *"What the system does very well is reward hard workers,"* most sources agreed. *"It's a good program for honoring Herculean efforts and nobody thinks that the people who get the high-tiered bonuses don't deserve them."*

> ## *"It's a good program for honoring Herculean efforts."*

Our interviewees across the board tended to start a little later (10am) and leave the office any time between 6pm and 11pm. *"It's very flexible,"* said one source when discussing HH's stance on office-based hours, *"even if the work itself is inflexible!"* Thankfully, *"super late nights aren't too frequent; there are some all-nighters but they always involve working with the team on something exciting."*

Offices

The New York HQ was remodeled in 2017: *"Now it's very modern and sleek, which makes you feel very professional! Plus it's based in a great location across from Battery Park – if you're on the best side you get a beautiful view of the water."* DC was going through renovations at the time of our calls. *"They're much needed,"* said relieved juniors here. Some nostalgic souls *"will likely miss the old school law firm feel,"* but most *"welcomed all the glass, standing desks and the new streamlined colors – it was looking a bit old and stodgy!"* The extent of cross-office collaboration varies by practice group; we heard that ties with the Paris base are generally strong, especially in HH's international trade group – *"people are going to Paris all the time!"*

Strategy & Future

DC managing partner Bill Stein tells us Hughes Hubbard's *"strategy as a mid-size firm is to focus on the areas that we're very strong in and bring the most value to our clients."* Alongside *"cutting-edge work"* in international arbitration, Stein highlights *"an extremely successful year of lateral partner hiring"* that has bolstered areas like anti-corruption and international trade. The Trump administration has prompted *"a lot of new work"* in the latter area, *"as our clients have needed to understand what direction to take following policy changes."* To find out more from Stein about the firm and what sets it apart from others, visit chambers-associate.com

See firm profile on p.653

Hunton Andrews Kurth LLP

Lawyers per state

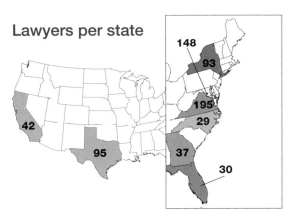

Largest US office: Richmond
US offices: 15
International offices: 5
First-year salary: $160,000 – 180,000
Billable hours: 2,000 target
Summers 2018: 50 (14 1Ls, 36 2Ls)
Revenue 2017: undisclosed
Partners made in 2018: 14
Famous for: forward-thinking approach; variety of mainstream and niche practices

Fresh from a major merger, this Richmond-born firm is on the hunt for its next generation of *"thought leaders"* in core areas like energy, financial services and real estate.

IT may have Southern roots dating back to 1901, but don't go thinking that Hunton is stuck in the past. *"Law firms have to innovate,"* global managing partner Wally Martinez tells us, *"and that means making better use of technology and offering cross-disciplinary solutions. We have broken team lines to bring those solutions to bear."* Such remedies are focused on four key industries: financial services, energy, retail & consumer products, and real estate investment & finance. *"75% of our revenue comes from those areas,"* Martinez points out, adding that the firm's industry focuses *"allow us to become thought leaders – our lawyers are expected to host talks on and publish articles about those areas. Anyone joining the firm can expect to be integrated into one of those industry areas right off the bat."*

"You have to look broadly at the world and ascertain what the future will be."

Innovation in 2018 came in the form of a merger with Andrews Kurth, which aims to, as Martinez puts it, *"strike a bolder geographic footprint in key markets and establish ourselves as a powerhouse in Texas."*

The opportunity to get early involvement in such matters was a draw for our associate sources, as was Hunton's

reputation in both mainstream and more niche practice areas: real estate, corporate, environment and privacy and cybersecurity were all mentioned as areas of particular interest. All of these practices come highly recommended in *Chambers USA*, where the firm picks up its biggest haul of rankings in its home state of Virginia, but also receives accolades for its work in Texas, DC, Florida, Georgia and North Carolina. Other notable strengths include IP, capital markets, bankruptcy/restructuring, labor & employment and climate change matters.

Strategy & Future

"You have to look broadly at the world and ascertain what the future will be," Martinez explains. So what has appeared in Hunton's crystal ball recently? *"There's been a lot of talk in the US about implementing the European public-private partnership model, but we've already taken a leaf out of the UK's book on that as we saw it coming – you look at things that will be coming in and you adapt."*

Hunton currently has 14 domestic offices dotting both coasts and the Texas market, as well as five international bases across Europe and Asia. Will it be adding to its ranks any time soon? Martinez reveals nothing concrete: *"We like to follow the flow of business; you see clients focusing on certain jurisdictions and you realize that in order to get the work done you will need to expand. But expansion for us does not mean just planting a flag and hoping people rally around it."*

On chambers-associate.com...

• Get hired at Hunton Andrews Kurth

The Inside View

See firm profile on p.654

Rankings in *Chambers USA*

Banking & Finance

Bankruptcy/Restructuring

Capital Markets

Climate Change

Corporate/M&A

Energy & Natural
   Resources

Environment

Intellectual Property

Labor & Employment

Latin American Investment

Litigation

Outsourcing

Privacy & Data Security

Projects

Real Estate

REITs

Retail

Tax

For detail on ranking tiers and ranking locations, visit
www.chambersandpartners.com

The Work & Offices

After sampling three practice areas as summers, associates "talk with the hiring partners to establish what you are interested in. They then look at which practice groups have a need." The process "definitely pinholes you right off the bat, which is great if that's what you want to do." Of the pinholes available, Hunton's litigation group took the largest share of the juniors on our list, followed by corporate and then corporate finance and real estate. A small number joined Hunton's administrative law, labor & employment and energy and infrastructure groups.

But where do they complete this work? Richmond, being the biggest office, sheltered the most associates (around a third) and was deemed "a fairly typical office building – I don't know if there's anything to brag about, but it's very nice!" DC and Dallas took on a similar number (around a fifth each); the latter "is in a diamond-shaped building that was designed by a famous architect – we recently renovated our floors and now all the offices have slick and modern glass paneling." Hunton's Park Avenue perch in New York is "absolutely beautiful. I went to a lot of interviews with various firms and this office is the best. It's also attached to Grand Central Station so most people don't have to walk outside if they don't want to!" The firm's LA, McLean, Miami and Atlanta offices nabbed a couple of associates each as well.

The newly merged firm will add Dubai and Silicon Valley to its network, but elsewhere – Texas, DC, NY, North Carolina and internationally – the two firms will be bolstering their legacy footprints.

"I've already taken 35 full depositions and defended 12 of them."

Junior litigators "occasionally filed on behalf of plaintiffs, but 90% of the work has been on the defense side." There are sub-groups to delve into, including teams dedicated to retail and consumer products, securities, environment and energy matters. Those in Richmond found that while

Recent work highlights

- Successfully defended Alfa Laval – a manufacturer of food processing equipment – against contamination claims worth over $4 million
- Advised ExxonMobil on a range of environmental and energy matters, including those tied to the shift in administration from Obama to Trump
- Helped Yahoo! manage the fallout from a cybersecurity attack that compromised around three billion user accounts
- Advised on a combined $375 million mortgage and mezzanine loan for the NYC skyscraper 70 Pine Street

"every now and again we have to pitch in on document review, the partners feel that our time is better spent getting more practical experience." This included opportunities to travel and take depositions; one associate had "already taken 35 full depositions and defended 12 of them." Sources in some of the smaller offices "basically do everything: I've done discovery work, case management, drafted motions, communicated with opposing counsel..." The size of these offices allowed associates to "enjoy a varied workload, but at the same time there aren't a lot of people here to share the responsibility, so you have to be able to multitask and put in a lot of hours."

The corporate finance and real estate group "represents developers, buyers and sellers – especially in the New York market – as well as banks that are making loans to large companies." Associates were certainly kept busy: "The deals operate on short timeframes – typically three months – and you're often juggling seven at a time!" As for tasks, "the more senior attorneys are in charge of the loan documents, so juniors do things like getting opinion letters, reviewing title reports and agreements affecting the property, and taking care of zoning stuff." Sources praised the group "for throwing us in early – you're on the phone all day with clients and the other side." Those hungry for more responsibility were not disappointed, as "very quickly you get to do more senior stuff," like running smaller deals where "you draft the sale and purchase agreement and monitor the transaction till closing."

"The deals operate on short timeframes."

Over in Richmond, corporate associates had encountered "a large variety of matters, from acquisitions to capital markets stuff to general financing to corporate governance." Those in Dallas were also impressed with the available mix: "We handle private equity transactions, fund formations and M&A." Across the offices, what juniors did depended "a lot of where in the life-cycle the deal was." Most found themselves "doing first drafts of primary documents, such as the asset purchase agreement, as well as the key ancillaries. Then there's also the more junior as-

See firm profile on p.654

Diversity	Partners (%)	Associates (%)
Women	19.6	50
White	89.3	81.7
Black/African American	3.2	3.7
Hispanic/Latin American	3.6	5
Asian	3.6	6.7
Mixed/Other	0.4	3
LGBT	0.7	1.3

sociate things like reviewing contracts, doing due diligence and formulating schedules." For more on Hunton's environmental and privacy and cybersecurity work, visit our website.

Training & Development
Hunton's 'client service curriculum' consists of *"sit-down events for associates that cover a breadth of topics, such as the firm's finances and how to interact with staff, to more legal-focused sessions on things like how to craft an argument for a brief."* Other courses include project management and budgeting. Here's the deal: *"You take what you want to take – they often occur over lunch and are particularly useful if you are about to get exposure to something that you haven't done on the job before."*

The extent of informal feedback was partner-dependent, but we heard from plenty of sourcesthat had had this experience: *"Oftentimes a partner will come back to me with mark-ups of a document I've drafted to show me the style they prefer – they take the time to explain the changes, which is critical for improvement."* The formal review process was spoken about positively: *"We write a self-assessment in March, then the partners and counsel we've worked with write up their reviews in April, and in June we have our sit-down review meeting. All the feedback is attributed, so we know exactly who said what and what they think of you!"*

Culture
Juniors were wary of overplaying the 'Southern vibe' (*"We're Southern to the extent that Southern means hospitality and geniality"*) and identified Hunton's caring side as the most discernible strand in its culture. *"Even when I interviewed at the firm I felt like people cared about me – in fact, my interviewers reached out to me beforehand to take the time to talk to me – and that's been consistent throughout my experience."*

"...Southern to the extent that Southern means hospitality and geniality."

How does this care manifest itself? Well, sources generally felt Hunton's senior lawyers were keen mentors. One junior recalled: *"There was an issue that I didn't quite understand and I went to one of the partners and they sat me down and ran me through the relevant concepts."* Insiders put this kind of behavior down to Hunton consisting of *"people who had the credentials to go to any firm they wanted but decided to come here. Some of our senior lawyers have known one another for 30 years and they're invested – they want the same thing for young associates."*

Judging by the number of social activities we heard about, it certainly sounds like Hunton's lawyers like spending time together: practice group lunches, happy hours, events for big football games, cooking classes and *"gatherings to celebrate people's birthdays and weddings"* were all highlighted in our interviews. *"We're not doing anything wild but it all produces a good atmosphere!"*

Hours & Compensation
Both the corporate and corporate finance and real estate groups came with highly variable hours. During quieter periods associates could be working between 9:30am and 5pm, but as deals ramp they could be toiling away until 2am for a week. Litigators regularly worked nine to ten-hour days, but also experienced lengthier stints: *"On the day of a trial I got into the office at 6am to ensure everything was ready, and was back in the office after court until midnight as we had a conference with the client."* Thoughts on how achievable the 2,000-hour billing target is varied depending on practice area. Those in the administrative group in particular found it to be *"a high number – it's something I'm concerned about."*

Associates felt *"appropriately compensated"* but did find *"the payment structure a little obscure."* Juniors start on a market-rate lockstep salary, but at around the 8th year associates transition to a *"performance based, case-by-case system."* With bonuses, sources understood that hitting the 2,000 hours target made them bonus eligible, but also spoke of *"rumors that you need someone to advocate for you as well,"* which the firm emphasized was more procedural than it sounds: to keep it performance-related, a case it made to the associates' committee. *"While we don't publish a scale of salaries, we offer total compensation that is competitive,"* says corporate finance partner (and former hiring partner) Tom Hiner. *"Each associate's total compensation is determined based on quality of work, economic performance and overall contribution to the firm, as well as market factors."*

See firm profile on p.654

Pro Bono

Associates can count 50 hours of pro bono toward their billing target: *"The informal expectation is that you'll do that 50. If you don't, you won't get penalized but they do track people who aren't doing it and send them emails with opportunities."* Sources estimated that *"around 30% of associates will do more than 100 hours,"* and if they do, they become proud recipients of an award named after the firm's cofounder E. Randolph Williams.

"There's not really a central person you go to for assignment," sources revealed, *"as there's a variety of people who are involved in different areas."* Our interviewees had *"leapt right in"* on custody matters, veteran issues, eviction lawsuits and animal abuse work. Juniors can also secure *"a lot of work"* from Hunton's two 'neighborhood pro bono offices' in Charlottesville and the Church Hill area of Richmond. The latter *"does a lot of landlord/tenant cases, while Charlottesville is known for immigration and domestic violence work."*

Pro bono hours

- For all US attorneys: 41,964
- Average per US attorney: 63

Diversity

"I think the population of diverse candidates that want to be in Richmond is quite low – often we lose them to firms in DC and New York," one junior posited. Another agreed that perceptions of Richmond might have an effect: *"If you're not familiar with Richmond then you might be concerned about it being an old-fashioned Southern city and not a welcoming environment – which is 100% wrong!"* Still, in other offices the location had yielded more diversity. One junior who'd spent time in the Miami office told us *"it's diverse from an ethnicity perspective, with Hispanic lawyers choosing to come here."*

Overall, juniors felt that Hunton *"is making a conscious effort to invest in diversity,"* and frequently pointed to the firm's 1L summer associate diversity program, where *"we take on diverse 1Ls in Richmond and Dallas – the hope is that we get them to return as 2Ls."* In addition, female sources had attended *"women in law events, which were held for the firm's clients as well as its female attorneys."* We also heard of *"informational events that explore different cultures"* and *"partners talking about diversity efforts during lunchtime seminars."*

"...around 30% of associates will do more than 100 hours."

See firm profile on p.654

Irell & Manella LLP

Lawyers per state

121

Largest US office: Century City
US offices: 2
International offices: 0
First-year salary: $180,000
Billable hours: 2,000 target
Summers 2018. 20
Revenue 2017: undisclosed
Partners made in 2018: 3
Famous for: work-life balance; all things IP; allowing its juniors to take ownership

This doyen of disputes is a product of its surroundings: big Californian tech and Tinseltown brands keep Irell looking sharper than sharp.

WITH clients ranging from media megastars like Warner Bros. and Disney to tech giants like Tesla and Uber, Californian-born Irell's work remains tip-top. It may be a relatively small operation (its 121 attorneys are split between two offices in Century City and Newport Beach), but Irell attracts clients with worldwide reach, allowing associates to work on *"very important, complex cases in lean teams."*

"We have an enormous reputation for IP," managing partner Ellisen Turner – who took the reins in February 2018 – tells us, *"but it's a common misconception that we're only an IP firm. We're great in that area – I think we're the best – but we are phenomenal in a wide array of fields."* Chambers USA certainly honors Irell's IP prowess with a tiptop ranking in California, but also rates its securities, media & entertainment, general commercial litigation, tax, life sciences and bankruptcy expertise. While the majority of Irell's lawyers work in its litigious teams, the firm does have transactional capabilities in areas like M&A, real estate, private equity and debt finance.

"Our lawyers in life sciences are knocking it out of the park."

Strategy & Future

Turner adds that while the firm has no goal to open more offices, new recruits in the future can expect to see a firm that's *"a bit larger, with more practice areas – at the moment our global investigation and anti-corruption practice are expanding, while our lawyers in life sciences are knocking it out of the park."* The recent appointment of Department of Justice prosecutor Jason Linder also bodes well for the firm's future, Turner tells us: *"Jason was an associate here, then he went to the DOJ and worked across every major industry in the US. Now he's back and he'll be enhancing our global investigations and anti-corruption practice."*

The Work

The vast majority of Irell's juniors work in its broad litigation practice – only a couple of the second and third years on our list were assigned to the firm's corporate practice. A free-market system of assignment allowed our sources to *"control your own career path and reach out to the different partners you want to work with."* This system was popular with our interviewees, who prized the freedom it gave them: *"I don't want to specialize! I want to try out lots of different types of work and form my own practice."* They also felt shielded from the potential negative effects of a free market, as *"no one falls under the radar or is left behind: you're supported and guided because the firm is small enough to give you a lot of training and mentorship."*

"I don't want to specialize!"

On chambers-associate.com...

- More on getting hired at Irell

The Inside View

See firm profile on p.655

Rankings in *Chambers USA*

Intellectual Property	Media & Entertainment
Life Sciences	Tax
Litigation	

For detail on ranking tiers and ranking locations, visit
www.chambersandpartners.com

Recent work highlights

- Secured a $506 million judgment against Apple for infringing a 'computer microarchitecture' patent owned by the Wisconsin Alumni Research Foundation
- Delivered an appellate win for client Tesla Motors, which affirmed a previous dismissal of a shareholder class action against the company and its CEO Elon Musk
- Acted for ZOLL Medical Corp. after Philips filed a $217 million damages claim; a federal jury rejected it and instead ordered ZOLL to pay 3% of what Philips originally sought for the infringement of its defibrillator technology patents
- Represented Warner Bros. during a class action lawsuit that challenged the way in which Warner Bros. (and other studios) accounted for home-video royalties over the course of several decades

Litigators are therefore free to sample the raft of matters that fall under the practice area, from media and entertainment disputes to securities cases to IP issues to government investigations to insurance fallouts. Many of our sources had taken on patent cases and *"really loved them – Irell is one of the few firms that allow you try this work without a science degree."* One raved about being given *"huge responsibility on a large-scale, complex patent litigation case: I got to take on deposition work with experts, which has made me much more confident. Plus we secured a really great settlement."*

Across all specialties juniors agreed that there are *"meaningful opportunities and the chance to exercise early responsibility."* As cases are prepared for trial, juniors had found themselves *"drafting expert reports and preparing witness outlines – you get a wide range of experiences that you don't expect as a first year. You're not doing hours and hours of doc review – you're managing doc review while drafting things and doing research."*

Training & Development

New recruits can expect two days of orientation training when they join, which covers *"all the basics like computer training, and then a few weeks later you get to go on the retreat to Palm Springs!"* This three-day excursion was unanimously popular among associates, who told us: *"It's wonderful. There are workshops and trainings, but overall it serves as a great introduction to Irell – a fun weekend where the new associates can meet the partners and bond from the beginning. It's relaxing too; some people play golf, some go to the spa etc..."* Upon their return litigators get into the training spirit by undertaking a two-day deposition training program, which sees juniors *"perform a mock deposition – the firm hires actors to play the witnesses!"* This is followed by regular lunchtime trainings *"on a different topic between January and May in your first year."*

"You get to go on the retreat to Palm Springs!"

All new starters are also assigned an associate mentor upon arrival. *"They're your official mentor but they're mostly a safety net,"* interviewees agreed. *"The people I go to are the partners I've built relationships with – I do that because I can and because they're there for me."* Other sources also bestowed praise on their seniors' approach to mentoring: *"You get close mentorship from all levels. We'll get support if something doesn't go right the first time."* Aiding this support network is a 'gap lunch' program which enables juniors to take more senior associates to lunch on the firm's dime: *"There's a huge emphasis on associate peer mentoring. It's another way to form mentorships that you create yourself."*

Pro Bono

"The firm definitely encourages pro bono," juniors told us. *"Irell has a 'one for one' policy, so all pro bono hours count as billable and there's no maximum amount that you can do."* How maximum is maximum? *"One first year racked up over 1,000 hours – when they say that Irell puts its money where its mouth is, it's absolutely true. The firm is happy if you are building and developing valuable skills."*

"...all pro bono hours count as billable."

Our interviewees had been building those valuable skills on a smorgasbord of matters, including those relating to domestic violence, civil rights, gang violence, construction and copyright law. *"A lot of the pro bono around here is related to immigration and asylum matters. Those cases are all local, whereas some of the copyright stuff has been sourced in the UK."* Sources were on the whole eager to *"take advantage"* of Irell's generous stance on pro bono, and not just because *"the good wouldn't be done otherwise."* It also allows newbies to *"take ownership"* of the pro bono they take on: *"We handle the entire case ourselves!"*

Pro bono hours
- For all attorneys: 9,590
- Average per attorney: 101

See firm profile on p.655

The Inside View

Diversity	Partners (%)	Associates (%)
Women	9	42
White	84	83
Black/African American	2	0
Hispanic/Latin American	2	2
Asian	13	13
Mixed/Other	0	2
LGBT	2	2

Culture & Offices

The concept of 'ownership' came up again and again in our interviews as a defining cultural trait: *"You're encouraged to take it! It's the thing that makes somebody do well here in general. You're not meant to feel like a cog in a machine."* This emphasis on ownership makes Irell a *"'choose your own adventure' sort of place,"* which values flexibility in various contexts (as you'll see from the stance on working from home, below). *"They let you work how you want. My door can be open but I can also shut it for days on end if I want – you can switch depending on your mood."* Ultimately, *"it's a 'do your own thing' culture,"* another interviewee summed up, with the firm's social staples – like Friday night happy hours and monthly breakfasts – *"there for you to be involved in them as much as you want. Some people just want to work and go home and that's accepted and normal."* Most people make the effort to attend Irell's annual all-attorney retreat: *"Last year it was held at Monarch Beach Resort! It lasts for a couple of days, and you can bring your family. One of the partners turned to me and said: 'Isn't this nice? If we were a bigger firm we wouldn't be able to do this!'"*

Get Hired

"We need them to be great because we unwind the Gordian knots that clients get into – and that requires creative lawyering." says managing partner Ellisen Turner. For more insight into what Irell's looking for in future recruits, visit chambers-associate.com

With its reputation for hiring top scoring graduates and promoting an intellectual vibe, juniors were pleasantly surprised when they arrived at Irell: *"I thought it was going to be an aloof, intellectual and judgmental place, but everyone I met blasted that misconception! I've loved talking to the people here and working with them."* A warm atmosphere was reported in Irell's Century City HQ, where there's *"a sense of familiarity – we know each other's names and say hi to one another in the halls."* The vast majority of the firm's juniors are based here (the Newport Beach office only housed one junior on our list), and the sources we spoke to loved it: *"Century City is great! I'm infinitely happier than friends of mine in New York. You can actually live in a house here and still be a 15-minute walk away from work."* While the office itself is *"a bit dated,"* sources did highlight that they get a $500 decorating budget for their individual offices, which come with some stunning views: *"I watch the clouds roll in from the ocean,"* one relayed dreamily.

Hours & Compensation

The hours *"aren't that different to what they are at a typical BigLaw firm,"* said juniors, *"but they trust you to be responsible and shape your own schedule to get the work done."* This was especially true in the Century City office, where working from home is quite common: *"I work from home one day a week on average – sometimes two or three days. A partner once said to me: 'I don't care if you work from the moon as long as you do your work!'"* When they are in the office, juniors tended to work between 8/9am and 6/7pm on average, with some logging back on *"for an hour or two"* at home to wrap up any outstanding tasks. When cases do go to trial, the hours increase as *"you're in court all day and then come back to the office to get everything ready for the next day – but it's fine because you know it's coming up and can plan ahead."* Fortunately, *"after a long trial they encourage you to take vacation. In fact, it's expected."*

> *"...after a long trial they encourage you to take vacation."*

All of this hard work goes into meeting Irell's 2,000-hour bonus threshold. *"If you hit that you'll get a lockstep bonus that's determined by class year. They might bump you up if you're almost at 2,000 so you get a bonus – but that's not guaranteed."* The target number *"has been tailored to incentivize a realistic amount of work,"* juniors told us, with one adding: *"It doesn't put me in competition with my peers, as we're all working to bill the same amount."*

Diversity

Ellisen Turner hit the headlines back in fall 2017 when it was announced that he would become Irell's first African American managing partner (and, from our research, the first of an AmLaw 200 firm). *"Our diversity committee's job is to think about these things and make them better. We bring in consultants and speakers to give us guidance,"* Turner tells us. Among Irell's situation-improving initiatives are pre-law outreach programs; a $15,000 scholarship program for diverse law students; and an implicit bias-combating interview technique during OCI season. So far, associates are impressed by Turner's efforts: *"Ellisen is putting a huge focus on increasing diversity here. We're excited about his tenure."* Read more from Turner on chambers-associate.com

> *"It's a 'do your own thing' culture."*

See firm profile on p.655

Jackson Walker LLP

Lawyers per state

385

Largest US office: Dallas
US offices: 7
International offices: 0
First-year salary: $180,000
Billable hours: 1,950 to be in good standing
Summers 2018: 27 (13 1Ls, 14 2Ls)
Revenue 2017: $249.4 million (+1.1%)
Partners made in 2018: 6
Famous for: loyalty to Texas; independence; highly-rated real estate work

The Texas market may be getting crowded, but Jackson still walks the walk.

MANY a firm has started with a homestead in the South, but few have shown the dedication that Jackson Walker has. For 130 years the firm has kept its lawyers based in the Lone Star State; today JW has over 380 of them, working out of seven offices across Texas. Its loyalty to the region has paid off, as JW snags a top *Chambers USA* ranking for its real estate expertise in Texas, as well as nods to its capabilities in areas such as general commercial litigation, labor & employment, corporate/M&A, healthcare and energy (with regards to electricity work). JW's investment funds practice is also gaining traction in *Chambers USA.*

Much like the firm itself, associates also demonstrated an unwavering loyalty. Many hoped to hunker down and *"work hard in order to make partner – the people that come here very much want to be a part of this firm."* Others added that JW *"shows a high degree of interest in its own people. They really invest in the associates here, and it was made clear early on that if I was hired it would be on the partnership track."* Most of our sources had roots in Texas, either through their upbringing or later education, but managing partner Wade Cooper tells us: *"We're open-minded about a candidate's connection to the state. It's easier to hire people from Texas, but we wouldn't foreclose on somebody who demonstrated what we look for."* Intrigued out-of-towners should therefore read on too.

On chambers-associate.com...

- Get hired at Jackson Walker

Strategy & Future

"There has been a lot of consolidation in the Texas legal market," continues Cooper, *"but we have remained true to our strategic plan."* That plan involves *"maintaining our independence and continuing to grow within the state of Texas. We're not looking to merge with another large firm just to get bigger."*

"...maintaining our independence and continuing to grow."

In an increasingly crowded market, Cooper tells us that JW isn't *"a competitor to the Wall Street firms with respect to capital markets work, but in areas like real estate, funds, power, regulatory and labor we think we can compete with anybody. A lot of Texas firms are backing out of those areas to focus on high-rate energy and capital markets work, which we think means there is a great opportunity to be the go-to firm is those aforementioned areas."*

The Work

Most of JW's juniors were based in its litigation, corporate & securities, and real estate departments. The odd outlier found a home in smaller groups like ERISA, labor & employment, healthcare, and land use. A free market system of work assignment is in place across most groups. Sources explained that *"the system doesn't work perfectly every time, but it's better than just being allocated to an attorney. You get to have a say in who you work for, and that contributes a big part to job satisfaction."*

See firm profile on p.656

Rankings in *Chambers USA*

Bankruptcy/Restructuring	Healthcare
Corporate/M&A	Immigration
Energy & Natural	Labor & Employment
Resources	Litigation
Environment	Real Estate

For detail on ranking tiers and ranking locations, visit
www.chambersandpartners.com

"*Across the state we handle pretty much any type of business dispute you can think of,*" litigators told us. In particular, our sources had come across cases in the media, construction, energy and aviation industries, and their practice had covered the likes of fraud, negligence, IP, securities and white-collar matters. "*What I like about JW is that we have a number of clients that range from small to large, so associates gain a variety of perspectives,*" said one satisfied source. "*I've worked on large cases where I'm the fourth chair for a media outlet, but I've also gone out to the Justice of the Peace courts to represent small clients, which has been great for my development.*" Doc review and handling discovery responses are unavoidable on those larger matters, but smaller cases can mean "*working with just a partner: you get to go to hearings, take depositions and write several dispositive motions.*"

"...our role is to mitigate any economic risks."

The corporate & securities department handles a plethora of transactional and regulatory matters. Juniors here said that half of their work was "*straight-up M&A where we represent the buyers and sellers of public companies, while 30% of it revolves around private equity matters – the rest is taken up with SEC compliance advice and miscellaneous contract work like employment or consulting agreements.*" On the investment funds side, "*we represent institutional investors during various deals, but often primary investments: our role is to mitigate any economic risks.*" With "*around 100 investor clients all around the world,*" sources here dealt with "*multiple time zones every day – once I had a call at 4am!*"

Over in real estate sources described three main streams of work: "*There's a finance side that handles deals where real estate is being used as collateral; there's leasing work; and there's also an energy arm – we have a pretty substantial group that does due diligence for wind and solar farms in Texas.*" The nitty-gritty work involves producing initial drafts of contracts, sitting in on calls, and "*playing a key role during the closing stages of a deal to make sure all the documents are good and the buyers are all up to date.*"

Recent work highlights

- Obtained a motion to dismiss a patent infringement suit on behalf of McKesson Healthcare and three other companies
- Served as co-counsel to Blackstone Real Estate Partners as the private equity firm acquired more than 15 multi-state portfolios worth over $20 billion
- Defended Warner Brothers during a defamation case that centered on a TMZ story on a police report
- Advised financial services firm Parkwood on its $50 million purchase of an interest in Riverside Investment Management Company

Training & Development

A week of "*pretty extensive training*" gathers all new associates in Dallas and quickly orients them to navigate life at the firm. Corporate and litigation juniors then go through a series of formal sessions that are tailored to their practice. For deal doers, the series is called "*the lifecycle of a company, and the sessions are really enjoyable.*" Litigators were also pleased: "*They teach you the different tools you need as a trial attorney. They go over deposition and oral advocacy skills, as well as motions and evidence objections – it's absolutely fantastic.*" Those in the smaller groups get more informal, hands-on training, with one telling us that "*each partner has taken it on as their responsibility to teach and guide me.*"

Culture

"*One of the mottoes that they like to use is: 'we take our work seriously but not ourselves,'*" associates revealed, and in practice they felt that "*the firm does hire people that fit into such a mindset and environment.*" On the work side, "*you can't be the type of person that just wants to have assignments handed to them; you need to have a big personality and be willing to go out and mingle with clients. We are all results-oriented people who are dedicated to their clients.*" On the less serious side, "*this is a firm where if it gets to 6pm and you want to go out for a beer with your colleagues, you can. A lot of people are laid back, and when it comes to stepping away from the desk and the phone, it's clear that people enjoy spending time with each other.*"

"We take a lot of pride in our longevity."

A close-knit vibe therefore dominates at JW: "*The firm has been around for 130 years, so we take a lot of pride in our longevity, which is reflected in our culture.*" The tendency of JW's lawyers to stick around for the long haul means that there's "*a bunch of attorneys who have only ever worked here – they're all friends and have been coworkers for 30 years or more. They're successful and effective – the top dogs in Dallas.*" This led some to suggest that there's a slight 'old boys club' feel to the firm: "*It's not insidious but it's there, and is evident when only certain peo-*

See firm profile on p.656

The Inside View

Diversity	Partners (%)	Associates (%)
Women	22.4	44.3
White	89	72.2
Black/African American	2.5	5.2
Hispanic/Latin American	14.	7.2
Asian	5.8	5.2
Mixed/Other	0.4	10.3
LGBT	-	-

ple are taken to lunch or appear to get preferential treat-ment." Others agreed that *"that sentiment lingers with the older partners,"* but dismissed the potency of its effect.

Offices

The associates on our list were based in JW's Dallas, Austin and Houston offices. The Dallas HQ housed the most, and residents here told us that *"we moved around two years ago to a brand new building that's 1,000 times better than our old offices! It's all glass and open spaces, and we have top-notch technology: everyone has tablets, the desks rise automatically to accommodate standing positions and there are some super fancy coffee machines."*

"We have top-notch technology."

The Austin base is located downtown, *"right on the river overlooking the State Capitol building."* Also on the plus side is the fact that *"there are lots of affordable apartments and condos nearby, which is great as you can walk to work."* Houstonites revealed that *"most of the offices are fairly small, but overall there's a nice mix of openness and privacy in the design, which I appreciate."*

Hours & Compensation

Associates must bill 2,000 hours in order to be considered for a bonus, but to keep up with your peers 1,950 is the basic billable requirement. This figure doesn't include a required 100 hours of firm citizenship work, which covers pro bono, and all the various tasks that fall under firm citizenship, such as business development and CLE. The 2,000-hour figure was dubbed *"a general expectation – a decent number of people do not hit it, and failure to do so is more accepted in some groups than others. Corporate & securities, for example, tends to be a lot more intense about hitting it."* Thoughts on how bonuses are calculated were mixed, with some Austin-based juniors telling us

that *"it seems a little subjective – it's not completely trans-parent,"* while those in Dallas said: *"It's very clear and fair. The system is tiered, so if you hit certain hours benchmarks your bonus goes up. They also pay associates a percentage of their originations, which is a nice little perk."*

"Thankfully nights like that are rare."

"Every person is different," when it comes to working hours. Some of our interviewees were early risers and got into the office by 7am and left at 5:30pm, while others preferred to work between 9am and 7pm. On the whole, *"if you work at a large law firm you can expect to work a lot,"* and busy times saw corporate & securities juniors working until 2:30am on occasion, while litigators had pulled the odd *"all-nighter – we had a very tight turna-round, and there's just nothing you can do about it! Thank-fully nights like that are rare."*

Pro Bono

Some juniors felt that *"they really encourage us to par-ticipate in pro bono"* via the 100 citizenship hours re-quirement, while others didn't think that figure provided enough motivation: *"We would do more of it if we were in-centivized to do so."* A partner on the pro bono committee sends out emails once a month, and many opportunities come through Texas Legal Aid and local entities. Sources had worked with schools and churches, attended advice clinics on starting up businesses, handled divorces, and filed petitions during international adoption cases.

Pro bono hours
- For all attorneys: 7,671
- Average per attorney: 20

Diversity

JW's efforts were deemed most effective when it came to gender diversity, and many interviewees mentioned the firm's women's group, JW², which *"meets once a quarter: there's always a great turnout, and they bring speakers in to discuss the issues that women face in the workforce. I feel they have really empowered me by giving me the tools I need."* There's *"not much racial diversity"* but juniors did tell us that JW has *"put an emphasis on it and has prior-itized it through formal programs and committees."* These include participation in recruitment events hosted by the Dallas Consortium on Minority Hiring and the Univer-sity of Houston Black Law Students Association.

See firm profile on p.656

The Inside View

Jenner & Block LLP

Lawyers per state

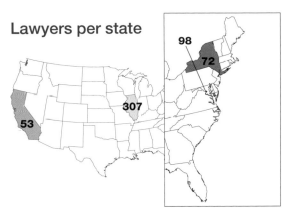

98

72

307

53

Largest US office: Chicago
US offices: 4
International offices: 1
First-year salary: $180,000
Billable hours: 2,100 target
Summers 2018: 44 (39 2Ls, 5 SEO)
Revenue 2017: $448.5 million (-2%)
Partners made in 2018: 13
Famous for: litigation prowess in areas like media & entertainment and insurance; commitment to pro bono; LGBTQ inclusion

This formidable Chicagoan is a force to reckoned with in the courtroom and a champion of pro bono and diversity.

"JENNER'S culture of inclusivity – it's the portrait, the identity of the firm," beamed our interviewees. The view from the top supports this, with managing partner Terry Truax telling us: *"We have an excellent commitment to working with a diverse team of extraordinary talent, to pro bono and to engagement with communities."* This reputation was not lost on Jenner's junior associates, who targeted the firm especially for its dedication to these areas: *"I didn't apply to any other BigLaw firms – only Jenner!"* We'll explore their thoughts on pro bono and diversity shortly…

Jenner is also well known for its capabilities in the courtroom, and Truax highlights that *"complex commercial litigation is the defining aspect of who we are."* On this front, Jenner picks up some superb *Chambers USA* rankings for its insurance, media & entertainment, general commercial and IP expertise. The firm also has a transactional arm, which contains practices like corporate, real estate, internet & technology, and communications. Future deal-doers are encouraged to seek out Jenner too, as *"our transactional group is really growing – we're growing our client base and making sure we're doing everything we can to secure repeat clients,"* juniors here told us. Most newbies join the firm's Chicago HQ, but Jenner's domestic

presence extends to New York, DC and LA. In 2015 the firm made its first foray overseas and opened a London branch that's currently focused on litigation work.

Strategy & Future

"We're very much known for our complex commercial litigation practice in the US," Truax explains, *"but I like to think that this area and others are beginning to take a foothold in London and Europe."* Commenting on the London office, Truax tells us that *"the strategic focus there is on gaining leverage into further litigation, investigation and public international law opportunities."* Alongside strengths in appellate and white-collar, Truax is eager to tell us about another practice that's recently taken flight: *"We've made a great effort to develop our aviation practice and have been fortunate to recruit a team of excellent lawyers to build that out."*

"Complex commercial litigation is the defining aspect of who we are."

Jenner's also been rounding out its energy offering beyond its historical specialty of electric utility companies, and while corporate remains *"a smaller portion of the firm, it continues to be an area we want to be locked into,"* says Truax. *"I'm certainly interested in seeing that develop on a smaller scale that's still high-end."*

On chambers-associate.com…

- Find out more about Jenner's LGBTQ diversity
- How to get hired at Jenner
- Jenner's offices and social life

See firm profile on p.657

The Inside View

Rankings in *Chambers USA*

Appellate Law	International Arbitration
Bankruptcy/Restructuring	Labor & Employment
Corporate Crime &	Leisure & Hospitality
Investigations	Litigation
Corporate/M&A	Media & Entertainment
Environment	Real Estate
ERISA Litigation	Tax
Insurance	Telecommunications
Intellectual Property	Transportation

For detail on ranking tiers and ranking locations, visit
www.chambersandpartners.com

Recent work highlights

- Advised Charlotte-headquartered snack maker Snyder's-Lance on its $4.9 billion agreement to be acquired by Campbell Soup Company
- Wrote and filed an amicus brief that supported the plaintiffs who are challenging President Trump's ban on transgender recruits in the military
- Conducted an internal investigation for General Motors' board of directors, which was tied to the events leading up to the recalls of faulty ignition switches
- Obtained $13.15 million in damages on behalf of the Estate of Elaine Steinbeck, following a series of legal battles over the rights to seminal US author John Steinbeck's works

The Work

The overwhelming majority of second and third-year juniors (76%) were working in Jenner's litigation practice. A handful were sprinkled across smaller groups, including bankruptcy, corporate, private wealth, government contracts, and communications, internet and technology. Positions in the latter two groups were concentrated in the DC office. Across the groups an open market system of work allocation dominates, though there are assignment partners on hand to help juniors if needed. Our sources liked this set-up, and found it *"really beneficial, as it gives you more control over the type of matters you want to work on. Plus everyone's really nice – it's not scary to walk up to a partner!"*

In litigation, juniors *"start out as generalists for the first three years and are exposed to a variety of areas before declaring a specialism in the fourth year – some people have primary and secondary groups."* Areas available for sampling include complex commercial, aviation, energy and IP litigation, as well as arbitration and government investigations. Patent matters enabled one source to *"be in charge of an expert witness, which involved communicating with them and getting them ready for the trial while also preparing the related report. The fact they trusted me to be a part of that process meant a lot to me."*

"It gives you more control over the type of matters you want to work on."

Complex commercial matters, meanwhile, can be *"very large, with 20 attorneys or so working on them, so they often involve a lot of gathering, organizing and summarizing facts."* On arbitrations juniors had *"gotten the opportunity to go to a hearing and draft a lot of the required documents – it's a really great responsibility and I feel like an important part of the team."* Government investigations, on the other hand, *"involve a lot of writing and figuring out what the law is when there's a gray area. You're also drafting interview outlines for witnesses, attending those interviews and putting together the subsequent interview memo that's*

circulated to the team and the client. I feel challenged and not drowning in mundane things!"*

"About 10% of the firm is corporate and it's growing and it's great," Jenner's deal-doers told us. Though most people walking through the door end up in litigation, some people do switch practices: *"A person in my year came in thinking 'I'm going to only do litigation' and now is mostly doing transactional work and really enjoys that."* Associates here can expect to work on *"small to midsized M&A deals, but we also support other departments and counsel clients on topics like privacy, advertising and marketing."* Tasks include drafting memorandums and risk assessments, as well revising promotional agreements and, of course, due diligence.

Diversity

"Everything you've heard about Jenner is true!" our interviewees exclaimed. They were lightning quick to praise Jenner as *"a very inclusive place"* that's *"genuinely committed to creating an environment that's comfortable for people of all backgrounds."* Current trends bode well for the future configuration of the partnership too: 62% of Jenner's 2018 partner class were LGBTQ, ethnically diverse and/or women. In addition, *"we have strong female role models at the firm, like Susan Kohlmann, who is the managing partner of the New York office."*

"It's about creating a culture where diversity is normalized."

Jenner has one of the highest percentages of LGBTQ associates recorded by the firms in our guide, which means *"you don't feel 'exampled' by your LGBTQ identity because there are so many of us here!"* Diversity is encouraged through the firm's many affinity groups, with one source telling us: *"They put their money where their mouth is. They recently held an attorneys of color networking event in Chicago and flew in attorneys from all over the country to attend."* Another associate emphasized that *"it's*

See firm profile on p.657

The Inside View

Diversity	Partners (%)	Associates (%)
Women	29.8	45
White	91.7	73.5
Black/African American	2.1	3.5
Hispanic/Latin American	2.1	4.5
Asian	2.5	15.5
Mixed/Other	1.7	3.0
LGBT	5	12

not just about the numbers; it's about creating a culture where diversity is normalized. By saying 'partner,' for example, rather than assuming someone has a 'boyfriend/girlfriend.'"

Pro Bono & Culture

Jenner's emphasis on diversity is "reflected in the pro bono that we do," juniors felt. The firm worked on the milestone Lawrence v. Texas case that paved the way for equal marriage in the US and it's currently working on fighting North Carolina's transphobic 'bathroom bill.'

"What's most important about Jenner's culture is the pro bono. Everyone here has this unwavering dedication to giving back to the community," sources emphasized. Pro bono is so embedded in Jenner's culture that one associate told us: "I can't remember which cases were pro bono and which were client billable!" It's not uncommon to hear of associates spending a few hundred hours a year on pro bono matters, which provoked one interviewee to say: "It's astounding to me how much pro bono my colleagues and I have done." The firm's pro bono matters span areas such as immigration, prisoners' rights, criminal defense, family law, trademark infringement and election law. "There are incredible and exciting opportunities," juniors agreed, with one adding: "I've seen about five of them on my email today!"

"Everyone here has this unwavering dedication to giving back to the community."

Associates also reasoned that "because Jenner has its reputation for pro bono, it attracts people who value doing good." This creates a supportive atmosphere all around, with one source recounting a day "when I came in with a cold: everyone on my team was wishing me well and trying to lighten my workload – they didn't have to do that! I couldn't ask for a better workplace in that sense."

Pro bono hours
- For all US attorneys: 90,254.6
- Average per US attorney: 168.4

Hours & Compensation

Jenner has an "all-around target" of 2,100 hours, "which encompasses 2,000 hours of billable and pro bono work, and 100 firm approved hours for things like recruitment activities, CLEs – even office meetings!" Hitting 2,100 hours makes associates bonus eligible, but the amount they get is determined "on a case-by-case basis." On the whole, sources had no qualms with the system, and appreciated that "all attorneys are treated individually."

"There's certainly enough work to keep you busy."

Most felt that "there's certainly enough work to keep you busy." This steady tide of matters translated into consistent 9am to 7/7:30pm days, with some evening and weekend work from home when required. "The workload has been more manageable than expected," one litigator sighed in relief, but some of those in the smaller departments did highlight that "the craziest weeks have seen me bill 70 hours, but that doesn't happen regularly – most of the time you're hitting 40 to 45 each week." Juniors also praised the "great home technology system we have – a lot of people live in the suburbs, so they can put the kids to bed and log back on around 8pm."

Training & Feedback

A weeklong orientation in the Chicago HQ gets newbies "up to date on how the firm works – it's housekeeping training really." Transactional lawyers subsequently undertake an additional week of 'corporate boot-camp' in November. "In terms of ongoing training, there are all sorts of CLEs you can go to," with litigators highlighting the benefit of writing workshops and tailored group sessions on particular niches. "We also had an informative CLE on recognizing implicit bias – it was very helpful to detect the biases I have and ensure they don't affect anyone."

"It's great to get your feet wet and receive instantaneous feedback."

Our interviewees' favorite training program was Jenner's two-day deposition workshop. "It's intensive and lasts from 8am until 5pm both days. They bring in actors to play the defendants and you practice giving the deposition in front of partners. It's great to get your feet wet and receive instantaneous feedback." On the subject of feedback: the firm's chief talent officer, Charlotte Wager, received praise from associates regarding the formal review process. "She reviews each person extensively. She knows me by name and what cases I'm on – having Charlotte is a huge benefit!"

See firm profile on p.657

The Inside View

Jones Day

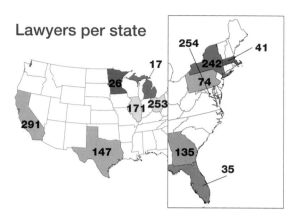

Lawyers per state

254   41   17   242   26   74   171   253   291   147   135   35

Largest US office: Washington, DC

US offices: 18

International offices: 25

First-year salary: $180,000 ($160,000 in Cleveland, Columbus, Detroit, Miami, Minneapolis and Pittsburgh)

Billable hours: 2,000 target

Summers 2018: 214 (29 1Ls, 176 2Ls, 9 SEO)

Revenue 2017: undisclosed

Partners made in 2018: 32

Famous for: being bigger and better known than almost every other firm

With 125 years of winning 'bigly' behind it, Jones Day is one of America – and the world's – most prestigious legal names.

CLEVELAND'S city motto, 'Progress & Prosperity,' has clearly been taken to heart by its most successful legal offspring. Jones Day's reputation as a powerhouse firm precedes it the world over and we hardly need to tell you it picks up *Chambers USA* rankings across ten states and DC, and is top of the heap in antitrust, construction, restructuring and labor & employment nationwide. The firm doesn't officially publish its revenue figures, but be assured it sits comfortably among the global titans.

An institution it may be, but evolution is key to success, and the firm can hardly be accused of standing still. Jones Day has often been in the news thanks to association with the Trump administration, with 13 attorneys taking up positions there. Meanwhile, its already formidable global offering increased to 27 overseas offices when a new one opened in Melbourne during the writing of this very paragraph. *"The international focus of the firm"* appealed strongly to associate insiders, alongside its enduring *"Midwestern values."*

The Work

All new starters report for duty to the New Lawyers Group and *"try whatever projects they want for up to a*

year. You're not permitted to join a group officially until June." Sources were unanimously positive about the scheme, pointing out *"it lets you sample different areas and see where you fit. You also get specialist experience in different kinds of law that helps your practice long-term."* Work assignment is overseen by at least one coordinator in each office, but the onus is on associates to get experience with the teams they're interested in, so being assertive is essential. Some pointed out *"you can end up taking work for the sake of it and not enjoying it, or feel like you're behind peers at other firms who specialize straightaway."* Once a junior's found their niche, they apply to join a group; the local team leader has final say.

Business & tort litigation is the most common home for newbies. Commercial disputes, securities fraud litigation, arbitration and white-collar investigations are all on the menu there, alongside some IP cases in California especially. *"Whatever the case calls for, I do,"* one interviewee told us; *"it could be anything from running document review to writing substantive motions or preparing witnesses for depositions."* In smaller offices in particular *"it's hard to hide and when work piles up it can feel like you're drinking from a fire hose,"* but sources agreed that *"there's a good support system in place."* On larger projects involving a squad of associates *"you can feel more like a cog in a wheel,"* and early client contact can be hard to come by, but litigators suggested *"Jones Day is very much a firm that offers opportunities to grow regardless of what year you're in."*

On chambers-associate.com...

- Get hired: interview insight
- Interview with firm-wide hiring partner Sharyl Reisman

The Inside View

See firm profile on p.658

Rankings in *Chambers USA*

Antitrust	Government
Appellate Law	Healthcare
Banking & Finance	Insurance
Bankruptcy/Restructuring	Intellectual Property
Capital Markets	Labor & Employment
Construction	Latin American Investment
Corporate Crime &	Life Sciences
Investigations	Litigation
Corporate/M&A	Products Liability
Employee Benefits &	Real Estate
Executive Compensation	Retail
ERISA Litigation	Tax
FCPA	

For detail on ranking tiers and ranking locations, visit
www.chambersandpartners.com

Recent work highlights

- Defended McDonald's in the largest National Labor Relations Board litigation ever brought forward, alleging 181 distinct legal violations
- Represented six colleges and universities in a multi-district litigation alleging that they failed to warn football players of the effects of concussions
- Advised tobacco company Reynolds American during British American Tobacco's $49 billion acquisition of 57.8% of RA's shares not already owned by BAT
- Lead debtors' counsel to coal giant Peabody during its reorganization, reducing the debt burden by $5.2 billion over pre-filing levels

M&A is the second most popular destination. We heard *"most matters are within the $100 and $500 million range, but some will be $10 million and others several billion dollars."* Representing both public and private clients, JD often handles cross-border mergers. Massive matters like these require multiple juniors for the due diligence process, but on *"smaller deals with just a partner you're involved in the whole project."* Juniors got a taste of drafting on both and found it *"a good way to bolster your skills."* One declared they'd *"been uncomfortable with the work a couple of times, which is what you need."*

"I've been uncomfortable with the work a couple of times, which is what you need."

Smaller teams were more likely to offer client contact early on, which some detected was *"firm strategy for newcomers, to get you experience quickly."* Banking & finance juniors took on *"a lot of organization; much of my job is herding cats."* There's some overlap with real estate, which encompasses private equity funds investing in real estate backed assets as well as *"more traditional lease and purchase cases."* Associates focused on fund work *"noticed my responsibility growing on each fund, so I've gone from drafting smaller agreements to putting together letters for a multi-billion dollar fund."* There's also a transactional wing in IP, plus patent prosecution and litigation. Research and writing *"comes early on, but when things slow down there's more discovery"* for clients spanning the software, pharmaceutical and telecommunications sectors.

Training & Development

Newbies from across the world are flown into DC to take part in the New Lawyer Academy, involving a series of presentations and workshops. First-years get *"a lot of training ranging from practical skills to sessions with vari-*

ous partners. After that it slows down and becomes more ad hoc." Litigators participate in multi-day NITA trainings; transactional associates go through the M&A boot camp. *"Most training is on the job,"* though, *"it's helpful to an extent."*

The associate review process is a lengthy affair, beginning in February with a report on all the matters that the reviewee has dedicated more than 25 hours to. That's sent to senior lawyers for review, who pass on *their* own review to the US practice group leader, *"ensuring consistency between offices."* Associates get a written statement from their practice group leader in summer, which *"can be a little too late to help, but it's useful for evaluating your overall growth."*

Get Hired

"It's easy to tell if somebody's the Jones Day type – intelligent but not competitive. If you come in wanting to be number one above other juniors… that's not what we want." Find out more interviews dos and don'ts at www.chambers-associate.com

Diversity

The good news first: associates suggested *"we're doing great for gender diversity; they really push a message of strong female leadership."* Eighteen of the firm's offices have female partners-in-charge. Several interviewees commended Jones Day for promoting women in traditionally male-dominated areas like M&A, and *"there's a female partner in charge in Dubai, upending a huge gender norm there."* Reports on the firm's racial diversity were less positive, though. *"There's a healthy handful of minorities but there could certainly be an improvement. A lot of people here point out the legal market lacks ethnic diversity but that's kind of a cop-out."* The 2017 new partner class came in for praise, and the firm does run *"a lot of initiatives through the diversity committee; partners take out minority associates and check in on how they're doing."*

See firm profile on p.658

The Inside View

Diversity	Partners (%)	Associates (%)
Women	25	49
White	89	81
Black/African American	1	3
Hispanic/Latin American	5	6
Asian	4	8
Mixed/Other	1	2
LGBT	-	-

Since 2016 Jones Day has also hosted a 1L Diversity Conference dubbed 'Perspectives and Pathways.'

Eighteen of the firm's offices have female partners-in-charge.

Culture & Offices

Given the firm's history and prestige it's no surprise that *"Jones Day is quite traditional"* – several offices still expect business formal attire – but newcomers were surprised to find *"it's less stuffy than expected. The firm's Midwestern roots still inform its attitude; there's less of the politicking you get at New York firms."* They also suggested that smaller class sizes help to keep out BigLaw's worst tendencies, and reported *"people who are really competitive tend to stick out."* While overall *"there are more shark-like attorneys in M&A and litigation"* than elsewhere, even juniors in those departments claimed *"everyone's a team player and is willing to chip in."*

"Going to another office, the only differences are where the cafeteria and restrooms are."

Jones Day embraces the idea of being 'one firm worldwide' strongly enough to splash it in massive letters on the website homepage. *"It's pretty accurate,"* interviewees confirmed. *"Going into another office, the only differences are where the cafeteria and restrooms are; you're definitely working for the firm and not just for your office."* Californians seemed to break most with Jones Day's overall vibe, reporting *"we're a lot different to people in Chicago or New York, and we work different hours as we're fortunate to have good weather most of the year."*

Physically speaking, the offices themselves are pretty varied – while DC is *"quite stunning; it's two buildings combined with an atrium that's recently been redone."* Atlanta has an Instagram-friendly *"rose-gold exterior. It's smaller than a typical law firm high-rise; we have the whole building."* JD New York is the largest office, and the team's just relocated to the financial district. Pleased with their new location, New Yorkers found *"the only drawback is as a junior I'm now in an internal office."* As for the OG Cleve-

land base, the facilities are *"better than they used to be! We've done a ton of renovations and have our own cafeteria, gym and 24/7 valet service."* Inter-office collaboration varies by practice group, but *"people come and go from different offices all the time"* and international travel is far from rare.

Each office hosts its own happy hours on a Thursday or Friday, plus *"a number of scattered socials"* often organized by an affinity group. More so than most, *"litigators and the New Lawyers Group are very social,"* though all things considered *"it's not that social here compared to other firms. If I want to just go home after work, it's fine."* Things do ramp up in summer, during which *"the firm puts on a couple of events a week,"* and there's no missing an excuse to roll out the bunting for anniversaries like the 30-year-old Chicago office had recently.

Pro Bono

Juniors in every office were keen to stress *"pro bono gets treated like any other assignment; it's seen as our obligation to give back."* The firm's two largest pro bono programs are the Unaccompanied Minors Project, aiming to help mothers and young children who have crossed the border into the US gain refugee status and apply for citizenship; and a dedicated site at the US Immigration and Customs Enforcement detention facility in Laredo. Transactional attorneys aren't left out – they can advise on clinics for local small businesses, or handle disputes.

"I'm blown away by the firm's commitment."

Getting opportunities like *"arguing a motion in front of a federal court in my first year,"* interviewees were *"blown away by the firm's commitment. It's always encouraged and I've never heard partners complain about anyone taking too much on."* Correspondingly, *"there's no limit on how many pro bono hours we can count as billables; they're in the same column in our hours breakdown."*

Pro bono hours
- For all US attorneys: 159,392
- Average per US attorney: undisclosed

Hours & Compensation

There's a 2,000 billable hours goal, and associates found *"it's definitely a target, not a requirement."* One admitted *"I didn't know we had a target!"* – those more in the know said *"it's easily achievable and there's no sense that not reaching it would be the end of the world, or will derail you from partnership."* Working hours can bounce between *"coming in around 10am and leaving at 5pm"* and *"getting a lot done so you're here until 9pm."* We heard surprisingly

See firm profile on p.658

few late night war stories: *"I can count on one hand how many times I've been in past 10pm,"* and weekend work was the exception not the rule. *"Nobody's watching to see if you're here or not, it's about getting the work done."*

"It creates a less competitive atmosphere when people aren't fighting for hours."

Jones Day are a tad funny when it comes to money – associates get black box annual raises rather than a bonus. The secrecy provoked mixed reactions, including some worries that *"it leaves you feeling a bit powerless"* and confusion as to how raises are determined. Most, however, appreciated *"not having to stress about the hours you work. That's part of the collegial environment, it creates a less competitive atmosphere when people aren't fighting for hours."* It's hard to pin down where the average lies compared to other firms. One junior thought: *"We're probably making less than some, but I appreciate the system and I know if I work really hard I can make more than market."*

Strategy & Future

If you've seen Jones Day in the news recently, there's a high chance it's because of the firm's links to the Trump administration. Firm-wide hiring partner Sharyl Reisman explains the firm has a *"large number of lawyers with government experience because of our rich heritage of lawyers serving in high-level government posts."* She went on to add that *"we have been fortunate to have several lawyers join us from the outgoing Obama administration, and we have had several lawyers from Jones Day join the current administration. Government experience is of great value to our clients."* Jones Day's already impressive global growth continues apace, most recently in the form of *"a new office in Melbourne, demonstrating our growing strength in Australia,"* Reisman tells us. *"Our new offices and entry into new markets reflects focused and deliberate growth to meet our clients' needs, not growing just for the sake of getting bigger."* For the full interview, visit www.chambers-associate.com.

Coming soon on chambers-associate.com... Jones Day's lawyers take us behind the scenes of their corporate department.

See firm profile on p.658

K&L Gates

Lawyers per state

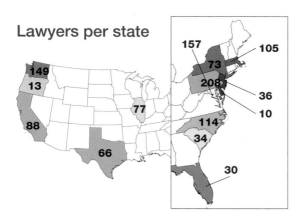

157
105
73
149
13
208
36
77
10
88
114
34
66
30

Largest US office: Pittsburgh
US offices: 23
International offices: 22
First-year salary: $120,000-$180,000 (varies by office)
Billable hours: 1,950 target
Summers 2018: 47 (8 1Ls, 39 2Ls)
Revenue 2017: $989.9 million (-16%)
Partners made in 2018: 17
Famous for: merger-based growth strategy; distinctive branding; global coverage; its legacy firm's connection with Bill Gates's father

With more than a decade of rapid expansion behind it, this global firm is now focused on maximizing cooperation across its vast platform.

"THE tentacles of the firm go back 150 years when you look at our constituent legacy firms," says K&L's recruitment and integration partner Craig Budner. While that description may conjure up images of some rampaging creature from a 1950s B-movie, we assure you that there's nothing to fear here – unless you're terrified of global law firms that is. For K&L Gates has a much gentler disposition than its formidable size (which encompasses 45 offices worldwide) might imply, as global managing partner Jim Segerdahl explains: *"There are lots of moving pieces and interrelated parts. But as complex as it is, it really boils down to an organization populated by people dedicated to working together to deliver great service to clients from what I regard as an amazing platform. We constantly emphasize teamwork and collaboration, and bringing together the best resources to deal with our clients' challenges – that is what we do day-in and day-out."*

Segerdahl took the reins from long-serving managing partner Peter Kalis in 2017; Kalis had overseen the firm's growth for two decades and helped to spearhead the 2007 merger between Seattle's Preston Gates and Pittsburgh's Kirkpatrick & Lockhart, which gave us the K&L Gates we

know today. While there has been a change in leadership, Segerdahl confirms that *"our basic mission as a highly integrated global firm has remained the same."* Chambers Global certainly acknowledges K&L's capabilities across Europe, the Middle East and the Asia-Pacific region.

On its home turf, K&L picks up an array of *Chambers USA* rankings across the markets it operates in. Top awards at a state level go to the firm's corporate/M&A & private equity, general commercial litigation, healthcare, bankruptcy/restructuring and environment expertise. Its nationwide nods, meanwhile, include energy, government relations, insurance disputes, investment funds and transportation work in the shipping sphere.

Strategy & Future

Given its recent history, will K&L be getting even bigger any time soon? *"I think it's not likely that any firm could keep up with quite the expansion pace that we've been on over the last ten years,"* Segerdahl reflects. *"It has been a remarkable run. We are fortunate to have reached the point where we're on five continents, so I think it's fair to say that the pace of expansion does not need to be on a par with the track over the past ten years or so."* However, Segerdahl is quick to qualify: *"That's not to say we will ignore positive strategic opportunities as they arise; indeed, we will always embrace and pursue opportunities to strengthen our positioning."* For more from Segerdahl, go to chambers-associate.com

On chambers-associate.com...

- Getting hired at K&L Gates: acquaint yourself with advice from the firm's recruitment and integration partner Craig Budner
- Interview with global managing partner Jim Segerdahl

See firm profile on p.659

Rankings in *Chambers USA*

Bankruptcy/Restructuring	Insurance
Corporate/Commercial	Intellectual Property
Corporate/M&A	Investment Funds
Energy & Natural	Labor & Employment
Resources	Litigation
Environment	Real Estate
Government	Technology
Healthcare	Transportation

For detail on ranking tiers and ranking locations, visit
www.chambersandpartners.com

Recent work highlights

- Represented oilfield services company Halliburton in connection with insurance coverage issues arising from the 2010 Deepwater Horizon disaster
- Acted for Microsoft as it contributed to a $1.4 billion investment in an Indian-based electronic commerce company, Flipkart Group
- Represented EB Holdings II – the holding company for a global metals outfit – during its restructuring, which involved €1.8 billion in outstanding debt
- Provided strategic advice to the Greater Washington Board of Trade on various matters, including the Board's response to a DC-based paid family leave bill, which affects all businesses in the region

The Work

Juniors are assigned to a primary practice, but can also select up to five secondary practices to take on work from. *"You do have a legitimate opportunity to seek assignments from other groups – it's quite free-flowing."* A free market system exists across groups, but there are some checks in place to ensure that juniors are getting enough work: groups in Seattle have official workflow coordinators to *"keep a handle on things and make sure that major projects get staffed,"* while others elsewhere simply have *"partners who coordinate and manage it among themselves; they get on the same page and know who's available."* Sources reported varying levels of success in the free market, but appreciated the opportunity to move around: *"You may be doing something for partner A who then has a lull, so you just go over to partner B who's super busy."*

K&L's complex commercial litigation and disputes (CCLD), corporate/M&A, and investment management groups housed just over half of the juniors on our list. CCLD covers several types of litigation, including securities, real estate, toxic tort, class action, government enforcement and environmental matters. Our sources here had often worked on the defense side of cases, for clients in a range of industries, from oil and gas to financial services. *"In the first year my tasks were more piecemeal,"* one source reported, charting their progress. *"I supported people writing motions, did research tasks for arguments, and interpreted case law. Now I have control of at least one of my own cases. I do doc review, but typically in anticipation of depositions."* Other second-years had also played a prominent role during cases: *"I'd write and spearhead everything and come up with the strategy. I didn't get to take the deposition, but I managed it – the questions I wanted asked got asked. I wasn't being a potted plant!"*

"It was a great way to jump in and get my name out there."

Corporate juniors had worked on a mix of M&A deals, securities offerings and commercial lending transactions, as well as some general corporate governance matters. In the beginning, *"you mostly assist with due diligence projects, but you soon get to start managing those projects, and get a chance to revise portions of agreements."* Sources found that venture capital and emerging growth-oriented work came with *"lots of client contact,"* and were pleased with how quickly responsibility levels ramped up: *"I got to be the sole associate on a $50 million asset purchase. I participated on calls and saw the project through from beginning to end. It was a very enjoyable experience and it happened a lot earlier than I thought it would."*

K&L's investment management practice has a sizable presence in DC and Boston, and we heard that there's currently a push to grow it in New York. Associates found the work to be cyclical: *"Over the summer it's very slow, so there's more research, reading and training. During the fall and winter it's busier, so we update filings – there's a lot of reviewing comparative documents to see what was done last year versus what the client wants to do now."* One highlight was *"helping to write a client alert with a pretty senior partner. They let me work on it like two months after I started; I know that at some places they don't put juniors' names on the byline, but my name was in. It was a great way to jump in and get my name out there."*

Training & Development

Associates have midyear reviews and *"more formal"* annual evaluations too. For the latter, *"you write a self-evaluation based on the firm's associate competencies for your level, and select partners/seniors you've spent more than 25 hours working with to review you. You then get a written consensus message based on those reviews."* Sources praised this system for being *"a two-way dialogue; they'll be other partners in the meeting with you, and they want to get your thoughts."*

"...constant in-house CLEs on every subject you can think of!"

See firm profile on p.659

417

Diversity	Partners (%)	Associates (%)
Women	24	43
White	88	81
Black/African American	2	3
Hispanic/Latin American	2	4
Asian	6	8
Mixed/Other	2	4
LGBT	2	4

There's certainly no shortage of formal training on offer: *"There are constant in-house CLEs on every subject you can think of!"* In addition, *"they also put on special programs from time to time. For example, they hosted an associate pitch competition once, where everyone got materials to help us become acquainted with client development-type activities."*

Get hired

How could a hotdog car boost your chances of impressing a K&L Gates recruiter? Visit chambers-associate.com to find out and discover tips from recruitment and integration partner Craig Budner.

Hours & Compensation

To bag a market-rate bonus at K&L associates have to meet a target of 1,950 hours. Those who *"bill beneath the threshold can still receive a bonus, but it's just not at market rate, sigh…"* one junior commiserated. Perceptions of how achievable K&L's billing target is varied across our interviews. Litigators found it *"pretty achievable,"* while those in investment management went ten steps further and confidently described it as *"extremely achievable."* Corporate juniors, on the other hand, said that it's *"relatively rare to hit it, mostly because you have a couple of months where the work's jammed in and then a couple of months where nothing much is happening."*

This unsurprisingly translates into some see-sawing hours for corporate associates: *"When it's not busy I get in by 10am and hopefully leave by 7pm, but on a busy day I'll get here by 8am and sometimes don't leave until midnight."* Investment management sources also mentioned staying until *"3am once a quarter or so,"* while litigators worked fairly standard ten to twelve-hour days. Associates appreciated being able to work remotely in the evenings, especially those with children. We spoke to several men and women with young families who felt supported by the firm, and were encouraged by recent changes in maternity and paternity policies: *"They now offer 18 weeks paid maternity and six more unpaid. They've extended paternity leave too – it was six weeks paid, now it's twelve."*

Culture

"I think it is unique," one Pittsburgh-based source commented when discussing K&L's culture, *"because despite being a big firm it actually feels small, as we have a more tight-knit environment here; people know what's going on in their co-workers' lives, and in my group we interact with the partners all the time."* Other interviewees across the network also felt that their offices boasted a more intimate feel, with one DC resident homing in on K&L's *"emphasis on cooperation: there's not a cutthroat feeling at all, and even the really busy seniors are always willing to sit down and explain something to me. They care about your world outside of the office, and if it's obvious that you're stressed they'll tell you to take care of yourself. I feel cared for, and that's rare."*

"...despite being a big firm it actually feels small."

Juniors also appreciated the *"honest feeling that you get from people; when I interviewed here I didn't get the canned responses that I got elsewhere. The partner said that 'yes, sometimes we work crazy hours, but when we don't have to we don't just sit around in the office.' He said that he was going to hang out with his kids that afternoon as his trial had been canceled."* And so while *"work is extremely important, so is family."* Therefore *"people are pretty respectful of your time outside of the office – they don't make up deadlines that aren't real, and they'll work with you if you have obligations beyond work."* This approach means that *"while the firm does set aside money for social events, which is nice, we don't have the kind of culture that you see at other firms where everybody hangs out together all the time – people generally like to go home and do their own thing."*

Offices

K&L Gates has too many domestic offices to describe individually – a whopping 23 that line both coasts and dot a fair few markets in between – but they do have something in common: *"They're all decorated in line with the firm's branding and colors. They're all white and spacious – a bit like an Apple store!"* The Pittsburgh HQ was home to the largest contingent of juniors on our list, but the firm's Seattle, DC, Chicago, New York and Boston bases also took on a significant proportion each. Associates had worked out of other locations on occasion and appreciated that when they did *"everyone very much saw me as a distant relative who'd come to visit. The same goes the other way too – I treat visitors like that and take them out to lunch or drinks after work."*

"Everyone very much saw me as a distant relative who'd come to visit."

See firm profile on p.659

K&L has a further 22 offices around the globe. How much juniors get to interact with their overseas colleagues depends on their practice group, sources felt: *"Transactional folks working on cross-border deals probably have more contact. On the litigious side it varies; the construction group does a lot of international arbitration work in Dubai, so they second people to the office there, while the insurance group sends people to London."*

Diversity

We spoke to a number of diverse associates, including people of color and LGBT juniors, and the feedback was unanimous: *"You can be yourself at work."* A number of these associates flagged the firm's commitment to diversity as one of its draws. Across the offices, female sources praised the Women in the Profession (WIP) group: *"They hold monthly lunches and usually bring in a speaker; we've had talks on topics like public speaking, effective communication and financial planning."*

"You can be yourself at work."

The LGBT group in Pittsburgh is particularly active, as this junior explained: *"We've hosted internal events with the WIP group; we organized a joint happy hour and theater trip with one of the firm's major clients; and following the Pulse tragedy in Orlando we hosted a fundraiser, which the firm sponsored. We also have quarterly video conference calls with LGBT representatives from across the network to touch base."*

Pro Bono

All pro bono hours count toward K&L's billing target. Our interviewees had found it *"pretty easy to take it on in addition to billable work – the firm definitely encourages it."* This encouragement was borne out in the fact that some of our sources had billed around 400 pro bono hours within a year.

"...a lot of people are very passionate about it."

Every office has its own pro bono coordinator, but juniors also told us that they'd been able to launch their own projects: *"People bring in things – one associate established a program to assist asylum seekers with their applications, while someone brought in a project to guide transgender folk through the legal process that enables them to change their names."* Our sources had also worked on matters tied to educational services, veteran assistance programs, prisoners' rights cases and anti-trafficking initiatives. *"The options are quite varied to say the least,"* one junior confirmed. *"One of our programs combats 'revenge porn'; we've formed an alliance and a lot of people are very passionate about it."*

Pro bono hours
- For all US attorneys: 49,138
- Average per US attorney: 42

See firm profile on p.659

The Inside View

Kasowitz Benson Torres LLP

Lawyers per state

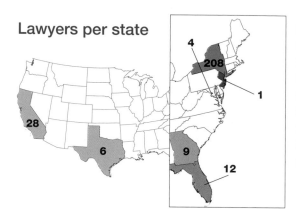

4
208
1
28
6
9
12

Largest US office: New York
US offices: 9
International offices: 0
First-year salary: $180,000
Billable hours: no requirement (2,150 for full bonus)
Summers 2018: 13 (2Ls)
Revenue 2017: undisclosed
Partners made in 2018: 9
Famous for: representing Trump; aggressive litigators

Confidence and independence are needed to succeed in this pack of "bulldog litigators."

FORMED by an exodus of 19 lawyers from Mayer Brown in 1993, Kasowitz is one of the few major firms younger than most of its associates. But you'd be foolish to equate age with ability. While Kasowitz has neither the numbers and international reach of Skadden or Latham, nor the pedigree of 'white-shoe' outfits like Cravath or Milbank, what it does have is drive and a reputation for *"bulldog litigators, so we definitely command respect among the legal community,"* one source asserted. The *Chambers USA* rankings confirm this assertion: Kasowitz is recognized among 'The Elite' for general commercial litigation in New York (and for some other areas too).

> **"We are not a Republican firm or a Democratic firm: we are a litigation firm and we believe everyone is entitled to legal representation."**

No conversation about Kasowitz is complete without mentioning the *"elephant in the room:"* President Trump. Name partner, founder and *"benevolent dictator"* Marc Kasowitz has represented the president in a variety of hairy situations over the years, including defending

him during the Russia investigation in 2017. However, political matters like this are not a big line of work for the firm and associates say they don't indicate a particular political lean among Kasowitz attorneys either. *"We are not a Republican firm or a Democratic firm: we are a litigation firm and we believe everyone is entitled to legal representation,"* asserted one interviewee. Another commented: *"From the outside you only see a snapshot of the firm. Some of the cases we have taken on make us look one-sided in the political sphere, but that's not case."* One candid junior told us: *"I'm a bleeding-heart liberal and I don't think I'm in the wrong place."*

Culture

Upon arrival, juniors are *"walked through the history of the firm"* during initial training. This includes a look at some of Marc Kasowitz's most notable cases, which shows that while the firm's work beyond Trump is not political it doesn't shy away from contentious issues. For example, in the mid-90s Marc Kasowitz represented tobacco giant Liggett Group as it broke ranks with the tobacco industry to settle smoking-related litigation claims, saving it millions in potential liabilities over smoking deaths. Juniors felt that cases like this were emblematic of *"the aggressive legal stances we take: we're always looking for the win."* While this may make you think the firm is full of alpha males, sources were quick to say that *"being a lone wolf wouldn't work here. When I have a new case, the first thing I do is go to other associates and start spitballing ideas."* Another source believed: *"Our bulldog attitude in law*

On chambers-associate.com...

- Get hired at Kasowitz
- 'The Big Interview' with Marc Kasowitz
- Interview with co-managing partners Cindy Kelly and Wally Schwartz

See firm profile on p.660

The Inside View

Rankings in *Chambers USA*

Bankruptcy/Restructuring	Litigation
Insurance	Real Estate

For detail on ranking tiers and ranking locations, visit
www.chambersandpartners.com

doesn't translate into our personalities. Nobody has ever been crass or directly critical of me."

"Our bulldog attitude in law doesn't translate into our personalities."

Still, Kasowitz is certainly not for those who like having their hand held: *"You have to be able to stand up for yourself and be confident in your work,"* said one source. *"I have had multiple experiences of sending a piece of research through to a partner, only to have the phone ring five minutes later with them asking me to explain my research and how I got to my conclusion."* This is not a firm for those who want to be eased into practising law slowly. *"People are eager to challenge you, for example partners in the way they delegate work to you,"* one interviewee said. Co-managing partner Wally Schwartz echoes juniors' views, describing Kasowitz's culture as *"a perfect combination of being nasty when you have to be and being helpful for each other: it works."*

Get Hired

"First and foremost, be sure you want to do litigation. Don't tell me you're not sure as it means you didn't do any research." Visit chambers-associate.com to find out more from Kasowitz's associates about how to impress the firm's recruiters.

As the firm's longstanding managing partner, Marc Kasowitz has traditionally maintained a tight grip over the firm, but sources indicated that changes were afoot. In September 2017, following a string of exits, the firm appointed Cindy Kelly and Wally Schwartz as co-managing partners of administration. As a result, associates felt that *"there is a lot more structure and a greater number of defined mechanisms for associates to communicate with the partnership and the partners to manage the business."* This includes a newly reinstated associate committee which conducts monthly meetings that have *"already seen things being accomplished."* For example, juniors were happy to report on the introduction of new standing desks, dual monitors and a push for more flexible working – more on that later. While juniors believed that Marc Kasowitz was in no way *"taking a back seat,"* they did take the appointments of Kelly and Schwartz as an indication that he was more willing to *"share responsibility"* in an *"attempt to match ourselves with other law*

Recent work highlights

- Defended President Trump in a defamation law suit bought by former Apprentice contestant Summer Zervos, claiming that state courts do not have jurisdiction over the president while he or she is in office
- Defended AMC against an unpaid contingent compensation claim concerning the series *The Walking Dead*
- Represented derivatives broker MF Global in a $3 billion accounting malpractice trial against PwC

firms." Schwartz tells us that while *"Marc continues to be the primary decision-maker in terms of the policies and priorities of the firm, we now have a more active management committee made up of an excellent staff of a senior level."*

Strategy & Future

Schwartz tells us that we can expect *"more of the same"* from Kasowitz in the future. *"Don't expect Kasowitz to turn into a firm that does everything and anything. Our focus will always be on litigation and we are always looking strategically at areas of litigation to expand into."* Go to chambers-associate.com to read more from Schwartz and co-managing partner Cindy Kelly.

Offices

Most of the firm's junior associates are based in the New York mother ship, though a handful are scattered across the other bases. Kasowitz has built up a national network of smaller offices over the years: Atlanta, Houston, Miami, Newark, Washington DC, Los Angeles, San Francisco and Silicon Valley. Each has no more than a dozen attorneys.

After a pilot programme in 2016, juniors now spend their first 18 months sharing an office with an associate one year more senior. *"It has worked out really well,"* one guinea pig explained. *"It provides us with another mentor and a person to ask questions in the first year."*

The Work

Nearly all Kasowitz's juniors are swallowed up by the firm's commercial litigation practice where they tackle anything from business disputes, antitrust and securities cases to IP and product liability. Only a handful of juniors each year join transactional areas such as real estate, bankruptcy and employment – they're usually put there because of prior work experience or their educational background.

Three assignment coordinators delegate work after reviewing associates' schedules, although many sources

See firm profile on p.660

The Inside View

Diversity	Partners (%)	Associates (%)
Women	23.1	43.3
White	84.6	77.5
Black/African American	3.3	5.8
Hispanic/Latin American	7.7	5.8
Asian	1.1	6.7
Mixed/Other	3.3	4.2
LGBT	1.1	4.2

pointed out that they receive a lot of their work directly from partners they had developed relationships with. Most were content with the system, noting that *"the firm is good at taking your preferences to heart. Where I've had autonomy, I've been able to carve out my own niche, but where I've been asked to work on a project where my views didn't completely align, the partners took that into consideration."* However, juniors also pointed out that the firm's *"meritocratic"* approach to work resulted in a system where *"some people become more sought after,"* reflecting that *"the firm could work harder with people who are falling behind."*

"We leave no stone unturned, everything is constantly being appealed."

Associates were happy to elaborate on how the firm's reputation for aggressive and creative litigation manifested in the approach to work. *"Many of the times when we have won, there has been very little precedent,"* one junior told us. *"This means we are always having to take different concepts from different areas and piece them together."* Another added: *"We leave no stone unturned, everything is constantly being appealed."* This approach leaves little breathing room for juniors who quickly discovered that any *"trepidations of being stuck doing doc review"* were unfounded. As one junior summarized: *"Six months in I was writing motions. In my second year I've been to trial, have second-chaired depositions and am about to first chair one."* Another second-year boasted of drafting a *"45-page appellate brief,"* as well as *"reading complaints, opposing motions to dismiss and drafting discovery documents. I don't know the last time I did doc review..."*

Hours & Compensation

Attorneys are tasked with getting 2,150 billable hours under their belt each year in order to get a full bonus. That's a high number, even for New York – one of the highest hours' targets of any firm in *Chambers Associate.* A junior commented: *"2,150 initially seems scary but once you break it down by weeks, it's not overly suffocating."* The nature of litigation work also means it's often easier to clock up hours in this practice than in an area like corporate.

"I usually shoot for a nine-hour day," one junior told us. *"I probably stay until 6 or 7pm most days. For a longer day I might be here until 8pm or 9pm."* Another busier source told us: *"On a normal day I come in at 9.30am and stay until 8.30pm. And I've worked a handful of weekends."*

"2,150 initially seems scary but once you break it down by weeks, it's not overly suffocating."

Sources implied that remote working isn't as easy as at other firms, noting that *"some partners see it as a right you have to earn – we are still quite traditional in that sense."* Still, associates were hopeful this was something that could be improved upon through the new associate committee. In addition, we also heard that the firm has recently upgraded its network to make remote working easier.

Hitting the hours' target is made easier by the fact pro bono, business development and recruitment tasks also contribute towards it. Bonuses are calculated by a combination of hours, reviews and participation in the likes of recruitment and professional development activities; doing well on all fronts affords attorneys a full bonus. Reviews are conducted close to bonus payouts to give juniors a better understanding of the amount they receive.

Pro Bono

Pro bono was something sources believed *"is going to take a huge step forward"* in the near future with *"even more opportunities coming from new partnerships we have."* David Abrams is the firm's pro bono coordinator and juniors commended him as *"phenomenal for making sure opportunities are made available to us."* Cases range from tenancy evictions and veteran assistance to child custody and immigration. One recent case saw the firm help a decades-old Baptist church in the Bronx retain its property in the face of foreclosure.

Pro bono hours
- For all attorneys: 11,749
- Average per attorney: 39.13

Training & Development

All juniors are assigned a mentor upon joining the firm who is very helpful for learning to *"navigate the different personalities at the firm and transitioning between years."* Incomers are also enrolled in 'Kasowitz University', *"a six-month training program run by two partners which stretches over a period of time rather than being front-loaded."* Every junior is assigned to a fictitious case and tasked with things like carrying out the discovery process, writing complaints and conducting mock

See firm profile on p.660

The Inside View

depositions.In addition, all associates have regular CLEs and *"access to a ton of other resources."*

Diversity

As well as the new associate committee, the firm's new infrastructure also includes a *"newly revamped"* diversity committee, headed by name partner Hector Torres. *"It's not just an email being blasted out every month,"* sources told us. *"Partners take the time to attend meetings with us and do things like purchase tables at minority events. And if, for example, you find a diversity conference happening elsewhere in the country, the firm will sponsor you to go."* Sources also felt the firm's newly established women's committee has made great steps in *"retaining and recruiting women."* The representation of women at the firm is roughly on a par with established New York firms like Cravath and Davis Polk. Kasowitz also recently joined the Minority Corporate Counsel Association (MCCA) and the Leadership Council on Legal Diversity (LCLD).

"Different interviewers have different styles and different questions that they like to ask. Some interviewers like to start off having candidates tell them something about themselves that's not on their resume, to get a fuller picture of a candidate. Others like to jump right into the resume and ask about more substantive experiences from the start."
— Hiring partner Marissa Holob,
Stroock & Stroock & Lavan

See firm profile on p.660

Katten Muchin Rosenman LLP

Lawyers per state

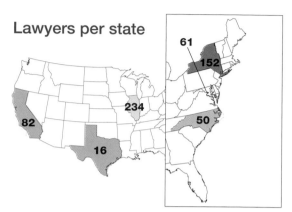

61
152
234
82
50
16

Largest US office: Chicago
US offices: 12
International offices: 2
First-year salary: $155,000 - $180,000 (varies by office)
Billable hours: 2,000 target (1,950 in Charlotte)
Summers 2018: 35 (10 1Ls, 23 2Ls)
Revenue 2017: undisclosed
Partners made in 2018: 11
Famous for: innovation and entrepreneurship

Katten has enough entrepreneurial spirit for nine lives.

ESTABLISHED in Chicago in 1974, Katten Muchin is a spring chicken compared to some of its peers, and it's this relative youth that informs a persistent mantra of ingenuity and independence. According to chairman Roger Furey, "*this works for associates because we offer them opportunities to work in new areas of the law that weren't around a few years ago. In addition to the traditional corporate and litigation practices, we have developed expertise in areas such as quantitative algorithmic trading, food safety outbreak law, sports law and cybersecurity.*" This adventurous approach appears to be working: Katten now has overseas bases in London and Shanghai, as well as 12 domestic offices (its latest addition to the network – a corporate-focused Dallas pad – opened in early 2018); its ever-rising profile in the legal world means that Katten is very much on the prowl for associates who can embody the qualities that have won the firm such riches. "*Cases are staffed leanly so we want people who can take the initiative and take on responsibility rather than just hiding and waiting for the phone to ring.*"

According to *Chambers USA*, the firm's best practices are real estate and white-collar crime in its home-state, Chicago. Beyond that, the firm gets an approving nod for real estate elsewhere, plus banking and finance, capital markets and sports law nationwide, media litigation in California, and healthcare and more general litigation in Chicago.

The Work

At the time of our research, a third of associates were on the firm's litigation team, while another third were evenly split between real estate and corporate. The remaining juniors were scattered throughout the various finance and tax groups. In Chicago, a staffing coordinator is sometimes used to assign work, but most interviewees gained their work by developing ongoing relationships with partners: "*In some ways it's on you to make sure you have a good caseload, but it gives you more control over what you're doing.*"

"In some ways it's like being a private investigator."

Litigation subgroups include white-collar defense, financial services, construction, healthcare and commercial litigation. Associates described "*a really interesting mix*" of work, including criminal and environmental litigation, and workplace and federal agency investigations. Sources found that "*because teams are staffed leanly you see the arc of the case and get more substantive assignments.*" That delivered a workload where "*on an investigation you'll be looking at primary documents and data and trying to put together pieces of the puzzle. In some ways it's like being a private investigator. That takes up half the time; the other half is traditional work like drafting motions and helping with briefs.*" One third-year told us: "*I've been doing a lot of reviewing reports and internal audits. Next year I'll be*

On chambers-associate.com...

- More on getting hired
- Interview with hiring partner Kristin Achterhof
- Interview with chairman Roger Furey

See firm profile on p.661

The Inside View

Rankings in *Chambers USA*

Banking & Finance	Litigation
Bankruptcy/Restructuring	Media & Entertainment
Capital Markets	Real Estate
Corporate/M&A	Sports Law
Environment	Tax
Healthcare	Transportation
Intellectual Property	

For detail on ranking tiers and ranking locations, visit www.chambersandpartners.com

Recent work highlights

- Teams from the real estate and sport departments aided the Milwaukee Bucks in connection with the development of their new arena.
- The real estate team works as counsel for the Miami World-center redevelopment, which will include a mall, residential condos, apartments and offices. The project is valued at $2 billion in aggregate.
- The corporate team in New York has represented Deerfield, an employee owned hedge fund sponsor, in a variety of healthcare transactions, including stock exchanges, financing and equity transfers.
- Advised Gamut Capital Management, a New York private equity firm, in the formation and fundraising of an investment fund which closed at $1 billion.

able to visit corporate offices to interview executives and personnel."

The corporate team has a particular focus on private equity M&A: "*We operate on both the buy side and sell side,*" juniors told us. "*There's a lot of diligence involved but there's an effort to include drafting so that we see progression as an associate.*" Another continued: "*On the one hand you're definitely in charge of as much as you can handle, but on the other there's a lot of junior work that isn't super advanced, so a lot of hours go toward that. I think that's just the nature of the work rather than associates being kept down.*" Sources particularly praised the amount of client contact: "*Because private equity firms are structured like law firms it makes sense to have associates talk to associates on the other side. It expedites the process and eases some of the anxiety.*" But corporate associates beyond Chicago felt "*the smaller teams contribute to the fact that corporate is a bit feast or famine. Sometimes there's no work and then there are crazy times because there isn't a huge support system.*"

Real estate is the only practice where the firm gets a top Chambers USA ranking. "*We're a full service group,*" associates told us. "*We do debt and equity work, and on the debt side we represent both lenders and borrowers.*" Larger deals have juniors working on titles and surveys and handling deal logistics: managing checklists, deliverables and closing binders. "*On smaller deals you're able to take on an active role drafting ancillary documents, compiling closing documents and helping with opinions.*" Taking the two together, one associate told us: "*The group approaches responsibility in a really positive way; I like to be involved and help run deals but at the same time I recognize that I'm still learning so I need that balance.*" As with corporate, "*there's a push for associates to meet people on the client side who are of a similar age and experience: the thought behind this is that the firm can grow with the client.*"

Culture & Hours

This approach to client contact is indicative of how the firm's insistent independence trickles down. "*I know this*

is in all the marketing but I really feel that it is entrepreneurial here. If you're motivated and you want to make your mark you can take it as far as you want. If you try to take the lead, nobody's going to say you're too junior." But is there anything else to the culture? One associate told us: "*The reason I chose Katten was because they really advertize themselves as being a nice place to work, while other firms focus on prestige or bonuses.*" Given its youth, the firm's bound to differentiate itself in this way, but associates felt that the firm lived up to this image. While a couple did mention "*a lack of interaction between practice groups,*" interviewees agreed: "*Generally people are kind, respectful of your time and not overly demanding.*"

> ### "If you're motivated and you want to make your mark you can take it as far as you want."

The billing target for associates in all offices except Charlotte is 2,000 hours (this can include up to 100 hours of firm-approved non-chargeable work, which covers activities devoted to pro bono, diversity & inclusion and practice content development). Juniors found this to be a reasonable target and some of our sources had cleared it easily. Associates clocked an average day of roughly 8am to 7pm, but that wasn't the full story. As one would expect, "*in transactional it varies*" – and that did mean leaving past 10 or 11pm on occasion. But this workload didn't seem to be overly pervasive. "*One of the things I like about working here is that I've been able to take vacations without being bothered by work.*"

There's time for a little socializing too, though it's far from work hard, play hard. Associates in Chicago told us: "*We've recently started an associate committee, but mostly the social scene's a little more informal.*" In the smaller DC office "*there's a weekly happy hour at 5.30pm which makes it easier for people with kids to attend.*" We also heard about holiday parties, team lunches and a firm-wide bas-

See firm profile on p.661

The Inside View

425

Diversity	Partners (%)	Associates (%)
Women	24.3	47
White	92.3	78.9
Black/African American	1.8	4.1
Hispanic/Latin American	0.7	5.5
Asian	4.3	10.6
Mixed/Other	0.3	0.9
LGBT	2.1	5.1

ketball team. "*One thing I will say is that associates are genuinely close friends.*"

Offices

Just under half of associates were based in Chicago, with ten in New York and around five in Charlotte, LA and DC. The firm's Windy City headquarters were described as being "*not the most modern,*" but we did hear that "*the firm's about to roll out new laptops, and the tech helpdesk is always on call.*" In DC juniors declared: "*I love the office here. It's right on the waterfront next to the Swedish embassy, and it's very light and modern. It's also right next to a creek and a bike trail. It's nice to be able to look out and see trees.*"

"*It's right on the waterfront next to the Swedish embassy.*"

Training & Development

Outside a yearly review, associates felt that "*feedback varies between groups.*" One had found that "*the best feedback has been what I've asked for. It's up to the associate to take the initiative. If you ask for feedback on a project, people are very happy to provide it.*"

As for training, juniors in litigation were most keen to tell us about a mock trial. "*You come in for the weekend and go through as a participant. You get to cross-examine a witness and see a closing argument, which is a really valuable experience.*" There's department-specific training outside litigation, plus optional CLEs and webinars: "*There's always a lunchtime session you can go to; you get emails constantly.*"

Diversity

Associates were certain that diversity was "*something the firm is pushing to do more of,*" while also being certain that there was a recognizable problem, with its diversity figures closely matching the BigLaw average. "*They do a lot for women here which has been really great,*" said one associate. "*There's women's mentoring and a group called the Women's Leadership Forum which organizes happy hours and lunches which anyone can attend. Both women and men do attend.*" To the firm's further credit, we heard about a new LGBT and minority committee that offers sponsored mentorship and annual conferences. And on the hiring side, interviewees involved in recruiting assured us: "*Diversity is always a priority during on-campus interviews.*"

Pro Bono

Associates can bill up to 100 hours of pro bono work "*no questions asked. If you go above that you can get more credit: you just have to ask and usually they're willing if you're doing legitimate work.*" We did hear of some associates missing out on pro bono during their entire first year; but nevertheless, another Chicago junior could report that: "*I've worked with the domestic violence legal clinic on immigration cases and for non-profit companies.*" There's also a mock trial put on in a local school and another associate told us: "*One thing they're particularly proud of here is the Jose de Diego Elementary School Clinic, which offers legal aid to people in the neighborhood.*" Finally, juniors added: "*You can tell in emails that the firm takes it seriously and that it's not just for marketing.*"

Pro bono hours
- For all US attorneys: 14,853
- Average per US attorney: 67.5

Strategy & Future

While the firm makes a lot of noise about pushing into new areas, a more existential test for firms over the coming years is the challenge of becoming more cost-efficient and staving off competition from all quarters, BigLaw or not. Promisingly, chairman Roger Furey is making all the right noises on this front too: "*We are doubling down on new ways to provide our service, like AI and analytics.*" Adding ballast to the firm's claims of rampant entrepreneurship, he said that "*we are giving our clients options outside of the hourly rate, thinking about how we can more creatively staff our engagements, and providing more visibility on the way we handle, manage and price our clients' services.*"

Get Hired

"*With all the marketing materials out there, law firms can start to sound the same,*" said one associate. "*So it's invaluable to talk to people and get a sense of whether they like their job and their environment.*" For more on recruiting at Katten, head to chambers-associate.com

See firm profile on p.661

King & Spalding LLP

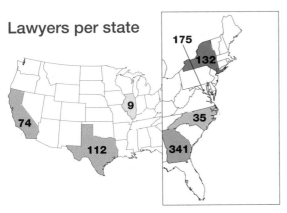

Lawyers per state

175
132
9
74
112
35
341

Largest US office: Atlanta
US offices: 10
International offices: 10
First-year salary: $155,000 - $180,000
Billable hours: no requirement
Summers 2018: 60 (9 1Ls, 48 2Ls, 3 3Ls)
Revenue 2017: $1.14 billion (+7.8%)
Partners made in 2018: 16
Famous for: being one of Atlanta's finest firms; international arbitration expertise; impressive growth over the last decade

With three decades of successive revenue growth behind it, Atlanta's K&S has well and truly entered the big league.

HAVING secured its crown as the new capital of hip-hop, and following Donald Glover's Emmy-winning series, Atlanta is pretty much the coolest place in America right now. As the city's biggest firm, does that mean King & Spalding is the coolest place to practice law? The recent appointment of now-former partner Christopher Wray as Director of the FBI is undeniably pretty awesome, as is the firm's seemingly unstoppable growth: over the past decade its ranks and revenues have swelled, propelling it past the 1,000-lawyer mark and the $1 billion revenue threshold. All of this has occurred under the savvy leadership of chairman Robert Hays, who has steered K&S since 2006 and has just been re-elected to serve a fifth term in his current role.

Hays has also overseen K&S' geographic expansion: in recent years it opened bases in LA, Tokyo, Moscow and Singapore, with services related to life sciences, energy and international arbitration in mind. Chicago became the 20th addition to K&S' network in 2017, and Hays tells us that it's *"fronted by former U.S. Attorney Zach Fardon. It's currently part of our white-collar crime and government investigations practice. Along with Zach, we*

hired a number of people who were also part of the U.S. Attorney's office."

Within its three broad arms of transactional, government & regulatory, and litigation practices, K&S picks up many a *Chambers USA* ranking. At a nationwide level, the firm's energy, healthcare, product liability and projects practices shine, while its biggest haul of tip-top nods are claimed in its home state – these include banking & finance, corporate/M&A, environment and general commercial litigation. Over in *Chambers Global*, K&S is considered one of the finest firms on the planet for international arbitration work.

Strategy & Future

"Over time, Chicago will become a multi-practice office," Hays explains, *"and we'll grow both transactional and commercial litigation practices there."* While *"we're open to the idea of additional office expansion if there's a compelling reason for it,"* Hays emphasizes that *"our primary focus going forward will be on building out the footprint we already have. We've added about as many offices as any firm in the past decade short of a merger."* He adds that *"we've had record levels of demand for our services,"* and highlights global disputes, government investigations and corporate finance as particularly booming areas right now. Read the full interview with Hays at chambers-associate.com.

On chambers-associate.com...

- Interview with managing partner Robert Hays
- Recruitment insight from Atlanta and DC-based hiring partners
- Get hired: associate recruitment tips and tricks

The Inside View

See firm profile on p.662

Rankings in *Chambers USA*

Antitrust
Appellate Law
Banking & Finance
Bankruptcy/Restructuring
Construction
Corporate Crime & Investigations
Corporate/M&A
Energy & Natural Resources
Environment
Food & Beverages
Government

Healthcare
Intellectual Property
International Arbitration
International Trade
Labor & Employment
Latin American Investment
Litigation
Products Liability
Projects
Real Estate
REITs
Securities
Tax

For detail on ranking tiers and ranking locations, visit
www.chambersandpartners.com

Recent work highlights

- Represented the University of Texas Southwestern Medical Center during the $292.5 million formation of a joint entity that will develop and operate a hospital campus in Frisco, Texas
- Defended consumer credit reporting agency Equifax against more than 200 class actions following its September 2017 data breach
- Advised SunTrust Bank in its capacity as administrative agent on the extension of a maturity on an unsecured $1.5 billion syndicated loan
- Represented fintech firm ZenBanx before Congress and U.S. financial regulators prior to its acquisition by online lender SoFi

The Work

All of the firm's summers get to sample various areas at K&S before putting forward their preferences to join a particular group. K&S' finance & restructuring, business litigation, special matters, tort & environmental and corporate groups snared most of the second and third-year juniors on our list. Some of the larger teams have staffing partners who gather availability reports: *"We guesstimate how many hours we have available and then they assign work. They're good when you start and you're in that ramp up period, but if partners are subsequently happy with your work they do pop in and give you matters more organically."* Those in smaller groups told us that *"assignment isn't very organized at all; nobody's there with a spreadsheet monitoring your hours."* Some *"would prefer more structure,"* but the majority agreed that *"K&S is good about allowing us the flexibility to move towards the areas we're interested in and the partners we want to work with."*

Business litigation is the largest disputes group, followed by tort & environmental, special matters (government investigations and white-collar) and international arbitration. *"We deal with securities litigation, class action defenses, contract disputes and a little bit of IP,"* business litigators explained. *"The majority of the work has involved drafting motions and basic documents, as well as assisting seniors with the bigger motions for summary judgment,"* a source revealed. The firm has a dedicated discovery center which juniors *"work closely with to manage e-discovery. It's an increasingly large part of the case process."* Conducting legal research and managing filings are also common tasks for juniors here.

The intriguingly-titled special matters department handles *"a lot of cases related to the Securities and Exchange Commission and Department of Justice – especially the fraud section."* Second-years get to assist with employee interviews and meetings with general counsel. *"We often travel to company HQs during cases,"* sources explained. *"I love our work. We basically do for companies what the FBI does for the government. I've used investigation skills to go through records to figure out who we need to speak to in order to find out what happened – I love interviewing people to find out what went wrong. A matter sometimes ends up at trial, and so we'll represent the company through the litigation."*

"I love interviewing people to find out what went wrong."

Previously separate entities, finance & restructuring are now one big happy family. The juniors we spoke to largely stuck to one side or the other, but there might be more overlap for future newcomers. Fledgling finance attorneys *"draft ancillary documents and chunkier security agreements but also monitor the checklist on deals. At first you've got partner oversight, but that reduces over time."* Individual offices can have different focuses: New York, for example, is big on securitization work, while Atlanta does more secured lending and Charlotte tends to concentrate on transportation finance. Cross-office staffing is common *"so you can lean toward what you're interested in."* Over in restructuring, the focus is on representing debtors, and Chapter 11 bankruptcies are big time-absorbers. *"I've been very happy taking the first draft or reviewing a draft from the other side,"* an interviewee said, *"but I'm also shepherding documents through and making sure everything gets implemented based on the negotiations that have taken place."*

On the transactional side, K&S' corporate juniors are mostly based in Atlanta. The practice represents both public companies and private equity funds. Atlanta is also home to a real estate team that's focused on *"financings, acquisitions and fund formations: day to day we're largely dealing with private equity funds. As a junior I'm*

See firm profile on p.662

The Inside View

Diversity	Partners (%)	Associates (%)
Women	22.5	47.8
White	91.7	81.9
Black/African American	2.7	5.2
Hispanic/Latin American	2.1	3.9
Asian	3.0	6.1
Mixed/Other	0.6	3.0
LGBT	1.2	3.0

reviewing partnership agreements, drafting offering documents and doing some research – nothing heavy!"

Training & Development

King & Spalding University (KSU) delivers a range of training programs for junior and mid-level associates. *"They do a really nice job with KSU,"* our sources thought. *"It offers various CLE credits through monthly seminars which either introduce or reinforce skills."* One told us how they *"wanted more of a foundation on the corporate side of things, so I was offered a four-part program that would give me a crash-course in that area."* Practice-specific training *"depends"* on the group in question: finance and restructuring juniors, for example, explained that *"we have basic training on protocols and practice, which are quite useful,"* while those in small practices said that *"we only have informal on the fly training: it's something that could be more solidified."*

Juniors found the formal review process to be *"very comprehensive: there's the opportunity to say what you'd like to get out of the experience and what you'd like to do going forward."* Interviewees especially liked the *"self plan"* part of the process: *"We draw up a two-page plan of what we'd like to do in the future. It's really helpful to plan your professional and business development."*

Offices

"One thing I've been impressed with is how interconnected everything is," a source reflected. *"Whenever there's a firm meeting or announcement every single office comes together for a conference."* Atlanta remains the center of the web and housed the largest percentage of the second and third-years on our list. *"We're the core tenant in our midtown building and we're currently undergoing a huge renovation,"* insiders revealed. *"We've opted for the more open, glass model. We're not just renovating for the sake of it – it's being done strategically and they took on board our input."*

> *"One thing I've been impressed with is how interconnected everything is."*

The DC and New York offices also take on a fair wedge of K&S' junior associates. The former is just a stone's throw away from both the White House and a grilled cheese bar (it's hard to say which is more exciting). *"We're split between two buildings – one is newer and has more open-floor space, while the other is older, darker and more traditional. The rooftops have beautiful views of the monuments though."* New Yorkers work in a similarly convenient midtown location, as *"the Rockefeller subway stop opens up into the building."* Renovations are underway here too, and *"once they're finished the problems we've had with lack of space will go away."* Phew.

Culture & Diversity

While there's *"definitely an umbrella K&S culture,"* associates agreed that it's one that's been stitched together from materials of various shades as *"all of the offices are pretty different."* Smaller bases and the DC office are *"more familial and laid-back. You don't see many lawyers late at night – everyone works hard then goes home."* In contrast, Houston is *"a lot more introverted,"* while the Atlanta HQ *"has a reputation for being stuffier, and it can feel a little sink or swim. That said, if partners are hard on you it's because they're trying to improve your career."* However, a shift in dress code to business casual has reduced perceptions of formality in Atlanta. While this wasn't such good news for the junior who'd *"bought six new suits just before joining,"* everyone else welcomed the change and appreciated that *"partners don't hold their status over you. It feels like you're working with them rather than for them."*

> *"...definitely an umbrella K&S culture."*

Though *"the firm tries very hard to encourage socializing,"* juniors gave conflicting reports on how successful K&S had been in this respect. *"A lot of the younger associates are more social, so we'll meet up for drinks; we'll go out for a happy hour two or three times a quarter but it's not super-regular,"* one more extroverted source revealed. Smaller offices were described as more tight-knit, while in the larger bases we heard that *"it's not uncommon to be in the office elevator with people who don't know who you are."* Most socializing tends to happen within practice groups. Some of the larger groups – like finance & restructuring – come together for *"group retreats: last year everyone from the group went to Atlanta and our clients gave talks."*

There's also a *"great retreat every year"* to celebrate diversity at the firm. *"There are fantastic panels with in-house counsel and partners of color, and they spend a lot of money putting us up in great accommodation."* Affinity groups include those for LGBTQ lawyers, women, and attorneys of color. Diversity efforts at the grassroots level include a $10,000 diversity fellowship and a 1L program that's held in conjunction with the Leadership Council on Legal

See firm profile on p.662

Diversity. Atlanta-based hiring partner Michael Paulhus tells us that K&S is *"focusing on expanding the pipeline of diverse candidates into our interviews to improve output. We're making sure the funnel is as broad as possible."*

Get Hired

"They're looking for compatibility and entrepreneurship – candidates who will take ownership of their own practice and not need a lot of help." Find out what else K&S is looking for at chambers-associate.com.

Hours & Compensation

Law is never a predictable beast, but K&S juniors reckoned *"an average day in the office would last between 8.30am and 6.30/7pm"* – a schedule common to the firm as a whole. When things get heavy *"it's not at all unheard of to be here until 11pm or midnight,"* especially in the Atlanta HQ. However, *"most partners allow for flexible schedules and they're very lenient with regards to teleworking."* Weekend stints *"aren't frequent"* and associates were keen to point out that *"people here are very cognizant of the notion that juniors can and should take time off. I've never been told no if I've asked for vacation."*

"Most partners allow for flexible schedules."

Although there isn't a formal billing target, we heard that it's necessary to rack up 2,050 hours in order to rake in a bonus; hours billed above this goal net associates more cash. Everybody we spoke to *"didn't have an issue meeting that – given how busy we are it's quite easy. A lot of associates bill more than that and it's rare to encounter someone at the super slow end."*

Pro Bono

Associates can count 100 pro bono hours toward their billable target, but we heard that *"you might be able to count more."* While this allowance was felt to be an incentive, juniors agreed that *"the onus is on us to make things happen – and to take on pro bono you have to be invested in it."* For those who are interested, K&S thankfully offers *"a lot of opportunities"* to take on both litigious and transactional pro bono. Our sources spoke of death penalty, asylum, domestic abuse, veteran and non-profit status matters. Each K&S office has links to local community organizations: Atlanta, for instance, has close ties to Habitat for Humanity.

Pro bono hours
- For all US attorneys: 36,708.8
- Average per US attorney: 37.8

See firm profile on p.662

The Inside View

Kirkland & Ellis LLP

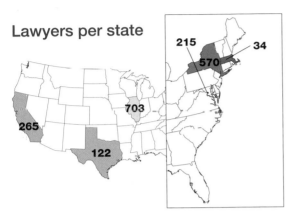

Lawyers per state

215   34
570
703
265
122

Largest US office: Chicago
US offices: 8
International offices: 5
First-year salary: $180,000
Billable hours: no requirement
Summers 2018: 283 (25 1Ls, 255 2Ls, SEO 3)
Revenue 2017: $3.165 billion (+19.4%)
Partners made in 2018: 78
Famous for: private equity prowess; entrepreneurial open assignment system

Kirkland has just climbed to the top of the *Am Law 100*. This should be a surprise to no one...

A NEW world record was made in 2017, when Kirkland toppled Latham from its perch atop the *Am Law 100* with its revenue of $3.165 billion – the highest sum ever earned by a law firm. This figure was the big headline, but behind it lies the recipe for Kirkland culture: talent; entrepreneurialism; hard work. As should be apparent, the firm's lawyers aren't the type to revel in their bounty: 2017 was an extremely busy year in DC, with the addition of the entire roster of lawyers from elite appellate boutique Bancroft (including former US solicitor general Paul Clement); next it carved out a new territory for its kingdom by opening a Boston office in May 2017, enhancing its private equity clout in the process.

Coming in with the impression that Kirkland was *"more energetic, young in spirit and cutting-edge"* than similarly massive firms, associates *"heard it was eat-what-you-kill. But when I got here I had a hard time imagining the people being aggressive – everyone was so nice!"* Newcomers were also more than pleased with Kirkland's broad panoply of strengths – *Chambers USA's* top-tier awards for bankruptcy, IP and investment funds are the jewels in Kirkland's nationwide crown, but other highly recommended practices include general commercial litigation, corporate/M&A, banking and finance, and antitrust.

On chambers-associate.com...

- Get hired at Kirkland
- Interview with co-hiring partner Jason Kanner
- Becoming a partner at Kirkland

The Work

Two thirds of the associates on our list were based in Kirkland's transactional group; around a sixth had joined the firm's litigation practice, while the rest were pretty evenly split between intellectual property and restructuring. Within every practice group the firm implements an open assignment system – *"they don't like it when we say 'free market', but that's what it is."* However, associates tend to get staffed directly on a matter initially *"to gain some traction."* This opinion on the system was commonly declared: *"I don't get why people think it's intimidating – if they do, this probably isn't the firm for them. It's a good model that lets you seek out the work you want to do."* Juniors aren't completely cast adrift though, as practice group heads send out weekly surveys to keep an eye on associates' workloads.

The transactional group covers general corporate work as well as specialist areas such as investment funds, debt financing, international trade and employee benefits. General corporate associates are *"supposed to try a little bit of everything as the firm doesn't want us pigeonholed too quickly."* Bread and butter work includes private equity and M&A deals. Lean staffing on these means *"you really do get thrown in from the beginning,"* with little shielding from client contact. Common junior tasks include producing first drafts of purchase agreements, conducting due diligence, negotiating schedules and running checklists. *"As you enter your third year, they encourage you to flex your managerial skills a bit more. It's been a good balance of responsibility overall – I'm sure I'll look back and long for the day I was doing checklists!"*

The Inside View

See firm profile on p.663

Rankings in *Chambers USA*

Advertising	Intellectual Property
Antitrust	International Trade
Appellate Law	Investment Funds
Banking & Finance	Life Sciences
Bankruptcy/Restructuring	Litigation
Capital Markets	Media & Entertainment
Corporate Crime & Investigations	Outsourcing
	Private Equity
Corporate/M&A	Products Liability
Energy & Natural Resources	Real Estate
	Securities
Environment	Tax
FCPA	Technology
Insurance	

For detail on ranking tiers and ranking locations, visit
www.chambersandpartners.com

Recent work highlights

- Represented Teva Pharmaceuticals during its $40.5 billion acquisition of Irish pharma company Allergan Generics
- Defended football team Los Angeles Rams and its owner during a $1 billion breach-of-contract lawsuit, which was brought after the team moved from St. Louis
- Advised tech giant Intel on an international patent infringement lawsuit brought by non-practicing entity Future Link Systems
- Worked on casino operator Caesars Entertainment's Chapter 11 restructuring of its operating company, which had a debt value of $18 billion

"It's a good model that lets you seek out the work you want to do."

Alongside general commercial cases, litigators are free to dabble in product liability, antitrust, securities and white-collar matters. *"Initially I was doing more general case management or administrative discovery work,"* one third-year reported, *"but now I'm the primary drafter of briefs and I recently took a deposition for the first time."* Massive international cases didn't involve *"actual doc review – we were coordinating the teams of reviewers instead."* Interviewees found they got *"a fair amount of client contact; it comes when it's appropriate and if they think you're capable."* They were also unanimously *"happy with the experiences available; the only thing getting in your way of trying new things is the stage the case is at in the cycle."*

IP litigators deal mostly with patent work, but there's also a copyright and trademark subgroup where *"you don't have to have as much of a science background."* Clients vary from pharmaceutical companies to software and mechanical outfits, and an equally varied work diet is normal: one junior *"worked on four entirely different areas in my first year alone, which included false advertising and trade secret cases."* Many took advantage of Kirkland's broad national (and international) reach *"litigating all across the country and in all the different courts – it's really cool."* One energetic source told us that they'd *"spoken with clients, drafted summary judgment briefs and second-chaired depositions – within the first two years we're expected to take our own though."*

Restructuring work *"involves a lot of travel, so we tend to bill more hours than other groups."* The length of cases means *"the open assignment system is less relevant, but* when cases do end after months (or years!) you're absolutely able to seek out what you want."* Kirkland primarily works on the debtor side of matters, representing *"very large companies – we just did the Toys R Us bankruptcy, for example."* The group's work is far from child's play though, and juniors swiftly took on *"a lot of discrete tasks,"* which included *"helping to negotiate a non-disclosure agreement and drafting motions to file in court."*

Training & Development

After completing an initial stint of general training, juniors begin practice-specific programs – the Kirkland Institute for Trial Advocacy (KITA) exists for litigators, while the Kirkland Institute of Corporate Practice (KICP) is there for transactional associates. These are *"something the firm works very hard on"*; full mock trials are on offer for KITA juniors, while multiple sessions every week are on the cards for KICP attendees – *"it's basically unparalleled skills-based training."*

Juniors appreciated that the annual formal review process is *"very personalized – it's all about how you've progressed and how you're rated against yourself, not others in your class. It's the most intense program I've heard of."* Associates list all the matters they've worked on and pick partners to review them; they get to read *"all their comments, so everything is very open."* Visit chambers-associate.com to find out more about Kirkland's two-tier partnership structure.

Offices

Kirkland now has eight domestic offices stretching from coast to coast. Its Chicago birthplace is *"a well-oiled machine – it's still driving things to an extent, though New York has rapidly closed that gap."* The Big Apple base is deep into *"one floor at a time"* renovations: *"It was already nice but they're making everything nicer. The glass doors will be a nice alternative to the more traditional and opaque 'white shoe' architecture we have now."* Other locations are getting facelifts too – DC is currently *"nice enough but*

See firm profile on p.663

Diversity	Partners (%)	Associates (%)
Women	24.6	39
White	86.9	76.0
Black/African American	1.7	2.9
Hispanic/Latin American	3.5	5.4
Asian	6.5	13.2
Mixed/Other	1.4	2.5
LGBT	2.3	4.5

a little old fashioned, so we're very excited about moving to a new space in 2019," while the burgeoning Houston office (opened in 2012) has "grown so rapidly we had to relocate – the new building has a fully stacked kitchen and common area."

"There isn't any trace of office hierarchy."

Cross-office work is conducted "on a case by case basis," but most found Kirkland "pretty collaborative" and didn't detect "any trace of office hierarchy." Larger groups – like Chicago's and New York's corporate squads – tend to be more self-contained. "When I do need to call someone, their picture pops up so I know what they look like!" Other interviewees – including some Chicago-based litigators and Houston housed deal doers – were getting actual face time with colleagues across the country, racking up frequent flier miles on matters involving multiple offices.

Culture & Diversity

Juniors acknowledged Kirkland's "reputation for being more cut-throat," but emphasized the extent to which they'd been left "stunned by the collegiality" witnessed upon arrival. "It is an incredibly competitive place, but that competitiveness is channelled against other firms!" One put the firm's enduring image down to "the expectation that you'll maintain a high workload here," while another simply dismissed it as the result of uninformed assumptions made by those "who are just jealous that they're not at this firm! It's not a sweatshop at all." Others suggested that having a more junior non-equity tier of partners had created a "younger, more amiable" environment compared to what they described as "the very formal and stiff" vibe at some of New York's native hotshots.

The relative youth of the non-equity partnership also helps to "reduce the hierarchical feeling that you might get at other firms," though some admitted that they "wouldn't go straight to an equity partner with a question." Attorneys from different levels get to mingle at alumni shindigs, holiday parties and other events hosted by departments. "From the summer onwards they encourage you to interact with peers wherever possible." There's "no expectation that the firm should be your primary social group," but many associates enjoyed "getting together informally for a drink. There are opportunities for us to bond and discuss our experiences."

"It is an incredibly competitive place, but that competitiveness is channelled against other firms!"

Kirkland's Women's Leadership Initiative regularly organizes events. At these, female associates were happy to see "that women are not only considered important, but are in positions of power." We were told that two of the four Chicago representatives on the management committee are women. Other plus points included "constant" roundtable events and open forums, as well as "a much more gender-balanced partnership class this year." Less positively, many admitted that "there's a lot of work to be done on the ethnic diversity front," with some dubbing their practice area "overwhelmingly white." The firm began a recruiting initiative called ALLSA in 2008 to reach out to minority student groups across the country, and, according to juniors, "a very diverse 2017 summer class" suggests their efforts are starting to pay off.

Pro Bono

With pro bono "treated the same as billable hours" many associates flagged it as a "favorite thing about the firm; if I'm looking for a new assignment it's realistic for me to choose pro bono work." Kirkland asks all of its attorneys to hit at least 20 hours, and one who'd shirked their charitable responsibilities "got an email every two days telling me I needed to do it! I felt really guilty that I hadn't done enough." The firm was perhaps happier with the interviewee who'd "put in 400 pro bono hours over a few months – the firm is giving me every opportunity." Such opportunities include landlord/tenant work, immigration cases and attendance at specialized clinics; some transactional attorneys had also used pro bono to try their hands at litigating. As befits Kirkland's competitive reputation, the firm hosts "little competitions between practice areas, to see which one can do the most pro bono!"

Pro bono hours
- For all US attorneys: 118,000+
- Average per US attorney: 63.7

Hours & Compensation

There's no official hours target for associates, but most bill somewhere around 2,000 each year – "that's not a hard minimum, but it's in the right ballpark." Bonuses aren't determined strictly by hours ("if you bill 1,800 you could still get one") but by a combination of work quantity, quality and the feedback obtained during formal re-

See firm profile on p.663

views. *"Bonuses start at market rate and go up above that depending on performance – it's the fairest method as it rewards hard workers."* Workaholics can potentially get a bigger pay packet for logging more hours, but we heard from sources who'd gone beyond 2,300 and were *"told in the review that it was too much: we're told to shoot for 2,100 hours, but saying no to work can be a challenge!"*

"There's no face-time requirement to factor in."

Every firm has its work martyrs, but Kirklanders told us that *"most people here want a life outside work – the firm's culture doesn't glorify being in all the time."* Many found themselves working ten-hour days in the office on average. *"There's no face-time requirement to factor in. A lot of people leave around 7pm to see their families and then log back on."* Juniors were also keen to highlight the extent to which hours can fluctuate, with late nights a fact of life in BigLaw. However, associates are encouraged to take vacations. *"I took two separate week-long trips as a first-year,"* one said, *"and the firm recognizes the importance of recharging and tries not to make you work while you're out."*

Strategy & Future

"The Boston office opening came out of nowhere, and I didn't realize we were looking to expand like that!" one junior exclaimed, while pointing to the firm's impressive financials. Another highlighted Kirkland's broad practice as a reason for the firm's continued confidence in growth: *"This is pretty clearly the best place for both private equity and restructuring work,"* they declared, *"so if the economy stays healthy we'll have a high volume of private deals, but if there's another downturn we'll get the best cases out of it."*

See firm profile on p.663

The Inside View

Kramer Levin Naftalis & Frankel LLP

Lawyers per state

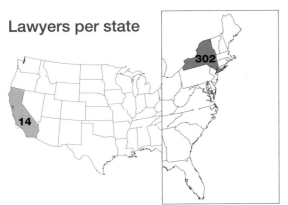

Largest US office: New York
US offices: 2
International offices: 1
First-year salary: $180,000
Billable hours: 1,950 target
Summers 2018: 15 (14 2Ls, 1 SEO)
Revenue 2017: $387 million (+9.9%)
Partners made in 2018: 5
Famous for: friendly work environment; advertising litigation; LGBT and pro bono initiatives; the most satisfied associates 2018

With its New York pedigree and enviable reputation in the courtroom, Kramer Levin presents BigLaw with an intimate twist.

KRAMER, Jerry Seinfeld's enigmatic neighbor, is a New Yorker. He sports an eye-catching bouffant, has a habit of dramatically bursting into rooms, and seems to have no regular source of income. Summary: he's a little 'different,' but people love him. Kramer Levin is a New Yorker too, and – somewhat surprisingly – the similarities stretch beyond name and location: it too is a little 'different.' Why? Well it carries a formidable reputation despite being smaller than many of its Big Apple peers, and (to the relief of our interviewees) it eschews those BigLaw stereotypes that leave law students drenched in a cold sweat. "*I wouldn't view it as the New York sweatshop type at all. There are busy times, but everyone is super nice, which helps!*" said one junior, while another added: "*People just wouldn't leave to go to another BigLaw firm.*"

"We don't need to be all things to all people."

Work-wise, the firm excels in advertising, white-collar and bankruptcy litigation, but Kramer doesn't just boast a stellar contentious practice: it picks up transactional nods from *Chambers USA* in areas like corporate, real estate, tax and capital markets. "*Though it might not be as well known among our generation as some of the global powerhouses, whenever you meet older lawyers they re-*

On chambers-associate.com...

- Insight on recruitment from associates and hiring partner Keri Ann Law

spect the firm for being top-notch," associates told us. Managing partner Paul Pearlman echoes this: "*We've always been known for the quality of our lawyering. We've been referred to as lawyers' lawyers. It is much easier to maintain that quality when you're smaller.*" To prove it, the firm recently represented New York mayor Bill de Blasio, and at the time of our calls was about to work on the Toys R Us bankruptcy.

Strategy & Future

Pearlman continues: "*I think we've carved out a niche in the marketplace by being smaller than many. Bigger does not necessarily mean better; we can satisfy our clients' needs, and we don't need to be all things to all people. We're content to solidify our place in the marketplace, while other firms are moving in lots of different directions.*" By solidifying, Pearlman means "*adding breadth and depth. For example, we brought Richard Farley in leveraged finance because we wanted to be representing lenders on the transactional side.*"

The Work

Kramer's litigation and corporate groups take the most juniors overall, while most of the rest go to intellectual property, real estate and creditors' rights (bankruptcy) teams. The remainder are spread around tax, land use, business immigration and employment. Each department has an assigning partner, and associates fill out a weekly email detailing their availability. Juniors leaned on their assigning partners for work to start with, but

The Inside View

See firm profile on p.664

435

Rankings in *Chambers USA*

Advertising	Immigration
Bankruptcy/Restructuring	Litigation
Capital Markets	Real Estate
Corporate/M&A	Tax

For detail on ranking tiers and ranking locations, visit www.chambersandpartners.com

Recent work highlights

- Represented New York mayor Bill de Blasio during an investigation into his campaign funding, which concluded without criminal charges
- Advised two of the largest investors in Puerto Rico – Franklin Advisers and Oppenheimer Funds – and some major bondholder groups regarding the island's bankruptcy proceedings and associated restructurings
- Acted for Toys R Us's creditors as the toy business filed for bankruptcy after accruing $5 billion of debt
- Represented professional sports gambler Bill Walters after he was accused of insider trading

soon *"the majority of long-term assignments come from asking around or developing relationships with partners. That's possible in an office with just a few hundred people."*

Litigators can sample a range of work, including advertising cases, white-collar crime matters and general commercial disputes. On the white-collar side, *"we often represent individuals within an organization, which means there's a more personal relationship with the client – as juniors we often interact with them."* All sources reaped the rewards of uber lean staffing. Some had *"client meetings with just me, a partner and another second year,"* while those preparing for trials told us: *"We are relied upon. I was drafting witness outlines, interviewing potential witnesses, dealing with expert testimony and preparing defense themes to be used at the trial. I got the full experience."*

While that all sounds wonderful, junior litigators still recounted stints of doc review, and corporate attorneys found themselves *"doing the customary due diligence. You can't take it personally: that is the hierarchy. It's about understanding the importance of it. Still, midlevel associates are interested in mentoring you to bring you up to speed."* The corporate group, which mainly serves middle-market private companies, has three branches: banking and finance, securities and M&A. *"As a first year you are free to work on anything,"* deal-doing sources told us. *"Because the staffing model can mean it's just you, a midlevel associate and a partner on a private equity matter, you become acquainted with the real mechanics of the deal. On top of junior things like drafting ancillary documents, you might also run the whole due diligence process and send memos to the other side."*

Offices

The vast majority of associates are based in New York, and despite *"having to wait in line for 20 minutes for the best salad places,"* they still found their midtown location *"great: we're in the center of Manhattan and the legal world – there are more than a dozen firms around us."* Inside, an office revamp *"is making more efficient use of the space, adding more glass and bringing in more light."* Kramer's interior decoration gurus relayed that they didn't have *"any complaints – it just needed to be brought into the 21st century via some additional flair."* Associates

share an office until their second or third year, which associates were happy with: *"We have a basketball hoop on the back of our door! It's nice to have a second pair of eyes for proofreading too, as well as someone to talk to."*

The only other domestic office, in Silicon Valley, has around 15 lawyers and specializes in IP litigation.

Culture

"We definitely work very hard, but this is a place that I look forward to journeying to every morning." All our interviewees offered similar caveats. *"It's just a little bit more laid back. I see ourselves as serious people who don't take themselves too seriously. When people are working they go all in, 100%, but everyone still gets along. There's no yelling."* Another junior added: *"If there's a conflict – say you're needed on two different deals – people are open to you talking to them to figure out how to get everything done on time so nobody gets upset. There's always an open channel of communication."* Once again, the firm's smaller dimensions are a benefit here: *"It's more collaborative and less bureaucratic because of its size."*

"They don't expect you to only exist as an employee."

Kramer people aren't just 2D lawyers either: *"The people here are really smart, but they have interests outside of law. As a result everyone is interesting, with certain hobbies or quirks."* And there's room to pursue these interests: *"The firm understands that you have a life outside of the firm. They don't expect you to only exist as an employee. This is not a firm where there's pressure to constantly hang out."* Still, for those who do feel like mingling with their colleagues we heard of monthly cocktail hours in the firm's atrium, a Christmas party and summer events. The lure of cocktails couldn't win over everybody though: *"I love it here, but it's a hard job and it's tiring. I want to go home when I'm finished, not to a cocktail party."*

See firm profile on p.664

The Inside View

Diversity	Partners (%)	Associates (%)
Women	15.3	38.6
White	91.8	74.3
Black/African American	2.0	2.3
Hispanic/Latin American	0	5.3
Asian	6.1	15.2
Mixed/Other	0	2.9
LGBT	3.1	2.3

Hours & Compensation

Associates must rack up 1,950 hours to get a bonus. That number, described as *"extremely achievable"* by our sources, was instituted relatively recently. The previous target was 2,150 and had attracted the ire of associates. *"The fact that they listened to us and made changes was impressive."*

Associates typically arrive at the office around 9:30am and leave between 7:30 and 8pm. *"If you do leave earlier, there's always the chance of getting an email and therefore doing more work from home. At weekends you won't be putting in full days, but there will be a few hours where you'll do work."* Hours can be unpredictably tough, especially in corporate. *"You have quiet weeks, medium weeks and really crappy weeks."* Early morning finishes occur, though infrequently enough to avoid grinding associates down. *"You do see people coming in with bags under their eyes, but there are always chances to catch a break and recharge."*

Pro Bono

"They both encourage and – more importantly – don't discourage doing pro bono." Backing up this statement, associates pointed to the fact that Kramer doesn't cap the amount of pro bono hours its lawyers can do, and that all of them count toward the bonus billing target. In addition, *"the firm holds an end of year pro bono awards ceremony, where we can see that most people – even partners – dedicate a significant amount of time to it."* Interviewees had worked on housing matters and with KIND (Kids In Need of Defense), to take on *"immigration status cases involving juveniles."* Kramer also has longstanding links to domestic abuse charity Her Justice, and offers its associates the chance to undertake a four-month pro bono secondment full-time via Brooklyn Legal Services.

Pro bono hours
- For all US attorneys: 25,946
- Average per US attorney: 85

Diversity

"There's room for improvement," was a typical response from associates when the question of diversity was raised. *"The partnership is heavily white and male, but hopefully that will change with time as our more diverse senior associates move into the partner ranks."* We did hear that *"the firm is taking steps to refine its partnership track and is making more of an effort to hire internally."* In addition, *"the diversity committee puts on events at the firm and does outreach events at law schools. There's also a Women's Circle, where groups of female attorneys meet – that's been well received, as it encompasses women from all levels."* Courtesy of founding partner Arthur Kramer, the firm has a historic connection to LGBT causes; together with his brother – the writer Larry Kramer – the firm helped to establish the Gay Men's Health Crisis in 1982.

Training & Development

New associates kick off proceedings with an orientation week that includes practice area-specific trainings. For corporate associates these covered *"contract drafting, due diligence and the different phases of a deal. Every comma matters in corporate work, and they alert you to all the things you might miss. It's a great overview."* Another associate told us there's *"a good bunch of CLEs afterward – maybe four or five a week – so many I can't keep track!"* However, despite the bounty of CLEs sources still agreed that *"the best training involves learning by doing."* Juniors also take a proactive approach to ensure they're developing matter by matter: *"After a project comes to an end I go to an older associate's office, schmooze, spend 20 minutes breaking down my performance and come away with some inside tips."*

See firm profile on p.664

The Inside View

437

Latham & Watkins LLP

Lawyers per state

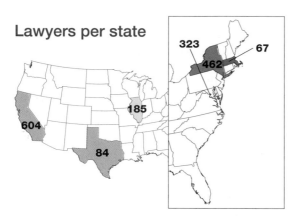

Largest US office: New York
US offices: 11
International offices: 19
First-year salary: $180,000
Billable hours: 1,900 target
Summers 2018: 196 (12 1Ls, 182 2Ls, 2 SEO)
Revenue 2017: $3.064 billion (+8.5%)
Partners made in 2018: 24
Famous for: giant revenue; unassigned junior associates

Latham may be a global giant, but thanks to its empowering self-assignment style, juniors did't feel like the small cog.

LATHAM is something of a high achiever. In 2017 the firm became the first to smash the $3 billion revenue barrier – that was the big headline, but to generate these sums in the first place you have to be doing something rather special. Take a look at *Chambers Global* and you'll see Latham's practices achieving rankings in 23 countries across the world, and leading the world in its global corporate, banking, energy & projects and high-yield products practices.

One might assume that world domination requires a steely resolve and sharp elbows, but associates insisted: *"Latham actually puts a ton of time and resources into developing a culture where people feel comfortable with one another."* Aside from looking to get a killer name on their resume, most had been *"drawn in by the unassigned program – I liked the idea that I didn't have to choose between transactional and litigious law up front."* Our associate sources found it empowering to carve their own career paths.

The staffing model may be quite fluid, but this does not result in any lack of distinction in each practice area's achievements: the firm's *Chambers USA* rankings are among the best of any American firm. The firm comes

top-tier nationwide in numerous areas including banking & finance, elite corporate/M&A, energy, environment, life sciences, projects, REITS and tax. State-by-state there are too many to list here, so have a look at *Chambers USA* if you're considering locations.

The Work

Associates begin life at the firm 'unassigned' so they can experience different areas, whether that's a variety of corporate assignments or figuring out whether they want to be a deal-doer or litigator. Each we spoke to was a *"huge fan of the system – getting hands-on experience in different groups is really helpful."* Work assignment is handled by a coordinator known as 'The Book' to whom associates submit weekly reports explaining what they're interested in taking on. *"Practice groups feed her assignments, and she matches people with projects."* Once they've found their niche, juniors steadily shift toward getting work from partners directly, but The Book is always open if things get quiet or you want to try something new.

Specialization tends to happen more quickly in smaller offices as *"you develop relationships much faster and it's difficult to fall through the cracks."* Does the broad scope of the unassigned system limit responsibility early on? *"I don't think so,"* one associate said. *"In your first year and a bit you're basically learning to be a lawyer anyway, and all the skills you learn are transferable between groups."* After two years (though most don't need all that time), associates are encouraged to formally align with one of the

On chambers-associate.com...

- Get hired: interview tips and tricks
- Interviews with vice chair Richard Trobman and hiring partner Manu Gayatrinath

See firm profile on p.665

Rankings in *Chambers USA*

Antitrust	Investment Funds
Appellate Law	IT & Outsourcing
Banking & Finance	Latin American Investment
Bankruptcy/Restructuring	Leisure & Hospitality
Capital Markets	Life Sciences
Climate Change	Litigation
Corporate Crime &	Media & Entertainment
Investigations	Outsourcing
Corporate/M&A	Private Equity
Employee Benefits &	Projects
Executive Compensation	Real Estate
Energy & Natural Re-	REITs
sources	Retail
Environment	Securities
FCPA	Sports Law
Financial Services	Startups & Emerging
Regulation	Companies
Healthcare	Tax
Insurance	Technology
Intellectual Property	Telecommunications
International Trade	Venture Capital

For detail on ranking tiers and ranking locations, visit
www.chambersandpartners.com

Recent work highlights

- Represented financial advisers Evercore during Whole Foods Market's $13.7 billion acquisition by Amazon
- Worked on the largest syndicated institutional term loan of all time, representing borrower Avago Technologies in a $17.8 billion matter
- Acted for the Florida Department of Environmental Protection on a water rights dispute with the state of Georgia
- Advised Energy Capital Partners on its $17 billion acquisition of electricity generator Calpine Corporation

firm's five core practices: corporate; finance; litigation & trial; tax; and environment, land & resources.

"Not the kind of place where you're stuck doing junior tasks for two years."

Incoming corporate associates had their fill of capital markets, IPOs, M&A, emerging companies and startup work, taking advantage of the unassigned system before committing to one subsection. *"When you start there's definitely a ramp-up period before getting more bigger-picture tasks,"* interviewees said, and they suggested their responsibility levels *"vary a lot by the size of the deal. On a lot of the startup work you're running the show and the partner's overseeing things."* That won't be the case in the firm's mega matters, representing institutional clients including Morgan Stanley and Bank of America: *"On larger-scale M&A and capital markets you're in a more narrow role focusing on diligence or legal opinions. It's not like you're marking up a purchase agreement on day one."* Associates nonetheless agreed that *"Latham is not the kind of place where you're stuck doing junior tasks for two years."* As in any transactional practice, the workload can be temperamental, but most felt *"the firm does a good job of managing everybody's time."*

"One of the main reasons" young litigators chose Latham was *"exploring a variety of practices, from white-collar investigations to consumer fraud class actions, trade se-*

crets, shareholder disputes and complex commercial litigation." Certain offices have specialties: you can trust that you'll be doing antitrust in San Francisco, for instance. Juniors handled *"everything from research to first drafts of motions and briefs; the partners are really good about giving us higher-level tasks."* One interviewee explained how varied things could get: *"I was on a high-profile investigation doing the unglamorous document review and putting binders together. At the same time, I was handling the majority of a motion to dismiss a class action, working one to one with a partner."* Some complained about a lack of client contact early on, but took on pro bono matters to fill this void.

Pro Bono

Pro bono hours all count toward the billable target. Everyone's expected to do at least 20, and the firm's committed to providing 60 hours per attorney. Most get their 20 done in a flash, and several associates told us: *"As a first year I did hundreds of hours. It's not something you're forced into but if you're interested, there's nothing stopping you."* One added the proviso: *"It was mentioned in passing that I should have a good balance with paid work."* Each office collaborates with local organizations: San Diego has a particularly strong tradition for immigration cases, while the New York team runs a pro bono partnership with a small business clinic. Veteran and asylum cases are also commonplace. If none of that tickles your philanthropic fancy, there's *"a lot of flexibility to bring in your own passion projects."* We heard about *"an associate who'd discovered a client organization helping transgender people complete name change applications. They ran it past the pro bono committee who thought it was a good idea."*

"A lot of flexibility to bring in your own projects."

Pro bono hours
- For all US attorneys: 190,536
- Average per US attorney: 111

The Inside View

See firm profile on p.665

Diversity	Partners (%)	Associates (%)
Women	22.8	43
White	90.2	73.4
Black/African American	1.0	3.8
Hispanic/Latin American	2.8	5.8
Asian	5.5	15.8
Mixed/Other	0.4	1.2
LGBT	3	5.2

Hours & Compensation

Taking 9am as an average start time, most associates were leaving by 7pm as *"nobody expects you to work late in the office. People often go home to have dinner with their families then work remotely."* We noticed attorneys were taking full advantage of flexible working policies – *"I'm sitting at home in my pajamas right now!"* – and all appreciated *"having that flexibility, when things do get busy in the office I'm not too stressed out."* Don't be fooled: Latham's lawyers do their time in the trenches when needed, especially in busy corporate teams. One source recalled that *"once or twice I've stayed until 2am, but there's been nothing too crazy."* The 'unlimited' vacation policy is similarly flexible, and drew mixed feedback as some felt *"it being nebulous means people don't always take it,"* though most associates had enjoyed at least some time off.

To be bonus eligible, associates must reach a target of 1,900 hours. They agreed *"it's a pretty low threshold and definitely achievable. The firm is busy right now so it's up to the associate to get there."* Though *"a lot of people end up over 1,900,"* sources clarified. *"Only just reaching it isn't looked down upon. The firm knows people won't be successful long-term if they're working constantly, and we definitely have time for a private life."* Bonuses work to a standardized system up until third year, when associates are rated from one to five in their biannual reviews – high performers are eligible for a tasty bonus-bonus.

Training & Diversity

Come review time, all partners who've worked with an associate review their work. A member of the associate committee then reads them the comments verbatim. Alongside this sits a formal academy program, for which first, third and fifth-year associates are flown out to one location for a series of condensed training sessions and conferences which summers and partners also attend. *"The first-year academy is really helpful for getting to know what the firm expects of you,"* juniors explained. First years also get 'core curriculum' sessions held every few weeks by partners and associates, sessions which feature presentations on different practice areas and key skills such as drafting and negotiation. Our interviewees reported: *"The training's been fantastic, the department-focused ses-*

sions in particular," but felt that *"informal training is more helpful. Partners are fairly approachable and never too intimidating to ask for help from."*

> *"We often get emails from the managing partner reminding us how much the firm values diversity."*

The academies also include presentations on unconscious bias in recruiting. *"The firm really stresses diversity's importance at every opportunity,"* associates said. *"We often get emails from the managing partner reminding us how much the firm values it."* Latham's 1L diversity fellowship expands the summer class to make room for candidates outside the normal recruiting routes, and the firm's also created an impressive number of initiatives including a three-day Diversity Leadership Academy for law students and midlevel associates, the Women's Leadership Academy and the associate-led Multicultural Promotion & Attainment Coalition (MPAC). *"There needs to be more work done to help progression of women,"* though, according to certain sources, who told us: *"I don't think we're where we need to be diversity-wise yet."* They suggested *"it hasn't been a huge success so far, but it's definitely top of the priority list."*

Get Hired

"Rather than filling up your resume with things you think will impress, include activities you're passionate about. Being a well-rounded person will get you far." Learn more recruitment tricks at www.chambers-associate.com

Offices

Housed in the infamous Lipstick Building, formerly home to Bernie Madoff's investment securities Ponzi scheme, Latham's New Yorkers considered it *"cool to be in such a recognizable place."* Following *"constant renovations,"* the office now features one open-plan floor on which many of the firm's first years sit, as well as a *"fun room with ping pong and foosball. There's more of a startup atmosphere than a typical BigLaw office."* Competitive Chicagoans dubbed their base *"much nicer than New York, it was redone two years ago and completely redesigned. Every office has a great view, though it's getting a little overcrowded..."*

A Boston associate suggested that *"in every location, Latham wants to be in a hip location,"* be that Beantown's tallest building or half a mile from the beach in San Diego. Interaction between the firm's 11 domestic and 20 international offices is fairly well oiled, and needs to be as *"almost every deal involves multiple offices."* If they're light on work or want to tackle something their own

See firm profile on p.665

The Inside View

digs doesn't offer, unassigned associates can contact colleagues in other locations to get staffed on matters.

Culture

Associates credited Latham with *"doing a good job of pushing a firm-wide culture. Calling ourselves a 'one-firm firm' is kind of corny but they have developed collegiality across the world."* We hear reports from every firm that *"elbows are less sharp here and big egos don't work well,"* but associates' suggestions that *"potential laterals have ended up not joining because of cultural and fit concerns"* imply that it's not all talk. Different offices do have distinct characters, particularly in sunnier, smooth-sailing California. New York on the other hand *"has a reputation for being fratty, and there is some truth to that in certain groups,"* but party-shy attorneys *"are able to find others they fit better with,"* be that in a sports team or diverse lawyers group.

"Potential laterals have ended up not joining because of cultural and fit concerns."

For those who want it, there's a fair amount of socializing in every office, including *"a lot put on by the firm"* – typically within departments in larger offices, while smaller ones are more likely to hang out as one big happy family.

Latham's partners clearly love a barbecue, as associates in several offices recalled *"the managing partner here inviting everyone to their house"* for one in summer, the peak social season. Nobody dared to review partners' cooking skills, but associates were *"really impressed with management's transparency. Every couple of months we have a state of the firm address breaking down the financials in more excruciating detail than I care to know."*

Strategy & Future

"Associates here are committed, but I don't know if they drink the Kool Aid," one declared. *"Everybody is pretty happy but if other opportunities come up they won't forgo those."* Some had concerns that the firm's sheer size limited partnership prospects, but were more than happy to have Latham's name on their resume. There's certainly room to shimmy around within the firm; hiring partner Manu Gayatrinath tells us: *"Latham has a broad base of practice groups, and is well positioned in various markets across the globe. A lot of our practice groups perform countercyclically, which helps us to weather market ups and downs pretty fluidly."* She clarifies: *"There haven't been any changes in what we are doing from a junior hiring perspective; we offer so many practices that the demand always seems to float at around the same level."* For more from Gayatrinath, head to www.chambers-associate.com

See firm profile on p.665

The Inside View

Linklaters

Lawyers per state

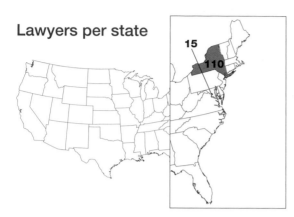

15

110

Largest US office: New York
US offices: 2
International offices: 27
First-year salary: $180,000
Billable hours: no requirement
Summers 2018: 23 (2 1Ls, 19 2Ls, 2 other)
Revenue 2017: £1.44 billion (+9.9%)
Partners made in 2018: 27 (2 in the US)
Famous for: international scope, transactional prowess and magic circle tag

Hailing from London, this prestigious magic circle firm packs its associates' schedules with cross-border work.

"EXCITING," "intriguing," "fun," "adventure" – words you'd typically see when browsing for your next vacation, but also used by juniors at Linklaters (or 'Links' as it's affectionately known) to describe their reasons for joining the firm. Yes, Links was the obvious choice for associates who wanted "not only international work but an international outlook." With its 29 offices across 20 countries and stated aim to be 'the leading global law firm,' our interviewees knew they'd found the one. However, with just two US offices in New York and DC, Links's "international flavor" comes with a more intimate twist compared to some of the larger domestic players it competes with.

Links's status as one of London's premier firms is rock solid, and in 2017 it posted a very healthy revenue of £1.44 billion (comfortably in the global elite). Behind such sparkling financials (and all those offices) is the firm's prowess, especially in transactional areas like corporate/M&A, capital markets, banking and finance, restructuring and energy – as its top rankings in *Chambers Global* attest. In fact, Links is ranked fourth in the *Chambers Global Top 30* of world-conquering firms, meaning – as juniors helpfully pointed out – that it naturally attracts "driven, open and curious people who are

interested in the world." If you recognize yourself in that description, read on…

The Work

Incoming associates are put into what Links calls 'the pool.' This system tracks associates' availability and aims to give them "exposure to multiple groups." Our sources felt that it had created "a more even distribution of work across the entire first-year class and high utilization rates." Some unexpectedly enjoyed practices they weren't initially interested in, while others had a more definite idea of the work they'd like to do and would've appreciated the chance to specialize earlier.

"You have to come up with a fund structure that accommodates around 200 investors!"

The bulk of second and third-year associates had settled into the investment funds, capital markets and dispute resolution groups; the rest were dotted between corporate, banking, projects, tax and financial regulation. In investment funds, "the diversity of clients is unmatched." Associates often acted for sponsors and had encountered investors from China, France, Singapore, Luxembourg, the Czech Republic and more. Such geographical scope makes for "one very big puzzle" work-wise, "as you have to come up with a fund structure that accommodates around 200 investors!" One source enthused: "As a junior you could be negotiating with investors on smaller matters, conducting fund reviews and drafting agreements."

On chambers-associate.com...

- Get hired: getting into Linklaters
- Interview with Tom Shropshire, Linklaters' global US practice head

See firm profile on p.666

The Inside View

Rankings in *Chambers USA*

| Antitrust | Latin American |
| Investment Funds | Investment |

For detail on ranking tiers and ranking locations, visit
www.chambersandpartners.com

Dispute resolution associates had worked on a hefty mix of white-collar defense matters, antitrust disputes, arbitrations, government enforcement actions and general commercial wrangles. They enjoyed composing *"a lot of correspondence with opposing counsel"* and found that *"research is definitely up there with one of the most frequent things we do; from that we draft motions and briefs and compose answers for seniors. Then there's the stuff that's pretty commonly done in litigation, like doc review."*

In capital markets, juniors are *"asked to do a bit of everything,"* including debt and equity deals, *"a sprinkling"* of banking work and some Latin America finance matters. Interviewees enthusiastically described *"drafting various transaction documents"* and *"client advisory memos."* There's also *"quite a bit of organizational work"* as juniors are often *"running the transaction: there's a lot of talking and emailing with the other side, a lot of client interaction and attending meetings – the days are pretty jam-packed! As a third year you're more like a fifth year in terms of the experience you get."*

Hours & Compensation

Links doesn't have a formal billing requirement, but some associates reported that there is an unofficial guide *"called 'the perfect ten.' The ideal is billing ten hours a day – and pro bono work can count – but it's just a goal."* Indeed, our sources didn't feel pressure to hit a specific number and highlighted that *"you're generally expected to work a similar number of hours as the people in your practice group."* Overall interviewees appreciated *"the more wholesome way of assessing performance: we have this concept of 'good standing,' which incorporates billables, pro bono and time spent developing internal 'know how' by drafting memos and updating informational sources."*

Cross-border work naturally means irregular hours: we heard from juniors rushing to get in by 6am to make a call, while others had left the office at 6am after staying up all night to get a filing done. Most said that they spent between ten and 12 hours a day in the office, but that can increase to between 15 and 17 hours during particularly busy periods. Our resilient sources took this in their stride: *"We have so much fun it makes it all worthwhile!"* In addition, *"the nice thing about being at an English-headquartered firm is that time off is sacred – people generally don't bug you on your time off and I've been able to do things on the weekends."*

Recent work highlights

- Advised German conglomerate thyssenkrupp on the €1.26 billion sale of its Brazilian subsidiary to a leading steel producer in Latin America
- Defended New York governor Andrew Cuomo during a broader lawsuit involving allegations of improper use of federal unemployment funds under the False Claims Act
- Acted for J.P. Morgan Securities as lead manager on Argentinian energy company Genneia's $350 million debut bond issue
- Advised telecommunications experts SoftBank Group on the launch of its $93 billion private equity fund

Culture & Offices

Most US associates call the New York office home (only one in our sample was based in DC at the time of our calls). It received lukewarm reviews: *"Overall it's fairly pleasant, but it's not extraordinary!"* On the plus side it benefits from *"nice views and a good Midtown location: it's accessible from anywhere in the city and close to a lot of clients, which is helpful."* Links's lease on the office space expires in 2020, so a move could well be on the cards…

English roots may inflect the culture in Links's US bases, but associates felt the firm's *"internationality"* was the real driving force behind it. *"Working with people from other cultures develops your interpersonal skills and keeps you open to new ideas,"* one source suggested. While people *"from the top down"* were described as *"kind, supportive and upbeat,"* it was also made clear that the approach to work was serious: *"It's certainly an environment that expects the best, and we achieve that by working together and making sure everyone is aware of the role they play and the expectations we have."*

> *"The nice thing about being at an English-headquartered firm is that time off is sacred."*

The social life may not be as *"institutionalized"* as it is in the London mothership, but the New York office sticks to the firm's Friday 'drinks cart' tradition – an informal *"get-together which allows us to enjoy a beer or glass of wine at the end of the day. I knew Linklaters was the firm for me when I heard about it!"* Juniors were also eager to tell us about attending the firm's global practice group retreats, which are held in various cities around the world: *"Links likes to emphasize how often we work with other offices, and the retreat allowed me to put faces to names."*

Training & Development

This isn't the only time juniors get to link up with their overseas colleagues. Summer associates can request to complete a stint in either Hong Kong or London, and all

See firm profile on p.666

Diversity	Partners (%)	Associates (%)
Women	17.1	45.2
White	85.4	57.8
Black/African American	2.4	3
Hispanic/Latin American	2.4	4.4
Asian	7.3	26.7
Mixed/Other	2.4	5.9
LGBT	7.3	4.4

first years descend on the latter for *"a fun week of training with new associates from across the firm."* After this, formal training varies from group to group, but one common thread was *"lunchtime sessions that are either hosted by partners or an external provider."* In addition there are *"always office-wide trainings on both discrete legal issues and career-based/administrative things."*

All juniors are assigned a mentor (either a partner or counsel) who they work closely with and meet for quarterly check-ins: *"These provide you with a good opportunity to just have an informal discussion about how things are going on both a micro and macro career level."* An associate's mentor also conducts an annual review, which incorporates feedback from *"five or more nominated colleagues you've worked with, regardless of their location."* There's also an informal midyear review.

Diversity

"In New York there aren't many female partners and men dominate the senior roles," but associates said the firm is *"fully aware of the problem and actively trying to change it."* A *"pretty strong"* women's group has *"different prongs to it,"* including a mentorship component and *"an initiative that aims to elevate female attorneys to partnership positions."* Drawing upon their time spent at global retreats, associates felt that female partner numbers were higher in Links's overseas offices. They suggested the imbalance could be a *"cultural thing"* in the US, and similarly so on a racial level. Networks exist for racially diverse associates; we heard that an Asian-American initiative is *"currently being revived by one of the seniors."*

"Working with people from other cultures keeps you open to new ideas."

Sources did praise the firm's efforts when it came to LGBT diversity: *"We are more diverse than other firms in that respect, and there are a lot of initiatives and partnerships with our clients to maintain and enhance that representation."*

Pro Bono

The *"big presence"* of pro bono at Links was an attraction for some associates. They get *"at least bi-weekly"* emails from a coordinator detailing available work from organizations such as the Urban Justice Center, Immigration Equality and New York Lawyers for the Public Interest. Juniors can also source their own projects too: *"If it's something you really care about, they'll help you set it up."* Some of our transactional sources found that deal volume prevented them from doing as much pro bono as they would've liked, while litigators felt they had more space in their schedules to fit it in. Interviewees had worked on human rights matters, corporate restructurings and labor law cases – one of which involved *"lots of ups and downs, a bench trial in front of a well-known judge, and, thankfully a decision in our favor!"*

Pro bono hours
- For all US attorneys: 5,867
- Average per US attorney: 50

Strategy & Future

Tom Shropshire was appointed global US practice head in 2017. He acknowledges the need for a bigger push in the US, and tells us that *"in some respects, competing with US firms, and – let's be specific – leading New York-based firms, is absolutely our ambition now. We want to make sure we have the highest-quality team doing the best-quality work in the market. However, we are not a deep incumbent New York law firm, so we have to find ways to position ourselves in the market in order to make ourselves attractive to both clients and talent."* You'll find our full interview with Shropshire on chambers-associate.com.

Get Hired

"Links can't afford to have people here who aren't super invested – they want people who are going to stick it out." For recruitment advice from Links associates, go to chambers-associate.com

See firm profile on p.666

Mayer Brown LLP

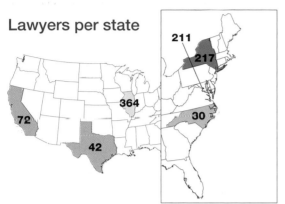

Lawyers per state

211
217
364
72
30
42

Largest US office: Chicago
US offices: 8
International offices: 18
First-year salary: $180,000
Billable hours: 2,000 required (2,100 target for bonus eligibility in most offices)
Summers 2018: 44 (5 1Ls, 37 2Ls, 2 other)
Revenue 2017: $1.31 billion (+4%)
Partners made in 2018: 18
Famous for: Chicago roots; nerd culture

For *"a gold star on your resume,"* where to look? Maybe Mayer Brown, a global giant which has propelled itself far and wide from its Windy City roots.

IT was just a decade ago that Mayer Brown took on its current name, but the firm's heritage stretches back much further – over 100 years in fact – to 19th century Chicago, where its headquarters still sit to this day. This is where most MB initiates wind up, and they agreed the firm offers a more forgiving environment than the traditional New York scene. *"Mayer Brown gives you the prestige of working for one of the best international firms in Chicago with a little less of a crushing workload than a New York firm,"* interviewees believed. The hours can still be long though and schedules demanding – more on that later.

Known for its work in finance, corporate and litigation, Mayer Brown is showered with *Chambers USA* rankings in 18 areas nationwide, and many more state to state. Many of these rankings come in its home state of Illinois, where the firm excels in antitrust, banking & finance, insurance, tax, technology & outsourcing, labor & employment, litigation and white-collar investigations. But Mayer Brown has flourished beyond the Windy City too: it has a further seven US offices and 14 more across the globe, with an office in Tokyo opening in 2018. *"It will allow us to better serve our large Japanese client base in all our offices,"* managing partner Kenneth Geller tells us. *"The office will start with a team on the ground focusing on project finance and M&A."*

On chambers-associate.com...

- Interview with managing partner Ken Geller
- Get hired at Mayer Brown

The Work

At the end of summer, incoming juniors rank the top three practice groups they'd like to join. *"Some groups take more people so you're more likely to get in,"* a junior said. *"Others are smaller and more competitive. I think of the end of summer as a sorority rush!"* There are minor variations between groups, but MB associates usually find their own work in a free-market system. By and large associates were happy with this. *"I really would hate having an assignment coordinator,"* one source said. *"This way I feel like I have control of the cases and people I work with."* Some associates pinpointed pitfalls: *"I'm very outgoing and it was hard even for me. You can get siloed into one group. You either need a lot of autonomy or actual regulation."* A source in finance was concerned about the volume of work the system faces them with: *"I might swing between 90-hour weeks and 20-hour weeks,"* they reported. *"The firm will work with you if you turn down work – but you have to be really busy to get away with it."* In Chicago, four partner-associate liaisons are there for support. *"They care about engaging with us,"* juniors reported, *"but it can be tricky for them to tell partners to lay off. They tell us how to write the email to say no to work."* We heard that litigation does have a more formal assignment system *"if a huge project comes in."*

> *"I have control of the cases and people I work with."*

Most associates on our list of juniors were in finance. *"Finance groups often come under the corporate umbrella, but at MB we're separate,"* observed one source. Juniors

See firm profile on p.667

Rankings in *Chambers USA*

Antitrust	Immigration
Appellate Law	Insurance
Banking & Finance	Intellectual Property
Bankruptcy/Restructuring	Labor & Employment
Capital Markets	Latin American Investment
Communications	Litigation
Corporate/M&A	Outsourcing
Employee Benefits &	Products Liability
Executive Compensation	Projects
Environment	Real Estate
Financial Services	Tax
Regulation	Technology
Government	Transportation

For detail on ranking tiers and ranking locations, visit
www.chambersandpartners.com

Recent work highlights

- Represented Wells Fargo in its $32 billion acquisition of GE Capital's commercial distribution finance and vendor finance platforms
- Successfully defended Chicago's former police superintendent against an employment discrimination allegation
- Represented Dell Bank in its first securitization in Europe worth €600 million
- Represented Canadian Imperial Bank of Commerce in its $3.8 billion acquisition of Chicago-based PrivateBancorp

tend to stick within one of the finance subgroups: general lending, funds, projects or (the biggest) securitization. One source rightly commented: "*I think the main reason finance isn't grouped under corporate is because we have such a strong securitization group.*" The firm is top-ranked nationwide by *Chambers USA* for securitization.

Finance clients include "*big investment banks, private equity funds and credit card companies*" like Morgan Stanley, Brookfield and World Financial Network. For juniors in Chicago "*there's not much face-to-face client contact, mainly because most clients aren't in Chicago. Lots are in New York, but really they're all over the country. I did get to go on a client visit out east.*" So what *do* juniors get up to? "*You'll send out the docs, collect comments, create new drafts, then put everything together at the end of the deal. Juniors handle the nitty-gritty of closings, so you get very familiar with ancillary documents.*" The nature of the work means juniors "*can start feeling a little isolated. A lot of the time you have to do a ton of work holed up in your office. You can come to work, bill ten hours, and not talk to anyone.*"

Corporate & securities has four subgroups: M&A, private investment funds, capital markets and technology transactions. Corporate sources noted that while work assignment is still free-market, "*partners distribute work to make an even balance.*" In M&A, juniors "*assist with deals, doing due diligence and a bit of drafting. I also help with joint venture projects and other things that don't fit squarely into M&A.*" Associates in funds "*help to bring in new investors and negotiate agreements for open-ended funds.*" The smallest group is technology transactions, which deals with "*digital service agreements, cybersecurity, big outsourcing deals and software licensing.*" The team handles contracts "*for things that have never been thought of before – AI, self-driving cars – so we have to be innovative.*"

Over in litigation "*you can do a bit of everything and specialize over time.*" That could include work from any of litigation's 'action groups' including antitrust and accounting malpractice. Clients include the "*household names*" of the corporate world – JP Morgan, Union Carbide, Google, Facebook, Nestlé, Bristol-Myers Squibb –"*which is really exciting, as it's cool to see what you're working on in the news.*" Litigators told us of "*two main types of work: fact-based discovery and legal research and writing.*" Associates said they also assist on depositions: "*I did all the doc review, a lot of preparing the client for interviews, and I was in charge of writing civil investigative demand responses.*" Litigators face their fair share of doc review. "*It probably made up 40% of my time last year,*" revealed one source, "*but I've also been able to handle first drafts of proceedings, document requests, letters to court and some of the less analytical documents. And I have a good understanding of how what I'm doing fits into the overall picture of the case.*"

Training & Development

All juniors are enrolled on a six-month fast-track training program, which has both general and group-specific weekly trainings. "*It's meant to match the tasks you'd be performing at that time, so earlier sessions are more basic like how to keep time and deal with administrative things, and later on it looks at how to engage with clients.*" For litigators group-specific sessions include "*how to prep a witness, create a deposition kit and draft documents – those are the sort of things I'd be doing.*" After suggestions from associates, the firm recently trialed a training bootcamp for finance and corporate associates – "*a few days where you learn everything all at once.*" Following good feedback, MB is looking to add some new elements to its first-year training curriculum in other groups.

"A few days where you learn everything all at once."

MB's mentor program connects associates with two partners as well as a midlevel "*for the social aspect.*" It was hit and miss, interviewees said: "*Some will tell you the program should be stronger, but the informal mentoring*"

See firm profile on p.667

The Inside View

Diversity	Partners (%)	Associates (%)
Women	20.3	41.4
White	89.2	69.0
Black/African American	1.2	4.7
Hispanic/Latin American	3.9	4.7
Asian	2.5	15.4
Mixed/Other	2.0	5.5
LGBT	2.2	3.7

is strong." Another source felt: "It's not a real program. I had to email to find out who my mentors were." Associates' have formal annual reviews and more informal checkups at six-month mark.

Hours & Compensation

Litigators were pretty satisfied with their working hours. "I'm in charge of pacing my tasks, so I can leave in the middle of the day to go to the gym." Working days usually last around ten hours, with some later nights and weekend work, particularly for those in finance and corporate. "It can be hard to get up at 5.30am when you were up until 2am the night before," reflected one interviewee. Juniors said their hours are shaped by client expectations, but wondered if the firm could make it easier to work remotely. "Most of my time is spent at the computer and on the phone, both of which I have at home," observed one source. "But it feels like three days a week I don't get to see my child in time before bed." Good news though: "One of the best things about Mayer Brown is that they encourage you to take time off."

"Even if you're on six or seven deals you can only do so much."

Associates have to bill 2,000 hours to move up a class. That figure "can include everything – client work, recruitment, pro bono, training, mentorship lunches, social events. It's incredibly hard not to hit it." There's a snag though. Hitting 2,000 won't get you your bonus. Outside the New York office (which has its own system), MB associates need to hit 2,100 hours of billable (or pro bono) work for a bonus, which was a sore point for some. "It's out of line with the market in Chicago," a junior said. "When you know your peers are getting a bonus for working fewer hours it's a little disappointing. From what I've heard, most don't hit the bonus target. As a first year you're just not capable. Even if you're on six or seven deals you can only do so much." Interviewees divulged that the associate committee had complained to the firm, and were now in talks to amend the rule. We'll report on progress in our next edition.

Pro Bono

Up to 200 hours of pro bono can count toward the bonus target, and first and second years have a 60-hour pro bono requirement. This was an easy reach for litigators, but associates elsewhere struggled. "You get too busy to do it," one said. Associates said pro bono immigration cases were commonplace. We also heard about a breach of contract case, a veteran appeal case, and helping a first-time home buyer.

Pro bono hours
- For all US attorneys: 58,175
- Average per US attorney: 66

Culture & Offices

Perhaps the best way to sum up being a junior at MB is this: "You know your place on the totem pole, but everybody treats you with respect." Associates described their colleagues as "reasonable, affable people who enjoy questions and the actual work." DC sources elaborated: "People joke we're a little nerdy and reserved, and I think that's true." It was a similar picture in Chicago: "We're known for being a bit of a nerd dungeon. I'm constantly impressed by the intellect of people – but they do also have an interest in music, literature, art." Associates said MB still has that BigLaw edge: "It's not what you see on TV shows with people yelling, but you definitely feel you have to prove you're devoted by being here as long as everybody else." We heard about a few instances where associates wanted a bit more clarity. A source reported: "A colleague was supposed to go and see a relative over Thanksgiving, but they were just told: 'Be available.' What does that mean? Can I work remotely? Do they want me in the office?"

"I'm constantly impressed by the intellect of people."

The Chicago office was said to be "family-oriented and have Midwestern values – we're less aggressive." With the exception of New York where "people want to be social," MB isn't the most actively sociable workplace. But in Chicago "the firm has built an attorney lounge for us to hang out with a TV, snacks, beer and wine." MB's next largest office is New York, followed by litigation-heavy DC and finance-focused Charlotte. The firm has a further three US bases: LA, Palo Alto and Houston, as well as 13 international offices. Associates said that "MB has a focus on practice areas more than offices," so cross-office work is common. And in a push to "create a more firm-wide community" in the finance group, juniors were recently told that (as part of the group's new bootcamp program) they'd get paired with partner mentors in other offices.

See firm profile on p.667

Diversity

Each office has its own diversity committees alongside a firm-wide organization and an associate diversity council. Of these, we heard Chicago's active associate-led LGBT group aims "*to help attorneys build relationships across different legal disciplines, provide opportunities for the firm to recruit and retain LGBT attorneys, and provide opportunities for LGBT attorneys to be visible at different events.*" The DC office hosted a firm-wide diversity retreat, and the women's forum there "*does a good job holding quarterly meetings about topics women show interest in, and the head of the firm came to speak to us at a roundtable about the firm's commitment to diversity.*"

"My sense is that the firm is very decentralized."

Strategy & Future

"*My sense is that the firm is very decentralized,*" an interviewee told us. "*There are a lot of smaller groups within the firm that are moving in their own direction, so it's hard to say one thing we're all gonna do moving forward when the firm has 13 offices with dozens of practice groups.*" But as far as being kept in the loop from a broader strategy viewpoint, associates felt it was "*hard to see how management could do better at a big firm. I do think they make an effort.*"

Managing partner Kenneth Geller gives some insight into MB's focus: "*In the US we have almost 1,000 lawyers and a full-service practice, so there's no practice group or capability that we're looking to add. The plan is to enlarge our presence in certain locations, particularly New York and the West Coast, and to enhance our offering in certain practices, particularly corporate.*"

Get Hired

"Look up and research the lawyers you're meeting with and know which areas or cases you're interested in." For more recruitment advice from Mayer Brown's juniors, head to chambers-associate.com

See firm profile on p.667

The Inside View

McDermott Will & Emery LLP

Lawyers per state

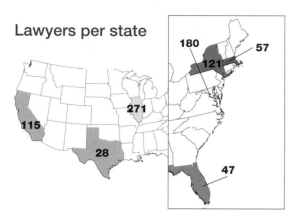

180
57
121
271
115
28
47

Largest US office: Chicago
US offices: 10
International offices: 8 (plus strategic alliance in Shanghai)
First-year salary: $180,000
Billable hours: 2,000 hours target
Summers 2018: 48 (6 1Ls, 41 2Ls, 1 3L)
Revenue 2017: $925.5 million (+1.8%)
Partners made in 2018: 27
Famous for: Reputable healthcare group; Chicago roots; private wealth

McDermott serves up a sundae of health, corporate, tax and more – but how does it keep its associates so sweet? The answer isn't ice cream, unfortunately.

MCDERMOTT still counts Chicago, where it was founded in 1934, as its largest office, but things have moved on a lot since then. "*We have important lawyers and professionals all over the world, so there isn't really a headquarters… unless you're talking to the Chicago kids!*" jokes chairman Ira Coleman. Add more of anything though, and things often get messy – so how does the firm, spread across 19 offices internationally, keep everything functioning as desired, and prevent a delicately arranged culture from melting away? "*I buy everybody ice cream,*" Coleman deadpans. In reality, however, that's a perk McDermott is yet to offer. Instead, Coleman explains: "*We really try to avoid folks who have a temper or who don't treat people well. They flush out of our culture very quickly. We've chosen not to bring in impressive groups that didn't match our culture, decisions we made very public within the firm.*"

After the Windy City, McDermott's most substantial domestic office is DC, where the healthcare group now surpasses Chicago's as the firm's biggest. And healthcare is the apple of McDermott's eye: its serious renown sees it scoop top-tier *Chambers USA* rankings in five states (and nationwide). Unsurprisingly, the all-encompassing

On chambers-associate.com…

- Interview with chairman Ira Coleman
- Get hired: recruitment insight from associates and hiring partner Eric Gilbert

practice was the main appeal for many associates. "*It's unique to be an associate in a place where you can find an answer to any question. Everyone specializes as they move up within the firm, so there's a specialist for every issue you might have.*" On top of healthcare, the firm's areas of particular strength span tax, litigation, private equity and M&A.

Strategy & Offices

Despite the cultural criteria for bold lateral hires, the firm has found opportunities to grasp. Chairman Ira Coleman describes how "*this year we added a five-person blockchain group from Debevoise, including partner Lee Schneider in New York. We think it's an important practice area, not just for cryptocurrencies, but also in our other power alleys, such as health and fintech.*"

The firm's current US footprint marks it out as a firm with the ability to bring its specialties to bear on a state's legal marketplace (it's worth checking the firm's *Chambers USA* rankings to see what it does well in each location). Coleman hints the firm will continue to take advantage of that: "*We partner with clients all over the world and are always looking at opportunities where it makes sense to establish a new office. In the near term, however, we're particularly excited to be expanding our presence on the West Coast, in San Francisco this year.*"

The Chicago office recently moved to a "*much more open and cheery*" space. "*People walk into the lobby now and*

See firm profile on p.668

The Inside View

Rankings in *Chambers USA*

Antitrust	Intellectual Property
Banking & Finance	Labor & Employment
Corporate/M&A	Life Sciences
Employee Benefits &	Litigation
Executive Compensation	Outsourcing
Food & Beverages	Privacy & Data Security
Healthcare	Tax
Insurance	Technology

For detail on ranking tiers and ranking locations, visit
www.chambersandpartners.com

Recent work highlights

- Advised Amazon on Texas corporate issues involved in its $13.7 billion acquisition of Whole Foods
- Acted for the National Football League on 12 concussion cases in Illinois
- Lead counsel for the Boston Beer Company and the Great Lakes Brewing Company after they were sued by Southern Glazer's Wine & Spirits for terminating business
- Represented a laboratory company, radiology practice and dental provider in a False Claims Act investigation regarding Medicare billing allegations
- Advised Saks Fifth Avenue on various employee benefit and executive compensation issues, including the establishment of a retirement plan for employees in a new Puerto Rico store

seem to be blown away. It helps us with our clients because, if the offices look this good, then the legal advice must be just as good!" Meanwhile, the *"beautiful"* DC office sits *"right in the heart of the city,"* just a few blocks away from Georgetown Law School. Besides Chicago and DC, the firm had junior associates working in New York, Miami, LA, Silicon Valley and Boston.

The Work

At the end of the summer program, associates rank their top three practice areas, before receiving offers for specific practice groups. Once through the door, it's up to them to find work through a free-market system that operates across groups. *"It's positive because if you want to do a type of work, you're free to go and find it. But if you're struggling, having more help and structure would also help associates who haven't had a chance to identify which stream of work they're interested in."* It did seem to have boosted collaboration, since associates described *"a lot of cross-group coordination."*

"You're part of a team that is working on transactions that are changing healthcare."

"They have a massive client list in the health sector," said associates, and related work spreads through the firm. Associates in the dedicated healthcare industry advisory group told us: *"You're getting the most interesting work, pushing the field forward, and asking questions that haven't been asked."* Sub-teams, labeled *"affinity groups,"* are numerous, but include digital health, health IT, privacy, private equity, fraud and abuse, managed care and nonprofit transactions. Thanks to the free market, associates *"aren't boxed in,"* but are *"usually encouraged to pick whether you want to be mostly transactional or regulatory. It's just such a big group otherwise!"* Experiences were unsurprisingly varied, but one associate recalled *"going from putting together ancillary documents to third-chairing transactions, to being on call all day with clients. I've done regulatory diligence for some of the largest healthcare deals in the country and it's satisfying to know you're part*

of a team that is working on transactions that are changing healthcare."

Under the corporate umbrella, groups include real estate, securities, finance and bankruptcy, *"but midmarket M&A is the bread and butter. The firm does deals as small as $10 million, though we have done deals as large as $1 billion plus. Private equity clients are predominant, but we also help companies with strategic transactions, often in the healthcare space."* Corporate work also extended beyond the actual transaction – associates had worked on *"internal reorganizations of corporations where, after they made an acquisition, they want to restructure the company in a more tax-efficient way."* Unfortunately, associate responsibility wasn't through the roof: sources found themselves *"mostly helping with diligence and ancillary document drafting."*

The tax teams also housed a number of juniors. Given that these form a smaller group, our sources reported that *"for better or for worse a lot of the work is substantive."* That included *"writing opinions on the tax consequences of a merger or a restructuring. There's the planning stage where you figure out the plan of action with the client, then you spend a couple of months writing those opinions."* McDermott started life as a tax practice, and the group works with recognizable clients like Microsoft and ExxonMobil. It takes on cross-border matters, but still tackles issues surrounding SALT (state and local tax).

Hours & Compensation

Associates reported a ten-hour working day to be the most consistent, but ebbs and flows were a fact of life (though less so in tax and private client). Most associates were familiar with clients' demands forcing them to stay beyond 10pm multiple times in a month, but, importantly, sources felt *"there aren't arbitrary deadlines. When I'm here late it's for a good reason. The partners aren't clamor-*

See firm profile on p.668

Diversity	Partners (%)	Associates (%)
Women	32	49
White	87	77
Black/African American	2	6
Hispanic/Latin American	3	4
Asian	8	10
Mixed/Other	1	3
LGBT	3	2

Get Hired

"I've seen people talking about learning Aboriginal languages and trying to climb the Seven Summits." Hiring partner Eric Gilbert explains how you can put your quirky interests to good use in your McDermott interview. Go to chambers-associate.com to find out more.

ing for you to work weekends." Still, a few wanted to have more options on where they worked: *"I sound like such a millennial, but I would like to see more flexibility to work from home."*

The 2,000-hour target includes 100 pro bono hours and 75 hours of professional development – *"you can use those hours to sit in on calls or negotiations."* That target was felt to be *"very, very achievable"* across groups, and further reward is given at the firm's discretion, but there was still some resentment around its timing: *"They aren't handed out until three months into the following year, so if you leave the firm in April you might get your bonus, but you had to wait that long to get it, and now if you go to another firm you've lost four months of the year."*

Training & Development

For their annual reviews, associates nominate partners to evaluate them, and also submit their cutesy-named 'I Love Me' memo, which is a chance for associates to *"write down everything you've achieved over the past year,"* or, in other words, *"to write about how wonderful you are!"* This self-evaluation gets submitted to the associate review committee, which is made up of partners across the firm, meaning *"a corporate partner in London could be reviewing a health associate – all they have to go on is a piece of paper!"*

While the reviews look back, juniors look forward, with an Associate Development Plan: *"You sit down with your mentor and talk about the goals you want to achieve. It could be 'I want to work with this partner' or 'I want to do a presentation to the practice group.'"* Extra training is rolled out through MWE University. Session frequency varies by group (altogether, sessions focusing on a range of practices occur weekly), and attendance is *"just short of compulsory."* One corporate associate vouched for them: *"I try to go as often as I can because it's helpful for the work that's done here."* Another attendee from the health group was reminded of law school: *"It doesn't teach you how to do everything, but it's useful for the background."*

Culture

"McDermott doesn't play on some sort of ivory tower white-shoeism. It's very much low key and enjoyable. I can get away with making fun of people!" Of course, *"there are definitely high expectations, but then also a lot of individuals are more than willing to spend time going through a document with you highlighting what you did right and wrong."* This was echoed again and again by associates: *"'Go figure it out' is not the tone that permeates our hallways."* Instead the firm paves an alternative route to high standards and loyalty. *"My biggest fear is disappointing the partners because they're too nice. There's more pressure than if they weren't."*

> *"My biggest fear is disappointing the partners because they're too nice."*

Juniors could see the benefits of *"working alongside folks in their seventies and everything in between. You have to be able to navigate different backgrounds, ages and practice groups – it provides a great opportunity to collaborate and learn."* However, they highlighted that *"a lot of partners are married and have kids in the suburbs, which removes a social aspect. A lot of people travel with work, so if you love spending a lot of time with people in the office, that's not something you'll necessarily get."* The firm is seemingly looking to improve on its social offering with a newly-launched retreat to Colorado Springs, a first for the juniors. *"We'll all be flown out to Colorado for training events, presentations, and, if it's anything like the partner retreat at the same location last year, there'll be opportunities for golfing, horseback-riding, spa days and happy hours!"* The DC office also recently launched a welcome committee to help integrate new attorneys *"so that you're not standing at a firm event alone with a drink hoping someone will talk to you."*

Diversity

When we checked in with associates, they were proud to tell us that *"all of the women partners are currently in Miami for a summit. They're working on goals and initiatives related to closing the gap between women and men in McDermott."* Similarly, we also heard about *"a diverse attorney summit this past year, which all of the racially*

See firm profile on p.668

The Inside View

diverse attorneys were flown out to." And beneath these grand events, associates could point to some promising realities. A DC associate told us: *"There is a group that supports young working mothers, who are helpful for navigating how to start a family while working. Some of the most recent people who made partner were young women with newborns – that certainly says something."* In fact, the firm promoted ten women to partner in the US for 2018. There is also a mentorship program for ethnically diverse lawyers and an LGBTQ affinity group.

Pro Bono

As we mentioned, associates can bill up to 100 pro bono hours, but once they hit the 2,000 target, the cap for pro bono is removed. Up until a couple of years ago, the firm didn't have a cap at all. One associate felt that: *"As someone who's extremely proud of our pro bono work, it would be nice if we were still following that practice, but I understand it was a business decision to improve the health of the firm."* However, associates were clear that they felt the firm supported their pro bono escapades: *"They'll champion someone who just won a pro bono case equally to someone who just won a big regular case."*

Matters associates had worked on included adoption work and a case focused on special education. There are also programs such as Partners in Reading: *"You pair up with a third grader and hang out for an hour reading. Either you read to them, or, if they feel up to it, they read to you."*

Pro bono hours
- For all US attorneys: 37,388
- Average per US attorney: 47.4

See firm profile on p.668

The Inside View

Milbank, Tweed, Hadley & McCloy

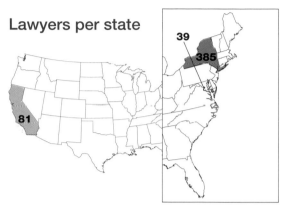

Lawyers per state

39
385
81

Largest US office: New York
US offices: 3
International offices: 9
First-year salary: $180,000
Billable hours: no requirement
Summers 2018: 63 (59 2Ls, 2 1Ls, 2 others)
Revenue 2017: $916.5 million (+ 7.1%)
Partners made in 2018: 7
Famous for: being the trusted advisers to New York's elite families and financial institutions; projects, transportation and bankruptcy expertise

A move to New York's trendy Hudson Yards development is *"ushering in a new era of Milbank being cool,"* say juniors at this esteemed Wall Street-rooted firm.

"I THINK that this whole thing about us being 'white-shoe' is ridiculous!" one source asserted with a polite but slightly exasperated guffaw. *"That's a dated preconception!"* roared others, offering a consensus that any association of the firm with blanched footwear and stuffiness should be ditched once and for all. This reputation stems from an illustrious history that has seen Milbank advise some of New York's most prominent families (like the Rockefellers and the Vanderbilts) and financial institutions (like Chase Manhattan Bank, as it was previously known). Status and prestige mean that *"a lot of people expect the firm to be very aggressive, but the culture here is actually quite benign,"* interviewees declared, eager to get the truth out there.

"Our Wall Street roots don't fit so much anymore."

They hoped that Milbank's upcoming move to the oh-so-hip Hudson Yards development in November 2018 would finally dislodge these outdated associations. Chairman Scott Edelman tells us that *"the firm has been based downtown for 150 years, and now we're moving to one of the coolest new neighborhoods in New York. Milbank is a contemporary modern law firm and our Wall*

Street roots don't fit so much anymore. We are moving to a space that is consistent with the Milbank of today."*

The Milbank of today is a global outfit with 12 offices placed strategically across the US, Europe, Asia and Latin America. Despite this coverage, sources were quick to distance Milbank from *"the mega-global law firms like Skadden and Paul, Weiss. We tackle the same quality of work but as the firm's intake is a lot smaller it makes it feel more intimate."* That quality of work is celebrated in *Chambers USA*, which deems Milbank a nationwide force to be reckoned with in the world of projects; other areas of note include Milbank's aviation finance and bankruptcy/restructuring capabilities. Its general commercial litigation and corporate/M&A practices are ranked in the 'elite' and 'highly regarded' categories, respectively.

Strategy & Offices

It's fair to say that our sources (the vast majority of whom were based in the New York HQ) were more than just a little bit excited about the move. *"It will definitely be a shock in terms of modernization!"* they exclaimed, especially because *"some of the technology here feels slightly outdated."* One interviewee cited Milbank's current digs at 28 Liberty Street as their *"main criticism of the firm, as the office structure can sometimes inhibit cooperativeness."* That's all set to change though, as Edelman reveals that *"one of our goals is to create a more unified culture through the new space. We want to create some common areas that*

On chambers-associate.com...

- Get hired: recruitment at Milbank
- Interview with chairman Scott Edelman

The Inside View

See firm profile on p.669

453

Rankings in *Chambers USA*

Banking & Finance	Litigation
Bankruptcy/Restructuring	Projects
Capital Markets	Real Estate
Corporate/M&A	Tax
Latin American Investment	Transportation

For detail on ranking tiers and ranking locations, visit www.chambersandpartners.com

Recent work highlights

- Represented Dutch financial services company Rabobank throughout a multijurisdictional internal investigation tied to potential manipulation of the Libor and Euribor reference rates
- Advised solar project developer Onyx on its tax equity partnership with Royal Bank of Canada Capital Markets to finance 16 projects across six states
- Acted for investment manager Borealis Infrastructure as it acquired a stake in Chilean gas company GNLQ
- Represented the Official Committee of Unsecured Creditors during the Chapter 11 bankruptcy of TK Holdings, which through its subsidiaries develops and manufactures safety products that are installed in vehicles across the world

will allow our employees to bump into each other, to meet and communicate and conduct business."

At the same time, sources felt that the firm was already pretty unified across its domestic locations. *"We don't have New York Milbankers or LA Milbankers. We are all just Milbankers,"* one proud associate declared, offering a summary that could serve well as Milbank's latest advertising slogan. *"The offices very much feel like different floors of the same building rather than three different locations."* Around 20% of the second and third-year juniors on our list were based in Milbank's LA and DC offices.

What about the cumulative effect of these offices' recent efforts? *"We've been continuing to build on our past successes and have had another great year,"* says Edelman. In particular, he highlights the firm's civil litigation, financial restructuring and global projects practices as booming groups, while the firm's white-collar and investigations work is currently *"one of our most exciting growth areas."*

The Work

Milbank's current first years are the *"test subjects"* for a new system which allows budding transactional lawyers in New York to rotate through three (out of seven) deal-oriented groups for four months at a time. Work across most groups is allocated via a dedicated assigning partner. *"We send over weekly availability reports, and it's nice to have someone looking at your schedule – it means there isn't too much pressure to take on too much,"* a corporate source told us. Litigators also *"preferred the set-up to going out and having to hunt for work,"* while those in leveraged finance relayed that *"it's a little less formal here: if you like working with someone and they like working with you, then not everything has to go through the centralized system – the assignment partner is more there to fill the gaps."*

The firm's litigation group housed the most juniors on our list. *"The group takes in everything,"* said sources here, describing a mix of work that spanned *"big bankruptcies, regulatory matters, probate work, commodities-based class actions and even IP stuff."* Chambers USA praises the group's work on a range of commercial, securities and white-collar matters, and clients here include private

equity funds, global investment banks and individual investors. *"It's a new step every day,"* litigators revealed. *"They keep you at a good pace, and once you've mastered something you move onto something else."* One expanded for us: *"For sure, there's doc review, but you also get to do legal research to ascertain the counterarguments we can put together; you get to review depositions to see how different parties interact and you can take a first stab at drafting motions and declarations."*

"There are a lot of elements to deals that make them interesting."

"We do everything domestically and abroad," said juniors in Milbank's large global project, energy and infrastructure finance group, *"whether it's financing gas-processing facilities, or building roads and ports, or developing solar plants and wind farms."* A lot of the matters here are tied to projects in Latin America, and interviewees had worked on deals occurring in Mexico, Guatemala, Chile and Colombia. As they entered their third year, sources were *"expected to start drafting the core finance agreements"* and enjoyed the fact that *"there are a lot of elements to deals that make them interesting; you're coordinating with local counsel and tons of parties, including sponsors, lenders, suppliers, government agencies, environmental consultants and engineers."*

Other transactional groups with a fair number of juniors included global corporate and global leveraged finance. *"There are no designated first, second and third-year tasks,"* those in corporate told us; *"it's very much a meritocracy."* They added: *"We do a lot more private than public deals, especially in the energy sector. Even as a first year I was able to take on a lot, which was very daunting, but I felt well supported."* It's a similar story in leveraged finance, where *"our bread and butter is acquisitions, and the players are financial institutions and equity firms. As a junior I get my hands dirty by doing first drafts of credit*

See firm profile on p.669

Diversity	Partners (%)	Associates (%)
Women	14	42.3
White	87.7	74.5
Black/African American	1.8	4.6
Hispanic/Latin American	6.1	7.7
Asian	3.5	9.7
Mixed/Other	0.9	3.6
LGBT	2.6	3.6

agreements and term sheets. If you're willing to step up and take it on, no one will refuse you on the basis of your year."

Pro Bono

Despite the withdrawal of Milbank's fellowship scheme (which allowed associates to take on three months of uninterrupted pro bono work) sources were adamant that the firm hadn't waned in its commitment to this noble pursuit: *"The assumption is that if you're not busy you'll take on pro bono matters. They have increased the minimum requirement to 25 hours and placed an emphasis on everyone doing a bit more throughout the year. Plus there's no cap on how many hours you want to commit to pro bono – it's all billable."*

The firm also makes an extra effort to accommodate individual preferences: *"When I expressed an interest in holding governments to account for abuses of power, they had a case prepared for me within the week,"* one dedicated junior reported. Matters are circulated weekly via an email that's sent out by Milbank's pro bono director. Our interviewees had worked on immigration, adoption, name change, disability benefits and death penalty matters. The firm's Advocacy@Milbank program (see below) also gives all first-year litigators an opportunity to represent individuals in appellate matters.

Pro bono hours
- For all US attorneys: 44,215
- Average per US attorney: 86

Training & Development

This year's cohort were also keen to highlight Milbank's commitment to training: *"They don't just pay lip service to it. This is a firm that spends a lot of time and money developing you as a lawyer."* It all kicks off with the 'Windstar' training scheme for summer associates: it's a ten-week program which charts the life-cycle of a hypothetical company (Windstar) from inception and financing through to bankruptcy and restructuring. Just before they start for real, all new juniors descend on the New York HQ for a week of orientation, which *"covers all the IT stuff and gives you a sense of what to expect."*

From then on *"training is very group-specific: some have very regular CLEs, while others take a more informal approach, which involves juniors sitting down with the seniors on deals and having a stab at something."* Sources in the projects group had experienced the latter approach, while those in corporate praised their *"group-specific CLEs, where we talk about specific agreements, provisions and developments in the law."* Litigators were also pleased, and flagged the benefits of a two-day deposition training in New York, which is part of the firm's Advocacy@Milbank program (this provides juniors with sessions on various skills – like persuasive writing and oral argument – from the first through to the sixth year).

> *"This is a firm that spends a lot of time and money developing you as a lawyer."*

However, the centerpiece of Milbank's training scheme arrives in the third year, when all associates are enrolled on the Milbank@Harvard program: *"We go to Harvard for a week, and attend sessions presented by professors from the business and law schools – it gives you a good financial and business background to supplement the work that you're doing."*

Culture

Interviewees felt that *"overall there's a big culture of being welcoming and warm,"* which sits in stark contrast to *"the stereotypes you hear about with regards to what New York firms are like."* Praise was bestowed on chairman Scott Edelman for *"trying to cultivate a Milbank culture as a whole. For years Milbank has been viewed as stuffy and old-school, but Scott has been pushing the firm away from that and ushering in a new era of Milbank being cool. While we respect and appreciate our roots in Wall Street, we know that we can't rest on our laurels and not move forward."* Alongside the upcoming move to Hudson Yards, juniors cited a newly-instated 'jeans Friday' and the firm's spring party as signs of a cooler direction: *"Last year's was held at the Whitney Museum, which is located in the hip meatpacking district – it was quite a step away from the typical formal party."*

See firm profile on p.669

The Inside View

455

Hours & Compensation

"It can't be overstated how important it is not to have bill-able hours targets," juniors told us. This interviewee spoke for many when they said: *"This month, for example, has been a bit slower, and not having to worry about targets has been great. Having billable goals means that you're stressed when you're super busy and stressed when you're not. This way is better for group mentality and it means that we can focus on the quality of the work we're doing."*

"...the unpredictability is just part of the job."

"Even if there was a target we'd hit it," sources added, pointing to plenty of work and potentially long hours. Corporate sources said: *"Our time tends to ebb and flow more, so some weeks can be very tiring. Today I got in around 9.30am and I have no idea when I will leave; the unpredictability is just part of the job."* Litigators, mean-while, were *"generally working 40 to 50 hours a week, with some 60-hour stretches – on monster matters you need to check your emails constantly!"* Thankfully, Milbank has done *"a good job of reforming the tech systems to make working from home just like working in the office."* All first years are given new laptops and iPhones to make remote working easier. *"They are good about where you work. At 6.30pm I'll go home and pick it up from there – you just work as long as you need to get stuff done."*

Diversity

"It doesn't feel un-diverse," was a typical response to questions on this topic. At the same time, juniors felt that *"there's still some way to go."* One area flagged for improvement was gender diversity, with juniors in groups like projects and litigation citing a lack of female representation in the partnership. *"The building blocks are there,"* however, with female interviewees highlighting the efforts of the Women@Milbank affinity group: *"Our monthly meetings are fantastic – our female partners take three hours out of their day to talk to us. Part of it is about bonding and part of it is about mentoring."* There are also affinity groups for Latin American, Asian Pacific Islander and LGBT attorneys, as well as a dedicated group for associates of African descent (aADAM).

Coming soon on chambers-associate.com... Milbank's lawyers take us behind the scenes at their project finance team, and bring to life their complex practice.

See firm profile on p.669

The Inside View

Mintz Levin Cohn Ferris Glovsky and Popeo PC

Lawyers per state

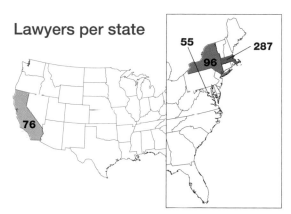

Largest US office: Boston
US offices: 7
International offices: 2
First-year salary: $180,000
Billable hours: 2,000 target (incl. 1,850 billables)
Summers 2018: 16 (4 1Ls, 12 2Ls)
Revenue 2017: $400 million (+7.4%)
Partners made in 2018: 6
Famous for: life sciences, healthcare and technology expertise

An ever-increasing revenue has kept this Boston-headquartered outfit in Mintz condition – and it's anticipating further growth.

"IT'S very much a Boston institution," was a common first response from juniors when asked to describe Mintz. "We're a go-to firm in the market here because of our strong ties to the city." And Mintz has got the financial results to prove it, as managing member Bob Bodian explains: "We followed our best year ever in fiscal 2016 with our best year ever in fiscal 2017. Over those two years our revenue grew by 23% and profits grew by over 20%. We are now in the middle of our 2018 fiscal year and we are on pace to do even better than last year."

Mintz associates were therefore eager to tell us that the firm has reached "a key moment in its development because of the amazing growth we've witnessed." Sources partly pinned this success on Mintz having "developed its expertise in midmarket transactions, especially in the life sciences space. The Boston office is really tech focused as we have so many startup companies in the city, and we've homed in on that to drive our growth."

Bodian tells us that life sciences and healthcare work is what Mintz is "nationally known for," but also flags energy, technology, telecommunications and private

equity as key areas. In terms of thriving practices, "our corporate groups are really strong right now – especially M&A and capital markets – but so is our litigation practice. We have been hiring laterals into our busy practice areas." We should add here that not all of Mintz's fine legal expertise is concentrated in Boston: the firm has six domestic offices across California, DC and Connecticut, and one overseas base in London. The bulk of Mintz's *Chambers USA* rankings are clustered in Massachusetts, but the firm receives nationwide affirmation for its healthcare and life sciences work.

> *"We're growing, we're getting busier, and we're doing more work for some of our bigger clients."*

Strategy & Future

"We are going to stay in our geographic footprint, and we will maintain our industry focuses," Bodian confirms. Mintz will be getting bigger, however: "We are going to keep hiring high-quality laterals. We will become more leveraged, so the ratio of associates to partners will increase. There will be more associates, but the class sizes will not be like they are at big New York firms. We are growing, we are getting busier, and we are doing more work for some of our bigger clients. The associates are really busy, so we need more of them."

On chambers-associate.com...

- Interview with Boston-based hiring partner Bret Leone-Quick
- Life in Mintz's IP practice
- More on offices & culture

The Inside View

See firm profile on p.670

Rankings in *Chambers USA*

Banking & Finance	Healthcare
Bankruptcy/Restructuring	Insurance
Corporate/M&A	Life Sciences
Employee Benefits &	Litigation
Executive Compensation	Real Estate
Environment	Retail

For detail on ranking tiers and ranking locations, visit
www.chambersandpartners.com

The Work

At the time of our calls, Mintz's corporate, litigation and IP practices took on the majority of its second and third-year juniors; a handful could be found dotted between its public finance, real estate, health law, employment and antitrust groups. Each group has an assignment partner *"to help you out if you're a little bit slow,"* but overall *"there's definitely more of a free-market system: you'll reach out to partners or they'll pick you personally based on your experience."*

In corporate, the team *"helps to form a lot of startup companies, primarily in the life sciences and tech industries."* This involves working with *"local entrepreneurs who wouldn't typically come to a BigLaw firm, so it's cool that we get to advise them on their relationships with big investors."* Outside of emerging companies and venture capital work, matters cover *"a mix of everything – securities, public offerings, M&A and licensing."* Capital markets deals were singled out for being *"staffed leanly: I'm putting together lots of closing documents and I helped with the drafting process for the primary agreements."* M&A transactions, meanwhile, were deemed *"fun, as you get to see how all the different levers work and where you can negotiate."*

> *"...it's cool that we get to advise them on their relationships with big investors."*

Litigation associates *"get pulled in on all kinds of things – we're working on contract disputes, property cases, some trademark and copyright matters. It's a broad spectrum and I really enjoy having that diversity."* Because of this array of work, *"we definitely don't specialize straight away – you're encouraged to take on different types of cases."* Juniors can expect to do some doc review and *"a ton of research,"* but also get a crack at *"drafting briefs, preparing for depositions, analyzing evidence and drafting correspondence to clients."* When it comes to case strategy, *"the seniors want to hear what we think; one of the partners says, 'If you can prove me wrong, I love that!' They want to know what holes their opponent in the courtroom will poke in their theories."*

Recent work highlights

- Represented Philips North America as it acquired Cardio-Prolific, a US-based company that develops treatments for peripheral vascular disease
- Defended emerging company Crescendo Biosciences during a $169.6 million dispute over the supply of parts to perform Crescendo's diagnostic test to manage the effects of rheumatoid arthritis
- Successfully defended US computer software company NextGen Healthcare against a patent infringement lawsuit filed by Preservation Wellness relating to its electronic medical records system
- Handled a portfolio of patents for life sciences researchers at the University of California San Diego, which cover antibodies and binding agents that can be used to treat a certain type of leukemia

Training & Feedback

A weeklong 'Base Camp' program welcomes juniors to the firm. It brings them all together in the Boston HQ for *"high-level training in everything: the doc review system, available technology resources, etc..."* Juniors praised the level of detail it contains: *"It's almost overwhelming! But fortunately they give you loads of printouts to keep."* This is followed by *"periodic training sessions"* throughout the year, which are typically held over lunch. Those in corporate were particularly impressed: *"They cover everything – we had a guy come in to teach us about basic accounting practices, but we've also had overviews of statutes and gone through different forms."*

All newcomers are paired up with mentors (typically a senior associate). *"We have full confidentiality with our mentors so you can speak freely and not worry about it having an impact on future reviews. The firm gives us a budget every month to have lunch with them."*

Pro Bono

Once associates bill 1,850 hours of standard client work, all the pro bono hours they've accrued can count toward the firm's 2,000 target for a bonus. Most juniors agreed that a proactive approach is required: *"It's really up to you to follow your interests and actively seek out opportunities."* Those who are feeling particularly active can call upon Mintz's dedicated pro bono chair, who *"will link you up."*

> *"...we receive training on how to do it."*

While Mintz lets its associates decide whether they have time for pro bono, we still heard that *"people generally have pro bono matters on the go and take them as seriously as paying client assignments."* In addition, *"the firm does encourage it and we receive training on how to do it during the Base Camp program."* Mintz's Domestic Vio-

See firm profile on p.670

The Inside View

Diversity	Partners (%)	Associates (%)
Women	24.5	48
White	91.3	77.7
Black/African American	2.5	4.6
Hispanic/Latin American	2.5	5.6
Asian	3.75	9.3
Mixed/Other	0	2.5
LGBT	3.3	2.5

lence Project is a key avenue for pro bono work, but we also heard of *"a ton of opportunities"* that spanned political asylum cases, protective orders for victims of sexual abuse, custody battles, veterans' matters and 'incubator' advice sessions for startup companies.

Pro bono hours
- For all US attorneys: 14,598
- Average per US attorney: 30

Offices & Culture

Almost two thirds of the juniors on our list were housed in the Boston HQ; the remaining third were split between the San Diego, New York and DC offices.The hot topic for Boston associates was the upcoming renovation of the office. *"We're downsizing so the idea is to make the space feel more open – we'll be having glass walls put in, for example."* Some juniors were a little worried at the thought of losing their current view onto the world via their office window. Bodian tells us: *"Everyone will have their own office, but my expectation is that associates will have interior offices for the first few years at the firm."* Still, the renovations sound pretty snazzy: *"We're doing a floor-to-ceiling gut renovation, and all of our systems will be updated,"* Bodian adds.

Get Hired

"I look for someone who's knowledgeable about the firm and can clearly demonstrate why they want to be here," one associate-turned-interviewer told us. To find out more about how to wow, check out our interview with Mintz's hiring partner Bret Leone-Quick on chambers-associate.com.

Bostonians frequently described the culture in terms of how collaborative it is: *"It's one of the reasons I came to Mintz. Everyone helps each other, and I can go into anyone's office to ask how we're approaching something and why we're doing it that way."* Juniors often felt that their efforts were recognized: *"Often the partner who's in charge of the group will send out an email on a Friday to thank the team for all the work they've put in – it goes a long way*

to making you feel appreciated and noticed." That appreciation can take a financial form too, as Bodian reveals: *"Because we had such a strong financial year, we increased the bonus pool. We took half a million dollars and gave it to our staff, totally apart from our regular staff bonuses, and we added $200,000 to the discretionary bonus pool for our lawyers."*

Hours & Compensation

On average, juniors across the offices got in between 9am and 10am, and left between 6pm and 8pm. Many then log back on for a few hours when they get home. Over in litigation, filing deadlines can mean a week of 10pm exits, while corporate juniors also experience *"midnight finishes a few days in a row"* when certain deals close.

A bonus is granted to associates if they bill 2,000 hours in a year. The amount they subsequently receive is not solely *"based on hours – your performance reviews also play a part."* For newcomers the bonus policy is bittersweet: *"Because of the way Mintz's fiscal year runs, you're not eligible for a bonus the first year that you're here. However, that means that you don't have to worry about hours, which takes the stress off a bit."* Others added: *"The bonuses for juniors fall in line with the market, but as you get more senior they fall below."* There were also mixed opinions on how achievable Mintz's 2,000 hours bonus target is, with corporate juniors in particular concerned: *"It's so hit and miss with the type of work we do."*

Diversity

This junior put it quite bluntly: *"They've done a good job – I don't look out at a sea of white faces."* Many of our other interviewees agreed, and highlighted some of the initiatives Mintz has put in place, including its sponsored 1L summer position for a diverse candidate and its various affinity groups. The LGBT group *"isn't huge, but we have a decent number of partners and associates involved across the offices. We organize both social mixer events and volunteer activities with local LGBT nonprofits."*

Mintz's women's initiative organizes a well-being week every fall and our female sources felt that there's *"a supportive environment for women: our affinity group recently held a meeting across the firm via videoconference – every single person introduced themselves and we discussed what we can do to help one another's careers."* The firm also recently increased its primary caregiver parental leave period to a fully-paid 18 weeks. Also of note is the firm's overarching minority affinity group (MIATTY), which hosts an annual retreat in a different Mintz office each year: *"All minorities firmwide are invited and it lasts for two days – we talk about how we're going to address issues and move forward."*

The Inside View

See firm profile on p.670

Morgan, Lewis & Bockius LLP

Lawyers per state

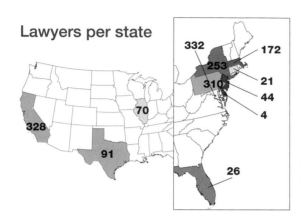

- 332
- 172
- 253
- 310
- 21
- 44
- 4
- 70
- 328
- 91
- 26

Largest US office: Philadelphia
US offices: 17
International offices: 13
First-year salary: $180,000
Billable hours: no requirement
Summers 2018: 87 (11 1Ls, 76 2Ls)
Revenue 2017: $2 billion (+7.6%)
Partners made in 2018: 28

Famous for: enormous headcount; representation of President Trump; 'trailblazing' chair Jami McKeon

With a *"magnetic leader"* in the form of firm chair Jami McKeon, associates felt this Philly-founded juggernaut would continue to expand for all the right reasons.

"IT was a no-brainer," said associates when asked why they opted to launch their careers at Morgan Lewis. *"It has that neat mix of great brand recognition, interesting front page work, prestigious clients, cool assignments for associates and an entrepreneurial spirit – we're not resting on our laurels; we have the hunger to keep getting better."* The onboarding of hundreds of ex-Bingham McCutchen lawyers in 2014 saw ML's headcount swell enough to see it become the largest firm in the US, but juniors assured us that *"we're not gobbling up firms for the sake of growth – we're making acquisitions in a strategic way, when there's a specialty required."* Recent additions have strengthened ML's healthcare practice in Houston, its tax group in Chicago, its funds clout in Hong Kong, its sports expertise in California, and its IP prowess in Shanghai. Across the globe, ML has 30 offices planted in North America, Asia, Europe and the Middle East.

Those *"prestigious clients"* include Coca-Cola, Google, Gap, JPMorgan Chase, Toyota and (the firm's most famous client right now) President Trump, who the firm has advised since its combination with Bingham. When it comes to the expertise that draws in these big names, tax is certainly a strength for ML; its practice is rated by *Chambers USA* as one of the best in the country. Among

its reams of rankings, other nationwide highlights include capital markets, corporate/M&A, ERISA litigation, labor & employment and immigration.

Much of this year's praise was centered on firm chair Jami McKeon: *"She's a trailblazer. There's an amazing amount of momentum behind her. Most associates and partners feel the firm is taking steps to be the go-to firm in the 21st century, in large part because of Jami and her team."* McKeon is *"traveling a lot but resident in the Philly HQ – sometimes I run into her in the cafeteria and she's just like any other partner I could approach."* Juniors also felt that ML's decision to keep Philly as its flagship base (instead of New York) sends out the message *"that we're a big firm with a more sustainable approach, which makes a lot of people stay for their entire careers."*

Diversity & Strategy

A diversity and inclusion committee is led by a *"full-time director who's based in New York. It meets regularly and launches different initiatives and programs."* Each office also comes up with its own initiatives, as this San Francisco junior revealed: *"Our office recently hosted one of the firm's mock interview programs with diverse law school students – they came in, did the interview and received feedback."* There's also ML Women, which is led by the firm's chair, Jami McKeon. *"They recently organized an event where senior female attorneys came to our office to give us advice – it's a strong initiative,"* one female source commented.

On chambers-associate.com...

- More on getting hired at Morgan Lewis
- Interview with firm chair Jami Wintz McKeon

See firm profile on p.671

The Inside View

Rankings in *Chambers USA*

Antitrust	Investment Funds
Banking & Finance	Labor & Employment
Bankruptcy/Restructuring	Latin American Investment
Capital Markets	Life Sciences
Corporate/M&A	Litigation
Employee Benefits &	Media & Entertainment
Executive Compensation	Outsourcing
Energy & Natural	Products Liability
Resources	Projects
Environment	Real Estate
ERISA Litigation	Retail
Financial Services	Securities
Regulation	Startups & Emerging
Healthcare	Companies
Immigration	Tax
Insurance	Technology
Intellectual Property	Telecommunications

For detail on ranking tiers and ranking locations, visit
www.chambersandpartners.com

"It's incredibly empowering and exciting to have a woman chair."

Other female interviewees told us that *"it's incredibly empowering and exciting to have a woman chair. We're really lucky to have Jami."* Explaining her vision for the firm, McKeon tells us: *"Over the years some firms have really narrowed their focus to chase after only the most profitable work – we, in contrast, have maintained our focus on being a relationship firm, so local and global clients can come to us with any issue or matter that needs a resolution anywhere around the world."* To read more from McKeon on diversity, work-life balance and how technology has changed the practice of law, visit chambers-associate. com

The Work

"We have pretty much every type of practice group but I'd say the three primary categories are litigation, corporate business transactions, and labor & employment," juniors explained. Of these, ML's litigation group is the biggest. As with all groups, there's an assignment coordinator on hand to dole work out, but overall it's *"a fairly fluid, open system – the coordinator keeps an eye on everyone's hours, but you can also get work more organically from partners who have seen your skills or your bio online and give you a direct call."*

Litigators enjoyed being exposed to a variety of different cases: *"When you come in the door you could be working on white-collar, antitrust, general commercial, regulatory, financial services or IP matters. If you develop an interest then you can delve deeper into that area."* On large

Recent work highlights

- Represented publisher Pearson as it sold a 22% stake (worth $1.2 billion) in Penguin Random House to German outfit Bertelsmann
- Secured a victory for Toyota against various fraud-based consumer protection claims tied to the automaker's 'Smart Key System' used within some of its vehicles
- Filed a successful motion to dismiss a lawsuit on behalf of Amazon, which asserted that the online giant's workers should be paid for their time spent passing through the company's security screening system during meal breaks and at their shift's end
- Acted for Google during litigation against the IRS over a tax deduction relating to a stock option issued to another company

mortgage-backed securities cases sources were working in *"pretty defined teams – I was on the offensive discovery team, focusing on those issues and helping the team take depositions."* Breach of contract cases were quite common, *"as they come up in almost every industry, from insurance to healthcare."* Those who'd taken on white-collar work found themselves on *"small investigations where you're the one going through the docs and preparing how we're going to represent witnesses. This week I'm heading to the DOJ and attending government meetings – it's a much more strategic role."*

The corporate business transaction group (CBT) is structured slightly differently office to office, but broadly covers M&A, securities, real estate, energy, outsourcing, finance and investment management work. Juniors in the larger offices sample various areas for a couple of years and then formally join a subgroup. Those initial years therefore come with a broad sweep of work: *"On bond offerings I helped with the logistics of audit committee presentations; on real estate deals I helped to draft a lease; on investment management matters I was assisting with the sale of fund interests; and on M&A transactions I was doing due diligence to look out for potential restrictions."* As juniors enter their third year, *"you become more focused on specific types of deals. You're expected to have a deeper knowledge of them and make judgment calls on how documents should look and work – it's challenging but exciting."*

Juniors had a lot of pride in the strength of the labor and employment group: *"It's able to maintain a separate identity, whereas in other firms it's often subsumed under larger litigation or corporate departments."* Its subgroups include labor/management relations; individual employee litigation & arbitration; immigration; and occupational safety and health administration (OSHA).

See firm profile on p.671

The Inside View

461

Diversity	Partners (%)	Associates (%)
Women	23.6	50.3
White	91	73
Black/African American	1.6	5
Hispanic/Latin American	1.3	4.8
Asian	5.3	14.2
Mixed/Other	0.8	3
LGBT	2.7	4.8

Training & Development

Reviews come thick and fast at ML: summers receive two, *"both of which were substantive, with written feedback."* First years also get two (midyear and end of year), and are assigned *"a rating of either 'adequate' or 'inadequate': it's always good to hear that you're doing good, get an official rating and have a sense of what the partnership is looking for in an associate."* Beyond this stage, subsequent annual reviews follow this format: *"In November the partners you've worked with fill out questionnaires about you and your work, then meet to discuss the feedback. Then in January you sit down with two partners you usually work with, and they summarize the consensus and give you the chance to voice any concerns or grievances."* We also heard that the firm is putting more of an emphasis on formulating professional development plans with its associates going forward.

Formal training varies by practice group. There are *"monthly sessions in litigation, which cover things like direct examination and arbitration – things you're likely to encounter."* As litigators get more senior they attend the firm's trial skills and trial academy programs – during the latter they receive *"deposition training with a mock client, which is very cool."* Over in CBT juniors attend *"weekly sessions, which are mandatory for first years. The firm also runs an M&A Academy throughout the year for all attorneys, which provides a more in-depth review of all aspects of M&A."* Every junior is also assigned a partner and an associate mentor, and praise was bestowed on ML's overall culture of *"mentoring, coaching and teaching. Partners take you under their wing. They don't want to get me out of their office as quickly as possible. They want to teach me why things need to be done a certain way."*

Culture & Offices

ML has a whopping 17 domestic offices and a further 13 overseas. The juniors on our list were spread over 13 of the US bases, from LA to Houston to Chicago to New York; the last of these housed the largest group (about a fifth of second and third years), while ML's Philadelphia HQ and DC office followed closely behind. As you might expect from such a large firm, sources reported some differences in atmosphere depending on the office. *"It's*

not formal or stuffy," a DC source stated, *"but at the same time it's certainly not casual and laid back – there are no jeans and polo shirts. It's a bit like a judge's chambers."* You may well find some jeans and polo shirts in San Francisco though, *"as we're a little more casual,"* while New Yorkers told us: *"Those negative connotations that Manhattan firms suffer from aren't present here. There are a lot of associates from different backgrounds and we're very welcoming. It's a respectful, professional place, and people will stop and ask you what you're up to and how that deal went – we're not looking to get away from each other!"*

"You won't get ahead by standing up and saying 'me, me, me, I did this!'"

In the Philadelphia HQ, associates felt *"the tandem package of ML and Philly is a really easy sell."* They drove home the *"tangible benefits of a city that's not New York, which has an insane cost of living! I feel able to work on my student debt, and potentially buy a house in the city within a couple of years of working."* The design of the office *"reflects the trust the firm gives us – we have actual walls and doors as opposed to those cool glass and steel structures, where everyone knows if you're not in your office."* With a more *"family-oriented"* workforce, younger associates did find the social scene here to be a little lacking, but *"there's a focus on creating a sense of community, so every other Wednesday there's an office-wide snack time – a chance for people to mix and mingle with colleagues you wouldn't otherwise encounter."*

Across office lines associates agreed that there's an overall *"culture of sharing credit. You won't get ahead by standing up and saying 'me, me, me, I did this.' It's clear the firm is geared around helping each other out, and we're very focused on producing an excellent product as a team."*

Hours & Compensation

ML doesn't have a billing requirement, but reaching 1,900 hours generates a bonus if associates are in good standing. However, given that this number was often described as *"very achievable,"* our sources had racked up more than this amount: *"My issue has been keeping below 2,200!"* exclaimed one corporate junior. The fact that all pro bono hours count as billable is *"really helpful for first years, as you can get yourself busy very quickly and let the regular client billable work build up more organically."* Juniors also told us that outside of the official parameters the extent of billing pressure can vary by office, as this DC-based source revealed: *"If you don't get 2,000 hours they're like 'why not?'"*

"My issue has been keeping below 2,200!"

See firm profile on p.671

The Inside View

Inevitably this means some tough schedules. Some litigators reported working consistent 12-hour days in the office (*"as I'd rather stick it out and then get out of here until morning"*), while a corporate junior highlighted that *"deal flow has been higher than it's ever been, which translates into long hours for everyone. I find solace in the fact that when I'm up late so is the client! The client has as much motivation to get it done."*

With this in mind, sources emphasized that ML *"realizes that it's an issue and works with us to make sure work-life balance is respected."* One *"really nice feature"* is a *"formal remote working program, where the firm helps you to set up a home office and allows you to spend two days each week working remotely."* Juniors must wait until their third year to sign up to the program, and we heard mixed responses from those who had: one praised it for being *"very flexible – at this moment I'm speaking to you from my home,"* while others felt that in practice *"it really just equates to one day working remotely."*

Pro Bono

Every full-time attorney is 'challenged' to rack up a minimum of 20 pro bono hours. *"If you don't you're not eligible for a full bonus, but everyone meets the challenge anyway and most do far more than that."* At the junior level, there were those who hadn't *"had time to invest much, but still cleared about 50 hours,"* while others had billed *"hundreds of hours – it's all counted the same as regular billables, so there's no reason not to do it."* The San Francisco office does *"a lot of guardianship and asylum cases, as well eviction defense work. We're also involved with Swords to Plowshares, which works with veterans to secure benefits."* In Philly, litigators were *"extensively involved"* in their pro bono matters, *"defending depositions and writing complaints and motions."* New Yorkers, meanwhile, had picked up matters through Volunteer Lawyers for the Arts.

Pro bono hours
- For all US attorneys: 101,870.8
- Average per US attorney: 62

"Find a law firm and practice that suits your intellectual passions. It's important for law students to figure out the type of environment they want, and choose a firm that aligns best with that. It's a tough profession. If you have an affinity for the work and the type of clients the firm represents, you'll have a much more fulfilling career."

– Wilson Sonsini managing partner
Douglas Clark

See firm profile on p.671

Morrison & Foerster LLP

Lawyers per state

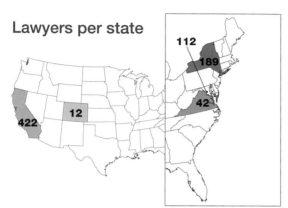

- 112
- 189
- 42
- 12
- 422

Largest US office: San Francisco
US offices: 8
International offices: 8
First-year salary: $180,000
Billable hours: undisclosed
Summers 2018: 86 (17 1Ls, 69 2Ls)
Revenue 2017: $1.06 billion (+12.4%)
Partners made in 2018: 7
Famous for: social justice pro bono; liberal attitude; tech smarts

For tech pro MoFo there's no such thing as a pro bono no-no.

THOUGH MoFo's amusing moniker actually hails from its abbreviated call name on a 1970s technology called 'teletype,' the firm's decision to keep it reflects a lot about the firm. Its website speaks of 'the MoFo mojo,' which associates described as *"a type of cool – we take our work seriously but we're not uptight. Everyone's down to earth while being amazing at what they do."* This is reflected in the firm's commitment to social justice through its women's rights and pro bono work.

Despite the firm's size, diversity in work and geographic spread, one thing that united all associates we spoke to was the fact that they'd been *"super busy this year."* We asked managing partner Craig Martin just why there's been so much going on at the firm this past year. *"It's a result of investments the firm's been making over several years. Different practices have yielded some very large matters – that has translated into associates being really busy on extremely interesting projects,"* he tells us. This flurry of activity has certainly paid off: MoFo recently posted a record revenue result and broke the billion-dollar mark in 2017.

MoFo's reputation for working with technology businesses is reflected in its client list: BlackBerry, Uber, Honda, Nikon and Yahoo! are just the tip of the tech client iceberg. The firm acts for businesses active in de-

veloping areas of technology and science all across the world, including booming markets in Korea and Singapore. Martin tells us: *"We really do think of ourselves as a technology firm. That is largely a reflection of the clients we represent. For example, we acted for Toshiba on the $18 billion sale of its memory card business. That was the largest private equity deal ever in Asia."*

MoFo unsurprisingly picks up *Chambers USA* rankings for its technology teams, as well as its intellectual property and privacy & data security groups. Other areas of note are finance, M&A, outsourcing, environmental law, government contracts and general commercial litigation.

The Work

Many new junior associates join litigation while a smaller but sizable chunk are in corporate. Some end up in finance and a few join tax. Work assignment is a casual affair. Assigning partners do exist, but not in all groups. Many associates in groups with a free-market system said that they'd prefer to have a more active assigning partner to turn to – *"it'd help level the playing field in terms of hours."*

Litigators, while generalists, can explore different subgroups: antitrust, employment, securities and white-collar, commercial litigation and IP litigation. Palo Alto focuses mainly on IP. Clients across litigation subgroups vary from Uber to big pharma to *"a case about barbecue sauce,"* but the main theme is that there are *"lots and lots of big tech clients."* One interviewee told us of their involvement in a case: *"I've been involved in drafting a motion to dismiss against a complaint, replies to summary*

On chambers-associate.com...

- Get hired at Morrison & Foerster
- Interviews with managing partner Craig Martin and chief legal talent officer Diane Cardona Downs

The Inside View

Rankings in *Chambers USA*

Antitrust	Labor & Employment
Appellate Law	Life Sciences
Banking & Finance	Litigation
Bankruptcy/Restructuring	Outsourcing
Capital Markets	Privacy & Data Security
Corporate/M&A	Products Liability
Environment	Projects
FCPA	Real Estate
Financial Services	REITs
Regulation	Startups & Emerging
Government	Companies
Intellectual Property	Tax
International Trade	Technology
IT & Outsourcing	Venture Capital

For detail on ranking tiers and ranking locations, visit
www.chambersandpartners.com

Recent work highlights

- Represented Paul McCartney in his lawsuit against Sony over copyright interests in Beatles songs including 'Yesterday', 'Hey Jude' and 'The Long and Winding Road'
- Represented BlackBerry in an International Trade Commission investigation that alleged that certain Android devices manufactured and sold by BlackBerry and other respondents infringed a patent owned by Singapore-based audio device manufacturer Creative
- Advised the Raine Group as financial adviser to Caesars Interactive Entertainment during its $4.4 billion sale of online casino games business Playtika to investors including one of China's largest gaming companies
- Advised Clean Energy Fuels on the $180 million sale of its renewable gas business to BP
- Acted for Toshiba in a $1 billion damages claim against Western Digital over interference in a deal to sell its chip unit

judgment and expert discovery." Then there's the typical junior associate legal research, memo writing and doc review which you'll find at any BigLaw firm, though juniors told us: "*It has taken up less time than I thought it would.*"

In corporate, juniors are split between the tech transactions, patents and general corporate subgroups (the last of these covers private equity, M&A and venture capital). In tech transactions, MoFo has "*clients ranging from multinational, multibillion-dollar corporations to startups that are just trying to get off the ground with a new app or gadget.*" Juniors draft development and manufacturing agreements as well as "*bigger asset agreements.*" The work is "*a roller-coaster – it's feast or famine.*" In the private equity and M&A practices, there's "*a very strong focus on energy and 90% of that is renewables.*" One associate elaborated: "*I enjoy working on renewable energy transactions, as it's for a good cause.*" Juniors can expect to "*help with anything from running diligence to drafting project contracts and purchase agreements.*" The big-name clients lawyers work with were seen as a bonus. "*I love working for a huge client that everyone knows about,*" one interviewee said. "*It's really cool!*"

Training & Feedback

For induction "*everyone comes to the San Francisco HQ and gets an intro to the mechanics of the firm*" – that's every new attorney from every office, worldwide. There are training sessions on practice area basics, communicating with clients and developing your own practice, as well as lots of socializing. "*It's a great opportunity – I met colleagues from the other side of country who I now work with regularly.*"

After the induction, first years get weekly mandatory training on practice area specifics such as discovery, responses to complaints and merger agreement clauses. Some juniors suggested that "*weekly training can feel like too much when you have a significant workload.*" Associates preferred on-the-job training: "*The best way to learn is to wait until the first assignment comes in and fumble your way through the dark till you get to the other side!*"

Pro Bono

"*Pro bono is a huge part of the culture here,*" interviewees agreed. Many associates we spoke to spent a quarter or a third of their time on pro bono. We even heard of one associate who billed 1,000 hours on a single pro bono case in a year – "*and it wasn't their only one!*" To get involved in pro bono all you have to do is "*say 'here are my interests' and the coordinator will find you something almost immediately.*"

"They practice what they preach when it comes to women's rights."

Work on offer includes immigration, veterans and housing cases. MoFo also takes on reproductive rights cases, including one case that aims to protect medics who work in abortion clinics. "*A lot of firms wouldn't take on such politically polarizing work,*" one interviewee observed. "*In a hostile political environment the firm's stepped forward to take a position. They practice what they preach when it comes to women's rights.*"

Pro bono hours
- For all attorneys across all US offices: 63,266
- Average per US attorney: 90

See firm profile on p.672

Diversity	Partners (%)	Associates (%)
Women	23.1	45.9
White	84.2	62.2
Black/African American	2.3	3.6
Hispanic/Latin American	4.2	4.9
Asian	9.2	23.9
Mixed/Other	0	5.2
LGBT	3.4	6.1

Culture

Many associates told us the emphasis on pro bono *"makes for a kinder culture."* The pro bono work reflects the culture at large – *"when we had the Northern California fires, the firm immediately decided to put together a handbook to help people affected who'd lost their homes. A whole bunch of people volunteered to write it and hand it out around California."*

Associates told us MoFo *"cares about our community. People here are focused on well-being and happiness."* Associates weren't shy to tell us about their political leanings either. *"We don't exclude non-liberal people,"* said a junior, *"but we do have a super liberal culture. That has to do with our roots in San Francisco, so for example we're very LGBTQ friendly and we have more of a startup mentality."*

Startup mentality? In a firm founded in 1883? This we had to hear more about. *"I wear jeans almost every day,"* said one interviewee in California. So far, so startup. *"The firm really cares about its workers and about being really relaxed and cool at the same time."* That fits the model too. And here's something else: *"I feel like it's a little bit quirky here. We're all very open with each other – we work together but we socialize together too. For example, we have a regular catered attorney lunch where people come together and converse about life and politics. That can get a little touchy, but luckily we're all pretty much on the same page politically!"*

Offices

At the time of our calls, there were a dozen or so juniors in the midsize offices in LA, DC and Palo Alto, with a handful in Denver, San Diego and Northern Virginia. Most associates were in the firm's two largest offices, New York and San Fran, which each had 20 to 30 juniors at the time of our research.

Despite being on opposite sides of the nation, one associate told us, *"the New York and San Francisco offices actually feel quite similar, which I wasn't expecting. For example, they're both in very modern buildings and really focused on sustainability."* This environmental focus is not surprising given the amount of work the firm does with sustainable energy clients. Associates were proud of their firm being *"super eco-friendly – we're encouraged to compost, recycle, print double sided."* It even affects the way electricity is used – *"the lights have sensors, so they'll shut off by themselves. Sometimes if I don't move for too long in my office, I have to move around to turn them back on!"*

> *"Super eco-friendly – we're encouraged to compost, recycle, print double sided."*

MoFo's biggest office is in San Francisco's financial district. As you walk in, there's *"an open space with loads of beautiful artwork,"* some of which is a bit… *"weird."* The conference rooms have *"amazing views of the Golden Gate Bridge and the city."* New York associates said that due to the firm's San Francisco origins, MoFo *"disrupts that reputation of what a New York law office is"* with its *"laid back"* feel. The DC office is apparently a little dated, so associates were excited about a planned move in 2020. *"Everyone is looking forward to moving into a space that's more designed for how modern law firms function,"* a junior said. Palo Alto associates described the office as *"like a little campus with a courtyard and pond in the middle."*

Diversity

MoFo was the first BigLaw firm to have an openly gay chairman – Keith Wetmore. Associates agreed in general that *"MoFo tries really hard, but it doesn't feel the most diverse place, that's for sure!"* Despite this, there are *"tons"* of affinity groups: 28 to be precise – for women, LGBTQ attorneys, people of color, working parents and veterans.

"Affinity groups do a great job of organizing community service events," a junior told us. One NYC-based group painted a mural in Hamilton Park. Other than that, affinity groups *"do lunches, grab drinks, and invite in motivational speakers and leadership coaches."* A few California groups for people of color *"put on an event where diverse people who own vineyards presented on how their companies succeed. And then we did some wine tasting!"* Every two years the firm invites its diverse attorneys to its 'Diversity Summit,' complete with lectures and schmoozing opportunities. Plus, there's a diversity and inclusion team that's *"very active: it checks up on people regularly."*

Hours & Compensation

MoFo's billing target is 1,950 hours regardless of office. Associates told us: *"It's easy enough to meet, as we've been pretty busy."* Everyone who hits 1,950 gets the same bonus, although *"there's also an additional payout for anyone who bills 2,500."*

See firm profile on p.672

The Inside View

It's pretty typical to work ten or 11 hours on any weekday, though when and where that gets done isn't particularly important. *"It's as flexible as possible for BigLaw,"* juniors agreed. Many work from home one or two days a week and we heard of departments where *"what's great is that most people don't come in on Fridays."* MoFo uses a system whereby lawyers accrue holiday entitlement: 15 days maximum for first, second and third years everywhere but New York, where they can earn 20.

"Every mom I know took their entire six months off. There's no stigma."

The flexibility for parents was noted across the board, with the parental leave policy extended further in 2017 to 20 weeks. *"This is why I love MoFo,"* shared one happy interviewee. *"You get six months' fully paid maternity leave."* You also accrue vacation days while you're on leave. *"What's notable is that pretty much every mom I know took their entire six months off. There's no stigma."* One associate told us: *"MoFo have recognized it's hard to keep women in BigLaw, especially moms. They're doing what they can to help that."* Reduced-hour schedules are available not only for parents, but any attorney at the firm.

Strategy & Future

The buzzword for MoFo attorneys in 2017 was 'busy.' *"It's been a good year for business,"* one associate observed. *"We've got a number of large clients who have significant cases, and some matters that have been going on for years are coming toward closing or trial."* Associates noted that the firm *"has placed a strategic priority on the renewable energy sector in particular,"* although they added that decisions made by the Trump White House could have an adverse effect on renewables growth.

Managing partner Craig Martin tells us: *"I'm hoping that the people who choose to join MoFo are going to find a firm that is in many ways very similar to the firm they're reading about now."* According to Martin that's a firm which *"continues to invest strongly"* to bring in the *"exciting deals and cases"* that currently come its way.

Get Hired

Words of wisdom from juniors included the recommendation to *"look for other experiences outside of law school that'll help you deal with the logistical and unexpected challenges that come up daily."* For more advice from MoFo's associates, go to chambers-associate.com

See firm profile on p.672

Munger, Tolles & Olson LLP

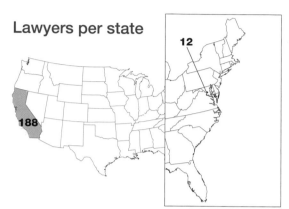

Lawyers per state

12

188

Largest US office: Los Angeles
US offices: 3
International offices: 0
First-year salary: $180,000
Billable hours: no requirement
Summers 2018: 20 (2 1Ls, 18 2Ls)
Revenue 2017: Undisclosed
Partners made in 2018: 6
Famous for: low leverage model; democratic processes; strong litigation offering; pro bono commitment

Lean staffing and a democratic approach are the big draws at this perky West Coaster.

THE reasons why juniors targeted Munger are pretty clear-cut: *"Two things stood out,"* one representative interviewee told us. *"The first was that the partner to associate ratio was pretty close to 1:1, which means that you get to work closely with the partners and have more client contact. The second was the overall culture of the firm: we are small and have a flat structure, which leads to democracy; associates get to vote on new hires and offices, for example, which is a pretty appealing prospect."* We'll delve further into how these two aspects influence the associate experience shortly…

In the meantime, let's return to this point about Munger's size. It is indeed quite small, clocking in at 200 lawyers spread across three offices in LA (the HQ), San Francisco and DC. The DC office, co-managing partner Sandra Seville-Jones tells us, *"was opened at the tail end of 2016 with former Solicitor General Don Verrilli. We are thrilled with how that office is starting to grow and it provides people who are interviewing with us opportunities to practice in three major cities."*

With regard to Munger's overall practice, Seville-Jones sees the firm's trial practice *"as our backbone; people know that we are willing to go to trial and that we're formidable*

opponents. We do also have a strong transactional practice, which is important as it enables us to be a full-service firm." Chambers USA reveals that litigation is certainly Munger's forte, with top regional rankings awarded to the firm's media, white-collar, securities and general commercial expertise. However, Munger's corporate/M&A know-how also picks up a high nod in Southern Cali, while its real estate and tax practices are acknowledged too.

The Work

Before they start, associates specify whether they wish to join Munger's litigation or corporate group. Most of the juniors on our list had pitched up in litigation, where they are assigned a specific partner to help them find work for their first six months. Once litigators get settled, a more free-market system reigns: *"You might get a random call from someone, or you might get offers from partners you've worked on successive cases with, or you can just ask partners to keep you mind if certain opportunities come in."* Juniors liked the system, but did flag that *"the hard part is finding the right balance and knowing how much is too much."*

Munger's litigation practice covers various areas, including antitrust, class actions, insurance, securities and white-collar. Juniors can remain generalists, but a few of our sources had *"focused in on a couple of areas."* Interviewees were pleased to tell us that *"this is not a place where people say 'first and second years can't do that.'"* So what does that mean in practice? *"Well, within*

See firm profile on p.673

Rankings in *Chambers USA*

Antitrust	Litigation
Appellate Law	Media & Entertainment
Corporate/M&A	Real Estate
Energy & Natural	Securities
Resources	Tax
Labor & Employment	

For detail on ranking tiers and ranking locations, visit
www.chambersandpartners.com

Recent work highlights

- Defended Warner Bros. and TMZ against a copyright infringement lawsuit brought by Sisyphus Touring – a company co-owned by Jared Leto – over TMZ's use of video footage featuring Jared Leto discussing Taylor Swift's music
- Representing Plains All American Pipeline during its defense against several class actions stemming from an oil spill off the Californian coast in 2015
- Acted for Bank of America during a case that questioned its role as a trustee of dozens of residential mortgage-backed securities (RMBS) trusts
- Continues to advise the Chan Zuckerberg Initiative (CZI) – a philanthropic company formed by Facebook's Mark Zuckerberg and his wife, Dr. Priscilla Chan – on various corporate matters

five months of being here I did my first deposition for a $900 million breach of contract case. I was deposing the individual at the center of the case." Our sources had still been *"doing the things that junior associates do, like coordinating discovery,"* but were able to *"spend the bulk of the time drafting substantive motions and having input during internal strategy meetings."* Plus, the amount of client contact is reportedly *"shocking: our case teams are small, so they trust us to give clients updates and there are opportunities to visit clients on-site."*

"I was deposing the individual at the center of the case."

Corporate newbies state whether they'd like to join corporate, tax or bankruptcy subdivisions, but we heard that there's still some flexibility to move between each strand. Those in the corporate group told us that *"it's a generalist practice, so juniors get a chance to do a bit of everything – M&A, capital markets, funds work, some corporate governance."* Clients vary from *"entertainment post-production companies to asset management firms to biotech names in Silicon Valley."* On the whole sources found that this group provides *"a good opportunity to get substantive associate experience mixed with standard junior work."* On the standard side there's due diligence, the preparation of ancillary documents and the requirement to *"keep track of everything."* The more substantive stuff ramps up in the second year, with one interviewee flagging their role as *"the lead associate on a deal, which enabled me to draft the main agreement."*

Culture

Many sources felt that Munger's *"low leverage, 1:1 partner to associate ratio"* had a significant influence on the culture. Working closely with seniors on projects *"translates into a level of comfort when it comes to more social interactions,"* juniors told us. *"The ratio has informal benefits, as we can all sit and have lunch, mingle, and not be divided by seniority."* Munger's collection of committees also dampen down the sense of hierarchy. There are committees devoted to many aspects of firm life, including policies, diversity and recruitment. Decisions are made via a show of hands that registers the approval or rejec-

tion of a certain proposal. *"The democratic process is absolutely fantastic,"* gushed one interviewee. *"As a first-year associate I was sitting on five of the firm's committees – all of which were internal governance ones – and I could say whatever I wanted, vote, and know that my voice was being taken seriously."*

"The democratic process is absolutely fantastic."

Juniors also suggested that Munger's low leverage attorney pool attracted *"people who are more independent"* and eager to take on responsibility early. In addition, *"we do draw in the kind of people that do clerkships – the type that see their career in law as an intellectual exercise. It is more of a cerebral firm in that respect, with people who like to discuss the issues and think through the challenges."* With a fair number of ex-clerks joining the ranks, Munger's incoming lawyers tend to be a bit older, *"and many people have families, so they have commitments that draw them away from work at the end of the day."* This doesn't bode well for a particularly buzzing social life, but sources generally felt that there was *"a happy medium"* at Munger: *"People can partake in as much as they like. There's no pressure to go and party at the end of the week."* Social activities include weekly 'sherry-sips,' bi-weekly lunchtime gatherings and an annual firm-wide retreat, which is typically held in Southern California.

Pro Bono

Does Munger support pro bono? *"Absolutely"* was the resounding answer from juniors. *"There's no cap on pro bono and it counts just the same as billable hours. It provides us with opportunities that are not always available from the work conducted for paying clients, so they encourage us to develop our skills and make a difference in the

Diversity	Partners (%)	Associates (%)
Women	24	45
White	82	70
Black/African American	0	6
Hispanic/Latin American	4	10
Asian	12	9
Mixed/Other	2	5
LGBT	2	9

community." Munger is one of the highest pro bono billers per attorney in our guide.

Munger has a longstanding relationship with KIND (Kids in Need of Defense), but we heard from associates who'd picked up work on behalf of various causes: some had taken on asylum matters, while others had clocked up hours on pro bono arbitrations and education cases *"which involved taking depositions and getting hands-on experience during a trial."*

Pro bono hours
- For all attorneys: 25,696
- Average per attorney: 135.5

Training & Development
Munger is *"definitely a place where you learn by doing,"* juniors revealed, highlighting the benefits of low leverage again: *"We have such easy and ready access to partners at the firm. I like knowing that they are directly reviewing my product, which allows me to learn from them and demonstrate that I'm growing as an attorney."*

Corporate juniors explained that *"having a formal training program is a bit much for just a small group of new starters,"* while litigators emphasized that there are still some sessions available to steer them in the right direction: *"Shortly after starting we did a day of training, which covered all aspects of litigation, like discovery and strategy, and since then we've had other sessions on briefs and depositions – within the first six months we probably do about 30 hours of formal training."* The firm also emphasized to us that it has been increasing the amount of formal training it offers.

Hours & Compensation
Munger doesn't impose any billing requirements or goals on its associates, who told us that *"people typically end up billing somewhere between 1,800 and 2,000 hours. There's not an expectation to go much over that, but if someone has a big trial they can shoot through to the mid 2,000s."* Base-level compensation is market-rate, but bonuses are

allocated based on each individual's contribution. Hiring partner Carolyn Hoecker Luedtke explains that *"there's no formula – bonuses are based on lots of things: somebody may have had a year where they billed an extraordinary number of hours, or they may have achieved an extraordinary result on a matter, or done something fantastic to contribute, like help to run the summer program – all of these things are recognized."*

"They trust people to do what works best for them."

"Compared to lawyers in New York, we have one of the more favorable work-life balances," interviewees also pointed out. Most of them got into the office by 9am and left by 6.30pm, and only logged back on at home *"if needed."* There are, of course, busy times: litigators had *"pulled a couple of all-nighters, but they're highly abnormal,"* while corporate associates reported being *"plugged in from home at 2am – clients expect you to be on call at all times."* Juniors did appreciate having the flexibility to work from home *"on days where you feel you'd be more productive doing so. Every lawyer here has their own way of doing the job, and they trust people to do what works best for them."*

Diversity
"We're not as diverse as we should be," associates concurred, *"but the firm is thoughtful in a way that reflects the very real problem of the lack of diversity in the profession."* Those thoughts do translate into action: *"During last year's 2L summer recruiting season we decided to switch to behavioral interviewing as it tends to do a better job of avoiding bias, and because we are smaller and have this democratic process we were able to get buy-in from the entire firm."*

Juniors can also volunteer to be part of the diversity committee, and some associates were part of a subcommittee focused on pipeline issues. For law students, Munger has a 1L diversity summer program and a diversity scholarship; pre-law students can participate in the MTO Fellows Program, which allows them to gain experience at the firm.

Strategy & Future
"All areas are going to receive attention," says co-managing partner Sandra Seville-Jones, who explains: *"We develop by looking at the issues that our clients face and by letting our lawyers pursue their interests in the law – if they have a passion they can take it and grow it."* She adds that Munger's *"entertainment practice and Silicon Valley-oriented work will be very important to the firm's future."*

See firm profile on p.673

Nelson Mullins Riley & Scarborough

Lawyers per state

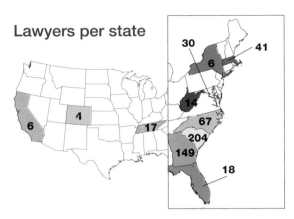

Largest US office: Columbia, South Carolina
US offices: 18
International offices: 0
First-year salary: $95,000 to $170,000
Billable hours: collections target (see hours & compensation)
Summers 2018: 48 (28 1Ls, 20 2Ls)
Revenue 2017: $405.4 million
Partners made 2018: 23
Famous for: friendly Southern vibes; collections goals

"Very transparent and calculated expansion" has helped South Carolina-born Nelson Mullins break the Am Law 100 for the first time in 2017.

IN 2017, Nelson Mullins joined the ranks of the top 100 US law firms. Its impressive 18.4% increase in revenue between 2015 and 2016 propelled the ambitious firm up 15 places, placing it at 88th on the coveted Am Law 100. Chairman Jim Lehman says: *"We feel like we were one of the best kept secrets in the Am Law200, so we're glad to see people can see what we've been doing and accomplishing for clients more now."*

Nelson Mullins' roots date back 120 years, to when founder Patrick Henry Nelson established the firm's current headquarters in Columbia, South Carolina. Today, the firm has done its share of growing: it maintains an extensive presence in its home state, but also boasts offices along the whole length of the East Coast, including the semi-recent addition of NY in 2015. Growth-mode didn't stop there, this time setting its sights further west with offices in Denver, and most recently in sunny LA. Juniors were attracted to the fact NM has *"complex and interesting work from prominent clients, but it's not based anywhere like New York or DC. It has a Southern personality which is conducive to people being friendly and not cutthroat."* In *Chambers USA*, the firm performs best in the Carolinas, particularly in corporate, litigation and environmental work.

On chambers-associate.com...

- Get hired at Nelson Mullins
- Interviews with chairman Jim Lehman and hiring partner Jim Rogers

The Work

The firm is broadly divided into litigation and transactional, then associates might work for a more specific team within that. Assignment varies somewhat between offices and practices, but more often than not there is an assigning partner/team leader. But assignment is still pretty fluid: *"Typically you start working with partners, who later ask you to get involved on projects. You have to check with your team leader on workflow and whether you have the capacity to take on that assignment."* Others described having a partner who *"manages our group, and as things are coming in he deals out the work according to who is busy and who isn't."* Juniors reckoned *"you're not micromanaged until things are overflowing."*

Just under two-thirds of the junior cohort can be found in litigation. General litigators could be *"working on a few different things at once on any given day. You get a broad exposure."* Areas that crop up a fair bit tend to include commercial, product liability, premise liability and professional negligence, among others. Other sub-teams within litigation specialize in areas such as complex contract litigation, employment litigation and regulatory. *"I've actually been most surprised at how hands-on it's been – I've been able to take leading roles in preparing depositions for important witnesses, and been in the room when they've been deposed. You're trusted to be client-facing, not just being kept hidden in the office."* Other junior litigators listed *"drafting documents like motions to dismiss and motions for summary judgment"* as well as research and initial case reviews. Some even mentioned *"getting to attend mediations and hearings, and sit second*

See firm profile on p.674

Rankings in *Chambers USA*

Corporate/M&A	Litigation
Environment	Products Liability
Healthcare	

For detail on ranking tiers and ranking locations, visit www.chambersandpartners.com

Recent work highlights

- Secured a number of trial wins on behalf of Bayer in a series of product liability cases alleging that a blood-thinning drug caused internal bleeding
- Served as discovery counsel in data breach multidistrict litigation for Anthem and 12 other companies facing over 100 putative class actions related a large cyberattack with extensive concurrent federal and state inquiries
- Represented Panera in a lawsuit against Papa John's International and a former employee for misappropriation of Panera's trade secrets and breach of contract regarding a noncompete
- Advising Compass Therapeutics, a startup life sciences company, on its intellectual property and patent prosecution strategy

chair for those." Sources admitted: *"Some assignments are more overwhelming than others, but at the end of the day I reckon I've had more experiences than associates at other BigLaw firms and I appreciate that."*

"I've actually been most surprised at how hands-on it's been."

Corporate takes the remaining third of juniors. Similarly to litigation, there are subgroups and teams under the wider corporate umbrella. *"A lot of them perform overlapping work, but it's broken down like that to manage people's workloads better,"* one interviewee reflected. Most groups do some form of M&A work (*"mostly mid-market deals"*) but there's also venture capital financing, preferred stock financing and debt financing. *"From day one, I had drafting responsibilities. I just expected to come in and do due diligence, but that wasn't the case."* Juniors initially drafted disclosure schedules, board and stock consents, and other ancillary documents. As associates progress, they can *"get more involved in drafting some of the main documents, like purchase agreements."* That's not to say associates never do due diligence: on larger deals, this is a common task for juniors, though as they move up, some third years have *"taken on overseeing and coordinating the due diligence."* Many agreed *"one thing I love about the firm is the high level of responsibility early on in our careers, especially in contrast to peers at larger firms, who still seem stuck in the back doing signature pages."*

Pro bono

"I haven't encountered a firm that is as committed to pro bono as Nelson Mullins," one source claimed. Any hours after 20 count toward an associate's billables: *"Other firms do pro bono, but we incentivize it – it makes sure people realize the importance of it."* Juniors got involved in a range of matters, including adoptions, disputes with landlords, domestic violence cases, appellate defense, veterans clinics and the unaccompanied minors project, to name a few. Pro bono clients are *"treated as paying clients – the firm dedicates a lot of time to it."* That said, some found *"it can sometimes be difficult, knowing big paying companies need stuff done too. Associates appreciate the commitment, but find it hard to balance it alongside the commitment to billable hours."* However, sources also found that their team leaders *"do a great job of helping us if we want to take on a project, and help guide us through it."*

Pro bono hours

- For all attorneys: 31,536
- Average per associate: 73

Culture

"I think because of its Southeastern roots, the firm has retained that Southern culture of friendliness and hospitality. We've not got so big that we've watered down our culture – we're not some faceless BigLaw firm." As a result, *"if you are a person who gets a bit too big for your breeches or you are disrespectful, you'll be rooted out very quickly."* More interviewees reckoned *"it seems very flat in terms of hierarchy. The firm has intentionally made sure everyone is equal. All the offices are the same size – it doesn't matter if you brought in $500 million or $10 million to the firm."* Although, be reminded this is still a law firm with partners leading it – some hierarchy is inevitable.

"One time we did a zip line."

"The firm is a place where everyone takes their work seriously, but not themselves." Beyond the obvious requirements to excel academically, juniors reckon the firm looks for *"people who would be pleasant to work with"* as well as those who can *"take initiative and seek out things beyond what is asked of them – someone who will go the extra mile."* Or as one source put it: *"We don't want a robot coming in."* Overall, the aim is to have *"someone who is presentable to a client, who works hard and enjoys what they do."*

Although associates are undeniably friendly and personable, many admitted that the social scene was a bit lacking. *"Initially we tried to organize monthly associate nights out, which we did for a while. But then I think everyone got super busy, and somewhere along the way we dropped the ball."* That said, juniors are eager to *"try and revive it."* The Atlanta office has *"an awesome rooftop terrace, stocked with wine and beer. On Fridays, attorneys can go up there*

See firm profile on p.674

Diversity	Partners (%)	Associates (%)
Women	22	44
White	94	78
Black/African American	1	8
Hispanic/Latin American	1	3
Asian	2	6
Mixed/Other	2	7
LGBT	1	2

and hang out." Other than that, there are regular events planned during the summer when summer associates are at the firm, which every attorney can attend. Examples have included baseball games, wine and beer tasting, and *"one time we did a zip line."*

Offices

Columbia and Atlanta are the biggest of the firm's 17 US offices. Its presence in South Carolina covers Charleston, Greenville and Myrtle Beach in addition to Columbia, while North Carolina offices cover Charlotte, Raleigh and Winston-Salem. Other offices across the US can be found in Boston, Denver, Huntington, Jacksonville, LA, Nashville, NY, Tallahassee and DC.

On top of the much-loved roof terrace, the Atlanta office boasts *"probably the best views in all of Atlanta."* Juniors also praised its location in Atlantic Station – *"well positioned to avoid traffic."* One slight problem some pointed out was space: *"We're expanding rapidly, so we're running out of space. I don't know what the plan is, but I heard we might be picking up another floor."* The Columbia office is *"right on Main Street"* in the top floors of a relatively new building.

Hours & Compensation

Nelson Mullins does things a little differently when it comes to hours. Instead of your traditional yearly billable hours target, attorneys at Nelson Mullins have a collection goal. In other words, *"at the end of the year you are judged by the amount you billed out to clients, and money actually has to collect to be eligible for the goal."* Associates have a 1,900-hour goal, then that multiplied by their rate is their collection goal.

"The compensation is a bit more like how partners are compensated."

According to juniors, this unique system comes with a number of both pros and cons. *"The compensation is a bit more like how partners are compensated. It makes more business sense to make sure the client pays, but then obviously if the client doesn't pay, you won't get your collection."*

Others reflected that *"in theory, if you bill 1,900 hours at your goal rate and every bit gets collected, you should surpass your goal. However, in reality that's not how it happens. It's a bit like communism – it sounds better in theory."* That said, some conceded that *"if you hit your collection target, you may well have worked fewer than 1,900 hours."* Corporate attorneys generally found it easier to hit their collection target as they have higher billable rates; however, they also admitted there was a higher chance compared with litigation that money might not collect.

Average day-to-day hours find associates getting in between 8am and 9:30am, and leaving the office anywhere between 6pm and 8:30pm. If busy that becomes *"drastically different."* When asked if there was much weekend work involved, juniors said: *"Not every weekend. Maybe a few hours on a Sunday once or twice a month."*

Get Hired

"I want to get to know the personality: why they want to practice, what their end game is, and whether they're enjoyable to be around." To find out more about interviews at Nelson Mullins, head to chambers-associate.com.

Training & Development

"We have an associates' committee training program that puts on seminars about twice a month. They are either practice area focused, or focused on how to be a successful attorney." These can cover topics from how to research effectively to how to bill your time. The firm also gives you billable credit for these sessions. *"I think the practice area ones are the most successful because they provide substantive help with actual day-to-day assignments."*

Diversity

"The firm acknowledges the issues with diversity and constantly works to improve it." Many expressed that diversity has been *"identified as a core value for the firm"* and that *"they're always look at recruiting diverse candidates."* Juniors felt the main issue was surrounding retention, especially of female attorneys. To tackle this, sources highlighted participating in a *"diversity panel that brainstorms ideas of how to better recruit but also retain diverse lawyers."* Another initiative is the women's leadership program – *"where equity partners take on the mentoring of a female partner to get them to equity partner."* There have also been Women and Business Development webinars, led by female partners, discussing what women need to do to garner more business. Nelson Mullins also offers a diversity scholarship to students from diverse backgrounds.

See firm profile on p.674

Strategy & Future

Juniors praised the firm's transparency when it comes to its strategy. *"The firm has done an excellent job of building organically, and building through smart business sense – not just for the sake of it. It's very calculated expansion."* Sources also highlight the firm's range of practices, meaning *"if one industry contracts a bit, the firm doesn't have all its eggs in one basket so we're not going to just collapse. Other areas of the business can pick up the slack."* Chair Jim Lehman adds: *"We feel like we're on a good path now. We'll likely continue to grow and continue with the strategy we developed ten years ago as it has continued to work well."* He speculates in saying: *"I expect we'll be larger, though I don't expect we'll be expanding internationally. We'll continue to grow domestically with additional lawyers and maybe additional geographies."*

"The greatest challenge is that the amount of money spent on outside legal services since the recession has not recovered from its pre-recession levels. The greatest challenge is therefore getting a bigger piece of what is for all intents and purposes a stagnant pie. Law firms, in my view, have to find where they are at the top of their game, find their niche and take more of the market share there. That's not to say that there are not great opportunities for great legal work; the legal issues facing clients are staggering, but law firms have to find their niche.

They are going to [specialize more] in the areas where there is a need for their services and where we as outsourced lawyers can bring value – not in areas where clients can keep it in-house. It's certainly going to be hard in this time of a stagnant legal market to be all things to all people – it's simply not cost effective."
– co-managing partner Susan Murley, WilmerHale

See firm profile on p.674

Norton Rose Fulbright

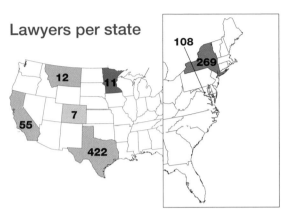

Lawyers per state

108
269
12
11
7
55
422

Largest US office: New York

US offices: 11

International offices: 47

First-year salary: $180,000

Billable hours: 1,800 client chargeable (New York and DC); 1,900 client chargeable (all other US offices)

Summers 2018: 83 (14 1Ls, 69 2Ls)

Revenue 2017: $1.958 billion (+16.1%)

Partners made in 2018: 10

Famous for: rapid expansion over the last eight years; global vision; projects, finance and energy expertise

Going global doesn't mean that you have to forsake an appealing culture, as ever-expanding NRF shows...

"IT'S been a big year," says US managing partner Daryl Lansdale, commenting on the events that have marked Norton Rose Fulbright's 2017. First came its merger with Vancouver's Bull Housser in January, followed by its headline-generating combination with New York-head-quartered Chadbourne & Parke in June, *"which expanded the New York and DC offices significantly,"* Lansdale tells us. *"We're now one of the top 25 firms in New York City by number of lawyers – 300 in total, which we're very proud of. Our US headcount has now increased to 1,000 lawyers, while we're at 4,000 globally."* But this combination wasn't just about numbers: synergies in areas like project finance, bankruptcy and white-collar investigations made the union particularly attractive.

"We remain the largest firm in the state of Texas."

NRF's appetite for mergers wasn't quite sated though: at the time of our call with Lansdale in late 2017, NRF was in the process of finalizing its tie-up with Australia's Henry Davis York. These mergers are just the latest in a long line of savvy additions that have propelled NRF's rapid ascent in recent years: in 2010, London-based Norton Rose kickstarted its strategy to become a major global

contender, and since then has drawn firms from Canada, Australia, South Africa and, of course, the US into its fold. The firm's global revenue puts it among the top ten, and its *Chambers Global* rankings say this is one of the world's most capable internationally.

The 'Fulbright' part of the equation arrived in the form of 2013's merger with Fulbright & Jaworski, which was especially known in Texas for its strengths in litigation. *"We remain the largest firm in the state of Texas, which continues to be a very important jurisdiction for the firm,"* Lansdale points out. Most of the firm's *Chambers USA* rankings honor its prowess in the Lone Star State, with top marks going to its antitrust, bankruptcy/restructuring and healthcare expertise. On a nationwide basis, NRF is rated highly for its projects know-how, especially in the renewable energy and liquefied natural gas spaces. The firm also picks up nods for its transportation, energy, international arbitration and tax practices.

Strategy & Future

"Our lawyers will continue to sell themselves not only as experts in law but in our clients' specific industries," says Lansdale. NRF's focus is on six key industries: financial institutions; energy; infrastructure, mining and commodities; transport; technology; and life sciences and healthcare. For more from Lansdale visit chambers-associate.com. On the domestic front, juniors relayed that *"traditionally we've been known as a Texas powerhouse, but we're very committed to growing our coastal presences in the US."*

On chambers-associate.com...

- Get hired: recruitment at NRF
- Interview with US managing partner Daryl Lansdale and hiring partner Doug Wabner

The Inside View

See firm profile on p.675

475

Rankings in *Chambers USA*

Antitrust	Intellectual Property
Banking & Finance	International Arbitration
Bankruptcy/Restructuring	Litigation
Corporate/M&A	Products Liability
Energy & Natural	Projects
Resources	Retail
Environment	Tax
Healthcare	Technology
Insurance	Transportation

For detail on ranking tiers and ranking locations, visit
www.chambersandpartners.com

Recent work highlights

- Represented the Ullico Infrastructure Master Fund as it acquired a portfolio of renewable energy assets including solar facilities in California and a wind farm in Oklahoma
- Acted for pharmaceutical company Boehringer Ingelheim during multidistrict antitrust litigation involving allegations of a pay-for-delay scheme over a generic version of a stroke drug
- Advised ROFIN-SINAR Technologies – a developer of laser-based components – on its $1 billion sale to US company Coherent
- Represented AWAS – one of the world's largest commercial jet aircraft leasing companies – during the purchase and leasing of various aircraft to major airlines in Latin America, North America, Asia and Europe

The Work

The second and third-year juniors on our list were allocated to a vast range of practices: 25 teams in total. The Chadbourne merger added considerable clout to the firm's projects and commercial litigation practices, which now join the corporate, M&A and securities group as the three most populated teams – together they account for just over 40% of the juniors in our sample. The method of work assignment depends on the team. In larger ones, like projects, *"there's a partner who's responsible for making sure people are busy, but we still follow quite a free-market approach – the onus is really on me to find deals."* In the smaller groups, some juniors got the bulk of their work from senior associates, while others were assigned to a *"main partner"* right off the bat, but still had freedom to pick up matters from others.

NRF's projects team housed the largest cohort of juniors. Sources here told us that the group *"predominantly represents lenders and sponsors in relation to secured transactions that require creative thinking."* Projects involving renewable energy sources like wind and solar power frequently crop up, and a few of our interviewees had been able to work on those tied to liquefied natural gas. *"They get you involved in a good variety of deals,"* said one junior here, who went on to explain that their role involved *"a mix of drafting and process management – you definitely need to keep organized! You're making sure that all the documents have been signed, that the borrower has met all of the conditions precedent, and that all of the parties have submitted everything in order to move the deal to a point where money can be lent."* What's the best thing about this practice?*"I enjoy my work because I get to see something that's good for society being built. It's nice to be able to help facilitate that infrastructure growth."*

"I've represented investors from Australia, South Africa and Canada."

The firm's commercial litigation practice covers many specialties, including antitrust, insurance litigation, healthcare disputes, trade secrets and class action defens-

es. Some of our sources had got involved in the team's data protection and cybersecurity work, which is *"a great area to practice in, as you gain expertise quickly; you're dealing with the same laws and regulations on a daily basis, and you have to be responsive – it's the kind of area where if a client calls because there's been a data breach you have to get on the phone with them immediately."* Clients across the team vary from *"proprietors to the biggest multinational organizations to our core oil and gas clients."*

"When I was in law school I thought that if you went to a big firm you'd be doing grunt work for years but that's not the case," one finance source told us. *"I get meaningful work and see it contribute to the final product."* In fact, juniors we spoke to across the firm's teams said that they'd experienced high levels of client contact – even in commercial litigation, where client interaction is usually harder to come by. Dealing with international clients and lawyers across NRF's global network is also a common experience, with interviewees in small transactional teams telling us that they'd *"represented investors from Australia, South Africa and Canada and built good relationships with the international offices. Part of the appeal of working here is having that coverage all over the globe."*

Culture & Offices

Of NRF's 11 US offices, only two – San Francisco and Minneapolis – had no second or third-year juniors at the time of our calls. The firm's Houston and New York offices tied when it came to taking on the largest segment of juniors, but DC and Dallas also took on a fair number. A few were working out of Austin, Denver, LA, San Antonio and St. Louis. *"We're seen as the home office for the US,"* those in Houston proudly told us. *"We're spread out over seven floors, and the offices are nice and new – there's been a significant investment in making the space more modern, and they've paid attention to design so there are quite a few open breakout areas where people can collabo-*

See firm profile on p.675

Diversity	Partners (%)	Associates (%)
Women	21	47
White	92	70
Black/African American	2	6
Hispanic/Latin American	2.5	6
Asian	3	12
Mixed/Other	0.5	6
LGBT	1.5	1

rate." New Yorkers also had *"no complaints"* when it came to their Midtown lodgings, which were perfectly pre-aligned for the merger between NRF and Chadbourne: both firms were already based in the same building, one on top of the other.

"...having genuinely nice people around makes all the difference."

That surely bodes well for cohesion, but on a broader level did juniors feel that there was enough intermingling between locations and practices? *"The firm does push a one-firm culture – particularly since the Chadbourne combination – and there is an emphasis on working seamlessly across offices,"* sources replied. Many did feel that they were very much part of a global firm, and echoed this junior in one of the smaller offices, who explained that they were *"on the phone with international offices daily – I definitely feel part of the bigger picture!"* On the whole, *"there are many programs and webinars that share information about the overall firm and support its 'one firm' methodology."* Interviewees also felt that NRF's strategy helped to foster cohesion *"as we're focusing on development by industry rather than practice, so we're bringing in people from different practice areas to concentrate on our six core industries."*

Beyond work, NRF runs a global charity initiative: *"The entire firm participates to raise money for a certain cause – this year it's the Nelson Mandela Foundation. We also participate in the MS 150, which is a charity bike ride between Austin and Houston; people from across the firm globally come to take part, and lawyers' families here in Texas host people."* That does make NRF lawyers sound like a very decent bunch of people, and our sources were quick to emphasize this: *"Generally our culture is shaped by the fact that we have really good people here – people who aren't jerks! It sounds simple but it makes coming to work so much better; we can have tough days and work late nights, so having genuinely nice people around makes all the difference."*

Training & Development

When associates first join, they attend a three-day orientation program in one of the larger offices, *"which covers training, but is also good for getting to know the other attorneys starting in your class."* Upon returning to their home offices, formal training continues via 'academy' programs tailored to litigators and transactional associates: *"We'll go through negotiation tactics, for example, as well as the business components of transactions."* Sources found these sessions *"most beneficial"* but just wanted them *"to last a little longer!"* Still, after the academies are completed, *"you can do CLEs at the firm's expense, so you can continue to develop your practice."* Our third-year insiders were also looking forward to attending one of NRF's 'international academies,' which bring together associates from across the firm at various points throughout their careers to attend sessions on the likes of networking, business development and leadership skills.

"It's a transitional time," said juniors when commenting on feedback. A new *"level system"* has been introduced, which will *"make formal feedback more extensive – they spent a lot of time earlier in the year explaining the experiences that are tied to each of the levels, but we're still not sure how everything will be factored in yet."*

Diversity

Several interviewees mentioned NRF's 2020 vision, which aims to create a 30% female partnership by – you guessed it – 2020. *"I've seen female representation improving at the management level and I've been impressed with what the firm's done so far. There's been a significant effort to invest in mentor/champion relationships as women progress into their sixth year and beyond,"* one source commented.

"...always working on new initiatives."

One Houston-based interviewee added: *"I'm diverse, and I feel very fortunate to look around and see that I'm on a par with other people."* Juniors also credited the firm's diversity director, *"who's always working on new initiatives,"* likeunconscious bias training, for example, *"which is a great step forward, as generally it's not something people like talking about, and it forces you to look at yourself and your behavioral patterns."* Praise was bestowed on NRF's support of its affinity groups as well: *"The firm has a budget for all of them, so we can get together on a quarterly basis and discuss what we see and what we would like to change."*

Hours & Compensation

At the time of our calls sources across the US faced a 2,000-hour billing target to qualify for a bonus; up to 100

See firm profile on p.675

hours could consist of a mix of pro bono and other approved non-billable work.Juniors found this target *"not easy, but achievable if your group is busy."* However, they also mentioned that the system was about to change: those in New York and DC will be aiming to hit 1,800 client-chargeable hours in order to be considered for a bonus (they will also be able to count up to 300 hours of credited non-chargeable hours toward bonus considerations); elsewhere, juniors will be shooting for 1,900 client-chargeable hours, and will be allowed to submit up to 100 credited non-chargeable hours to inform the bonus that they get. Credited non-chargeable work covers pro bono, as well as participation in the likes of diversity and inclusion, recruitment, mentoring and practice development activities. Check in with us next year to discover what juniors make of this new system. For now, *"people feel that they are fairly compensated and that the work-life balance here is reasonable; there are other firms that pay more and offer bigger bonuses, but they also expect a lot more from you."*

Pro Bono

"At the top level we have a pro bono committee, but each office also has a pro bono coordinator who organizes associates' participation," juniors explained. In Texas, juniors had picked up matters through the Houston Volunteer Lawyers service, and came to the aid of those impacted by Hurricane Harvey: *"We put in place this phone bank service called Legal Lines, which enabled our lawyers to give quick advice to people on things like housing issues."*

Elsewhere, insiders had worked on death penalty appeals, asylum cases, and name change matters for transgender clients – *"they're really great to do, and they're discrete so can be accommodated into your schedule easily."* Interviewees were also *"pleasantly surprised"* by the number of more corporate-oriented opportunities available, with some highlighting their experience drafting contracts for theater groups.

Pro bono hours
- For all US attorneys: undisclosed
- Average per US attorney: undisclosed

Get Hired

"We want lawyers with a global mindset because we're a global business with international and domestic needs," says US managing partner Daryl Lansdale. For more tips on getting an offer from Norton Rose Fulbright head to chambers-associate.com.

See firm profile on p.675

Nutter McClennen & Fish LLP

Lawyers per state

138

Largest US office: Boston
US offices: 2
International offices: 0
First-year salary: $160,000
Billable hours: 1,900 target
Summers 2018: 7 (1 1L, 6 2Ls)
Revenue 2017: $90 million (+0.7%)
Partners made in 2018: 4
Famous for: co-founded by pro bono pioneer Louis Brandeis; being a Boston bigwig; work-life balance

Bostonian through and through, sources went nuts for Nutter's work-life balance and 'tight-knit' environment.

CO-FOUNDED by pro bono pioneer Louis Brandeis, this Boston firm has stuck to its people-oriented roots. For a start, associates hailed how *"a good work-life balance is a clear part of the culture."* Then there's the firm's refined size. With 138 attorneys, Nutter promotes a *"tight-knit working environment. Younger associates spend a lot of time together outside of work – we're an intimate family."* Only a handful of juniors join each year, and this select group are told that *"the firm intends to make us partner some day. It's something the people of the firm care about. They invest in you and support you on that path from day one."*

But choosing employee-driven policies and a select class size doesn't mean the work's small-time. Nutter picks up strong rankings from *Chambers USA* in banking& finance, litigation and real estate, with further rankings in environment and labor & employment.

The Work

At the time of our calls, there were four junior associates in litigation, three in private client, two in IP, and one in both tax and corporate & transactions. In order to dish out work fairly, associates must complete weekly capacity reports to their department chair, *"saying if you*

On chambers-associate.com...

- Get hired: recruitment insight from hiring chair Christopher Lindstrom

have space for more work, or if you're totally maxed out." Associates are then assigned cases or deals. *"But as time passes you tend to get work informally through partners you've worked with in the past."*

Litigation is Nutter's largest department, spanning business and commercial, product liability, environmental, IP, white-collar, and employment and labor litigation. *"Though we're based exclusively in Boston, our client base isn't,"* said one junior. *"I'm working on cases that are Europe-based, Canada-based – all sorts."* Sources in this department were clear: *"Doc review is a big part of any junior associate's life! I do about five 20-70 hour doc review projects a year."* However, associates got their hands on more complex tasks too: *"I've done scheduling conferences and written motion arguments. If you've written the motion and helped prepare for it, you can go to court. You're involved fully in the case."*

The work in private client *"is about collecting assets, doing estate tax returns, then a lot of estate planning, tax planning and foundation work."* Clients are typically *"nonprofits, donor-advised funds, individuals and families. Clients stay with us their whole lives."* And, in a certain way, beyond it. *"When a client dies, we'll help the family deal with their affairs, administer estates, make filings – we get everything squared up so that the family can deal with part of the grieving process administratively."* Associates were involved everywhere, *"having all types of correspondence with clients, including personal meetings. You develop relationships with partners' clients and become a point of contact. You never have the same day twice."*

See firm profile on p.676

The Inside View

Rankings in *Chambers USA*

Banking & Finance	Litigation
Environment	Real Estate
Labor & Employment	

For detail on ranking tiers and ranking locations, visit
www.chambersandpartners.com

In the smaller departments, associates were keen to tell us they still felt like *"an integral part of the firm."* Corporate & transactions associates begin their experience *"doing any type of corporate work that needs to be done."* The department handles regulatory work, M&A, and banking and finance (including work with startups), so there's plenty to cover. Meanwhile, IP associates waxed lyrical about getting face-time with clients. *"I like working with more sophisticated, diverse clients. Being in Boston our clients include large biopharma companies, research institutions and startups which have spun off those institutions."*

Pro Bono

"Nutter's history is rooted in pro bono work," said associates. And it's true: co-founder Louis 'The People's Lawyer' Brandeis helped to start the pro bono tradition in the US. Flash forward 140-odd years and you'll still find that *"Nutter takes pro bono very seriously. You can count unlimited pro bono hours toward your billable total."*

Nutter is heavily involved with the charity KIND (Kids in Need of Defense), which *"represents undocumented minors to make sure they're not deported. The organization shares our office space, so we can walk over to them and ask questions. It's really convenient."* Associates are *"encouraged to be proactive in bringing opportunities to the attention of the firm. Everyone's free to pursue whatever projects they're interested in."* And sure enough, during our research we heard about one pro bono pro (a junior associate) formulating a pro bono relationship with the New England based AIDS Action Committee.

Pro bono hours
- For all attorneys: 7,490
- Average per attorney: 53

Offices

Aside from the Boston office, Nutter has a much smaller office in Hyannis, though associates rarely visit. The HQ is found in Boston's seaport district, *"a pretty trendy up-and-coming Boston neighborhood. There's construction everywhere and a ton of restaurants – seemingly every day a new building pops up! It's a great neighborhood to work in."*

Recent work highlights

- Advised the Massachusetts-based Commerce Bank and Trust Company on its acquisition by Berkshire Hills Bancorp, a deal valued at $209 million
- Represented Fidelity Bank in connection with government and internal investigations, plus a multidistrict class action, all concerning Telexfree, and the alleged $3 billion international pyramid scheme
- Worked with Northeastern Retirement Services on its acquisition by the bank holding company Community Bank System, in a deal valued at $140 million
- Represented the City of Haverhill, Massachusetts, on the closure of a landfill and the permitting process for the development of solid waste and organic waste management facilities

"My office and the managing partner's are the same size."

Attorneys' offices are the same size for everybody, from junior associates to the managing partner. *"There's no large corner offices for partners. My office and the managing partner's are the same size. The office is a physical manifestation of the attitude that we're all equal. It shows that they're putting a lot of faith and respect in you."* Still, partners do get one bonus. *"They often have the water view, so they get that little perk!"*

Culture

Many associates couched their experiences in terms of the Nutter 'family,' telling us: *"Literally when you walk through the door, you get the sense of a family environment. Everyone's proud of and invested in the firm."* Unlike firms with legions of faceless associates, Nutter's compact size means *"you get to know people very quickly. It's such a comfortable place to work – people appreciate your opinion from the beginning."* Another associate believed *"it's not an environment where you should feel intimidated to talk to the big partner in their big chair. You can walk up to the managing partner and ask silly questions – I ask her about 20 questions a day!"*

"People appreciate your opinion from the beginning."

Like the best of families, Nutter ushers in the holidays together; the office conference center is furnished with decorations, and an open bar is provided. There's also an annual associate reception with *"a band, beer and excellent food. It's only for associates, so you can let your guard down a little bit."* More regularly, free doughnuts (in the morning) and pizzas (in the evening) are distributed on Wednesdays – these help to nudge associates over the midweek hump. *"If you have to work late, you try and*

See firm profile on p.676

Diversity	Partners (%)	Associates (%)
Women	25	59
White	97	70
Black/African American	0	10
Hispanic/Latin American	3	5
Asian	0	5
Mixed/Other	0	10
LGBT	1	2.5

make it a Wednesday!" If that weren't enough, there are 'Wine Down Thursdays' where the firm *"sets out wine and cheese – we unwind and get ready for Friday."*

Diversity

Associates found that *"Nutter is an inclusive place, but the numbers don't reflect that. They do a good job with associate gender diversity, but racial diversity needs work."* Hiring chair Christopher Lindstrom tells us: *"There is a great deal of progress that needs to be made – that's true for Boston as a whole and it's true for us. We place great emphasis in terms of hiring and hosting diversity and inclusion events, and working with the area law schools."* On that front, associates mentioned *"a speaker series which works with local law schools, doing talks on topics affecting communities of color. We had the first African American woman to serve on the Supreme Court of Massachusetts speak!"*

Another positive was the tenure of managing partner Deb Manus. *"I take a sense of pride in knowing my firm has a female managing partner because it's so rare,"* said one interviewee. *"It's a badge of pride the firm wears."* However, one female partner doesn't tell the full story. *"One of the issues is the amount of women at the equity partner level. There needs to be representation across the board."*

Training & Development

Associates' training begins with the aptly titled 'Nuts and Bolts' program: *"Six or seven sessions on different topics – written discovery for example."* One source described how *"as a junior associate you can feel like there's information overload, so breaking it down this way is really helpful."* Nevertheless, some associates felt that *"there should be some more training to communicate the expectations for junior associates."*

"They think you'll become a partner."

Meeting those expectations gained importance since *"when the firm hires associates it's because they think you'll become a partner."* That opportunity is, of course, a mas-

sive positive. *"They invest in every associate here,"* was a common refrain, backed up by the firm's mentoring program. First years have partner and associate mentors, and second years, a partner mentor. *"Me and my mentor went for lunch every month like clockwork,"* said one junior, but many more found frequent everyday interactions with *"aware and willing"* partners just as valuable.

Hours & Compensation

Nutter's billable hours target is 1,900, plus an additional 100 hours of *"firm commitment hours: networking, training and pro bono."* Interviewees agreed that *"associates, and especially juniors, don't hit that target. You shouldn't feel stressed about that. If you do hit it, people are impressed. It's a big achievement."* The private client department regularly clocks in at 7:30am – *"our clients are older and they wake up early!"* – but average hours among interviewees settled around 9am-6pm, with *"people often logging in for a couple hours once they get home."*

To that end, associates spotted a *"trend toward more flexible working."* On offer there's a policy to work one day a week from home, or an 80% reduced-hour schedule. *"It doesn't impact your career – I know people have been elevated to partner while on an 80% schedule."* Interviewees continued to advocate Nutter's work-life balance by telling us: *"Weekend work is very rare. In three years I've only worked two weekends."* The snag? A salary that dips below the $180,000 benchmark. But associates opined: *"I understand we're not going to be at market – we chose to have a life outside of work."*

Get Hired

"I'm looking for people who hold up a great conversation, with curiosity and intellect," says hiring chair Christopher Lindstrom. For more on the firm's approach to recruiting, and advice on getting hired, head to chambers-associate.com

Strategy & Future

"We're always looking at our alignment to our economy and the world," says Nutter's managing partner Deborah Manus. *"For example, we recently welcomed Seth Berman as a partner to lead our privacy and data security practice. There isn't a client anywhere that doesn't care about data privacy."* Manus also points to recent growth in the firm's banking and financial services, IP litigation and real estate practices. With regard to the latter, Manus explains: *"There is a tremendous amount of real estate development happening in Boston right now. The city is literally rising all around us. Our robust real estate practice covers all phases of permitting, financing, leasing and development."*

See firm profile on p.676

O'Melveny & Myers LLP

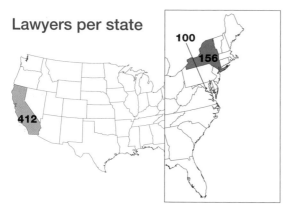

Lawyers per state

100
156
412

Largest US office: Los Angeles
US offices: 7
International offices: 8
First-year salary: $180,000
Billable hours: undisclosed
Summers 2018: 80 (4 1Ls, 70 2Ls, 6 other)
Revenue 2017: $738 million (+1.8%)
Partners made in 2018: 6
Famous for: being LA elite; litigation prowess; Sopranos mention

O'Melveny's star-studded clientele draws associates in, and its sunshine culture keeps them there.

OF all the issues making waves in 2018, the #MeToo movement must be among the most talked about, and, hopefully, consequential. From a business perspective, revelations about the behavior of powerful men have sent company boards and shareholders into a spin. To regain some semblance of control, law firms are brought in as a steadying hand, to conduct investigations. So it is that litigation expert O'Melveny & Myers was called upon, not for the first time, to manage a high-profile situation. When Paul Marciano, chairman of clothing brand Guess, was called out by model Kate Upton in allegations of sexual misconduct, O'Melveny was hired to head up the company's probe.

Look elsewhere, and you'll find O'Melveny intervening in cases, and deals, of a similar stature. The firm was chosen as lead trial counsel to defend the huge $85 billion AT&T-Time Warner merger from a DOJ attempt to block it (President Trump had vowed to halt the deal during his presidential campaign).

This headline-grabbing work is the tip of an O'Melveny iceberg: the firm has fifteen offices across three continents, but its roots go deepest in the Golden State. It has five offices there, including the HQ in downtown LA. The firm's best *Chambers USA* rankings come in California

nia too, and a notable ranking in capital markets demonstrates why O'Melveny's growing transactional work shouldn't be ignored. On that front the firm recently bagged three M&A partners in Century City.

The Work
The balance among juniors is roughly 70:30, litigation to transactional. For the first two to three years, litigation associates are unassigned, *"floating from one practice group to another based on your interests."* A work coordinator is on hand in each office, but associates could also find work in a more free-market way. Most associates were happy with the co-existence of these two systems. *"I knew I didn't want a firm where it was all informal. That scared me – what if people don't like you? I liked the availability of that formal channel."*

Litigators had worked on white-collar and investigations, securities litigation, bankruptcy, antitrust and general commercial litigation, seeing matters focused on food and beverages, sports, oil and energy, media and entertainment and more. *"At the junior level you get the opportunity to experience and develop familiarity with a whole bunch of litigation sub-genres and I think that is very helpful."* And right from the off, associates are thrown into the thick of it: *"My very first day they assigned me to a ten-week antitrust trial. It was an incredible opportunity for my first day of work to go to court. That said, those ten weeks were the hardest I've worked in my life, so it balances out."*

On chambers-associate.com...

- Learn how to get hired from O'Melveny's hiring partner Allen Burton

See firm profile on p.677

Rankings in *Chambers USA*

Antitrust	Intellectual Property
Appellate Law	International Trade
Bankruptcy/Restructuring	Labor & Employment
Capital Markets	Litigation
Employee Benefits &	Media & Entertainment
Executive Compensation	Products Liability
Environment	Projects
ERISA Litigation	Securities
Insurance	Tax

For detail on ranking tiers and ranking locations, visit
www.chambersandpartners.com

Recent work highlights

- Acted for Donald Trump and Trump University in two class actions brought by former students seeking payment refunds
- Represented Disney in a copyright dispute over the animated movie Zootopia
- Acted for Fox in its claims accusing Netflix of poaching Fox executives
- Represented Goldman Sachs in its underwriting of a $1.7 billion public offering by biotech company Thermo Fisher Scientific

Associates by and large felt integrated: *"On a white-collar matter, I'm the second most junior person on a team of seven, but one of the partners running that will routinely call me or swing by my office to hear what I have to say. If I pitch an idea he gives me credit. I feel as though I'm a full member of the team."* With that, came client contact for some: *"I was asked to put together a PowerPoint for a big client from overseas, and to present it!"* Instead of heaps of doc review, juniors find themselves tasked with *"making sure we don't miss deadlines on a case, making sure partners know what's coming up, and keeping track of documents. I routinely draft documents and send them to a partner who will edit it. Because partners have a number of cases they won't know the case in such detail – but I need to."*

"You're reading talent agreements of actors whose work you might enjoy."

On the corporate front, the firm recently began putting associates into groups when they join, *"but it's not rigid. I can still take on assignments from other groups. The firm recognized some people in corporate didn't get the training experience that was necessary to progress as fast in departments with very specific skills."* Groups include M&A, finance, project finance and development, and capital markets. But some did feel constrained: *"I mostly do capital markets and not necessarily because I picked it, it's sort of where I got stuck. I wish I'd had more opportunities to try other groups and work with different people."* Associates working on M&A *"had to do a lot of diligence. We do a lot on the buy side so we look into the company that the client would be buying and make sure there are no hidden risks to help make sure the transaction will go smoothly."* Entertainment deals make this less dull: *"You're reading talent agreements of actors whose work you might enjoy."* In capital markets matters, an associate recalled *"keeping tabs of the progress of the transaction. I'm the one making sure everyone knows what stage a document is at at any given time. I'm like a mini-manager. On smaller transactions they're keen to make your training as fast as possible – I've talked to clients, taken a first stab at drafting some sections, and researched compliance on an IPO."*

Training & Development

New associates get an overview of the firm basics at an orientation, which is followed by a 'Global Academy' program. We heard that due to different start dates for incoming juniors, there can be a bit of a delay between the orientation and the academy for those who join earlier – not that our sources seemed to mind too much: *"I think it would have been hard for them to put us through months of training straight away, so I'm glad it was staggered, but it did give you an 'oh my gosh I don't know what I'm doing' feeling for a while."* Annual reviews include a self-evaluation, and then, *"every couple of years associates get to review partners anonymously. Consultants come in for detailed interviews with the associates to get feedback on what's working, and what's not. That's really valuable."*

Juniors are assigned two mentors – a partner and an associate. *"I feel more comfortable going to my associate mentor with day-to-day questions like, 'When is it too early to take vacation?' My partner mentor's role is to make sure I'm getting to do things I want to in my career. I can ask, for example, 'How can I take a deposition? Have you heard of any cases I could get on?'"* And associates receive other opportunities to rub shoulders with partners in the 'take a partner to lunch' program: *"Any associate can take any partner to lunch once a month."* Play your cards right and it can lead to work: *"There's a partner who works on investigations I'm interested in, so I asked them to lunch and asked about cases. They had a new investigation, and I got on it."*

Get Hired

Associates told us: *"We want someone who can lead but not someone who's gonna plow through while they're leading. We don't even have partners like that."* For insight on the recruitment process from hiring partner Allen Burton, head to chambers-associate.com

See firm profile on p.677

The Inside View

Diversity	Partners (%)	Associates (%)
Women	20.5	48.1
White	88.9	72.6
Black/African American	2.6	3.1
Hispanic/Latin American	1.1	6.3
Asian	7.4	13.6
Mixed/Other	0	4.4
LGBT	3.2	5.6

Hours & Compensation

At the time of our calls some sources were a bit hazy about how many hours they should be aiming to bill each year, but the firm recently made it clear that 1,900 is the target to shoot for. Fortunately, this number didn't fill our interviewees with apprehension: *"I've exceeded 1,900 in the two years I've been here."* Associates who *"demonstrate a superb quality of work are also eligible for a merit bonus."*

"Since I've been here – over a year – I really haven't had any down months."

Tough schedules were more of a pressing concern: *"Since I've been here – over a year – I really haven't had any down months. It's good in the sense that if the firm is busy, time passes really quickly, but of course nobody would complain if we could have long lunches for a week."* In saying that, associates felt those in charge did what they could to alleviate the pressure: *"Managers try hard to organize work so that it doesn't bleed into evenings unless there's an unexpected rush. I had concert tickets last week and I told people I really wanted to go. There was no pushback."* Similarly, associates' vacations weren't disturbed: *"I remember responding to a few emails in the first year and getting angry emails back saying, 'You're on vacation!'"*

Culture & Offices

Despite demanding hours, associates underlined the fact that *"although people get stressed, no one makes other people feel anxious. One assistant has been here for 35 years and that's not an aberration. You wouldn't work here for 35 years if there were screamers."*

The O'Melveny culture isn't far off the laid-back vibe its California home is famous for, and associates choroused: *"This is really where O'Melveny shines."* For starters, juniors felt they could make connections. We heard of junior buddies skiing together, and *"frequently having wine in somebody's office on Friday evenings. When you're doing some difficult work, it's great that you have people you can commiserate with."* Furthermore, *"everyone sees themselves as a mentor to everyone more junior than them. I see myself as mentor to first-years."* Having said that, *"everyone is pretty assertive and independent – they'll be able*

to figure out how to get something done without completely relying on other people."

Step inside the *"boisterous"* 'mothership' office in downtown LA, and you'll find *"people telling jokes and walking around chatting. On Fridays there's a farmer's market across the street, so partners knock on doors to grab lunch and you get a train of people getting food together."* A highlight is the associate and counsel lounge, *"with couches and games, a foosball table, a basketball game, and there are some snacks and drinks. I just wish there were more opportunities to use it!"* A short drive away in the Century City office, associates here were just as proud of the culture: *"We're hard-working but laid-back, and conscious of community: we have a policy in several offices whereby if we donate to charity then we get to wear jeans."* O'Melveny also has offices in New York, San Francisco, Newport Beach, Silicon Valley and Washington, DC.

Diversity

Associates were keen to tell us about O'Melveny's annual Diversity Day, an event *"celebrating the diversity of the firm. You're meant to express your own diversity, so one year everyone was asked to submit a photo of themselves showing something colleagues might not know about you. I found out one was an avid hunter, and one assistant grows prize-winning tomatoes."*

"There are, like, 10,000 affinity groups!"

Associates could readily relay the firm's multitude of diversity programs, and their involvement with them. *"There are, like, 10,000 affinity groups!"* exclaimed one excitable associate. That may be a slight exaggeration, but we heard of a women's affinity group, a Jewish lawyers group, a Persian group, a Catholic lawyers group, an Asian-American group, a Hispanic group, an African-American group, and an LGBT group. To give one example of these groups' activity, the latter *"works closely with LGBT groups at local schools. We have a scholarship program at USC Gould law school."*

Pro Bono

"One of my favorite things about the firm is that pro bono is counted one-for-one toward the billing target, and legitimately encouraged. It's not something we play up to Chambers Associate to make us look good!" That's us told then. There's no cap on pro bono, and some sources had clocked 200 hours in a year. Associates are free to seek out their own pro bono work but there are also two pro bono counsel (one in New York, one in LA) and a dedicated partner to help distribute matters. We heard about projects with environmental and civil rights groups, and associates were dazzled by the court time and writing

See firm profile on p.677

experience available. Highlights included "*doing an entire deposition by myself for seven hours*" on an immigration case, and "*a handful of cases representing LGBT organizations, in response to various state laws aimed at restricting rights for LGBT couples and individuals.*"

Pro bono hours
- For all US attorneys: 72,092
- Average per US attorney: 118

Strategy & Future

The headline-grabbing work at O'Melveny is no accident. "*We like to be in play for those very attractive, top matters. We want to be tapped to try these major cases, and work on cutting-edge deals,*" says firm chair Bradley Butwin. And that means identifying the hot new areas of work. "*We recently formed a dedicated fintech practice advising early-stage companies and investors on regulations. We have quickly built up teams in areas of demand – we're looking to build upon our strong healthcare, trial and cybersecurity practices too.*" The firm also recently added a sports team.

But, above all, Butwin says, O'Melveny's strategy is client-driven: "*We've got a very loyal and dedicated group of clients who come back to us again and again and our goal is to make sure we continue to stay on top of their needs and grow with them.*" That informs a reserved attitude toward expansion too. "*The firm's goal is to be in practices and locations where clients need us, as opposed to pursuing a 'plant the flag' strategy.*"

> *"Brexit seems to have settled down in terms of the way it affects us in the States, and the cross-border work between Europe and the US. Initially everyone was like "what's going to happen?" and running around with their hair on fire. My impression is that we don't know what's going to happen so we better just get on with life. We've been spending a lot of time with big financial institution clients doing planning. Other clients have said that once there's more clarity on what's going to happen, they will adjust accordingly."*
> – Freshfields US regional managing partner Peter Lyons

See firm profile on p.677

Orrick, Herrington & Sutcliffe LLP

Lawyers per state

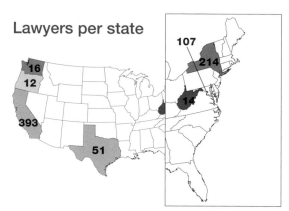

Largest US office: New York
US offices: 12
International offices: 13
First-year salary: $165,000 - $180,000
Billable hours: no requirement (2,000 encouraged)
Summers 2018: 64 (10 1Ls, 53 2Ls, SEO 1)
Revenue 2017: $975 million (+4.9%)
Partners made in 2018: 15
Famous for: being from California; tech and startup clients

This colossal Californian offers an eclectic range of services to techies, financiers and oil giants alike.

ORRICK may not have the disruptive power of an Uber or an Airbnb but it definitely likes to help businesses that do: Microsoft, Apple, Pinterest and Netflix have all sought Orrick's services. Alongside its core strength in the technology market, the firm focuses on finance and energy & infrastructure, with Credit Suisse, Wells Fargo and Chevron all on the client list. In line with its West Coast origins the firm also has something of a reputation for being a bit more laid back (for BigLaw), which drew in a few of the associates we spoke to. Sources said that *"people are understanding of the fact you want to have a life outside of the office"* and said there is a *"change in culture"* taking place, with an effort being made to *"encourage working from home and agile working."*

The current plan hardly seems to be hurting the firm. Across its 12 domestic and 13 international offices Orrick pulled in $974.6 million in revenue in 2017. *Chambers USA* awards the firm rankings for an array of practices, including top marks for appellate law, projects and energy across the US and recognition for areas including capital markets, intellectual property, and work for startups.

The Work

Orrick's juniors are spread across the firm's eclectic mix of practice areas. Litigation takes in most followed by technology, energy, intellectual property, public finance, supreme court & appellate and real estate. Banking & finance, corporate and white-collar litigation had just a couple of juniors at the time of our research. Most juniors enter the New York, DC and San Francisco offices, with a few each year joining the smaller offices in Silicon Valley, Houston, Sacramento, Orange County and Seattle.

Across offices work is typically handed out by a coordinator, though the degree to which juniors' work streams are determined by the coordinators varies. For example, litigators found that it's *"a very controlled system so you don't have to go around asking for work,"* while those in the Supreme Court appellate practice reported *"a volunteer system where matters are circulated so people can do stuff they're interested in and the work is distributed fairly."* Technology juniors experienced *"an informal system in which you get about 80% of your work from partner mentors. It helps to be a self starter as there's no platform you can pull assignments from."*

"It's fun to dig into the legal questions and learn new things."

Orrick's supreme court & appellate group is spread across San Francisco, New York and DC, though *"casesare staffed across locations so your physical placement is irrelevant."* The team represents the mighty of the financial

On chambers-associate.com...

- Get Hired: interviewing at Orrick

See firm profile on p.678

The Inside View

Rankings in *Chambers USA*

Antitrust	IT & Outsourcing
Appellate Law	Labor & Employment
Banking & Finance	Latin American Investment
Bankruptcy/Restructuring	Litigation
Capital Markets	Native American Law
Corporate/M&A	Products Liability
Employee Benefits &	Projects
Executive Compensation	Real Estate
Energy & Natural	Startups & Emerging
Resources	Companies
Insurance	Venture Capital
Intellectual Property	

For detail on ranking tiers and ranking locations, visit www.chambersandpartners.com

Recent work highlights

- Helped Wells Fargo restructure Chesapeake Energy, the largest natural gas producer in the US
- Defended Netflix in a spat with Fox where the latter is trying to sue the former for allegedly stealing staff
- Represented Billy Bush during his exit negotiations with NBC after he was suspended from the Today show following his appearance in the infamous Access Hollywood tapes with Donald Trump
- Helped Pinterest acquire search engine Jelly in a deal worth $1.14 billion

and tech world tackling *"the biggest and most important legal questions. It is all very interesting and relatively high-level as cases are at the appeal level."* Juniors *"research and draft a litany of briefs. One recent example was a lengthy memo evaluating the weaknesses of the legal theories the government was relying on."* Juniors even sometimes get to draft entire briefs. *"It's fun to dig into the legal questions and learn new things, but there is a bit of a learning curve. I have not yet had time to obtain relevant background knowledge on all the areas of law I am doing research on."*

Litigation clients include *"financial institutions, telecommunication businesses and consumer products firms"* like Citigroup, Hemlock Semiconductors and PayPal. Juniors get to explore various areas, which *"is a good way to take some control. For example, I don't particularly like white-collar work but I don't have to take any on."* Juniors work on discovery, *"handling case development, getting documents produced and reviewing what has been done so far,"* but the work gets *"really exciting when you are putting together a cross-examination during a trial."*

The Technology Companies group handles corporate work for tech companies – *"everything from setting up companies to taking them public, securing them financing, helping them manage their board and merging them."* Juniors spend their time *"responding to emails, reviewing documents and negotiating deals."* The firm works with startups and recently founded businesses like 23andMe and Stripe, so juniors may find them directly opposite clients providing advice. *"You could be talking a founder through a difficult situation or producing a capitalization model in Excel,"* a junior reported. Given the financial bent of the work, *"it's hugely helpful being numerate. Associates have an easier time if they can make their way around an Excel spreadsheet."*

The energy & infrastructure team handles two types of matters. Public-private partnership work involves *"repre-*

senting either a developer partnering with a public entity or vice versa to get the tax benefits needed for a project like an airport, bridge or tunnel."* Then there is more *"traditional"* project finance and energy work. Juniors spend their days helping partners turn agreements. One explained: *"I go into the document, make the first edits and send them to the partner. Sometimes I send it back to the client or I take questions from opposing counsel."* Those hoping for an easy ride, be warned! Sources found it *"a hell of an experience: you have to learn a lot quickly and are always kept on your toes. The hours can be brutal: you can spend nights working until 2am busting your ass. You have to do that to get the right experiences to develop."*

Training & Culture

While opportunities will come at you thick and fast, Orrick's management wants associates to take up those experiences which suit them best. 'Chart your own course' is the big strapline on its careers web page. In this vein the firm has what it calls a 'Talent Model' career development program, which essentially gives associates the freedom to move more quickly up the career ladder if they perform exceptionally. In practice, associates thought *"it tends to be quite rigid, but at least we do have opportunities to advance outside the traditional lockstep system."*

"One of the best parental leave policies."

Another way Orrick offers associates choices in their development is through external career coaches. The setup helps juniors to feel *"totally free and open to discuss career goals,"* a source told us, whether that be inside the firm or elsewhere. *"You do hear stories about folks saying that they're not happy and are ready to do something different and the firm has been very supportive of them."*

Orrick also attempts to give its lawyers more flexibility through an agile working system. This enables associates to *"work remotely a couple of days a week or a month."* Alongside this the firm *"has one of the best parental leave*

See firm profile on p.678

The Inside View

Diversity	Partners (%)	Associates (%)
Women	22.5	47.7
White	78.2	57.7
Black/African American	3.0	2.9
Hispanic/Latin American	1.3	4.3
Asian	7.7	13.4
Mixed/Other	9.7	21.7
LGBT	2.7	5.1

policies" – it offers 22 weeks of paid primary care giver leave, the most generous offering of any firm featured in *Chambers Associate*. *"It's pretty cool how flexible it is."*

Insiders traced all these flexible supportive policies to Orrick's origins as a *"Californian firm, meaning it's a bit more laid-back than a typical New York firm."* Sources emphasized that the working culture also means informal feedback is good too. *"Partners are pretty good at sitting down with you and saying,' Next time think about this,"* one reported. In addition, *"people are genuine so mentoring does not feel forced. For example, as a summer a lot of the senior associates take you out to lunch and give you off-the-cuff advice on how you should handle certain situations or people in the firm."*

Social Life & Offices

Given associates' positive views of their colleagues, we wondered if they got up to much together socially. Well, yes they do. On top of summer program events and an annual diversity and inclusion retreat there are numerous things going on in each office. Those in the finance, energy and tech-focused New York office can participate in things like *"a Mentoring and Margaritas program, karaoke nights"* and occasional fun and games in the office during quieter moments. In DC, home to a good part of the firm's energy and appellate practices, *"it's very common on a Friday to hear, 'Hey does anyone want to grab a beer tonight?'"* and in energy-centric Houston the *"managing partner is a big fan of running so we recently did a cross-country trail run."*

On the West Coast, in the firm's full-service San Francisco HQ juniors were happy to discover *"a partner in the public finance group who organizes happy hours every Friday"* as he has a bar cart in his office. *"It's a nice way to create a sense of community – people have busy lives so it can sometimes be hard to meet outside the office."* Finally, juniors nearby in the tech and IP-focused Silicon Valley office experienced a working environment that is *"more suburban, meaning things tend to be little more quiet. Alot of folks just want to get home to their family."*

Hours & Compensation

Orrick is still a BigLaw firm, so despite all this fun and flexibility plenty of hard work awaits newbies. To be bonus eligible, the firm suggests a guideline of billing 2,000 hours, though some associates bag a bonus despite not meeting this figure. Generally sources felt the target *"is going to push you, but it's not completely unrealistic."*

Start times range from 8am to 9.30am with work finishing between 6.30pm or 7pm on a normal day, though litigators typically finish later, perhaps as late as 10pm. As is the case at any BigLaw firm hours do fluctuate, meaning that during busy times associates could have their heads down till *"10pm or midnight."* One source told us: *"The latest night I ever had was staying till 5am, though that was in extraordinary circumstances."*

Diversity & Inclusion

Sources felt that *"diversity and inclusion aredefinitely a focal point and something that everyone at the firm from top to bottom cares about."* Practically speaking, Orrick organizes an annual Dive/In ('diversity and inclusion') program, 'a worldwide celebration of the different backgrounds and cultures that constitute our global community' according to the firm's website. Associates reported that *"we invite guest speakers"* and *"artists from different backgrounds come in and display their art."*

Orrick's diversity stats are perhaps slightly better than those of its competitors, but insiders felt that *"there is room for improvement. For instance when you look at our management committee there are plenty of women but there are not many people of color."* Five of the 11 members of the management committee are currently women or from a minority background.

> *"When the travel ban came in we did a lot with the ACLU and the National Immigration Law Center."*

Pro Bono

Juniors can take on pro bono cases from *"a fantastic coordinator who handles all pro bono inquiries."* An interviewee reported: *"You can go to him and say, 'I'm interested in immigration pro bono,' and he will basically have five cases you can help with."* Other opportunities include things like *"campaigning for bail reform, financing nonprofit energy projects and writing papers on policy issues."* We heard that lawyers at the firm were involved in matters related to President's Trump travel ban in 2017. *"When the travel ban came in we did a lot with the ACLU and the National Immigration Law Center,"* a source reported.

See firm profile on p.678

The Inside View

Pro bono hours
- For all US attorneys: 93,617
- Average per US attorney: 134

Strategy & Future

CEO Mitch Zuklie splits Orrick's strategy into four parts. The first is a focus on three sectors: technology, energy & infrastructure and finance. Zuklie comments: *"Increasingly we find clients asking for market insights because innovation is outpacing regulations. We think a sector focus helps us provide such insights."* The second strand of the strategy is *"being the best place to work,"* says Zuklie. *"That means a commitment to coaching and feedback and a great respect for women and diversity."* And *"being a leader in technology and innovation"* is the third part of the strategy. As an example Zuklie highlights *"Orrick Labs, an internal project launched in November 2017 designed to develop legal technology for us which we cannot get in the marketplace."* And finally, aiming to *"achieve financial results to reinvest in our people, our clients, our firm and our communities"* rounds off the firm's guiding philosophies.

To learn about becoming a lawyer in California, visit chambers-associate.com

See firm profile on p.678

Patterson Belknap Webb & Tyler LLP

Lawyers per state

200

Largest US office: New York
US offices: 1
International offices: 0
First-year salary: $180,000
Billable hours: 2,100 target (incl. 250 nonbillable)
Summers 2018: no summer program
Revenue 2017: $192.7 million (+3.8%)
Partners made in 2018: 1
Famous for: being fans of judicial clerks; litigation prowess

Patterson is a New York litigation powerhouse with a lot of time for judicial clerks and even more for pro bono.

THAT old cliché that 'this firm punches above its weight' is somewhat overused in legal marketing, and should be reserved for exceptional occasions: a Patterson review is one of them. Although no punching goes on here; this is *"a humane place to practice law,"* noted associates, contrasting the firm's inner culture with its formidable courtroom persona. This 200-strong firm makes a worthy opponent to any of the huge names in litigation, and in advertising litigation, Patterson is itself a huge name, winning a top-tier nationwide ranking in *Chambers USA.* The directory also bestows rankings on the firm's IP, securities litigation, media & entertainment, and real estate practices.

This New York firm is no herd-follower – a mentality that begins at recruitment, with the firm's penchant for hiring from clerkship (although not exclusively). Our sources drew comparisons with the BigLaw stereotypes and insisted that this is *"by no means a sweat shop."* With a clerkship behind them, juniors at Patterson are expected to be a little more independent. They found working in *"smaller and leaner teams of two or three"* beneficial to their development and told us partner interaction is a reality from day one.

The Work

While litigation takes the heavy load of the firm's shiny new recruits, Patterson sends a few into the noncontentious practices: corporate, tax, real estate, trusts and estates and employee benefits. *"Our work often overlaps,"* explained one litigation attorney, *"especially with tax-exempt organizations. I got to work on a big commercial case that Patterson has been advising on for the past 15 years, so there's plenty of interaction across the firm."*

"Everyone at the firm is encouraged to be a generalist"

Asked if they found the litigation focus at all limiting, our interviewees all chorused that the work was *"really diverse, with varied cases and big-name clients"* – dropping names like Coca-Cola and Johnson & Johnson into the conversation. *"Everyone at the firm is encouraged to be a generalist,"* we learned. *"I really didn't know the type of litigation I wanted to do, so the fact that you can try all the different areas Patterson offers was a huge advantage,"* one third-year told us. *"There are a few people who have advanced degrees in science who choose to do mostly patent work,"* but those with less focus can get experience on internal investigations, patent cases, cybersecurity, FCC matters, product liability and nonprofit work. The media, entertainment and false advertising practices offer associates some particularly toothsome work: some of the latest clients include Hershey's, L'Oréal, Time Warner and Standard & Poor's.

On chambers-associate.com...
- Get hired: the route to Patterson
- Diversity at Patterson

See firm profile on p.679

The Inside View

Rankings in *Chambers USA*

Advertising	Litigation
Intellectual Property	Real Estate

For detail on ranking tiers and ranking locations, visit www.chambersandpartners.com

How do juniors know where to begin? "*There's a formal structure in place – there are two assigning partners that all matters go through,*" which ensures that all attorneys are "*well rounded and handling a good balance of cases.*" A source added: "*The assigning partners are kind of a buffer to help you maintain your sanity and work balance and make sure you get to do the things you want to do.*" We've also been told that "*it's up to the associates to take the initiative with the work available and create their own career paths.*"

"*One of the other nice things about Patterson is partners are willing to take you to hearings,*" explained one newbie, "*and even though I'm quite junior, I've had cases where I've been staffed with just one partner.*" Attorneys have plenty of responsibility from the get-go, and should be prepared to take the lead on briefings, motions, independent depositions and legal drafting.

Training & Development

Newbies are enrolled onto a formal training program called 'Litigation Nuts and Bolts' that takes attorneys through all aspects of the litigation life-cycle, "*from drafting a complaint, to drafting a settlement – and everything in between.*" These sessions are also attended by writing and public speaking experts to help polish your courtroom skills.

"There is an expectation that you're going to raise your hand"

Check-ins with the assigning partners are organized every two months for newbies. Juniors are also assigned to an 'Associate Learning Group', consisting of six associates and a partner. Each group plans three social events throughout the year, perhaps to a theater or a high-end restaurant: "*It's such a valuable opportunity to socialize with the associates outside of the office, as well as get some extra mentorship from the partner.*" Juniors also get informal mentoring with a midlevel associate throughout the year, "*which is great, as you always have someone you can call for if you need help.*"

"*I've never run into a situation where I couldn't handle the work,*" associates reflected. "*There is an expectation that you're going to raise your hand and ask for help if you need it,*" explained one junior, and that doesn't preclude knocking on managing partner Lisa Cleary's door.

Recent work highlights

- Defending Johnson & Johnson in a $450 million dispute accusing the pharmaceutical heavyweight of infringing a competitor's patent on hydrogel contact lenses
- Representing Coca-Cola in a series of cases attempting to ban the sugary giant from participating in public debate about weight management as their drinks are sweetened
- Defended The Hershey Company in a class action accusing the chocolate maker of deceptively labeling its products, due to the company's sourcing of cocoa from an African region that includes the use of child labor
- Represented Charter Communications in its action against the New York City Police Department for withholding and charging for video footage requested under New York's Freedom of Information Law

As one insider revealed, "*you feel completely comfortable speaking with her. She is genuinely interested in any problems that you might have and understanding how things could be better.*"

Get Hired

Patterson hires mainly from clerkships. Learn more about the recruitment process at chambers-associate.com.

Strategy & Future

"*I think we're a bit lower-profile,*" said one insider. "*The firm made the choice to stay small and not merge in the 80s and 90s.*" One associate pointed out that "*we have always been a relatively cautious and conservative firm in the sense of expansion. We have a relatively unique thing here and it would be a shame to lose it.*"

Patterson has seen a recent change in leadership however, and while Lisa Cleary remains managing partner and co-chair for another term, she was joined by Peter Tomlison who inherited the role as new cochair in April 2017. "*We are really continuing to focus on our litigation strengths,*" Lisa told us, "*and even though we're only a single office, we are able to service our clients across the United States.*" The key to Patterson's ongoing success? "*We are moving forward on a number of technological fronts to modernize all aspects of our practice going forward to provide the best service client possible,*" Lisa explained. "*We can create virtual offices in a nanosecond with our crackerjack IT team.*"

Culture & Offices

"*Patterson has all the prestige of a big New York firm, except we're not drowning in 30 offices and 1,500 employees,*" one insider explained. "*But the one thing that is annoying*

See firm profile on p.679

The Inside View

Diversity	Partners (%)	Associates (%)
Women	18	43
White	90	76
Black/African American	2	5
Hispanic/Latin American	2	3
Asian	6	11.4
Mixed/Other	0	4.6
LGBT	12	8.6

about our office is that we are right off Times Square so we have to deal with that on a daily basis."

"We're a little more alternative – or at least, as alternative as you can get in a corporate law firm."

Our sources thought their firm attracts *"the type of people who aren't just in it for the money,"* but definitely for *"the love of the law."* Others described their fellow attorneys as *"a little bookish, but not in a negative way"* and *"very intellectual."* According to one litigator, Patterson can be classed as *"a little more alternative – or at least, as alternative as you can get in a corporate law firm. The associates in particular have a wide variety of interests and career ambitions."* Others have pointed out that *"it's a really down-to-earth place that values individuality. People will introduce me as 'this is my colleague', not as 'this is my associate'."*

For all its contrasts to the BigLaw stereotypes, Patterson is still no easy ride. *"Lawyers here need to be able to stand up for themselves,"* insiders thought. *"People take their work very seriously here, not least because there are complicated issues and a lot of money at stake,"* declared another source, *"but you don't hear people screaming or slamming their doors."*

It's not all work and no play; attorneys and partners have been spotted *"letting their hair down at the Winter Party... but only to the extent that nobody wants to be the one acting out the story the next morning."* Associates have also praised the firmwide events as providing *"plenty of opportunity to do some internal networking,"* with the latest party hosted at the Grand Hyatt Hotel. *"The firm rented out a big ballroom, there was an open bar with every kind of food you can imagine,"* and while everyone had drink in hand, juniors were mindful to *"sip their drinks very slowly"* in the presence of the powers that be. Asked if associates would change anything about the culture, one ventured: *"I would definitely adopt a casual dress code. I'm not sure it's something the firm is ready to do yet, but I think it will happen one day."*

Hours & Compensation

The hours requirement is 1,850 billable and a further 250 of citizenship, which includes pro bono. Translating that into a typical day's work, most attorneys we interviewed were in the office between 9.30am and 7pm, and while the firm's new recruits were *"pleasantly surprised by how little I've had to work on the weekends,"* there's no escaping the inevitable: *"The nature of the work means there will be between five to ten occasions of the year when you need to stay at the office past midnight."* This was a relief to our sources: *"I was worried about being a lawyer in New York. I didn't think I'd be able to find a place where I'd enjoy the work and also have a life outside work, but so far I've been able to accomplish both of those things at Patterson."*

"I didn't think I'd be able to find a place where I'd enjoy the work and also have a life outside it."

"I feel like it's a good balance between the salary and hours I put in," reported one insider, *"I know that I'm making market."* Associates are also eligible for a bonus upon hitting both their targets, however if they fail to hit the right figure on either of those, the amount of bonus the attorney gets is reviewed on a case-by-case basis (provided they've hit 2,100 hours overall).

Pro Bono

Attorneys are expected to jump straight into the vast pool of pro bono from the moment they step through the door. Patterson has seen a 100% pro bono participation rate for well over a decade. Notable examples include working with the Corporation Counsel where you'll be defending multiple depositions, exercising your writing skills and sitting in the hot seat. It also means that *"you get a lot of contact with the partner, as often it will just be the two of you trying to help this person,"* chimed one junior. *"It also gives me an opportunity to take a lead role, so it's really rewarding for both of us."*

Aside from depositions and smaller housing projects, the firm has its fair share of veterans' initiatives, domestic violence cases and landlord/tenant matters to get involved with.

Pro bono hours
- For all attorneys: 23,301
- Average per attorney: 139

See firm profile on p.679

The Inside View

Paul Hastings LLP

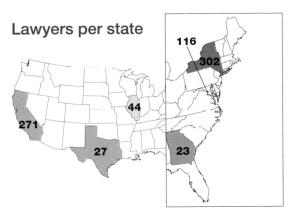

Lawyers per state

116
302
44
271
27
23

Largest US office: New York
US offices: 11
International offices: 11
First-year salary: $180,000
Billable hours: 2,000 target
Summers 2018: 82 (7 1Ls; 75 2Ls)
Revenue 2017: $1.118 billion (+4%)
Partners made in 2018: 16
Famous for: its LA office skyscraper which keeps getting destroyed in movies/on TV; competitive edge

"There's a mentality that we have to be the best and do the best. And we need people who can sprint with us."

PAUL Hastings is a big international legal brand with strategic bases in the world's economic hubs. Once a Californian firm, Paul Hastings' identity has shifted as it has grown: New York has emerged as the firm's largest office and the natural epicenter for its global network. Although the Cali factor can be felt in some top clients – Disney, Google, Blizzard – several others – Goldman Sachs, United Airlines – signal the firm's eastward trajectory. The culture, too, is decidedly un-Californian and quite *"fast-paced,"* said one LA associate. *"They have extremely high expectations."* As one associate put it: *"You're playing with the Dodgers! There's a mentality that we have to be the best and do the best. And we need people who can sprint with us."*

In a firm that likes to be always on the move, lawyers only get to stand still when using their standup desks – *"I stand 80% of the day!"* The forward-looking environment, the glass walls filling the place with sunlight *"and all that fancy stuff – I love it!"* associates told us.

The firm's go-getting attitude shows in the *Chambers USA* rankings it hauls in by the dozen. In Chicago, Texas and Georgia, Paul Hastings is recognized mainly for its corporate, finance and real estate work. In DC, California and New York, a much more diverse array of practices win applause: IP; antitrust; media & entertainment;

Latin American investment; and environment to name a few. Nationwide and globally, the firm receives acclaim for its labor & employment practice.

The Work

The biggest groups for junior associates to join are litigation and corporate, followed closely by employment and real estate. The smallest group on offer is tax, which welcomes just a few juniors each year. Although *"you're encouraged to bounce around,"* once associates have a foot in the door they're able to pursue assignments and build a practice in specific areas. Work allocation is office and group-specific: one NYC associate told us, *"Most of my work flows through the staffing partner."* Whereas an LA source told us, *"It's a free market system – it's doled out fairly informally."*

"I just turned off The Today Show because one of our plaintiffs is being interviewed!"

Corporate subgroups available include M&A, private equity, investment management, project finance, and private investment funds. The work spans from *"the usual banks work"* to multibillion tech supply transactions. Across all groups juniors told us, *"In the beginning it started out with a lot of typical rote junior work; due diligence, drafting smaller items, research assignments, marking up documents."* But this soon developed into *"pretty substantial work. Once on a relatively small M&A matter, I was mostly driving the deal. I was doing most of the drafting, correspondence and driving the closing."*

On chambers-associate.com...

• Get hired: recruitment tips and advice
• Interview with managing partner Greg Nitzkowski

The Inside View

See firm profile on p.680

493

Rankings in *Chambers USA*

Antitrust

Banking & Finance

Bankruptcy/Restructuring

Capital Markets

Climate Change

Corporate/M&A

Employee Benefits &
   Executive Compensation

Environment

FCPA

Intellectual Property

Investment Funds

Labor & Employment

Latin American Investment

Leisure & Hospitality

Litigation

Media & Entertainment

Real Estate

Tax

For detail on ranking tiers and ranking locations, visit
www.chambersandpartners.com

Litigation encompasses subgroups such as white-collar investigations, IP, securities, and general commercial. *"It can get more specialized in NYC or LA,"* one associate from a smaller office told us, *"here we're all in the general pool, we're not pigeon-holed because of our geographic location."* Associates wanted to tell us about something called 'good doc review': *"It's not just doc review, it's a lot more engaging. My actual tasks are digging through emails, chronology of events, and control failures. It's doc review where you're putting together facts – it's been a lot of my work and I've loved it."* As well as that, juniors can expect to work on interview outlines, sit in on interviews, do some drafting of trial preparation documents and respond to subpoenas and requests for discovery.

The employment juniors are mostly based in California. The group is *"the flagship department of the firm and it's super well known."* Clients include companies in technology, entertainment and the service industry, and cases are frequently discrimination-based. *"The caliber of work we get is unique,"* thought one associate. *"Two of our cases right now are in the news. I just turned off The Today Show because one of our plaintiffs is being interviewed!"* As for the work, *"we do a lot of motion writing for summary judgment, drafting deposition outlines, responding to discovery. Sometimes we even do witness interviews."*

Pro Bono

There's an expectation that associates will bill at least 25 pro bono hours, with an overall goal of 75 hours, but there's an unlimited amount of pro bono hours that can be billed: *"They're very honest about wanting you to do pro bono."* Work is handed out by local pro bono coordinators in each office.

"...a great way to develop skills and get your foot in the door."

"There are a lot of opportunities to work on very cool pro bono matters." Juniors work with organizations such as

Recent work highlights

- Defended Activision Blizzardin a putative class action lawsuit alleging senior artists are misclassified as exempt from overtime, concerning the classification of senior video game artists as creative professionals
- Represented The Lightstone Group on several development transactions in six projects across NYC and Hollywood totaling over $1.5 billion
- Provided counsel to RBC Capital Markets and Merrill Lynch, Pierce, Fenner & Smith in the $3.75 billion acquisition of DigitalGlobe, a provider of high-resolution Earth imagery services, by MacDonald, Dettwiler and Associates
- Represented Boehringer Ingelheim resulting in the invalidation of all claims of a key patent covering the rheumatoid arthritis use for AbbVie's immunosuppressive drug Humira, the world's top-selling drug product
- Secured dismissal of claims against Google and its parent company Alphabet regarding their confidentiality, data security, and conduct policies of roughly 65,000 employees nationwide. This is the first case of its kind against a Silicon Valley giant, and the final result is likely to affect how the industry approaches these policies in the future

the Innocence Project, Kids in Need of Defense, Sanctuary for Families, the American Civil Liberties Union and the Homeless Advocacy Project. There's also the opportunity to advocate for criminal justice reform, *"drafting amicus briefs for hot topic social issues before the Supreme Court."* And for developing your own career at Paul Hastings, *"pro bono is a great way to develop skills and get your foot in the door with a partner you may want to work with in the future."*

Pro bono hours
- For all US attorneys: undisclosed
- Average per US attorney: undisclosed

Training & Feedback

After a two-week orientation that's *"a bit repetitive,"* first-years will go to the (almost unpronounceable?) 'PHThrive', *"a three-day workshop in Chicago for all first-years to meet each other and get the basic skills; interfacing with clients, firm policies, and also sessions on group-specific training."* Anyone who's trained at Paul Hastings will know the firm plays on its PH acronym with gusto – *"we have a lot of quirky names!"* The overall training program gets the catchy acronym PH DNA (Paul Hastings Developing New Associates). Many agreed that the best thing about these initial sessions is making new 'PHriends': *"While the training programs are slightly helpful, the main purpose is to meet everyone and do some inter-firm networking. That part I did really appreciate."*

See firm profile on p.680

The Inside View

Diversity	Partners (%)	Associates (%)
Women	22	43
White	88	65
Black/African American	3	5
Hispanic/Latin American	3	4
Asian	6	23
Mixed/Other	1	3
LGBT	3	3

"You get to see these more advanced stages of the case."

Although the coaching program has no PH-based acronym, sadly, it does *"help us a lot,"* concurred associates. *"Our coaches took us to lunch on the first day and I'm still in contact with my coach all the time."* Associates are given 150 hours of budget relief where for the first twelve months you can bill for work and not bill the client; *"it's a good way to ask partners you don't work with, 'Hey, can I come in and sit on this call with you?' You get to see these more advanced stages of the case that give you a perspective of what the overall goal is."*

Culture & Offices

The Big Apple base is Paul Hastings' largest office, followed by LA and Washington, DC. The firm's other offices also take juniors in varying numbers: Atlanta, Chicago, Orange County, Palo Alto, San Francisco, San Diego and Houston. As one associate put it: *"It's hard to describe the culture of the whole firm at all. The culture differs office to office, department to department, floor to floor."*

The New York office is above Grand Central Station, so *"you can avoid the weather and go straight up!"* In NY associates agreed, *"I think the LA-ness seeps into our office – it's more laid back than other firms around here!"* On each floor there are two PlayStations; *"it demonstrates the culture here – on a Friday afternoon you can just go and pick up a controller and relax."*

In DC, associates told us *"everything else is on an informal level, but I wouldn't say we're super social. Most people have families and a life outside the company and people tend to respect that."* Another told us, *"In a nutshell, the culture's best characterized as mutual respect."* An associate from another smaller office told us, *"We're relaxed – NY is buttoned up in suits every day, but here were have our jeans on!"*

"The culture differs office to office, department to department, floor to floor."

The LA office is in the very center of Bunker Hill in downtown LA. Despite what the Manhattan associates think about their Cali cousins' lifestyle, we were told, *"LA can be super busy. It's very fast-paced."* This pace is set by the partners: *"They're the rainmakers of the firm. They have extremely high expectations and it creates a pretty intense atmosphere. There's a sort of warrior culture – a mentality of 'if you can't take it, you're not good enough'."*

Associates in New York spend their first two years in an open-plan interior working area known as the 'In-Zone,' though *"some people call it the bullpen!"* Thoughts about this were mixed: *"I like it for the opportunity to collaborate with other people."* Others said, *"The downside is that it's distracting – you can't make private phone calls from your desk, you have to go to the designated phone booth."* One associate told us, *"I have to look through a partner's office just to see outside!"*

Once you're in the third year, you get your own office. The firm's smaller offices have been open-plan glass for quite some time, but the bigger bases have been adapting to this layout in recent years. *"There's a lack of private space. The way you relax when you get into your own office and close the door, that doesn't exist."* Though people did in general praise that *"I get sunlight basically all day and the views are great. We can see the sunset every day."*

Diversity

Associates agreed that *"in terms of gender, it's great. Something I noticed when I first got here is how many senior people are women."* However, associates would *"like to see more racial diversity."* Associates expressed a general consensus that *"the firm tries really hard to take diversity very seriously."* Those natty acronyms get a resurgence in diversity initiatives: there are several PHANs (Paul Hastings Affinity Networks) for minority attorneys and staff, as well as their allies. *"The women's PHAN is probably the most active. They have a program where you can go to lunch with female partner as a mentor opportunity."* PHANs put on seminars that get broadcast to all offices of the firm; *"recently a managing counsel at McDonald's told us about how when he's looking for lawyers, he always picks the only diverse person. It was really interesting."*

Hours & Compensation

"That's how it is on the books, but that's not how it is," an associate told us on the firm's policy of unlimited vacation. *"On the one hand no one tells you not to take it, but at the same time any vacation has such a massive impact on everyone else it's hard to take. Every time I try to take vacation, it's ended up having to fall through."* We heard were told of an associate who *"was on vacation with their*

See firm profile on p.680

family and a partner just said, 'I'm flying you back early,' and brought them back."

"There's an expectation that you'll be broadly available."

Reassuringly, we came across few associates who'd pulled many all-nighters – in most offices and departments, *"generally by 7 it's mostly empty"* and people head home to finish up anything which couldn't wait. *"That said, there's an expectation that you'll be broadly available. There's never a time at night you just shut off or stop responding or working."*

Weekend work depends on the case. While one source said, *"I billed 12 hours this weekend and 18 last weekend,"* that was the upper end, and most people we spoke to billed about half a day each weekend. As such, our sources had no problems meeting the 2,000 billable hours mark: *"It's not like some sort of do-or-die cutoff. They don't judge you by your hours because you don't have control over your hours."*

Managing partner Greg Nitzkowski recognizes that this end of the legal profession is a *"stressful job driven by demands of clients which are frequently unreasonable and hard to contain within day hours."* Nitzkowski told us about the firm's investment in mobile working tools to ease the pressure. *"I've never liked the 'life balance' moniker – to me it's about 'life flexibility.' We should have all the tools that provide people with that flexibility."*

Strategy & Future

Over the past couple of years the firm's M&A, private equity, finance, IP and white-collar litigation practices have undergone a healthy amount of growth, but labor & employment is still, rightly, viewed as the firm's jewel in its crown. Go online to read the full interview with managing partner Greg Nitzkowski and learn about his vision for the firm.

See firm profile on p.680

Paul, Weiss, Rifkind, Wharton & Garrison LLP

Lawyers per state

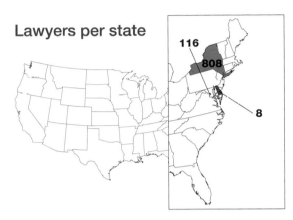

116

808

8

Largest US office: New York
US offices: 3
International offices: 5
First-year salary: $180,000
Billable hours: no requirement
Summers 2018: 148 (7 1Ls, 136 2Ls, 2 3Ls, 3 SEOs)
Revenue 2017: $1.3 billion (+6.6%)
Partners made in 2018: 4
Famous for: home-grown partners; pro bono prestige; New York litigation renown

Those with *"a love for intellectual stimulation"* and a passion for pro bono might want more than a slice of Paul, Weiss.

"OUR goal is to have the very best talent you possibly can have under one roof," says Paul, Weiss chairman Brad Karp. To that end, the firm's demonstrated a healthy appetite for proven talent, bringing in big-name lawyers from Kirkland & Ellis, Cravath, Dechert and Simpson Thacher in recent years. But Karp insists that *"from a law student's perspective, our goal is to continue to attract the best talent in the world and to nurture that talent. The matters we handle are extraordinarily complicated and invariably cutting-edge, so we want the best minds collaborating on creative solutions. What distinguishes Paul, Weiss is that we're old-fashioned in terms of our culture and values. So many firms are bottom-line motivated. We've done exceptionally well from a profitability perspective, but we're all about the culture."* Juniors supported this sentiment: *"I think there is a focus on the core human characteristics of individuals – yes, the job requires a certain level of intellectual rigor, but you have to have a cultural fit."*

> *"We're playing a leading role on a wide range of crucial issues that we hope will improve social justice in our country."*

Part and parcel of this *"cultural fit"* is Paul, Weiss' penchant for pro bono. The firm famously worked on landmark cases such as *Brown v. Board of Education*, and *United States v. Windsor*. Today, Karp says: *"We're playing a leading role on a wide range of crucial issues that we hope will improve social justice in our country. We have dedicated teams of lawyers fighting to protect a woman's right to choose, to enforce refugee rights, to oppose unconstitutional travel bans, to block voter disenfranchisement, to safeguard LGBT rights, and to improve our criminal justice system."*

Back to that bottom line though. *"The main thing that attracted me was the impression I got that both litigation and corporate practices were thriving."* It's true: the firm's flourishing. *Chambers USA* awards it multiple stellar litigation and regulatory rankings, plus impressive marks in bankruptcy, capital markets, tax, media & entertainment, corporate/M&A, and real estate (among numerous others). *"The firm's profits have been climbing for the past 20 years and it keeps attracting big-name partners. It continues to go uphill rather than staying stagnant."*

On chambers-associate.com...

- Interview with chairman Brad Karp
- Get hired: more insight on the firm's recruitment from associates

The Work

Over half of associates could be found in litigation, roughly a third in corporate, while the remainder were spread across more specific areas like bankruptcy, employee benefits, personal representation, real estate and tax. Both litigation and corporate juniors begin as gen-

See firm profile on p.681

Rankings in *Chambers USA*

Antitrust	FCPA
Banking & Finance	Financial Services
Bankruptcy/Restructuring	Regulation
Capital Markets	Intellectual Property
Corporate Crime &	Investment Funds
Investigations	Litigation
Corporate/M&A	Media & Entertainment
Employee Benefits &	Private Equity
Executive Compensation	Real Estate
Energy & Natural	Retail
Resources	Securities
ERISA Litigation	Tax

For detail on ranking tiers and ranking locations, visit
www.chambersandpartners.com

Recent work highlights

- Defending the multinational biopharmaceuticals company AbbVie over allegations that thousands of customers who used Androgel, a testosterone replacement therapy, suffered serious side effects.
- Represents ExxonMobil in wide-ranging climate change-related investigations and litigations brought by state attorneys general. It forms part of a movement to investigate what energy companies knew about climate change, and whether they misled people on the issue.
- Advised the Kraft Heinz Company in its proposed $143 billion acquisition of UK-based global consumer goods company Unilever. The acquisition was ultimately unsuccessful.
- In connection with the acquisition of Jimmy Choo, the firm advised fashion brand Michael Kors in its $2 billion senior secured credit facilities.

eralists (corporate juniors work across four sub-groups for their first two years) and both have a formal work assignment system that juniors can take advantage of. *"The first couple of assignments are assigned through that, but once you start working with people you like, on subject matters you like, you can pretty much control your destiny within the firm. Then if you need work, you can ask the assigning partner."* Choosing to take work through the assigning system brought benefits. *"It can be difficult to say no when a partner directly asks you to work on something, but if there's someone in between, you can be candid and say when you're too busy to take it on."*

Due to the generalist nature of their work, litigators had gathered a range of experiences. Sources mentioned working on bankruptcy matters, M&A litigation, white-collar investigations, securities class actions, and employment cases, among others. Many juniors praised being able to *"participate in depositions and witness prep,"* getting direct client contact. *"It's been valuable; you're not just a fly on the wall watching. I was told from the beginning that 'you need to participate in depositions because you're a lawyer. You can't just sit there and watch.' It was helpful."* One junior found it *"a little intimidating at first because I was barely an attorney, but I think the firm provides a lot of support for you to be confident in what you're doing. There's a good balance between supporting you, but letting you run with your assignment."* Other tasks involved discovery, drafting initial versions of motions, and preparing presentations for the government.

The growing corporate practice covers four main groups: funds, securities, M&A, and finance – the largest being M&A. *"Usually when we start out, we can indicate what group we're interested in and can get assigned to those matters, but generally you're free. We're encouraged to try out tasks within all of the four corporate groups."* Clients include large multinational corporations from the energy, technology, media, sports and entertainment industries,

plus private equity companies. Similarly to litigation, *"one thing the practice does well is getting younger associates client contact very early on. I feel like I've been able to get more than you'd expect from a second or third year."* On top of early client contact, juniors had conducted legal research and due diligence, drafted contracts and negotiated nondisclosure agreements. *"The partners are more than happy to give you substantial work as long as you're ready for it, though it does depend on the type of deal or clients."*

"...very much human, and humane."

Training & Development

When they first start, juniors can expect intensive training during their first week, followed by periodic sessions over the next few months. Litigators remembered *"training on how to prepare litigation documents, how to do doc review, how to actually produce the documents, as well as any ethical issues tied into the practice."* Corporate juniors had training on each of the various corporate sub-groups and on the *"junior associate-specific tasks"* within those. Both sides also receive training on computer equipment and the firm's available resources.

Formal reviews happen once a year. In addition to being reviewed, juniors have the opportunity to conduct 'upward reviews.' Associates *"get to review anyone we work with who is two years our senior or more. It has often led to improvements in teaching and behavior based on that feedback, which I feel is important."*

Culture

"We're the nice New York firm: we're courteous to opposing counsel, to each other – we're just polite. It is discouraged to be competitive, cutthroat, or mean." This amiable modus operandi ensured that *"the firm is very welcoming for*

See firm profile on p.681

Diversity	Partners (%)	Associates (%)
Women	21	40
White	87	78
Black/African American	3	5
Hispanic/Latin American	1	3
Asian	7	11
Mixed/Other	2	3
LGBT	6	6

first-year associates. Coming into a law firm is very daunting, but Paul, Weiss makes it feel as seamless as possible." Once they've crossed the threshold, associates found that *"bringing your perspective to the table is something that is valued here."* In fact, while being *"a place where people appreciate hard work,"* Paul, Weiss' people are *"very much human, and humane."*

Like most humans, Paul, Weiss' associates like to let their hair down occasionally. *"The firm does a lot of events for us, but I think associates naturally bond and hang out outside the firm."* Some of these events included a casino night, Shakespeare in the Park, a firm retreat, and various holiday events. The highlight of the social calendar is perhaps the annual MoMA summer garden party, which *"everyone at the firm is encouraged to go to."*

Sources also placed importance on the firm's forward-thinking outlook. *"There's an understanding that the legal profession is changing, and Paul, Weiss wants to be a part of that change."* Juniors raised the example of *"President Trump announcing the travel ban; the firm moved quickly to help lawyers who wanted to be on the ground helping people, and encouraged people to go if they wanted to. When the firm cares about issues, it acts."* Many felt *"our chairman is very much for taking us into a new era for the firm."*

Hours & Compensation

There's no official billing target at Paul, Weiss, with bonuses paid in lockstep. Sources agreed the annual average is about 2,000-2,100 billable hours, *"but that's not a hard requirement. People will well exceed that and others won't reach it – it's not really an issue."* In other words: *"People work as hard as they can without burning themselves out."* On an average day, juniors might get in to the office at 9:30am and hope to get out by 7pm, though some leave earlier and log back in at home. Busier periods can see attorneys arriving closer to 8am, and leaving anywhere up to 2am. One source *"had a five-week stretch of those hours."* Juniors understood hours could be *"up and down,"* telling us: *"When you're on a live deal or case, it's going to be awful, but once it's signed or closed, it's quieter and you can enjoy that."*

Offices

The firm has three US offices, with its New York HQ taking the vast majority of attorneys. DC and Wilmington, Delaware make up the rest of the US presence, while globally, the firm has offices in Toronto, Beijing, Hong Kong, London, and Tokyo. The DC office is *"almost exclusively litigation-focused,"* while NY runs the gamut of the firm's practices.

"Every floor has a kitchen stocked with about 24 different drink products."

The New York office benefits from a handy midtown Manhattan location, and sources loved how *"every floor has a kitchen stocked with about 24 different drink products – it's only a small thing, but it's awesome."* One floor was recently turned into the new conference center *"with cutting-edge equipment and all the new gadgets."* The only grumble interviewees had related to *"space issues."* Specifically, juniors told us that *"from second year you get your own office, but it's a small internal office. You don't tend to get an external office until fourth year. It can be claustrophobic, especially in the summer – sometimes you don't see daylight."*

Pro Bono

"A lot of firms pay lip service to pro bono, but I think Paul, Weiss is better than others." One only has to look at the firm's history to show it doesn't just talk the talk on pro bono, but walks the walk (see our website for more on Paul, Weiss' history of pro bono). *"It was explained by partners that if the firm has committed to taking on a pro bono matter, then it is to be treated in the same manner as a paid matter, with the same level of professionalism and diligence."* Naturally therefore, pro bono hours are counted the same as billable hours. Juniors had got their teeth into matters including criminal appeals, asylum cases, housing discrimination cases, and transgender legal name changes, among others. Besides the feel-good factor of doing something good for those in need, pro bono also provided juniors with *"more hands-on, substantive experience. Partners recognize and encourage that."*

Pro bono hours
- For all attorneys: 100,563
- Average per attorney: 100

Diversity

"In this industry diversity is a major issue, if not a crisis, but I think our firm makes great efforts to support and encourage diversity, both in recruiting and supporting those here." The firm has a number of initiatives and programs in place, one of which is a mentoring program for diverse associates. *"It's a three-year program where you're assigned*

See firm profile on p.681

to a partner mentor and they guide your development as a diverse associate at the firm. Although all partners respect diversity, you feel more comfortable discussing issues with your specific diversity mentor." Sources also mentioned "a special program for women above a certain level of seniority, where they counsel you on the best path to partner." Paul, Weiss also has a number of affinity groups: Asian-Pacific Lawyers, Black Lawyers, Family, Latino Lawyers, Pride @ Work, and Women.

Get Hired

"Students need to show their passion for being at Paul, Weiss, the work we do and their passion for learning." For more insight on getting hired, go to chambers-associate.com

Strategy & Future

"Historically we've been a litigation-heavy firm, but our corporate practice has been really booming recently. It's becoming comparable to litigation." Chairman Brad Karp estimates that the split between transactional and non-transactional work is "about 50:50; the firm is more balanced today than it has been at any time in our history." Other than that shift, sources reckon: "People generally feel very comfortable. This is a place where you're going to have a stable job, with stable clients. It's not going anywhere."

Still, juniors reckoned: "The firm is very focused on being the top firm in the world. Not in an arrogant way, but in a concerted, conscious way." Brad Karp tells us: "We're focused on five key practice areas: litigation, white-collar/regulatory defense, public company M&A, private equity, and restructuring. Our goal is to ensure that we remain the world's leading law firm in each of these five practice areas." Nevertheless, juniors emphasized that "we're not trying to steer away from those Judge Rifkind values – we step up when firms need to step up. We still want to be that firm."

See firm profile on p.681

The Inside View

Perkins Coie LLP

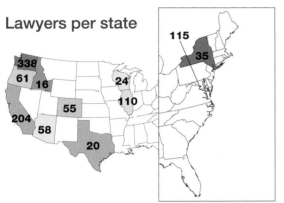

Lawyers per state

Largest US office: Seattle
US offices: 16
International offices: 3
First-year salary: $105,000 (Anchorage) - $180,000
Billable hours: 1,850 - 1,950 required
Summers 2018: 62 (18 1Ls, 44 2Ls)
Revenue 2017: $786 million (+0.6%)
Partners made in 2018: 18
Famous for: liberal vibe; tech clients

Perkins Coie LLP also has an office in Alaska with 11 attorneys

Seattle may have given the world Starbucks, grunge music and the doughnut maker, but for the aspiring lawyer only one Emerald City creation should matter: Perkins Coie.

GIVEN that they work for a firm that houses one of the nation's top political law groups, you can be sure Perkins Coie's attorneys kept a close eye on 2016's presidential race – and be pretty certain which candidate they favored. *"We represent a lot of Democratic bodies, and it should go without saying Perkins is generally a liberal firm,"* one junior said, *"but it's not aggressively so. There's no hostility to different points of view."* Partner Marc Elias acted as general counsel to the 'Hillary for America' campaign (you can read a full interview with him on our website), and even after Clinton's defeat the firm has continued to *"actively fight the Trump administration"* where it can.

It's not all politics at Perkins though – its vast array of *Chambers USA* rankings stretch across ten states and encompass both litigious and transactional strengths; top praise goes to areas like IP, white-collar crime, natural resources, and corporate and commercial. Nationwide, technology is an important focus, especially with regards to startups, fintech, data security and renewable energy. But the good rep goes beyond sterling work, as interviewees made clear: *"Perkins is also known for treating*

associates fairly; there are lots of opportunities to excel and take on interesting work."

The Work

Most Perkins rookies find themselves in the firm's business, commercial litigation or IP practice groups (all of which divide into subgroups, into which the firm directly hires). A handful slip into smaller teams like political law or product liability. Juniors tend to communicate directly with partners and associates to get staffed on matters – *"there's an entrepreneurial spirit to it and the responsibility is primarily on us"* – but a weekly check-in keeps management aware of associates' availability, and most interviewees felt *"the firm is generally pretty good at keeping tabs on our workload."*

Subgroups in the business department include corporate governance/transactions; emerging companies & venture capital; financial transactions/restructuring; private equity; and tech transactions & privacy. In most groups, deals can involve *"any kind of company,"* from industry giants to blooming new businesses. A junior's day to day *"fundamentally consists of drafting,"* whether that's general commercial agreements, client memos or more specific documents. *"Quite quickly we get a lot of direct client contact and responsibility,"* but juniors still have *"the ability to say no to work. Managing your own workload is very much respected – hell, it's encouraged."* Interviewees

On chambers-associate.com...

● Get hired: more info on recruitment at Perkins Coie
● Interview with director of recruiting and retention Mike Gotham

The Inside View

See firm profile on p.682

Rankings in *Chambers USA*

Bankruptcy/Restructuring	Native American Law
Corporate/Commercial	Natural Resources
Corporate/M&A	Privacy & Data Security
Environment	Products Liability
Government	Real Estate
Insurance	Retail
Intellectual Property	Startups & Emerging
Labor & Employment	Companies
Leisure & Hospitality	Technology
Life Sciences	Transportation
Litigation	Venture Capital

For detail on ranking tiers and ranking locations, visit
www.chambersandpartners.com

Recent work highlights

- Represented InfiniLed – an Irish developer of nanotechnology products – as it was sold to Facebook-owned virtual reality company Oculus VR
- Acts as general counsel for the Democratic National Committee
- Acted for HTC after a $1 billion lawsuit was brought against it and Beats by consumer electronics firm Monster Cable and its founder
- Won Supreme Court voting rights victories in Virginia and North Carolina

found that responsibility was ramped up on smaller matters; one enthusiastically recounted being *"given work typical of a fifth-year within twelve months,"* thanks to the leaner staffing model at Perkins (a feature across groups).

"I take charge of everything including frequent interaction with the client."

Options for litigators include antitrust, business litigation, construction, environment, insurance recovery, securities, and white-collar/investigations. Juniors aren't always restricted to one subset, with some reporting *"a really broad practice that covers a bit of everything."* Most at least dabbled in the technology sector, where clients range from giants like Facebook and Twitter to ambitious start ups. Working closely with the latter, associates got to *"take charge of everything including frequent interaction with the client. Those opportunities are rarer on larger matters, where we'll usually have a discrete task,"* like managing discovery, drafting briefs or filing motions. *"It's been an appropriate learning curve,"* sources agreed, *"supervision is there when you need it but I also have the ability to work independently and take on a lot of responsibility."* Things move even faster in small niche groups – we heard of at least one junior getting to argue in court.

A mix of large pharmaceutical companies, smaller tech startups, universities and other institutions fill the client roster in IP. Attorneys there choose to specialize in patent prosecution, patent litigation or trademark & copyright. *"Right off the back I'm the primary client contact on smaller cases,"* one IP junior ethused. *"Overall the seniors in the group have been pretty good about listening to what type of work associates want to do and making sure that happens at some point."* Associates in smaller departments also had relatively free rein: *"I'm surprised how much discretion I have and I think they trust juniors more at this firm."* In some cases, their work had a more local dimension compared to matters in the three largest practice groups,

resulting in less cross-office collaboration but more immediate client contact.

Offices

Many associates – particularly those in smaller offices – work with colleagues across the US. Some juniors felt that decision-making has become more centralized as the firm's expanded, but others reported that *"partners have enough authority in the smaller offices to not make them feel like satellites. At the same time it's nice that the bigger bases make an effort to pull us onto relevant projects."* Different digs have different specialisms: DC is the political law capital, for instance, while Palo Alto is an emerging companies hotspot.

"The bigger bases make an effort to pull us onto relevant projects."

Perkins Coie's bases can often be found within Wi-Fi range of their tech clients; one, for instance, is situated in *"the Pearl District, one of the hottest places in Portland,"* while another is nestled in SoMa, the *"epicenter of start ups"* in San Francisco. Those in New York liked the *"nice location"* of their 30 Rockefeller Plaza home, and added: *"We're split between floors 22 and 25, which is tricky, but it's great to work at 30 Rock!"* The Seattle HQ may never have inspired a network comedy, but sources labeled it *"a great building that balances modern and traditional styles. We all have sit/stand desks after the office was remodeled five years ago."*

Training & Development

Following a firm-wide new starter's retreat in October (hosted in Seattle), monthly departmental training sessions are broadcast by video conference across offices. Associates agreed that *"training is one thing the firm could improve on, as it feels quite broad. It would be more helpful to tailor training to more individual situations."* On the job learning therefore plays a major role in associate development, and it's something that *"happens naturally: I'm*

See firm profile on p.682

Diversity	Partners (%)	Associates (%)
Women	24.8	48.7
White	87.9	71.2
Black/African American	2.5	4.8
Hispanic/Latin American	3.1	6.3
Asian	4.9	13.8
Mixed/Other	1.6	3.9
LGBT	2.5	3.9

never scared to email a partner or senior counsel with a dumb question."

In addition to informal feedback, there's a *"very elaborate"* annual review system. First, juniors submit a self-evaluation to a partner outside their office and practice group. This allotted partner also receives evaluations from (nominated?) lawyers that an associate has worked with, and after collating the material arranges a meeting to suggest areas for improvement. *"It's very goal-oriented, and a really good process,"* sources said, though they admitted its usefulness is dependent on how much time partners can spare for it. To round everything off, juniors also receive a written summary of their performance from the associate evaluation committee.

Culture & Hours

Looking back fondly at their law school days to draw a comparison, one Perkins associate suggested the firm's atmosphere *"is like walking into the school library and hanging out with a study group. Everybody here really likes the law, and there's no competitive vibe among associates."* Others credited the lack of strife to *"people having a West Coast attitude"* whether they're in Seattle, California or the Eastern Seaboard. This extends to all attorney levels too: *"Very senior partners will just pop into my office and say hello."* Painting a picture of a *"pretty social environment in terms of amiability and sharing anecdotes in the hallway,"* interviewees nonetheless suggested *"there's not a lot of after-hours socializing,"* something some wanted to turn around. *"The social side depends on the practice group, and in some people have developed really strong relationships."*

Dishing out *"nothing but extreme praise"* when the time came to talk of transparency, sources reported that management *"is very open to disclosing financials and firm strategy to associates"* through quarterly meetings in each office. Director of recruiting and retention Mike Gotham cites *"transparency and accessibility of management"* as two keys planks of the firm's culture, citing extensive meetings with lawyers in different offices on the new bonus program as an example.

"Even if you don't hit hours targets, partners won't look down on you."

Previously based solely on the number of hours billed, associate bonuses are now determined via a more *"holistic"* approach, which takes into account broader firm contribution, client service and business development. *"It's still a bit unclear how that will affect us exactly,"* sources felt, *"but even if you don't hit hours targets, partners won't look down on you or hold it against you."* That said, most felt their goals were *"very achievable given the amount of work available, though it can require some work/life balance sacrifice."*

Perkins doesn't keep too close an eye on its associates' comings and goings, and new parents or those with commitments outside work are free to *"work normal 8.45am to 5.15pm office hours then go home – that's fully respected."* For others, the *"deviation in hours can be massive,"* but a flexible approach to remote working means juniors can be home in time for dinner, log back on later and still notch up the expected number of hours. Billing targets (ranging from 1,800 to 1,950 hours) and salaries are linked to local markets – for more information on recent changes, visit our website to read the full interview with Mike Gotham.

Pro Bono

There's no cap on the number of pro bono hours associates can count towards their billable targets. *"The firm is pretty highly committed to pro bono – I've never heard of anybody being told to do less, and one associate down the hall has billed 200 hours to one matter!"* However, we did hear that a case has to be made for matters that are likely to go above 100 hours.

Immigration and asylum matters are a Perkins mainstay; they've become even more common following the executive orders introduced by President Trump. Our sources also took on LGBT rights cases, landlord/tenant disputes and will drafting matters, and often took the lead on them. *"We get to run our own cases, but every week we also get matters circulated, which we can work on with support from partners."* Those who want to go the extra mile can apply for the Sher Kung Memorial Pro Bono Fellowship, which allows associates to devote six months wholly to pro bono.

Pro bono hours
- For all attorneys across all US offices: 56,717
- Average per US attorney: 60.8

See firm profile on p.682

Diversity

Gender diversity is *"strong among the associates and there are a lot of women at every level,"* but sources noted the industry-wide issue of firms struggling to maintain those numbers. The firm offers a reduced hours option so that attorneys working at a certain percentage of their expected billables will not have their progress to the partnership hindered – a scheme devised to ensure working mothers aren't disadvantaged. *"We did have one women on reduced hours for most of her tenure, and she made partner the first year she was up for it. They love to highlight her but she is an outlier at the moment."* Turning to racial and socioeconomic diversity, *"there's a lot to be improved, but the firm's attuned to it and trying to increase representation. The partnership group doesn't seem as ethnically diverse as it could be; associate-wise it's better but there's a long way to go."*

"It's great to see female partners helping other women make informed career decisions."

Two firm-wide diversity retreats take place every other year: one for women, and one for all other minorities. *"I went to this year's not knowing what it would be like,"* one source said, *"and it turned out to be an outstanding program. It's great to see female partners helping other women make informed career decisions."* The firm has several affinity groups and offers a 1L diversity fellowship scheme.

Strategy & Future

Perkins Coie prefers gradual refinement to revolutionary change. Mike Gotham tells us: *"The firm's offices have grown over the last several years as the economy has continued to strengthen. And we have more offices now as well. Our recruitment has kept pace with that growth."*

See firm profile on p.682

Pillsbury Winthrop Shaw Pittman

Lawyers per state

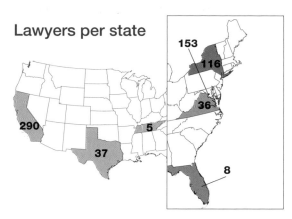

Largest US office: Washington, DC

US offices: 14

International offices: 7

First-year salary: $180,000

Billable hours: 1,950 target (bonus eligible at 1,900 and 2,000)

Summers 2018: 33 (all 2Ls)

Revenue 2017: $589.5 million (+2.8%)

Partners made in 2018: 7

Famous for: friendly folks; diversity milestones

It's not just dough that keeps Pillsbury's attorneys happy – the relatively relaxed culture, interesting practices and tight-knit office network are also key ingredients.

DIG around Pillsbury's website and you'll find a brochure titled 'The people here are really nice: and other nasty rumors about us.' It's full of wry observations like *"associates are just as valued as partners: it's hard to know whom to kiss up to,"* and plays up the firm's reputation as one of BigLaw's cuddlier beasts to the nth degree. Chairman David Dekker explains: *"Our hope is that money is not the only glue holding the firm together, this should also be a great place to come to work."*

Our associate sources assured us it's not all firm-generated hype, having *"noticed a lot of attorneys have been here their entire career. The people here are very welcoming and I'm genuinely happy to see them every day."* But these nice guys don't tend to finish last: cream of the crop *Chambers USA* rankings for IP, construction, technology and outsourcing stand out among others spanning corporate/M&A, insurance and more. Perhaps the firm's California heritage is what makes this a *"pretty relaxed"* place to be, despite all this success and expansion across 14 US offices – DC is now the largest base. An appealing array of practice areas and a commitment to diversity make this an attractive place to work.

The Work

Litigation and corporate are the two most common newcomer destinations, but other groups including environment, executive comp, finance, IP, real estate and public practices in DC recruit one or two juniors each year. In most departments, work assignment involves *"a bit of both partners approaching you and vice versa; it's more informal than at some other firms."* A partner oversees associates' workloads in larger teams to make sure nobody's got too much on their plate, and *"partners tend to be very on top of who's doing what. We submit self-assessments to let them know what we can and would like to take on."* Through this, our interviewees could guide their practice in the direction they chose.

"A lot of work comes from semiconductors and startups."

Open-minded corporate juniors tended to play the field initially, flirting with M&A, funds, venture capital and startup work. *"Companies come to us as a one-stop shop,"* they explained, with clients varying from local institutions to multinational big hitters. Down in future-focused Silicon Valley *"a lot of work comes from semiconductors and startups, but we also have some public clients."* Newbies cut their teeth assisting partners and handling diligence, before progressing to drafting and direct client contact. *"We get a lot of hands-on experience here. I think if that's what a junior's looking for then Pillsbury is the best place to do that."* Happy with their progress, sources pointed out: *"Early responsibility is the best way to learn.*

The Inside View

Rankings in *Chambers USA*

Construction	Intellectual Property
Corporate/M&A	International Trade
Employee Benefits &	Outsourcing
Executive Compensation	Real Estate
Energy & Natural	Retail
Resources	Startups & Emerging
Environment	Companies
Food & Beverages	Tax
Government	Technology
Insurance	Transportation

For detail on ranking tiers and ranking locations, visit
www.chambersandpartners.com

Recent work highlights

- Worked on IT corporation NTT Data's $3 billion acquisition of Dell's IT services and outsourcing
- Represented semiconductor manufacturer Exar in its $700 million cash sale to hardware company MaxLinear
- Acted for New York University in $1.47 billion litigation against Factory Mutual Insurance after denial of coverage of losses incurred by Superstorm Sandy
- Advised Citibank as part of $1.35 billion three-tranche syndicated loan facility for mobile phone network provider Digicel

We staff leanly so there's never a moment I'm wasting my time."

Insurance, antitrust, real estate, white-collar and classic commercial litigation are all up for grabs for young litigators. The clientele here is similarly varied, with a tech leaning in California especially (*"a lot of young tech startups come in on the corporate side, then we help them with litigation matters"*). Practice area teams tend to be smaller than the BigLaw norm, so *"you don't always get as varied a workload as in a place with 50 partners doing different things,"* but on the plus side *"juniors get a lot of experience early on."* Most moved quickly from research and document review to drafting reports and briefs, with some also logging court appearances.

Encouraged to push themselves, interviewees told us: *"I haven't been spoon-fed, but folks are really patient with me asking questions. I've really been able to take control of tasks given to me."* The story was similar in smaller departments, from which associates reported: *"You progress based on the ability you demonstrate rather than your class level"* and took *"sometimes terrifying"* early responsibility in their stride.

Training & Development

On top of training by doing (*"the really helpful side,"* according to some), first-years are all enrolled at Pillsbury University (PU), the firm's practice area-tailored CLE training department. *"The corporate group is big on monthly classes,"* while litigators can have a go at NITA's mock trial program – one junior declared it *"very good, you have three really intense days to put things together."* First-years can count 150 hours of PU training toward their billable requirements.

Following an informal midyear self-evaluation with two partners, associates go through a more rigorous end-of-year process centered on *"business development goals – it's a useful exercise."* Some had a *"mixed experience"* with

immediate feedback, but others reported: *"It's rare I don't hear back from the partner about a piece of work I've submitted."* The firm also runs a mentorship scheme which, aside from some complaints about delays replacing departed mentors, came in for praise.

Diversity

Pillsbury has a history of promoting female talent – it was the first Am Law 100 firm to be led by a woman, and one of the first to extend benefits to same-sex domestic partners. Living up to that legacy, 75% of the incoming 2017 partner class were women, and five of the firm's offices have female managing partners. Associates also commended *"good alternative work arrangements for lawyers with children"* and *"a strong LGBT initiative."* Every other year an 'attorneys of color' conference takes place and in 2017 the firm launched an LGBT retreat too. *"It ended with a practical discussion of steps we could take to recruit people from diverse backgrounds and help them progress. There've been some good ideas of how we can do better."* With some way still to go, *"the firm's willingness to put on events and contribute to causes has never been in question."*

75% of the incoming 2017 partner class were women, and five of the firm's offices have female managing partners.

Get Hired

"When interviewing I ask what adversity they've faced – it doesn't have to be a life or death situation, but I'd like to hear about how they work through challenges." For more interview advice, visit Pillsbury's profile on www.chambers-associate.com

Offices & Culture

San Francisco is the firm's birthplace (on the West Coast, at least), and its base there is *"in an older building, but*

See firm profile on p.683

The Inside View

Diversity	Partners (%)	Associates (%)
Women	23.5	46.7
White	88.4	70.0
Black/African American	1.6	3.9
Hispanic/Latin American	2.3	5.3
Asian	6.6	16.2
Mixed/Other	0.6	3.9
LGBT	3.6	3.9

the views are fantastic." Silicon Valley's newer office is contrastingly "more like a startup: we have video game machines in a collaborative area. the snacks are great, we get fed so well!" Over on the East Coast, the New York base's Times Square location "can be annoying, I sometimes don't leave until after 8pm when the streets are emptier," whereas DC's "location and facilities are top-notch. We can go up on the roof to hang out." Juniors agreed the firm has "worked very hard to integrate its offices," with a lot of collaboration in corporate and finance in particular. There's an incentive structure that rewards partners who staff matters across offices, which sources felt had "helped build the one-firm culture" since the legacy firms came together.

"Before starting here I bought some new suits as I anticipated being in one every day," one source recounted. "I was simultaneously pleased and disappointed to find we're a business casual firm!" Some felt this was "reflective of the California roots of the Pillsbury wing," but New Yorkers reported: "The culture here is more similar to Big Apple firms. Hitting billable targets is really pushed, but everyone still gets along really well." What do juniors put the firm's famous friendliness down to? "People seem to care about Pillsbury because most started as summers," they reasoned, plus "you work directly with partners a lot so it's not super hierarchical."

"You work directly with partners a lot so it's not super hierarchical."

Associates get pretty chummy too, with one shamelessly declaring: "We're an awesome group! There's a lot of camaraderie and goodwill to each other, and not a lot of cattiness, which is important working in law." Happy hours and outings "both organized and impromptu" provide opportunities for out-of-hours socializing, and juniors revealed: "We're trying to do more bonding events." As well as post-work soirées, the firm also hosts regular meetings to run associates through current and projected financials. There's also a yearly "road to partnership" session, and while "making partner isn't an easy slam dunk, we hire small classes for a reason and it's a real possibility" for those who want it.

Pro Bono

With no cap on the number of pro bono hours associates can bill, all attorneys are expected to contribute 25 hours annually. "The firm really pushes it, you can grow skills and give back at the same time" via monthly legal pitstop clinics and citizenship workshops as well as pro bono matters. Immigration and asylum cases have become particularly commonplace under the Trump administration. On top of that, corporate juniors worked pro bono for fledgling startups – "something that's definitely championed" – and Pillsbury's different offices collaborate on fundraising with local organizations.

Pro bono hours
- for all attorneys across all US offices: 42,216
- average per US attorney: 79.4

Hours & Compensation

A firm-wide billing target of 1,950 sits between thresholds of 1,900 hours to earn half the market bonus and 2,000 to get the full monty. First-years might struggle to get over the bar, but after that "there's more than enough work to go around, especially within corporate." Associates pointed out that "the cross-office firm structure means you can get work from anywhere across the country," and while "the requirements are important, if you're showing up and doing good work but billing 1,800 hours nobody will kick you out."

"It's really helped me keep my sanity."

7pm was the average home time for associates, within a wide range. "I've been fortunate to not have a ton of weekend or super late night work," one said, "it's really helped me keep my sanity." Pillsbury offers four weeks paid vacation; we heard "the firm is so flexible" and encourages juniors to take a decent amount of time off.

Strategy & Future

Chairman David Dekker tells us Pillsbury's "had 18 strong lateral partners join the firm during 2017," but suggests these and the opening of a new Miami office are "focused strategic additions, not an indication that we are looking to open a number of new offices over the coming year." The firm's been embroiled in high-profile merger talks three times over the last few years. Dekker explains: "Most firms in today's market would say merging is a possibility, but we don't feel compelled to merge. Certainly, we'd like to improve the breadth and depth of certain practices, and if there was a proposed combination that made that possible we wouldn't rule it out." To find out more about where Pillsbury will be going in future, read the full interview at www.chambers-associate.com.

See firm profile on p.683

507

The Inside View

Proskauer Rose LLP

Lawyers per state

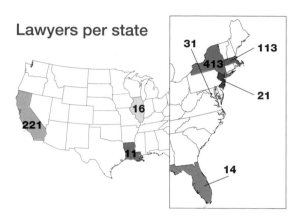

31   113
413
21
16
221
11
14

Largest US office: New York
US offices: 8
International offices: 5
First-year salary: $180,000 (New York, Boston, LA, DC and Chicago)
Billable hours: no requirement
Summers 2018: 63 (6 1Ls, 55 2Ls, 2 others)
Revenue 2017: $890.3 million (+4.4%)
Partners made in 2018: 10
Famous for: highly rated labor & employment practice; trusted adviser to the sports, media and entertainment industries in particular

Talents both mainstream and niche meet at this glitzy New Yorker, which has more A-listers on its books than an Oscars invite list.

IF firms could call upon their clients to help throw a party, Proskauer's would arguably be the best. Food would be supplied by the award-winning Blue Hill Farm restaurant, while live music would be performed by U2, Lady Gaga and Ariana Grande. The venue? MoMA would work well, as would the Lincoln Center. Some Major League Baseball clubs would help the party go with a swing, and enter some NFL and NBA teams, and you have something akin to a high net worth Woodstock.

This rather glamorous client roster has been acquired thanks to Proskauer's sterling reputation for labor & employment, sports, and media & entertainment work – all of these practices are awarded high marks in *Chambers USA*. *"A handful of firms are known for their strength in these practices but none of them have the clients we do,"* one thrilled associate declared. And while it's clear that Proskauer has *"strength in a lot of niche practice groups,"* juniors were also eager to get across that *"our firm is definitely a full-service one,"* with many other talents besides. These include Proskauer's work for investment funds, as well as its expertise in the capital markets, corporate/M&A, healthcare, insurance, and general commercial litigation spaces. All in all, Proskauer has

earned over 60 *Chambers USA* rankings between its eight offices nationwide.

Strategy & Future

Chairman Joseph Leccese tells us: *"2017 was a solid year for us: our bankruptcy team has been particularly busy, as we're representing the Financial and Oversight Management Board in connection with Puerto Rico's restructuring. In the transactional area our fund formation, private credit and M&A practices have continued to be very strong."*

"We want to continue to be at the cutting edge of all the major issues that affect employers."

Going into 2018 Proskauer is focused on *"trying to serve asset managers in every respect,"* Leccese adds. *"We brought in a large lateral group from Stroock that specializes in large mutual funds, which has really rounded out our asset management offering and provided us with an enormous amount of additional regulatory expertise."* The emphasis in litigation is on *"continuing to develop star trial lawyers, while in labor & employment we want to continue to be at the cutting edge of all the major issues that affect employers."*

The Work

Proskauer's corporate department took on the majority of juniors (almost 60% of those on our list). The litigation and labor & employment groups took on a significant

On chambers-associate.com...

- Get hired: how to get in the door
- More on the firm's offices and the Proskauer Institute

See firm profile on p.684

Rankings in *Chambers USA*

Banking & Finance	Labor & Employment
Bankruptcy/Restructuring	Latin American Investment
Capital Markets	Leisure & Hospitality
Corporate/M&A	Litigation
Employee Benefits &	Media & Entertainment
Executive Compensation	Private Equity
ERISA Litigation	Real Estate
Healthcare	REITs
Immigration	Sports Law
Insurance	Tax
Intellectual Property	Technology
Investment Funds	

For detail on ranking tiers and ranking locations, visit
www.chambersandpartners.com

Recent work highlights

- Represented Morgan Stanley as it took on the role of financial adviser to Starwood Waypoint during the real estate investment trust's $20 billion merger with Invitation Homes
- Successfully defended Lady Gaga against a copyright infringement suit brought by a French sculptor, who alleged that the singer's Born This Way album artwork infringed her work
- Secured a positive outcome for The New York Times on a partial motion to dismiss a class action filed by two of the newspaper's employees, who alleged that they were discriminated against on the basis of their age, race and gender
- Served as legal counsel and strategic adviser to Los Angeles 2028 (LA28) in connection with the city's successful bid to host the 2028 Olympic and Paralympic Games

chunk of the remaining associates, while a few joined areas like tax, real estate, private client and healthcare. Most juniors in the larger corporate, litigation and labor groups begin life as generalists, but in *"a recent change in approach the firm is requiring corporate juniors to join a designated subgroup after one year instead of two."* Legal directors are present in each group to get juniors ramped up when they first start and to serve as a safety net *"if you get stuck."* On the whole a more entrepreneurial approach is encouraged, and most juniors appreciated the opportunity to *"shape your path within certain parameters and foster relationships with partners who want to invest in you."*

Subgroups in corporate include private investment funds; private credit; private equity and M&A; capital markets; TMT; and restructuring & bankruptcy. The department is especially recognized in *Chambers USA* for its mid-market work in industries such as real estate, healthcare, finance and sports. On the capital markets side, our sources found themselves *"commenting on prospectuses, coordinating opinions, making sure filings comply with securities laws and reviewing credit facilities."* Others had been able to work on deals *"where it's just me, a partner and senior counsel, which allowed me to manage the process and complete first drafts of terms in agreements."*

Labor & employment is *"a huge practice area: the majority of associates do employment work, while some exclusively focus on labor matters – some do a bit of both."* The employment side is mostly contentious in nature, and spans class actions, wage and hour disputes, harassment claims, trade secrets cases and more. There's also some advisory work for employers like *"large telecom businesses, banks and major league sports teams."* On single-plaintiff cases *"you can do everything, including fact-gathering, conducting interviews and drafting motions to dismiss – the partner would work with me and deliver feedback."* Sources felt they played an integral role: *"As a junior you're the one*

who's closest to the facts, so even when a partner takes the first cut at something they'll ask for your opinion."* Labor-oriented work – which involves managing the relationships between unions and companies – was deemed by some to provide *"more hands-on opportunities, especially with regard to hearings and second-chairing depositions."*

Litigation covers *"general commercial, antitrust, contract, IP and white-collar disputes."* Interviewees here weren't *"stuck doing doc review all day,"* and when it came to motions *"you're more or less in charge of the minor ones, but can still have a crack at drafting the bigger ones too."* Often *"there's one person between you and the partner, especially in the IP/entertainment practice where they like to keep things lean. On the more partner-heavy cases you can do most of the research."*

Culture & Offices

Just over half of the juniors on our list were based in Proskauer's New York HQ. Boston and LA claimed around a fifth each, while the rest of our sample were spread thinly between the firm's Newark, Chicago, New Orleans, DC and Boca Raton offices. New York *"is the firm's flagship office, so it's bigger, pristine and can feel a bit more intimidating compared to other Proskauer offices (Boston is more relaxed, for example), but going by New York standards it's still pretty casual."* The building itself was *"built within the last ten years and is beautiful; we're right off of Times Square, which is perfect for transportation links, and the offices get lots of light thanks to floor-to-ceiling glass."* Juniors here share offices for the first two years before earning their own. *"The firm is flexible about allowing associates to work in different offices,"* said Newark juniors, who journeyed across the Hudson to work in the New York mothership from time to time. Further connections are fostered via Proskauer's videophone system, which enables frequent cross-staffing on matters:

The Inside View

See firm profile on p.684

Diversity	Partners (%)	Associates (%)
Women	17.1	48
White	92	74.3
Black/African American	2.7	2
Hispanic/Latin American	2.7	5
Asian	2.2	15.1
Mixed/Other	0.5	3.5
LGBT	1.8	3.3

"It's very much a seamless system, and I feel just as integrated with teams in the other offices as I do with those in my own."

"To fit in here it's imperative to have a sense of humor and to be able to roll with the punches."

So what are the unifying cultural traits across Proskauer's various bases? *"The people here are the type you'd want to grab a beer with,"* juniors suggested, adding: *"Other firms are too OCD about things and want to harp on about details to the nth degree. The result is that people become bland, dry and lose their energy."* They therefore agreed that Proskauer's more *"laid back and casual"* stance produced *"a sense of ease between associates and partners,"* and plenty of room for personalities to shine: *"Everyone has one! They try to avoid people who can't hold a conversation. People here have diverse interests, which means you can have thoughtful conversations on topics outside of the law and develop relationships that are not based solely on work."* Hiring partner Michael Mervis adds: *"A sense of humor is important. We are not looking for students who are accomplished but can't find the humor in things; we are a very team-oriented place."*

Training & Development

The 'Proskauer Institute' brings together all new associates in New York for a week of introductory training. *"It's a crash course that covers a lot of business training, and they bring in people from Columbia University to host sessions. It can feel a bit like that training is occurring in a vacuum, as during the first week you don't really know how to apply it and might forget points – something like it later on or a refresher would be beneficial."*

After this initial blast, first-years attend mandatory monthly trainings within their practice groups. *"There's a core curriculum program where seniors present to us on tangible topics and issues, like what to do when you receive a complaint."* Some of our sources found these sessions too general: *"They're for everyone in corporate, so there could be sessions on securities law and you can't do anything with that info as you're not focusing on that*

area." However, associates agreed that *"informal, on-the-job training is effective, and the associates and partners do take the time to explain things to you."* Labor & employment juniors were also happy to attend *"weekly meetings to discuss the latest developments in our group, how they are affecting our client population and our long-term strategy for dealing with them."* Departmental-specific sessions continue beyond the first year, and the firm also provides every associate with an annual budget which they can spend on external programs and Bar Association activities.

Pro Bono

"This is our 143rd year as a firm and we have a strong legacy of pro bono work that goes back generations," chairman JosephLeccese tells us, pointing to the success full-time pro bono partner Bill Silverman has had *"marshaling enthusiasm in our ranks and securing access to the best cases."* These efforts have not gone unnoticed by our sources, who told us that they *"love that Proskauer is passionate and committed to pro bono work. You can be riding the train in the morning, read about some horrendous decision our president has made and you can be sure that within an hour of getting to work, there will be an email saying something like 'Proskauer is teaming up with X to stand against Y' – it's very reactive to current needs."*

"It's very reactive to current needs."

There's no official limit to how many hours associates can commit to pro bono and every hour counts as billable. As a result, our interviewees had devoted time to advising human trafficking clinics, working on veteran assistance projects, facilitating Uvisas and representing those who've suffered domestic violence.

Pro bono hours
- For all US attorneys: 46,755
- Average per US attorney: 56.3

Get Hired

"Our questions are intended to draw out what makes candidates tick and how they will fit within our culture," says hiring partner Michael Mervis. Find out more about Proskauer's recruitment process on chambers-associate.com.

Hours & Compensation

There are no official billing requirements at Proskauer, but informal targets *"vary by practice group,"* juniors told us. In labor & employment, for example, *"there's an unspoken expectation that you'll reach 2,000 hours; they gen-*

See firm profile on p.684

erally track what the rest of the group is doing and if you ask the partner what the average is they'll tell you." Over in corporate and litigation juniors felt that billing 1,800 hours would stand them in good stead. While most juniors were grateful *"not to face the intensity of having to hit an exact number,"* those in corporate (*"where work-flow is more subject to peaks and troughs"*) admitted that *"there is some anxiety about working out how low your hours can go before you end up not receiving a bonus."* All bonuses are merit-based, however, and interviewees highlighted that the amount isn't significantly altered by the number of hours billed: *"Here you can bill 1,700 or 2,500 hours and you'll still get a similar bonus."*

Across the practice groups, the average working day lasted between 9/9.30am to 7/8pm. Of course, those hours are extended during busy times: *"You're at a BigLaw firm so people will expect you to put in some pretty serious hours at some points."* For litigators this meant working until 8.30pm and *"much later than that at times – sometimes for half the month, sometimes for all of it!"* Those in labor & employment were consistently busy, but found they didn't have to work *"under any unnecessary circumstances"* and received plenty of advanced warning when required to work additional hours (*"if you tell me on a Tuesday that I'll have to work Saturday then I'm fine with it!"*).

Diversity

"Over the last five years the firm has done a lot to incentivize women to stay," our female sources informed us. Two programs in particular were highlighted: *"There's a women's sponsorship program for fourth and fifth-year associates, which pairs up a number of women each year with senior partners, in order to equip them with the tools needed to succeed at a senior level. They also launched a parental leave program which enables primary caregivers to take paid leave for up to six months, and then for the following six months work 75% of your hours for 100% compensation."* These efforts were well received by female interviewees, with one telling us that *"the firm is responsive to our concerns – I feel comfortable enough to raise my observations with the male partners I work with."*

"Over the last five years the firm has done a lot to incentivize women to stay."

See firm profile on p.684

Reed Smith LLP

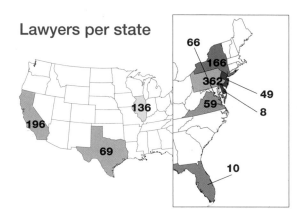

Lawyers per state

66
166
362
49
59
8
136
196
69
10

Largest US office: Pittsburgh
US offices: 15
International offices: 12
First-year salary: $130,000-$180,000
Billable hours: 1,900 target (2,000 to be bonus eligible)
Summers 2018: 59 (9 1Ls, 50 2Ls)
Revenue 2017: $1.119 billion (+4.1%)
Partners made in 2018: 17
Famous for: international reach, especially for shipping; Pittsburgh steel heritage

BigLaw on paper, though less so in culture, international Reed Smith is *"still very much in growth mode."*

"IF you're in BigLaw, you're a small cog in a big machine. Nobody knows who you are, and you will be working from sun up to sun down." Such appraisals of BigLaw life are cynical, but they remain prevalent – and it's down to firms to challenge them. This particular view originated from a source adamant to avoid *"going down 'that' route for the sake of it."* Similarly, another of our sources described being averse to *"using BigLaw as a springboard for a career."* The fact that Reed Smith won the affection of such exacting associates only demonstrates the strength of its offering. *"They were the first firm I interviewed with, and the more firms I interviewed with after, the more I realized how special they were,"* one source explained. *"It didn't feel stuffy or inauthentic."*

Add a bountiful business encompassing 1,800 attorneys and 28 offices worldwide, and any residing cynicism evaporates. Despite its existing magnitude, associates found themselves attracted by the fact that *"Reed Smith is a firm still very much in growth mode."* The firm has planted flags in Frankfurt, Singapore and Miami in recent years, while also boosting its European head count by 10% after taking on more than 50 lawyers from KWM in September 2016.

On chambers-associate.com...

- Get hired: tricks and tips for getting into Reed Smith
- Interviews with global managing partner Sandy Thomas and chief diversity officer John Iino

The firm services clients in all sorts of matters, excelling in certain states across bankruptcy, insurance, finance, M&A, labor & employment and more general litigation. This work crosses industries including entertainment & media, life sciences, shipping and finance, and its full breadth of expertise wins it 43 *Chambers USA* rankings.

The Work

Summers chose broadly whether to pursue a path in litigation or business & finance, each of which houses a number of subgroups. Complex litigation is the biggest litigation subgroup, while others include IP, life sciences, labor & employment, and data security & privacy. Transactional associates split into corporate & transactional advisory, real estate, energy & natural resources, and financial services, among others. Despite the divisions, sources emphasized a degree of flexibility. *"There are associates who, after trying litigation for a few months, are now fully transactional lawyers a year later."* Upon choosing either path, associates naturally gravitate toward a group which they are then placed into more formally after a few years. One junior who strayed into IP territory recalled *"one project turning into two, two turning into five, five turning into ten until I was doing exclusively IP ligation."*

"I felt like a fully fledged lawyer."

Complex litigation associates gain work via a free market, and cover a great breadth of work, especially since *"the insurance recovery, labor & employment and IP*

See firm profile on p.685

The Inside View

Rankings in *Chambers USA*

Antitrust	International Arbitration
Banking & Finance	Labor & Employment
Bankruptcy/Restructuring	Life Sciences
Construction	Litigation
Corporate/M&A	Products Liability
Healthcare	Real Estate
Insurance	Tax

For detail on ranking tiers and ranking locations, visit www.chambersandpartners.com

Recent work highlights

- Successfully dismissed a multibillion-dollar FCA (False Claims Act) suit from the US Department of Justice on behalf of healthcare provider HCR Manor Care
- Represented NRG energy in the $425 million sale of the Aurora and Rockford generating stations in Illinois
- Achieved an insurance bad-faith verdict for Mine Safety Appliances, achieving more than $50 million in damages for the company as it took on North River Insurance
- Defended M&T Bank successfully in a nationwide class action which alleged insufficient communication over the repossession of customers' vehicles

groups can also draw on associates from the group." Sources were happy to report that *"juniors do everything. There is some inevitable doc review but a lot of that gets pushed down to our contract attorneys and discovery team."* The breadth of work meant associates could, for example, see a mix of *"small, local, commercial real estate cases,"* and *"big national trials related to medical devices."* One junior recalled joining a *"trade secrets, fraud and conspiracy case early on. The case had been fast-tracked to be tied up in nine months so I hit the ground running. I was writing outlines for all of the depositions, going through all the discovery and then before trial, preparing the witnesses. Sitting across the table and talking strategy with the partner, I felt like a fully fledged lawyer rather than a junior associate."*

A fair amount of due diligence awaits corporate juniors, but sources were happy to report ongaining *"more substantive writing tasks as you get higher up."* Juniorsalso highlighted working on *"more significant issues on the regulatory and compliance side,"* throwing up opportunities for juniors to *"coordinate solutions with clients, draw up benefit plans structures with partners and coordinate research on agreements."* One corporate associate described working with clients across the spectrum, *"from local businesses to large international clients in deals ranging anywhere between $50 million to in excess of $1 billion."*

The energy & natural resources group offers incomers a blend of transactional and regulatory work, serving construction and utilities clients, wind turbine manufacturers, plus oil and gas producers and transporters. Juniors reported *"conducting compliance training for clients, revising documents and refitting memorandums."* The work varies between office. DC provides a regulatory angle through work with theFederal Energy Regulatory Commission. The firm's Houston base, which has seen growth in recent years, provides associates with more of a *"transactional slant,"* whereas the firm's HQ in Pittsburgh takes on a mix of both, with a notable environmental practice included too.

Training & Development

The firm's training resource, Reed Smith University, operates both internally and with the help of external providers. It's also linked to CareeRS, a firm-wide career development program which follows a litigation or corporate track. After a typical first week of introductory training, associates continue with training classes one to two times a week. *"The training tends to be more focused on general skills that are applicable across the board,"* sources noted, adding that *"we also have free membership of the PLI (Practising Law Institute) which has some more practice group specific training on it. It's very much on us to sign up for things."* First-years are also invited to pick their own careers advice mentors *"who help put together a plan of what your first year is going to look like."*

Juniors carry out yearly self-reviews too. *"It's not just something you can bang out in a couple of hours. Essentially you have to evaluate your performance in everything from business development to leadership skills. It can feel kind of laborious but it does make you sit down, really reflect on what you've done, and set up a game plan for next year. "*

Pro Bono

Associates can count 120 hours of pro bono work as billable, for individual cases or as part of the firm's formal program. Cases range from asylum, immigration, and domestic abuse to corporate governance matters and nonprofit mergers. Several juniors mentioned their involvement in the Name Change Project, which helps transgender people to change their names. That often sees associates pair up with local law students to help draft any necessary documents required by the court. *"Pro bono is something that is clearly important to the firm because when you walk down the halls, each of the offices have plaques showing how much pro bono you have done,"* one Chicago associate observed. *"The firm has a lot of relationships with nonprofits and if you want go out and forge your own relationships, the firm will encourage you to do that."*

See firm profile on p.685

The Inside View

Diversity	Partners (%)	Associates (%)
Women	23.3	48.7
White	88	77.9
Black/African American	4.1	5.1
Hispanic/Latin American	2.2	6.3
Asian	4.6	8.1
Mixed/Other	1.1	2.6
LGBT	2.2	3

Pro bono hours
- For all US attorneys: 56,310
- Average per US attorney: 59

Culture & Offices

As mentioned previously, associates found the firm's cultural merits clearly on show right off the bat. *"After my OCI, I followed up by thanking one of my interviewees. They then spent an hour personally helping me to prepare for the callback, explaining what the firm was like and how to best prepare myself. My face hurt so much from smiling and laughing – there was just such a great energy."*

> *"My face hurt so much from smiling and laughing – there was just such a great energy."*

Collaboration in particular came to the fore in discussions about the firm's culture. Departments aren't *"siloed,"* and associates told us: *"The firm does an excellent job of dividing the work, encouraging attorneys to meet each other by acknowledging expertise in other groups."* For a few associates each year, there's even the possibility of embarking on an international secondment to tighten those cross-border bonds. Still, sources identified some differences between offices. For example, the firm's LA office was highlighted as being a lot quieter, owing to the fact that *"a lot of people work remotely."* Sources interpreted this as *"good for those who like a flexible schedule, but bad for those who like having partners around."* Those in Chicago felt they had more of a *"unique, small-firm feel,"* owing to the fact that they *"used to be a prominent Chicago firm before being 'acquired' by Reed Smith."* Across all offices though, sources agreed that Reed Smith is a place of *"less criticism and more encouragement,"* where juniors can *"feel comfortable making mistakes and approaching partners."*

Most juniors reside in Chicago, Pittsburgh, Philadelphia, San Francisco and New York. A handful could also be found in each of the other California offices, as well as Texas and DC, with a few spread across the firm's Virginia and New Jersey offices. All juniors have their own offices except in New York, where space is significantly more expensive.

Diversity

37.5% of partners are female or otherwise diverse at Reeds, reflecting an above-average commitment to diversity which recently saw the firm signing up to the Mansfield Rule. Similar to the NFL's Rooney Rule, this *"mandates that law firms will be required to certify, with respect to specific appointments such as partnership, director and committee positions, that the considered talent pool is at least 30% women and minority attorneys,"* according to John Iino, the firm's chief diversity officer. *"Last year we set out our 2020 plan where we identified four specific strategic drivers: quality aligned with productivity, revenue, raising brand awareness, and the fourth is the recruitment and retention of diverse talent. When diversity is one of the firm's four strategic pillars you know that the attention on this is at the highest level."*

His impressive rhetoric is validated by juniors' own experiences, and they praised the strength of the firm's affinity groups. WINRS (Women's Initiative Network of Reed Smith) *"has a huge presence in the firm,"* one source explained, and provides *"support through a backbone of strong women."* The group frequentlyputs on seminars on topics such as communication and networking. We also heard of juniors being sent to a number of external events, including leadership programs and statewide conferences. Even in regions typically considered less diverse, associates highlighted that *"we do a lot to push LGBT initiatives."*

Hours & Compensation

Juniors must aim to hit 1,900 billable hours, but profit-sharing bonuses only kick in at 2,000. *"They're not going to fire you if you don't hit that,"* sources assured us, adding that *"they will work with you to make you more productive and efficient."* Most juniors reported getting in between 8am and 9am, and leaving somewhere between 6:30pm and 8:30pm, with *"few breaks where you aren't billing."* When really stretched, associates reported 12-hour days, andfor many associates a typical week included a few hours working from home in the evening, though sources stressed that most *"try to avoid working weekends."*

The firm doesn't look too harshly on juniors taking time off: *"I was worried about my reputation after taking a week off early on in the year but the partners encouraged me to do so – it definitely hasn't affected my reputation with the firm."* Similarly another associate happily reported *"taking a couple of weeks off to recharge after a major trial."* One thing to note is the regionally dependent sal-

See firm profile on p.685

ary. New York falls in line with Cravath's $180,000 salary for first years, but other offices are less generous.

Strategy & Future

The firm recently opened a Miami office, a move that was *"a reflection of our increasing amount of Latin American work, and the importance of our international arbitration practice,"* says global managing partner Sandy Thomas. He adds that *"the firm is one year into our four-year plan. We have a very specific spreadsheet which measures our progress against annual objectives."* At its heart is a sector-based strategy, which is focused on the life sciences & healthcare, finance, media & entertainment, energy & natural resources and shipping industries. *"We want to deepen our expertise with those clients,"* says Thomas.

Get Hired

"With other interview teams you could tell that they hadn't ever met and the process seemed like a burden, but with Reed Smith it seemed like they were excited to talk to you. It was much more of a dialogue than forced interview questions." Find out more about the process of getting hired by Reed Smith by visiting chambers-associate. com.

See firm profile on p.685

The Inside View

Ropes & Gray LLP

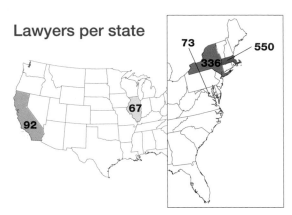

Lawyers per state

73 550
336
67
92

Largest US office: Boston
US offices: 6
International offices: 5
First-year salary: $180,000
Billable hours: no requirement
Summers 2018: 175 (6 1Ls, 164 2Ls, 3 3Ls, 2 SEO)
Revenue 2017: undisclosed
Partners made in 2018: 12
Famous for: private equity; Bostonian roots

Like a modern-day Paul Revere, Ropes & Gray is riding out valiantly from Boston. It has a plan to grow in the US and internationally.

"ROPES is the place to be if you want to practice law in Boston." A bold claim, declared proudly by a number of Ropes associates who were confident in their choice of a firm that combined the perks of BigLaw with an *"as-good-as-it-can-be work-life balance."* Just what 'as good as it can be' means we'll come to later, but with ten top *Chambers USA* rankings in Massachusetts and the largest lawyer head count of any firm in the state, Ropes' reputation as a *"regional powerhouse"* is certainly well deserved.

"We've entered 2018 in a very strong position."

Ropes is not a firm content with being a big fish in the little pond of Beantown, however. The majority of its US lawyers are actually based outside the Bay State – the New York office in particular is chunky in size and ranked by *Chambers USA* for litigation, corporate and other areas. The firm is also Chambers-ranked in Chicago, California, DC and nationwide. International expansion has been the name of the game in the past decade with new offices opening in Tokyo, London, Shanghai and Seoul. London, Hong Kong and New York are key to the firm's five-year growth plan that culminates in 2020. *"The firm ended 2017 with solid momentum, which means we've en-*

tered 2018 in a very strong position," managing partner David Chapin tells us.

It's not all been plain sailing though: at least 22 partners left the firm in 2017 including seven who joined Kirkland & Ellis in London, Hong Kong, New York, Chicago and Boston. To stem the tide of departures, associates have been offered retention bonuses of up to $50,000 to stay. David Chaplin asserts: *"Elite attorneys continue to move from other top-tier firms to us, and our clients are bringing their most challenging and interesting work to us."* Our sources didn't appear too concerned: *"The firm's leadership has been very transparent about the departures – we knew internally before it was in the news. I don't think many of us have plans to leave."*

The Work

The overwhelming majority of Ropes' junior associates work within the broad corporate and litigation groups. The remainder can be found in tax & benefits, private client and business restructuring. In the two 'supergroups' most associates start out as generalists. In corporate, juniors select two 'buckets' to draw work from, picking from general corporate; private equity; investment funds; and healthcare, real estate and life sciences. The litigation practice covers business & securities, government enforcement, antitrust and IP. (One thing to note is that a number of the firm's IP lawyers left by mutual consent in 2017 to set up their own boutique, but Ropes still has a significant IP practice.) After two years juniors join one specific subgroup.

On chambers-associate.com...

- Get hired: tips from hiring partner Peter Erichsen
- Interview with managing partner David Chapin

See firm profile on p.686

Rankings in *Chambers USA*

Antitrust	Healthcare
Banking & Finance	Intellectual Property
Bankruptcy/Restructuring	Investment Funds
Capital Markets	Labor & Employment
Corporate Crime &	Life Sciences
Investigations	Litigation
Corporate/M&A	Privacy & Data Security
Employee Benefits &	Private Equity
Executive Compensation	Real Estate
FCPA	Tax

For detail on ranking tiers and ranking locations, visit
www.chambersandpartners.com

Recent work highlights

- Advised Bain Capital on the €2.27 billion sale of cosmetics maker Carver Korea to Unilever
- Secured victory for Boston Children's Hospital in a dispute over stolen data that contained potentially valuable research on cutting-edge anti-obesity drugs
- Has advised global investment management giant PIMCO on the formation of over 25 hedge funds and private equity funds totalling over $25 billion in assets since 2010
- Acted for Massachusetts-based biotech multinational Bioverativ on the $825 million acquisition of True North Therapeutics

Ropes has a formal work assignment system. *"There is an entire staffing department dedicated to getting you a wealth of experience in your first two years so you can make an educated decision about what you want to do next."* Each practice area has an associate development manager (ADM) who takes in requests for juniors from partners and senior associates and then dishes out assignments. Interviewees said around half their work comes from the ADM – the rest comes from *"attorneys coming to you directly: a lot of people reconnect with those they worked with during their summer, and when you begin developing a specialty the same people keep coming back to you."* Most sources were content with the system, though some litigators in Boston highlighted that *"recent turnover in the centralized staffing team has brought with it some growing pains; there doesn't seem to be a lot of insight from the staffing partners into the work associates are doing."* Juniors also called for more clarity on the time needed for assignments. One said: *"What's advertised as a five-hour task could turn into a much longer project which becomes difficult to plan around."*

"There is an entire staffing department dedicated to getting you a wealth of experience."

Private equity and investment management are a particular focus of the corporate group, and clients include *"some of the best"* in the industry like Blackstone, PIMCO, TPG Capital and Bain Capital. *"You have to assist these big firms with hedges that are incredibly complicated,"* an interviewee reflected. Associates cut their teeth conducting reviews of registration statements, drafting regulatory applications, liaising with clients, drafting ancillary documents and coordinating strategy with partners. *"I appreciate the fact that I could immediately interact with clients as a first and second year,"* one source said.

The firm's healthcare practice, which sits within corporate, is top-ranked nationally by *Chambers USA*. Juniors *"get to see a range of transactional work through the lens*

of the healthcare sector," an interviewee said. *"I've done private equity work, looked into tax exemptions, and dealt with mergers and acquisitions of academic medical centers. There's also a great deal of regulatory research. Some clients might want a 50-state survey of regulators looking into specific rules that might affect their products or activities."*

Over in litigation, one budding junior provided us with a snapshot of their working life: *"On my favorite case, I was on a trial team which ended up taking a case to trial in state court. Initially I did the document review and preliminary research to support the claim, but as the case went on I did the preparation for depositions, attended the trial and even got to examine a witness."* Another junior told us: *"At the start I was reviewing discovery documents and helping to develop the facts. During the later stages of the case, I was involved in drafting motions to compel and deposition outlines."*

Training & Development

If you love to learn, you'll be pleased to hear that *"Ropes is a firm that prides itself on its formal training,"* sources agreed. *"We have resources on anything you can imagine."* These include dedicated writing coaches and *"tons of helpful materials that you can print out and refer to later."* A program called 'Bills, Bills, Bills' – not the Destiny's Child song – offers associates instruction on *"how to bill correctly so partners don't have to go back and correct things."* All this is supplemented by practice-group specific training. One litigator sung the firm's praises for offering *"a practical deposition workshop right before I had a real one!"*

"We have resources on anything you can imagine."

While all our interviewees appreciated *"the great job the firm does in providing the best opportunities for formal training,"* some sources – particularly in litigation – felt this sometimes comes at the expense of informal on-

See firm profile on p.686

The Inside View

Diversity	Partners (%)	Associates (%)
Women	24.7	48.5
White	85.4	72
Black/African American	2.1	4
Hispanic/Latin American	0.4	2.8
Asian	1.7	11.2
Mixed/Other	10.5	10.1
LGBT	2.1	5.4

the-job training. An interviewee reflected: *"With some partners it feels like my work is going three levels up the food chain without me receiving feedback despite it being changed into something completely different."* Sources acknowledged having *"different experiences with different partners,"* with some noting that *"there is a tendency among some partners to be professorial."*

Pro Bono

Asked for evidence of the firm's commitment to pro bono, sources pointed to the fact that *"Ropes lawyers were physically in the airports trying to get people through after Trump's executive order banning people from certain countries from the United States."* The team was headed up by Boston-based pro bono cochair Jennifer Rikoski. In November 2016 the firm also joined GLBTQ Legal Advocates & Defenders and the Massachusetts Transgender Political Coalition in launching a program to provide legal guidance to help transgender people update identity documentation.

On average, Ropes attorneys record over 100 hours of pro bono a year and we heard of some associates billing upwards of 500 hours *"without anyone saying it's too much."* Associates agreed that the firm *"encourages you to use pro bono as a chance to gain experiences you don't normally get – I've done lots of writing that I hadn't had enough experience of on paid work."* An unlimited number of pro bono hours can be counted toward the billable hours target.

Pro bono hours
- For all US attorneys: 132,385
- Average per US attorney: 119

Diversity

With women accounting for almost a quarter of the partnership, Ropes is at the higher end of the spectrum compared to other firms when it comes to gender diversity. Sources did point out that they'd like to see an increase in the representation of ethnic minorities; at the moment just under 15% of partners are from a minority ethnic background, which is around the average recorded by

the firms in our guide. *"We do have a dedicated diversity partner and there are initiatives in place, but the firm still isn't where it needs to be,"* one source asserted. Associates pointed to a Women's Forum and diversity lunch initiatives as evidence that the firm is making efforts but also acknowledged that *"it takes more than lunches and dinners to change the statistics."*

On the positive side it's worth adding that the firm has elected Julie Jones to start as chair in 2020 – the first woman to hold that post in the firm's 152-year history. Ropes also puts its money where its mouth is: its Roscoe Trimmier Diversity Scholarship provides five 2Ls with $25,000 each.

Culture & Hours

As mentioned above associates said the work-life balance at Ropes is *"as good as it can be."* What does that mean? *"I think it has something to do with being a behemoth in Boston,"* one junior mused, adding: *"I think that here your time is respected more than at the big Wall Street firms. The partners are compassionate and are generally concerned about your welfare when you're working late into the night."* What's that? Working late into the night? Yes, a regular day in the office may be a reasonable 9am to 7pm, but prospective juniors should still expect to work some long slogs typical of a top firm. *"During the busiest periods,"* one associate reported, *"I'm in the office until 8pm and then go home, log in at around 10pm and work until midnight."* Working from home is made sweeter by the $500 associates receive to set up a home office. One interviewee enthused: *"With two large screens and a wireless keyboard and mouse, my home setup is now nicer than my work setup!"* Most of our interviewees said they take advantage of the firm's *"flexible approach to working"* by working at least one day every two weeks out of the office.

> *"I think it has something to do with being a behemoth in Boston."*

Associates also found that *"any fears of getting a bad reputation for taking time off"* were unfounded. One reported: *"I had to take two week off during the middle of a deposition and the senior associates were more than understanding. The firm wasn't emailing me constantly – my coworkers are always there to pick up the slack. Even partners sometimes muck in on work way below their pay grade, which I hugely respect."* Our interviewees also appreciated the firm's *"below-market billable hours target"* which they felt afforded *"more time and space to figure things out independently."*

Our interviewees appreciated the option Ropes offers of becoming a career associate or counsel as alternatives to

See firm profile on p.686

the path to partnership. One said: *"We have quarterly meetings with an attorney development partner who discusses our long-term plans, even if those might not be with the firm. We are proud of people who go into state and local government or in-house positions – leaving the firm is not considered a taboo subject."*

Offices

Juniors here acknowledged that *"Boston definitely feels like the HQ, but New York also has its own identity."* (The recently expanded New York office shares a building with Fox News and *"famous correspondents are recognizable by their large hair and make-up."*) We heard that *"there is a bit of friendly rivalry between the offices – we are jealous that Chicago has jeans Friday which we don't!"* However, other sources mused that the amount of cross-staffing means that *"any serious rivalry is impossible,"* adding that *"communication is almost completely seamless."* The firm also maintains a *"visitors policy,"* allowing associates to work out of other offices freely in what is *"a good opportunity to meet attorneys in other offices who you frequently work with in person."*

Strategy & Future

"Our strategy has been to sustain our momentum, and to grow at the same time," managing partner David Chapin tell us. *"The firm is expanding in areas that play to our strengths, in particular private equity, bankruptcy, M&A and investment funds - as they all complement the outstanding practices we have around the world. We're also focused on things we think we do well, and we're investing in those areas, including advising large financial institutions."* For more from Chapin, go to chambers-associate.com

Get Hired

"We have a more thorough and in-depth evaluation process than most firms. We're looking long-term, so we want to make as thoughtful a decision as possible," hiring partner Peter Erichsen tells us. To find out more about what this process involves, read our full interview with Erichsen on chambers-associate.com

The Inside View

See firm profile on p.686

Schulte Roth & Zabel LLP

Lawyers per state

19

331

Largest US office: New York

US offices: 2

International offices: 1

First-year salary: $180,000

Billable hours: 2,000 target

Summers 2018: 41 2Ls

Revenue 2017: $424.1 million (+3.6%)

Partners made in 2018: 2

Famous for: world-dominating hedge funds expertise; intimate scale; vibrant social scene

Schulte may put the 'fun' in investment fund management, but its top-quality work and enviable client list show that it means business.

ESTABLISHED in 1969, Schulte is a New York-centered firm with impressive credentials in the investment management space. *"Schulte is known for its funds expertise, and it permeates everything at the firm,"* juniors told us, who added that it was this *"very interesting line of work"* that attracted them in the first place. The firm's hedge funds know-how in particular picks up top awards in both *Chambers USA* and *Chambers Global*, giving Schulte kudos on both the national and worldwide stage. Despite this international renown, Schulte has a small physical presence that consists of just three bases: on home soil, its New York HQ is accompanied by a 19-lawyer DC office, which has a growing reputation for white-collar and government investigations work. Overseas, a base in London rounds out the firm's offering.

Our interviewees felt that Schulte's more navigable size forged a sociable and more relaxed culture: *"It's a smaller firm so you get to know everyone much better. I feel lucky to be part of a class of 30 rather than 80."* But as chair of the executive committee Alan Waldenberg explains, a smaller scale means that Schulte also attracts those on the more ambitious and confident side of the personality spectrum: *"It's an easier place to shine but it's also a more difficult place to hide compared to our competitors. If you*

On chambers-associate.com...

- Interview with chair of the executive committee Alan Waldenberg
- Tips from associates on getting hired

want to go through the motions and sit in a big pool of associates this isn't the place for you."

Those who had decided that Schulte was the one for them typically found themselves based in the New York HQ (DC usually takes on one or two newbies each year), which *Chambers USA* also acknowledges for its corporate/M&A, bankruptcy/restructuring, real estate and tax expertise.

Strategy & Future

"I always say, if it's not broken, don't fix it," chair of the executive committee Alan Waldenberg tells us. Schulte's plans for the future are therefore crystal clear: *"We want to continue to grow in our core practices but we don't see any need to shift course. We're not going to start new practice areas or open 27 foreign offices in five years' time just because our competition has."*

The Work

Around a quarter of the associates on our list were based in the investment management practice, but the firm's litigation and M&A and securities practices also housed a fair number of juniors. The remainder were split between the finance, individual client services, structured finance and derivatives, real estate, business reorganization, and tax groups. Each group has an assignment coordinator, but the extent to which they are relied upon varies by practice. What typically happens is that *"as you progress things become more 'free market' – you gravitate toward*

See firm profile on p.687

The Inside View

Rankings in *Chambers USA*

Bankruptcy/Restructuring	Investment Funds
Capital Markets	Litigation
Corporate/M&A	Real Estate
Employee Benefits &	Tax
Executive Compensation	

For detail on ranking tiers and ranking locations, visit
www.chambersandpartners.com

Recent work highlights

- Advised over 400 hedge fund manager clients on the formation and structuring of numerous multibillion-dollar funds, including large fund operators like Centerbridge Partners, Perella Weinberg Partners and Trian Fund Management
- Represented the former chief scientist of pharma company Merck during various securities actions that arose out of Merck's decision to withdraw its arthritis drug Vioxx from the market in 2004
- Acted for Cerberus Capital Management – one of the world's largest private equity fund managers – as it purchased Bushkill Group, a vacation property ownership company, from Resorts Group

the partners you enjoy working with, or you're asked to work for a specific client."

Those in investment management work *"primarily on hedge fund formations and management matters."* Juniors had helped to form *"funds worth over $1.5 billion"* and enjoyed *"taking these entities through the launching to the trading phase."* They also praised the lean staffing model (teams often consist of just a junior, a mid-level and a partner), but admitted that at times *"it's a bit trial by fire."* On the plus side small teams mean that there's *"regular contact with clients, who inquire about certain forms and so on; I'm currently helping with a fund's strategy and the client calls me twice a week."* The highs include *"learning how to do launches by just doing them,"* which gives juniors exposure to subscription documents. Matters typically cover multiple jurisdictions, including the Cayman Islands and the UK.

"You can build your own niche here."

The litigation department works on *"a plethora of matters,"* and juniors don't typically specialize in one area. Sources had dipped their toes into SEC work relating to hedge funds, proxy litigation matters, white-collar crime cases, government investigations and regulatory issues. Associates generally praised the variety of work available, which included *"drafting everything from complaints and motions to substantive briefs."* Those on regulatory matters revealed: *"The bulk of my time is spent drafting letters to government agencies, and I've spent a ton of time preparing witnesses."* Many were *"thankful"* for the amount of face time they got with partners: *"A lot of firms tell you they'll give you all these experiences but I've really found that to be true here."*

Over in M&A and securities, the group encompasses traditional M&A, shareholder activism, capital markets and securities work. *"I focus on one sub-group, but if I wanted to take on something else it would be very easy to ask them to bring me in on it. You can build your own niche here,"* one insider explained. *"On a complex deal the senior attorney oversees the more primary documents, but juniors still get to handle entity formation checklists, ancillary documents and signature pages."* With M&A deals, tasks depend on whether Schulte is representing the buyer or the seller: *"On the seller side you get to be responsible for data requests, negotiating nondisclosure agreements, and turning edits on share purchase agreements. On the buyer side you're doing more due diligence – someone has to do it and that someone will always be the junior!"*

Training & Development

An orientation period in New York gives juniors a chance to *"figure out the IT and billing systems, as well as the more substantive stuff like the nature of the client base – associates can come in with very little knowledge of hedge funds and that type of entity."* Following this, associates attend various *"boot camps"* that are tailored to their practice. Litigators, for example, *"go through training sessions for the first two years; right off the bat they're hosted by partners and associates every week, and they focus on specific things like how to draft pleadings and respond to document requests – they're really valuable for first-years."* M&A associates had enjoyed a similar experience: *"There seem to be boot camps every other week!"*

Culture

Most firms see a spike in social activity during the summer, but Schulte really knows how to host a memorable summer program. We heard of associates enjoying Beyoncé and Nicki Minaj concerts, go-karting expeditions and excursions to Nike's flagship store to design their own sneakers. The fun doesn't stop there, however: *"The firm really does foster the idea of hanging out together. There are monthly associate lunches in huge conference rooms, parties all the time, and movie evenings where they rent out a theater and show movies before general release."* Other sources highlighted how social their practice group was: *"This team hosts impromptu happy hours and we recently did an escape room. Our social events usually involve an unreasonable amount of food too…"*

See firm profile on p.687

The Inside View

Diversity	Partners (%)	Associates (%)
Women	12	42
White	89	73
Black/African American	2	2
Hispanic/Latin American	2	3
Asian	3	13
Mixed/Other	1	2
LGBT	2	4

"...you can have a beard. It doesn't matter."

Back in the office, interviewees pitched the overarching culture as "*laid back and friendly; it's a little more casual, which I like, and people often stop by to chat.*" The firm promotes a more dressed-down, "*less prim and proper*" environment, which is most evident on "*jeans Fridays.*" However, on any given day "*it's very rare to see someone in a tie if they don't have a meeting or court appearance scheduled. You can dress how you want; you can have a beard. It doesn't matter. You can be yourself – many people have different personalities here, so there's no need to conform.*"

Offices

The firm's midtown office in Manhattan has been undergoing a revamp of late, so "*everything's brand new; it's all glass and very hi-tech, with sit/stand desks that go up and down electronically.*" The tech upgrade includes a new phone system "*called 'Loop Up,' which enables you to see who's talking when you're on a call with multiple people.*" At the time of our calls, the firm was also in the process of distributing laptops that associates can dock at their desks to serve as their main computer (making it easier for juniors to work remotely if needed).

Hours & Compensation

Juniors must reach a target of 2,000 hours each year to qualify for a bonus, and they can count 200 hours (and potentially more if they petition) of time spent on any mix of pro bono, marketing, writing, recruitment and other approved non-billable work toward it. "*It's transparent,*" sources reported merrily. "*The compensation system is pretty fair: the salaries are all lockstep and there are additional payment tiers for the bonus when you bill 2,300 and 2,500 hours – it's nice to know you'll be rewarded.*"

"It's nice to know you'll be rewarded."

The 2,000-hour target means that "*you need to fill up the majority of your day.*" But what that day looks like often depends on the individual: "*There are people who prefer to work from 9am until 7pm, and have that consistent eight-*or nine-hour grind, while others will work some 15-hour days and then some where they leave by 3pm.*" Those in investment management explained that "*you can foresee the long days and plan accordingly,*" while their colleagues in other transactional groups like M&A and securities said that "*it really does fluctuate; I've done a couple of true all-nighters, and there are times when I'm here until 2am, but that's not the norm.*"

Diversity

"*On observation, no, we're not very diverse,*" associates declared, "*but once you're here on the inside you see that we do a very good of promoting it, especially with regards to women; we also have a small but strong LGBT community that does a good job.*" While "*we don't have that many women in leadership positions, those who are take on an incredible amount of responsibility.*" Sources put the lack of diversity in the partnership down to the fact that "*not many people make partner here, and that limits the potential for renewal.*"

Pro Bono

There is a senior attorney who coordinates pro bono and circulates opportunities around the firm: "*He's extremely active, and is constantly sending around emails, which is nice because you don't have to seek the work out.*" Litigators told us that "*pro bono is becoming a bigger deal, but the reality is that most associates are too busy to take on huge projects. There are associates that prioritize them though.*"

Those in the transactional groups, however, explained that "*if you want to do it you can, but you don't get the feeling that it's encouraged.*" Others agreed: "*You're not forgiven for getting behind on your billable work because you've been on pro bono.*" Those who'd taken on projects had worked on matters related to family law, the Innocence Project, green card/U visa applications and liability waivers for charities. All attorneys are encouraged to log a minimum of 30 pro bono hours each year.

Pro bono hours
- For all US attorneys: 12,289
- Average per US attorney: 36

Get Hired

"We want people who want to get their feet wet as soon as they walk through the door," says chair of the executive committee Alan Waldenberg. For more recruitment insight from Waldenberg and Schulte's associates, go to chambers-associate. com

See firm profile on p.687

The Inside View

Seward & Kissel LLP

Lawyers per state

15
156

Largest US office: New York
US offices: 2
International offices: 0
First-year salary: $180,000
Billable hours: 2,000 target
Summers 2018: 11 (11 2Ls)
Revenue 2017: undisclosed
Partners made in 2018: 1
Famous for: investment funds, maritime finance; associate satisfaction

A New York midsizer specializing in shipping and hedge funds: not the obvious backdrop for one of the happiest associate cohorts in our guide.

SEWARD associates are a happy bunch. When we asked them why things are going well for them their responses didn't reveal any kind of magic formula or especially fancy perks – there aren't ball pits or PlayStations littering the office, for example. Instead, the firm's secret to success is humbler and much more lawyerly: associates just *"genuinely like their job."* The reasons for this satisfaction soon became clear in our interviews: *"You really do feel very involved in the assignments,"* reflected one associate. Another added: *"We're doing top-quality work, but the size isn't overwhelming."* The firm is just shy of 180 lawyers, most in New York and a few more in DC. The size, associates told us, *"means lean staffing,"* fostering independence in the juniors, who *"generally work directly with a partner."*

In addition, our annual research shows that firms with a certain specialist leaning are home to happier associates, and Seward is well known for its expertise in hedge funds and shipping work. These two pillars receive strong rankings in *Chambers Associate*, and Seward's reputation in the former is more than just well established– the firm set up the world's first hedge fund, A.W. Jones & Co., in 1949. According to managing partner James Cofer, these practice areas will remain key focuses. The firm will *"continue to grow its capabilities in the investment man-*

agement space. In the shipping industry we are looking for more things to do, whether that be restructuring debt, innovative finance techniques or capital markets."

The Work

In the NY office, future associates list their top four preferences and are informed of their placement beforehand. The majority of incomers end up in investment management, with the next largest group going to corporate finance, leaving a few to head into litigation, employee benefits and tax. Things are less regimented in the DC office, which only offers places in investment management. It's a *"much smaller office, you start out getting assignments from all the partners and then you find your own niche."*

"I love learning about how people from different countries run their companies."

Seward's investment management group can claim an impressive market share, counting 40% of the top 100 hedge funds as clients, based on assets under management. The department does *"a lot of structuring and launching of funds. We also deal with a fair amount of offshore counsel in the Cayman Islands and the UK, so we end up with a decent amount of international exposure."* The work itself might involve *"reviewing and providing advice on marketing materials for our clients, or providing comments on their website disclaimers. A lot of time,*

On chambers-associate.com...

- Get hired: more on recruitment at Seward

See firm profile on p.688

The Inside View

Rankings in *Chambers USA*

Corporate/M&A   Transportation
Investment Funds

For detail on ranking tiers and ranking locations, visit www.chambersandpartners.com

however, will be spent drafting or revising." DC associates found that their work was much more research-focused. The partners *"point you in the right direction and then it's a deep dive. They trust you right off the bat but there are some strong personalities in this office, so you have to be assertive."*

Corporate finance includes capital markets, real estate, debt finance and the business transactions group *"which is really an M&A group."* The team can be found running anything from high-profile shipping transactions to midmarket M&A work. Newbies spend their days *"making sure nothing fell through the cracks. I was looking at underlying documents and contracts, as well as getting on calls on all times of day and chasing things down – it was great hands-on experience!"* Daily tasks vary based on the niche. Those in distressed debt trading did some drafting *"but not as much as other attorneys do,"* while the international and shipping-focused capital markets lot faced the challenge of *"coordinating with four different times zones,"* and this was seen as a bonus: *"It's really great! I love learning about how people from different countries run their companies."*

The employee benefits group primarily focuses on ERISA. Clients are typically on the employer side, though the firm does on occasion act on the employee side. Sources told us there was *"a lot of drafting counterparty agreements, and reviewing private fund documents. There are a lot of rules underlying the investment of defined pension plans so we help investment managers understand what those rules are and address any concerns they could cause."* While this may not sound like a laugh a minute, sources we spoke to thought: *"It is excellent! The group is just the best. They are very good at being hands-on and spent a lot of time training me."*

Pro Bono

In New York, pro bono activity *"depends on the department; for example, litigation recognizes it as part of your billable hours and is respectful of that."* Those on the transactional side found less opportunity, but we did hear that there's a dedicated transactional pro bono partner on hand to help these associates find relevant work. *"The firm ensures that if you don't have 50 hours of pro bono by the end of the year you will have them, but the attitude toward pro bono is if you want to do it that's great but no one is going to bother you."* Those in DC felt they did less than

Recent work highlights

- Helped Monagasque shipping company Scorpio Tankers merge with Navig8 Product Tankers in a $1.1 billion deal
- Acted for Emerging Global Advisors on its merger with Columbia Threadneedle Investment
- Represented oil and shipping company Dynagas in a $480 million loan agreement which involved working across six different jurisdictions
- Defended Dutch bank ING against approximately 48 actions in the US

their NY peers. The firm has a longstanding relationship with Her Justice, which marshals public-spirited lawyers to help low income women in NY, and we heard of divorce and immigration cases being taken on too.

"It's a very natural way to learn and individualize your work."

Pro bono hours
- For all US attorneys: 6,028
- Average per US attorney: 35

Training & Development

Most training was delivered on the job, which sources welcomed. *"It's a very natural way to learn and individualize your work. There could be more formal training but the system is effective."* Formal reviews occur at the end of each year, though as with the training, feedback was more readily available informally. But it's not all ad hoc: incoming associates have an introductory week that covers *"how firm infrastructure works, who to contact to do what and that kind of stuff."* Litigators get biweekly informal lunches and those in employee benefits have weekly meetings at the start to cover the technical aspects of their work. In corporate finance, *"it's more 'here is the work, try to figure it out.'"* That doesn't mean that there's no formal training on offer here at all: we heard that the firm hosted 20 courses for its corporate finance associates over 2017. On a broader level, the firm also covers the cost of a Practising Law Institute (PLI) membership, which offers unlimited training courses.

Offices

Associates in the Battery Park Plaza offices were impressed by their milieu: *"It's beautiful. It's been renovated recently and it's all cherry wood-colored furniture with various artworks."* And while some took issue with the quality of the view from their window – *"just a bland, black office building"*– others enjoyed resplendent panoramas *"out to Brooklyn and to the Statue of Liberty."* Generally junior associates share offices up until their third year. DC Associates were equally chirpy about their workplace: *"Everyone loves our modern office! We have*

See firm profile on p.688

Diversity	Partners (%)	Associates (%)
Women	11	43
White	92	82
Black/African American	0	4
Hispanic/Latin American	2	2
Asian	6	11
Mixed/Other	0	1
LGBT	0	1

half a floor down in the Mount Vernon area and we have a lot of happy hours in the kitchen."

Hours & Compensation

Sources in litigation and corporate finance reported 9am to 9:30am start times and end times between 6pm and 8pm. Late nights for litigators could last until midnight, and a few in corporate finance reported doing a deal closure on just three hours of sleep. Those in the employee benefits group found their hours to be slightly lighter around deadlines.

There is a billable requirement of 2,000 hours to get a bonus but it is not a *"minimum to stay employed; I have never felt any push that I have to get it."* Generally associates felt sufficiently compensated for their efforts, particularly given the recent bump first years received, matching the market rate of $180,000.

"They really have let me run with things and I have learned a lot about how to be an attorney."

Culture

To learn that *"the firm is a face-time place in the sense they like you working from the office and not home"* seems at odds with what you'd expect from one of the most satisfied associate cohorts. However, *"you do see people every day and it is bustling in the office."* The close contact with senior lawyers was also appreciated, particularly as partners were willing to *"keep you in the loop and walk you through any questions you have – though when they give you work they expect you to figure it out."* Regular partner mentorship has a big impact on associate satisfaction, our research shows. *"They really have let me run with things and I have learned a lot about how to be an attorney."*

Firm social events occur mainly during the summer associate program, which includes *"a baseball game, a retreat to the Wintergreen resort in the Blue Ridge Mountains (for those based in the DC office), a restaurant night, bowling, a trivia night."* There are also happy hours and lunches, and most socializing is informal: *"People are sociable around the building."*

"We want people from different backgrounds. Not only is it the right thing to do, it provides better service to our clients."

Diversity

The firm is *"enthusiastic about increasing diversity but the vast majority of lawyers are white. They are starting to make an effort to get more diverse candidates but right now it does not show up in the numbers."* One source believed *"the firm is starting a diversity initiative but I am not exactly sure what that will involve,"* and another said: *"I think we are trying to start a women's initiative but as of now nothing has been formally created."* Associates seemed unclear, so we turned to Jim Cofer for the firm's line on the initiatives: *"We have a diversity initiatives committee and an associate-led women's initiative. We want people from different backgrounds. Not only is it the right thing to do, it provides better service to our clients."*

Strategy & Get Hired

One hint for those eying up a junior associate position: do your homework. *"One thing I am surprised by is the lack of basic research about the firm. For example, the DC office does not do hedge funds, it does regulated funds. If candidates interview with some knowledge about regulated funds, that would make them stand out."* For those wondering what the future holds in store there should not be too many surprises. According to Jim Cofer, *"we are not trying to be all things to all people, we try to be focused on particular practice areas and will continue to do more things for people in our current industries."* Go online to learn more about the hiring process.

See firm profile on p.688

Shearman & Sterling LLP

Lawyers per state

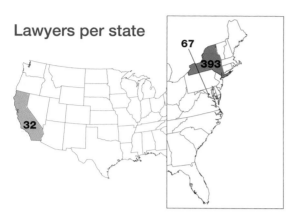

67
393
32

Largest US office: New York
US offices: 5
International offices: 16
First-year salary: $180,000
Billable hours: no requirement
Summers 2018: 56 (2 1Ls, 51 2Ls, 3 SEO)
Revenue 2017: $917.5 million (+0.6%)
Partners made in 2018: 8 (in the US)
Famous for: prestigious history, international work

Shearman & Sterling gives a lesson in international presence.

OUR Shearman & Sterling 101 begins with a history course – the firm was founded nearly 150 years ago, and has built up *"a universally respected reputation"* in the time since. *"I was attracted by the old prestige of the firm,"* several associates told us, *"we helped Ford go public in the '50s and represented the Rockefellers."* Next lesson, geography: Shearman has offices in Africa, Asia, Europe and the Americas, is home to lawyers from 80 different countries and interviewees proclaimed it *"the most global among the upper ranks of New York firms. They deal with complex issues for clients all over the world."*

But the most important class for your education is, of course, law, and Shearman earns gold stars for capital markets, general commercial and securities litigation, Latin American investment, projects and various other areas, according to *Chambers USA.* Its signature practices also include international arbitration. By securing a $50 billion award for former Yukos shareholders, the firm broke the record for the largest ever arbitration case – a record previously also held by Shearman!

The Work

Nearly all new starters begin associate life in Shearman's NYC mothership. Most start as generalists in either the corporate or litigation pools, then dive deeper into one niche a couple of years in. *"Officially we have to rank our*

preferences *after a few years and then the partners meet to decide who goes into what group, but midway through second year people tend to focus on the practice they're leaning toward,"* one explained. *"I appreciated that Shearman didn't make me choose straight away – law school doesn't prepare you for that!"* A few groups including tax, antitrust and compensation, governance and ERISA sit outside the pool.

General corporate associates submit a monthly ranking to their group coordinator stating three areas they'd like work from, and *"they do their best to defer to your preferences."* However, *"at the end of the day, you'll end up being put on something if you have the time."* M&A, capital markets, real estate and project development finance all fall into the bucket. Those with international aspirations were pleased to *"work across multiple jurisdictions, from the US and UK to China and the Middle East."* There's *"a lot of diligence no matter which group you're working in,"* but sources generally agreed *"with the philosophy of getting into the weeds as a junior, so you understand all the underlying principles."* Other responsibilities vary by area – capital markets involves *"pretty consistent first cracks at drafting background documents,"* while real estate *"generally throws you in more quickly – you're drafting leases pretty early on."* Partners generally *"aren't hard-asses, if you're struggling they won't drill you into the ground,"* and do a good job of explaining the bigger picture.

> *"...multiple jurisdictions, from the US and UK to China and the Middle East."*

Litigation also has an assigning partner who *"looks at your hours over the past week and month and is aware*

On chambers-associate.com...

- Get hired: recruitment knowledge
- Interview with senior partner David Beveridge

See firm profile on p.689

The Inside View

Rankings in *Chambers USA*

Antitrust	Financial Services
Banking & Finance	Regulation
Capital Markets	International Arbitration
Corporate/M&A	Latin American Investment
Employee Benefits &	Litigation
Executive Compensation	Projects
Energy & Natural	Real Estate
Resources	Securities
Environment	Tax
FCPA	Technology

For detail on ranking tiers and ranking locations, visit
www.chambersandpartners.com

Recent work highlights

- Represented Bank of America and Wells Fargo in a number of oil and gas companies' Chapter 11 bankruptcies
- Sought US court confirmation of a $50 billion award from the Russian Federation on behalf of former controlling shareholders of Yukos, the largest potential award in arbitral tribunal history
- Acted for healthcare website WebMD in $2.8 billion sale to portfolio firm Internet Brands
- Worked for Citibank and J.P. Morgan in connection with a $10 billion revolving credit facility for pharmaceutical giant Johnson & Johnson

of your interests. When push comes to shove, if you have bandwidth you'll end up taking the case." Sources downloaded a whole internet's worth of investigations, arbitration and commercial, M&A and securities litigation to their dockets. Financial institutions are the main clients – "we tend to represent underwriter banks a lot" – but there's healthcare, media and technology companies too. Direct client contact may not be "a huge part of the group; corporate associates get a lot more," but juniors were happy with what got served up. "I haven't done much document review, except on an emergency basis" one announced, "there's been a lot more drafting and research to do. Senior associates and partners don't hesitate to put juniors in charge of larger processes."

There was some upheaval in antitrust in 2017: the DC team took on several lateral hires but global head Stephen Mavroghenis jumped ship to Quinn Emanuel in Brussels. US associates didn't seem fazed though, declaring themselves "very happy" with their workload – "I couldn't have expected better. I've done a lot of merger analysis memos and antitrust risk assessments." The group seesaws between litigation and counseling work with corporate clients across finance, healthcare, defense, retail and other industries. "Being in a small group tends to lead to significant client contact," a colleague in compensation, governance and ERISA shared. Their group "touches almost everything: deal work, offerings, employment agreements, Section 16 filings for companies, they're all in the day-to-day." Juniors got to walk through document changes with clients, after drafting ancillary agreements themselves.

Training & Development

After an initial orientation week in their home offices, new starters flock to New York for a first-year conference. Later there's one for mid-level associates, then another called 'Associate Leadership Academy' for high-achieving sixth and seventh years. Litigators told us "something that sets Shearman apart is its exceptional programs throughout the year." Not to be outdone, trans-

actional juniors declared that "Shearman does a really good job covering the breadth of corporate practices." One wily source "calculated that if I went to every lunch training event, I'd only have to buy my own lunch two or three times a month!"

Associates get one formal review a year: "We select reviewers and submit them to an online system, where they rank us in categories and can provide comments." There's also an annual 'Snapshot' career development meeting to talk through what they'd like to do more of in the future to build their skills.

Culture & Diversity

"You definitely feel like you're part of something historic – this firm was established a year before the Canadian Constitution!" We'll smugly correct this associate's error: Canada's constitution technically predates Shearman's 1873 foundation by a good few decades. But you get the point: it's old, and with that come questions about its culture reflecting such esteemed white-shoe origins. "Shearman used to get that," admitted one source, "but people here are their whole selves, nobody's putting on a 'lawyer suit' when they come in and there's no fratty, bro culture." That's especially true in DC, which feels "a bit more casual than New York. The atmosphere is a little more relaxed and button-down." Sources generally felt that "although there is obviously a hierarchy, partners don't seem like demigods," and some gleefully revealed they regularly went out for lunch with their seniors.

> "Nobody's putting on a 'lawyer suit' when they come in."

Across the firm as a whole, associates felt pretty chummy with colleagues. "It's more social than I expected," one told us, enjoying bi-weekly office happy hours and an environment in which "even on the average Tuesday, a bunch of people will go to the bar. The firm's generally been doing more associate and firm-wide events recently." This comes after insider info from last year that the associate

See firm profile on p.689

The Inside View

Diversity	Partners (%)	Associates (%)
Women	17	39.2
White	75	59.2
Black/African American	1.8	4.5
Hispanic/Latin American	2.7	4.5
Asian	5.4	16.6
Mixed/Other	15.2	13.7
LGBT	0.9	5.3

committee was pushing for more socializing outside the traditional summer associate period. Most felt they and the firm had done *"a good job."* Less party-hard sources stressed *"there's no sense that you're not part of the group if you skip a happy hour. The social life doesn't get as crazy as at some other firms, but I do have friends here who I'll hang out with outside work."*

Shearman got a similarly encouraging review on the diversity front, with most interviewees agreeing *"it's taken into consideration when we're recruiting, and any issues we have aren't specific to Shearman."* Some felt that the firm's international nature helped boost diversity, particularly its International Associate Program which allows lawyers qualified in other countries to do a one-year internship in New York. Others argued *"racial diversity is probably the category we do least well in. It's tricky because the attitude is there and the firm really talks about issues but I don't see the impact of it in our ranks."* Affinity groups in place to address the divide include WISER for women, BLAQUE for black lawyers and AVALANCHE (no, really) for Asian attorneys. Given that *"the last five years of incoming classes have been incredibly diverse,"* the priority going forward looks to be *"making sure that carries up to partner level – it's relatively stagnant at the moment."*

Offices

Shearman's New York home on 599 Lexington Ave is *"really cool from the outside, very different from a typical Manhattan office building."* Its beauty, though, is… skin deep. *"A little dated"* was the diplomatic description, but one associate didn't hold back, declaring it *"the worst among the big firms. The pink walls and light brown wood are just old-fashioned."* As things stand, juniors share an office for two years before getting their own. The firm is contemplating relocating in 2020, as part of a *"modernizing"* rebrand. Team DC moved to new lodgings in 2016 complete with *"glass walls and much more modern amenities, including standing desks. The glass was a point of contention but associates are generally really happy."* Shearman's smaller offices in Menlo Park and San Francisco also take a newbie or two each year.

"Very different from a typical Manhattan office building."

Given the firm's international reputation, it's no surprise that cross-office communication and collaboration is silky smooth. *"I went to the other coast for a friend's wedding and I spent some time working there,"* a junior related, adding: *"It was very easy to pretend I was home."* A sojourn overseas is also a real possibility, and every year a few entry-levels get the chance to work abroad permanently as US track associates in one of Shearman's international offices.

Pro Bono

"I know people who've done hundreds of pro bono hours at the expense of billable work and nobody's told them not to." This associate testimony reflects sources' big thumbs-up for Shearman's pro bono efforts. Notable highlights include a program sending attorneys to Africa with Lawyers Without Borders, and a 15-year collaboration with the International Criminal Tribunal for Rwanda. More recently there's been *"a giant jump across the board reacting to the Trump administration. We had people heading to JFK as soon as the executive order went out."* Asylum and immigration cases are currently *"a hot commodity."* Everybody's mandated to do 25 hours of pro bono, and *"in the last couple of years the firm established that if you don't reach the minimum two years in a row, you lose your bonus."*

Pro bono hours
- For all attorneys across all US offices: 35,554
- Average per US attorney: 85.5

Hours & Compensation

There's no official billables requirement for Shearman associates. Those we spoke to suggested *"somewhere around 2,000 is what most aim for – an unofficial target I hear floating around is 2,050, but that might just come from other firms."* Most suggested it's *"something I don't think about often. There seems to be plenty of work going around."* In 2016 the firm announced a more solidified remote working policy wherein associates can work two days a month from home; they even get a laser printer if they fancy it. When in the office, juniors tended to work until about 7pm or 8pm on average. *"Busy days can stretch until midnight or later, but I very rarely pull all-nighters. At the most extreme end, I'll be in the office 70 hours a week,"* one said.

Salaries and bonuses follow a *"quite rigid lockstep"* in sync with the market. *"If there's work to be done and someone isn't billing they might not get a full bonus,"* and similarly *"if you go above and beyond they'll compensate you ac-*

See firm profile on p.689

The Inside View

cordingly." Sources found it *"encouraging to know you'll be rewarded if you have one of those years of having to work 2,900 hours."* Without an hours target, associates found it pretty easy to take at least some of their four weeks allotted vacation: *"I forgot to take any until September and got reminded I had a bunch of weeks stored, it's a good amount."*

"...something I don't think about often. There seems to be plenty of work going around."

Strategy & Future

Four fifths of Shearman's offices are outside the US, and it isn't done expanding its global reach: senior partner David Beveridge tells us the firm is*"looking to open an office in South Korea. That will happen in the near future."* That said, the US isn't being left out of the party, and he reveals *"New York and DC have been the strongest growth areas in the US"* over 2017. Will Brexit, the Trump administration and other protectionist developments affect Shearman's cross-border ambitions? *"It's hard to predict now,"* Beveridge explains, *"but uncertainty inevitably affects the volume of transactions. It's a looming risk."* For more insight into the future of Shearman & Sterling, read the full interview on www.chambers-associate.com.

"You definitely feel like you're part of something historic – this firm was established a year before the Canadian Constitution!"

See firm profile on p.689

Sheppard, Mullin, Richter & Hampton LLP

Lawyers per state

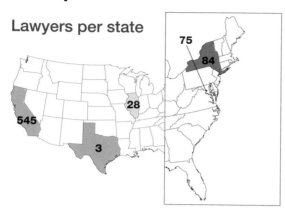

75
84
28
545
3

Largest US office: Los Angeles

US offices: 10

International offices: 5

First-year salary: $180,000

Billable hours: 1,950 required (1,800 client-charge-able)

Summers 2018: 29-30 (1-2 1Ls, 28 2Ls)

Revenue 2017: $671.1 million (+10.5%)

Partners made in 2018: 16

Famous for: measured growth; Cali roots; industry focuses in areas like healthcare and energy

Slow and steady wins the race: this Californian firm's cool approach leaves satisfied associates feeling invested in and integrated.

TURNING 90 is a big deal. It's an impressive feat in itself, but Sheppard Mullin also had a number of other achievements to look back on as it reached this milestone in 2017: ten domestic offices, a further five overseas, and a secure status as one of California's best law firms. Its years of experience in the Golden State are reflected in its collection of *Chambers USA* rankings, which encompass areas like media and entertainment, litigation, labor and employment and corporate/M&A. On a nationwide scale, Sheppard's government contracts and Native American law practices come in for particular praise; its non-Cali offices can be found in New York, DC and Chicago.

"...not stagnating, and moving forward in a predictable way."

Chairman Guy Halgren explains the approach behind the firm's success: "*We have a concept we use called 'the 20-mile march,' which came from business consultant and author Jim Collins: it involves sticking to a consistent plan, not chasing the next big thing, not stagnating, and moving forward in a predictable way. We generally like to target a 5-10% increase in production and attorneys per year. In terms of scope, we consider ourselves to be a strong national firm with international reach.*"

On chambers-associate.com...

- More on getting hired at Sheppard Mullin
- Interview with chief HR officer Bess Sully

For current associates, this approach was attractive – especially since it's seen the firm post growing revenue stats every year since 1992. But that's not all: for those returning to their Cali homeland after law school, Sheppard offered a local "*power center – it's not like joining an East Coast firm's outpost in California, where the big decisions aren't made and you don't feel incorporated in the firm.*" For those based outside the state, Sheppard has "*the best of both worlds: the BigLaw experience and pay scale, but in the context of a smaller operation that's highly respected.*" No matter the location, associates identified this firm-wide perk: "*It's a place where you can push to develop your career and get responsibility early. It's not a firm with lots of institutional processes and hoops that take a longer time to jump through.*"

The Work

Sheppard's corporate, business trial and labor and employment groups take the bulk of new associates, while the remaining are divvied between IP, government contracts, finance and banking, and real estate. All departments have practice group leaders, but the extent of their involvement in assignment varies. For example, an IP source told us that their hands-on PG leader was "*really awesome at making sure everyone's busy,*" while business trial interviewees spoke of a more 'free market' system where PG leaders provide a safety net if necessary: "*You can go to them if you haven't got anything going on.*" Overall, sources noted that "*industry groups are just as important as practice groups. You might find yourself doing vari-*

See firm profile on p.690

Rankings in *Chambers USA*

Antitrust	Healthcare
Banking & Finance	Insurance
Bankruptcy/Restructuring	Labor & Employment
Construction	Litigation
Corporate/M&A	Media & Entertainment
Government	Native American Law

For detail on ranking tiers and ranking locations, visit
www.chambersandpartners.com

Recent work highlights

- Secured a $9.1 million victory for financial services outfit Tullett Prebon during a lengthy dispute with a former employee
- Represented YouTube network Machinima during its $85 million sale to an affiliate of Warner Bros. Entertainment
- Represented Bank of China as it made a $390 million loan to real estate developer Crescent Heights to finance a 40-story luxury rental tower in LA
- Acted for clothing retailer Forever 21 as it sued Gucci over the fashion brand's trademark registrations featuring a certain sequence of colored stripes

ous work for certain clients rather than certain work for various clients."

The corporate group is a case in point: *"Within our practice we have several industry groups, and I focus a lot of my work on healthcare,"* one source revealed. Other juniors had worked on *"a wide variety of deals, including mergers, asset purchases and reorganizations, as well as public company filings."* The industry focus can add a *"regulatory component to what we do; I've drafted memos on federal and state healthcare laws, plus compliance with privacy and life insurance rules – a lot of the time it relates to the underlying transaction that's going on."* Those who focused on telecommunications worked for *"satellite and cable operators"* and contributed to *"filings for FCC spectrum sales, but also conducted research for memos, assisted with negotiations and drafted documents."*

"...business development is very important, even at associate level."

Sheppard's business trial group covers various strands, including securities, insurance, professional liability, private wealth and bankruptcy litigation. The free-market system means that you see *"a wide selection of cases,"* with one source telling us they'd recently worked on *"a securities class action, some contract disputes, False Claim Act cases and trusts and estates matters."* Another explained: *"While we have some large institutional clients, we don't have the same number as, say, Cravath or Skadden, so business development is very important, even at associate level. It also means that smaller, multimillion cases allow us to cut our teeth on substantive work, like applying our research to writing first drafts of motions and entire briefs."*

In the *"litigation-oriented"* labor and employment group, recent shifts in California's laws have produced *"a lot of class action work related to wage and hour issues."* Juniors mixed these with *"single plaintive cases, which tend to involve harassment, discrimination and wrongful terminations. They're more interesting as there's an investigative angle to them; you're fact gathering and getting to know people in order to uncover the back story and office politics."*

Training & Development

Associates were optimistic about the training program Sheppard has been rolling out: *"It involves structured presentations on the various aspects of being an associate and succeeding in a law firm – there's also some substantive legal stuff, but it's more general and not practice-specific."* However, we did hear of practice-specific training sessions *"videoconferenced out of Cali,"* and a focus on client development in several groups: *"The partners really encourage us to take steps on that front, whether it's tagging along to networking events or attending a conference, for example."*

There is a formal mentoring program (which sees juniors paired up with a partner adviser) but juniors felt *"the real strength here is informal mentoring,"* with one enthusing: *"I have several associates that I consider as mentors – they push me with bigger assignments and provide me with feedback. It's an organic thing, and I feel I can connect with anyone in the group."*

Culture & Offices

Almost 70% of the juniors on our list were based in Sheppard's Cali bases. Of these, the LA, San Francisco and Century City offices took on the most, and were widely praised for having a *"family-friendly"* feel: *"I meet a lot of hard-working people, but everyone is also easygoing – just nice Cali people."* In the LA HQ, niceties are formalized via an annual 'associate appreciation day,' the most recent of which saw *"the partners take us out to see Top Gun Live – it was a blast!"* Others in Cali told us they were looking for *"a BigLaw firm that's a little laid back, somewhere where people aren't just cordial but actually friends with you – and that's rung true so far."*

"If they smell a fake, they don't like it."

Just over a sixth of our juniors were in the New York office, which sources summed up as *"not stodgy or ultra-conservative, but still work hard/play hard; it's not abnormal for one of our secretaries to gather everyone around at*

See firm profile on p.690

Diversity	Partners (%)	Associates (%)
Women	19.6	49.4
White	87.5	69.5
Black/African American	3.1	3.6
Hispanic/Latin American	1.9	3.6
Asian	4.7	12.9
Mixed/Other	2.8	10.5
LGBT	2.5	3.1

5pm on a Friday and say 'we're gonna have some scotch' – whoever's available to chat is welcome, and it's all very natural and comfortable." Over in DC, interviewees also felt the Cali vibe infusing the office, making it stand out in comparison to more 'traditional' East Coast firms: *"It's pretty casual and not too buttoned-up, with partners willing to talk to associates and interact with them socially. We're not a hard-partying bunch though – a lot of people want to finish the working day and go home to their families."*

Diversity

Minority associates approved of what they saw as a culture of open-mindedness: *"I interviewed with firms with higher diversity numbers, but Sheppard felt like the firm I could be most comfortable being myself at. They value authenticity; if they smell a fake, they don't like it."*

One source wanted *"more time spent on unconscious bias training to further address why some attorneys don't get the same caliber of work,"* while another suggested this solution: *"Every minority associate needs both a mentor and a partner sponsor that really stands up for them and ensures they are getting exposure."* Juniors did feel that the firm's good intentions were evident, with one interviewee – a member of a diversity network – telling us: *"We have phone conferences once a month to talk about the progress we've made in recruiting, to share any concerns we've had – we have some well known partners in the group, and whenever there's been an issue immediate action has been taken by the firm leadership."* The firm also told us that a diversity mentorship scheme is currently being devised.

Hours & Compensation

The majority of our interviewees had enough work to allow them to reach Sheppard's 1,950 billing target, which makes them bonus eligible. Once juniors bill 1,800 hours to standard clients, they can use 150 hours from any mix of pro bono, business development and educational activities to get them to the desired figure. Juniors also spoke of *"proactive partners"* that step in to assist if they

notice an associate billing lower hours. A full market bonus is paid out if associates reach 2,000 hours, while 10% above market is awarded at 2,200 and 20% above market is dished out at 2,400. Discretionary amounts are also paid out to recognize the likes of client originations and other work conducted on behalf of the firm.

Ten-hour stints in the office were fairly normal because *"it's BigLaw and there are expectations,"* but our sources still felt there was time for life outside of work: *"I'm going to a basketball game tonight and went to a hockey game last week. I'm not here 24/7."* Associates described *"a culture of boundaries, which encourages us to have a work/life balance. If someone has an important event, there's an understanding it will be respected."*

Pro Bono

Associates were pleased with the firm's pro bono commitment: *"My practice group has a 100% attorney participation goal and they really do push it."* Juniors identified both specific pro bono coordinators and partners that *"constantly send out opportunities,"* so getting staffed on matters wasn't deemed difficult. Asylum cases were common among the juniors we spoke to, with one highlighting their experiences *"as the lead attorney for two hearings, drafting a 35-page brief, and going to a declaration for several witnesses."*

Pro bono hours
- For all US attorneys: 28,669
- Average per US attorney: 38

Strategy & Future

Chairman Guy Halgren tells us that over 2017 *"the continuing growth of our healthcare and energy work in particular has been impressive."* Geographically, *"our strategic plan has focused on growing our New York and DC offices to the level of at least 100 attorneys in each by 2018, and we're right on track."* Halgren adds that Sheppard will continue to adjust to broader technological changes in the industry: *"We hired our first chief innovation officer this year; he is responsible for bringing together all the different AI resources for attorneys to use in their practices."*

Get Hired

"We want to understand how a candidate may build on our values and how the firm can assist the candidate in his/her career development." For more hiring advice from chief HR officer Bess Sully, go to chambers-associate.com.

See firm profile on p.690

The Inside View

Sidley Austin LLP

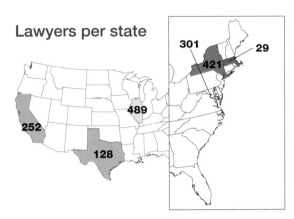

Lawyers per state

301   29
421
489
252
128

Largest US office: Chicago
US offices: 10
International offices: 10
First-year salary: $180,000
Billable hours: 1,800 requirement to advance to the next year
Summers 2018: 168
Revenue 2017: $2.04 billion (+5.7%)
Partners made in 2018: 16
Famous for: 'all bases covered' approach to client service; formidable appellate law expertise; hedge fund know-how; Midwestern culture

This Chicagoan-gone-global has shown that giant rewards can come through being financially cautious.

"2017 was a really successful year for Sidley," executive committee member Anne Rea tells us. *"We surpassed $2 billion in revenue – a new milestone for the firm – and we're continuing to grow in virtually all our offices across the US, Europe and Asia."* So what's the secret behind this success? *"We have a diversified range of services,"* Rea explains, highlighting the firm's *"three prongs"* of transactional, litigation and enforcement, and regulatory services. *"That diversity helps position us to be successful in any market."*

Of these prongs, litigation clout is perhaps what Sidley is best known for: its appellate law practice picks up top *Chambers USA* marks across the US, while other contentious strengths include general commercial, white-collar, securities, insurance, product liability and IP disputes. Standout areas in its two remaining prongs include financial services regulation, investment funds, corporate/M&A and capital markets securitization work. Unsurprisingly, newbies were attracted to Sidley's *"reputation for being great in a number of areas,"* but it wasn't just status that sealed the deal for our sources: *"You just get a good vibe from the people you speak to here. During the callback I kept waiting for the catch, but it didn't come: you get to work with really decent people at a top global firm."*

Strategy & Future

"We have a different business plan than some firms," Rea adds. *"Some start to grow by narrowing their offering to what is most profitable. We have a long-term vision which is to have the services that meet the full range of our clients' needs."*

"We're pursuing a strategy of smart growth."

"We're seeing a strong transactional market right now," says Rea, *"and we think the tax legislation in the US is going to drive more transactions in the coming year."* While it's clear that Sidley's focus is on providing an expansive offering, it is at the same time cautious when it comes to growth, as associates revealed: *"We're pretty conservative with budgeting and finances, and 'slow and steady' with decision-making – we're pursuing a strategy of smart growth, of growth where it makes sense to expand our footprint."*

Offices

Sidley's ten domestic offices are spread out across the major markets in the US: the majority of the juniors on our list (almost 70% combined) were based in the firm's Chicago HQ and New York office. The DC, LA, Century City and Dallas bases also took on a significant number, while just a handful joined the firm in Palo Alto, Boston, San Francisco and Houston.

On chambers-associate.com...

- Get hired at Sidley Austin
- Interview with executive committee member Anna Rea

See firm profile on p.691

The Inside View

Rankings in *Chambers USA*

Antitrust

Appellate Law

Banking & Finance

Bankruptcy/Restructuring

Capital Markets

Climate Change

Corporate Crime & Investigations

Corporate/M&A

Employee Benefits & Executive Compensation

Energy & Natural Resources

Environment

ERISA Litigation

FCPA

Financial Services Regulation

Healthcare

Insurance

Intellectual Property

International Arbitration

International Trade

Investment Funds

IT & Outsourcing

Labor & Employment

Latin American Investment

Leisure & Hospitality

Life Sciences

Litigation

Media & Entertainment

Privacy & Data Security

Products Liability

Real Estate

REITs

Securities

Tax

Technology

Telecommunications

Transportation

For detail on ranking tiers and ranking locations, visit www.chambersandpartners.com

Recent work highlights

- Defended Deloitte China against a securities fraud claim after it was discovered that substantial sums were being embezzled at a China-based distance education company by its CEO and various other insiders
- Advised real estate investment trust Starwood Waypoint on its $21 billion merger with Invitation Homes, forming the largest single-family rental company in the US
- Represented JPMorgan Chase Bank as administrative agent of a $1.2 billion credit facility for insurance outfit Brown & Brown
- Serves as primary US counsel for London Stock Exchange-listed Man Group, and advises the active management business on a variety of activities, including new fund launches, the acquisition of new managers and regulatory matters

Chicago is the *"home base"* and Sidley has an office building to match its status: *"We're right downtown in 'The Loop,' and we're the flagship tenant in the 38-story building, so we all get our own offices."* The firm won't be moving any time soon (*"we've renewed our lease for another ten years"*) and renovations are currently underway: *"The office is pretty good as it is, but we want to keep up and be modern."* Sources were excited to *"have the opportunity to look at mock-ups of what the new space will look like, and weigh in on the color schemes and lighting."* New Yorkers were also anticipating a design overhaul: *"Right now we're working out of what looks like a traditional corporate law firm setting – no bells or whistles. We're going to redesign it to look more cutting-edge."*

The Work

When it comes to assignment, a more informal system permeates most offices and practices. Sources largely agreed with this interviewee, who told us: *"I love the more free-market system, as it allows me to get the work I want. I can fill my time with the things I've chosen as opposed to things that have been chosen for me."* There are some safety nets in place though. In commercial litigation, for example, there are *"a couple of partners who serve as junior associate coordinators, and if you're looking for a particular type of case they can help you get staffed on it."* Over in global finance, meanwhile, there's a *"pod system, where you're initially allocated four assigning attorneys – a mix of partners and senior associates – who represent a cross-section of the group's work. They're like training wheels –*

they help you get started, then naturally fall away as you develop a rapport with people."

Litigators were abundant in this year's cohort. The majority (a quarter of the firm's second and third-year US juniors) were in commercial litigation, where Sidley has a reputation in many industries, including healthcare, financial services and defense. Tasks included *"pretty much everything under the sun"*: sources oversaw preliminary discovery matters, prepared and attended depositions, and drafted the likes of motions and briefs. Many found that *"the days of sitting and doing doc review for hours on end are very few and far between."* One source highlighted that *"from the moment I walked in the door, if you showed you were competent and serious about your work, you were treated like a true lawyer and expected to solve problems – not to constantly write memos to file."*

"...a steep learning curve, but it's good for progression."

On the transactional side, groups like M&A, global finance and investment funds took on a significant number of juniors. M&A sources could do *"public company work, private equity, finance – everything under the M&A umbrella."* They told of *"negotiating purchase agreements, putting together issues lists, working on ancillary documents and coordinating with opposing counsel."* They also explained that *"as you get more senior, you get more exposure to the drafting of main purchase agreements."* Furthermore, associates relayed: *"We don't really get staffed on deals by our class year – some firms are strict about allocating tasks for certain year groups, but here we don't do that as much. People are willing to give you responsibility for what you can handle."* As a result, there's *"a steep learning curve, but it's good for progression."*

See firm profile on p.691

The Inside View

Diversity	Partners (%)	Associates (%)
Women	25.3	45.8
White	88.4	69.4
Black/African American	1.7	5.1
Hispanic/Latin American	1.7	6.2
Asian	7.3	15.9
Mixed/Other	0.9	3.3
LGBT	-	-

Global finance covers *"traditional lending work, acquisition finance, structured finance, securitization and more,"* busy associates here informed us. The group often represents *"large banks as administrative agents for syndicated financings, or companies as borrowers."* Juniors spent their time on *"deal management and making sure things run accordingly,"* as well as on drafting ancillary documents and other agreements. *"I started drafting primary transaction documents by the middle of my second year!"* one exclaimed. To top it off, juniors emphasized that there's *"client interaction from day one – there was no hiding us from them."* Investment funds sources revealed that the group's focus is on hedge funds and private equity fund managers. *"We analyze existing documents with annual regulatory updates in mind, and help draft letters for clients and investor-facing documents."*

Culture

"It's more a hybrid of Type A and Type B traits," said juniors of Sidley's culture.But what exactly does this apparent oxymoron mean? *"We're the lawyer-type to a certain extent – outwardly, we're competitive when representing clients against others – but we're collaborative and helpful to each other, rather than aggressive."* Interviewees gushed that *"any Sidley lawyer across the office or country will talk to you and share their wealth of experience."* Others added that this helpful stance made Sidley *"more family-friendly – it's not that 'work hard, play hard, Wall Street in the 80s' type firm. People can work hard then go home to their families."*

"It's more a hybrid of Type A and Type B traits."

As a result, many appreciated that *"there's not that sense that you need to go and hang out with people after work all the time – the social side is there, but it isn't invasive."* Those who are interested can attend some lively gatherings: *"There are holiday events across the offices that people make an effort to go to. Last year in Chicago we had a really fun black-tie party to celebrate the firm's 150th anniversary. It was great to get dressed up and meet new people."* A variety of social events also take place over the summer, and we heard of activities such as cooking classes, sports games, comedy shows and bar crawls.

On the more 'Type A' side of the spectrum, juniors added that Sidley fosters a culture where *"associates are empowered to take on more responsibility and contribute to developing business."* Several sources highlighted that *"business development is becoming an increasing focus, even among associates. It's a very competitive world in the BigLaw space, so they want people to think about those opportunities from an early stage."*

Training & Development

An office-specific orientation kicks off proceedings for the first week, and is followed by a three-day program in Chicago *"which brings every new associate from across the world together."* After that, practice-specific training begins. Litigators were happy that *"they've recently revamped the training to better reflect what you're doing at each stage of your career. Juniors work on motion drafting, while mid-levels start training on arguing motions, and seniors do mock trials."* Transactional associates, meanwhile, attend 'Corporate College.' *"We get various presentations on M&A, capital markets, fund formations and tax issues – the whole gamut of transactional work. We also get homework assignments, like filling out a due diligence matrix for a pretend client."*

Associates have reviews twice a year. *"It's a formal process, and every matter where we've billed 50 hours or more has to be submitted for review; matters below 50 can be submitted at your discretion."* Once reviewing attorneys have had time to write up their thoughts, juniors *"meet with two or three partners to go over their feedback. You have the opportunity to ask questions about anything that was written. It's very helpful."*

Hours & Compensation

Juniors must bill 1,800 hours a year in order to progress to the next year, and 2,000 hours in order to qualify for a bonus. *"Almost everyone receives a bonus,"* relieved juniors told us across the groups, with those in commercial litigation and global finance especially confident: *"You would have to actively avoid doing stuff to not hit the hours."* Bonuses are discretionary and allocated via *"an honor system – if you're putting the work in you get what you deserve."* This led some to describe bonuses as *"a bit of a black box,"* but sources found that *"generally if you're exceeding hours, expectations and receiving positive reviews you can expect an above-market amount."*

"People are good about not creating false deadlines."

See firm profile on p.691

On an average day, most sources reported being in the office for around ten hours (usually 9/10am until 7/8pm), but this naturally depended on what was going on with the case or deal. If there's more work to do in the evenings, *"most people go home to have dinner with their families"* and log back on afterward. The amount of weekend work varied, with those in global finance telling us that they'll work *"at least a couple of hours every weekend,"* while those in commercial litigation and investment funds did so occasionally when matters required it: *"People are good about not creating false deadlines and making you work on weekends for something that doesn't need to be done until the following week."*

Pro Bono

Once associates hit their 1,800-hour advancement requirement, up to 200 hours of pro bono can count toward their bonus threshold. *"There are always whispers that you won't get dinged for doing more than that, and they may consider some hours above that when deciding on your bonus."* While most interviewees agreed that Sidley is *"very committed to pro bono,"* they also flagged that *"there's no requirement for you to do it"* and some of our transactional sources hadn't done any: *"The work just hasn't freed up space."* Litigators had been more consistently involved, however, with one telling us: *"I've done 200 hours every year that I've been here. Sometimes more!"*

"You can basically take your pick of whatever interests you."

When it comes to getting staffed on pro bono matters, *"there are a few dedicated attorneys who will email us about opportunities and provide trainings."* Sources did praise the variety of matters available, and told us: *"You can basically take your pick of whatever interests you, whether that's veterans' cases, insolvency matters, traditional landlord/tenant disputes or immigration issues."* On the transactional side, there is *"some interesting corporate-related work,"* like micro-finance projects and opportunities *"to review commercial contracts for companies in developing countries."*

Pro bono hours
- For all US attorneys: 119,323
- Average per US attorney: 66.8

Diversity

Many agreed that Sidley's committee on the retention and promotion of women was *"a particular strength"* and *"very active."* The group *"holds seminars throughout the year on things like how to handle work-life balance, childcare and going on parental leave."* There's also a reduced work schedule that's *"available to all attorneys for family reasons. It's primarily used to help with childcare, but it's also available if you have elderly parents that need looking after or something."* Alongside this, one source added: *"Every year since I've been here the new partnership appointments have been 50:50 split between men and women. That's not to say that the partnership itself is near that 50:50 split, but it's getting there and that's important to see."*

**On chambers-associate.com...
Sidley's media & entertainment lawyers take us behind the scenes at their fascinating practice.**

See firm profile on p.691

Simpson Thacher & Bartlett LLP

Lawyers per state

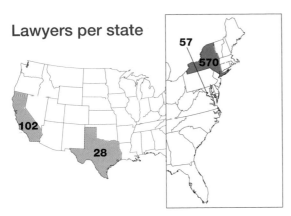

Largest US office: New York
US offices: 5
International offices: 6
First-year salary: $180,000
Billable hours: no requirement
Summers 2018: 108 (10 1Ls, 98 2Ls)
Revenue 2017: $1.376 billion (+5.7%)
Partners made in 2018: 11
Famous for: mega deals; encouraging healthy competition

If you prefer congenial teamwork to wrestling glory away from your colleagues, take note: this venerable New Yorker is deliberately *"set up to avoid a cage match."*

FOR new associates, Simpson Thacher *"stood out as a firm that had it all."* Year in, year out, Simpson's prestigious reputation plays its part in enticing fresh talent: *"We're certainly proud of our heritage."* That's a heritage reaching back to 1884, making it as old as *The Adventures of Huckleberry Finn.* And just as that novel's reputation as one of the greats has endured, so too has Simpson Thacher's – it remains comfortably nestled in the upper echelons of BigLaw. *"There's a sense of putting our heads together for something larger than us. Partners talk about previous partners, and building on the work they've done."* That work includes advising on the five biggest LBOs in business history, dabbling in eight-digit deals, and picking up the phone to big-name clients like Google, Microsoft, Hilton, JP Morgan and DreamWorks. And it's very much got the stamp of approval from *Chambers USA:* its clutch of nationwide rankings reveals transactional and litigious strengths, with top praise awarded to the firm's banking, capital markets, corporate, insurance disputes, private equity, real estate, securities litigation and tax practices.

So it's got the prestige and then some, but like your mother keeps telling you, looks aren't everything. What about personality? Current associates were keen to tell us that *"there's a culture of positivity that carries on from generation to generation, so you have a never-ending cycle of good people coming to the firm. The best thing about working at Simpson is being at the forefront of something that has potentially never been done before, with some of the brightest people in the industry."* Prestige? Check. Interesting work? Check. Personality? Check. *"If I could hit the reset button I'd end up at Simpson again."*

The Work

Simpson's sizable corporate group claimed the bulk of junior associates on our list, while litigation took just over a quarter. The rest were sprinkled between real estate, tax, and executive compensation and benefits. As it currently stands, corporate juniors rotate through three out of four sub-groups (M&A, capital markets, banking and credit, and funds) before typically choosing a specialty. This system is about to undergo a slight change; from 2018 incoming first-years will rotate through two. The current lot appreciated rotating instead of diving straight into a group – *"you could make a premature and awful choice that way! Rotating gives you an extra layer of knowledge before specializing."* But not everybody does: Simpson's backing of the generalist means there are partners *"who take pride in doing everything, even 20 or 30 years into their career!"*

On chambers-associate.com...

- Get hired: recruitment advice from Simpson's juniors
- Interviews with chairman Bill Dougherty and hiring partners Krista Miniutti, Nick Goldin and Rajib Chanda

See firm profile on p.692

Rankings in *Chambers USA*

Antitrust

Banking & Finance

Bankruptcy/Restructuring

Capital Markets

Corporate/M&A

Employee Benefits &
    Executive Compensation

Energy & Natural
    Resources

Environment

Financial Services
    Regulation

Insurance

International Trade

Investment Funds

Latin American Investment

Litigation

Private Equity

Real Estate

Securities

Tax

Technology

For detail on ranking tiers and ranking locations, visit
www.chambersandpartners.com

Recent work highlights

- Represented ChemChina during its $43 billion acquisition of Swiss biotechnology company Syngenta
- Advised 21st Century Fox on a $12.2 billion loan to finance its acquisition of pay-TV broadcaster Sky
- Represented Hilton in multiple debt offerings amounting to $1.8 billion
- Defended SeaWorld against investor allegations of under-reporting the negative impact the documentary Blackfish had on attendance and ticket sales
- Acted for Twitter in a series of securities class actions

"You can become an expert in just a few years."

Associates identified *"meritocracy"* as the common denominator between the corporate groups: *"You don't feel like a paper pusher, you feel like an actual attorney."* M&A may entail *"more typical junior tasks, like diligence"* but we also heard of associates getting to *"strategize with a partner on a complicated deal, bouncing ideas back and forth. It was really cool to have those high-level discussions where no idea was a bad idea."* In funds, *"everyone does everything. You can expect to do some drafting and coordinating, and when the fund is actively fundraising, organizational aspects become entirely mine."* By the end of a stint in banking and credit, capable associates were *"getting to run the closing process on deals for both borrowers and lenders."* The split in capital markets is roughly *"60/40 debt over equity deals from both the issuer and underwriter side."* The group's lean staffing made for *"a frustrating, terrifying, but ultimately good learning experience. If I had one complaint, it'd be that there have been times where I've had too much responsibility and not enough oversight, but on the upside you can become an expert in just a few years."*

There's no rotation system in litigation, which is governed by a generalist approach. Associates had sampled *"a hodgepodge"* of different matters, like government investigations, IP cases, securities disputes and insurance work. During an antitrust case, associates were *"working with an Israel-based client, our colleagues in the London office and local councils across the world. At one point we had all these different clocks on the wall and spent a lot of time working out the math!"* Common tasks for junior litigators include pouring through discovery materials, writing briefs and even conducting client interviews: *"You don't get sidelined with junior tasks. The fact is you're too valuable to be doing photocopies."* Sources typically jumped on cases at different stages in the litigation cycle, allowing for plenty of variety: *"You could be working on discovery for one and an appellate brief for another."*

"The fact is you're too valuable to be doing photocopies."

A centralized staffing program across all groups and offices ensures *"work is allocated based on availability."* Everyone gets the same amount of work, so *"you don't feel as if you're busting your hump when someone else isn't."* Sources were glad that the system gave them *"one less thing to worry about,"* and also found it *"easy to just raise your hand and say, 'I'm interested in X type of work, could you keep me in mind when it comes around?' That actually works amazingly."*

Training & Development

First-years are assigned a partner and an associate mentor: *"They don't throw mentors blindly at you; they allocate based on who's taken an interest in you and as a result you can tell people are invested in your development."* On top of these formal channels, more informal wisdom is in bountiful supply: *"The benefit of a large firm with so many specialties is that there's always someone to teach you something you wouldn't otherwise know."* An initial blast of *"general skills training applicable to your group"* scored positive reviews: *"I learned about negotiating and how to effectively read and mark up contracts, for example."* This is followed by monthly 'lunch and learn' sessions, which were described as *"extensive and robust."*

We did hear mixed feedback when it came to annual reviews. First-years get two reviews and found it *"really cool to get that feedback early on: a partner sits you down and goes through the various reviews filled out by people you've worked with. There's a good amount of constructive criticism."* Others were less impressed: *"My mid-year review wasn't particularly useful – it lasted ten minutes and the partner said, 'We'll talk in more detail when there's more to go on.'"* However, juniors did appreciate getting to give anonymous *"upward"* reviews: *"It's a great thing for accountability."*

See firm profile on p.692

The Inside View

Diversity	Partners (%)	Associates (%)
Women	20	43
White	89	70
Black/African American	2	4
Hispanic/Latin American	3	2
Asian	5	17
Mixed/Other	1	6
LGBT	3	5

Hours & Culture

With no official billing requirement, new associates can sometimes wonder if they're billing the right amount, but there's no need to panic: "*I had lower hours at the beginning and was a little concerned it would come up in my review, but actually I was pleasantly surprised. They just told me it would pick up.*" And after a while, "*you just don't think about it. You enjoy the slower days because you're not worried about hitting a certain number.*" Associates receive a lockstep bonus and are encouraged to take vacation: "*I can't think of anyone who hasn't taken the full amount.*"

Full vacation, standardized bonuses and no billing requirement... Associates felt all of these factors (along with the centralized staffing) shaped the firm's overall culture: "*It's set up to avoid a cage match situation. No one is hoarding work. There's enough stress in BigLaw without having to figure out politics.*" With a white-shoe legacy comes an inevitable preconception of stuffiness, but associates were quick to set the record straight: "*It's not too stuffy or too relaxed – it's like Goldilocks, they've got it just right.*" Across the board, juniors were comfortable with their colleagues: "*It's supportive from junior to partner level. I called someone up at midnight one Saturday and they walked me through every step of an assignment.*" Another junior added: "*The stratification here doesn't leave you intimidated by senior people. The worst I got was a disappointed sigh which, frankly, I deserved!*"

"It's set up to avoid a cage match situation."

Another reason why juniors weren't so worried about billing hours is because they work so many: "*Days can be wild.*" Fortunately for litigators, "*no one is interested where I'm working from,*" but in corporate Simpson "*isn't as permissive as other firms*" and often expects juniors to be in the office. We spoke to associates who regularly worked 12-hour days and more, particularly in corporate: "*I plan to be here late every night.*" This lifestyle "*sometimes*" allows for a social life, but can be "*so bad people usually just want to go home and go to bed. Occasionally you think you have your weekend, then an email comes through and suddenly it's gone. I wish some people would lose my number!*"

On the plus side, when associates are holed up together into the wee hours "*you have a nice sense of camaraderie – my friends at other firms will tell you I'm the happiest of the bunch!*"

Offices

"*No matter where you live*" in NYC, it's a breeze getting to Simpson's "*super centralized*" HQ, where the majority of associates are based. Situated across the street from Grand Central, the "*open and light*" office recently had a glass interior fitted – part of the "*glass wall movement*" sweeping the nation's law firms. Now that they're used to the transparent space, associates had only one lamentation: "*I can't take my shoes off late at night because people can see!*" More than making up for these footwear-related anxieties is the "*unbelievable*" cafeteria: "*It's among the best in the city. The staff put a smile on my face every day. I have friends at other firms who want to come.*"

The firm has another four US offices located in Palo Alto, LA, Washington and Houston.

Diversity

Simpson's diversity mentoring program gives diverse associates the option of being paired up with a mentor for just over 12 months: "*I met up with mine to chat for an hour once every three weeks.*" So far, over 200 associates have signed up for the program. In addition, there's a diversity retreat, which allows "*diverse associates to get together to talk about what needs to be focused on, before taking our suggestions to partners.*" Simpson has affinity groups for women, ethnic minorities and LGBT associates, as well as an Urban Education Initiative which partners with local schools in New York and LA to expose diverse students to the profession from a younger age.

Further up the ladder, "*it would be nice to have more female partners, but you can find role models in different groups. I'm most aware when I'm the only woman on a case, and there's been a decent number of those. I always feel respected, but it's a little shocking that in a big group of people we can't wind up with more of a balance.*" Female juniors on the whole felt that "*it's hard being a woman in BigLaw, but the firm makes it easier.*"

Pro Bono

"*There's no minimum hour requirement, but pro bono is valued just as much as the work we do for paying clients.*" We spoke to associates who'd racked up 150-plus pro bono hours and had the goods to show for it: "*You get an award for doing more than 100 hours. I think a lot of people get them.*" Some of the cases we heard about involved spousal support issues, unemployment benefits, rent

The Inside View

disputes and harassment complaints: "*A school district reached out to us because a parent was harassing teachers at a school. We were able to persuade the detective to issue an arrest warrant, and after that's effectuated we can go get a protective order.*"

"You get an award for doing more than 100 hours."

The firm is also "*pretty heavily involved in immigration matters; we do permanent residency applications and amicus briefs. The environment is another longstanding focus for Simpson, and we also host pretty regular clinics with small businesses to help get them off the ground.*"

Pro bono hours
- For all US attorneys: 48,359
- Average per US attorney: 63

Strategy & Future

"*We want to continue to capitalize on our strengths with regards to our institutional client platform,*" chairman Bill Dougherty tells us. With no plans to expand its geographic footprint at the moment, Simpson's focus is on developing its current offices. In the US, the firm's been building up its regulatory capabilities in DC in particular. On a more firm-wide level, Dougherty explains that "*our technology practice is critically important for the future; technology is disrupting industries all around us, so we want to make sure we remain very present in that space and continue to work with the new wave of technology companies, like Airbnb and Tesla, whose offerings we participated in last year.*" For more from Dougherty, visit chambers-associate.com

Get Hired

"*We're not into people who are just focused on trying to sell themselves in interviews; just be a normal person at lunch and feel free to talk about your life – not just the law!*" For more recruitment tips from Simpson's juniors and hiring partners, go to chamber-associate.com

See firm profile on p.692

The Inside View

Skadden, Arps, Slate, Meagher & Flom LLP & Affiliates

Lawyers per state

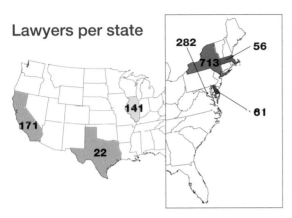

282
56
713
141
171
61
22

Largest US office: New York
US offices: 8
International offices: 14
First-year salary: $180,000
Billable hours: 1,800 target
Summers 2018: 203 (32 1Ls, 171 2Ls)
Revenue 2017: $2.58 billion (+3.5%)
Partners made in 2018: 10
Famous for: formidable global standing; mega M&A but strength in both transactional and contentious areas

Sinking its teeth into some of the juiciest work the Big Apple has to offer, this hulking megafirm has an ironclad reputation for fierceness and quality.

HOLLYWOOD loves a good origin story, especially when it's cranking out the latest in a seemingly endless stream of superhero movies. Perhaps for the next one they should consider a film based on the origins of Skadden, one of BigLaw's most celebrated tales. The firm came together on April Fool's Day (we kid you not) 1948 when Marshall Skadden, John Slate and Les Arps united to take on New York's white-shoe elite. Just as Marvel's Avengers devastated the city's landscape in the titular film, Skadden tore up the status quo by taking a fierce stance in both the boardroom and the courtroom. Its boldness paid off big time: today Skadden is a formidable international giant, and a world leader when it comes to mega M&A deals.

And if you're looking for legal superheroes in the firm's corridors of power, you'll find plenty to choose from – *Chambers USA* bestows over 30 top rankings on Skadden's expertise across both the country as a whole and eight individual states. Alongside corporate/M&A, standout areas include antitrust, securities litigation, real estate, tax and political law. One particularly insightful source summed up Skadden's appeal: *"The beauty of the legal market is that it's always evolving, and a firm like*

Skadden – with its diverse practice and footprint – can shine no matter what's happening." This junior echoed the thoughts of many when they said: *"I knew that whichever group I ended up choosing, it would be at the top of its field."* Sources also acknowledged the firm's prestige and fearsome reputation, but several said that they *"kept on making connections with people during the interview process, so it quickly became apparent that this was a comfortable place to be."*

The Work

Around half of Skadden's annual intake of juniors slots into the corporate and transactional group, while most of the rest join a litigation or a regulatory team (which includes tax). Centralized work allocation systems exist in each department, though over time associates get tasks more directly from partners. One explained that *"there's a very healthy give and take. It's well organized, but it also provides you with a nice way to build organic relationships."* Groups conduct weekly staffing meetings to make sure nobody's getting snowed under or going begging for work – the latter situation is rare, but can happen in *"more cyclical, up-and-down"* transactional practices.

Most corporate associates are allocated to a sub-group right off the bat, but those in New York rotate through two teams for eight months at a time before picking their poison. M&A is the largest subdivision, and newbies here tackle *"a lot of diligence, but also get to draft ancillary documents and shareholder rights plans, which you don't necessarily expect to do as a junior."* Sources felt there's *"as*

See firm profile on p.693

The Inside View

Rankings in *Chambers USA*

Antitrust	Intellectual Property
Banking & Finance	International Arbitration
Bankruptcy/Restructuring	International Trade
Capital Markets	Investment Funds
Chancery	Latin American Investment
Corporate Crime & Investigations	Litigation
	Media & Entertainment
Corporate/M&A	Private Equity
Employee Benefits & Executive Compensation	Products Liability
	Projects
Energy & Natural Resources	Real Estate
	REITs
FCPA	Securities
Financial Services Regulation	Sports Law
	Tax
Government	Technology
Healthcare	Telecommunications
Insurance	

For detail on ranking tiers and ranking locations, visit
www.chambersandpartners.com

Recent work highlights

- Represented Yahoo! during its $4.83 billion acquisition by Verizon Communications
- Acted for BMW throughout international arbitration proceedings brought by manufacturing and distribution firm Whitesell
- Defended Barclays during its long-running litigation with the Federal Energy Regulatory Commission, which accused the bank and four of its former executives of manipulating the energy market
- Advised Disney on its $1 billion acquisition of a 33% stake in software company BAM Technologies

Litigators commit to either traditional commercial litigation or a subset like insurance or political law. Generalists take on *"everything from securities to breach of contract cases... anything big enough for someone to hire Skadden for. The variety of work is something I appreciate."* Variety is also the name of the game when it comes to associates' tasks, which range from *"bread and butter legal research to document review to conducting employee interviews."* Is it a mix that keeps junior happy? *"I don't think I have any complaints,"* said one, *"not all the work is tied to the most crucial aspect of a case, but when I want to try something, the partners make an effort to get me in on it."* On the whole, *"it's an egalitarian environment, and the responsibility available can be high."* Interviewees were also happy to try their hand at international work – some even enjoyed a spell overseas.

much responsibility available as you'd like, though you do have to prove yourself before people trust you." For some, it was too much too soon: *"I feel we could do with a bit more supervision, though mid-level and senior associates are good at explaining things to you."* They also flagged that M&A can be more hierarchical than other departments (*"some partners are more hands on than others"*) but at the same time interviewees praised the early client contact they'd received.

"It's an egalitarian environment, and the responsibility available can be high."

Banking, corporate restructuring, antitrust, finance and investment management also fall under the big corporate umbrella. Skadden traditionally serves debtor clients in restructuring matters, but associates *"also worked with liquidators; in the past few years there have been a lot of oil and gas bankruptcies."* Interviewees struck gold by *"getting to run discovery production – doing that as a second-year was a great experience."* Corporate finance newbies worked primarily on IPOs and high-yield deals, and whetted their appetite with diligence from the off. *"What's awesome is that you get out of that space quickly. I've drafted disclosure documents and a lot of ancillaries."* The antitrust team, meanwhile, is split between transactional and litigious wings. One associate who'd straddled the divide reported: *"I've helped with discovery and led client calls as a first-year. On the corporate side, there's been some document review, but also presentation preparation and white paper drafting."*

Training & Development

Associate life at Skadden begins with three days in New York, which kick off a four-week training program called ACE [Associates' Comprehensive Education]. This includes a two-week mini-MBA. *"We spent over a month just training,"* an interviewee reflected, *"which was difficult to appreciate at the time, but now I'm really glad we had it. However, the program could last for two months and we'd still have a lot to learn!"* It's helpful, then, that group-specific training sessions come further down the line. Juniors also receive annual reviews (first-years get two), and get the process underway by selecting the partners they've worked sufficient hours with to evaluate them. *"If there are any issues they're addressed as early as possible, and people tend to be willing to give quick face-to-face feedback."* Interviewees deemed the approach to feedback *"fine"* overall: *"There could always be more, but what we do get is always really respectful – I've never been yelled at or chewed out!"*

See firm profile on p.693

The Inside View

Diversity	Partners (%)	Associates (%)
Women	22.4	47
White	91.6	71.3
Black/African American	1.4	4.9
Hispanic/Latin American	2.8	5.2
Asian	4.2	14.8
Mixed/Other	0	3.9
LGBT	1.7	4.7

Offices & Culture

Skadden's New York HQ is by far the largest base, and housed the largest contingent of associates on our list. There's an on-site gym and cafeteria to keep attorneys fit and fed, but juniors here summed up the building as *"nothing outstanding – it's a big Times Square office. The location isn't ideal, but we're moving in 2020."* Lawyers are headed for Manhattan West, near Hudson Yards. The DC office took on the next largest chunk of juniors, who told us that their newly renovated digs were *"what New York is aiming for; the office is a lot more open and bright, with glass panels, which really improves team morale."* The rest of Skadden's second- and third-years were split between its Boston, Chicago, Palo Alto and Wilmington offices, but the firm also has domestic bases in LA and Houston. Nobody outside of the New York mothership felt left out of the loop at the firm – *"it never feels like we're a satellite, and if most of the case team is here then we're in the driver's seat"* – and communication between the offices is well oiled both within and beyond the US.

"...we do like to have fun."

Several found that the firm's culture wasn't quite what they expected coming in – in the best possible way. *"I heard it was like a sweatshop,"* said one, *"and while there are ups and downs and people expect a lot, that's not true at all."* Many noted that *"New Yorkers do tend to be in the office for longer, so there's more of a work/life balance in the other offices,"* but at the same time *"the personality of the firm is pretty uniform across the board; Skadden puts a premium on personality, and we're not just a bunch of robots!"* The myth-busting continued when it came to assumptions that *"there's a fratty drinking culture – that's 100% false. It's not like people are chugging beer in the office."* Instead, sources reasoned that this reputation stems from *"people incorrectly using the word fratty as a synonym for social, and we are social – we do like to have fun."*

Fun can be had at numerous events, both on a firm-wide and office-specific basis. The biggest event in the Big Apple sees the firm *"rent out the ice skating rink at Rockefeller Center, so we can have a full dinner and dancing."* Let's hope Skadden's New Yorkers wore the appropriate footwear... Sporting and political events serve as common so-cial outlets, and most offices have weekly happy hours or non-alcoholic gatherings. *"Maybe other firms are jealous because we have cooler events than them and spend more time together,"* one associate boasted. There is quite a full program on offer, after all: departments also run social events throughout the year (the frequency depends on the team), as do Skadden's affinity groups, which bring in speakers to address attorneys – recent examples include Democratic National Committee chairman Tom Perez and civil rights activist Connie Rice.

Pro Bono

Declaring Skadden *"tremendously supportive"* of pro bono, associates pointed out that *"all pro bono hours are chargeable to billables, which really incentivizes us to do it. I've been able to commit a significant amount of time to cases and can direct them."* First-years in particular tend to pick up a decent amount of pro bono both to build experience and to fill gaps in their time. *"Sometimes partners will signal if I'm doing a lot and need to get more paid work, but I never feel like I shouldn't be doing pro bono,"* one junior explained. Immigration and asylum, nonprofit incorporation, community development and domestic violence cases are all common at Skadden, and various offices conduct specialized 'Impact Projects.' These include monthly 'Military Mondays' clinics in New York; a Palo Alto-based program that involves Skadden's lawyers giving legal guidance to high school students; and a partnership between the LA base and the Creative Rights Agency and Learning Rights Law Center, which has launched a sexual and cybercrimes awareness program. *"The firm is pretty open to our own ideas too,"* associates told us.

Pro bono hours
- For all attorneys across all US offices: 181,644
- Average per US attorney: 136

Hours & Compensation

Juniors can put 100 'productive work hours' (i.e. time spent doing things like shadowing or writing articles) toward the firm's 1,800 billable target, as well as an unlimited amount of pro bono. Noting that *"it's a lower goal than a lot of peer firms,"* most agreed *"it's very achievable and there's no real excuse not to meet it."* They also put the lower target down to *"some of the more specialist groups where there might not be as much work to go around."* Bonuses are lockstep for the first seven years, and after that point a discretionary element is introduced. Some go-getters grumbled that *"there's no benefit to billing more – lockstep almost rewards being less efficient,"* but less fiercely competitive juniors argued that *"lockstep creates more of a team feeling, as there's no incentive to hog all the work."*

See firm profile on p.693

543

"You're only here that late if something cool is happening."

Most associates felt their schedules left room to enjoy being people as well as lawyers, but noted *"it's difficult to schedule weekday plans as you never know what can come up."* Work hours can be extremely varied, especially in corporate, though non-New Yorkers were more confident about getting out by 7pm. Empire City sources admitted *"there are always busy times but it's not as bad as I expected,"* with one clarifying: *"I've only stayed beyond midnight once or twice; you're only here that late if something cool is happening."* An average day for some lasted between 10am and 8pm, but ultimately *"it really depends on what's going on."* In M&A, for example, *"there are days when I leave at 2pm and days when I leave at midnight."* More positively, interviewees felt encouraged to take at least a couple of weeks of vacation each year, and could do so without being bombarded by e-mails.

Strategy & Future

Though some felt *"transparency is something the firm could improve on,"* others pointed out that *"every year, the managing partner gives a State of the Firm address"* to keep them in the loop of broader developments. Skadden is also keen to get associates' ideas on how to improve things: executive partner Eric Friedman tells us that *"this year, we've built upon our reputation for innovative legal work and advanced our culture by inviting the entire firm to submit ideas for how to improve Skadden. Almost 200 ideas came in, 55 of which were from summer associates."* Walking the walk to match the talk, Friedman confirms Skadden will be implementing around 30 of the proposed ideas. To read the full interview and find out more about how the firm's shaking things up, head to chambers-associate.com.

Get Hired

"Everyone here is an alpha and a good teammate at the same time – I don't know how they get the balance right but they do!" To gain more insight into what Skadden's looking for in a candidate, head to chambers-associate.com.

See firm profile on p.693

Snell & Wilmer LLP

Lawyers per state

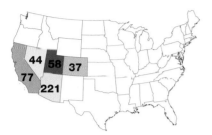

Largest US office: Phoenix

US offices: 8

International offices: 1

First-year salary: $115,000 - $160,000

Billable hours: 1,800 - 1,950 (varies by office)

Summers 2018: 25 (5 1Ls, 20 2Ls)

Revenue 2017: Undisclosed

Partners made in 2018: 6

Famous for: strength in the Southwest, particularly in areas like corporate, litigation and environment;commitment to local communities; emphasis on business development

Life's swell at Southwesterner Snell: it's *"a regional firm with impact"* and a focus on more than just business.

"OUR region has a lot of growing cities, and that's very attractive to lawyers," says firm chair Matt Feeney. *"People come here to raise their families."* Snell's juniors also highlighted the appeal of the Southwest, and observed that *"a lot of our attorneys have come from the Midwest – there's a strong group from Iowa and Kansas, and that's definitely influenced the atmosphere of the firm and contributed to its culture of politeness and congeniality."*

Pioneers who cross the Great Plains will find that Snell has much more to offer than a thriving location and a warm culture. Our interviewees were particularly vocal about this firm's desire to nudge its associates toward the partnership via an early focus on business development. *"They are very forthcoming about wanting you to become a partner, and they invest a lot in us to enable that to happen,"* one chirpily revealed. Snell therefore attracts those who are *"looking to set down some roots, stay and have a career."* That kind of loyalty extends beyond the firm, as Snell *"wants to give back to the community – they really encourage us to get involved in their volunteer projects."* Feeney also underscores this point: *"I believe people want to be part of something that is more than just a business*

enterprise – something that also does right by its communities."*

Then there's the reputation for great work, of course. In its home state of Arizona, Snell comes out on top for its corporate/M&A, environment, general commercial litigation and real estate expertise, but *Chambers USA* also dishes out accolades for the firm's work in Colorado, Nevada and Utah. While its offices may be concentrated in the Southwest, Feeney tells us that *"we view the firm as regional in geography only; we're pleased with our ability to serve clients both nationally and internationally."* The firm's overseas capabilities are enhanced by an office in Los Cabos, Mexico.

Offices

Working relationships between neighboring offices were common, and often originated from the associates' desire for certain work, although they are also facilitated through gatherings like the annual firm retreat: *"Each year everyone comes to Phoenix for a couple of nights and a lot of PowerPoints! We see the firm's numbers, then we break out into our practice groups and interact with people from the other offices. It builds a sense of community."* Almost half of the juniors on our list were based in the Phoenix HQ, while the remaining half were split between its LA, Las Vegas, Salt Lake City, Orange County, Denver, Tucson and Reno offices.

On chambers-associate.com...

- Interview with firm chair Matt Feeney
- Get hired: recruitment insight from hiring committee chairs and current associates
- More on Snell's IP work

The Inside View

See firm profile on p.694

Rankings in *Chambers USA*

Corporate/M&A	Litigation
Environment	Native American Law
Labor & Employment	Real Estate

For detail on ranking tiers and ranking locations, visit
www.chambersandpartners.com

Strategy & Future

"I wouldn't say we are trying to broaden our offering," says firm chair Matt Feeney, *"we are trying to deepen it in certain areas."* In particular, Feeney highlights growth within the life sciences and biotech subsets of the firm's practice. Elsewhere, *"one of our goals is to be the preeminent natural resources group in the West. Environmental, water, regulatory – those are areas we do have growth in. We're also seeing growth in the cybersecurity area; we had partner James Melendres join us from the DoJ."*

"One of our goals is to be the preeminent natural resources group in the West."

This growth has prompted Snell to expand its reach, but not by opening fully fledged offices, but 'presences' in both Albuquerque and DC. With an uptick in oil and gas work under Trump, Snell is currently *"exploring alternative models in Texas,"* Feeney tells us. *"Partners are considering a similar presence in Houston or Dallas to see if there is room for a firm like ours. We will continue negotiations with existing firms, but we're also open to establishing something that enables us to move into the market more slowly."*

The Work

Snell's second- and third-year juniors were split between 11 practices, but the firm's corporate and securities, commercial finance, and IP groups held the highest concentrations. Associates get assignments in different ways depending on location. The Phoenix HQ has a more open-market system, for example, while *"work often just lands on your desk"* for those elsewhere. Phoenix associates *"never found it difficult to source work. During the summer program a senior associate assigns us projects so you meet loads of lawyers, which meant I already had working relationships when I started."* A 'litigation pool' allows the department's first-year associates to dip their toes into a number of sub-groups. *"I like the variety,"* said one litigator, *"as it gives me a break but still helps me to hone skills for my primary practice."*

Industry-specific subgroups within the *"catch-all"* commercial litigation group include financial services, IP, securities, real estate, 'special' litigation and compliance, construction, white collar, and election and political law.

Recent work highlights

- Advised Global Water Resources – a water utilities company operating mainly in Phoenix – on its IPO; shares were offered at $6.25 each, and the matter totaled $8.4 billion
- Acted for the Utah Department of Transportation after a road construction project was delayed, in a matter worth over $100 million
- Represented oil and natural gas company MarkWest Energy during a contested $300 million insurance claim, which resulted from a pollution incident
- Won a case on behalf of hospitality company Diamond Resorts International, after an employee accused it of forcing them to resign for whistle-blowing and sought over $500,000 in damages

The freedom to source work between them saw our interviewees working on the likes of *"real estate, civil conspiracy, retail, civil negligence, tort and soft matters – you're not just exposed to typical breaches of contract."* Clients range from large financial institutions to far smaller companies, which provide good opportunities for fledgling litigators: *"On those smaller matters I've been the primary contact for the client."* As well as drafting motions and pleadings, associates had attended court hearings and taken depositions. *"My highlights have been taking two expert depositions and writing part of a summary judgment. I really felt I was playing an instrumental role in the team."*

"You're not just exposed to typical breaches of contract."

Corporate and securities associates had covered most aspects of their department's work. *"I've been involved in M&A deals and private placement offerings."* Certain partners *"specialize in biomedical companies and start-ups,"* which involves *"overseeing securities offerings to get those entities started,"* as well as *"handling company formation matters, like preparing articles of organization, charter documents and operation agreements. It's pretty cool stuff and it's relatively easy, so a young associate can do it."* Sources found that *"partners are good at not withholding the interesting work. A lot of what you do as a young associate can be mundane, but there's enough of the more complex stuff thrown in to make it exciting."* Rather fittingly for the Wild West, interviewees had also handled *"client wrangling"* to ensure information was submitted on time during the due diligence process.

Culture & Development

"I don't know if it's official policy," one source pondered, *"but we have a well-known and well-enforced no-jerk rule. If someone is being a jerk, it gets to senior people very quickly and gets shut down."* Associates went on to paint a picture of a culture with a community ethos where

See firm profile on p.694

The Inside View

Diversity	Partners (%)	Associates (%)
Women	16.3	42
White	92	85
Black/African American	0	1.8
Hispanic/Latin American	5.4	3.2
Asian	1	5.7
Mixed/Other	1.5	4.6
LGBT	1	1.8

"everyone is available to talk and laugh with. We're a firm that's full of polite, professional people."

This politeness coincides with a rather formal dress code: *"We are still required to wear a full suit every day. People may think we are formal or stuffy as a result of that, but it's not the case."* We heard tales pointing to a healthy social life across the board at Snell: in Denver there's a partner who hosts a wine-tasting event; in Phoenix there are weekly basketball and volleyball games to keep lawyers energized; and in Salt Lake City there's a much-loved tradition of *"going to each other's houses to watch* The Bachelor *– it's good to keep up with it!"* On the whole, *"there are less firm-sponsored events, but that's because they bring in people who want to spend time with each other. It's the whole mindset of the place and in any given week I'm invited to at least two social activities."*

"We have a well known and well-enforced no-jerk rule."

Further bonding is enabled by Snell's COACH mentoring program, which is designed to help junior lawyers find their feet and position themselves firmly on the path to partnership. In assigning formal mentors, *"the firm ensures you're speaking to the 'grey-hairs' in the firm. It breaks down barriers."* Furthermore, *"they want us to work on business development right out of the gate. I brought in my first client with the help of my mentor; they are your best resource for helping you to progress toward the partnership."* Making partner was flagged as a realistic prospect: *"The partner track is pretty clear. They focus on you building up a book of business and we have lunch talks with successful partners and associates, who pass on their knowledge to us."*

Hours & Compensation
Average associate hours were pretty reasonable for BigLaw: our sources were usually in the office by 8.30am and out by 6pm, but timings did vary. While we never heard of anyone pulling an all-nighter, some of our sources had stayed in the office until midnight on occasion. Encouragingly, *"partners are frank about saying; 'Don't overwork, this is not a grind shop.' Your bonus*

doesn't increase at a rate that makes doing 2,400 hours worth it. They don't want you working like that."

On the subject of bonuses: 1,900 hours is the target to shoot for in Salt Lake City, Phoenix and Denver; those in LA should reach 1,950; and in Reno, Tucson and Vegas it's 1,800 hours. *"They are well-known marks, and the people who really want to get there can do so,"* thought Phoenix-based sources. *"It's not a number that will keep you from seeing your family and is in line with the city's average."* They also felt their base salaries were in line with the market, but described their bonuses as *"lower compared to other local firms."* Snell's closed compensation system means that bonuses *"aren't talked about in the same way as they are at other firms."* Our sources mostly agreed with this junior, who felt that *"it simply comes down to trusting the people making the decisions – and I think we have the right people in charge to make us feel confident that decisions are being made fairly."*

Diversity
Around half of our interviewees could specifically name the firm's diversity initiatives. These include a student diversity scholarship (the FAR program), the Women's Initiative (which provides flexible working schedules that *"allow women to stay on the partnership track"*) and a legal writing internship for diverse students. Many partners also sit on the boards of community-oriented charities, which are often directed at particular minority groups.

Pro Bono
The firm's pro bono commitments also take on a community slant. A Phoenix-based junior told us: *"We're very involved in community outreach. Once a month I help at the Homeless Legal Assistance Project, to answer legal questions from those in need."* Our sources had also volunteered at a tax assistance program, worked for a charity, and written wills for veterans. Completing 50 hours of pro bono is encouraged and a technically unlimited amount (pending approval) can count toward Snell's billable target.

Pro bono hours
- For all US attorneys: 11,870
- Average per US attorney: 28.8

Get Hired
"We have a credo that talks about what you can do for the firm, for the community and for our clients. We want people who fall within that credo, so we look for those who are already involved in the community," says Anne Meyer, co-chair of the hiring committee. For more recruitment insight, go to chambers-associate.com.

See firm profile on p.694

The Inside View

Squire Patton Boggs

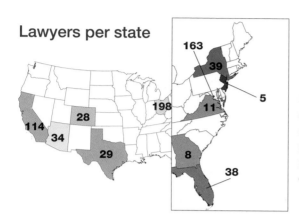

Lawyers per state

163
39
198　11　5
28
114
34
29　8
38

Largest US office: Washington, DC
US offices: 18
International offices: 29
First-year salary: $135,000-$180,000
Billable hours: 1,950 target (1,900 for first-years)
Summers 2018: 30 (7 1Ls, 23 2Ls)
Revenue 2017: $1 billion (+1.7%)
Partners made in 2018: 12
Famous for: numerous mergers; growth culture; political lobbying

It's business as usual for Squire Patton Boggs, which is continuing to hire lateral partners and merge with like-minded firms.

SQUIRE Patton Boggs really knows how to kick off the New Year with a bang. Each year there's something new and exciting hitting the legal headlines: early 2018 saw the firm announce that it had nabbed three partners from Dentons to launch a new office in Atlanta.

With this addition, Squire has 18 US offices and 47 worldwide – at the time of writing at least. The firm in its current form came about through the 2014 merger between Ohio-founded Squire Sanders and DC-headquartered Patton Boggs, which brought together two firms with storied histories. Squire now seeks to get the attention of students across the country, from coast to coast. *"I was attracted to the complexity of the work and the clients,"* one junior told us. Those clients range from industrial businesses like Goodyear Tires, Amtrak and Valvoline to UnitedHealth and an Ohio golf club. Others noted that all the mergers mean Squire is *"a large firm with a medium-firm feel – it's the best of both worlds."* Sources felt the most appealing part of Squire was its *"strong international presence, with a number of offices all over the world."*

On home turf, Squire excels in *Chambers USA* in its home state of Ohio. Areas such as banking and finance, corporate M&A, and natural resources and environment earn top-tier rankings, while areas including bankruptcy/restructuring, labor and employment, and general

commercial litigation follow closely. The firm also picks up one or two *Chambers USA* rankings in New York, Florida and Arizona, plus national recognition for its government relations practice (previously a core area of expertise for legacy firm Patton Boggs in DC).

The Work

At the time of our research, juniors could be found dotted across ten of the firm's US offices, with the largest numbers in DC and Columbus. Litigation and corporate take in most juniors, with others spread across areas including public policy, financial services, IP, environment, government investigations and real estate.

An informal work assignment system permeates most groups, which means a hefty amount of independence for juniors. *"I'm the only person who knows everything I'm working on,"* one interviewee asserted, *"so it's really up to me to manage my time and workload, and understand whether I have too much or too little on my plate."* The system has both pros and cons – a pro is that *"there's no gatekeeping – you get opportunities you wouldn't otherwise get."* Others, however, highlighted that *"at times all things are busy at once which can be overwhelming."* Juniors in some groups mentioned submitting their availability every two weeks, which is *"so that they can make sure the firm is allocating work correctly if a partner needs an associate and doesn't immediately have someone in mind."*

On chambers-associate.com...

• Interview with global managing partner Fred Nance

"It's really up to me to manage my time and workload."

See firm profile on p.695

Rankings in *Chambers USA*

Banking & Finance	Government
Bankruptcy/Restructuring	Insurance
Corporate/M&A	Labor & Employment
Employee Benefits &	Litigation
Executive Compensation	Natural Resources

For detail on ranking tiers and ranking locations, visit
www.chambersandpartners.com

Litigators have a variety of areas they can get their teeth stuck into. *"We handle contract disputes, environmental litigation, antitrust litigation, healthcare litigation, and some regulatory work for organizations like the DEA."* Some offices have a narrower focus. For example, a West Coast source explained: *"Product liability is probably the biggest focus in this office, as well as IP and employment litigation."* Others highlighted being involved in international commercial litigation which means *"large cases perhaps involving foreign governments or large international corporations."* Past clients have included Fiat Chrysler and the DOJ. Juniors' responsibility levels increase over time. *"In my first year I did a lot of research and memos, but now in my second year I've hardly done any research,"* one source told us. *"Instead, I've been drafting briefs and arguing motions in court, attending case management conferences and taking depositions."* Tasks like doc review and trial prep come up too.

Corporate attorneys cover *"M&A, corporate governance, startup work, and both private and public company work"* across industries including healthcare, financial services, technology and real estate. Sometimes the firm acts for government agencies too. Juniors told us they had *"drafted significant portions of purchase agreements and commercial transaction documents."* Some also reported regular client contact: *"I got to speak to the client directly despite how junior I was!"* Others reckoned they spent more time on classic tasks like due diligence and reviewing agreements. *"Squire staffs quite leanly,"* another source commented, *"so I've had the opportunity to work on more than just diligence. I've drafted and negotiated things like contracts and employment or shareholder agreements."*

The public policy team in DC is home to a couple of juniors. *"The work ranges from actual law to arguing the case for whatever a client's issue is up on Capitol Hill,"* a junior informed us. *"We do work with foreign clients who may not understand how something becomes law."* It's a junior's task to *"track legislation's progress through Congress; for example, tax reform or immigration, which have been in the news frequently. I would draft memos on how different versions of a bill might affect our client's business, and – once the law has passed – engage with the client on what points will affect them."*

Recent work highlights

- Advised Sterling Bancorp, a regional bank holding company, on its merger with Astoria Financial Corporation in a stock-for-stock transaction valued at $2.2 billion
- Represented Ohio's KeyBank as administrative agent in negotiating, documenting and closing a $400 million credit facility for Lincoln Electric Holdings
- Defended the State of Colorado against filings brought by the State of New Mexico alleging that Colorado is responsible for the release of three million gallons of acidified water and mine waste into the Animas River
- Represented Columbus' Muirfield Golf Club in a trademark suit against TCGC Properties, alleging the infringement of the 'Memorial Tournament' trademark

Offices

While the firm has no official headquarters, juniors still felt that the Cleveland office (where Squire Sanders was founded in 1890) functioned as the 'nerve center'. However, DC is the firm's biggest office and, at the time of our calls, housed the most juniors. Those in Columbus described themselves as *"the little brother"* to Cleveland as the latter *"is the biggest Ohio office."* The third Ohio office in Cincinnati is the smallest of the three.

The DC office was recently remodeled, although *"not all the floors are finished yet."* Sources found it to now have a *"very modern, clean and sleek feel."* Interviewees praised the showers in the building, so if associates fancy a workout before the real work, they can shower after. Everyone gets their own office, though sources reported that newbies have to wait until their second-year for an exterior office. San Francisco associates had noticed the growth of the office since the firm's merger with 50-lawyer Carroll Burdick in 2016. Interviewees also noted the existence of health/wellness rooms in certain offices across the network, which come equipped with sofas and provide a handy space for associates to have a moment of peace if they require it.

Culture

With the merger between Squire Sanders and Patton Boggs feeling like something of days past for current newbies (think back to the year of Ellen DeGeneres' Oscar selfie and the Ice Bucket Challenge), most agreed the only effect on the culture had been that *"now we are a large firm, but with a medium-firm feel because of all the mergers. That was never lost."*

"It's still corporate, but I feel like I have a lot of freedom here."

Sources also believed that Squire *"is a large global firm, but doesn't have that high-pressure feel."* They elaborated:

See firm profile on p.695

Diversity	Partners (%)	Associates (%)
Women	23.1	51.6
White	84	80.3
Black/African American	4.6	2.5
Hispanic/Latin American	4.2	4.5
Asian	5.7	9
Mixed/Other	1.5	3.6
LGBT	-	-

"It feels very conversational – I feel very comfortable saying what I feel." As a result, the term *"pretty laid back"* came up a lot when juniors were describing the culture. That said, juniors added: *"It's still corporate, but I feel like I have a lot of freedom here. It's pretty much what you make of it."* An entrepreneurial approach was also valued: *"You get opportunities, but it's about taking them and creating something out of them. The firm values your efforts to bring in clients, network and engage in your community."*

Sources also noticed that *"people love to socialize – events are pretty well attended and we always have seasonal things like holiday parties and regular happy hours."* There are occasional weekend gatherings too, though *"we usually leave weekends for people's friends and family outside of work."* In the summer, social calendars are busier. A source reported: *"In 2017 we did bowling and wine tasting, with some dinners and a rooftop party thrown in!"*

Training & Development

"I would say most of the training has come through gaining experience and learning on the job," a source told us. This was the general consensus all round, though interviewees did emphasize that the firm is *"really encouraging of CLEs – one came with an attorney tool kit which I've referred back to several times."* There are also a couple of NITA trainings for litigators. Some felt training was an area that could be improved, though many admitted: *"I've been fortunate to work with partners who have taken the time to mentor and teach me. The partners are willing to teach at this firm, and I've benefited from that more than any general group training."* The firm told us that it has recently revamped its training program, which starts over the summer and continues into the first year under the banner of 'SPB University'.

Hours & Compensation

First-years are eased into the firm with a billing target of 1,900 hours, increasing to 1,950 from the second year onward. *"My understanding is that it is a goal, and not something you'll be fired over if you don't meet it,"* a source told us. Not that it matters too much, as most juniors found it to be an achievable target. An average day looked something like 9am to 6pm in the office, though *"leaving at six doesn't mean I stop working – I go home, and work from there."* The ability to work remotely was praised across the board – *"it's a super awesome thing about the firm!"* Despite this, occasional late nights in the office are unavoidable. *"I have been here until midnight or the early morning, but that is a pretty rare occurrence,"* a junior reported. Another joked: *"When it's deal time I pretty much live here,"* though they emphasized *"that is the minority of the time."*

> ## "I have been here until midnight or the early morning, but that is a pretty rare occurrence."

Associates are paid different amounts in different markets, but it ain't all about the money, and juniors we spoke to were generally happy with their salary. That said, when it comes to bonuses there was some uncertainty: *"It's one thing people complain about – it's not transparent. If you meet your billables, you're not necessarily going to get a bonus. It's a subjective system."*

Pro Bono

A firm-wide pro bono committee and dedicated coordinators in Cleveland and Dallas help to staff attorneys on projects. Up to 100 hours of pro bono can count toward associates' billing targets. Experiences with pro bono varied among our interviewees. One source felt: *"I don't think they necessarily present us with lots of pro bono opportunities, but they're willing to support pro bono opportunities we might bring in."* Several sources recalled doing pro bono during their summer, specifically *"free advice clinics on various housing issues."* Some associates had recently been involved with the Tenant Advocacy Project, child custody issues and consumer protection cases, while others had drafted agreements and contracts for nonprofit organizations. The firm also does a fair bit for work for KIND (Kids In Need of Defense), takes on matters for veterans' groups and runs its own 'Public Service Initiative' that is focused on high-stakes cases like death penalty appeals. Associates who had got into pro bono agreed that *"it's a nice opportunity because you're completely in control of those cases and you get different experiences than on billable work."*

Pro bono hours
- For all US attorneys: 18,599
- Average per US attorney: 26

See firm profile on p.695

The Inside View

Diversity

Juniors noticed good gender diversity at the associate level, where *"the male-to-female ratio is equal"* – male partners still outnumber female partners four to one though. Associates in different offices had different opinions on the extent of the racial diversity around them. Most found that *"racial diversity is not so great"* although all agreed *"the firm makes a point to communicate that it is committed to diversity."* Interviewees also noted that global managing partner Fred Nance is African American. Nance is a member of the firm's global board, which is 50% diverse; he is also one of the leaders of the firm's diversity committee, which works on developing diversity initiatives. One such initiative is the Women's Enterprise Group, which addresses advancement and retention of women.

Strategy & Future

"Squire is entrepreneurial, so it is always looking outwards," a junior believed. *"It's very much a global firm, with more offices outside the US than inside. I feel we have more visibility in the global market than ever before."* So what's the plan going forward? Juniors broadly guessed that *"it seems the goal is to continue moving forward and staying healthy financially. We're trending in the right direction."* Others added that they couldn't foresee *"anything major coming up"* (like more mergers), but were eagerly awaiting the firm's annual meeting for more info on Squire's plans: *"The managing partner and several other partners make a presentation on the financial health of the firm and where they want it to go. They also tell us what the firm is interested in; technology is obviously a huge thing, and the firm is going to engage with technological advances and modernize accordingly."* Go online to read our interview with global managing partner Fred Nance.

See firm profile on p.695

The Inside View

Sterne, Kessler, Goldstein & Fox P.L.L.C.

Lawyers per state

126

Largest US office: Washington, DC

US offices: 1

International offices: 0

First-year salary: $180,000 (2,000 hour track)/$165,000 (1,900 hour track)

Billable hours: 1,900 or 2,000 target

Summers 2018: 6 (6 2Ls)

Revenue 2017: undisclosed

Partners made in 2018: 5

Famous for: IP focus and emphasis on hiring those with relevant academic and practical backgrounds

These self-proclaimed 'nerds' have a knack for all things IP.

"THERE are a lot of different ways people describe our culture: collaborative, committed to science... but what I'd say is that we're a little nerdy!" says recruiting committee chair (2017) Paul Ainsworth. Yes, DC-based Sterne Kessler is full of science and engineering whizzes who are also legal masterminds (over 50 of its professionals have earned PhDs in these areas). Though dealing exclusively in IP matters, managing director Mike Ray tells us: "I tend not to use 'boutique' to describe us because that word infers 'small' – and we're not small at all." One thing that certainly isn't small is Sterne Kessler's client list, which includes global mega brands like Apple, adidas and Volkswagen.

"We'll continue to be a well-balanced and market-leading IP firm."

"This firm blew up by responding to activity in the IP field," associates told us, before helpfully explaining: "It started out as a patent prosecution firm in the late 70s. Then when litigation became the hot topic in the industry, the firm branched out and brought in the relevant people." On the patent prosecution side, Sterne Kessler receives top marks from *Chambers USA*, especially for its expertise in industry sectors like computer software, life sciences and engineering. Litigation work, meanwhile, is on the rise, as Ray points out. "We've had two litigators join us

in DC recently, and they've been accelerating the growth of our litigation practice – biosimilars and electronics are two very hot areas right now in that regard."

All of our associate interviewees had relevant previous experience connected to the firm's practice areas. That doesn't mean that all of them came in wielding hefty PhDs (although some of them did) – we heard of some that had worked at the Patent Office, while others had started at the firm as tech specialists (see our interview with Paul Ainsworth online) or took up internships on the Federal Circuit that exposed them to patent litigation.

Strategy & Future

"The International Trade Commission is increasingly becoming an important place to litigate patent cases," says managing director Mike Ray. "We're involved in 10% of the cases that are heard there – for a single office with 130 lawyers we're making a great impact. In the district courts, we're seeing battles fought in the area of biologics, which presents enormous opportunity for our firm," Ray notes. This influx of litigation matters "hasn't come at the expense of our prosecution work. We'll continue to be a well-balanced and market-leading IP firm." For more from Ray, see the full interview on chambers-associate.com

On chambers-associate.com...

- Interviews with managing director Mike Ray and recruitment chair Paul Ainsworth
- Sterne Kessler's DC office

The Work

Juniors join a specific practice group from the beginning of their summer at the firm. Most work in Sterne Kessler's electrical, biotech and mechanical groups, which handle a mix of both patent prosecution (the process of

See firm profile on p.696

The Inside View

Rankings in *Chambers USA*

Intellectual Property

For detail on ranking tiers and ranking locations, visit
www.chambersandpartners.com

applying for patent status) and patent litigation work. A handful work in the firm's dedicated IP litigation group. All groups expose juniors to the firm's inter partes review (IPR) work, which it calls patent office litigation. When it comes to assignment, *"the directors of each group will meet and talk about workloads. It balances the work among associates and levels the playing field – there's no unhealthy competition or 'me vs. you' going on."*

Over in the mechanical group, *"we do utility patents and a lot of design patents – I do half and half, which gives me some variety."* Some spent their first few months at the firm *"drafting briefs for IPR matters – I was the primary drafter and it was a good challenge."* Sources had also conducted *"freedom to operate and landscape searches"* on the patent prosecution side: *"You're evaluating how strong a patent is by taking all of the institutional knowledge we have to make sure it doesn't fall into the same trap that other patents did – it helps broaden your understanding of the law and sharpens your ability to spot relevant issues for the client."*

"I was the architect of the document."

In electrical, the work (as the name implies) revolves around *"electrical engineering technology – everything from consumer products to computer architecture and semiconductors. Most of my time has been spent on prosecution matters, where I interview inventors, draft the application, send it off to the partner for internal review and then file it for client review."* Life in biotech is even more technical: *"We deal with pharma-related inventions, mostly compounds, formulations and chemical entities. I have clients ranging from a couple of guys making investments up to global pharma companies."*

Devoted litigators deal with clients from all of the above categories. They reported working on a mix of patent office litigation and district court cases, and highlighted the group's appellate work at the Federal Circuit, as well as a small but growing trademark subgroup with a mechanical focus. *"Especially at the beginning you'll be doing a lot of legal research and spot assignments where you just see a small part of the puzzle."* Weightier assignments are in store though: *"I've drafted motions to dismiss for Patent Office litigation cases. The partner was reviewing it but I was the architect of the document, which allowed me to see the bigger picture – it's much more meaningful and enjoyable."*

Recent work highlights

- Successfully defended US biotech company ImmunoGen against an inter partes review filed by a competitor, which centered on a patent covering ImmunoGen's breast cancer drug Kadcyla
- Continues to implement Apple's global design protection efforts – in 2016 Sterne Kessler orchestrated over 900 patent filings in more than 20 countries for the technology giant
- Assisted Verizon and Verizon Wireless with trademark clearance and prosecution – the firm typically clears over 500 trademarks for the company each year
- Defended Teva Pharmaceuticals against a Hatch-Waxman lawsuit that alleged that it and several other pharmaceutical companies had infringed patents covering a drug called Restasis, which is used to increase tear production in sufferers of 'dry eye disease'

Pro Bono

IP isn't an area traditionally associated with pro bono, and juniors did admit that pursuing such matters is *"an option, but they don't push it – no one's going to be knocking on your door saying you've got to do pro bono work."* Our sources had attended trademark clinics for members of the public, and helped inventors with limited resources to pursue securing a patent. *"The firm does send of a few emails about getting involved,"* and has recently broadened its scope: *"Over the past year we've been getting involved in immigration and legal aid refugee matters. I'm glad that the firm is finding a way to become involved in the issues in our community."* Pro bono hours can count toward the firm's billable targets, but the specific amount is dependent on the pro bono practice's budget each year.

Pro bono hours
- For all attorneys: 1,120 approx
- Average per attorney: 8.6

Training & Feedback

The initial two-week training period was described as *"extensive: some of it involves getting familiar with the computer systems, but we also get an introduction to patent prosecution, a session on how to draft applications, and trips to the Patent Office and the Federal Circuit to witness oral arguments at court. It's great for hands-on observational training."*

After that, there are mandatory weekly sessions for all first and second-year associates: *"They prioritize it to make sure we stay sharp. The focus of the sessions ranges from recent Federal Circuit decisions that will affect our work to refreshers on the basics of patent practice. They held a recent one on design patents, which was very informative."*

The Inside View

See firm profile on p.696

Diversity	Partners (%)	Associates (%)
Women	25.5	27.1
White	78.2	72.9
Black/African American	3.6	2.9
Hispanic/Latin American	5.5	1.4
Asian	12.7	22.9
Mixed/Other	0.0	0.0
LGBT	1.8	4.3

Culture

An associate's practice group can determine the extent to which they work with other colleagues. In groups like electrical and biotech *"the work product is more individually generated – most people work by themselves or with just a director,"* while in litigation *"there's more collaboration."* Regardless of the group, associates agreed that *"people are encouraging and have a lot of time for us – they're willing to stop what they're doing to help you understand what needs to be done and not make you feel stupid!"* Sterne Kessler's practice group directors came in for particular praise: *"They always welcome questions, suggestions and challenges – we have our opinion and we are encouraged to voice disagreement. There's an emphasis on positive engagement."*

"Most of us are introverts," one associate in the electrical group told us, adding: *"We're scientists, so there's not a lot of powwow going on in general!"* Others told us that the firm is *"very family-oriented,"* with this junior summing up the approach in most groups: *"Occasionally we'll go out for drinks, but most often I'll head home to be with the family."* While Sterne Kessler might not have a raft of social excursions planned every week, its practice groups still host happy hours and the summer period comes with a spike in events (we also heard that the firm's barista bar draws a steady crowd).

Diversity

We heard mixed reports on gender diversity depending on the practice group juniors were in. Those in litigation, for example, said there were *"a lot of women here; three of our latest hires were women and one of the partners who runs a lot of the everyday mechanics is also a woman."* The mechanical group, meanwhile, was described as being *"predominantly male."* This associate explained: *"Part of the issue is that we're an IP firm, and we reflect the number of women going into science and engineering and following*

those areas through to law school – these are areas where women have traditionally been under-represented, but I see potential and the possibility of improvement."*

"We reflect the number of women going into science and engineering."

Many sources told us that Sterne Kessler *"feels inclusive and very accepting,"* and praised the events organized by the firm's diversity committee: *"They put a lot of energy into it: we had a person of color from NASA come to speak to us a couple of months ago, and we had an HR representative from Google come to speak to us about inclusion."*

Hours & Compensation

Associates can choose between two billable target tracks: 1,900 or 2,000 hours. *"The majority of people are on 1,900,"* juniors revealed. *"It's in most people's interest to be on that track – you don't want to oversell and underdeliver."* If those on 1,900 end up billing 2,000 in the end, *"you're compensated for it as if you were on the 2,000 track, but you'd get that amount in a bonus at the end of the year."* There's also a reduced hours scheme that allows attorneys to go down to 1,800, 1,700 or 1,600 hours with a proportionate dock in pay. One told us that *"trying to make 1,900 in the first year was quite stressful. Taking the dock in pay was worth it to alleviate the stress."*

"You don't want to oversell and under-deliver."

Interviewees tended to put in around ten hours a day at the office, with the majority arriving between 8:30am and 9am, and leaving between 6pm and 7pm. *"Patent prosecution is more consistent while the hours in litigation can fluctuate a bit more,"* sources told us, with late nights potentially running to 10pm *"a few times a week"* depending on workload. In general, working weekends is *"not a regular thing"* and evening work is *"kept to a minimum."*

Get Hired

"Most of our interviewers here are focused on the candidates' transcripts, how well they did and the technical courses they took," says recruiting committee chair (2017) Paul Ainsworth. Find out more about getting hired at Sterne Kessler on chambers-associate.com

See firm profile on p.696

Stroock & Stroock & Lavan LLP

Lawyers per state

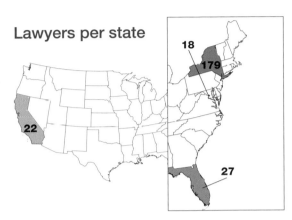

Largest US office: New York
US offices: 4
International offices: 0
First-year salary: $180,000
Billable hours: 2,000 target (incl. 200 non-billable)
Summers 2018: 17 (1 1L, 16 2Ls)
Revenue 2017: $251 million (-7.3%)
Partners made in 2018: 6
Famous for: New York heritage; real estate expertise; midsized dimensions that provide quality work and a low partner to associate ratio

This midsized firm has Stroock a nice balance: it's small enough to cultivate a *"familial atmosphere"* and big enough to provide *"stability and sophisticated clients."*

NOT long before our calls with Stroock's juniors, the firm had announced its role advising a developer on a major new waterfront project in Long Island City, Queens – which is notable for two reasons. First, it showcases Stroock's New York heritage and ongoing involvement in the city (*"We've been around since the late 1800s and we're steeped in the community,"* sources were quick to tell us), and second, it exhibits one of the firm's core strengths: real estate. *Chambers USA* tips its cap to Stroock's development, financing and zoning work in New York in particular.

But there's a lot more to Stroock than a beating heart in Manhattan and a talent for handling the legal dimensions of its urban landscape. Over the years Stroock has expanded its geographic reach by opening offices in LA, Miami and DC, and its practice is composed of many areas besides real estate: other highlights in *Chambers USA* include bankruptcy/restructuring, employee benefits & executive compensation, IP and insurance; on a nationwide basis its international trade practice is highly regarded.

Our associate interviewees were fully aware of Stroock's reputation, but also chose it for its more midsized measurements: *"I wanted a firm that had a low partner to as-*sociate ratio to ensure I got exposure, could grow as an attorney and do substantive work."* While small enough to provide that experience, juniors also felt that Stroock was big enough to provide stability thanks to a balanced spread of practices (which ranges from corporate to financial restructuring to litigation): *"The legal industry is vulnerable to change right now, but Stroock can give you that BigLaw stability."*

The Work

Stroock's litigation department took in the biggest number of associates on our list, followed by corporate and real estate. The rest went to the financial restructuring, tax, and business practices. Each department has an administrative partner who's tasked with distributing work: *"It's somewhat traditional in that sense. In the beginning all matters come down through them, which ensures you become familiar with the broader practice group."* However, as times passes *"a lot of reciprocation goes on, where if you've consistently worked for certain partners they begin to ask for you directly."* Our sources liked the blend of both assignment channels, and repeatedly flagged the benefits of Stroock's lean staffing arrangements: *"There's never more than two or three associates on a deal, and I'm always the only junior. It's a hands-on firm and they do a good job of giving us responsibility early on."*

Litigators *"particularly enjoyed how different each case can be."* A more generalist approach saw juniors sample matters tied to lobbying rules, real estate advertising reg-

See firm profile on p.697

The Inside View

Rankings in *Chambers USA*

| Bankruptcy/Restructuring | International Trade |
| Insurance | Real Estate |

For detail on ranking tiers and ranking locations, visit
www.chambersandpartners.com

ulations, discrimination claims, loan agreements, mergers and civil investigations. *"The most common things are research and legal analysis, but you're not just writing up information while the partner makes all the decisions – it's very much a collaboration where your ideas and theories are exchanged and worked with."* Other tasks included journeying to clients' offices for fact-gathering exercises, drafting outlines for witness examinations and responding to subpoenas. *"By the beginning of your second year you can expect to start taking cases from cradle to grave and driving them forward."*

"...taking cases from cradle to grave."

It's also *"pretty general under the corporate umbrella,"* where associates had dabbled in a mix of M&A, finance and funds work. On the finance side, *"we tend to represent the borrower during refinancings,"* and for juniors this meant *"a lot of paper! There's a lot of coordination and management to be done."* M&A deals, meanwhile, *"tend to have larger teams, so juniors are usually tasked with turning comments on the more minor agreements."* Juniors felt that funds work offered the most responsibility, as *"they keep you very involved, from leading on some calls to doing a lot of drafting: there are a preset number of documents that go into setting up the fund, and I take a first crack at them before they're reviewed by partners."*

The real estate department is *"completely full-service and standalone, as opposed to being an ancillary bolt-on like it can be at many other firms."* Associates therefore saw *"the whole range: acquisitions, dispositions, lending work, joint ventures and leases – we do everything!"* Some of our interviewees had specialized early and taken on a lot of lending work: *"We represent the lenders, and the deals can range from $20 million to half a billion. I get to draft documents like signature pages and speak to the client on the phone three or four times a week – not so much to give legal advice, but to be the point person that manages the deal flow and gets it closed."*

Training & Development

Juniors agreed that *"you have to be proactive to get regular feedback,"* but were grateful to have two formal reviews each year (one in June and one at the end of the year). *"You ask for feedback from everyone you've worked for, and they review around 15 aspects of your performance. Once everyone's had their say you sit down and talk through it*

Recent work highlights

- Advised pharma giant Pfizer on various real estate transactions, including the sale of its worldwide headquarters in New York and the $6 million renegotiation of an office lease in San Francisco
- Represented international chemical company Solvay during its $6 billion acquisition of US defense contractor Cytec
- Obtained a dismissal for accountancy juggernaut Grant Thornton after a federal lawsuit that sought $100 million in damages was issued against it for alleged securities law violations
- Acted for KUKA, a German manufacturer of industrial robots, as its $5 billion acquisition by a Chinese investor came under the scrutiny of the Committee on Foreign Investment in the United States (CFIUS) and the Directorate of Defense Trade Controls

all with the administrative partner." The implementation of several clear review categories was popular: *"It's created more transparency, and it allows partners to give more substantive feedback instead of just checking boxes."*

Formal training manifests itself in *"a great deal of CLE sessions; there's an active program that usually runs one or two events a month, covering business development, personal marketing and practice-specific talks."* For litigators, the pinnacle of Stroock's formal training is the summer mock trial. Participants found it *"invaluable"* as a learning experience: *"You can write outlines for cross-examinations all day, but until you're standing on that podium with everyone watching, there's no substitute."*

Hours & Compensation

Juniors work to meet a 2,000-hour billing target, but can put 200 hours of 'non-billables' – like pro bono and time spent on business development activities – toward it. Sources in groups like litigation and financial restructuring described the target as *"attainable if you're willing to put in the hours,"* but those in more transactional groups like corporate and real estate found it more challenging: *"It's been a slow summer so I'm not going to make it – I don't think there are any consequences as they prefer us to work more for experience and training at the start of our careers."* Those who fall short of the hours target by a small amount may still be considered for a bonus, as the firm also looks at factors like good performance, efficiency and the overall activity within a particular practice.

"They prefer us to work more for training and experience."

Ten-hour days in the office were normal, with many sources working between 9am and 7pm. When deals ramp up so do the hours – the record we heard of was

See firm profile on p.697

Diversity	Partners (%)	Associates (%)
Women	19	42
White	91	78
Black/African American	0	5
Hispanic/Latin American	4	7
Asian	5	6
Mixed/Other	0	4
LGBT	1	2

one junior staying overnight and leaving at 11am the next day. That's on the intense end of the scale though – normally *"you're not expected to stay super late, and you won't find people regularly eating dinner here. People tend to leave by 7:30pm."*

Culture

Stroock's size means that *"we still work for sophisticated clients but can do so in a more familial atmosphere where the partners care about our well-being."* This all helps to create a *"not super competitive or cutthroat environment – people pitch in for doc reviews, and there's a 'collective action' approach to any problems that arise."* There's *"still a hierarchy"* but *"often you'll find everyone conversing with everyone – the secretaries, the paralegals, the librarians. You develop a rapport with a whole bunch of people."* This was all true in the offices outside of the New York HQ as well, as this LA interviewee testified: *"We're not cogs in the wheel – we have a tight-knit environment here where my practice group chair knows me by name and knows all about my family."*

> ## "You develop a rapport with a whole bunch of people."

On the social side, interviewees had enjoyed happy hours, bowling excursions and *"dinners to give us time to bond away from the office."* There was some hankering for *"a little more interaction between departments,"* but themed monthly events in each of the firm's offices were deemed helpful for fostering further unity: *"We've had a Halloween one, a baseball one, a beach themed one and even a pie contest!"*

Offices

The majority of juniors were based in Stroock's flagship New York office on Maiden Lane. Its downtown location in the heart of the financial district also comes with *"some of the best views in Manhattan."* While *"the office space itself is not the greatest,"* renovations are underway to spruce the place up: *"The renovated areas look much nicer: we've opened up a beautiful new cafeteria downstairs, every floor has a new bathroom, and our lobby has*

also been done." Once the common areas are done, the individual offices will be made shiny and new too. Juniors currently share an office for their first two years at the firm, before getting their own in their third year.

Diversity

As with most firms, Stroock gets *"less diverse the higher up the ranks you go,"* but juniors felt that the disparity was *"not through lack of effort on the firm's part,"* and praised the firm for making a *"huge effort to increase diversity over the last three years."* They added that Stroock is *"committed to retaining diverse professionals,"* and partly does so through a series of *"active, visible affinity groups that plan events and talks to bring awareness to issues or simply to celebrate diversity."* The firm's LGBT group hosts a *"very well-attended annual dinner that people look forward to,"* while the women's group *"meets at least once a month for lunch, a cocktail hour or a speaker event – before we meet we read up on articles in order to discuss gender disparity in the legal market."*

> ## "...huge effort to increase diversity over the last three years."

Pro Bono

Juniors were *"pretty active"* on the pro bono front, with one excited to tell us that they'd written *"about a third of an amicus brief to the Supreme Court on a voting rights case."* Stroock doesn't *"force pro bono on you but strongly encourages people to take it on – they give out nice medals and I have one sitting on my desk!"* On the whole sources felt that *"it's valid to prioritize pro bono work because the firm values it and the efforts from our leadership are genuine."* Some of the organizations associates worked with included IMPACCT Brooklyn, the Urban Justice Center, the Brennan Center for Justice, the Center for Reproductive Rights and Her Justice.

Pro bono hours:
- For all attorneys: 15,974
- Average per attorney: 64.7

Strategy & Future

"We're targeting greater growth in our financial restructuring, real estate, financial services and litigation practices," co-managing partner Alan Klinger tells us. He adds that 2017 saw Stroock refocus its strategy along key industry lines: *"The strategic planning process over the past year led us to approach the business from an industry rather than a skills-based point of view. We looked at the way clients purchase our services and subsequently reorganized the firm into eight core business units that are focused on the needs of our leading clients. In some areas, for example, we've combined litigators and transactional lawyers into a business unit in order to show our clients that we truly understand their business and can advance their interests."*

See firm profile on p.697

Sullivan & Cromwell LLP

Lawyers per state

52
607
65

Largest US office: New York
US offices: 4
International offices: 9
First-year salary: $180,000
Billable hours: no requirement
Revenue 2017: $1.4 billion (+3%)
Summers 2018: 152 (5 1Ls, 129 2Ls, 15 3Ls, 3 other)
Partners made in 2018: 7
Famous for: Perfectionism, intellect and high-flying alumni

If the *"pursuit of excellence"* is your top priority, you'll find this New York stalwart a very suitable place to launch your career.

FOR chairman Joe Shenker, the most surprising thing about being at Sullivan & Cromwell is *"how little it has changed* [since joining in 1980] – *in terms of our culture, approach to work and pursuit of excellence."* That pursuit especially attracted the high-fliers on our junior associate list, who flagged *"the sharpness"* of the firm's attorneys as a major pull factor. These learned lawyers keep S&C at the top, as exemplified by its array of top *Chambers USA* rankings in areas like corporate/M&A, capital markets, tax, litigation, financial services and real estate. Further proof of the firm's excellence comes via an inspection of its alumni ranks, which contain the likes of Jay Clayton (chair of the US SEC) Norris Darrell (former president of the American Law Institute), Peter Thiel (cofounder of PayPal) and international human rights lawyer Amal Clooney.

Its headquarters may be in New York, but S&C also has a further three domestic bases and nine offices across Europe and the Asia-Pacific region, giving the work an *"international flavor."* Most recently, after a 16-year hiatus in geographical expansion, office number 13 opened its doors in Brussels. Shenker explains why: *"We don't believe in opening offices simply because other people are doing so, or based on a 'field of dreams.' We only launch new offices to respond to specific practice and client needs and*

we want each of our offices to be the best in its jurisdiction. Our opening in Brussels is the result of expanding cross-border work, and increasing European regulation."

The Work & Pro Bono

Juniors are mostly split between two broad practices at S&C – 'general practice' and litigation. Only a handful on our 125-strong list had settled into the firm's tax and 'estate & personal' practices. Those in GP found that there was enough flexibility to allow both free-rein sampling of various areas and a more targeted approach: *"I can say exactly what I want to do – I'm not forced into a bunch of areas I absolutely don't want to do. We're free agents for M&A, capital markets, restructuring – anything that falls under general practice for two years."* After two years, juniors choose a group to specialize in, but the majority also pick a secondary group to continue working in to maintain a broader practice. A centralized assignment system initially takes away the slog of having to find work, but functions more as a backup: *"You are encouraged to ask for work. I've only got a few deals through the system. Most have come through partners or seniors knocking at my door."*

"I'm not forced into a bunch of areas I absolutely don't want to do."

Our GP sources had dabbled in debt offerings, leveraged financings, joint ventures, public and private M&A deals, and fund formations. One junior had recently been busy *"helping a private equity client purchase a portfolio*

On chambers-associate.com...

- Get hired: more on the route to Sullivan & Cromwell
- Interview with chairman Joe Shenker

See firm profile on p.698

The Inside View

Rankings in *Chambers USA*

Antitrust	Financial Services
Capital Markets	Regulation
Corporate Crime &	Insurance
Investigations	Investment Funds
Corporate/M&A	Latin American Investment
Employee Benefits &	Litigation
Executive Compensation	Projects
Energy & Natural	Real Estate
Resources	REITs
Environment	Securities
FCPA	Tax

For detail on ranking tiers and ranking locations, visit
www.chambersandpartners.com

Recent work highlights

- Advised industrial gases company Praxair on its $73 billion merger with Linde
- Acted for AT&T during its acquisition of Time Warner, which was worth $107.7 billion in total
- Represented Amazon as it acquired Whole Foods for $13.7 billion
- Defended the Bank of Nova Scotia against allegations of manipulating the gold market
- Obtained an $814.9 million arbitration award on behalf of BlackBerry following a dispute with Qualcomm over royalty payments

---

company" and "*writing memos for banks on regulatory issues they could be encountering in the near future.*" Is there a typical day? "*You can typically expect to be on client calls or in meetings with partners, but it just really varies based on the deal.*" On restructuring matters juniors were "*helping to advise on the mechanisms used during the bankruptcy process, as well as reviewing court papers and drafting motions.*" During real estate financings they were "*assisting on the joint venture agreements between the financing party and the developer,*" while on M&A deals they gained "*exposure to everything from diligence to drafting various documents – it's pretty standard between your second and fourth year to really learn the finer details of drafting.*"

The litigation practice also has a formal assignment desk. Litigators recommended a "*forthright*" approach: "*The biggest mistake you can make with the desk is not to ask right off the bat for the type of work you want to do. I walked in terrified of being thrown onto a huge investigation that would keep me occupied for years, but the desk was very responsive in understanding what I wanted.*" Other fears didn't come to pass either: "*I expected to move to New York and get shut in a room to do doc review for two years, but I've been able to do more interesting work.*" We heard from juniors working on a case involving an automaker's diesel emissions: "*I'm one of 50-plus associates on the matter. I've been involved in briefing attorneys, communicating with consumers, drafting summary judgments and motions to dismiss.*" Another enjoyed their role as "*the lead associate on one of the issues tied to an internal investigation at a bank – many of these are focused on alleged antitrust violations and money-laundering activities, and they can go on to produce civil work.*" Other areas covered by the litigation group include white-collar, securities, product liability, arbitration, IP and labor & employment.

Juniors still had some time left over for pro bono. There's no limit on how many pro bono hours associates can bill, and some had taken full advantage of that: "*I've accrued a hefty amount of pro bono hours and it hasn't been an issue. I feel comfortable putting time into it and it's been a highlight for me.*" Our sources had worked on death penalty cases, immigration issues and matters that drew upon the Violence Against Women Act. GP associates found it easier to take on pro bono when they were summers, but did praise the firm for "*creating a lot of opportunities and encouraging us – whether we can do it or not just depends on our schedule.*"

Pro bono hours:
- For all (US) attorneys: 37,818
- Average per (US) attorney: 58

Training & Development

GP associates found that there were plenty of formal training opportunities: "*During your first year there's a two-day boot camp where you cover the basics, and throughout the year there are sessions held every few weeks on relevant topics, like how Brexit might impact deals, or the anatomy of certain agreements.*" Litigators, however, found the approach far more "*hands-on: here you learn by doing, because every case is so different – if you don't understand something you just go and ask.*"

Sources were positive about the formal review system: "*Every time you work so many hours with a senior associate or partner, they get prompted to review you. At the end of the year all of their marks and comments are collected and you have a formal review.*" While these reviews were deemed helpful, GP juniors highlighted the usefulness of "*informal check-ins with partners at the end of deals,*" and litigators emphasized the benefits of the firm's partner mentorship program: "*We're paired with a partner mentor within the first six months to discuss how to develop our skills – around things like taking depositions, leading client meetings and speaking with agency.*"

See firm profile on p.698

The Inside View

Diversity	Partners (%)	Associates (%)
Women	21	40
White	90	77
Black/African American	2	2
Hispanic/Latin American	4	4
Asian	4	15
Mixed/Other	1	2
LGBT	7	7

Hours & Compensation

While having no billing requirement *"takes the edge off a bit,"* we still spoke to juniors who *"always watch"* their hours *"to make sure they're up enough: generally people say that if you want to make partner you should be billing 2,000 a year, but that's not an official policy, just a guideline."* Sullivan isn't the kind of firm that attracts slackers anyway: *"Billing targets at other firms tend to be low and everyone here bills beyond them – we're self-motivated to find work and the firm is very busy."*

Ten to twelve-hour days were pretty standard: *"Most people work from the office every day, and transition home to do more in the evenings. You have to use your judgment: people don't mind if you go home at night to log back on, but if you're just launching a new deal they might not be so happy."* One associate reflected: *"The first six months were hard – my social life was in trouble. But a lot of us have learned what needs to be answered immediately and what can wait."* Sources did feel well compensated for their work though, and were big fans of the lockstep bonus system: *"It's 100% based on your year and pretty much everyone gets one."*

Culture

Associates remembered hearing *"horror stories about how scary, cutthroat and – for lack of a better word – mean New York firms were"* in their law school days, but were *"incredibly pleased with the respect factor and the number of good relationships you have with people here – it makes the job easier."* One junior explained how external perceptions of S&C being a more old-school 'white-shoe' firm still follow it around today, and added: *"That stereotype might've been applicable in the distant past, but definitely not now."* On the whole our sources agreed that S&C promotes a *"courteous and cordial"* atmosphere. *"Like any firm it has its crazies, but I've made really good friends!"*

"...the respect factor."

S&C is also *"big enough for almost anyone to fit in; there are outgoing people, quieter people who spend all day in their office – so many different personalities and micro-cultures."* For many, S&C's intellectual ethos stood out as the most discernible cultural strand. *"We're a bunch of client-friendly nerds!"* one source joked, while another added: *"It's a very organized and detail-oriented place. Everyone tends to be a perfectionist, and it's nice to know that everyone is as committed as you."*

When it comes to socializing, S&C is *"more on the quiet side,"* but the firm does host events for attorneys to let their hair down. For New Yorkers, the annual 'SullProm' was a highlight: *"It's a really fun formal event – there's a band and you can bring a date if you want!"* Over in LA, the associate group was close-knit: *"Tonight we're all going to a nearby hotel for an outdoor movie screening of Clueless."* Do the partners also go along to these nostalgic 90s teen movie nights? *"Well, no... but it's nice to have the chance to mingle without the pressure of your boss standing right there!"*

Offices

You'll find S&C's New York HQ in the financial district. Associates were *"incredibly grateful to be down here. There are some tourists on Wall Street, but nothing compared to the numbers in Midtown."* Inside, the decor *"reflects our status as an older, established firm,"* with one source affectionately comparing it to *"an old school mansion."* However, renovations are *"slowly but surely"* underway, with some of the completed floors deemed *"state of the art."* When junior get their own offices *"depends on which group you're in – some of my GP friends already have them,"* bemoaned one litigator. The views are worth waiting for, though: *"From my office I can see the Statue of Liberty and the helipad where I watched the Pope arrive!"*

Over in LA, associates loved being close to Beverly Hills and having their own offices from the start: *"If you're having the odd meltdown it's really nice to shut your door."* LA residents also described their office as *"less hierarchical because of its smaller size – we're exposed to leadership opportunities earlier as a result."* They gave a thumbs-up to inter-office communication too: *"It's totally seamless, whether I'm dialing China, Japan or New York. Pretty much every case I've been on has been staffed across various offices."* The firm's other US offices are located in Palo Alto and DC.

Diversity

While attending diversity events, associates noticed *"a number of partners who are extremely committed. It's the sort of issue you think only young lawyers care about – it's nice to know that upper management cares too."* Our female sources were happy with an 'office hours' initiative that sees *"female partners blocking off time every week for us to stop by and discuss whatever we'd like to discuss – it's a way for us to connect and socialize."* Female as-

See firm profile on p.698

sociates also found it encouraging that *"male attorneys attend lunches and roundtable discussions"* about gender diversity.

"I have faith in the firm."

"It doesn't feel particularly diverse from an ethnicity standpoint," sources agreed, but *"the firm is clearly making an effort to improve that."* There are various associate affinity networks that implement initiatives and programs. A member of one told us: *"I have faith in the firm. They've put in place a peer mentoring program that pairs first and second years up with more senior lawyers, plus I've attended conferences and monthly social events."*

Strategy & Future

"As new financial developments occur, we expand our practice areas to accommodate them," chairman Joe Shenker tells us. With that in mind, Shenker adds: *"Our technology work continues to grow – for example, bitcoin didn't exist ten years ago and now I get asked questions about it all the time."* Alongside a promising amount of fintech work, Shenker anticipates *"being involved in some interesting government spending plans tied to infrastructure development in the US."* The result of the 2016 presidential election also means that *"there will be regulatory and tax law changes"* for S&C's attorneys to advise on.

"...incredibly pleased with the respect factor and the number of good relationships you have with people here – it makes the job easier."

The Inside View

See firm profile on p.698

Thompson & Knight LLP

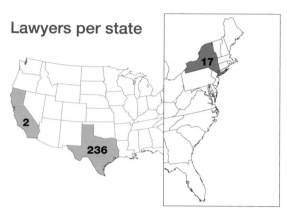

Lawyers per state

17
2
236

Largest US office: Dallas
US offices: 6
International offices: 4
First-year salary: $180,000
Billable hours: 1,900 target (2,000 after first year)
Summers 2018: 11 (3 1Ls, 8 2Ls)
Revenue 2017: $212.02 million (-0.6%)
Partners made in 2018: 5
Famous for: Texas and oil

This Texan titan is staring down the competition by sticking to its strategy of being a *"super regional firm."*

"A LOT more firms have moved into Texas recently so the competition is greater," managing partner Mark Sloan tells us. *"We know we have to adapt with the changing times."* It may well be fending off some of the national heavyweights that are edging their way in, but T&K's strong foundation in Texas should see it through: the firm celebrated its 130th birthday in 2017 and, together with its HQ in Dallas, operates three other Lone Star bases in Houston, Austin and Fort Worth. It also has something else that should thwart those out-of-towners' attempts to conquer the state: *"It's a very hot market and there's a lot of pressure on the lateral recruiting front, but one thing that sets us apart is that we have a lot of loyalty in our partnership,"* Sloan says.

"It's very rare to see people leave."

This wasn't lost on our associate sources, who told us that *"the firm attracts people who want to be in it for the long haul – they want people who want to make partner here. It's very rare to see people leave."* Consequently our interviewees felt that T&K *"really invests in its young associates, via training and both formal and informal mentorships."* Of course, what was on offer work-wise also played an

important role in attracting juniors: the firm's origins are clear to see in its *Chambers USA* nationwide ranking for oil and gas transactions, but T&K also receives a range of commendations for its Texas-based work in areas like real estate, tax, IP, healthcare and energy-related regulatory and litigation matters.

Strategy & Future

T&K's reach extends far beyond the confines of Texas though: it has additional domestic offices in New York and LA, and overseas outposts in Algiers, London, Mexico City and Monterrey. So is the firm looking to balloon into a global powerhouse anytime soon? Well, not quite, as Sloan explains: *"Our strategy is to remain a 'super regional firm,' so to speak. We're not focused on trying to become national or expanding all over. What we are focused on is strengthening our current bench and getting into new practices like cybersecurity. More than anything we listen to our clients, and we direct our resources to wherever they have a need."* Visit chambers-associate.com to read our full interview with Mark Sloan.

The Work

T&K's trial, real estate & banking, and corporate & securities departments took on the majority of the 27 associates on our list; a handful were assigned to the firm's finance, tax, IP, and bankruptcy & restructuring practices. Our sources revealed that there's *"a more free-market approach"* to work assignment in the transactional groups: *"The partners get in touch as and when they need*

On chambers-associate.com...

- Interview with managing partner Mark Sloan and hiring partner Jessica Hammons
- Get hired: recruitment advice for Thompson & Knight

See firm profile on p.699

Rankings in *Chambers USA*

Antitrust	Healthcare
Banking & Finance	Intellectual Property
Bankruptcy/Restructuring	Labor & Employment
Corporate/M&A	Litigation
Energy & Natural Resources	Real Estate
Environment	Tax

For detail on ranking tiers and ranking locations, visit www.chambersandpartners.com

Recent work highlights

- Represented Yates Petroleum Corporation during Yates's $2.4 billion merger with EOG Resources
- Advised an affiliate of Dunhill Partners – a commercial real estate investment firm – as it secured a $120 million refinancing for its property in Dallas's Design District
- Won a $65 million dispute for client Life Partners Creditors' Trust, which brought a case against its founder and former CEO, who was accused of perpetuating a fraudulent scheme connected with the sale of life settlements
- Advised SFC Energy Fund II on the formation and capitalization of a newly formed exploration and production (E&P) company, Armor Energy

you. It does all depend on experience, and often you'll get work because people have seen what you've been able to do on previous matters. As people progress they tend to work with a narrower range of partners." Over in the trial group, however, there's a more formal work assignment system that is overseen and coordinated by a departmental manager.

"The name of our group is trial, not litigation, which means that every lawyer here can show up, argue and actually see a trial through," said juniors in this practice. "Obviously we do a lot of work for our oil and gas clients," they added, highlighting their work on pipeline disputes, as well as "complex partnership, real estate and regulatory matters." Teams are staffed leanly ("a max of 15 attorneys") so "the learning curve is very steep: at the moment I'm taking the lead on drafting motions and working my way up to arguing in court. It's about getting the trust of the partners and showing them that you can handle responsibility."

Real estate & banking juniors told us: "We do lending and development work, but also have a big CMBS [commercial mortgage-backed securities] practice – one of the great things about being a junior is that you can sample all of those lines of work." Sources were pleasantly surprised to "do projects across the country – it's not just local work, and a lot of the banks we work for are national clients." When it comes to tasks, "the partners want you to get more than just the typical diligence experience early on; they'll give you as much as you can handle, and I've been able to get a lot of drafting experience on leasing, sale and loan agreements. You take a first stab at those and get comments from partners."

"...more than just your typical diligence experience."

Those in corporate & securities had gravitated toward the M&A side of things, but also spoke of a sizable private equity practice which "deals with both fund formation and the implementation of strategy." Interviewees here found that "you end up doing a lot of oil and gas deals, especially in the midstream and upstream areas." Like their real estate counterparts, sources felt that "you're not pigeonholed

with first-year work." On M&A deals "you can be working with a senior associate, which will mean that you're drafting the ancillaries and smaller documents for them, but on others it can be just you and a partner, and you'll be sitting in on the negotiations and doing a large part of the drafting on main purchase agreements." Oil and gas is what the finance group is "most famous for," but juniors here also pointed to "smaller, more diverse financings where banks lend to chemical, equipment and furniture companies, for instance." These generally bestowed more responsibility on juniors, "as you get to draft the main documents – on the oil and gas deals you're doing more organizational work like reviewing checklists and conducting searches."

Training & Development

New joiners spend their first three days in Dallas for some introductory training, before heading back to their home offices and starting their practice-specific run of CLEs. In real estate, for example, "we have weekly CLE meetings where partners present on topics to the whole group – they cover title and survey training for first years and it's so nice to have that ongoing education." A monthly business development program was recently introduced too: "It's broken down into sessions for first, second and third-year juniors, and focuses on the level of client development you should be aiming to do in those years, which is helpful."

Juniors get a formal end-of-year evaluation and a mid-year review too, which was appreciated: "You get a check-in and the opportunity to turn things around if you're not doing something so well. It's also a chance for you to make sure your career is developing in the way you want it to."

Culture & Offices

Two-thirds of the juniors on our list were based in T&K's Dallas HQ; Houston housed the majority within the remaining third, with just one or two juniors calling Austin, Fort Worth and New York home. Those in Dallas

See firm profile on p.699

Diversity	Partners (%)	Associates (%)
Women	25	45
White	92	87
Black/African American	1	5
Hispanic/Latin American	3	1
Asian	1	2
Mixed/Other	3	5
LGBT	1	3

Hours & Pro Bono

Billing 1,900 hours makes first years bonus eligible and allows them to advance to the next year's pay scale; after the first year juniors need to be hitting 2,000 hours (plus 200 hours in 'firm investment time') to achieve the same result. Our sources across the offices found the target fair (*"I thought it would be harder to hit than it actually is!"*) and were glad that the firm *"discourages people from going above 2,200 hours to avoid burnout and fatigue."*

loved the downtown location, which is *"within walking distance of lots of restaurants – we're right in the mix of things!"* Inside, *"the offices are really nice and modern, plus the IT support is top-notch – I've asked for their help at 3am before!"* The Houston office was also warmly received: *"We've just moved into a brand new space on Main Street; the office was built from scratch and we have everything we need. It's brighter too, which has been good for morale!"*

That doesn't mean that T&K associates don't work hard. Real estate juniors on leanly-staffed teams said they'd had to work late nights and some weekends, but were glad to report that *"the group is taking steps to improve staffing issues."* Corporate associates, meanwhile, said that preserving a work-life balance *"is more difficult because our schedules can be erratic; you can't really plan ahead, but when the slow times come you take advantage of them."*

"We have a team mentality and zero complaints."

Not that the firm needs too much of a morale boost, from the sound of things. *"There's a strong, cohesive culture here,"* associates agreed, comparing T&K to *"some of the bigger firms that have moved into Texas"* in recent years. This relieved junior told us: *"My girlfriend works at one of those firms and it sounds like a nightmare! Here people get along – we have a team mentality and zero complaints."* In this cohesive vein T&K invited all of its lawyers from across the network to celebrate the firm's 130th anniversary in *"a cool events space in Dallas."*

Many sources felt that T&K's partners played a major role in shaping the firm's culture. *"They foster it: many of them have families and therefore understand the need to have a work-life balance. They leave at 6:30pm most days, and there's no face-time requirement to stay here until they leave – they really trust you to get the work done."* The partners' approach also means that *"we all work closely together, so that it doesn't feel that everything's on you all the time – you feel very involved and that you can walk into anyone's office to ask questions. Having that level of interaction with the partners makes for a more relaxed environment."*

Fifty hours of pro bono can count toward the billable requirement, *"but you can apply for more to count, and I've never heard of any request being turned down."* Juniors pointed to *"a number of resources"* at their disposal, including a pro bono chair *"who sends out emails every couple of weeks,"* legal clinics and opportunities sourced via the Houston Bar Association. We heard of associates helping to revise a women's shelter's bylaws and assisting Habitat for Humanity with a project to build a hospital in Ghana.

Pro bono hours
- For all attorneys across all US offices: 3,212
- Average per US attorney: 26

Diversity

"The firm is making an effort but the desired outcome hasn't quite been achieved yet," associates concluded when it came to diversity. T&K's efforts to promote gender diversity received the most praise, with a female interviewee telling us: *"I feel very supported here. The women's organization gets together on a quarterly basis, and there are a lot of women in high-level partner positions across the different practice groups."* Sources agreed that *"they could do a better job at boosting ethnic diversity,"* but did flag the firm's emphasis on trying to do that during recruitment efforts. Hiring partner Jessica Hammons tells us: *"We've made great strides in this area: our fall class this year was 44% women and minorities, and 50% of our laterals were diverse too."*

See firm profile on p.699

Troutman Sanders LLP

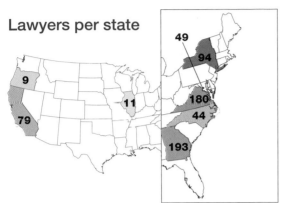

Lawyers per state

49
94
9
11
180
79
44
193

Largest US office: Atlanta
US offices: 13
International offices: 0
First-year salary: $155,000 - $180,000
Billable hours: no requirement/2,000 target
Summers 2018: 56 (17 1Ls, 39 2Ls)
Revenue 2017: $509 million (+3.8%)
Partners made in 2018: 9
Famous for: intimate working environment; Georgia roots; focus on energy, life sciences, insurance and banking & finance sectors

With more than a hundred years of Southeastern heritage to its name, Troutman's certainly a big fish in more than just its native Atlanta.

IS it a bird? Is it a plane? Is it a superhero who can breathe underwater and swim faster than Michael Phelps? Well no, not quite, but as a legal entity Troutman has well and truly demonstrated its power as one of Georgia's premier firms, with an influence that extends beyond the borders of the 'Peach State'; its 600 (plus) lawyers are deployed across 12 further domestic offices that give Troutman ample national coverage. The Sanders portion of the firm's moniker comes from its former chairman, Carl E. Sanders, who also served as Georgia's governor.

Making waves in diverse waters, Troutman earns top *Chambers USA* rankings in Georgia for its banking & finance, energy and environment work; in Virginia it also picks up gold for its environment expertise, as well as for its corporate/M&A, IP and real estate practices. Other highly rated areas include insurance, immigration and general commercial litigation – especially in Troutman's Atlanta HQ. Weighing up the firm, associates noted that it *"doesn't have a typical hierarchy, in the sense that people treat each other like equals,"* which means that new fish can *"dive right in and get their hands (fins?) dirty."* One interviewee put this down to a *"pretty low leverage: the Troutman ethos is to let attorneys develop skills from the start."*

Strategy & Future

Up until May 2018, Troutman maintained three offices in Asia (Hong Kong, Beijing and Shanghai) These closed following a strategic review that found insufficient overlap between the firm's Chinese practice and its focus on middle-market clients and the energy, life sciences, insurance and banking & finance sectors. *"We didn't know about the office closures until they leaked to the press,"* associates told us, *"but the firm is usually good at communicating to us its plans for the future."* The firm hosts regular videoconference meetings to keep attorneys in every office in the loop. Thankfully, these meetings *"demonstrate a long-term investment in associates. It's comforting to know the firm is in great shape and I appreciate knowing where the firm is going."*

The Work

Each year Atlanta takes on a sizable chunk of new associates. New York and Richmond are also big recruiters, but the DC, Charlotte, Orange County and San Francisco offices also hire regularly too. Finance & restructuring is the most common destination for rookies followed by IP; financial services litigation; real estate; business litigation; corporate; and multifamily housing finance. Work assignment in each group *"tends to happen quite organically,"* but in the larger teams *"the group leader is on hand to monitor associate hours and make sure that we're doing a good amount."* Associates found that *"the free market works better for some than others"* but appreciated *"getting to work with a wide array of partners."*

On chambers-associate.com...

- Get Hired: recruitment tips and tricks
- Interview with managing partner Steve Lewis

The Inside View

See firm profile on p.700

Rankings in *Chambers USA*

Banking & Finance	Environment
Bankruptcy/Restructuring	Immigration
Climate Change	Insurance
Construction	Intellectual Property
Corporate/M&A	Labor & Employment
Energy & Natural	Litigation
Resources	Real Estate

For detail on ranking tiers and ranking locations, visit
www.chambersandpartners.com

Recent work highlights

- Acted for Southern Power during its $395.5 million acquisition of Mankato Energy Center in Minnesota
- Advised Southern Company Gas and Northern Illinois Gas on a $1.9 billion syndicated credit facility
- Served as co-lead counsel to Capital One during five computer software patent infringement claims, which together were worth over $100 million
- Advised BNC Bancorp bank on its $1.9 billion acquisition by Pinnacle Financial Partners

The recently merged finance & restructuring group handles the likes of insolvencies, asset sales, infrastructure projects, and real estate and consumer lending deals. *Chambers USA* rates the Atlanta team's banking regulation practice in particular as top-notch. Transactions range *"from smaller matters to enormous hundred million dollar deals,"* and on all but the very largest mandates juniors *"run checklists, do due diligence and curate loan documents from start to finish."* Some were surprised to find themselves *"drafting the main documents as well as the ancillaries – it's pretty atypical for someone of my level."* That may sound a bit daunting, but sources assured us that *"we're never left out in the cold – all I need to do is raise my hand and partners will help."*

"All I need to do is raise my hand and the partners will help."

Business litigators handle a range of commercial and breach of contract disputes, while those in financial services litigation encounter an array of clients including credit card and mortgage lenders, banks and auto finance companies. Sources in the latter *"deal a lot with what we call the alphabet soup acts"* – an apt nickname for the likes of the Fair Debt Collection Practices Act (FDCPA) and the Home Owner's Equity Protection Act (HOEPA). *"I've done a lot of research but that will probably decrease over time,"* an interviewee commented, *"as the partners are really good at taking into consideration what experience you already have – at the same time they try not to overwhelm you with things you're not familiar with."* Business litigators had sampled healthcare, data, tort and real estate work, and in each area were *"thrown into the mix early on. Within my first year I'd drafted motions and pleadings, been to court and interfaced with opposing counsel."*

Multifamily housing finance is a distinctive Troutman niche; one associate estimated that the firm does *"at least 50% of the lender work in the sector nationwide."* The practice involves counseling banking clients on mortgages that are sold to secondary market investors. Associates in the team *"opened and closed small loan transactions,"* and were happy to report that *"client contact is definitely an integral aspect of our work."* Likewise, sources in the general real estate department told us that *"the great thing about Troutman is that you get to work directly with clients very early on."* Interviewees were pleased to *"experience a number of scenarios rather than just being siloed into one,"* and therefore dipped in and out of development, construction, leasing, purchase and sale matters.

Training & Development

First years converge on Atlanta for the New Attorney Orientation Program. All lawyers subsequently enroll at Troutman Sanders University, but overall sources agreed that *"most of the training is on the job and informal."* This approach was favored by some more than others. Financial services litigators, for example, felt they had *"significant oversight that enables you to subsequently take off with something,"* while their counterparts in business litigation *"would prefer more formal training – we'd benefit from more instruction."* Transactional juniors were happy to report that they'd received a program of *"significant trainings, where all associates go to one office for multiple days of CLEs, which take you through transactions, tell you what you should be looking at, and give you context for the things you're doing. They've been very helpful."*

Offices & Culture

Since 1992 Troutman's Atlanta HQ has sat in the Bank of America Plaza, which is Georgia's tallest building and the 15th tallest in the USA. At the time of our calls the firm was moving to lower, but freshly renovated floors – *"a huge ordeal, but the new space looks incredible!"* Richmond (the second largest office) has *"a beautiful view of the James River if you're lucky enough to sit on that side of the building,"* while DC is in a similarly *"great location. I brought my parents in and they thought it was very professional."* The New York team has relocated from the Chrysler Building (which *"everyone hated"*) to a sweet spot in 875 Third Avenue: *"It's a completely new construction. I don't want to say 'state of the art' as that's a cliché, but everything is modern and laid out well."* There's also *"a good amount of communication between the offices,"* associates reported. *"It's as if people are just down the hall!"*

See firm profile on p.700

Diversity	Partners (%)	Associates (%)
Women	19.6	50.9
White	88.5	73.4
Black/African American	2	8.2
Hispanic/Latin American	2.4	2.3
Asian	2.4	11.2
Mixed/Other	4.7	4.9
LGBT	1.7	4.9

"We're just normal people... as lawyers go."

Fishing for compliments was easy in the Troutman pond. Interviewees gushed: *"We have the best culture! I'm really good friends with associates in the other offices and wish I had more excuses to hang out with them."* Several suggested that *"there's a more intimate feel here. It's less hierarchical than other firms, and if I think a partner's wrong then I'm encouraged to speak freely."* In a more measured tone one summarized: *"We're just normal people... as lawyers go."* When asked whether a Southern vibe permeates the offices, New Yorkers felt that *"it's pretty different here"* and noted more of a 'city that never sleeps' culture: *"I really enjoy it. New York itself is largely populated with attorneys who have grown up here, so this office has more of an NY feel. To the extent that we interface with the other offices, we see the elements of our office that are Northeastern in character."*

Diversity

There were mixed reports on the diversity front – some insiders suggested that *"there are no real issues, especially with gender balance,"* while others argued that *"gender balance is definitely an area Troutman needs to continue working on"* through programs including its Parents' Group and Women's Forum. The latter hosts quarterly business development programs, mentoring sessions and firm-wide retreats in New York. *"It would certainly be beneficial to have more female associates in certain groups, so they are trying to boost the numbers."* All our interviewees noted that *"the firm is making a greater effort to recruit more diverse candidates"* – an effort that seemed to be paying off in Atlanta and the other larger offices more than in the smaller ones with narrower intakes.

"The firm is making a greater effort to recruit more diverse candidates."

Pro Bono

Nothing spurs people on more than a competition, so in 2017 each of Troutman's offices vied to see which could do the most pro bono proportionally. *"There was a prize for the office that secured the highest percentage of attorneys doing more than 30 hours, and another for the office that posted the highest percentage increase from last year."* This *"motivating of associates into friendly competition"* was one reason why sources felt *"the firm very much pushes pro bono,"* with the proviso that *"it's on the attorney to take up the opportunities."* However, even post-competition juniors still felt that *"there are big differences between the offices in terms of how much gets done."* For those who are interested, amicus briefs, prisoner litigation and immigration matters are all on the cards; Troutman also collaborates with organizations like the Atlanta Legal Aid Society to run clinics.

Pro bono hours
- For all attorneys across all US offices: 15,317
- Average per US attorney: 23

Hours & Compensation

Associate salaries vary by location, but are lockstep until the fourth year. In 2017 the firm abolished its minimum hours requirement in favor of a *"holistic review process,"* which it uses to calculate bonuses and *"minimize pressure on associates."* How the new system will work was a mystery to some, who felt that *"it leaves us with a lot of uncertainty – transparency is the main issue."* Others were more positive, however, and said that *"they're now considering the whole picture of someone's value to the firm, including community involvement and all sorts of other factors. You're not just a number."* We heard that 2,000 hours guarantees a bonus and is a good amount to strive for if you're eyeing the partnership track.

Juniors *"aren't expected to put grueling hours in"* and *"a typical day lasts from 9am to 7pm – it can be less, it can be more, and there are times when you do go home and log back on."* However, *"you can go for weeks without having to work at all from home,"* and 9pm was seen as a late night even in New York and Atlanta.

Get Hired

"Troutman is looking for ambitious people who'll go out and find the work they want – not those who will sit at their desk waiting for it to come to them." Find out what else the firm is looking for at chambers-associate.com

See firm profile on p.700

The Inside View

Vedder Price

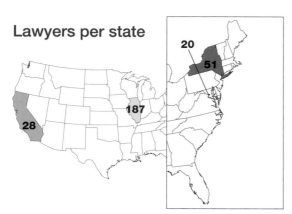

Lawyers per state

20
51
187
28

Largest US office: Chicago
US offices: 5
International offices: 2
First-year salary: $180,000
Billable hours: 2,000 target
Summers 2018: 13 (2 1Ls, 11 2Ls)
Revenue 2017: $252 million (+5.1%)
Partners made in 2018: 5
Famous for: a high-flying aviation practice and talent for all things transportation

They're soaring, flying – there's not a deal in transportation that Vedder can't reach, but that's not the only talent covered in this Chicagoan's fleet.

CHICAGO-born Vedder Price is *"known throughout the world"* for its transportation finance practice, especially in aviation. Associates in this practice were thrilled to be *"working at an industry leader: the people I'm surrounded by are the masters of what they do! Very few people come into transportation finance with some sort of background in it, and it's not an area that gets much press or publicity in the mainstream. I've managed to learn so much about the industry and how it affects the economy – there's never been a dull moment!"*

Though it earned its wings in aviation, Vedder is soaring in more ways than one. The firm offers *"a full-service suite"* that spans a host of practices within its corporate, litigation and labor & employment departments, as well as many sectors beyond transportation: insurance, healthcare and biotechnology to name a few. In addition to its first-class nationwide ranking in aviation finance, Vedder maintains *Chambers USA* nods in areas such as white-collar crime, corporate/M&A & private equity, banking & finance, and employee benefits & executive compensation.

As well as being attracted to its reputation and more navigable size, the associates we spoke to were excited about the prospect of staying at Vedder for the long haul: *"I landed at a place where the goal is to make everyone a*

shareholder one day. It makes you want to come to work every day when the firm is rooting for you to succeed and become a shareholder."*

Strategy & Future

"The firm is managed conservatively," associates told us. *"Vedder's not trying to take over the world or move into every market. We're focusing on continuing our good work in the spaces we already focus on."* Operating shareholder Doug Hambleton echoes these sentiments: *"One of our strategies is to keep up our edge in the aviation practice by focusing on incremental growth. It's a marathon, not a sprint."* With our readership in mind, Hambleton tells us that Vedder can offer students *"something increasingly rare among law firms – a very vibrant, sophisticated mid-sized platform."*

"It's a marathon, not a sprint."

Offices

Vedder's 187-lawyer Chicago HQ is flanked by four other domestic offices – two on the East Coast in New York and DC, and two on the West Coast in LA and San Francisco. The majority of associates, however, end up in the Chicago office (only two on our list of second and third years were based in New York, while one resided in DC). All associates get their own office from day one, but some do have to wait for a few years until they're upgraded to an office with a window. Chicagoans are based in *"the perfect location: right downtown by the river in the 'Loop,' which is easy to get to and has lots of restaurants nearby."*

On chambers-associate.com...

• Get hired: tips from Vedder Price insiders

See firm profile on p.701

The Inside View

Rankings in *Chambers USA*

Banking & Finance
Bankruptcy/Restructuring
Corporate/M&A
Investment Funds

Labor & Employment
Litigation
Transportation

For detail on ranking tiers and ranking locations, visit
www.chambersandpartners.com

Recent work highlights

- Advised Citibank on a $300 million loan financing for up to ten aircraft for a new joint venture called Bauhinia Aviation
- Secured a court of appeals decision in favor of tech client Oracle Corporation, which affirmed an earlier ruling to deny certification of a class of employees alleging failure to pay overtime and pay statement violations
- Defended insurance company Security Life during a $69 million-plus breach of contract case over the development and subsequent selling of a universal life insurance product
- Advised Tokyo-based Mitsubishi UFJ Lease & Finance Company (MUL) on a business alliance worth over $1 billion, which will expand MUL's existing rail leasing platform in North America

The offices here are currently being remodeled: *"Things are becoming more modern, with white walls and brighter spaces replacing the dark wood. They're also in the process of creating more windowed offices for associates."*

The Work

Two-thirds of the juniors on our list were assigned to its corporate department, which contains a range of subgroups: capital markets & securities; finance & transactions; global transportation finance (GTF); healthcare; and investment services. The rest of our sample were split between Vedder's labor & employment, litigation and IP practices. All groups run a free-market system of assignment: *"It's pretty organic. There's no central hub for getting work, which has pluses and minuses, but it gives you more agency to choose what you want to do."*

Under the umbrella of corporate, the GTF and finance & transactions subgroups housed the most juniors. *"Our group is definitely a niche for sure,"* said juniors in GTF. The group works with many a high-flying name in the finance and transportation sectors, including Air Canada, Macquarie Bank and Citibank. *"Working for big clients is pretty exciting,"* sources added, *"as you get to have one-on-one interaction with the directors of these major corporations."* As well as getting this *"significant client contact early on,"* associates can expect to delve into tasks such as drafting credit and security agreements and managing deal closings: *"When matters close it's your role to coordinate with local counsel in various jurisdictions. In any given day I'll be working with people in Egypt, Ireland, London – wherever the aircraft is!"*

Within finance & transactions there are further subgroups: *"M&A; corporate finance; and healthcare & regulatory compliance. It's very specialized, but as a junior you get to work across all three areas – you're a jack of all trades, but master of none – mastering takes time."* On the M&A side there's a lot of private equity work that sees juniors *"crawling before we walk: doing diligence is necessary to understand how corporate formation works. You get to see what the implications are of different structures like LLPs, for example."* Other tasks included drafting agreements, making and monitoring checklists, and managing the signature documents during closings.

"I'll be working with people in Egypt, Ireland, London – wherever the aircraft is!"

There's some freedom of movement between the litigation and labor & employment groups at Vedder. On the litigation side, *"we do a bit of everything – there's some real estate/construction work, a lot of contracts disputes – especially over restrictive covenants – and recently we've been getting into the data privacy area as well."* Juniors admitted that they do *"a lot of doc review,"* but much more besides: *"Matters here are staffed pretty leanly, so I've drafted briefs and motions from scratch, taken a couple depositions and second-chaired a trial after just six months of being here!"* Those who'd sampled labor & employment work had encountered discrimination and harassment cases, and hosted employment counseling sessions for clients.

Pro Bono

Vedder increased its number of billable pro bono hours from 30 to 60 in 2016. Associates appreciated the increase but noted that *"it's still a pretty small number."* One associate told us: *"For one case I billed 150 hours. There are a lot of people in my community that require pro bono assistance but I have to limit it. There's a chance they'll up it again in the future but for now it's a frustrating shortcoming."*

"There's a little bit of everything."

"The amount of credit you get is not liberal but the opportunities you get are," juniors insisted. *"We have a pro bono committee and the chair of that committee sends out regular lists of available cases. There's a little bit of everything: prisoners' rights cases, employment discrimination matters, interesting ABA projects…"*

See firm profile on p.701

Diversity	Partners (%)	Associates (%)
Women	18	45
White	92	76
Black/African American	1	6
Hispanic/Latin American	3	2
Asian	4	11
Mixed/Other	0	5
LGBT	2	2

Training & Feedback

The first week or so is all about *"getting acclimated to all the different departments and the resources you have at your disposal – it's crucial to understand the software you're using!"* After this settling-in period, associates can expect *"pretty frequent in-house CLE sessions"* that give them a *"detailed understanding"* of topics related to their practice area and the current market: *"They might be on things like how to evaluate an insurance certificate, or how to better understand our clients. We recently had one on cryptocurrency as it's taking over and everyone's talking about it!"*

A lot of praise was also bestowed on mentors, both formal and informal. On the formal side, juniors are appointed a senior associate mentor: *"It's definitely helpful to have someone you can pose questions to and help you figure out how things work."* Informally, we heard that seniors often go out of their way to take associates under their wing: *"I had a shareholder reach out to work with me on a monthly basis and orient me in this world of big regulatory issues."*

Hours & Compensation

After bumping up associate salaries to match the Cravath scale, Vedder raised its bonus eligibility threshold from 1,850 to 2,000 hours in 2017. Following their first year of trying to hit the new target, junior responses were mixed. Those in corporate subgroups like investment services and GTF told us: *"No one hurts for hours and most associates can hit 2,000 without a problem,"* while others revealed that *"the general consensus for litigation and employment is that it's a lot harder to hit your hours – I'm just barely squeaking into bonus territory this year!"* Keeping up with colleagues was advised, and associates receive *"anonymous hours reports each month"* to give them a clear sense of what the average in their group is.

"No one's expecting you to stay at your desk all night."

Associates are typically in the office between 9am and 7pm each day, and top that up with a couple more hours at home most nights. Vedder buys dinner for anyone stay-

ing after 7pm, but many associates told us they'd *"never used it because no one's expecting you to stay at your desk all night. There's no reason to be in the office until 11pm unless a transaction or filing needs to be tied up."* Those in litigation, labor & employment and even some corporate subgroups like investment services flagged the consistency of their hours, *"which makes for a nicer lifestyle."*

Culture

"The Midwest has a colder feel in general, but Vedder is a friendly and warm place," said our cheery sources. This level of perkiness was buoyed by the fact that *"everyone's close – there's no competitive edge to the culture here."* To exemplify this, interviewees told us that *"there's a class of attorneys here who started as summers together and now they're shareholders together. It's nice to see that they were able to cultivate relationships and not compete against each other, but support each other instead."* At the same time, an entrepreneurial approach is encouraged: *"You can make your practice what you want it to be. If you have an idea about something you can make your case and they'll support it."*

"You can come in, do your work, go home and have your life."

Associates also noted that Vedder's *"a firm where you can come in, do your work, go home and have your life. It's not a firm that tries to monopolize your time. It's very businesslike in that way, which I appreciate."*

Diversity

The firm does have an overarching diversity committee that implements and monitors initiatives, and the one our sources highlighted the most was 'WAVES' – Vedder's women's initiative, which stands for 'Women at Vedder Empowering Success.' *"It's a good program as it's led by senior female shareholders. There's an event every other month, whether it's a book group discussion of 'Lean In' or a meeting on how women have furthered their careers at the firm. It provides informal mentorship and a good opportunity to ask questions."* On the recruitment side, Vedder recently extended its diversity scholarship to cover a summer position in its New York office, on top of the one it already offered in Chicago.

Get Hired

Getting into Vedder is no picnic: pick up tips and tricks from associates at chambers-associate.com.

See firm profile on p.701

The Inside View

Venable LLP

Lawyers per state

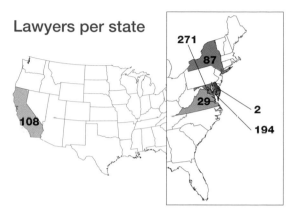

271
87
29
2
194
108

Largest US office: Washington, DC

US offices: 9

International offices: 0

First-year salary: $180,000

Billable hours: 1,900 target (1,950 to be bonus eligible)

Summers 2018: 42 (4 1Ls, 38 2Ls)

Revenue 2017: $540.5 million (+8.4%)

Partners made in 2018: 18

Famous for: its love for bocce; community connections, especially in Baltimore; nationwide strength in areas like advertising, privacy & data security and REITs

Its head may be in DC but its heart's in Baltimore; Venable offers quality work, a warm atmosphere and a rooftop paradise for bocce enthusiasts.

"THERE is just something about this city," Venable's Baltimore-based juniors told us. For one it was the winning mix of *"modern city living with a more homely, small-town feel,"* while for another it was the city's *"egalitarianism – it's a place where you don't have to be from an established family to make a difference."* It's the city where Venable was founded over a hundred years ago, and its ties to it are still strong: *"We're a huge presence in the city – not just as a law firm but as an active member of the community,"* sources told us. Indeed, one of the firm's partners, Kenneth Thompson, was recently appointed by a federal judge to help oversee a series of reforms being made to the city's police force.

Our sources were pleased to report that the Baltimore spirit has *"percolated through to our offices across the network."* These include the firm's DC HQ, as well as growing bases in LA, San Francisco, New York and Delaware.

For our sources, it was clear that Venable *"had the resources to attract high-quality work while promoting a more amiable atmosphere."* An inspection of the firm's *Chambers USA* rankings confirms this: on a nationwide level Venable is recognized in a range of areas, especially when it comes to advertising, real estate investment trusts

(REITs), privacy and data security, and government-related work. On a more local level, the DC office shines for its IP capabilities, while in its home state of Maryland the firm's healthcare, corporate/M&A and commercial litigation practices are particularly noteworthy.

Culture & Offices

Venable juniors were quick to distance themselves from the *"boisterous, out there for their own gain"* types that can be found in the profession. *"Here we have a very low a-hole quota,"* one DC insider candidly explained, while a Baltimore-based source added: *"Everyone is interested in getting to know you personally and my first week involved a series of partners and associates asking me how was I doing. The partners even know my dog's and my boyfriend's names, while I know the names of all their children!"* This level of acquaintance is aided by a reportedly even ratio of partners to associates – close to *"one to one"* – *"which allows us to get to know them more directly."*

"The partners even know my dog's and my boyfriend's names."

Almost half of the associates on our list were based in Venable's DC HQ, which recently moved to *"new, sleek and modern"* digs at 600 Massachusetts Avenue. Complete with *"glass walls everywhere, a beautiful rooftop and lots of common spaces for coffee breaks and catch-ups, it's a setup for success!"* That rooftop comes in handy for a *"grand unifying event"* each summer – a ten-week bocce tournament of course! What's bocce, we hear you ask?

On chambers-associate.com...

- All you need to know about bocce
- Get Hired: advice and tips
- Interview with Dan Moylan, co-managing partner

See firm profile on p.702

The Inside View

Rankings in *Chambers USA*

Advertising	Intellectual Property
Bankruptcy/Restructuring	Labor & Employment
Corporate/M&A	Leisure & Hospitality
Employee Benefits &	Litigation
Executive Compensation	Privacy & Data Security
Energy & Natural	Products Liability
Resources	Real Estate
Environment	REITs
Government	Retail
Healthcare	Technology

For detail on ranking tiers and ranking locations, visit
www.chambersandpartners.com

Recent work highlights

- Advised J.P. Morgan on its compliance with various regulations relating to its mortgage origination business
- Secured a win for cosmetic brush designer Artis as it took on Lilly Ghalichi's company Lilly Lashes, for selling brushes that infringed Artis's IP rights
- Advised actress Kate Hudson on her business relationship with an online sports clothing company, Fabletics
- Represented Sabra Healthcare REIT during its merger with Care Capital Properties, which created a new healthcare-focused real estate investment trust company

It's like the French game of boules, where players compete to throw their ball closest to the jack (a smaller ball). *"Everyone from the librarians to the facility staff to the summer associates are encouraged to participate,"* insiders explained. *"It strengthens a culture where people like each other – I think people outside the firm are jealous of our bocce court!"* Venable's Baltimore office was home to roughly a quarter of the juniors on our list, while a handful could be found spread between the LA, New York and Tysons offices.

The Work

The practice groups that drew in the most juniors were commercial litigation, regulatory, corporate, and tax and wealth planning. The odd one or two were beavering away in groups like bankruptcy, real estate, IP, labor & employment and government contracts. When it comes to getting work, *"associates don't need to be overly 'entrepreneurial,'"* relieved juniors told us. *"You have a practice group leader who helps to coordinate the work and from there partners approach you directly. It avoids the potential for a lot of the awkwardness that comes with a total free-market system."*

"...writing drafts and doing meaningful research from day one."

The firm's *"meritocratic approach"* means that *"crazy levels of responsibility"* are available for those who feel up to the challenge. *"At first I was drafting supporting documents and conducting research into securities,"* one commercial litigator told us, *"but now I coordinate directly with the partner, anticipate what needs to be done and supervise those at a more junior level."* We even heard of one associate playing a substantial role in Taylor Swift's case against former radio DJ David Mueller. Other junior litigators reported drafting disclosures and motions to compel, as well as preparing experts and attending depositions across a range of areas including white-collar, employment, fraud and contract law. *"They pile on substantive*

work early on," juniors reiterated. *"Doc review is part of our world when it has to be, but I've been writing drafts and doing meaningful research from day one."*

"The regulatory group is a sort of holding company for many different subgroups." Associates here can dip into teams focused on the likes of food and drugs, politics, nonprofit organizations, telecom, finance and advertising. *"As a first year you're softly 'assigned' to a particular group, but you can still get work from the other groups – as you become more senior you tend to specialize more."* Juniors in the nonprofit group reported working on *"everything from the formation to dissolution of organizations, which has included drafting applications for tax exemption."* Those who'd dabbled in the politics group described a *"research-heavy"* environment: *"One thing I do is manage lobbying queries for several clients who are engaged in multiple states. For example, sometimes they reach out with questions about giving a gift in a particular state."*

Hours & Compensation

First-year associates aim to bill 1,800 hours, but their target rises to 1,900 from their second year onward. *'Overall they like us to rack up around 2,200 hours, but that includes volunteering work, pro bono, business development and other non-billable tasks."* Bonuses kick in when associates hit 1,950 hours; 50 hours of pro bono can count toward this total, and the bonus amount rises for every additional 50 hours associates bill.

With a base salary that matches the Cravath scale for the first three years, juniors were grateful for the *"more relaxed hours"* at Venable, though we did hear of *"a plan to increase the hours expectations to reflect the rate of the pay we receive – it's not meant to change by a life-altering amount, however."* Co-managing partner Dan Moylan tells us he anticipates that *"the increase will be somewhere in the magnitude of 2% across the board, and we're considering implementing that in 2018."* For now, juniors in the Baltimore office were in sync with the city's early bird culture, with most getting into the office by 8:30am and

See firm profile on p.702

Diversity	Partners (%)	Associates (%)
Women	-	-
White	-	-
Black/African American	-	-
Hispanic/Latin American	-	-
Asian	-	-
Mixed/Other	-	-
LGBT	-	-

leaving around the 7pm mark; those in the DC office maintained a slightly later schedule, and typically left by 8pm. *"Super-busy periods where you're working 60-hour weeks are fortunately sporadic"* across the groups, and on the whole juniors found the firm respectful of *"family and vacation time."* Another praised the flexibility they'd encountered: *"As long as you are accessible you can also come in later, leave later or work from home."*

Pro Bono

Juniors in the Baltimore office emphasized the strength of *"Venable's relationships with multiple nonprofits which continually feed the firm work, like House of Ruth, which is a domestic abuse charity. Equally, if you have any ideas of your own, all you have to do is find a partner to supervise you and you're off to the races."*

"I get the sense that the Baltimore office has more long-standing connections than we do," one DC associate suggested. Still, the Gerry Treanor Pro Bono Fellowship gives associates from both offices the chance to complete a six-month stint at either Bread for the City (a charity for vulnerable DC residents) or Maryland Legal Aid in Baltimore. Overall, we heard of associates across the board tackling domestic abuse, immigration, elderly assistance, veteran and landlord/tenant cases. *"A lot of people at Venable also end up being judges or running for office,"* including former managing partner Karl Racine, who currently serves as the Attorney General for the District of Columbia.

Pro bono hours

- For all attorneys: 29,833
- Average per attorney: 43

Training & Development

Juniors again cited the more balanced partner to associate ratio here as *"it means you're able to work closely with them and learn from them."* This setup worked well for those who favored *"direct learning over formal sessions that are funneled through a hierarchical system."* However, for others the firm's *"more hands-on and feedback-based"* approach to learning didn't compensate for *"the lack of formalized training,"* though Venable has been making improvements on this front. Litigators told us of an *"upcoming and division-wide formal training that will last for three days,"* while those in corporate explained that *"what started off as an initial writing tips session has now started to morph into a more regular CLE program that gives a detailed breakdown of every stage of a transaction."*

Diversity

"It's getting better," hopeful juniors told us on the subject of diversity. They were most positive about efforts to boost gender diversity: *"The gender split in the associate ranks is 50:50 if not higher on the female side. There's room to improve at the partner level, but women are continuing to rise through the ranks."* Venable's WAVE (Women at Venable) group was credited for *"giving young female attorneys the tools and abilities to progress in their group and make partner. We have monthly meetings where the paths to the partnership are explained, but we also discuss how we can increase collaboration and involve more people in pitch meetings."*

Strategy & Future

Associates described the firm's management style as *"conservative,"* which they felt *"ensures constant growth – even through recession."* Co-managing partner Dan Moylan confirms: *"We will continue to grow but do so in a very particular way. We value our culture – we will make sure that the Venable of tomorrow is the same as the Venable of ten years ago in terms of culture."* He emphasizes that the firm has always favored *"strategic"* over *"opportunistic"* growth: *"In San Francisco, for example, we have looked at where growth and expansion could compliment our existing strengths in tax, corporate and real estate. You're are not going see any mega-mergers or anything like that."* For more from Moylan, go to chambers-associate.com

> ## Get Hired
>
> *"It gives us a chance to get a handle on who we think is impressive based on their interactions."* Head to chambers-associate.com to find out from hiring partner Bob Bolger how to impress Venable's recruiters.

The Inside View

See firm profile on p.702

Vinson & Elkins LLP

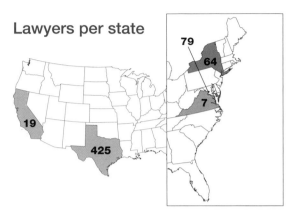

Lawyers per state

79
64
7
19
425

Largest US office: Houston
US offices: 8
International offices: 8
First-year salary: $180,000
Billable hours: 2,000 target
Summers 2018: 113 (30 1Ls, 82 2Ls, 1 SEO)
Revenue 2017: $727.5 million (+11.3%)
Partners made in 2018: 8
Famous for: energy pedigree; 'Jim's' - V&E's very own private Starbucks in Houston office

Well oil be damned – V&E's expansion out of its comfort zone definitely isn't a waste of energy.

"WHEN you Google us, the first thing you see is our transactional energy work," one junior told us. Indeed – that's why many associates sought out this Houston-headquartered firm in the first place: *"It's the energy capital of the US, and V&E has one of the best energy practices in the country."* *Chambers USA* clearly agrees, as it ranks V&E's oil and gas expertise in the highest nationwide category, as well as dishing out other nods for its electricity and related climate change know-how.

But there's far more to V&E than its pedigree in Texas tea, as our interviewees were keen to emphasize: *"We're impressive in other areas too! For one thing our litigation practice doesn't get the attention it deserves."* A closer inspection of *Chambers USA* reveals a clutch of other high rankings – especially in its home state – in areas like corporate/M&A, capital markets, general commercial litigation, real estate, tax, and technology. With fluctuations in the energy market – including those dips in oil prices – *"our management knows that we need to expand beyond it; we're still strong and steady in that area but around half of our clients are coming from other industries now. We're trying to expand our tech expertise on the West Coast, for example."* Juniors were very confident in the firm's overall approach: *"We've just celebrated our 100-year anniversary in 2017, and we have every intention of being around for the next 100 years too!"*

Strategy & Future

"We had a record year in 2017 with strong financial performance that really helps us retain and attract top talent," managing partner Mark Kelly tells us. *"Half the work we do is outside energy and in 2018 we're going to continue to expand in various areas: private equity and finance, white-collar, construction and IP. We recruited a number of partners over the last 18 months in IP in the Bay Area, Dallas, Austin and DC."*

On the topic of Vinson's steadily growing head count, Kelly explains: *"I want to make sure people are busy but not so busy that they're overwhelmed. That's not really our strategy or culture – we're more about moderate growth, quality people, a strong reputation and bringing in people who get along well with our group."*

The Work

At the time of our calls, the largest group (45%) of second and third-year juniors were working in V&E's M&A/capital markets group (MACM), while the following groups also took on a significant chunk of associates: complex commercial litigation; energy; finance; and tax. A few could also be found in the firm's labor and employment; environmental; IP; real estate; and restructuring practices.

In MACM sources reported a *"50:50 split between energy clients and clients from other sectors, like healthcare, transportation and even fashion."* V&E's energy expertise *"gives us a high deal flow, because energy companies always need*

On chambers-associate.com...

- Get hired: interview with hiring partner Doug Bland

See firm profile on p.703

The Inside View

Rankings in *Chambers USA*

Antitrust	Intellectual Property
Appellate Law	International Trade
Banking & Finance	Labor & Employment
Bankruptcy/Restructuring	Latin American Investment
Capital Markets	Litigation
Climate Change	Projects
Corporate/M&A	Real Estate
Energy & Natural	REITs
Resources	Tax
Environment	Technology
Government	

For detail on ranking tiers and ranking locations, visit www.chambersandpartners.com

Recent work highlights

- Represented TransCanada Corporation – the developer of the Keystone oil pipeline – as its subsidiary, Columbia Pipeline Group, acquired Columbia Pipeline Partners for $915 million
- Secured a win for Fortune 500 client Energy Transfer Equity, as it sought to terminate a proposed $38 billion merger with The Williams Companies
- Defended tech company Software AG after a competitor, GlobeRanger, filed a trade-secret misappropriation suit against it over the use of a radio frequency solution developed for the US Navy
- Advised the underwriters of Clipper Realty during the real estate company's $88 million IPO – the proceeds of which were partly used to fund the company's acquisition of commercial properties in New York

money – it's great to get your hands on different things." In the first few years, juniors are given *"freedom to bounce between areas that fall under the MACM umbrella, including private equity and shareholder activism matters."* On IPOs, interviewees had *"helped to coordinate changes to documents with other groups and drafted ancillaries, as well as portions of more complicated documents like stockholders' agreements, offering memorandums and prospectus supplements."*

"All associates do energy work – it trickles into everything here."

"As a commercial litigation associate you get exposure to different areas – one day it's a contract dispute, another day it's an oil and gas matter, and another it's an antitrust case." Other areas juniors mentioned included appellate, securities and regulatory work. On one dispute over a merger an interviewee *"did everything, including a lot of discovery and deposition prep – we had about 25 depositions in three weeks!"* On the staple breach of contract matters, *"I'll be consulting with the folks who are putting a deal together, and they'll be asking us about specific language used in the contract and the scope of what's enforceable."* Juniors especially liked the *"complex procedural issues"* that crop up in class action cases: *"We'll look at how we can shift things from the state to the federal court, for example – it's like putting together a puzzle."*

The energy transactions and projects group is split (as the title suggests) into *"two main sides: the transactions side, which covers M&A, structured finance and equity deals, and then projects."* The latter side involves *"the development of various energy assets, including fracking facilities, export terminals, fertilizer plants, solar parks and renewable energy facilities – those projects can go on for years!"* Transactions typically require first years *"to do the trench work like diligence and checklists, but when you progress to the second year you get a lot more responsibility: I've* drafted entire agreements from scratch on smaller deals and handled the communication with the client."*

Training & Development

A three-day orientation program in the Houston HQ welcomes all new starters to the firm. *"You get acquainted with the firm's culture and systems; they bring in new joiners from across the globe and place a heavy emphasis on making connections in different offices – it should be easy for you to just pick up the phone and call someone."* When juniors return to their home offices, the more *"substantive training"* begins in the form of regular CLEs: *"They cover things like offering processes and how to form certain documents. They give you a good general overview and don't go too deep into the weeds – most learning happens on the job."*

Hours & Compensation

There may be no formal billing target at V&E, but *"2,000 hours is the average that everyone tries to meet – it's also the number at which the firm has historically paid out a bonus."* That figure was deemed reasonable across groups, but juniors did point to *"ups and downs that make it harder to meet as a first year – you have a bit less control."* Bonus increases are tiered at 2,150 and 2,300 hours.

Texas-based sources typically worked between 9am and 6pm, while those in New York started and finished a bit later, working between 10am and 8pm on average. We did hear a few late night stories, especially from those in the transactional groups (*"last week I was here regularly until at least midnight,"* one MACM source told us). Some juniors preferred *"to put in the extra hours during the week so I can have a couple of days off at the weekend,"* while others *"generally take some work home every weekend – it's pretty standard to do at least a few hours."*

See firm profile on p.703

The Inside View

Diversity	Partners (%)	Associates (%)
Women	15	38
White	91	77
Black/African American	1	4
Hispanic/Latin American	3	4
Asian	2	10
Mixed/Other	2	5
LGBT	2	4

Pro Bono

"It's very encouraged," sources agreed when discussing pro bono. "The firm sends around email blasts and we also have a great firm-wide pro bono counsel – she'll look into what you want to do and try to make it happen!" An unlimited number of pro bono hours count toward the 2,000-hour bonus target.

Some of our sources had worked on guardianship cases where "people have become mentally incapacitated and need to have a guardian appointed to oversee their health and finances." Others had attended Lambda Legal clinics to "help transgender individuals change their gender on their licenses and passports – people weren't sure what Trump was going to do to impede that process." We also heard from those who'd assisted in the aftermath of Hurricane Harvey, by "helping people apply for funds from the Federal Emergency Management Agency to fix the damage done to their homes."

Pro bono hours
- For all US attorneys: 21,154
- Average per US attorney: 35

Diversity

As well as highlighting the presence of "some brilliant women and minority partners here," pretty much every associate we spoke to mentioned the new firm-wide diversity council that has just been created. The firm's previous diversity forum was described as "smaller, less transparent and only open to diverse lawyers." The new council, in contrast, "has been opened up to all attorneys; we've had such a positive response, with so many people wanting to get involved that we've broken it down into three subcommittees: recruitment, retention and business development." Though it's still in its early stages, plans on the cards include mentorship programs with law schools, recruiting events and a pipeline schools focus. "I appreciate that it's focused on concrete actions – we're talking about the specific things we can do to make a difference."

Culture

"At a BigLaw firm you're going to work hard – there's no avoiding that," a Houston resident stated, "but at a New York firm it's like 'get your ass in here on Sunday,' while at a Texas firm it's more like 'can you please help me this Sunday?'" Other juniors also appreciated "the general vibe of not freaking out all the time" and summed up the culture as "fairly casual but professional: casual because we wear jeans on a Friday and have little parties, and professional because when we're interfacing with clients that's how we behave."

"They bring in people to give us massages and health evaluations."

Though there's "no pressure" to attend, there are regular happy hours and dinners across the offices, as well as more office-specific events such as a wellness week in New York, where "they bring in people to give us massages and health evaluations." There's also an annual chilli cook-off in Houston: "It's a pretty intense competition! They bring in a couple of guest judges and they do a blind tasting. Last year we had about 40 entries." The most popular event of the year is Dallas's "casino party in summer. The firm rents out the top part of a hotel and sets up craps, blackjack and roulette, and gives you fake tokens to gamble with. At the end of the night, we put the tokens into drawings for prizes like Rangers tickets!"

Offices

The Houston HQ is the biggest in V&E's network, and was home to almost half of the second and third-year juniors on our list. "It's not so flashy from the outside, but inside we have a beautiful white marble stairwell in the lobby area." The office is also home to the country's only private Starbucks ("they call it Jim's but everything in there is Starbucks, which is pretty cool"). Sources here also noted that "this is very much a HQ; it's great to have a lot of resources and be where a lot of the great work is sourced."

Dallas is the firm's second-largest office and housed about a quarter of junior associates. "We were going to move to a different building, but we decided to stay because we really like the downtown location, so we're renovating instead. A year ago you'd have thought it looked like the movie 'Wall Street' from the 80s – it was all wood and gold. Now glass is coming!" V&E's DC, New York, Austin and Richmond offices all took on a handful of juniors each.

See firm profile on p.703

The Inside View

Waller

Lawyers per state

206
11
16

Largest US Office: Nashville
US offices: 5
International offices: 0
First-year salary: $130,000
Billable hours: 1,800 target
Summers 2018: 17 (3 1Ls, 14 2Ls)
Revenue 2017: undisclosed
Partners made in 2018: 9
Famous for: healthcare law; Tennessee heritage

This Nashville native receives another clean bill of health from its juniors, who point to further growth in industries outside of its core healthcare focus.

"HEALTHCARE work makes up a large percentage of our business," juniors were quick to tell us when describing their firm. *"We like to think of it as an advantage that we can leverage in the marketplace."* Waller is certainly in the right marketplace for such work: healthcare is one of Nashville's largest industries, with around 350 companies operating in the area. While healthcare is certainly Waller's beating heart, it also has other systems keeping its vital signs in order, as associates revealed: *"We're continuing to build our expertise in some exciting areas like hospitality, entertainment, private equity, white-collar and bankruptcy. We'll never lose our healthcare focus, but we don't to want to just have a boutique scope."*

Waller's remit expanded in 2016 when it acquired all of the lawyers from Austin-based firm Taube Summers, which was known for its bankruptcy and commercial litigation work. An inspection of Waller's *Chambers USA* rankings also shows that alongside healthcare, its other top-tier practices in Nashville include banking & finance, environment, real estate and general commercial litigation. Other industries of note include manufacturing, financial services, education, film, music and television.

Strategy & Future

"Waller does not want to be all things to all people," chairman Matt Burnstein informs us. *"Instead, we want to be a full-service law firm with around 240 lawyers who are well known and relied upon in specific industries."* Indeed, *"industry renown is a strategic goal."* Burnstein tells us that healthcare is Waller's number one industry: *"Our reputation in healthcare is well established, and behind that our financial services work has grown nicely – we have a thriving bankruptcy practice, for example."* Waller is also looking to enhance its reputation in retail and hospitality, as well as technology and advanced manufacturing: *"In each of those areas we've made notable lateral hires, including alcoholic beverage lawyers and patent prosecution and patent litigation attorneys."*

The Work

Waller's corporate, litigation and healthcare departments absorbed the most juniors on our list. A few could also be found in the firm's real estate, tax, IP, and labor & employment groups.

The corporate department draws in its share of healthcare clients, but also advises entities in the manufacturing and financial services industries. Juniors can expect a variety of deals, including mergers & acquisitions, joint ventures and private placements. Our sources had worked with *"a lot of private equity-backed clients in niche and up-and-coming markets within the healthcare sector, like dental management."* A bounty of smaller deals means that *"you can be juggling between ten and 15, so the*

On chambers-associate.com...

• Get hired: how to get into Waller

See firm profile on p.704

The Inside View

Rankings in *Chambers USA*

Banking & Finance	Labor & Employment
Corporate/M&A	Litigation
Environment	Media & Entertainment
Healthcare	Real Estate

For detail on ranking tiers and ranking locations, visit
www.chambersandpartners.com

work is varied and you get to do several tasks at once. It's *definitely been enjoyable.*" Such tasks included *"due diligence review, client interaction, marking up and drafting purchase agreements and ancillaries, and managing deals as part of a larger team."*

"Our healthcare laws continue to change constantly, so our work is interesting."

Lawyers in the corporate and healthcare departments frequently work together. Juniors in the latter liked *"the fact that the work here is challenging. Our healthcare laws continue to change constantly, so our work is interesting as it feels like we're trying to hit a moving target."* Much of a junior's workload will be regulatory-oriented: *"We'll be doing the compliance stuff and supporting our corporate lawyers on different transactions. We'll be reviewing due diligence, for example, or helping facilities to secure permits and advising them on the regulatory requirements for licensures."* Some had delved into some *"quasi-litigation work"* by getting involved in *"Certificate of Need hearings, when healthcare providers want to open a new service but need us to argue before the state board why that service is needed."*

Waller's contentious offering spans general commercial litigation and dispute resolution, as well as specialist areas like government investigations and white-collar crime. Litigators explained that *"banking and healthcare are the two big industries here, and we also represent a lot of high net worth individuals."* On the government investigations side, *"we defend a lot of healthcare clients – like hospitals and healthcare facilities – during False Claims Act cases."* Sources here were thrilled with what they'd been able to do so far, with this junior telling us: *"I've been at the firm for a year and a half and I've already participated in 15 depositions and taken some on my own. People are willing to give you as many opportunities as you want – especially if you ask for them!"*

Culture & Offices

The vast majority of Waller's juniors were based in its Nashville HQ – only one on our list was learning the ropes in the firm's Austin base. *"Being in Nashville is great!"* juniors exclaimed. *"We are in the hub; all of our*

Recent work highlights

- Represented Healthcare Realty Trust as it sought to acquire eight medical office buildings in Atlanta for $193.8 million
- Served as transaction counsel to Mississippi Baptist Health Systems during its merger with Baptist Memorial Healthcare, which created one of the largest nonprofit health systems in the US
- Acted for Athlon Sports Communications as it filed a lawsuit to determine the value of the shares held by its former CEO and three other shareholders who all dissented from a merger
- Advised H.G. Hill Realty Company on the acquisition, financing and development of a $75 million town center project in Brentwood – one of the fastest growing areas in Tennessee

board and partner meetings are held here, and all of our biggest clients deal with Nashville attorneys, so we feel privileged to be here." Sources were quick to add that *"that doesn't mean the other offices don't do good work. Birmingham, for example, does more finance work, while Austin is particularly focused on litigation and bankruptcy matters – the focus isn't really on healthcare there."*

Nashville residents were also pleased to get their own offices from the get-go, but *"the size of them varies depending on which floor you're on and how long you've been at the firm. No one has an interior office though, so we get great views over the city."* Such views are afforded as Waller occupies the top floors of the Nashville City Center office tower. *"We're currently renovating the rooftop patio so we can have lunch up there – they're adding a bar too."*

Undoubtedly the social highlight of the year is Waller's firm-wide retreat: *"In 2017 it was held in Nashville, and socialization is half of the intent behind it. They rented out hotels and invited spouses and families to come so everyone could meet one another. We also conduct an internal awards ceremony and bring in speakers to discuss topics that may be of interest."*

Overall, juniors felt that *"there are all types of people at Waller and that's a good thing."* There's room for those who want to *"work their tail off,"* but also plenty of space for those who want to *"maintain a positive family life outside of the office. That might be more of a Nashville versus New York cultural difference. Most of the partners here have families and they spend a decent amount of time with them – family is definitely a priority."*

Hours & Compensation

So just how long are juniors working? Sources reported that during *"an easy/non-crazy period it's something*

See firm profile on p.704

The Inside View

Diversity	Partners (%)	Associates (%)
Women	18	13
White	95	85
Black/African American	0.1	6.4
Hispanic/Latin American	0.1	0
Asian	3	3.8
Mixed/Other	0.1	3.8
LGBT	-	-

like 9am to 6pm, but during a busy period it's more like 8/8:30am to 7:30/8pm." Litigators reported working from home in the evening on quite a regular basis, while those in healthcare *"always remain present in terms of responding to emails in the evening – I do cut away from work at a certain time each night, and overall the hours aren't insane."*

Base salaries are lockstep for the first four years and juniors were *"happy that Waller matches the market – two of the larger firms in town recently raised their base pay and we stepped up to make sure our associates are being paid the same."* From the fifth year onward *"there are a range of lockstep values set for your year. Which one you get is determined by the compensation committee and your practice group, and is based on how you've been progressing and the meaningful contributions you make."* This is still a fairly new system, so sources were *"waiting to see how it settles in and works."* Juniors become eligible for a bonus in their second year, and only if they hit a 1,800-hour billing target. *"The compensation committee are quite opaque when it comes to how they determine the amount you get,"* but the word on the street is that *"it drastically increases if you bill 2,000 hours…"* The firm tells us that it uses its review process (see below) to convey to associates how it will be determining bonuses each year.

Training & Development

Formal training gets under way with a weeklong boot camp for newcomers, which *"takes you through Waller's systems and includes advisory sessions from senior associates on things like how to work well with partners and tricks they've learned – it's helpful as you get an idea of what partners want."* After that each practice group tends to host monthly lunchtime trainings *"on topics that are hot at the time"* as well as key skills: *"We've had ones on successful negotiation tactics, how to prepare for depositions – they're good as partners may not have time to offer that advice outside of those sessions."*

"…advisory sessions from senior associates on tricks they've learned."

There's also a mid and end-of-year review process, *"where the partners you've worked with report on what you've done and give you tips for improvement."* Further support comes in the form of a mentorship program that pairs juniors up with a senior associate (typically): *"In theory you're meant to meet up with them once a month, but often our schedules get in the way."* Fortunately, *"you do build up other mentoring relationships informally, and most of the partners are good at giving feedback – it's not usually in depth, but they highlight how you can develop."*

Pro Bono

"There are lots of different avenues for pro bono work," juniors told us. One of the main ones is a Nashville-based *"legal aid walk-in clinic, where we can go – often on the weekend – to provide advice. We do a lot of protection orders for family law matters there."* There's also a paralegal who *"sends out emails a couple of times a month, which contain descriptions of cases."* Juniors can also *"run a proposed project by a practice group leader – they are always very encouraging, and we can then take it up with a partner who's agreed to oversee it."*

Sources added that doing 25 hours a year was a *"loose guide"* and didn't feel that there was *"any discouragement to do pro bono."* However, sources did *"wish that they would offer billable credit for it – it's all extra time that you put in."*

Pro bono hours
- For all attorneys: 3,801
- Average per attorney: 16.6

Diversity

"The diversity initiatives have improved markedly over the past couple of years," juniors told us. *"Our chairman does a really good job of promoting it."* Recent changes include a new diversity board, which has been *"set up to promote further discussion of initiatives to ensure the firm is always getting better."* On the recruitment front, Waller has expanded its summer program by hiring diverse 1L candidates each year; three joined in 2017 and two are expected to take part in 2018.

The firm's annual retreat has also become a focus for addressing diversity issues. *"In 2016 one of the main speakers gave a presentation on diversity and we took away action points on hiring and staffing. The following year we had one on generational diversity. Overall there's a greater emphasis on seeking out diverse candidates and fostering a diversity of ideas."*

See firm profile on p.704

Weil, Gotshal & Manges LLP

Lawyers per state

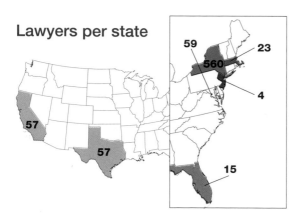

59
23
560
4
57
57
15

Largest US office: New York
US offices: 8
International offices: 9
First-year salary: $180,000
Billable hours: no requirement
Summers 2018: 136 (14 1Ls, 119 2Ls, 1 3L, 2 SEOs)
Revenue 2017: $1.39 billion (+10.3%)
Partners made in 2018: 7

Famous for: having a balanced set of practices that include top-notch bankruptcy and M&A lawyers; having an expansion strategy that's based on opening offices overseas instead of pursuing mergers

It may be famous for its stellar bankruptcy work, but a balanced set of prestigious practices will guarantee that this New York native sticks around for a long Weil yet.

WHEN the economy is in dire straits and companies are going bust left, right and center, it helps to have a globally recognized bankruptcy and restructuring practice to handle the mess. But the optimist in us knows things won't always be so bleak; when the economy picks itself up again, a slew of budding deals will emerge. Being able to thrive in both economic scenarios is partly where Weil's success lies: *"Weil isn't lopsided,"* associates eagerly pointed out. *"It has breadth with strong corporate, litigation, bankruptcy and tax departments."* Executive partner Barry Wolf also emphasizes that *"part of our business plan has always been to have a lot of balance in the firm. By this, I mean a balance of practice areas as well as a balance in geographies. "*

And it's not just talk – *Chambers USA* hands the firm high-class rankings in each of the four areas mentioned above, while *Chambers Global* positions it within its Top 30 of planet-busting hotshots – particularly due to its prowess in areas like private equity, restructuring/insolvency and corporate/M&A. Alongside being attracted to the firm's *"prestige,"* multiple sources were keen *"to get*

exposure to Weil's variety of practices over the summer." Their recruitment interviews with the firm's lawyers gave them the final nudge: *"The OCI and callback process can be exhausting, but the people at Weil seemed like regular people that didn't take themselves too seriously – that was important, as the work is already serious enough!"*

Strategy & Future

"Weil hasn't gotten to where it is by gobbling up lots of other firms," interviewees told us proudly. The firm's strategy has instead been focused on opening up new offices, especially overseas. These are integral to the firm's success, as Barry Wolf explains: *"We have a strong set of offices in Europe, so if the US economy is struggling, the EU economy might be strong and vice versa."*

At the same time, Wolf doesn't see any new bases or practices springing up soon. Instead, *"we're going to strengthen the areas that we have in terms of continuing to obtain more market share."* On the topic of financial performance, Wolf reveals that the past two years have been record breakers for Weil: *"Our 2017 performance exceeded 2016 by a meaningful amount in terms of profitability of the firm, which is really exciting!"* Revenue rose just over 10% to a hefty $1.39 billion. But Wolf wants Weil to be known for more than financial success: *"Our vision is to remain within the top tier of firms from both a financial perspective and from the perspective of the cutting-edge work that we do."* For more from Wolf, visit chambers-associate.com

On chambers-associate.com...

- Get hired at Weil
- Interviews with executive partner Barry Wolf and hiring committee members Jackie Cohen and Joshua Amsel
- Weil's offices

See firm profile on p.705

The Inside View

Rankings in *Chambers USA*

Antitrust	IT & Outsourcing
Banking & Finance	Labor & Employment
Bankruptcy/Restructuring	Litigation
Capital Markets	Media & Entertainment
Corporate/M&A	Private Equity
Employee Benefits &	Real Estate
Executive Compensation	Securities
Environment	Sports Law
Intellectual Property	Tax
Investment Funds	Technology

For detail on ranking tiers and ranking locations, visit
www.chambersandpartners.com

Recent work highlights

- Advised the transaction committee of tobacco products manufacturer Reynolds American on the company's $60.6 billion sale to British American Tobacco
- Served as counsel for Credit Suisse and some of its affiliates during a series of disputes over real estate loans which combined were worth billions of dollars
- Acted for Goldman Sachs and Bank of America Merrill Lynch as they put together a $13.7 billion arrangement to finance Amazon's acquisition of Whole Foods Market
- Represented Takata Corporation – a Japanese automotive component manufacturer – as its subsidiary filed for Chapter 11 protection in the US following the widespread product recall of a specific type of airbag that the company makes

The Work

Juniors are split between four main practice groups: litigation, corporate, tax, and business finance/restructuring. Corporate takes the largest chunk of associates (just over half of the juniors on our list), who join various subgroups including capital markets, banking & finance, private equity/M&A, structured finance, real estate, and technology & IP transactions. Litigation follows with around a third of associates; its subgroups include complex commercial litigation (CCL), securities, antitrust, employment, regulatory, and patent litigation. Tax and business finance/restructuring take on the remaining associates.

Most groups have a formal work assignment system in place: *"It's online and you put in what you're working on, as well as an estimate of how much time you expect to bill during the following week. The assigning partner then looks at who has capacity and assigns from there."* Others described more of a *"hybrid system"* in which the formal online system plays a part, but is *"more of a fallback – the informal side of going out and securing your own work takes precedent. You start to form relationships with partners and get to see what kind of work you really like, so you can start to make your own way a bit."* The formal system was appreciated though, especially in the beginning: *"Early on, not having to seek out your own work helps you to obtain a broader base level of experience."*

"There are many different ways of going about mergers and acquisitions."

Out of the corporate subgroups, private equity/M&A absorbs the most associates. On the public company side, there's *"large-scale post-IPO work for mature companies,"* which can include *"the buying and selling of other companies or divestitures of certain subsidiaries."* The private equity side involves similar things, but *"for PE funds. The main difference is that there's a lot less regulation as they're not publicly traded, so there are many different ways of going about mergers and acquisitions."* Tasks include *"a*

heavy amount of diligence," but also *"drafting confidential treatment memorandums, and assisting in developing public filings for companies."*

Banking & finance involves a lot of leveraged finance work, with a dollop of investment-grade matters on top. Depending on the deal, the group *"represents either the lenders or the borrowers."* Clients span a bunch of major banks, as well as various debt funds, corporate borrowers and well-known names from the private equity sphere. Juniors get *"a lot of drafting experience very early on"* in this group, which starts with ancillaries and progresses to more complex *"security documents, guarantees and credit agreements."* The capital markets subgroup works on IPOs and bond offerings among other matters. Juniors frequently work alongside their counterparts in M&A and restructuring, as *"there are always new warrants and new bonds on the table."* Sources were able to *"review and draft indentures and warrant agreements, filings, contracts, and other arrangements with third parties that are sometimes necessary."*

"Weil gives you work based on what you show you're capable of."

Over in litigation, most juniors join the complex commercial subgroup (CCL), which was fondly described as *"a grab bag of litigation."* The catch-all group does *"standard breach of contract disputes"* as well as *"business-related torts, class actions, trade secrets matters and internal investigations."* For anything more specific, there are tidy subgroups for the likes of securities, employment and antitrust disputes, among others. Across the board, litigators got involved with the *"inevitable"* discovery and doc review, but also researched and drafted client memos and motions to dismiss. *"Weil gives you work based on what you show you're capable of. If you prove yourself to be responsible, smart, engaged and invested in what you're doing, then the partner will be willing to let you take the*

See firm profile on p.705

The Inside View

Diversity	Partners (%)	Associates (%)
Women	24	49
White	89	74
Black/African American	2	5
Hispanic/Latin American	4	4
Asian	4	14
Mixed/Other	1	3
LGBT	2	4

first crack at something – something usually reserved for a more senior person."

Training & Development

Training kicks off with a weeklong orientation in New York. After that, most groups put on *"monthly, if not bimonthly, lunchtime training sessions – depending on the topic, it'll either be just for the relevant level of associate or for the whole group."* Those in the bankruptcy group were especially grateful for these sessions, *"as it's such a complicated area that you don't learn much about in law school – they take you through the whole bankruptcy cycle."* Corporate juniors were also pleased: *"If there's a new precedent or change in SEC regulations then they structure a lunch around the topic. Nothing beats actually doing it, but they help you understand in advance and give you something to refer back to."*

Formal reviews happen twice a year. *"You submit a list of recommended reviewers – more senior people you've worked with – and they in turn submit their feedback. You then meet with two partners to discuss the comments you've received and your professional development goals."*

Hours & Compensation

Weil doesn't require its associates to hit a billable target, which sources felt was *"one of the best things about being here."* Bonuses are therefore *"not tied to billable numbers, which takes the pressure off."* Instead, they are lockstep and class-based, as is the base salary, which follows the Cravath scale. People's personal billing goals ranged from 160 hours a month in smaller offices like Silicon Valley to 200 hours in New York: *"That's a pretty good benchmark, as you're definitely putting in the hours but not killing yourself."* As a general rule, interviewees explained that *"you should be making sure you are keeping up with whatever your group is doing – if your group is busy and you're not, that might be an issue."*

Day to day, most aimed to be in the office for around 9:30am, and usually left anywhere between 6:30pm and 8pm. The nature of deal work means those hours can fluctuate significantly: *"There are weeks where I leave at*

1am and weeks where I'll leave at 6pm," one corporate junior told us.Late finishes for litigators can stretch to midnight, but fortunately they don't work weekends *"super often – if I do then it would be for a couple of hours on a Saturday or a Sunday. Not the entire weekend."*

Culture

Despite lockstep compensation and the absence of billing targets, sources in New York still suggested that *"there's competition among associates – I don't know where it comes from, but it is competitive."* We think that this fellow New Yorker gave a good explanation when they explained that *"we're motivated people that want to work hard and do well; there's no undue external pressure to get things done because we just have that internal drive to get them done anyway."*

"The firm expects excellence but it doesn't require you to be a robot to achieve it."

This doesn't mean that everyone at Weil is a 'Type A' nightmare – quite the opposite: *"The firm expects excellence but it doesn't require you to be a robot to achieve it."* Many associates agreed: *"People do actually like each other and spend time together. There have been times during crazy deals where I've been on an internal call at 1am to discuss our work, and I've ended up chatting to people for an extra 20 minutes because they were so nice – I think that's indicative of the culture here."* There are also cultural differences between the offices, as this Silicon Valley interviewee revealed: *"Our office is a 'jeans every day' sort of place – New York and Dallas are viewed as being more intense, while SV is more levelheaded."*

Pro Bono

There's *"absolutely a big push"* on the pro bono front. There's a dedicated pro bono department based in New York, which is headed up by the firm's pro bono counsel; there are also regional representatives in each office to help distribute local opportunities. As a result, sources felt there was *"a smorgasbord of pro bono"* on offer – matters they mentioned included asylum work, veterans appeals, housing applications, prisoners' rights cases and corporate assignments for nonprofits. One highlighted that *"every time there's some big crisis – like the fires in California or a big earthquake or the current situation with refugees – the firm reaches out to us and says 'here's what you can do to help.'"* Weil has partnerships with organizations including Planned Parenthood, NYCHA (New York City Housing Authority), the Bronx Defenders and the Innocence Project. The aim is for everyone to complete 50 hours of pro bono a year.

See firm profile on p.705

The Inside View

Pro bono hours
- For all US attorneys: 50,913
- Average per US attorney: 42

Diversity

Many agreed that *"it does feel quite diverse at junior level, but it gets less diverse as you look up at the more senior ranks. In terms of diverse role models, it is lacking."* However, associates recognized the firm's efforts: *"Weil wants it to be a diverse place and devotes resources to improving the situation."* On top of the usual collection of affinity groups, Weil also hosts a 'diversity month' in November, which comes complete with *"lots of events, workshops and talks about what we can do to boost and support diversity."* Juniors felt these events *"weren't just token calendar entries – they really spend a lot of time pushing them. We also have mandatory diversity training, which even the most senior partners have to go to, and I think that's really valuable."*

Some practice groups fared better than others; the business finance & restructuring practice, for example, was praised for having *"a strong representation of women – around a third of the partners in my office are female. We have a women's breakfast every month so we can meet up."* Juniors had hopes that summer classes would continue to be more diverse: *"In my summer class seven out of ten were white males. I raised it with one of the partners, who said they weren't thrilled either, and the next summer the class was more diverse and representative – it's something people are aware of, talk about and work on."*

Get Hired

"We're not so focused on quantitative achievements..." Head to chambers-associate.com to find out what Weil looks for at interview.

**On chambers-associate.com...
Weil's lawyers take us behind the scenes at their private equity practice to help you fully understand what's involved.**

The Inside View

See firm profile on p.705

White & Case LLP

Lawyers per state

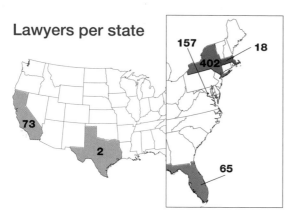

157
18
402
73
2
65

Largest US office: New York
US offices: 7
International offices: 43
First-year salary: $180,000 ($174,000 Miami)
Billable hours: 2,000 target
Summers 2018: 119 (8 1Ls, 109 2Ls, 2 other)
Revenue 2017: $1.8 billion (+10.4%)
Partners made in 2018: 31
Famous for: global prestige; highly regarded projects and energy practice

It takes resilience and *"intellectual curiosity about the law"* to thrive in W&C's *"seamless"* network of global offices.

THIS is a firm where working with offices across the globe is *"just normal day-to-day business"* for its associates, who actively sought such an experience while at law school. *"When I was looking I wanted to join one of the best global firms,"* one interviewee recalled, *"and the breadth of W&C's practice was certainly an initial draw."* Despite maintaining its headquarters in New York, the majority of W&C's lawyers (around two-thirds) are housed in its 34 overseas offices, which stretch across Europe, the Middle East, Africa, the Americas and the Asia-Pacific region. *Chambers Global* places the firm fifth in its Top 30 list of international megastars, and especially rates W&C's work in the projects and energy space, as well as its international arbitration, construction, finance and public international law expertise.

Such a scope came with clear benefits for our sources, who enthused about *"asking and answering questions no one has ever posed before."* Innovative lawyering was deemed exciting, as was the opportunity to contribute to headline-generating matters: *"One thing that makes an impression on me is how big the deals and cases we work on are. It's cool to see something in the news and say 'I'm working on that!'"* On its home turf, juniors help to power this global juggernaut from seven domestic of-fices (W&C expanded its presence on US soil in February 2018 by opening an office in Houston, which will strengthen its oil and gas offering). The New York HQ (alongside London) has been a key focus for the firm in recent years, and while W&C isn't in the habit of planting flag after flag in domestic soil, it did venture into the Boston market in 2016.

Strategy & Future

W&C is in the middle of its five-year growth strategy, and executive committee member David Koschik tells us how it's panning out: *"Our US lawyer head count is up to over 800 lawyers at this point, from 600-plus when we launched the strategy a couple of years ago."*

As W&C enters the second half of its current strategic plan, Koschik tell us that the focus will be on its disputes, capital markets and M&A practices. *"In terms of industries, we're very focused on four: financial institutions, private equity, oil and gas, and technology. We feel we have a substantial presence in those four globally, but feel we can and should be bigger in them in the US."*

The Work

W&C's commercial litigation and M&A groups absorbed the most juniors on our list. Other groups to take on a significant number included antitrust, finance, restructuring, EIPF (energy, infrastructure and project finance), and securities. In the majority of the firm's offices, both litigators and transactional-focused juniors typically

On chambers-associate.com...

- Get hired: more on recruitment at White & Case
- Interview with executive committee member David Koschik

See firm profile on p.706

The Inside View

Rankings in *Chambers USA*

Antitrust	International Trade
Banking & Finance	Latin American Investment
Bankruptcy/Restructuring	Litigation
Capital Markets	Private Equity
Corporate/M&A	Projects
Energy & Natural	Real Estate
Resources	Tax
Environment	Technology
Intellectual Property	Transportation
International Arbitration	

For detail on ranking tiers and ranking locations, visit
www.chambersandpartners.com

Recent work highlights

- Advised health benefits company Anthem on its proposed $54.2 billion merger with Cigna, a global health insurance services outfit
- Represented the Republic of Peru against a breach of contract claim brought by an Illinois company
- Acted for Japanese conglomerate Toshiba during antitrust class actions following allegations of an industry-wide battery price-fixing conspiracy
- Advised Disney on a series of debt offerings worth $15.8 billion in total

start off as generalists and join a 'pool' before specializing – litigators spend two years in the pool while their corporate counterparts do so for just their first year. During that time, a formal allocation system keeps juniors busy: *"You update a portal every week and indicate how busy you are, the matters you're working on, and the matters you're interested in working on in the future."* While assignment coordinators oversee this system, sources still found that they could *"express particular interests directly with people in the group – they can then clear your availability with the assignment team."*

Pool-based corporate juniors can sample work from five subgroups: M&A, project finance, capital markets, tax and banking. In the first year *"the two things you're typically doing are due diligence and cross-referencing checks for main purchase agreements – you've got to make sure the documents are in a good shape."* Others highlighted that responsibility can quickly ramp up: *"The culture of the group is to give you responsibility based on your commitment and capability. Trust is the key component and they like to delegate work to capable juniors."* For M&A juniors, working on multiple deals could become a bit of a puzzle, especially when they involved several jurisdictions. *"For example, you have to time wiring correctly so the money gets where it needs to be – if the bank isn't open it can throw a wrench in there! These deals can also mean that you're researching foreign laws or on conference calls at odd times. You also have to be aware of cultural norms."*

Fledgling litigators can sample a mix of commercial litigation, arbitration, white-collar, antitrust and IP matters during their time in the pool. Those who'd subsequently specialized in commercial litigation told us that *"there are a lot of general contract cases, but also securities disputes, bankruptcy matters and some class actions too."* We also heard of a dedicated social media group over in LA, *"which handles all sorts of litigation and gives compliance advice to such companies all over the world."* Responsibilities can *"vary a lot, from something more menial like bluebooking texts to conducting legal research for sum-* mary judgments to helping to prepare deposition outlines to even taking depositions."* Sources were pleased to report that *"most of the day-to-day involves legal writing: editing and drafting briefs, writing letters to the court and drafting discovery reports."* Litigators working with international offices were *"always aware of the time differences between the jurisdictions we work with. For example, I might have to handle something in the morning or forward something on at night if I need to consult local counsel in a certain country."*

Hours & Compensation

The firm's 2,000-hour billing target (which can include up to 200 hours of work from pro bono and firm-mandated activities, like *"writing articles, attending recruitment events and contributing to client pitches"*) was unanimously viewed as a reachable goal by our interviewees. One corporate junior even labeled it *"too easy,"* but was quick to add: *"I don't want them to put it up though – EVER!"* A handful of sources going well over the target weren't ruffled by working so much: *"I'd rather work 2,300 happy hours than 200 at a place I was unhappy with."* We suspect the 'super bonus' associates get at 2,400 might also keep a smile on their faces – hitting the 2,000 hours qualifies associates for a lockstep bonus.

"They don't want you chained to your desk."

"It's a little difficult but that's the cost of BigLaw," said one New York-based corporate associate on the topic of work-life balance. *"I usually get in by 10am and consistently work until 8pm or 9pm."* A securities source added: *"The hours can be very long and I'm still navigating juggling everything and making plans outside of work. During the summer we were really busy and almost every weekend you couldn't count on making plans."* There generally wasn't much of a face-time expectation across the offices though, which helped: *"They don't want you chained to your desk. Say I have an 11pm conference call with Asia, it's totally normal for me to go home and take it there."*

See firm profile on p.706

The Inside View

Diversity	Partners (%)	Associates (%)
Women	19	50
White	79	62
Black/African American	2	5
Hispanic/Latin American	6	11
Asian	10	17
Mixed/Other	3	5
LGBT	2	5

Others regularly left by 6pm and logged back on to do work at home in the evenings.

Training & Development

Formal training gets off to flying start with the New Associate Conference: *"They bring all the new associates across the Americas up to New York for three days of introductory training."* This format is repeated for 'milestone conferences' at the junior, mid and senior levels. *"The junior one I just attended covered deal and stress management training – it was very useful for identifying stressors and good ways to cope."* Ongoing formal training varied by group and office, and included monthly lunchtime seminars for litigators (*"a partner will talk about some aspect of our practice, and the sessions are always enjoyable"*) and 'boot camps' for corporate associates: *"They walk you through different agreements, and it would be helpful to do more of them as we progress and begin to draft more – at the moment they're held once every couple of months or so."*

All first years are put into 'mentoring circles' made up of a partner, a couple of seniors/midlevels and *"two to three"* juniors. Associates who'd hit it off with their circles found them helpful for bringing up concerns: *"As you transition into different roles it's great to bounce ideas off of a smaller group where you feel comfortable."* The circles provided a chance to have some fun too: *"Some meet up for karaoke, some get coffee and lunches, and one organized a gin-tasting!"* While some sources deemed the path to the partnership as *"extremely hard,"* they nonetheless praised W&C's culture of mentoring. *"There's a good sense of nurturing people to become one of us. Part of that involves putting you on the spot with partners and asking you what you think. People here want you to succeed."*

Culture & Offices

W&C's juniors felt strongly that the firm is *"truly international not just because it has offices everywhere, but because of how integrated it is. When they say 'one firm,' it's true. They staff matters across offices all the time, so I'm constantly working with people in London or Hong Kong.* Associates enjoyed feeling part of the W&C network. *"Despite being so big and spread out we're still able to feel*

like a family – I feel connected to the people I've worked with in other offices."* Juniors can even get healthily competitive with their overseas colleagues during the annual White & Case World Cup: *"All offices send teams to Europe for softball and volleyball tournaments. Last year it was held in Vienna and the year before it was in Hamburg. The New York team doesn't do as well – we need to beef up!"*

"I'm constantly working with people in London or Hong Kong."

Off the pitch and back in the office, New York associates told us the atmosphere *"isn't formal or stiff, but not exactly laid back either – it falls somewhere in the center."* They agreed that there's *"a strong team-oriented environment. When we're working late everyone is happy to eat dinner together, and people will say things like 'I'm a night person so I'll work until 3am, and you can pick this up in the morning.' People are good about making sure we don't lose our minds!"* In DC there was a similar vibe: *"It's a 'work hard' mentality and can get pretty serious, but there's an eye toward making sure people have time to relax. We had a big filing a month or so ago so we broke out the ping pong table to lighten the mood."* We also heard about other relaxation-encouraging perks: *"The firm has people come in to give us massages – we get pampered and spoiled!"*

The brand new *"all glass"* headquarters in New York was another highlight for associates. *"It's like a Silicon Valley tech office!"* The majority of the juniors on our list (just over 60%) were based in the New York mothership, which is now located within the 1221 Avenue of the Americas skyscraper. All of that glass has given the office a sense of openness and has made it a *"much more sociable"* place, with lots of *"collaboration spaces."* Other highlights included a cafeteria that *"overlooks the city all the way down to the Statue of Liberty."* W&C's DC office was home to the next largest cohort of juniors (almost 20%), while the rest were spread between the firm's other domestic bases in Boston, LA, Silicon Valley, Houston and Miami.

Diversity

As in previous years, sources identified W&C's international scope as a good foundation for fostering diversity. *"When you go to firm events people speak different languages and look different from one another – that's not the case when you attend other law firms' events."* W&C's range of affinity groups – which include networks for LGBT, Asian, Hispanic, black and women lawyers – came in for particular praise: *"The person in charge of ours does a great job of bringing people together for cultural events, and linking you up with partners for lunches – we get a lot of contact. There are partners who are the same race as*

See firm profile on p.706

me, so I feel like a person who looks like me could actually make it."

Pro bono

Associates could get pro bono work via a dedicated global manager based in New York, whose location was no obstacle for juniors in other offices: "*I emailed him about trying to meet my pro bono hours* [juniors are expected to bill at least 20 each year] *and he called me within five minutes to discuss. The responsiveness is great.*" First years are also assigned at least one pro bono matter to work on.

"*The firm has a close relationship with the UN in general,*" juniors revealed, "*so you can do research for them on genocide and war crime projects, for example.*" Other pro bono matters included wrongful convictions, immigration cases, environmental lawsuits and work stemming from Trump's travel ban: "*We supported nonprofits that were suing the Trump administration over the ban, so I did research related to that and some of us went over to JFK to help at the time.*"

Pro bono hours
- For all US attorneys: 68,759
- Average per US attorney: 75

Get Hired

"We're definitely looking for candidates with an international perspective – that's really important to the firm and I think the vast majority of people – if not everyone here – has international experience or some tie overseas." Find out more about getting hired on chambers-associate.com

On chambers-associate.com...
White & Case's lawyers take us behind the scenes at their antitrust and banking practices. Their vivid examples and stories bring these complex areas to life.

See firm profile on p.706

Wiley Rein LLP

Lawyers per state

241

Largest US office: Washington, DC
US offices: 1
International offices: 0
First-year salary: $180,000
Billable hours: 1,950 target
Summers 2018: 12 (1 1L, 11 2Ls)
Revenue 2017: undisclosed
Partners made in 2018: 6
Famous for: government contracts, TMT and insurance work; devotion to maintaining a single base in DC

One office, three key specialties: DC's Wiley wears a triple crown of government, insurance and TMT expertise.

FOUNDED half a mile away from the White House when Ronald Reagan called it home, Washingtonian Wiley Rein has remained loyal to the capital for 35 years, never feeling the need to expand beyond it. Prospective juniors *"really liked that it's invested in being a DC firm and not a global player with far-flung offices, as you get to know pretty much everyone you work with personally."* The DC grounding also provides *"less of a competitive New York-style BigLaw culture"* and a raft of government connections.

On the subject of these connections: the firm has a historic association with the GOP (former name partner Fred Fielding acted as White House counsel for two Republican presidents). Today, however, juniors told us that Wiley has *"become a lot more balanced in terms of political diversity"* within its ranks and works with both sides of the aisle. Its government-related work is still very much one of the three prongs on Wiley's trident of well-known specialties – insurance and telecommunications, media and technology (TMT) matters form the other two. All three practices merit gold star *Chambers USA* rankings, while other groups like IP, international trade, franchising and privacy & cybersecurity also get nods.

On www.chambers-associate.com...

- Get Hired: interview essentials
- Hiring tips from recruiting committee chair Rachel Alexander and chief talent officer Kay Nash
- Interview with managing partner Peter Shields

The Work

You guessed it: Wiley's government contracts, insurance and TMT practices absorb most of its incoming juniors, but you'll still find the odd one or two in areas like IP and international trade. In TMT and government contracts, there's a free-market work allocation system, which scored mixed reviews. Some had found it *"pretty easy, as you just walk around, get to know people and drum up work,"* while others didn't like the system *"at all, because it can be challenging to break into: before you get a chance to impress a partner, they may have already chosen someone they like working with and set them on the path for getting more assignments."* Insurance was less problematic, as an assigning partner *"is very good at what he does – I've worked with almost every partner in the group."*

Team TMT handles both litigation and regulatory work – the latter often has a specialist focus on Federal Communications Commission regulations. Junior tasks range *"from filing complaints to completing first drafts of motions; the coolest thing is getting to be the first pen on a lot of substantive writing projects."* Even juniors who'd worked primarily on the litigation side found that *"there hasn't been a great deal of document review,"* with one boasting: *"I haven't done a single one!"* A *"big portion"* of life here involves *"keeping abreast of developments in technology in general, to figure out how they relate to what we do."*

The *"bread and butter"* in government contracts is bid protest claims – which challenge the awarding of such contracts – but juniors had also worked on a sandwich

See firm profile on p.707

The Inside View

Rankings in *Chambers USA*

Government	Media & Entertainment
Insurance	Privacy & Data Security
International Trade	Telecommunications

For detail on ranking tiers and ranking locations, visit
www.chambersandpartners.com

filling of *"claims and counseling for companies under the Service Contract Act"* and employment cases. Enjoying a *"pretty consistent practice,"* sources' only protests were aimed at *"the short turnaround period for filings; it can affect your work-life balance as you only have ten days to respond and things can ramp up quickly."* On a more normal day, the workload centers on reviewing briefs and opposing counsel files: *"You can review around 60 documents then write up a brief. I feel like I've built substantive knowledge in my first year."*

"We're not bogged down in enormous document reviews."

Wiley's insurance group provides both coverage counsel and litigation services for insurers and insured policyholders in various fields, including employment, cyber liability and policy. *"Litigation offers more high-level work more quickly,"* juniors revealed, *"as cases move quickly and matters tend to be smaller, so we're not bogged down in enormous document reviews. Our area is kinda unique as there isn't a lot of discovery."* Instead, interviewees got to draft motions for summary judgment and some appellate briefs. In the beginning, it's common to be doing *"coverage analysis, where you analyze insurance policies and write first drafts of letters to the policyholder."* There are also research assignments us for grabs, *"where you look into discrete questions that a partner has on a certain state's laws."*

Training & Development

Newbies are assigned two associate mentors, usually from the same practice group. Everyone receives an annual review, *"which is helpful for ensuring you get substantive feedback from partners, as throughout the year things can get hectic and slip through the cracks."* First years also get a midyear review with a partner, *"who walks you through the progress you've made after getting feedback from people you've worked with."*

In addition to standard orientation sessions, first years have weekly practice-specific trainings in the form of a '101' series. It's more intensive for some groups than others. *"TMT needs more as it's so specialist – we've had a good number of modules exposing us to sources to use and the procedures for certain work products."* Insurance juniors, meanwhile, found there's *"a lot of learning on the job"*

Recent work highlights

- Acted for Republican National Committee to resolve a First Amendment challenge to the site plan and security regulations for the party's 2016 National Convention
- Represented Japanese insurer Tokio Marine during a $575 million claim brought by SunTrust Bank, which sought to recover the costs tied to litigation and investigations that arose from the credit crisis
- Sought to obtain regulatory approval for satellite manufacturer SSL MDA Holdings, which was looking to acquire Earth-imaging company DigitalGlobe for $2.4 billion
- Counsel to radio giant iHeart Media on an array matters, including transactions, license renewals and compliance with the FCC's ownership rules

but still pointed to a range of sessions *"that go through different types of policies."* A more advanced '201' series awaits juniors in year two.

Culture & Office

Being a one-office DC firm *"does have an impact"* on the working environment, juniors agreed. *"We're a cohesive group,"* one explained, adding: *"Overall it's a very genial culture and there's a lot of respect for having a life outside the firm."* It sounded like there was plenty of life within the firm too, as social events at Wiley range from winery tours to holiday parties and a fall festival *"where people can buy baked goods."*

Associates seemed pretty sweet on one another: *"Some of my best friends are my coworkers. Wiley does a really good job of hosting lunches and happy hours every so often."* But mingling isn't just reserved for happy hours, as *"being in a single office means you can always stop by and talk to somebody in person; everyone is really nice and wants to do a good job. No one wants drama!"* Across the board sources found *"Wiley more 'steady life' culturally. The firm tells you when you're a summer that it's a family-oriented place."*

"We're a cohesive group."

If you've just resurfaced from a *Stranger Things* binge you may be pleased to hear Wiley's office described as *"a building from the '80s,"* but we've often heard that the decor is *"a little outdated and basic. It's well taken care of but it's not a modern building."* Our interviewees found a certain charm in the retro vibes, though, and were pleased to get their own office from day one: *"They're not giving you tons of fancy snacks or coconut water but its being dated doesn't really matter – I prefer solid walls to glass anyway!"*

See firm profile on p.707

The Inside View

Diversity	Partners (%)	Associates (%)
Women	27	54
White	88	74
Black/African American	3	7
Hispanic/Latin American	3	7
Asian	6	12
Mixed/Other	0	0
LGBT	2	4

Diversity

Looking at the industry as a whole, one source had the *"sense that Wiley isn't behind the curve, but not quite ahead of it either"* when it came to diversity. Strong female representation at associate level was dubbed *"a plus,"* but translating this up to the partnership is *"an ongoing process. They have a pretty good approach to flexible working, which helps."* Though some suggested that *"racial diversity isn't better or worse than it is at your typical BigLaw firm,"* others were more conscious of deficiencies: *"We could be doing better given our size. I don't think it's very racially diverse, but they're working on it."* A pipeline scheme is available for diverse 1Ls, and the firm runs several affinity networks for ethnic minorities, LGBT lawyers and working parents.

> *"They have a pretty good approach to flexible working."*

Pro Bono

"It's great to have a pro bono partner here who really pushes it and does a great job of advertising projects," juniors reported. Those projects had included tax matters, landlord/tenant cases, immigration work and social security appeals. One junior enthused: *"I wrote two Supreme Court amicus briefs in my first year, which is ridiculous and incredible – it's great to be able to work on such substantive, high-impact projects."*

Despite this enthusiasm, juniors simultaneously found Wiley's approach to pro bono *"fairly frustrating"* due to the 50-hour cap it imposes on what can be counted toward the billable target. *"The policy is outdated and not on par with the wider industry. Pro bono matters can run on for much longer than that, and you could fill up 50 hours in two weeks – other firms are more generous."* Some sources had heard *"that if you hit 100 hours they'll consider counting it but it's a real black box."* The firm clarified that associates can apply for additional credit for high-impact pro bono cases.

Pro bono hours
- For all attorneys across all US offices: 13,151
- Average per US attorney: 48

Hours & Compensation

Juniors shoot for an annual billable target of 1,950 hours. *"I'd say it's achievable if you don't do much pro bono,"* said one, while another confirmed: *"The work is available and you can get there – I didn't have a problem making it even as a first year."* Some warned that *"Wiley is a face time-heavy firm: you're expected to be here between 9am and 6pm – it's not the kind of place where you can traipse in every day at 10:30am."* The average leaving time was 6:30pm, with late nights described as rare: *"There have been around 15 days where I've been here until 11pm – it's the exception rather than the norm,"* one second year explained.

> *"The work is available and you can get there."*

Juniors *"couldn't complain"* about Wiley's base compensation structure, which matches the Cravath scale for juniors' first four years in practice. After that, it switches to a merit-based system. Bonuses, however, are *"a bit of a black box: you take what you're given without any real explanation. The system could definitely be improved."* At the same time, other sources did make the point that *"we didn't come to Wiley expecting NY-level bonuses, and the trade-off of a better work-life balance is worth it."*

Strategy & Future

As a DC firm, government policy affects Wiley Rein acutely. Managing partner Peter Shields reveals *"during any administration change there tends to be an uptick in Washington work. Whether it's a Democratic administration that is stereotypically regulating or a Republican one that is deregulating, clients want to understand every facet and implication of the government's activity."* He highlights international trade as *"a high priority of this administration"* while noting that *"there's been more M&A activity and litigation as a result"* too. To read the full interview, visit www.chambers-associate.com.

Get Hired

"The firm is looking for team players... I've never done one project completely by myself." Wily Wiley wannabes will find plenty of helpful recruitment hints on chambers-associate.com

See firm profile on p.707

The Inside View

Willkie Farr & Gallagher LLP

Lawyers per state

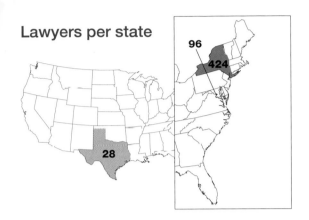

96

424

28

Largest US office: New York
US offices: 3
International offices: 6
First-year salary: $180,000
Billable hours: no requirement
Summers 2018: 55 (1Ls 6, 2Ls 49)
Revenue 2017: $772 million (+11.7%)
Partners made in 2018: 7
Famous for: insurance work; active social life

This 130 year old corporate stalwart is characterized by an active social life and a relatively relaxed approach to hours.

"PEOPLE here do talk about the collegial culture, doors always being open, yada yada yada..." said one Willkie associate jokingly, *"but to me what really matters is that partners here might just come into my office for a chat and will take us out for lunch or beers. And I literally have no hesitation in picking up the phone to call a partner if I'm slammed and I need more time to do something."* This is what associates felt defined working life at Willkie. Add to this a raft of social events, jeans-only Fridays and juniors being able to give anonymous feedback on their seniors (more on this later), and you can see why associates said Willkie *"attracts a lot of relaxed and laid back people."*

But these lawyers are no idlers: Willkie has a strong reputation for corporate and litigation in New York and nationwide. It has a clutch of rankings in *Chambers USA*: Willkie sits in the 'elite' category for M&A in New York and nationally, and at the top of the midmarket for litigation in the Big Apple. It also wins a top Chambers ranking for transactional and regulatory insurance work, plus nods for practices including bankruptcy, investment funds, antitrust, and telecom, broadcast & satellite.

The Work

Across the firm's three domestic offices in Houston, DC and New York – where the vast majority of juniors are based – the corporate and litigation groups snag just over half of all newbies. Here work is assigned formally with associates sending weekly reports to assigning partners (we hear that the firm will be shifting to an electronic allocation system in the near future). There are other ways of getting work, *"but mostly work filters through the assignment system."* Opinions were mixed on this: some sources really liked it, arguing it prevents *"fighting over the most interesting work or people getting too many hours."* Others thought *"it does not work as well as I had hoped. Halfway through my second year my assigning partner was very busy and unable to disperse work evenly."* In smaller teams, most of which are in New York, *"you just get a call or email from the partners."* Though some said this does result in uneven work distribution, *"if you are quiet you are not meant to feel bad and when I have been swamped I've not gotten emails saying 'hey can you look into this.'"*

"At first it's a lot to take in because you're working on four matters simultaneously and drawing on multiple areas of law."

On chambers-associate.com...

- Get Hired: how to go far at Willkie interviews
- Willkie and Major League Baseball

Corporate work at Willkie covers *"private equity, M&A, capital markets and a lot of complex insurance work."* Clients include banks like Morgan Stanley and Goldman Sachs, insurers MetLife, Assurant and Swiss Re, and

See firm profile on p.708

The Inside View

Rankings in *Chambers USA*

Antitrust	Investment Funds
Banking & Finance	Litigation
Bankruptcy/Restructuring	Private Equity
Corporate/M&A	Real Estate
Employee Benefits &	Securities
Executive Compensation	Tax
FCPA	Telecommunications
Insurance	

For detail on ranking tiers and ranking locations, visit
www.chambersandpartners.com

Recent work highlights

- Represented telecom provider Level 3 Communications when it was acquired by CenturyLink for $34 billion
- Advised MetLife on its multibillion-dollar spinoff of its US retail life insurance and annuity operations
- Represented a group of indigent transgender individuals in a challenge to New York State rules barring Medicaid coverage of transgender-related healthcare
- Acted for insurance broker and risk manager Marsh, which was assisting New Jersey Transit with a $400 million claim against its insurer over damages caused by Hurricane Sandy
- Helped Dallas-based Springbok Energy Partners launch a private equity firm and partnership with investor Natural Gas Partners

businesses like shipping company CMA CGM and food producer Bonduelle. Houston focuses on energy clients. Associates do *"anything from researching securities law to preparing signature agreements."* A number of juniors found that *"at first it's a lot to take in because you're working on four matters simultaneously and drawing on multiple areas of law."* That being said, colleagues were apparently *"happy to slow it down and talk you through what you are doing."*

The litigation practice covers antitrust, bankruptcy, white-collar and securities cases as well as FCPA investigations and matters relating to asbestos trusts. Clients include Citigroup, Bloomberg and Warburg Pincus. Different offices have differing focuses, with New York doing a lot of bankruptcy and insurance work, and DC big on government investigations. An associate told us: *"The majority of last year I was working on a case in the pretrial phase. I drafted letters, discovery requests and responses to discovery requests. I was the only junior on the team, and when we were doing a motion to dismiss I did the first draft of that."* Another source, who had been working on investigations, had a somewhat different experience: *"I worked with a team of people – some juniors, one senior and the partner – and typically did the doc review and privilege review that needed to get done. I also helped with research and drafting summaries of research. I did a lot of things sitting at the computer – I think some of the other juniors probably had more exposure to clients."*

What of the smaller teams? An asset management source was *"looking into clients that want to do a particular trade, researching federal securities law and drafting operating agreements."* An IP insider had *"been writing a motion to dismiss, discovery responses and discovery requests, as well as taking a couple of depositions."* Meanwhile, juniors in the communications & media team might spend their time *"filing comments with the FCC and researching policy issues and factual issues like what shows are on Netflix as opposed to Hulu."*

Culture & Social Life

Willkie has a reputation for being a more sociable firm than some of its New York competitors, and it's well deserved. *"There's a large amount of socializing informally,"* a New York transplant told us. *"People come from different parts of the country and so don't have a huge network in the city. Willkie does a great job of integrating us all together."* Integration efforts start with monthly 'informal gatherings' – a conference room is booked out, food is brought in and *"everyone comes to network and mingle."* We also heard of a bowling tournament hosted by the corporate team, the IP team doing an escape room challenge (at the suggestion of the partners), group happy hours, a yearly holiday party (*"it's a blast!"*), and summer events including an open bar in Central Park and outings to Broadway musicals like *Hamilton*. Willkie also organizes talks on topical issues, for example criminal justice reform and *"the tensions between equal rights and individual religious liberties."* Recent speakers include a former CIA analyst (who delivered a talk on North Korea) and author Kim Barker, who wrote *The Taliban Shuffle* – a memoir that covers Barker's time as a journalist reporting in Afghanistan and Pakistan.

"There is no pressure to bill a certain amount of hours."

There's clearly a lot going on and Willkie is definitely a good fit for juniors who want a firm with an active social life and a *"more relaxed"* day-to-day atmosphere. Sources did remind us that the focus remains on the work and social events are *"concentrated in the summer and the fall."*

Hours & Compensation

In keeping with the firm's more relaxed vibe, juniors felt they had a not-so-frantic time when it came to billable hours, primarily because they don't have a target to hit. *"One of the best things about compensation here is that*

See firm profile on p.708

The Inside View

Diversity	Partners (%)	Associates (%)
Women	15	43
White	91.8	78
Black/African American	1.4	4.2
Hispanic/Latin American	2	5.3
Asian	3.4	9.5
Mixed/Other	1.4	3.4
LGBT	3.4	3.7

there is no pressure to bill a certain amount of hours," sources agreed. "If I ever feel any it's because I want to be pulling my weight." This doesn't mean associates can slack off though. Corporate and litigation juniors usually come in between 9 and 10am and are out the door at 7 or 7:30pm when it's quiet, but if it's busier "you can be in the office till midnight every week." Smaller groups like government investigations have more consistent hours, with juniors arriving between 8:30 and 9:30am and leaving around 6:30 or 7:30pm.

Offices

Associates share an office till their second year and described the building in New York as "a bit of a mix with wood paneling and glass." In DC the office was "recently renovated and now feels a bit more modern." DC folks felt that in their office "the vibe is a little more laid back and reasonable on the hours" than New York, but those in the Big Apple contested this: "Corporate work can be intense, but I've never heard of the culture being different in DC."

Training & Development

After initial general training, "each department has its own boot camp where you learn what your day-to-day work will be like." In addition, each office hosts its own CLE lunches. Some associates felt the firm emphasizes on-the-job training so "it's really a trial by fire." The good news is that "everybody's always willing to give advice. I was run through subtle things like what kind of subject headings to use when something goes to a client."

"I was run through subtle things like what kind of subject headings to use."

Unusually, Willkie's review system works from bottom to top as well as top to bottom. Associates can fill out an online anonymous feedback form for any person they've worked with for over 25 hours. One insider loved the system: "Elsewhere I've worked with senior colleagues I thought were terrible and I could never express it." Another source did caution that "you always have to remain polite."

Pro Bono

While litigators have plenty of pro bono opportunities, transactional juniors had mixed opinions on their options. Some thought they had "a really robust set of opportunities," while others felt it's "hard to do substantive transactional pro bono." New York regularly works with Her Justice, which provides free legal services to women in poverty; juniors can also do a four-month externship with the organization, as well as with Mobilization for Justice in New York and the Washington Lawyers' Committee in DC. Sources said they felt comfortable spending as much time on pro bono as they wanted. One interviewee told us: "No one will say; 'Why are you doing pro bono, that's a waste of time!'"

Pro bono hours
- For all US attorneys: 44,634
- Average per US attorney: 79

Diversity

"Willkie tries very hard to create a diverse environment," sources said, pointing toward the Women's Professional Development Committee which is "a really great place to discuss any issues in the workplace." The firm also provides implicit bias training and diversity mentoring.

"We are not looking for unbridled growth."

Strategy & Future

Firm chairman Tom Cerabino says the firm intends to grow its M&A, private equity, litigation and investigations, asset management, restructuring and antitrust practices. That's not a particularly focused strategy, we're sure you'll agree, so don't expect any sudden growth spurts from Willkie any time soon. Cerabino told us: "Willkie's philosophy is to be careful in our growth. It's important for us that we know all our partners and maintain quality control. We are not looking for unbridled growth."

Get Hired

"It's not a question of just telling me what's on our website," says professional personnel committee chair Tom Henry. "You have to connect your own experience with that and show how it fits into what Willkie does." For more recruitment tips from Henry and Willkie's associates, go to chambers-associate.com

See firm profile on p.708

WilmerHale

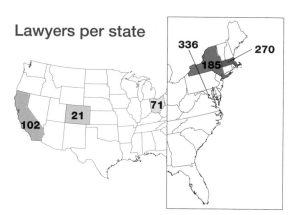

Lawyers per state

336 270
185
71
21
102

Largest US office: Washington, DC
US offices: 7
International offices: 5
First-year salary: $180,000
Billable hours: 2,000 target
Summers 2018: 92 (3 1Ls, 85 2Ls, 4 SEO)
Revenue 2017: $1.137 billion (+0.6%)
Partners made in 2018: 7
Famous for: academic style; industry-rousing support for pro bono; government-based alumni; top-notch expertise in appellate, life sciences and IP

Those with a genuine passion for the law should feel right at home at this *"academic"* firm, which is famous for its government work and influential commitment to pro bono.

THIS elite firm comes with dominant flavors from both DC and Boston, thanks to a 2004 merger that united top practices in the capital and Beantown. The resulting entity, WilmerHale, excels in the areas associated with these major markets – a point that wasn't lost on our shrewd interviewees. Those who targeted the firm in Boston did so because *"Wilmer is strong in technology and life sciences,"* while those who sought it out in DC were drawn to its standing in litigation and government-related work: *"I knew I wanted to work in government at some point. I attended a summer lunch where people with fascinating careers in the government came to speak, and many had worked at WilmerHale. I recognized that Wilmer was unique in that people worked at the firm, went into government and then came back."* Among the ranks of WilmerHale's famous alumni is Robert Mueller – a name known across the nation for his role investigating Russia's alleged interference with the 2016 presidential election.

In *Chambers USA*, WilmerHale's government work picks up high praise in the areas of congressional investigations and merger approvals. Elsewhere, top-ranked strengths nationwide include antitrust; appellate law; financial services regulation; IP; life sciences and securities regulation. Accolades are also won in the other domestic markets WilmerHale operates in – LA, Palo Alto, Denver and New York. But our interviewees typically wanted more than just stellar fee-earning work, as this source explained: *"I was only looking at firms with a strong focus and genuine dedication to public interest issues, and WilmerHale has lived up to my expectations in that regard."*

Pro Bono

You know pro bono's a big deal at a firm when one of its legacy partners authored *Justice and the Poor* – the influential book that kickstarted efforts to secure equal justice across the US in the early 20th century. As one junior affirmed: *"A big reason why I ended up coming back to Wilmer after my clerkship was because of its commitment to pro bono."* We heard of an unofficial aim for associates to have 100 hours of pro bono work under their belt each year, against 1,900 hours of fee-earning work. However, sources agreed that *"there's no discouragement from doing more,"* and technically an unlimited amount can count toward the annual billing target (see below) – many of our interviewees had billed in excess of 200 hours.

Associates need only to reach out to the firm's pro bono coordinators – who email out opportunities daily – to secure themselves assignments. *"It's not just first come, first served,"* interviewees clarified. *"If everyone wants to do an appellate brief, for example, then they try and ensure that everyone has a chance to do so."* On top of a whole host of clemency projects, family law matters and veterans'

On chambers-associate.com...

- Get hired: the way into WilmerHale
- Interview with co-managing partner Susan Murley

See firm profile on p.709

Rankings in *Chambers USA*

Antitrust

Appellate Law

Banking & Finance

Bankruptcy/Restructuring

Corporate Crime &
  Investigations

Corporate/M&A

Employee Benefits &
  Executive Compensation

FCPA

Financial Services
  Regulation

Government

Intellectual Property

International Arbitration

International Trade

Life Sciences

Litigation

Media & Entertainment

Native American Law

Privacy & Data Security

Private Equity

Real Estate

Securities

Startups & Emerging
  Companies

Tax

Technology

For detail on ranking tiers and ranking locations, visit
www.chambersandpartners.com

Recent work highlights

- Secured a favorable settlement for the Tohono O'odham Nation following the tribe's long-running dispute with the State of Arizona over the Nation's plans to open a gaming facility on its land near Phoenix
- Representing pharma giant AbbVie in some of the first cases to arise from the Biologics Price Competition and Innovation Act (BPCIA), which relate to the proposed sale of biosimilar products that allegedly infringe multiple AbbVie patents
- Helped Internal Revenue Service commissioner John Koskinen defeat an impeachment campaign mounted by the House Freedom Caucus via bipartisan advocacy and media outreach
- Represented Hilton Worldwide Holdings during a $6.5 billion transaction which saw Chinese conglomerate HNA Group acquire a 25% equity interest in Hilton from affiliates of Blackstone

work, sources also mentioned the relatively recent introduction of an internal civic engagement initiative: *"It's a firm-wide effort to discuss issues of public interest within the firm, and there have been some pro bono matters that have emerged out of those discussions – we were able to share information quickly about Trump's travel ban, for example."*

Pro bono hours

- For all US attorneys: 109,628.9
- Average per US attorneys: 118.3

The Work

WilmerHale's litigation/controversy department snaps up the majority of new starters (just over 60%); a fifth join the firm's transactional arm, while the rest are divided between the regulatory & government affairs; IP; and securities groups. All departments have assignment coordinators, but the extent to which they control workflow depends on the practice and location. In the DC-based litigation group, for instance, *"we have a happy medium between the coordinator formally handing out assignments and a free-market system that allows you to get work through your own network. It's a pretty decent balance, and it's nice to know that for the most part you can be proactive about managing what you work on."* In the transactional wing of the Boston office, however, *"all assignments go through the practice coordinator. They do a good job of making sure people are adequately staffed, and they're very receptive if you say you don't have the bandwidth to take on more assignments – they're looking out for you."*

"...taking international trips to attend interviews."

Most junior litigators remain generalists until their fourth year, when they begin to home in on a more specific practice area. However, even *"a lot of partners remain pretty broad across the spectrum."* For our interviewees, this spectrum often covered IP, appellate and investigation matters. *"I've had full responsibility for the content of amicus briefs,"* one source told us, *"from writing and submitting the brief to making the revisions and suggesting further avenues for research."* Another source had enjoyed playing *"detective"* on investigation cases, and found themselves *"drafting proposals, running productions"* and even *"taking international trips to attend interviews."* By the third year most juniors will have racked up some decent experience in the core litigator competencies. As one third year explained: *"I've done the first drafts, revisions and editing of two summary judgment motions; and the same for at least eight motions to dismiss. As far as discovery goes, I've second-chaired the defense of four depositions."*

WilmerHale's transactional department comprises corporate; tax; real estate; and bankruptcy & financial restructuring groups. Most of its juniors had joined the corporate group, and sources here revealed that they also start out broad. *"We deal with everything from emerging companies (which involves incorporating and setting them up, as well as financings) to large public companies that are undergoing IPOs or mergers and acquisitions."* On the emerging company side, juniors might be representing *"the founder who's straight out of grad school."* These venture capital-type deals mean that *"you work directly with the partners and the client from day one – at this stage in my career I'm doing the whole financing, which involves getting the documents from the other side, marking them up, liaising with the investors and drafting the primary financing agreements."* On larger M&A deals, a junior's role

See firm profile on p.709

The Inside View

Diversity	Partners (%)	Associates (%)
Women	25.4	49.6
White	88	75
Black/African American	3.6	5.6
Hispanic/Latin American	1.2	3.9
Asian	6	13.8
Mixed/Other	1.6	2
LGBT	1.2	6.1

tends to skew more toward project management, which sees them handling diligence and *"being the first point of contact for the deal. They really rely on junior associates to know the ins and outs of the deal and to keep everyone on track."*

Hours & Compensation

Thoughts on how achievable WilmerHale's 2,000-hour billable target is varied by practice group. In general, *"it's easier to hit your hours in litigation as you have a more consistent lifestyle (unless you're going to trial!),"* while in corporate *"things can be very up and down – if you have a slow month, it can be hard to bring those hours back up."* Fortunately, if juniors don't hit the target *"you don't get into trouble, but you won't have what you need to get a full Cravath bonus."* There's also a *"discretionary amount"* paid on top of the market-rate bonus if juniors get good feedback: *"There are a set of categories that they say they evaluate you on at the end of the year. I still think it boils down to the number of hours you work, but they leave room for things like community and client service, efficiency, teamwork, and participation in firm life."*

In corporate it's *"hard to give an average but ten-ish hours in the office is fairly common, as is a small amount of work at the weekend – usually just an hour or so."* When deals took off, sources had worked *"14 hours a day for a week; there was a period this fall when I was working every weekend. It really depends on what's going on – there's no consistency."* Although generally more stable, the hours in litigation can also peak around trials: *"There are times where I haven't worked after 7pm or weekends, and times when I'm doing 13 to 14 hours a day."* While these hours are fairly typical for BigLaw, insiders felt that they had a better work-life balance than they would have elsewhere.

Culture

"Nerdy" was a word that frequently cropped up during discussions of WilmerHale's vibe. Our interviewees put this down to associates' *"academic"* approach to work: *"Everyone is very open to debate and analytical about how to construct certain arguments or even a sentence. We don't just view law as a practice but as an ongoing con-*

versation about ideas." But despite a high concentration of *"individuals with highly impressive credentials,"* sources simultaneously felt that WilmerHale is a place of *"modesty,"* with one summarizing: *"Nobody is cocky here, and nobody takes credit for the work! Instead, my colleagues are generous when it comes to giving everyone credit."*

> *"We don't just view law as a practice but as an ongoing conversation about ideas."*

However, juniors did also elaborate on some perceived differences between groups. Corporate sources labeled their colleagues in litigation as *"the nerdier group"* and described themselves as *"the cooler team."* Similarly, one associate in the capital's regulatory team told us their *"conversations were more likely to be about The Bachelor and sports rather than a law review article."* (We were glad to hear that even top-notch lawyers like to indulge in trashy TV as well.) Insiders were also keen to emphasize that there's nothing *"bro-ish or frat-like"* about the atmosphere at WilmerHale, although there's a nice social life to be enjoyed if it's wanted: *"You don't have to attend social events if you don't want to! But this is the kind of place where people walk down the halls and say hello, and also keep their doors open, so there's a free exchange of conversation. Our weekly happy hours are therefore well attended, and we also have popular monthly attorney lunches."*

Offices

While WilmerHale has no official HQ, the Boston and DC offices informally serve as joint 'heads' of the firm. Together, these offices housed almost 60% of the second and third-year juniors on our list. *"The Boston office is based in a gorgeous building with spectacular views of the harbor!"* sources gushed, while also highlighting the perks of individual offices from the get-go. Our DC-based interviewees revealed: *"We're moving in five years' time,"* but for now had a very clearly defined set of pros to keep them happy: *"A good location that's right next to the metro, free coffee, a ping pong table, and a small but decent gym that's never busy."* Around a quarter of our sample were based in the New York office, which was described as *"the third power center in the network, as it's the next biggest and the fastest growing. It's an office that lures in candidates who want a more DC-type legal practice but in a New York setting, with all of its great food and art."* The rest of WilmerHale's juniors were split between its LA, Palo Alto and Denver offices. Overseas, WilmerHale has established bases in Beijing, Berlin, Brussels, Frankfurt and London.

See firm profile on p.709

Training & Development

Associates described training at Wilmer as *"very extensive."* After a few days of *"basic orientation on HR matters and how to bill time,"* newbies move swiftly on to their practice-specific sessions. On the transactional side there's 'Corporate University,' which hosts weekly trainings for the first six months. *"It takes us through the lifecycle of a company, and goes over what we should do for startups, IPOs and mergers, as well as how to do diligence and work with certain financial documents."* Litigators also get a burst of *"introductory contested matters training,"* followed by sessions across their first four months on the likes of writing and discovery. Overall juniors felt that *"they get it right. You do get a lot early on, and it can be like drinking from a fire hose, but the advantage is that you already know a whole universe of things that you could be expected to do."*

Diversity

Boston juniors felt their office wasn't *"particularly diverse,"* but did note that WilmerHale still fares better *"when compared against this legal market more generally. Boston has a very homogeneous legal environment and has always struggled with race. For women and LGBTQ lawyers it's better."* Those in DC, meanwhile, said that their base *"does feel diverse: I qualify as a diverse associate and we have regular roundtable discussion groups; there's a diversity holiday party; and I get emails every week detailing conferences I could attend."*

The firm's Women's Leadership Initiative (WLI) was repeatedly mentioned, and is broken down into office-specific groups. *"The WLI in LA is the most active by far,"* female juniors here beamed. *"We have monthly meetings and talk about different topics in the workplace and ideas for addressing certain issues. We have brought those issues to the attention of partners, and the fact that we're having these discussions is in itself a good thing."*

> ### "We have brought those issues to the attention of partners."

Strategy & Future

"We're doing very well," confident sources reported, highlighting the firm's most recent office opening in Denver in 2016, *"which demonstrated a commitment to our client base."* Others also felt that WilmerHale was *"well positioned"* for the future: *"Overall our goal is growth but at the same time we want to preserve the high-end work that we do. We'll be focusing on our strengths, and on the practice areas we do well in."* To read what co-managing partner Susan Murley has to say on WilmerHale's future, go online.

See firm profile on p.709

Wilson Sonsini Goodrich & Rosati

Lawyers per state

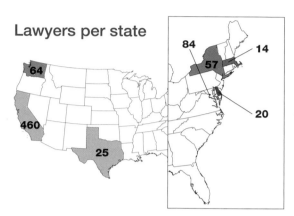

Largest US office: Palo Alto
US offices: 11
International offices: 4
First-year salary: $180,000
Billable hours: 1,950 target
Summers 2018: 48 (48 2Ls)
Revenue 2017: $797 million (+5.6%)
Partners made in 2018: 15
Famous for: Silicon Valley savvy; startup expertise

As a Silicon Valley veteran, this enterprising firm is looking for those who share its passion for technology, life sciences and emerging growth clients.

"WILSON is one of the marquee names in this market," associates in the firm's Palo Alto HQ proudly proclaimed. After planting its flag in Silicon Valley in 1961 – back when 'Silicon Valley' was still a newish nickname for the rising tech hub – Wilson immediately started working for the hippest startups and companies emerging in the area. *"There weren't a ton of large law firms here at that time, and Wilson quickly established itself as a prominent name in the technology space,"* a junior added. Today Wilson counts the likes of Google, Netflix, Tesla, Twitter and pharma company Mylan among its extensive client roster, and this collection of names proved very alluring for our sources: *"It was the technology slant that drew me. It's an exciting firm with interesting work and clients that are always coming up with new ideas,"* said one, while another told us that *"the banner headline here is the chance to work with both startups and big-name tech clients."*

However, some of our interviewees found that *"once I started here, I started working far more with life sciences clients, which turned out to be a welcome surprise."* Yes, together with emerging growth enterprises, life sciences completes Wilson's triumvirate of focuses; whether you join this firm as a deal-doer or a litigator, you can expect your work to be filtered through these specialized lenses. *"The tie that binds all the lawyers here is the affinity for*

representing the kind of companies we do," says managing partner Douglas Clark, so those with an interest and/or background in any of the above areas are very much encouraged to seek this firm out. Around 60% of Wilson's revenue comes from its corporate work, while the remaining 40% is gathered from the efforts of its litigation, IP and antitrust lawyers. *Chambers USA* especially rates Wilson's work in California, where it picks up top rankings for its M&A, venture capital, IT & outsourcing, capital markets and contentious securities expertise. It also picks up nods in DC, New York, Texas and Washington, and is considered a nationwide leader when it comes to startups and emerging companies.

Strategy & Future

"We're going to stick to our time-tested strategy, which is focusing on the representation of technology, life sciences and emerging growth enterprises," says managing partner Douglas Clark. In terms of geographic growth, Clark explains that Wilson's *"domestic footprint was rounded out with the opening of our Boston office two years ago, so we're not planning any further expansion in the US."*

"Innovation in the US drives the success of our practice."

On the subject of broader political and economic developments, Clark tells us that *"the drivers of our business are less affected by the current political landscape. Innovation in the US drives the success of our practice, and hope-*

On chambers-associate.com...

- Get hired at Wilson Sonsini
- Interview with managing partner Douglas Clark

See firm profile on p.711

The Inside View

Rankings in *Chambers USA*

Antitrust	Litigation
Capital Markets	Privacy & Data Security
Corporate/Commercial	Projects
Corporate/M&A	Securities
Employee Benefits &	Startups & Emerging
Executive Compensation	Companies
Intellectual Property	Tax
International Trade	Technology
IT & Outsourcing	Venture Capital
Life Sciences	

For detail on ranking tiers and ranking locations, visit
www.chambersandpartners.com

Recent work highlights

- Counseled Time Warner on competition issues and its strategy relating to a potential FCC review of its sale to AT&T
- Advised Yahoo! during its $4.83 billion acquisition by Verizon
- Defended Amphastar Pharmaceuticals against a $900 million patent infringement lawsuit filed by Momenta Pharmaceuticals and Novartis AG's Sandoz unit
- Represented privately-held biotech company Delinia throughout all IP matters tied to its $775 million acquisition by global pharma company Celgene

fully the government will remain somewhat out of that." For more from Clark, visit chambers-associate.com

The Work

Most of the firm's second and third-year juniors practiced within its corporate department, but the litigation group also picked up a significant number. A handful of juniors could be found honing their skills in Wilson's IP and antitrust practices.

Work allocation tends to be largely organic in most groups, although this differs slightly between teams and offices: corporate & securities juniors in the Bay Area, for example, participate in the firm's 'LAUNCH' program, which requires them to send through *"a weekly availability report, where you fill out the matters you're working on and then rank availability from 0 to 100% – it keeps partners in the know."* The program is designed to ensure that these juniors are exposed to a wide variety of matters in their first and second years at the firm. Litigators, meanwhile, explained that *"there's a bit more hand-holding when you first start, as juniors partners are assigned to keep track of your hours, but after that assignment becomes pretty informal – I like having the opportunity to say no to people if I'm too busy and yes to those I want to work with."*

Corporate juniors described working for three types of client:early stage startups; private companies that are not yet public; and *"the Googles of the world"* – large, publicly-traded companies. Sources explained that *"in corporate you get to work with a mix of these, and sample a mix of M&A deals, venture capital financings, IPOs and corporate governance matters. Associates typically cover the whole lot."* Interviewees reflected that *"a lot of the work revolves around document production, whether that's drafting financing documents or arranging filings."* On top of that, sources reported *"running diligence on IPOs and large M&A deals"* and assisting with *"regular corporate governance matters for startup companies, like producing*

board consents and stockholder consents." Working with startups gave juniors early client contact: *"At the beginning the learning curve is steep – a lot of the time you can take the lead with startups, so you end up with a lot of responsibility quickly. If they don't have an in-house lawyer, you sort of act like their general counsel."*

Many junior litigators were based in the department's securities and commercial litigation subgroup, but others were also housed in its IP/patent litigation and privacy and data protection groups. Securities and commercial *"primarily covers the regular commercial contract disputes, as well as class actions and SEC investigations on the securities side."* With the latter, juniors had been able to *"prepare interviews and sit in on them; these matters are leanly staffed, so our responsibilities are accelerated."* Other tasks included researching and writing briefs, although sources said that juniors were more likely to start conducting depositions on the commercial side of the group's work. Those in the patent group told us that *"the focus is on pharma patents, but we also do things in the hi-tech and electronics spaces too."* They added: *"If you demonstrate competence they'll give you more responsibility. I've argued a motion to compel and a motion to dismiss, and I've also taken/defended ten depositions in total."*

Culture & Get Hired

"Wilson Sonsini was one of the first Silicon Valley firms, so it embodies the pioneering spirit of its location," juniors reflected, before adding: *"But because of that, it is also an older firm – older than some of the firms that have popped up in the area. It's like the cool grandpa – it has some tradition, but it still matches current clients' needs and culture."* The firm's roots have an undeniable influence on its culture, which juniors described as *"informal, fast-paced and adaptive to what's going on in the primary sectors we service."* Many agreed that Wilson's an *"entrepreneurial place that's work-focused but also very respectful of your own time. People understand that you have commitments outside of work, and they encourage a work-life balance to the extent that that is possible within BigLaw."*

The Inside View

See firm profile on p.711

Diversity	Partners (%)	Associates (%)
Women	23.7	42.4
White	79.8	67.4
Black/African American	1.5	3
Hispanic/Latin American	5.4	3.9
Asian	12.8	20.5
Mixed/Other	0.5	5.2
LGBT	1	3

"It has some tradition, but it still matches current clients' needs and culture."

It's therefore not surprising to discover that Wilson's recruiters hunt for candidates with an entrepreneurial flair: "*They like people to take the initiative and be proactive, whether that's reaching out to colleagues to gather information, or just understanding what else can be done to help the partner and the client during a matter.*" The firm also tends to attract "*people with an interest in the start-up world, and especially those who have already worked in tech or life sciences in some way.*" For more advice on gaining an offer from Wilson, go to chambers-associate.com.

On the social side, juniors felt that the firm hits the right balance: "*Wilson holds events and promotes camaraderie, but that's not the focus.*" They noted that "*the younger associates get together quite often,*" but more seasoned attorneys tend to "*have families so aren't looking to spend a ton of time socializing outside of work.*" However, sources added that "*colleagues across levels do get beers or coffees together, and people mix well at the holiday events.*"

Offices

Wilson's Palo Alto, San Francisco and DC offices housed the majority of the firm's juniors. Its Boston, LA, New York, San Diego and Seattle offices also took on a few, while only one or two joined the firm's Austin and Wilmington bases. The Palo Alto "*mothership*" is "*right in the center of the city, which makes for an easy commute! PA is great in that it has that quiet, suburban feel, but also all the amenities that you'd expect in a big city.*" Life is pretty comfortable in the office too: "*All attorneys get their own offices, and there's a pretty flexible office movement program which allows you to request a new office if you don't like where you sit. I got a nice big office for a decent amount of time!*" Over in San Diego, excited associates told us: "*We've just finished remodeling the entire building; all of the offices have been redone with frosted glass panes and new furniture. It feels much more hip and in line with our clients!*" Overseas, Wilson has a presence in Beijing, Hong Kong, Shanghai and Brussels.

Training & Development

"*There's a bunch of formal training when you first start, which helps you get to know the firm and its policies,*" juniors reported, "*and then that's followed by subject-specific training.*" Corporate sources were especially pleased with their "*monthly meetings, which provide us with training webinars live from Palo Alto; we also have weekly trainings every Friday morning in our office, where we all take turns to present on topics, all the way from paralegals up to the managing partner of the office.*" Litigators were equally happy, and told us that "*they give you just the right amount for the next phase of your development, so they'll run deposition training at the end of your second year, for example.*"

Sources also found Wilson's "*excellent database helpful: it has all of the firm's precedents on it, and all of the firm's documents are constantly updated with annotations to give you background on how to use them and why.*" Rounding things off are Wilson's formal academy programs, which are run for associates in their first, third, fifth and seventh years at the firm. These gather all associates in the relevant year in one of the Bay Area offices for up to three days of training on a range of both professional and practice-specific skills, as well as networking strategies.

Hours & Compensation

Attorneys have to hit a 1,950 hours target to become bonus eligible, and sources were confident that "*most of us easily blow through that.*" Corporate juniors were the most optimistic, and while litigators told us that it's "*not hard to achieve,*" they did highlight that "*a decent number of people didn't reach it, but it wasn't a problem as far as we've been told.*" A hundred of these hours can be made up of non-billable work such as newsletter writing, interviews or client alerts, and juniors can also include an additional amount of shadowing hours (time spent observing senior attorneys performing high-value tasks). Bonuses are lockstep and match the market – "*people are generally happy with where we are!*"

Day to day, associates come in between 8:30am and 9:30am, and usually aim to leave anywhere between 5:30pm and 7pm. Corporate juniors "*may put in a couple of hours from home, and rarely stay later than 9pm in the office – the latest I stayed was 4:30am, but that's because a deal was closing and things needed to be done!*" IP sources found that "*there are a lot of manageable deadlines, although every once in a while something is dropped on you at the last minute,*" while litigators said: "*It's 50:50 as to whether I work at the weekend – if I do, it's always just for a couple of hours and not for a full day.*"

See firm profile on p.711

The Inside View

Pro Bono

All pro bono hours count toward Wilson's billable target. *"I billed about 300 hours last year,"* one source recalled, *"and didn't get any flak from the firm for that. People might miss a day or two at work to attend pro bono hearings, and that's completely fine and supported."* While some *"make it a point to build it into their practice,"* some juniors found that *"it can be hard to prioritize pro bono when the firm is busy."* Many sources agreed that although *"the firm as an institution is very committed, the realities of the practice can make it hard time-wise."* When associates did have the time, they reported getting involved with housing and eviction cases, child custody and guardianship matters, and a hefty amount of immigration and asylum work. Interviewees highlighted ties with multiple programs and organizations, but repeatedly mentioned Casa Cornelia Law Center, which focuses on human and civil rights violations.

Pro bono hours
- For all US attorneys: 37,593
- Average per US attorney: 72

Diversity

"I think it's quite diverse," thought one Palo Alto-based junior, *"and part of that comes from our being a Cali-based firm; we're quite well represented when it comes to LGBTQ individuals and ethnic minorities."* While this source's contemporaries agreed that representation is good at the junior level, they did highlight that the configuration *"becomes more traditional as you move up the ranks."* That is slowly changing though, and in 2017, 44% of the firm's latest partnership appointments were women or minorities. Our sources didn't speak of many formal initiatives, but did emphasize the work of Wilson's Women's Task Force: *"It's active, and hosts monthly meetings and outings that are well attended – they are trying."*

> **"Wilson Sonsini was one of the first Silicon Valley firms, so it embodies the pioneering spirit of its location."**

See firm profile on p.711

The Inside View

Winston & Strawn LLP

Lawyers per state

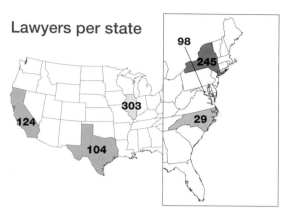

98
245
303
124
29
104

Largest US office: Chicago
US offices: 9
International offices: 7
First-year salary: $180,000
Billable hours: 2,000 required
Summers 2018: 83 (8 1Ls, 76 2Ls)
Revenue 2017: $978.5 million (+18.9%)
Partners made in 2018: 17
Famous for: Chicago's oldest firm; formidable litigators; going for growth

Winston & Strawn is embracing growth, modernity, and its associates too.

CHICAGO has produced some pretty big names over the years – generous Oprah, wizened Harrison Ford, unique Kanye… and seminal pop-punk band Fall Out Boy. But long before these folks were so much as a twinkle in their parents' eyes (even Harrison Ford), Winston & Strawn were building a Chicagoan legal legacy. Since 1853 the firm has branched further afield: there are now 16 bases in total, with international sites in locations like London, Paris and Dubai, but the firm still plays a pivotal role in the bustling Windy City. *Chambers USA* demonstrates the firm's expertise in Illinois, recognizing its credentials in areas such as labor & employment, transactional media & entertainment, IP, commercial litigation, white-collar litigation, and corporate M&A. Beyond Chi-town, highlights include an energy regulation practice in California, a shipping regulatory practice focused in DC, and a sports law team in New York.

Historically though, Winston's *"great reputation for litigation"* has been at the fore, and that had appealed to a lot of the juniors we spoke to. But this is changing. One transactional source noticed how *"at the time of interviewing, the firm didn't have that robust of a corporate practice, but since I've joined they've been acquiring more corporate groups, so it's turned out to be a great decision."* As well as a new Dallas office, the firm brought in a number of energy

lawyers, all of which underscore the firm's hefty appetite for growth. It's not done yet.

The Work

Over half of juniors could be found in litigation, a quarter in corporate, with the rest split between labor & employment, tax, real estate, energy, and employee benefits. The majority of groups gain work through a free-market system. *"You, the associate, are in the driver's seat. It's a matter of you approaching folks to engage with them. You can explore different types of matters and figure out what the firm has going on."*

And this isn't just limited to an associate's office: cross-staffing was rife throughout the firm's network. One junior recalled: *"I had an interest in antitrust work, but there wasn't much of that in my office. I expressed my interest and they were able to put me in touch with people in other offices."* Juniors appreciated that *"you have control over your work – the type, who you work with, the workflow. You are responsible for your career path early on."* Alternatively, if juniors are struggling to find work, *"a safeguard"* comes in the form of assigning partners.

"You, the associate, are in the driver's seat."

Litigation associates usually keep things quite general when they start. They're free to focus on specific sub-groups down the line if they desire, but the free-market system means the work they've picked up so far *"doesn't preclude you from branching off."* So sources had sampled heavily across a *"wide array of litigation matters"*: com-

On chambers-associate.com...

- Get hired at Winston & Strawn
- Interviews with managing partner Tom Fitzgerald and hiring partner Bill O'Neil

See firm profile on p.712

Rankings in *Chambers USA*

Advertising	Labor & Employment
Antitrust	Latin American Investment
Banking & Finance	Litigation
Bankruptcy/Restructuring	Media & Entertainment
Corporate/M&A	Projects
Energy & Natural	Sports Law
Resources	Tax
Intellectual Property	Transportation
International Trade	

For detail on ranking tiers and ranking locations, visit
www.chambersandpartners.com

Recent work highlights

- Won a victory for Beef Products in a defamation lawsuit against ABC, who had referred to its produce as 'pink slime'
- Acted for Goldman Sachs, Merrill Lynch, Credit Suisse and Morgan Lewis in the dismissal of a class action brought by shareholders of Party City against the party supplies company
- Represented The Chamberlain Group against Ryobi, a hardware manufacturer, achieving the verdict that Ryobi infringed two patents relating to a garage door opener and backup battery
- Represented Siligan Holdings, a consumer goods packaging supplier, in its $1.023 billion acquisition of WestRock Company, a dispensing systems business

plex commercial litigation, securities work, white-collar and regulatory work, antitrust, IP, and appellate. *"You name it, we probably do it,"* one added. And, as a large firm, *"the clientele runs the gamut of large corporate and institutional types – banks, insurance companies, electronics companies, steel producers and pharmaceutical companies, to name a few."*

Litigation juniors had reason to be happy. *"I've had a fair amount of substantive work early on. Within two months I drafted a motion to dismiss, which was really cool!"* For the most part though, this occurred on smaller cases. Sources admitted that *"with the bigger cases, it's usually more discovery-related things and a bit of doc review, though we do have an in-house doc review team, and we outsource some of it too."* Reflecting on it all, one source felt *"it's a good mix of substantive experience, without being thrown to the wolves."* Other tasks included drafting of briefs and pleadings, legal research and witness prep. *"They don't say 'once you're in X year you can do X tasks' – they do a good job of not pigeonholing you. Your responsibility depends on how the case is staffed, but also on what you've shown you're able to do."*

Over on the growing corporate side, attorneys usually end up leaning toward a particular area, such as M&A, securities work or finance. *"It's more typical to have a larger variety of work when you first start, then whittle it down."* Typical M&A work is usually *"middle market"* with larger, billion-dollar deals cropping up from time to time. Juniors started out *"drafting ancillaries, reviewing disclosure schedules and reviewing contracts,"* but could move on to oversee the diligence process. Again, there's an array of clients from diverse industries, but finance folks had mostly represented lenders (mostly banks and private equity funds). Those focused specifically on securities were *"doing daily securities filings, and a lot of drafting of the deal documents for bond deals."* One associate told us: *"It really depends on the partner. One partner has me doing a lot of the micromanaging because they're very big picture focused. I'd say it's 50:50 overall in terms*

of good substantive experience – there's still a lot that is outside of your wheelhouse."

Offices

Most of the firm's junior associates are based in Chicago or New York. DC has a little over ten, and the Dallas, LA and San Fran offices each have a handful. A select few also reside in Houston, Silicon Valley and Charlotte.

There was a buzz among folks in the Chicago headquarters, who each mentioned a recently built cafe: *"It's something they show every new recruit! Attorneys and staff can meet there and have lunch. There are coffee machines and pop machines, and TVs."* Juniors also praised the office location – each associate gets a window office with *"amazing views, as we're right on the river, overlooking Lake Michigan."* New Yorkers, who typically share an office to begin with, are stationed on top of Grand Central Terminal – *"once you're off the train you're basically at work."* That office is currently undergoing a renovation, while LA has just completed its own renovation, and comes complete with *"a wellness room – you can take a blanket in there if you're really tired!"*

Culture

"Winston is perceived as being pretty conservative, but I haven't felt that as much as I would have expected. It's been shifting – maybe ten years ago that perception was right, but recently the firm has put a lot of equity into its associates, focusing on training, longevity, happiness and diversity." Nowadays, juniors felt that *"all that's left of that old-fashioned legal conservatism is the Chicago office's old-fashioned look!"* Pushing preconceptions aside, associates summarized: *"There's a lot of hard-working people here, but they're also really personable and willing to help you out. They also understand the need to have a life outside of work."*

See firm profile on p.712

Diversity	Partners (%)	Associates (%)
Women	22.5	44
White	90	74
Black/African American	1.7	5.6
Hispanic/Latin American	3	5.3
Asian	4.3	9.5
Mixed/Other	0.7	5.3
LGBT	1.2	3.5

"The firm has put a lot of equity into its associates, focusing on training, longevity, happiness, and diversity."

Accordingly, the social side is also alive and well: in Chicago, attorneys have *"a weekly happy hour every Friday."* In classy New York, this is more commonly known as *"Martini Friday"* and is organized around a theme; prior themes have included Chinese New Year and the Oscars. During the summer, juniors were able to go to Cubs games, go on boat trips, and one remembered: *"Our year did a casino night where the firm brought in private dealers just for us."*

Hours & Compensation

Attorneys have a billing target of 2,000 hours, 1,900 of which must be *"hard billables"* – the other 100 can be pro bono, or 50 hours of firm citizenship and investment work. This includes working on things like pitches or recruitment. Sources felt that that allowance made a difference: *"When you take into account pro bono hours, it makes it much more attainable."* After associates hit their 2,000-hour target, any hours in excess of that (whether hard billables, pro bono or firm citizenship/investment contributions) go toward a further bonus.

"People are usually reasonable, but it's a roller-coaster."

On an average day, most sources were in the office for 9am and out by 6pm. *"Partners will often leave between 5 and 6pm, go home, eat with their family and then log on at night. That has trickled down; associates will do the same thing."* There's no formal vacation policy, and interviewees noted the level of informality. *"There's nobody waiting by my door to see if I get in at a specific time – there's no expectation for you to be in the office for the sake of it."* But, not to sugarcoat things, it's important to stress that associates are still exposed to fluctuations. *"When deals are closing it can be more like a midnight or 1am finish,"* said one corporate associate, while another told us: *"In the first three months of the year you will usually be leaving at eight or later."* Likewise, *"it's just the nature of litigation – people are usually reasonable, but it's a roller-coaster."*

Diversity

Associates struck a note of optimism on gender diversity. The firm's gender-neutral parental leave policy (which provides 20 weeks' paid leave) won praise from associates, who felt confident that *"at least in the near future, firm stewardship will have a fairer representation in terms of female partnership."* Many noted the appointment of Linda Coberly as the firm's first female managing partner of the Chicago office as a positive step in this direction (the Silicon Valley and San Francisco offices are also headed up by women).

"We realized that's not enough, and wanted to do more."

On ethnic diversity, associates felt that *"it's an area where the firm is improving."* Winston recently hired a new director of diversity and inclusion, Sylvia James, and has a full-time diversity committee that works alongside the firm's hiring committee to address diversity in recruiting. Hiring partner Bill O'Neil tells us more about the firm's plans to boost diversity: *"For our 2018 summer class, we are expanding our 1L program for diverse law students in partnership with the LCLD [Leadership Council on Legal Diversity]. Five to seven diverse 1L summers will join us this summer, and hopefully we'll make a favorable impression on them so that they rejoin us next summer. They will also be able to join a different office for their 2L summer."* Winston also has multiple affinity groups and recently *"sent a number of diverse attorneys to a conference in Orlando called Charting Your Own Course."* It is also a signatory of the Mansfield Rule.

Training & Development

Winston's 'Jumpstart' training program for juniors starts with a weeklong orientation, which brings *"all first years together in Chicago."* Once back in their respective offices, the program continues with ongoing department-specific training. *"There's also specialized sessions for different subgroups. Not all sessions are applicable to your practice, but you can pick and choose which to go to."* Litigators reported having trainings on depositions, and then *"once every couple of years they do a full mock trial and bring in actors."*

Reviews occur annually. *"In your first two years you get a summary review where you find out if you're doing well or not. From the following year, it's a real review. You get comments from everyone you've worked for and they assign you a number grade."* Two partners conduct the review, one of whom associates will have worked with. Associates also receive a written report summarizing the review.

See firm profile on p.712

Pro Bono

Every interviewee agreed on the firm's stance regarding pro bono: *"It's a high priority at our firm. They want all attorneys to be engaged in pro bono services."* Sources highlighted: *"They were pushing for 100% of attorneys to do at least 20 hours, and we were in the high 90s."* Although 20 hours is the minimum, the internal goal is said to be 35 hours. *"Obviously billable work is the priority, but there's respect for pro bono, so if there's an urgent deadline on a pro bono matter, the teams are respectful and you can devote time to that."*

As with billable work, associates could choose their own path. *"The firm is partnered with different organizations, but if you ever want a specific opportunity, you can let the pro bono department know and they'll work to find you something."* Juniors had worked on a range of matters, including juvenile defense matters, veteran work, asylum cases, discharge upgrades, and a significant amount of immigration work for the National Immigration Justice Center. One unique case involved *"defending a bunch of Star Trek fans who had written a fan-film and were being sued for copyright infringement."* They reached a settlement, so the fans can continue to live long and prosper...

Pro bono hours
- For all attorneys: 65,000
- Average per attorney: 73.5

Strategy & Future

The firm has recently changed its partnership structure, going from a two-tier structure (equity and non-equity partners) to a one-tier structure. That's a good thing for associates' career prospects, an issue the firm has looked at improving, but lateral hiring has accelerated too. Managing partner Tom Fitzgerald highlights: *"Since January 1, 2017, we've hired 89 partners, which is a record number for us."* Going forward, the plan is to *"fully integrate all these individuals that have come our way – that is very important to us. We think we can bring a lot of different services to clients that we haven't previously had the opportunity to do."* The firm has some serious momentum behind it, and Fitzgerald's *"most immediate goal"* is crystal clear: *"Revenues over one billion dollars."*

Get Hired

"Attitude, effort, and exuberance go a long way. A huge selling point is when someone can express their passion about wanting to come work with us," says hiring partner Bill O'Neil. To get as much insight as possible about recruitment at Winston, head online.

See firm profile on p.712

The Inside View

Leading Law Firms

Adam Leitman Bailey, P.C.

One Battery Park Plaza, Eighteenth Floor, New York, NY 10004

Tel: 212 825 0365   Fax: 212 825 0999
Email: info@alblawfirm.com
Firm website: www.alblawfirm.com
Linkedin: adam-leitman-bailey-p.c.

Twitter: @ALB_PC
Facebook: AdamLeitmanBaileyPC
Instagram: @alb_pc

Main areas of work

- Real Estate

Firm profile

By uniting many of the best real estate attorneys of our generation, Adam Leitman Bailey, PC has become one of New York's most prominent real estate law firms. The firm excels by solely practicing real estate law and only taking on projects and cases where it is among the best in the field. Adam Leitman Bailey, PC has achieved groundbreaking results in the courtroom, in the board room, at the closing table, in the lobbies of legislative bodies and in every other venue where talented legal advocacy is key to its clients' interests.

Recruitment

Recruitment outside OCIs:

Adam Leitman Bailey, PC advertise for externship positions on our website as well as through various law schools (i.e. New York Law School, Rutgers, Hofstra, and others).

Summer associate profile:

We choose the most talented applicants. When interviewing candidates for these positions, we look to see whether they have the potential to be great at our firm. Once we hire someone, the training, mentoring and teaching never stops. We strive for greatness in everything we do and expect our interns to do the same. We encourage you to express your opinions and share your ideas to improve our work.

Summer program components:

Our interns become lawyers in training and are part of the legal team and learn on the case or deal. Being assigned to active cases and made part of the team has given externs and interns the ability to produce amazing results. Only the very best law school students will make it at Adam Leitman Bailey, PC as we are considered among the best, if not the best, real estate law firm in New York City. Because Adam Leitman Bailey, PC practices only one type of law, all of our associates rapidly become experts. We have exciting cases that require hard work and sweat as well as the smartest most aggressive, passionate, loyal and committed students who are ready to change the world one real estate case at a time.

Interns will participate in a wide range of tasks that may include conducting case investigation, legal research and discovery; meeting with clients and experts; and preparing memoranda, briefs and other legal documents for administrative, judicial and transactional proceedings.

Head Office: **New York, NY**
Number of domestic offices: **1**
Number of international offices: **0**
Partners (US): **8**
Associates (US): **17**
Languages spoken: **13**

Contacts
Main recruitment contact:
Brianna Loverich
(bloverich@alblawfirm.com)
Hiring partner: **Adam Leitman Bailey**
Diversity officer: **Adam Leitman Bailey**

Recruitment details
Entry-level associates starting in 2018: **2**
Clerking policy: **Yes**
We offer externships for the Fall and Spring semesters and an associate program during the summer
Summers joining/anticipated 2018: **2 based in New York**
Summer salary 2018:
1Ls/2Ls/3Ls: **$11/hour**
Split summers offered? **No**

ADAM LEITMAN BAILEY, P.C.
NEW YORK REAL ESTATE ATTORNEYS

Firm Profiles

Akin Gump Strauss Hauer & Feld LLP

1333 New Hampshire Ave, NW, Washington, DC 20036

Tel: 202 887 4000   Fax: 202 887 4288
Recruitment website: www.akingump.com/en/careers
Linkedin: akin-gump-strauss-hauer-&-feld-llp

Twitter: @akin_gump

Main areas of work

Antitrust, communications and information technology, corporate, cybersecurity, privacy and data protection, energy, entertainment and media, environment and natural resources, financial restructuring, global project finance, government contracts, healthcare, intellectual property, international arbitration, international trade, investment funds, labor and employment, litigation, mergers and acquisitions, pro bono, public law and policy, real estate, Supreme Court and appellate and tax.

Firm profile

Akin Gump is a leading global law firm with more than 900 lawyers and advisors in the United States, Europe, Asia and the Middle East. The firm is widely recognized for its strength in transactional work, litigation, and regulatory and public policy, which allow the firm to provide a comprehensive suite of service for governments, companies and individuals worldwide. Collegiality, commitment, excellence, integrity and intensity form the bedrock of Akin Gump's core values. Akin Gump's dedication to the advancement of these values guides relationships within the firm and, most importantly, with its clients.

Recruitment

Law Schools attending for OCIs in 2018:

American, Berkeley, Boston University, Cardozo, Catholic, Columbia, Cornell, Duke, Emory, Fordham, George Mason, George Washington, Georgetown, Harvard, Howard, Houston, Michigan, New York University, Penn, UC Irvine, UCLA, USC, SMU, Stanford, Texas, Tulane, Vanderbilt, Virginia, Washington University, William & Mary

Recruitment outside OCIs:

Lavender Law, Loyola PLIP, On Tour Interview Program (CA), South West Region Black Law Student Association Job Fair

Summer associate profile:

Akin Gump seeks motivated candidates with outstanding academic credentials, overall achievement, leadership and interpersonal skills, and work experience. In addition, the firm looks for candidates who demonstrate the firm's core competencies: ownership, professional excellence, service and teamwork and client focus.

Summer program components:

Akin Gump summer associates work on real matters for real clients. Summer associates gain in-depth exposure to the firm's practice and hands-on experience with clients and work that interests them. With training, mentorship, teamwork and social activities, summer associates get a realistic and meaningful picture of firm life. Summer associates participate in pro bono projects through organisations with which Akin Gump has a pro bono partnership. These projects are geared to a summer associates' interests and maximize front-line responsibility while ensuring appropriate supervision from experienced attorneys. Summer associates receive feedback on a project-by-project basis and at mid-summer and end of summer reviews.

Number of domestic offices: 11
Number of international offices: 9
Worldwide revenue: $1,039,000,000
Partners (US): 267
Associates (US): 386

Contacts
Main recruitment contact:
David H Botter, Firmwide Hiring Partner.
For a complete listing of our recruiting contacts go to:
www.akingump.com/en/careers/lawyers/recruiting-process/contact-us.html
Diversity officer: Michele Meyer-Shipp, Chief Diversity & Inclusion Officer

Recruitment details
Entry-level associates starting in 2018: 53
Clerking policy: Yes
Summers joining/anticipated 2018:
1Ls: 13 - 15, 2Ls: 54, SEOs: 4
Summers joining/anticipated 2018 split by office: Dallas 1Ls: 3 and 2Ls: 7
Houston 1Ls: 3 and 2Ls: 7
Los Angeles 1Ls: 1 and 2Ls: 8
New York 1Ls: 3 - 5 and 2Ls: 18
Philadelphia 2L: 1
Washington, DC 1Ls: 3 and 2Ls: 13
Summer salary 2018:
1Ls: $3,500/week
2Ls: $3,500/week
1Ls hired? In some offices and through our Pro Bono Scholars Program
Split summers offered? Case by case
Can summers spend time in an overseas office? No

Akin Gump
STRAUSS HAUER & FELD LLP

Allen & Overy LLP

221 Avenue of the Americas, New York, NY 10020

Tel: 212 610 6300   Fax: 212 610 6399
Email: legalcareers@allenovery.com
Recruitment website: www.us.aograduate.com
Linkedin: allen-&-overy

Main areas of work

Banking, corporate, international capital markets, litigation, project finance, financial restructuring and insolvency, general lending, leveraged finance and tax.

Firm profile

We are one of a group of truly international and integrated law firms with approximately 5,000 people working in 44 cities in 30 countries. This network has allowed us to become one of the largest and most connected law firms in our peer group with a global reach and local depth that is simply unrivalled. As more than 65% of our work involves more than two countries, our US practice—which operates principally from offices in Hong Kong, London, New York and Washington DC—is fully integrated with our offices in Europe, Asia, South America, Australia and Africa. We believe we have a special culture at Allen & Overy, which is founded on quality work, excellent working partnerships and collegiality.

Recruitment

Law Schools attending for OCIs in 2018:

- Albany Law School
- Brooklyn Law School
- Cardozo Law School
- Columbia Law School
- Duke University School of Law
- Fordham University School of Law
- Georgetown Law School
- Harvard Law School
- Howard University School of Law
- New York University School of Law
- Northwestern University Law School
- UCLA School of Law
- University of Chicago Law School
- University of Michigan Law School
- University of Pennsylvania Law School
- University of Virginia School of Law

Recruitment outside OCIs:

For a full list job fairs and resume collects we participate in please visit:

www.us.aograduate.com/Meet-Us/In-Your-Area/

Summer associate profile:

At Allen & Overy, we operate in a dynamic, challenging environment which fosters creativity as well as professionalism. Our attorneys handle the most sophisticated and complex domestic and cross border transactions and cases for our clients. The ideal candidate should possess determination, vision, creativity, strength and breadth of character. He or she should be committed to working as part of an international team. One of the best features of the Allen & Overy team is the strength of the personal and professional relationships formed between colleagues. We maintain strong camaraderie around the world.

Summer program components:

We recruit on campus for all four summer programs (New York, London, Hong Kong and Washington, DC). We typically host around 18-20 summer associates in New York, three to four in London, one to two Hong Kong and four to five in Washington DC. Summer associates are treated as full-time associates and we make a point of offering considerable responsibility, working on top-quality transactions in various areas. We place great value on feedback and go to great lengths to match individual preferences with the work we assign. Summer associates can expect to receive ample partner attention and to gain invaluable experience. We take mentoring and development seriously and both are fundamental aspects of our program. We also expect our summer associates to have fun and plan social events to integrate them into our firm culture.

Head office: New York, NY
Number of domestic offices: 2
Number of international offices: 42
Partners (US): 45
Senior Counsel (US): 12
Associates (US): 128

Contacts
Main recruitment contact:
Erin Manna,
Manager of Lateral Recruitment
Hiring partners: Charles Borden (DC),
Laura Hall (NY)
Diversity officer: Elizabeth Leckie, Partner

Recruitment details
Entry-level associates starting in 2018: 21
Clerking policy: Yes
Summers joining/anticipated 2018:
2Ls: 22, 3Ls: 0, SEO: 0
Summers joining/anticipated 2018 split
by office: NY: 1
Summer salary 2018:
2Ls: $ 3,500/week
Post 3Ls: $3,500/week
Split summers offered? Occasionally,
summer associates have spent time in
other offices with US capabilities on a
case by case basis
Can summers spend time in an overseas
office? Yes, we run parallel summer associate programs in New York, London,
Hong Kong and Washington DC.

ALLEN & OVERY

Alston & Bird LLP

One Atlantic Center, 1201 West Peachtree Street, Atlanta, GA 30309-3424

Tel: 404 881 7000   Fax: 404 881 7777
Email: erin.springer@alston.com
Recruitment website: www.alston.com/en/careers
Linkedin: alston-&-bird-llp

Twitter: @AlstonBirdLLP
Facebook: Alston-Bird-LLP

Main areas of work

Alston & Bird provides a full range of services to domestic and international clients. Our core practice areas are intellectual property, complex litigation, corporate, and tax, with national industry focuses in healthcare, financial services and public policy.

Firm profile

Founded in 1893, Alston & Bird is a leading national AmLaw 50 firm. Counseling clients from what was initially a local context quickly expanded to regional, then national levels and now spans a global economic environment. Alston & Bird has overlaid its broad range of legal skills and business knowledge with a commitment to innovation and technology. Alston & Bird has been ranked on *Fortune* magazine's '100 Best Companies to Work For' list for 19 consecutive years, an unprecedented accomplishment among law firms in the United States. The recognition speaks to the culture of the firm and the environment in which we practice law and provide service to clients. Alston & Bird has been consistently recognized as a US law firm providing superior client service in the *BTI Most Recommended Law Firms*. This recognition results from interviews with approximately 300 corporate counsel at Fortune 1000 companies.

Recruitment

Law Schools attending for OCIs in 2018:

American, Cardozo, Columbia, Cornell, Duke, Emory, Fordham, Georgetown, George Washington, Georgia, Georgia State, Harvard, Hofstra, Howard, Loyola – LA, Mercer, Michigan, NYU, Northwestern, SMU, Stanford, Texas, UC Berkeley, UC Hastings, UC Irvine, UCLA, UNC, USC, Vanderbilt, Virginia, Wake Forest, Washington & Lee

Recruitment outside OCIs:

BC/BU Job Fair, Georgia State Southeastern IP Job Fair, Lavender Law, Loyola Patent Interview Program, NEBLSA Regional Job Fair, Pennsylvania (ATL Program), Sunbelt Minority Job Fair

Summer associate profile:

Our lawyers have diverse backgrounds, varied social, cultural, civic, and educational interests and our summer associates are no exception. We value hard work, scholastic excellence and strong interpersonal skills.

Summer program components:

Our summer program provides students with substantive work for real clients, hands-on training opportunities, lawyer pairings to help foster relationships, and a firm-wide retreat. Summer associates work closely with their mentors to identify projects from our database that will allow for an authentic experience based on their legal interests. In addition to formal training programs, we offer out-of-office experiences to attend depositions, client meetings, hearings and other hands-on learning experiences. Associate contacts ensure that summer associates have plenty of opportunities to interact with attorneys throughout the summer.

Head Office: Atlanta, GA
Number of domestic offices: 9
Number of international offices: 2
Worldwide revenue: $730,579,255
Partners (US): 345
Associates (US): 366

Contacts
Main recruitment contact: Erin L Springer
(erin.springer@alston.com)
Hiring Partner: Elizabeth A Price
Diversity officers: Cari Dawson and John Latham

Recruitment details
Entry-level associates starting in 2018: 46
Clerking policy: Yes
Summers joining/anticipated 2018:
1Ls: 9, 2Ls: 46
Summers joining/anticipated 2018 split by office: Atlanta (ATL): 26,
Charlotte (CLT): 9, Dallas (DFW): 4,
Los Angeles (LAX): 2, New York (NYC): 7,
Raleigh (RTA): 1, Silicon Valley (SVA): 4,
Washington, DC (WDC): 2
Summer salary 2018:
1Ls: $3,000/week (ATL, CLT, RTA) or $3,5000/week (DFW, LAX, NYC, SVA, WDC)
2Ls: $3,000/week (ATL, CLT, RTA) or $3,5000/week (DFW, LAX, NYC, SVA, WDC)
Split summers offered? Yes, first half required
Can summers spend time in an overseas office? No

ALSTON & BIRD

Arnold & Porter Kaye Scholer LLP

601 Massachusetts Avenue, NW. Washington, DC 20001-3743

Tel: 202 942 5000 Fax: 202 942 5999
Email: recruiting@arnoldporter.com
Recruitment website: www.arnoldporter.com/en/careers
Linkedin: Arnold & Porter Kaye Scholer LLP

Twitter: @arnoldporter
Facebook:
Arnold-Porter-Kaye-Scholer-LLP

Main areas of work

Our 1,000+ attorneys in 13 offices practice across more than 30 areas, including antitrust, corporate and finance, intellectual property, life sciences and healthcare regulatory, litigation, real estate, and tax, provide clients a multi-disciplinary approach to their most complex legal issues.

Firm profile

Arnold & Porter is recognized for its regulatory experience, sophisticated litigation and transactional practitioners, and leading multidisciplinary practices. We are the firm of choice for 133 Fortune 250 companies. The firm's core values of excellence in the practice of law, maintaining the highest standards of ethics and professionalism, respecting and promoting diversity and individuality among our colleagues, and maintaining a deep commitment to public service and pro bono work, keep us grounded, focused, and evolving to meet new opportunities and challenges.

Recruitment

Law Schools attending for OCIs in 2018:

Arnold & Porter interviews students from over 40 law schools across the country.
Please visit our website for a complete list of job fairs and on campus interview programs.

www.arnoldporter.com/en/careers/law-students-trainee-solicitors/careers-recruiting-events

Recruitment outside OCIs:

Please visit our website for interviewing and application options outside of OCIs.

www.arnoldporter.com/en/careers/law-students-trainee-solicitors/careers-recruiting-events

Summer associate profile:

Our firm is a collection of independent, diverse personalities who share a common devotion to first class legal work and client service. We seek candidates with outstanding academic and extracurricular achievements, relevant work experience, as well as strong interpersonal skills and references.

Summer program components:

Our summer associates experience first-hand the firm's strong commitment to excellence, diversity, pro bono work, and professional development, working side-by-side with our attorneys on actual client matters. We seek to match assignments to the interests each summer associate has identified, including pro bono work. Our summer associates participate in the firm's extensive training programs, including attending a retreat in one of the firm's US offices. All summer associates have mentors and receive feedback on each assignment. Our summer program features a mix of events designed to appeal to a broad range of interests.

Number of domestic offices: 9
Number of international offices: 4
Worldwide revenue: $951.5 million
Partners (US): 299
Associates (US): 467 (includes 47 staff attorneys)

Contacts
Main recruitment contact:
Jennifer Gewertz, Firmwide Director of Attorney Recruiting
Hiring partners: Ellen Fleishhacker, Catherine Schumacher, Darren Skinner
Diversity officer: Anand Agneshwar, Diversity & Inclusion Committee Chair; Brenda Carr, Director of Diversity & Inclusion

Recruitment details
Entry-level associates starting in 2018:
Anticipated 56 (includes 8 clerks)
Clerking policy: Yes
Summers joining/anticipated 2018:
1Ls: 8, 2Ls: 57, 3Ls: 0, SEO: 0
Summers joining/anticipated 2018 split by office:
Washington DC: 33, New York: 17,
San Francisco/Silicon Valley: 6,
Denver: 3, Chicago: 2, Houston: 2,
Los Angeles: 2
Summer salary 2018:
1Ls: $3,465/week
2Ls: $3,465/week
Split summers offered? Case by case
Can summers spend time in overseas office? No

Arnold & Porter

Axinn, Veltrop & Harkrider LLP

114 West 47th Street, New York, NY 10036

Tel: 212 728 2200   Fax: 212 728 2201
Email: recruiting@axinn.com
Recruitment website: www.axinn.com
Linkedin: axinn-veltrop-&-harkrider-llp

Main areas of work

Antitrust, intellectual property and complex litigation.

Firm profile

Axinn is a different kind of law firm. It combines the skills, experience and dedication of the world's largest firms with the focus, responsiveness, efficiency and attention to client needs of the best boutiques. Axinn was established in the late 1990s by lawyers from premier Wall Street firms with a common vision and has been joined by lawyers from the best firms and law schools who share that vision. Axinn is devoted to providing the highest conceivable quality of service in three practice areas: antitrust, intellectual property and high-stakes litigation. Axinn achieves that goal through world class skills and deep trial experience. Time and again, major companies have turned to Axinn for their biggest deals and cases, often on the eve of trial.

Recruitment

Law Schools attending for OCIs in 2018:

Berkeley, UChicago, Columbia, UConn, Duke, Fordham, George Mason, George Washington, Georgetown, Harvard, UMichigan, NYU, UPenn, Stanford, UVA, Washington University in St Louis, Yale

Recruitment outside OCIs:

We visit various diversity and practice group focused job fairs, including NEBLSA and the Patent Law Interview Program.

Summer associate profile:

Axinn is a top tier boutique practicing in antitrust, IP and high-stakes litigation. It seeks students who have achieved academic excellence and are entrepreneurial. Candidates must be among the top 25% of their law school class. Top 10% class ranking, law review and moot court experience is preferred. For the antitrust group, Axinn prefers that candidates have an economic or finance degree/background. Science or engineering backgrounds are preferred for candidates who wish to work in IP. Patent bar admission is a plus for IP candidates.

Summer program components:

During their summer with Axinn, associates attend internal meetings and seminars to familiarize themselves with lawyers, clients and a range of projects that comprise our practice. In addition, Axinn attorneys and outside professionals provide training in such topics as legal writing, litigation strategy and how to effectively utilize firm resources and support services. Each training experience emphasizes *'learning by doing'* and serves to enhance opportunities for summer associates to develop, exercise and build confidence in their skills. Each summer associate is assigned a partner and associate mentor, who are available to prioritize assignments and act as a sounding board. Axinn combines the prestige of a large firm with the collegiality of a boutique. Summer associates are invited to join events such as wine tastings, theater, sporting and museum outings and cooking classes.

Head Office: New York, NY
Number of domestic offices: 3
Number of international offices: 0
Partners (US): 25
Associates (US): 40

Contacts
Main recruitment contact: Rachel Rosado (rrosado@axinn.com)
Hiring partners: Daniel Bitton, Jeremy Lowe and Thomas Rohback
Diversity officer: Jeremy Lowe

Recruitment details
Entry-level associates starting in 2018: 7
Clerking policy: Case by case basis
Summers joining/anticipated 2018: 9
2Ls: 9
Summers joining/anticipated 2018 split by office: New York: 4, Hartford: 2, Washington DC: 3
Summer salary 2018:
2Ls: $ 3,461 per week
Split summers offered? Case by case basis

Baker Botts LLP

One Shell Plaza, 910 Louisiana, Houston, Texas 77002-4995

Tel: 713 229 1234   Fax: 713 229 1522
E-mail: recruiting@bakerbotts.com
Recruitment website: www.bakerbotts.com/lawstudents/
Linkedin: baker-botts-llp

Twitter: @bakerbotts
Facebook: BakerBottsLLP
Instagram: @bakerbotts

Main areas of work

Based on our broad experience and our in-depth knowledge of our clients' industries, we are recognized as a leading firm in energy and technology. Core practice areas include project development and finance; corporate transactions; complex business litigation; international arbitration; antitrust; intellectual property; environmental; compliance and enforcement; tax; employee benefits; and real estate.

Firm profile

Baker Botts is a globally respected law firm with 725 lawyers and 14 international offices. We are driven by the highest ethical and professional standards. This professionalism, combined with industry knowledge and insights and our understanding of the law, helps us to deliver effective, innovative solutions for our clients.

For more than 175 years, Baker Botts has delivered results-oriented services, establishing us as a leading law firm. Our reputation is complemented by our leadership in government, the judiciary and our communities. Regardless of size, sector or jurisdiction of a client, our commitment is to help achieve their business objectives

Recruitment

Law Schools attending for OCIs in 2018:

Baylor, Berkeley, Cardozo, Chicago, Columbia, Cornell, Duke, Fordham, Georgetown, George Washington, Harvard, Houston, Loyola Patent Program, Michigan, Northwestern, Notre Dame, NYU, Pennsylvania, SMU, St. John, Stanford, Texas, UC Hastings, UCLA, UC Davis, USC, Vanderbilt, Virginia, Washington University, Yale, Bay Area Diversity Career Fair, Boston College/ Boston University Job Fair, Harvard BLSA Job Fair, Lavender Law Job Fair, San Francisco IP Job Fair, Southeastern Minority Job Fair, Texas in NY and DC Job Fairs, Veterans Legal Career Fair.

Recruitment outside OCIs:

Write-ins, Referrals, Judicial Clerkships, Baker Botts Winter 1L Open House (all US offices)

Summer associate profile:

Baker Botts lawyers are selected from the top graduates among the best law schools. We have formally established a set of core attributes we seek in candidates; some of which include leadership, collegiality, dedication, and commitment to excellence.

Summer program components:

Our philosophy is to allow summer associates to sample work in practice areas in which they are interested. Written and oral work evaluations are strongly encouraged and monitored. Each summer associate has both partner and associate advisors. All summer associates receive formal performance evaluations during the summer program. Baker Weekend, the cornerstone of our summer program, brings together summer associates and lawyers from all seven of our U.S. offices for a weekend of training and social events. Our summer associates learn about our firm through interactive panel discussions and informal break-out sessions with firm leadership and enjoy socializing with each other and our attorneys in a fun, casual setting.

Head Office: Houston, TX
Number of domestic offices: 7
Number of international offices: 7
Partners (US): 243
Associates (US): 340

Contacts
Main recruitment contact:
Elizabeth Krichmar, Director of Recruiting
Hiring partner: John Martin,
Partner-in-Charge, Recruiting
Diversity officer: Kathy Bowman-Williams,
Director of Diversity

Recruitment details
Entry-level associates starting in 2018: 56
Clerking policy: Yes
Summers joining/anticipated 2018: 103
(1Ls: 32, 2Ls: 71)
Summers joining/anticipated 2018 by office: Austin: 13, Dallas: 23,
Houston: 32, New York: 16, Palo Alto: 6,
San Francisco: 4, DC: 9
Summer Salary 2018:
1Ls: $3,642/week
2Ls: $3,642/week
Post 3Ls: $3,642/week
1Ls hired? Yes
Split summers offered? Splits between
offices are limited and available on a
case-by-case basis
Can summers spend time in overseas
office? No

BAKER BOTTS

Bracewell LLP

711 Louisiana St., Suite 2300, Houston, TX 77002

Tel: 713 223 2300   Fax: 800 404 3970
Email: recruiting@bracewell.com
Recruitment website: www.bracewell.com/careers
Linkedin: Bracewell LLP

Twitter: @BracewellLaw
Facebook: bracewell.llp
Instagram: @bracewellllp

Main areas of work

- Antitrust/Competition
- Corporate & Securities
- Energy
- Environmental Strategies
- Finance
- Financial Institutions
- Financial Restructuring
- Government
- Intellectual Property
- International Practice
- Labor & Employment
- Litigation
- Private Investment Funds
- Public Finance
- Real Estate & Projects
- Strategic Communications
- Tax
- Technology
- White Collar Defense, Internal Investigations & Regulatory Enforcement

Head Office: Houston, TX
Number of domestic offices: 8
Number of international offices: 2
Worldwide revenue: $278,698,000
Partners (US): 158
Associates (US): 196

Contacts
Main recruitment contact:
Jennifer Queen, Chief Talent Officer
Hiring Partners: Austin: Victoria Ozimek
Dallas: Jon Leatherberry
Houston: Cle Dade and Chris Dodson
New York: David Ball
Washington, DC: Kirk Morgan

Recruitment details
Entry-level associates starting in 2018: 17
Clerking policy: Yes
Summers joining/anticipated 2018:
1Ls: 11, 2Ls: 28
Summer salary 2018:
1Ls: $3,461.54/week
2Ls: $3,461.54/week
Split summers offered? No
Can summers spend time in an overseas office? No

Firm profile

Bracewell LLP is a leading law and government relations firm primarily serving the energy, finance and technology industries throughout the world. Bracewell's industry focus results in comprehensive, state-of-the-art knowledge of the commercial, legal and governmental challenges faced by its clients and enables Bracewell to provide innovative solutions to facilitate transactions and resolve disputes.

Recruitment

Law Schools attending for OCIs in 2018:

Baylor, Columbia, Duke, George Washington, Georgetown, Harvard, Lavender Law, Loyola Patent Law Interview Program, Northwestern, NYU, On Tour Interview Program, SMU, South Texas College of Law, Southeastern Minority Job Fair, The Consortium, Thurgood Marshall, University of Houston, The University of Texas, UVA, Vanderbilt

Recruitment outside OCIs:

We participate in resume drops at law schools across the nation and accept write-in candidates via our website.

Summer associate profile:

We look for candidates who have distinguished themselves academically and actively participate in law school and professional legal organizations. Successful candidates possess a strong work ethic and are self-motivated. Given the firm's collaborative culture, we also look for individuals who are team players.

Summer program components:

The firm offers summer associate programs in all US offices, though demand in each office is determined from year to year. These programs vary by location, but typically range in length from eight to ten weeks. During this time, summer associates have the opportunity to explore different areas of the law by working on actual matters. Summer associates attend hearings, depositions, trials, negotiations and client meetings. They also hone legal writing skills by helping research and draft agreements, briefs, articles and blog posts. In addition, summer associates are encouraged to explore the local community and attend attorney dinners, summer associate lunches and a summer associate retreat.

BRACEWELL

Brown Rudnick LLP

One Financial Center, Boston, MA 02111

Tel: 617 856 8200   Fax: 617 856 8201
Recruitment website: www.brownrudnick.com/careers
Linkedin: brown-rudnick

Twitter: @BrownRudnickLLP
Facebook: Brown-Rudnick-LLP
Instagram: @brownrudnickllp

Main areas of work

Bankruptcy and corporate restructuring; complex litigation and arbitration; corporate, securities and M&A; distressed debt and claims trading; emerging companies; energy, utilities and environmental; finance; funds; government contracts; government law and strategies; healthcare; intellectual property; intellectual property litigation; international dispute resolution; life sciences; real estate; tax; white collar defense and government investigations.

Firm profile

Brown Rudnick, an international law firm with offices in the United States and Europe, represents clients from around the world in high stakes litigation, international arbitration and complex business transactions. Clients include public and private corporations, multinational Fortune 100 businesses and start-up enterprises. The firm also represents investors, as well as official and ad hoc creditors' committees in today's largest corporate restructurings, both domestically and abroad.

Founded more than 70 years ago, Brown Rudnick has over 250 lawyers providing advice and services across key areas of the law. Beyond the United States, the firm regularly serves clients in Europe, the Middle East, North Africa, the Caribbean and Latin America. With its Brown Rudnick Center for the Public Interest, the firm has created an innovative model combining its pro bono, charitable giving and community volunteer efforts.

Recruitment

Law Schools attending for OCIs in 2018:

- Boston College
- Boston University
- Columbia University
- Fordham University School of Law
- Harvard University
- Howard University School of Law
- New York University
- University of California – Irvine
- University of Connecticut
- University of Pennsylvania
- University of Texas
- University of Virginia

Recruitment outside OCIs:

- Boston Lawyers Group Job Fair
- Hispanic National Bar Association
- Lavender Law Career Fair
- Loyola Patent Job Fair

Summer associate profile:

Brown Rudnick recruits summer associates who are highly intelligent and creative and also possess those personal qualities that define our firm: hard driving but value oriented and pragmatic, entrepreneurial, always honest and ethical and highly collaborative.

Summer program components:

Brown Rudnick allocates significant energy and resources to provide each summer associate with a first hand experience of life as a lawyer at our firm. We offer a wide range of assignments, provide a robust training curriculum, including core legal and writing skills, business development and networking skills, as well as a fun social calendar.

Head Office: Boston, MA
Number of domestic offices: 6
Number of international offices: 2
Worldwide revenue: $192,200,000
Partners (US): 85
Associates (US): 75

Contacts
Main recruitment contacts:
Heather L. Cannady
(hcannady@brownrudnick.com)
Molly I. Childs
(mchilds@brownrudnick.com)
Hiring partner: Jeffrey L. Jonas
Diversity officers: Sunni Beville,
Ari Joesph

Recruitment details
Entry-level associates starting in 2018: 8
Clerking policy: Yes
Summers joining/anticipated 2018:
1Ls: 1, 2Ls: 10
Summers joining/anticipated 2018 split
by office: Boston: 5, Washington DC: 1.5,
New York: 3.5, Orange County CA: 1
(We have one summer splitting between
NY and DC)
Summer salary 2018:
1Ls: $3,461/week
2Ls: $3,461/week
Post 3Ls: $3,461/week
Split summers offered? Case by case
Can summers spend time in overseas
office? Case by case

Cadwalader, Wickersham & Taft LLP

200 Liberty Street, New York, NY 10281

Tel: 212 504 6000   Fax: 212 504 6666
Recruitment website: www.cadwalader.com/makehistory
Linkedin: cadwalader-wickersham-&-taft-llp

Twitter: @Cadwalader

Main areas of work

The firm offers legal representation in antitrust, banking, business fraud, capital markets, corporate finance, corporate governance, energy, executive compensation, financial restructuring, healthcare, intellectual property, litigation, mergers and acquisitions, private equity, private wealth, real estate, regulation, securitization, structured finance and tax.

Firm profile

Cadwalader, Wickersham & Taft LLP, established in 1792, is a leading legal advisor to many of the world's top financial institutions and corporations, with offices in New York, London, Charlotte, Washington D.C. and Brussels. Lawyers provide counsel on sophisticated and complex transactional, litigation, and regulatory matters to help our clients break new ground, achieve their business goals, and overcome challenges.

Recruitment

Law Schools attending for OCIs in 2018:

American, Berkeley, Boston University, Brooklyn, Cardozo, University of Chicago, Columbia, Duke, Emory, Fordham, George Washington, Georgetown, Harvard, University of Michigan, Northwestern, NYU, Penn, Vanderbilt, University of Virginia and Washington University.

Recruitment outside OCIs:

We accept student applications through resume collections, on-campus resume drops, referrals, write-ins and job fairs.

In 2018 we will be participating in the following job fairs: BU/BC NYC Job Fair, Cornell NYC Job Fair, Emory NYC Job Fair, Lavender Law, MCGC NYC Job Fair, MCGC DC Job Fair, NEBLSA Job Fair and The Law Consortium DC Job Fair.

Summer associate profile:

Cadwalader is a community of talented and driven individuals committed to innovation and premier client service. We seek candidates with a record of academic and personal achievement, who exhibit excellent communication skills and professionalism, and who are analytical and creative thinkers.

Summer program components:

Under the supervision of experienced attorneys, summer associates have an opportunity to make meaningful contributions to ongoing projects. You will work on diverse and challenging assignments in a variety of our practice areas, participate in substantive and skill building sessions and take on pro bono work. Our goal is to expose you to the various aspects of the practice of law: meeting with clients; participating in strategy and negotiation sessions; conducting research; drafting memos, documents and pleadings; and attending closings, depositions and court appearances. Associate and partner mentors will work closely with you throughout the summer. In addition to getting feedback on individual projects from supervising lawyers, you will also participate in mid-summer and end-of-summer formal evaluations.

Head office: New York, NY
Number of domestic offices: 3
Number of international offices: 2
Worldwide revenue: $408,000,000
Partners (US): 77
Associates (US): 172
Other Attorneys: 72

Contacts

Main recruitment contact:
Tara Conlon,
Director of Legal Recruitment
(tara.conlon@cwt.com)
Hiring partners: Anne Tompkins
Diversity officer: La Tonya Brooks,
Manager of Diversity & Inclusion

Recruitment details

Entry-level associates starting in 2018: 21
Clerking policy: Case by case
Summers joining/anticipated 2018:
2Ls: 35, SEO: 2
Summers joining/anticipated 2018 split by office:
New York: 27, Washington, DC: 5,
Charlotte: 3
Summer salary 2018:
1Ls: $3,462/week
2Ls: $3,462/week
Split summers offered? Case by case
Can summers spend time in an overseas office? No

CADWALADER

Cahill Gordon & Reindel LLP

0 Pine Street, New York NY 10005

el: 212 701 3000

Recruitment website: www.cahill.com/careers

Main areas of work

Antitrust, bankruptcy and restructuring, communications, corporate, corporate finance, corporate governance and investigations, crisis advisory, executive compensation and employee benefits, environmental, insurance, intellectual property, litigation, media, pro bono, real estate, tax and trusts and estates.

Firm profile

Cahill has thrived for nearly a century by focusing on the most significant opportunities and complex legal challenges facing leading financial institutions and global businesses. Cahill is a firm where you can shape your own legal career. We believe that lawyers who practice in diverse areas are happier and more productive. We do not require immediate specialization and do not have formal departments or rotation policies. While among the most profitable New York-based law firms, our size is conducive to regular interaction between partners and associates. Opportunities abound for interesting work and unparalleled on-the-job training.

Recruitment

Law Schools attending for OCIs in 2018:

Albany, Boston College, Boston University, Brooklyn, Columbia, Cornell, Duke, Fordham, Georgetown, George Washington, Harvard, Howard, New York University, Northwestern, University of Michigan, University of Pennsylvania and University of Virginia (with job fairs and write-ins from a dozen more).

Recruitment outside OCIs:

As a complement to our campus interview process, we review all additional direct submissions. We encourage candidates interested in our firm to contact us with inquiries about our Summer Program and associate opportunities.

Summer associate profile:

The firm seeks academically strong candidates who display good judgment, self-confidence and enthusiasm for the practice of law.

Summer program components:

Summer associates at Cahill gain first-hand experience of what it would be like to be an associate at Cahill. With substantive assignments and opportunities to gain valuable public interest work experience and attend client meetings, negotiations, court appearances and networking events, Cahill's summer associates develop a true understanding of the firm's practice. Formal and informal training, personal mentoring and comprehensive evaluations are components of the firm's summer program.

Head Office: New York, NY
Number of domestic offices: 2
Number of international offices: 1
Worldwide revenue: $387,651,000
Partners (US): 66
Associates (US): 201

Contacts
Main recruitment contact: Donna Manion, Director of Legal Recruiting (dmanion @cahill.com)
Hiring partner: Brockton B. Bosson and Sheila C. Ramesh
Diversity officers: Stuart Downing and Susanna M. Suh

Recruitment details
Entry-level associates starting in 2018: 38
Clerking policy: Yes
Summers joining/anticipated 2018:
2Ls: 44
Summers joining/anticipated 2018 split by office: NY: 44
Summer salary 2018:
2Ls: $3,500/week
Split summers offered? Yes, with government or public agencies.
Can summers spend time in an overseas office? No

Choate Hall & Stewart LLP

Two International Place, Boston, MA 02110

Tel: 617 248 5000
Email: legalrecruiting@choate.com
Recruitment website: www.choate.com/careers

Linkedin: choate-hall-&-stewart
Twitter: @ChoateLLP

Main areas of work

Private equity and M&A, finance and restructuring, life sciences and technology companies, intellectual property and related litigation, government enforcement and financial litigation, insurance and reinsurance, complex trial and appellate, and wealth management.

Firm profile

Choate is one of the nation's premier law firms. Choate conducts its national and international practice through a single office model, with all lawyers under one roof in Boston. The firm's associate-to-partner ratio is low, affording junior lawyers opportunities to play important roles on matters and facilitating rapid career development. Lawyers know each other well and work together in dedicated client teams. That familiarity, proximity and continuity allows them to share knowledge easily and respond to clients' needs efficiently, seamlessly and immediately.

Recruitment

Law Schools attending for OCIs in 2018:

Boston College, Boston University, Columbia, Cornell, Georgetown, Harvard, New York University, Northeastern, Suffolk, University of Virginia and Yale

Recruitment outside OCIs:

Choate collects resumes via a resume drop at many other schools.

If we do not offer this at your school, qualified candidates may submit their resume to legalrecruiting@choate.com.

Clerking policy: Choate offers progression credit, as well as a one-time clerkship bonus, to candidates who join the firm immediately following the completion of a federal district or circuit court clerkship or a federal or state supreme court clerkship

Summer associate profile:

Choate seeks candidates who have a record of academic excellence and professional achievement. We value proven leadership, dedication to team success, a strong work ethic and the ability to approach challenges thoughtfully and creatively. We seek candidates who offer perspectives and talents shaped by a broad range of socioeconomic, racial, ethnic, professional and personal backgrounds.

Summer program components:

Throughout the summer, Choate's summer associates are involved in real work with real clients. In recent years, summers have performed legal research, drafted memos and briefs, helped prepare transactional documents, conducted diligence, reviewed documents, participated in deal closings, assisted in fact gathering, drafted estate planning documents, observed depositions, negotiations and trials and worked on pro bono matters. Each summer associate is matched with a junior associate, mid-level associate and partner mentor, who provide guidance and feedback. The summer training program provides the opportunity to develop professional skills, to learn about the firm as a business and to have the experience of working at the firm as well as to develop important legal skills, such as writing.

Head Office: Boston, MA
Number of domestic offices: 1
Number of international offices: 0
Worldwide revenue: $236,250,949
Partners: 63
Associates: 97
Other Attorneys: 21

Contacts
Main recruitment contact:
Elaine Cohen Bortman, Chief of Legal Recruiting and Talent Development
Hiring partners: Diana Lloyd, John Nadas
Diversity officer: Choate has a Diversity & Inclusion Committee which includes partners from a range of departments and is chaired by the Managing Partners.

Recruitment details
Entry-level associates starting in 2018: 15
Clerking policy: Yes
Diversity fellowship: Yes
1L Fellows receive a position in Choate's summer program and are eligible for a stipend of up to $25,000
Summers joining/anticipated 2018:
1Ls: 2, 2Ls: 13
Summer salary 2018:
1Ls: $3,462/week
2Ls: $3,462/week
Split summers offered? No

Cleary Gottlieb Steen & Hamilton LLP

One Liberty Plaza, New York, NY 10006

Tel: 212 225 2000　Fax: 212 225 3999
Recruitment website: www.clearygottlieb.com
Linkedin: cleary-gottlieb-steen-&-hamilton-llp

Twitter: @ClearyGottlieb
Facebook:
Cleary-Gottlieb-Steen-Hamilton

Main areas of work

Antitrust, banking and financial institutions, bankruptcy and restructuring, capital markets, corporate governance, cybersecurity and privacy, derivatives, economic sanctions and foreign investments, energy, environmental, executive compensation and ERISA, financial technology, global crisis management, intellectual property, investment funds, international arbitration, international trade and investment, leveraged and acquisition finance, litigation and arbitration, mergers, acquisitions and joint ventures, private clients, private equity, private funds, pro bono, project finance and infrastructure, public international law, real estate, securities and M&A litigation, sovereign governments and international institutions, structured finance, tax, white-collar defense and internal investigations

Firm profile

Cleary Gottlieb is a pioneer in globalizing the legal profession. Since 1946, the firm's lawyers and staff have worked across practices, industries, jurisdictions and continents to provide clients with simple, actionable approaches to their most complex legal and business challenges. The firm has 16 offices in major financial centers around the world. However, we operate as a single, integrated global partnership, not a US firm with a network of overseas locations. The firm is fluent in the many languages of local and global business, and Cleary's consistent success in multiple jurisdictions earned Cleary *Chambers and Partners'* inaugural *"International Law Firm of the Year"* award. The firm employs approximately 1,200 lawyers from more than 50 countries and diverse backgrounds who are admitted to practice in numerous jurisdictions. Cleary was among the first international law firms to hire and promote non-US lawyers as equal partners around the world.

Recruitment

Law Schools attending for OCIs in 2018:

Boston College, Boston University, Brooklyn, Cardozo, Chicago, Columbia, Cornell, Duke, Fordham, George Washington, Georgetown, Harvard, Howard, Lavender Law Career Fair, McGill, Michigan, Midwest - California - Georgia Consortium, National Law School Consortium, NEBLSA Job Fair, New York Law School, NYU, Northwestern, Notre Dame, Ohio State, University of Pennsylvania, Stanford, Texas, Tulane, Washington University, Washington and Lee, William and Mary, UC Berkeley, UCLA, USC Gould, Vanderbilt, Virginia, Yale

Summer associate profile:

We seek candidates who are confident in their abilities and creative in their thinking. We look for academically strong men and women of all races and nationalities who are enthusiastic about practicing law. We place a premium on openness, diversity, individuality and collegiality and look for candidates who do so as well.

Summer program components:

Our summer program is designed to provide summer associates with real world preparation to jump-start a successful legal career. We offer summer associates the flexibility to enjoy assignments in many practice areas or to focus on a particular discipline. The summer program consists of formal and informal training, partner and associate mentoring, optional overseas office rotations, pro bono work, comprehensive evaluations and social/networking events.

Head Offices: New York, NY and Washington, DC
Number of domestic offices: 2
Number of international offices: 14
Partners (US): 108
Associates (US): 481

Contacts
Main recruitment contacts:
Donna Harris (NY) (dharris@cgsh.com)
Georgia Emery Gray (DC)
(gegray@cgsh.com)
Hiring partners: Elizabeth Lenas (NY) and Michael Mazzuchi (DC)
Diversity officers: Sandra Flow (NY), Lewis Liman (NY) and Katherine Mooney Carroll (DC), Alexis Collins (DC)

Recruitment details
Entry-level associates starting in 2018: 120
Clerking policy: Yes
Summers joining/anticipated 2018:
1Ls: 4 (DC), 2Ls: 108, SEO: 7
Summers joining/anticipated 2018 split by office: NY: 90, DC: 18
Summer salary 2018:
2Ls: $3,461/week
Split summers offered? Yes
Can summers spend time in an overseas office? Yes

Firm Profiles

CLEARY GOTTLIEB

Clifford Chance US LLP

31 West 52nd Street, New York, NY 10019-6131

Tel: 212 878 8000   Fax: 212 878 8375
Email: sarah.posner@cliffordchance.com
Recruitment website: www.cliffordchance.com/usrecruiting
Linkedin: clifford-chance-americas / clifford-chance-llp

Facebook: CliffordChanceGrads
US Twitter: @CC_Americas
UK Twitter: @CC_UK_PR

Main areas of work

NY: Banking and finance, capital markets, corporate/M&A, private funds, insurance, litigation and dispute resolution, real estate and tax, pensions and employment.

DC: Banking and finance (with a specific focus on project finance), litigation and dispute resolution and structured finance.

Firm profile

Clifford Chance offers the opportunity to join a major US practice and the world's leading international law firm. We are the first fully-integrated worldwide firm to provide coordinated legal advice to the world's leading financial institutions, corporations and governments. The combination of a large US presence with unparalleled resources in Europe, Asia Pacific, Latin America, Africa and the Middle East makes us uniquely qualified to handle complex cross-border and domestic transactions, disputes and investigations.

Recruitment

Law Schools attended for OCIs in 2018:

- American
- Brooklyn
- Columbia
- Cornell
- Duke
- Fordham
- Georgetown
- George Washington
- Harvard
- Michigan
- NYU
- Penn
- St. John's
- Virginia

Summer associate profile:

We believe in giving our lawyers a high level of exposure and responsibility from the very beginning. Over the ten-week program, our clerks will work on a wide variety of assignments to not only gain exposure to our full range of practice areas, but to get to know the partners and associates in those departments as well. Through close attorney contact, formal training, time spent in one of our offices abroad, and social events that explore the city, our summer law clerks receive a realistic vision of what it means to be a Clifford Chance lawyer.

Summer program components:

We believe that the best learning is done on the job. In addition to the hands-on experience they'll receive working alongside our partners and associates on real assignments, our summer law clerks also participate in formal training programs focused on legal writing, corporate transactions, negotiations, as well as a seminar specifically geared toward working as an international lawyer. Feedback is given on a formal and informal basis, allowing our clerks to have a clear idea of their development.

Head Office: London
Number of domestic offices: 2
Number of international offices: 30
Worldwide revenue: $1,985,000,000
Partners (US): 72
Associates (US): 201

Contacts
Main recruitment contact:
Sarah Posner
(sarah.posner@cliffordchance.com)
Hiring Partner: Nicholas R. Williams (NY)
Steve Nickelsburg (DC)
Diversity officer: Zarrar Sehgal

Recruitment details
Entry-level associates starting in 2018: 28
Clerking policy: Yes
Summers joining/anticipated 2018:
1Ls: 1, 2Ls: 18, 3Ls: 0, SEO: 1
Summers joining/anticipated 2018 split by office: NY: 17, DC: 3
Summer salary 2018:
1Ls: $3,461.54/week
2Ls: $3,461.54/week
Split summers offered? Case by case
Can summers spend time in an overseas office? Yes

**CLIFFORD
CHANCE**

Cooley LLP

175 Hanover Street, Palo Alto, CA 94304-1130

Tel: 650 843 5000
Recruitment website: www.cooley.com/careers
Linkedin: cooleyllp

Twitter: @cooleycareers
Facebook: CooleyLLP

Main areas of work

Advertising, antitrust and competition, appellate, artificial intelligence, asset recovery, blockchain, capital markets, class actions, commercial litigation, communications, compensation and benefits, copyright, corporate, corporate restructuring and bankruptcy, cyber/data/privacy, debt finance, education, emerging companies, employment and labor, estate planning, financial services, fintech, fund formation, government contracts, healthcare, insurance, intellectual property, international anti-corruption/FCPA, international arbitration, investment funds, life sciences, M&A, patent counseling and prosecution, patent litigation, private equity, product compliance and product liability, public companies, real estate, regulatory, securities and governance, securities litigation, shareholder activism, social enterprise and impact investing, tax, technology transactions, trade secrets, trademark, venture capital, virtual and augmented reality, white collar and regulatory defense.

Firm profile

Cooley's lawyers solve legal issues for entrepreneurs, investors, financial institutions and established companies with a significant emphasis on technology, life sciences and other high growth industries. Clients partner with Cooley on transformative deals, complex IP and regulatory matters and bet-the-company litigation, where innovation meets the law. Cooley goes to great lengths to maintain the culture of teamwork, collaboration, respect and excellence upon which it was established in 1920. Cooley strives to maintain an environment of diversity and inclusiveness and to create opportunities for professional growth. It is proud to be the top-ranked law firm on *Fortune's 100* Best Companies to Work For list.

Cooley considers its commitment to the communities in which it operates to be one of its highest priorities and each year performs thousands of hours of pro bono legal services and other forms of community service.

Recruitment

Law Schools attending for OCIs in 2018:

Please refer to the Events portion of our website for a list of the job fairs and campuses we will visit during the 2018 OCI season.

Recruitment outside OCIs:

Interested students are also welcome to send in their applications outside of the OCI process. For a list of legal talent career contacts by office, please visit: www.cooley.com/careers.

Summer associate profile:

Successful summer associates are highly motivated, independent thinkers, with a collaborative spirit and an entrepreneurial mindset. They have excelled both in and beyond the classroom. They recognize that the greatest successes are those achieved by a team. They take ownership, inspire confidence and are motivated by a shared sense of purpose.

Summer program components:

Cooley's summer program is designed to give participants an unfiltered introduction to life and practice at the firm. It enables them to experience Cooley's commitment to providing extraordinary legal services in a professional and collaborative environment. Comprehensive training opportunities are provided through 'Cooley College' Constructive feedback is provided at the conclusion of each assignment and in formal mid- and end-of-summer feedback sessions. Assigned mentors ensure that each summer associate is integrated into the firm over the course of the program.

Head Office: Palo Alto, CA
Number of domestic offices. 10
Number of international offices: 3
Worldwide revenue: $1.07 billion
Partners (US): 300
Associates (US): 600

Contacts
Main recruitment contact:
Carrie Wagner, Chief Legal Talent Officer
(cwagner@cooley.com)
Diversity officers: DeAnna Allen, Partner
Frank Pietrantonio, Partner
Amie Santos, Director of Diversity and
Inclusion

Recruitment details
Entry-level associates starting in 2018: 51
Clerking policy: Yes
Summers joining/anticipated 2018:
1Ls: 8, 2Ls: 51, SEO: 1,
Google Legal Summer Scholar: 1
Summers joining/anticipated 2018 split
by office: Boston: 9, Colorado: 2,
Los Angeles: 2, New York: 9,
Palo Alto: 17, Reston: 3, San Diego: 5,
San Francisco: 8, Seattle: 2,
Washington DC, 4
Summer salary 2018:
1Ls: $3,462/week
2Ls: $3,462/week
Split summers offered? Yes
Can summers spend time in an overseas
office? No

Firm Profiles

Cozen O'Connor

One Liberty, 1650 Market Street, Suite 2800, Philadelphia, PA 19103

Tel: 215 665 2000   Fax: 215 665 2013
Email: jcaughie@cozen.com
Recruitment website: www.cozen.com/careers
Linkedin: cozen-o'connor

Twitter: @cozen_oconnor
Facebook: CozenOConnor
Instagram: @cozenoconnor

Main areas of work

Business/corporate, commercial litigation, construction, criminal defense and internal investigations, government and regulatory, insurance coverage, institutional response, labor and employment, intellectual property, real estate, private client services, subrogation and recovery, transportation and trade.

Firm profile

Established in 1970, Cozen O'Connor delivers legal services on an integrated and global basis. As a first-generation law firm, we have not forgotten our entrepreneurial roots and continue to provide top-notch client service at unparalleled value as we have grown to one of the top law firms in the country. Our business and litigation practices serve clients in the most effective and efficient manner, with professionals across disciplines working collaboratively to resolve any matter.

Recruitment

Law Schools attending for OCIs in 2018:

Georgetown, Harvard, Howard, NYU, Penn, Penn State, Seattle University, Temple, UVA, University of Washington, Villanova, GW, Fordham, University of Miami

Recruitment outside OCIs:

We participate in a walk-around program, The Law Consortium – Philadelphia, and two job fairs, The Philadelphia Area Diversity Job Fair and the Northwest Minority Job Fair.

For students at non-OCI schools who wish to apply outside of these programs, please submit application materials at www.cozen.com/careers/law_students beginning in July.

Summer associate profile:

We seek summer associates who embody the best characteristics of our attorneys. These are candidates who have distinguished themselves from their peers in academics, legal writing ability and oral advocacy skills. Our summer associates have diverse backgrounds including, but not limited to, prior work experience, military service and a demonstrated commitment to serving their communities through volunteerism.

Summer program components:

We provide our summer associates with a realistic experience of the responsibilities and high level of performance expected of our associates. They take part in an extensive firm orientation and weekly training programs, such as a trial skills workshop where they have learned to prepare and present an opening statement. We provide writing mentors and associate mentors to provide advice and guidance. Summer associates are invited to practice group meetings and to attend hearings, depositions, or client meetings with attorneys. Social events and teambuilding activities are scattered throughout the program to help each summer associate become better acquainted with each other and the firm's attorneys.

Head Office: Philadelphia, PA
Number of domestic offices: 24
Number of international offices: 3
Worldwide revenue: $416 million
Partners (US): 444
Associates (US): 169

Contacts
Main recruitment contacts:
Jill M. Caughie (jcaughie@cozen.com)
Mindy Herczfeld (mherczfeld@cozen.com)
Hiring partners: Dan Luccaro,
Lezlie Madden
Diversity officer: Lynne Espy-Williams

Recruitment details
Entry-level associates starting in 2018: 16
Clerking policy: Yes
Summers joining/anticipated 2018:
1Ls: 6, 2Ls: 23
Summers joining/anticipated 2018 split
by office: Chicago: 2, Denver: 1,
Houston: 1, Los Angeles: 1, Miami: 1,
Minneapolis: 1, New York: 3, Philadelphia: 10, Pittsburgh: 1, Santa Monica: 1,
Seattle: 2, Washington DC: 5
Summer salary 2018:
1Ls: $2300-2973/wk, varies by office
2Ls: $2500-3173/wk, varies by office
Split summers offered? Case-by-case
Can summers spend time in an overseas
office? No

Firm Profiles

Cravath, Swaine & Moore LLP

5 Eighth Avenue, New York, NY 10019

l: 212 474 1000   Fax: 212 474 3700
ecruitment website: www.cravath.com
nkedin: cravath-swaine-&-moore-llp

Facebook: cravath
Twitter: @cravath

Main areas of work
orporate, litigation, tax, executive compensation and benefits, trusts and estates.

Firm profile
ravath is known as one of the preeminent law firms in the country. Each of our practice
eas is highly regarded and our lawyers are widely recognized for their commitment to
e representation of our clients' interests. We believe the development of our lawyers
our most important long term objective. Our partners come almost exclusively from
e ranks of our own associates. We recruit the most talented law students and have our
artners directly train the next generation of associates. Through our rotation system —
system in which corporate associates 'rotate' from one practice group to another and
tigation associates 'rotate' from one partner to another — associates work directly with
small team of partners and associates. We have found that this system enables even our
most recently hired associates to work directly with our clients and to quickly assume
ubstantial responsibility for important matters, while at the same time preventing undue
pecialization.

Recruitment

Law Schools attending for OCIs in 2018:
Berkeley, Boston College/Boston University Job Fair, Brigham Young University New
York Interview Program, Cardozo, Chicago, Columbia, Cornell Job Fair, Duke, Emory Job
Fair, Fordham, George Washington New York Job Fair, Georgetown, Harvard, Harvard
BLSA Job Fair, Howard, Lavender Law Career Fair, LeGaL LGBT Career Fair, Michigan,
Midwest-California-Georgia Consortium, Northeast BLSA Job Fair, New York University,
Northwestern, Stanford, Texas, Texas New York Job Fair, Tulane/Washington University
Job Fair, Vanderbilt Job Fair, University of Pennsylvania, Virginia, Yale.

Recruitment outside OCIs:
Clerkship hiring

Summer associate profile:
Our summer program is designed to provide law students with an experience that mirrors
the life of a first year associate. Summer associates experience the day-to-day working life
of a Cravath lawyer and gain valuable hands-on experience working directly for, and with,
our clients.

Summer program components:
Prior to the summer, we collect department and assignment preferences (type of matter
or practice area, specific teams or partners). Upon arrival, summer associates are assigned
to a partner from their selected department, along with an associate mentor. This partner
is responsible for assigning work, providing feedback, integrating summer associates fully
into their teams and ensuring that the experience resembles that of a first-year associate.

Additionally, there are a number of social and cultural activities including a party at the
Central Park Zoo, Broadway shows, Hudson River Sail, the Apollo Theater, Shakespeare
in the Park and various professional sporting events.

Head Office: **New York, NY**
Number of domestic offices: **1**
Number of international offices: **1**
Partners (US): **84**
Associates (US): **412**

Contacts
Main recruitment contact: **Lisa A Kalen
(lkalen@cravath.com)**
Hiring partners: **Michael A Paskin,
D Scott Bennett**
Diversity officer: **Kiisha J B Morrow**

Recruitment details
Entry-level associates starting in 2018: **92**
Clerking policy: **Yes**
Summers joining/anticipated 2018:
1Ls: **5**, 2Ls: **82**, SEO: **2**
Summers joining/anticipated 2018 split
by office: NY: **87**
Summer salary 2018:
1Ls: **$3,500/week**
2Ls: **$3,500/week**
Split summers offered? **Yes**
Can summers spend time in an overseas
office? **Yes**

CRAVATH, SWAINE & MOORE LLP

Firm Profiles

Crowell & Moring LLP

1001 Pennsylvania Avenue, N.W. Washington DC, 20004-2595

Tel: 202 624 2500   Fax: 202 628 5116
Recruitment website: www.crowell.com/careers/lawyers
Linkedin: crowell-&-moring-llp

Twitter: @Crowell_Moring

Main areas of work

Advertising and product risk management, antitrust, aviation, bankruptcy and creditors' rights, C&M international, digital transformation, e-discovery and information management, environment and natural resources, energy, financial services, government affairs, government contracts, healthcare, insurance/reinsurance, intellectual property, international dispute resolution, international trade, investigations, labor and employment, litigation and trial, plaintiff's recovery, privacy and cybersecurity, tax, mass tort, product and consumer litigation, trade associations, trade secrets, transaction and corporate/securities, and white collar and regulatory enforcement.

Firm profile

Crowell & Moring LLP is an international law firm with more than 500 lawyers representing clients in litigation and arbitration, regulatory, and transactional matters. The firm is internationally recognized for its representation of Fortune 500 companies in high-stakes litigation, as well as its ongoing commitment to pro bono service and diversity. The firm has offices in Washington, DC, New York, Los Angeles, San Francisco, Orange County, London, and Brussels.

Recruitment

Law Schools attending for OCIs in 2018:

Berkeley, Chicago, Columbia, Cornell, Duke, Fordham, George Washington, Georgetown, Harvard, Howard, Loyola, Maryland, Michigan, Northwestern, NYU, Rutgers, University of Pennsylvania, UC Hastings, UC Irvine, UCLA, USC, University of Virginia

Recruitment outside OCIs:

We participate in the following job fairs: Lavender Job Fair, On Tour Interview Program (in LA), Bay Area Diversity Career Fair

Summer associate profile:

The firm looks for highly qualified, entrepreneurial candidates with diverse backgrounds.

We prefer candidates with law review, journal or moot court experience and/or strong relevant legal employment experience, including judicial clerkships; as well as demonstrated leadership capabilities.

Summer program components:

The diversity in our summer program reflects the diversity of our firm at large. We want summer associates who take the practice of law and client service more seriously than they take themselves, who will contribute to the life of the firm, and who share our sense of responsibility to the community.

Most of our junior associates come from our Summer Associate Program. We want you to go back to law school knowing who we are, what we do, and how we do it. Work for summer associates includes mostly short-term projects that will allow you to experience as many practice areas and as many lawyers as possible.

Summer associates have the opportunity to participate in workshops and seminars on such topics as 'The Law Firm as a Business' and 'Oral Advocacy Training'. In addition, the firm offers summer associates opportunities to accompany Crowell & Moring attorneys to 'Live Events', which are real-world activities such as court hearings, client meetings, depositions, presentations and negotiations, to observe our lawyers in action.

Head Office: Washington, DC
Number of domestic offices: 5
Number of international offices: 2
Worldwide revenue: $418.7 million
Partners (US): 188
Associates (US): 149
Counsel/Sr Counsel (US): 141

Contacts
Main recruitment contact:
Torey Phillips, Director of Attorney Recruiting and Development (tphillips@crowell.com)
Hiring partner: Ryan Tisch
Diversity officer: Melanie Priddy

Recruitment details
Entry-level associates starting in 2018: 20
Clerking policy: We encourage clerkship opportunities.
Summers joining/anticipated 2018:
1Ls: 1, 2Ls: 20
Summers joining/anticipated 2018 split by office: Washington, DC: 10, New York: 4, Los Angeles: 3, Orange County, CA: 2, San Francisco: 2
Summer salary 2018:
1Ls: $ 3,462/week
2Ls: $ 3,462/week
Split summers offered? Case by case
Can summers spend time in an overseas office? No

Firm Profiles

Curtis, Mallet-Prevost, Colt & Mosle LLP

01 Park Avenue, New York, NY 10178-0061

el: 212 696 6000   Fax: 212 697 1559

mail: recruitment@curtis.com

Recruitment website: www.curtis.com

inkedin: curtis-mallet-prevost-colt-&-mosle-llp

Twitter: @curtislawfirm

Main areas of work

Curtis represents clients across industry sectors, including multinational corporations and financial institutions, governments and state-owned companies, money managers, sovereign wealth funds, family-owned businesses, individuals and entrepreneurs. Curtis' attorneys provide legal services in international arbitration, renewable energy and climate change, project finance and infrastructure development, international tax, mergers and acquisitions, private equity, restructuring and insolvency, litigation, banking and finance, capital markets, investment management, international investment, corporate law and real estate.

Firm profile

Curtis, Mallet-Prevost, Colt & Mosle LLP is a leading international law firm that provides a broad range of legal services to clients around the world. The firm operates worldwide throughout its offices in Europe, the United States, Latin America, the Middle East and Central Asia. Curtis' international orientation has been a hallmark of its practice for nearly two centuries. Curtis attorneys are trained as internationalists with a deep understanding of the cultural as well as business sensitivities associated with conducting business across borders.

Recruitment

Law Schools attending for OCIs in 2018:

UChicago, Columbia, Duke, Fordham, Georgetown, NYU, St. John's, and UPenn

Recruitment outside OCIs:

Targeted search, resume collects, write-ins, and hiring from judicial clerkships

Summer associate profile:

The Curtis Summer Program is small and highly selective. Curtis chooses approximately five to ten second-year law students to participate in our program. The summer program, which lasts ten weeks, starts in late May and ends in July. Grades and scores are not the only criteria for selection. Curtis looks for students who are confident, independent thinkers.

Summer program components:

The summer program is designed to give students a realistic view of the practice of law while also teaching them real world lawyering skills in a hands-on environment. Our summer associates quickly become assimilated as each summer associate is matched to a partner mentor and an associate advisor.

Summer associates receive assignments through our dedicated team of assigning associates. Throughout the summer, summer associates join our lawyers in meetings, closings, depositions and court proceedings. Formal trainings includes lectures, workshops, panel discussions and lunchtime programs on relevant topics.

Head office: New York, NY

Number of domestic offices: 3

Number of international offices: 14

Worldwide revenue: $155,000,000

Partners (US): 52

Associates (US): 74

Contacts

Main recruitment contact: Krystal Reese (kreese@curtis.com)

Hiring partner: Carl Ruggiero

Recruitment details

Entry-level associates starting in 2018: 6

Clerking policy: Yes

Summers joining/anticipated 2018:

2Ls: 10

Summer salary 2018:

2Ls: $180,000

Split summers offered: No

Can summers spend time in an overseas office? No

Curtis, Mallet-Prevost, Colt & Mosle LLP

Davis Polk & Wardwell LLP

450 Lexington Avenue, New York, NY 10017

Tel: 212 450 4000   Fax: 212 701 5800
Recruitment website: https://careers.davispolk.com
Linkedin: davis-polk-&-wardwell-llp

Main areas of work

Capital markets, mergers and acquisitions, credit, litigation (including antitrust, bankruptcy, general commercial, IP, securities litigation and enforcement, and white collar and government investigations), tax, private equity, investment management, restructuring, corporate governance, intellectual property and technology, financial regulation, derivatives, FinTech, environmental, executive compensation, real estate and trusts and estates.

Firm profile

Davis Polk & Wardwell LLP is a global law firm. For more than 165 years, its lawyers have advised industry-leading companies and major financial institutions on their most challenging legal and business matters. Davis Polk ranks among the world's preeminent law firms across the entire range of its practice. With more than 900 lawyers in New York, Northern California, Washington DC, London, Paris, Madrid, Hong Kong, Beijing, Tokyo and São Paulo, the firm operates from key business centers around the world to provide clients with seamlessly integrated legal services of the highest caliber.

Recruitment

Summer associate profile:

We seek to hire applicants from a variety of backgrounds with outstanding academic and non-academic achievements, leadership skills and creativity and with a demonstrated willingness to take initiative. We strive to find exceptional lawyers who share our commitment to excellence.

Summer program components:

Our summer program is designed to allow students the opportunity to experience work as a junior associate. Summer associates are encouraged to work on matters in any practice area of interest. There are no required rotations. Work assignments are made through two associates who take leave from their regular practices to assist each summer associate in shaping their summer work experience. In addition to working with our attorneys on the firm's current billable and pro bono matters, summer associates have the opportunity to attend practice area overviews and participate in multi-day interactive training sessions and workshops. The program also includes a wide range of cultural, social and mentoring activities to assist summer associates in getting to know their peers and our attorneys.

Head Office: New York, NY
Number of domestic offices: 3
Number of international offices: 7
Lawyers (US): 820

Contacts
Main recruitment contact:
Cristobal V Modesto
(cristobal.modesto@davispolk.com)
Hiring partners: Maurice Blanco and
Dana Seshens

Recruitment details
Clerking policy: Yes
Summers joining/anticipated 2018: 175
(1Ls: 7, 2Ls: 159, Other: 9)
Summers joining/anticipated 2018 split
by office:
New York:145 (1Ls: 7, 2Ls: 131, Other: 7)
Northern California: 17 (2Ls: 15, Other: 2)
Washington DC: 2Ls: 13
Summer salary 2018:
1Ls: $3,500/week
2Ls: $3,500/week
Split summers offered? Yes
Can summers spend time in an overseas
office? Yes

Davis Polk

Debevoise & Plimpton LLP

919 Third Avenue, New York, NY 10022

Tel: 212 909 6000
Email: recruit@debevoise.com
Recruitment website: www.debevoise.com

Linkedin: debevoise
Twitter: @Debevoise

Main areas of work

Debevoise & Plimpton LLP has three main areas of practice: corporate (including mergers and acquisitions, private equity, investment funds, insurance, banking, leveraged finance, business restructuring and workouts, asset management, capital markets, corporate governance, structured and project finance, aviation finance, healthcare and life sciences, intellectual property, media and telecommunications, real estate, energy and environmental law), litigation (including white collar/regulatory, international dispute resolution, intellectual property, general commercial litigation, cybersecurity and data privacy, insurance, securities, antitrust, employment, bankruptcy and products liability) and tax and employee benefits.

Firm profile

Debevoise & Plimpton LLP is a premier law firm with market-leading practices, a global perspective and strong New York roots. The firm's clients look to it to bring a distinctively high degree of quality, intensity and creativity to resolve legal challenges selectively and cost efficiently. Deep partner commitment, industry expertise and a strategic approach enable the firm to bring clear commercial judgment to every matter. The firm draws on the strength of its culture and structure to deliver the best of the firm to every client through true collaboration.

Recruitment

Law Schools attending for OCIs in 2018:

Benjamin N Cardozo, Brooklyn, Columbia University, Cornell University, Duke University, Fordham University, Georgetown University, Harvard, Howard University, New York Law School, New York University School of Law, Rutgers University, St. John's University, Stanford, Tulane University, University of Chicago, University of Michigan, University of Pennsylvania, University of Texas Law School, University of Virginia, Washington University, Yale

Recruitment outside OCIs:

We conduct resume collections at many schools for which we are not able to attend their on campus interviews.

Summer associate profile:

Debevoise searches for dynamic, analytically strong and professionally curious individuals with an interest in and enthusiasm for the challenging deals and matters on which the firm works. In addition, the firm is interested in individuals from an array of different backgrounds as it prefers that its lawyer population is as diverse as its clients.

Summer program components:

Debevoise's summer program is structured to provide participants with the flexibility to explore as many practice areas as they wish. In order to accommodate the individual's evolving interests, the firm has chosen not to impose an assignment system that 'rotates' participants through different areas of the firm. There are opportunities throughout the summer for formal evaluations, while informal feedback is given on a continuous basis. Social events are held for summer associates, which provide them with the chance to connect with other lawyers, of all levels, at the firm.

Head Office: **New York, NY**
Number of domestic offices: **2**
Number of international offices: **7**
Worldwide revenue: **$822 million**
Partners (US): **134**
Associates (US): **417**

Contacts
Main recruitment contact: **Sandra Herbst**
Hiring partner: **Nicole Mesard**
Diversity officer: **Rachel Simmonds-Watson (Diversity Manager)**

Recruitment details
Entry-level associates starting in 2018: **75**
Clerking policy: **Yes**
Summers joining/anticipated 2018:
95 (excluding SEOs and returnees)
Summers joining/anticipated 2018 split by office: **NY: 93, DC: 2**
Summer salary 2018:
2Ls: **$ 3,500/week**
Split summers offered? **Yes**
Can summers spend time in an overseas office? **Yes**

Debevoise & Plimpton

Dechert LLP

Cira Centre, 2929 Arch Street, Philadelphia, PA 19104-2808

1095 Avenue of the Americas, New York, NY 10036-6797

PA Tel: 215 994 4000 / NY Tel: 212 698 3500

Email: legal.recruiting@dechert.com

Recruitment website: www.dechert.com/careers

Linkedin: dechert-llp
Twitter: @dechertllp
Facebook: DechertLLP

Main areas of work

Dechert delivers legal expertise and commercial insight in our core practices: antitrust; banking and financial institutions; bankruptcy, business restructuring and reorganization; corporate; employee benefits and executive compensation; energy and natural resources; finance; financial services and investment management; intellectual property; international arbitration; international tax and private client services; international trade and government regulation; life sciences; litigation; real estate; and pro bono.

Firm profile

Dechert is a global law firm focused on sectors with the greatest complexities, legal intricacies and highest regulatory demands. With 27 offices in the United States, Europe, Asia and the Middle East, the firm offers attractive locations in which to live and work. Dechert is a leading global law firm for pro bono services. The American Lawyer recently ranked us as the top law firm for international pro bono work. We are also proud of our diverse and inclusive culture. Dechert was named one of the 'Best Places to Work for LGBT Equality' by the Human Rights Campaign and also received a perfect score for the sixth year in a row in the *Corporate Equality Index.*

Recruitment

Law Schools attending for OCIs in 2018:

American, Berkeley, Boston College, Boston University, Chicago, Columbia, Cornell, Duke, Fordham, George Washington, Georgetown, Harvard, Hofstra, Michigan, Northwestern, NYU, Penn State, Stanford, Temple, University of Connecticut, UNC, University of Pennsylvania, University of Texas, UCLA, USC, UVA, Vanderbilt, Villanova.

Recruitment outside OCIs:

Dechert delivers distinctive and exciting opportunities, provides extensive training and mentorship, and offers its lawyers the experiences needed to become experts in their field. We welcome applications from experienced lawyers seeking sophisticated work and a collegial environment.

Summer associate profile:

In addition to a strong academic background, we seek candidates with excellent communication, leadership, management and client relations skills indicating a high likelihood of success as a lawyer at the firm.

Summer program components:

Summer associates will discover firsthand what it's like to be a lawyer at one of the world's most respected and dynamic global law firms. Our summer associates do not formally rotate through practice groups or departments; rather, they work across all the practice groups. A variety of work assignments allows summer associates to gain a broad perspective and get a close-up view of the practice of law. Beyond client-based assignments, we encourage summer associates to attend closings, depositions, hearings, oral arguments, trials, negotiations, and board meetings. Summer associates are assigned at least one associate mentor and one partner mentor and attend practice group meetings and training. We offer summer associate-specific training sessions throughout the program. Through our program, we provide summer associates with a realistic view of what it's like to practice law at Dechert.

Main Offices: Philadelphia / New York
Number of domestic offices: 13
Number of international offices: 14
Worldwide revenue: $978,000,000
Partners (US): 209
Associates (US): 371

Contacts

Main recruitment contacts:
Alison Bernard, Chief Talent Officer (alison.bernard@dechert.com)
Hiring partner: James A Lebovitz, Firmwide Hiring Chair
Diversity officers: Hector Gonzalez, Deputy Chair for Diversity;
Satra Sampson-Arokium, Director of Diversity and Inclusion

Recruitment details

Entry-level associates starting in 2018: 48
Clerking policy: Yes
Summers joining/anticipated 2018:
1Ls: 6, 2Ls: 37
Summers joining/anticipated 2018 split by office: Boston: 5, Charlotte: 3, Hartford: 1, New York: 13, Philadelphia: 12, Silicon Valley: 1, Washington DC: 8
Summer salary 2018:
1Ls: $3,461.54/week
2Ls: $3,461.54/week
Split summers offered? Yes
Can summers spend time in an overseas office? Yes, case by case

DLA Piper LLP (US)

1251 Avenue of the Americas, 27th Floor, New York, NY 10020

Tel: 212 335 4500   Fax: 212 335 4501
Recruitment website: www.dlapiperlegalcareers.us
Linkedin: dla-piper

Twitter: @DLA_piper
Facebook: DLAPiperGlobal
Instagram: @dlapiper

Main areas of work
DLA Piper's core practices in the US are corporate, employment, finance, government affairs, intellectual property and technology, litigation, real estate, restructuring and tax.

Firm profile
DLA Piper is a global law firm with lawyers located in more than 40 countries throughout the Americas, Europe, the Middle East, Africa and Asia Pacific, positioning us to help clients with their legal needs around the world.

Recruitment

Law Schools attending for OCIs in 2018:
TBD

Recruitment outside OCIs:
We participate in job fairs and resume collects at numerous law schools throughout the US.

Summer associate profile:
We promote a culture that is inclusive of all, where everyone has the opportunity to grow their career and where pathways to success are transparent. We look for well-rounded, energetic and entrepreneurial people. We generally recruit from the top 1/4 to the top 1/3 of law school classes.

Summer program components:
During the summer, with guidance from lawyers in the roles of mentors, we provide summer associates with a stimulating, realistic and exciting taste of law firm life. Summer associates experience challenging days filled with client work, relationship-building opportunities and enriching activities.

All summer associates attend a retreat hosted by one of our offices. During this three-day gathering, summer associates get to know one another and participate in team building and training activities.

Our goal is for summer associates to experience what it is like to be on the DLA Piper team and, through the summer experience, envision their future as a knowledgeable, highly skilled, well-rounded DLA Piper lawyer.

More than 90 offices in 40 countries
Worldwide revenue: $2,634,093,805
Partners (US): 612
Associates (US): 543

Contacts
Main recruitment contact:
Stacy Silverstone,
Director of Legal Recruiting
(stacy.silverstone@dlapiper.com)
Hiring partner: Christina L. Martini,
National Hiring Partner - Associate Recruiting
Diversity officer: Genhi Bailey

Recruitment details
Entry-level associates starting in 2018: 34
Clerking policy: Yes
Summers joining/anticipated 2018:
1Ls 15, 2Ls 50
Summer salary 2018:
1Ls: $3,461/week in most markets
2Ls: $3,461/week in most markets
Split summers offered? No
Can summers spend time in an overseas office? No

Duane Morris LLP

30 S. 17th Street, United Plaza, Philadelphia, PA 19103

Tel: 215 979 1000   Fax: 215 979 1020
Recruitment website: www.duanemorris.com/site/careers.html
Linkedin: duane-morris-llp

Facebook: DuaneMorrisLLP
Twitter: @DuaneMorrisLLP

Main areas of work

Business reorganization and financial restructuring; corporate; employment, labor, benefits and immigration; energy, environment and resources; private client services, health law, intellectual property, litigation and real estate.

Firm profile

Duane Morris LLP, a global law firm with more than 800 attorneys in offices across the United States and around the world, is asked by a broad array of clients to provide innovative solutions to today's legal and business challenges.

Recruitment

Law Schools attending for OCIs in 2018:

Duane Morris LLP, a global law firm with more than 800 attorneys in offices across the United States and around the world, is asked by a broad array of clients to provide innovative solutions to today's legal and business challenges.

Summer associate profile:

Duane Morris strives to attract the best law students and to offer the ideal environment for lawyers at the beginning of their professional lives. We endeavor to improve our Summer Associates Program each year to make Duane Morris a meaningful and valuable destination for summer associates. The firm's summer associates rated the firm's program #1 nationally in *The American Lawyer's* 2017 Summer Associates Survey and a #1 ranking in the Philadelphia City ranking for 2017.

Duane Morris offers interesting challenges to law students who participate in our summer program. We believe the program offers a realistic picture of our practice to aspiring attorneys who have an interest in sharing our goals and serving our clients. Our program balances challenging work assignments with constructive feedback, work-related activities outside the office and enjoyable social events.

Summer program components:

The growth and development of each Duane Morris attorney furthers the central goals of the firm to provide the best legal services possible, to develop and build client relationships, and to ensure the stature and reputation of the firm with its clients. Duane Morris' Attorney Professional Development Program provides its summer associates and associates with comprehensive training and mentoring to support development of individual knowledge, skills and abilities in three broad categories: legal skills and substantive law, best business practices for the firm and practice development. Aside from these specific responsibilities, the mentors help introduce the summer associates to other lawyers in the firm and provide general guidance on any matter, whether or not related to particular work assignments.

Head Office: **Philadelphia, PA**
Number of domestic offices: **21**
Number of international offices: **8**
Partners (US): **397**
Associates (US): **324**

Contacts
Main recruitment contact:
Jennifer Davis, Manager of Legal Recruitment and Personnel
Hiring partner: Kelly D Eckel, Esquire
Diversity officer: Joseph K West, Esquire

Recruitment details
Entry-level associates starting in 2018: **15**
Clerking policy: **Yes (federal only)**
Summers joining/anticipated 2018:
1Ls: **1**, 2Ls: **20**
Summers joining/anticipated 2018 split by office: **Philadelphia: 13,**
Cherry Hill, NJ: **1**, Miami: **1**, New York: **4**, San Diego: **1**, Chicago: **1**
Summer salary 2018:
1Ls: **$2,788/wk (Phila)**
2Ls: **$3,173/wk (Phila/NY/Chicago)**
        $2,692/wk (Cherry Hill/Miami)
        $2,884/wk (San Diego)
Split summers offered? **Case by case**
Can summers spend time in an overseas office? **Case by case**

DuaneMorris®

Dykema Gossett PLLC

00 Renaissance Center, Detroit, MI 48243

Tel: 313 568 6800　Fax: 855 255 4354
Recruitment website: www.dykema.com
Linkedin: dykema-gossett-pllc

Twitter: @dykema
Facebook: DykemaGossett1

Main areas of work

Dykema provides counsel to business entities worldwide on a wide range of business issues. Our practices include business, commercial, financial services, product liability and appellate litigation; automotive; corporate finance; energy; real estate; dental; government policy; IP and IP litigation; bankruptcy; labor and employment; health care; tax; environmental and insurance.

Firm profile

With nearly 400 attorneys and professionals in 13 offices across the country, Dykema delivers the highest quality counsel and exceptional client service from a work environment that thrives on collaboration, diversity and inclusion. Associates have autonomy and are given responsibility and client access early. Dykema provides an extensive professional development program including abundant legal skills and business development training. Given the firm's culture of collegiality and teamwork, many have made Dykema their home since the start of their careers.

Recruitment

Law Schools attending for OCIs in 2018:

Baylor, Detroit Mercy, Illinois, Michigan, Michigan State, Notre Dame, OSU, St. Mary's, Southern Methodist (SMU), Texas Tech, U of T–Austin, Wayne State

Recruitment outside OCIs:

Dykema has a long tradition of hiring from schools outside OCIs. Our current firm-wide hiring partner was such a candidate. We also attend job fairs for diversity and geographic outreach.

Summer associate profile:

A successful summer associate shows initiative, excellent analytical skills and strong writing ability. We look for associates who are willing to work hard, have demonstrated leadership potential and enjoy working in a team environment. We urge our associates to take advantage of all the firm offers to help them learn our practice and our culture. Advisors, practice area activities, professional development training and social events combine to accomplish this goal.

Summer program components:

Dykema's summer program offers challenging assignments and a real life law practice experience with opportunities to participate in client, court and other formal settings. A firm-wide summer retreat is held in early June. A key component is a writing workshop with a professional writing instructor. This retreat, along with our advisor program, training, substantive practice experience, and social events have greatly contributed to the success of Dykema's summer program.

Head Office: Detroit, MI
Number of domestic offices: 13
Worldwide revenue: $212,000,000
Partners (US): 276
Associates (US): 141

Contacts
Main recruitment contact: Sarah K Staup
(sstaup@dykema.com)
Hiring partner: Lisa A Brown
Diversity officer: Sherrie L Farrell

Recruitment details
Entry-level associates starting in 2018: 11
Clerking policy: Yes
Summers joining/anticipated 2018:
1Ls: 3-4;　2Ls: 16
Summers joining/anticipated 2018 split
by office: Chicago: 4; Dallas: 2; Detroit: 5;
Bloomfield Hills: 2; Grand Rapids: 1;
Lansing: 2; Ann Arbor: 1;
San Antonio: 2-3
Summer salary 2018:
1Ls: $2,300-2,900
2Ls: $2,300-2,900
Split summers offered? No

Epstein Becker & Green, PC

250 Park Avenue, New York, New York 10177-1211

Tel: 212 351 4500   Fax: 212 878 8600
Recruitment website: www.ebglaw.com/careers
Linkedin: epstein-becker-&-green-p-c-

Twitter: @ebglaw
Youtube: ebglaw

Main areas of work
- Employment, Labor & Workforce Management
- Health Care & Life Sciences
- Litigation & Business Disputes

Firm profile
Epstein Becker Green (EBG) is a national law firm with a primary focus on health care and life sciences; employment, labor, and workforce management; and litigation and business disputes. Founded in 1973 as an industry-focused firm, EBG has decades of experience serving clients in health care, financial services, retail, hospitality, and technology, among other industries, representing entities from startups to Fortune 100 companies.

Recruitment

Law Schools attending for OCIs in 2018:
- American University
- Benjamin N. Cardozo
- Boston University
- Brooklyn
- Case Western Reserve University
- Columbia
- Cornell
- Fordham University
- George Washington University
- Harvard
- Loyola University Chicago
- New York University
- Seton Hall University
- St. Louis University
- University of Houston
- University of Maryland
- University of Virginia

Recruitment outside OCIs:
The firm also collects resumes from 25 law schools, participates in several career fairs, and receives over 500 resumes from law school candidates who apply directly with the firm.

Summer associate profile:
EBG looks for law students who have a demonstrated interest (through experience and/or education) in health law or in labor and employment law. EBG prefers students who are in the top third of their class and prefer law journal experience.

Summer program components:
EBG's Summer Associate Program is designed to provide a comprehensive picture of practice at the firm as well as training in substantive areas of the firm's core practices and is the primary source of new associates. Summer associates are assigned a broad range of projects that otherwise would be preformed by junior associates. They get the opportunity to work on client projects, pro bono projects, and client development projects.

Head Office: New York
Number of domestic offices: 14
Number of partners (US): 132
Number of associates (US): 128

Contacts
Main recruiting contact:
Amy Simmons, asimmons@ebglaw.com
Hiring partner: Carrie Valiant
Diversity officer: Carrie Valiant

Recruitment details
Entry-level associates starting in 2018: 9
Clerking policy: No
Summers joining/anticipated 2018:
1Ls: 2, 2Ls: 8
Summers joining/anticipated 2018 split by office: DC: 5, New York : 4, Newark: 1
Summer salary 2018:
1Ls: $1,850/week
2Ls: varies
Split summers offered? considered on a case-by-case basis

EPSTEIN
BECKER
GREEN

Finnegan, Henderson, Farabow, Garrett & Dunner LLP

901 New York Avenue, NW, Washington, DC 20001

Tel: 202 408 4000   Fax: 202 408 4400
Recruitment website: www.finnegan.com/en/careers/
Linkedin: finnegan-henderson-farabow-garrett-&-dunner-llp

Twitter: @FinneganIPLaw
Facebook: finnegan

Main areas of work

Our practice includes all aspects of patent, trademark, copyright, and trade secret law, including counseling, prosecution, licensing, and litigation. We also represent clients on IP issues related to international trade, portfolio management, the Internet, e-commerce, government contracts, antitrust, and unfair competition.

Firm profile

Finnegan offers full-service IP legal and technical experience in virtually every industry and technology—from electrical and computer technology, industrial manufacturing, consumer products, medical devices, and biotechnology to pharmaceuticals, chemicals, and alternative energy.

Recruitment

Law Schools attending for OCIs in 2018:

Alabama; American; Arizona State; Berkeley; Boston College; Boston University; Emory; Florida; George Mason; George Washington; Georgetown; Georgia; Georgia State; Harvard; Hastings; Howard; Maryland; New Hampshire; Pennsylvania; Santa Clara; Stanford; UC Davis; USC; UCLA; Vanderbilt; Virginia; Washington.

Recruitment outside OCIs:

- Bay Area Diversity Career Fair
- Chicago Patent Law Interview Program
- Midwest-California Consortium Interview Program
- National Law School Consortium
- SFIPLA Bay Area Job Fair
- Southeastern Intellectual Property Job Fair
- Southeastern Minority Job Fair
- The Law Consortium

Summer associate profile:

For starters, the summer associates are smart, willing to work hard, and committed to excelling in intellectual property law. They are expected to demonstrate the ability to analyze complex legal issues, write clearly and persuasively, show initiative, manage time effectively, and assume responsibility for projects. Above all, they're expected to be team players who work — and play — well with the rest of the team.

Summer program components:

During Finnegan's Summer Associate Program, you'll be exposed to the full range and diversity of an intellectual property law practice. You'll receive real work assignments involving litigation, Patent Trial and Appeal Board (PTAB) proceedings, prosecution, licensing, trademark, copyright, and the drafting of opinions and briefs. You'll receive specialized training that complements your legal studies in areas such as legal writing, patent application filing strategies, overview of licensing, and an overview of PTAB and litigation best practices. You'll meet peers drawn from top law schools across the country and have ample opportunity to socialize with Finnegan partners and associates — all in structured circumstances that stress professionalism, training, and development.

Head Office: Washington, DC
Number of domestic offices: 5
Number of international offices: 5
Worldwide revenue: $309,116,000
Partners (US): 121
Associates (US): 134

Contacts
Main recruitment contact: Laurie Taylor
Hiring partner: Scott Burwell
Diversity officer: Raj Gupta

Recruitment details
Entry-level associates starting in 2018: 22
Clerking policy: Yes
Summers joining/anticipated 2018:
1Ls: 3, 2Ls: 29
Summers joining/anticipated 2018 split by office:
Washington, DC: 24
Atlanta, GA: 3
Palo Alto, CA: 2
Reston, VA: 2
Boston, MA: 1
Summer salary 2018:
1Ls: $3500
2Ls: $3500
Split summers offered? No
Can summers spend time in an overseas office? No

FINNEGAN

Firm Profiles

Fish & Richardson PC

One Marina Park Drive, Boston, MA 02210

Tel: 617 542 5070   Fax: 617 542 8906
Email: recruiting@fr.com
Recruitment website: www.fr.com/careers
Linkedin: fish-&-richardson-p-c-

Facebook: FishLegalRecruiting

Main areas of work

Fish & Richardson offers top-rated litigation, patent, regulatory, trademark, and copyright services to help clients maximize the value of their intellectual property.

Firm profile

Fish & Richardson is a global patent prosecution, intellectual property litigation, and commercial litigation law firm with more than 400 attorneys and technology specialists in the U.S. and Europe. Fish is the #1 U.S. patent litigation firm, handling nearly three times as many cases than its nearest competitor; a powerhouse patent prosecution firm; a top-tier trademark and copyright firm; and the #1 firm at the Patent Trial and Appeal Board, with more cases than any other firm. Since 1878, Fish attorneys have been winning cases worth billions in controversy — often by making new law — for the world's most innovative and influential technology leaders.

Recruitment

Law Schools attending for OCIs in 2018:

Boston College, Boston University, Columbia, Emory, Fordham, Georgetown, George Washington, Harvard, NYU, Santa Clara University, SMU, Stanford, Texas Tech, UC Berkeley, UC Hastings, University of Houston Law Center, UCLA, University of Michigan, University of Minnesota, University of Pennsylvania, University of Texas, Boston Lawyers Group Job Fair, Delaware Minority Job Fair, Patent Law Interview Program (Chicago), Southeastern IP Job Fair

Recruitment outside OCIs:

We also hire from judicial clerkships, job fairs, write-in applications, and our attorney referral program.

Summer associate profile:

Fish seeks students with excellent academic credentials and superior writing ability, and for many positions, a scientific or technical background is preferred (required for patent prosecution candidates).

Law students are a great fit for our summer program if they: convey a sincere career interest in intellectual property, always want to know how things work; thrive in a fast-paced, deadline oriented environment; and are motivated to take on challenges.

Summer associate components:

Summer associates at Fish participate in challenging work assignments, training with industry leaders, and activities that foster relationships with their future colleagues.

Summer projects may include preparing patent and trademark applications and conducting research for litigation cases, as well as opportunities to attend client meetings, depositions, and even trials.

The highlight of our summer training and integration is a firmwide retreat that features an award winning writing workshop, business development training, and an associate led discussion of life in Big Law. Summer associates bond with other students and attorneys across the firm, and establish relationships they will carry through their careers.

Throughout the summer, each office plans activities to welcome summer associates into the firm and city in which the office is located. Each summer associate is provided a mentor to answer questions and provide guidance. And all of our attorneys are invited to provide in-depth feedback which summer associates receive in their mid-summer and end of summer reviews.

Head Office: **Boston, MA**
Number of domestic offices: **11**
Number of international offices: **1**
Worldwide revenue: **$416.8 million**
Partners (US): **182**
Associates (US): **162**

Contacts
Main recruitment contact:
Kristine McKinney, Chief Legal Talent and Inclusion Officer
Hiring partner: **Betty Chen**
Diversity officer: **Kia Scipio,**
Diversity & Inclusion Manager

Recruitment details
Entry-level associates starting in 2018: **17**
Clerking policy: **Yes**
Summers joining/anticipated 2018: **25**
1Ls: 10 (SEO: 7), 2Ls: 15 (SEO: 4)
Summers joining/anticipated 2018 split by office: **Atlanta: 2, Boston: 5, Dallas: 2, New York: 2, San Diego: 2, Silicon Valley: 3, Twin Cities: 3, Washington DC: 6**
Summer salary 2018:
1Ls: $3,500 per week
2Ls: $3,500 per week
Split summers offered? **Yes**
Can summers spend time in overseas office? **No**

Fitzpatrick, Cella, Harper & Scinto

1290 Avenue of the Americas, New York, NY 10104

Tel: 212 218 2100 Fax: 212 218 2200
Recruitment website: www.fitzpatrickcella.com
Linkedin: fitzpatrick-cella-harper-&-scinto

Main areas of work

All areas of intellectual property law, including patents, trademarks, copyrights, unfair competition and trade secrets.

Firm profile

We have one of the premier patent litigation practices in the nation and also prosecute more than twice as many patents as any other New York-based firm. The quality and experience of our attorneys is second to none. In addition to superior legal qualifications, the overwhelming majority of our attorneys hold scientific or engineering degrees and many also have substantial industry experience. Our attorneys also have a long history of pro bono work, as well as active involvement in bar associations and community organizations.

Recruitment

Law Schools attending for OCIs in 2018:

American, Boston College, Boston University, Brooklyn, Cardozo, Columbia, Fordham, George Mason, George Washington, Georgetown, Harvard, New York Law School, New York University, Notre Dame, Pace, Rutgers, Seton Hall, St John's, University of New Hampshire and the University of Pennsylvania, Yale

Job Fairs/Consortia: Cornell Job Fair, Emory in New York, New York Interview Program, University of Connecticut NY Job Fair, and the Loyola Patent Interview Program

Recruitment outside of OCIs:

We are happy to receive direct submissions from 2L law students throughout the year, and 1L law students beginning on December 1st.

Summer associate profile:

Fitzpatrick is looking for a diverse group of summer associates with science or engineering degrees. Our summer associates are team-oriented, motivated and have excelled academically. We like to see candidates that are enthusiastic about IP.

Summer program components:

Summer associates will have significant involvement in intellectual property matters, including playing substantive roles in litigation teams. Each summer associate has a partner and associate mentor to provide counsel and advice with assignments.

Fitzpatrick will also provide formal training through seminars, a legal writing course, a fact investigation course and deposition workshop.

Head Office: New York, NY
Number of domestic offices: 3
Partners (US): 49
Of Counsel (US): 5
Associates (US): 55

Contacts
Main recruitment contact: Nicole Cohen
(ncohen@fchs.com)
Hiring partner: Ha Kung Wong
Diversity officer: Elizabeth Holowacz

Recruitment details
Entry-level associates starting in 2018: 6
Clerking policy: Yes
Summers joining/anticipated 2018:
2Ls: 9
Summers joining/anticipated 2018 split by office: New York: 9
Summer salary 2018:
1Ls: $ 3500
2Ls: $ 3500
Split summers offered? Only in exceptional circumstances

Fitzpatrick | we are IP.

Foley & Lardner LLP

777 E. Wisconsin Avenue, Milwaukee, WI 53202-5306

Tel: 414 271 2400 Fax: 414 297 4900
Email: rbradley@foley.com
Recruitment website: www.foleyrecruiting.com
Linkedin: foley-&-lardner-llp

Main areas of work

With more than 1000 attorneys spread across 21 domestic offices and three foreign offices, Foley's market-leading platform includes business law, government and public policy, international, intellectual property and litigation. Adding depth to our bench strength, we address and anticipate client needs across more than 30 core practice areas and nine cross-disciplinary industry teams.

Firm profile

Foley provides award-winning business and legal insight to clients across the country and around the world. Creating legal strategies that help meet our clients' needs today — and anticipate their challenges tomorrow — Foley is continually recognized by our clients and the legal industry for our exceptional client service, thought-leadership, value and innovative strategy.

Recruitment

Law Schools attending for OCIs in 2018:

Law Schools: Baylor University, Boston College, Boston University, Columbia, Cornell, Duke, Florida State, Fordham, Georgetown, George Washington, Harvard, Howard, Marquette, Michigan, Minnesota, Northwestern, Notre Dame, NYU, SMU, Stanford, Texas A&M, Texas Tech, UC Berkeley, University of Chicago, University of Florida, University of Houston, University of Illinois, University of Iowa, UCLA, University of Miami, University of San Diego, USC, University of Texas, Vanderbilt, Virginia, Wisconsin, Yale

Job Fairs: Bay Area Diversity Career Fair, Lavender Law Conference Job Fair, Loyola Patent Law Interview Program, SFIPLA, Sunbelt Minority Job Fair, Southern Legal Interview Program, University of Oklahoma Job Fair (Dallas & Houston)

Recruitment outside OCIs:

We fill the majority of our hiring needs through OCI but always consider all other applicants who apply to the positions posted to our online career center at www.foleyrecruiting.com. Specific needs outside of OCI are posted to that same online career center.

Summer associate profile:

Foley is looking for summer associates with an entrepreneurial spirit who bring diverse life and work experiences. Key attributes also include intellect, academic achievement, judgement and leadership abilities and excellent communication and interpersonal skills.

Summer program components:

We aim to introduce our summer associates to life as a Foley associate. Making significant contributions from day one, our summer associates are immersed in real world, practical experiences. Work is assigned on a project basis, which allows summer associates to experience a variety of practice areas and choose projects that match their interests. Summer associates receive a dedicated mentor and our Foley Academy training programs highlight Foley's culture, practice areas and strategic goals while developing and strengthening professional skills. To round out the experience, our summer associates participate in entertaining social events, including a firmwide retreat, where summer associates hear directly from firm leadership, participate in interactive workshops and training programs and build and strengthen relationships with our attorneys and other members of their class.

Head Office: Milwaukee, WI
Number of domestic offices: 21
Number of international offices: 3
Worldwide revenue: $830 million
Partners (US): 482
Associates (US): 402
Of/Special Counsel (US): 153

Contacts
Main recruitment contact:
Rebecca S Bradley (rbradley@foley.com)
Hiring Partner: Bob Scher
Diversity officer: Eileen Ridley

Recruitment details
Entry-level associates starting in 2018: 53
Clerking policy: Bonus and advanced standing provided for federal clerkships and clerkships with the highest court in any state
Summers joining/anticipated 2018:
1Ls: 21, 2Ls: 60
Summers joining/anticipated 2018 split by office: Boston: 9, Chicago: 11, Dallas: 6, Detroit: 2, Houston: 4, Jacksonville: 4, Los Angeles: 5, Madison: 2, Miami:1, Milwaukee: 19, New York: 1, Orlando: 2, San Diego: 4, San Francisco: 1, Silicon Valley: 1, Tampa: 1, Washington DC: 8
Summer salary 2018:
1Ls: $2,700-$3,500
2Ls: $2,700-$3,500
Split summers offered? Case by case.
Can summers spend time in an overseas office? No

FOLEY & LARDNER LLP

Firm Profiles

Fox Rothschild LLP

000 Market Street, Philadelphia, PA 19103

Tel: 215 299 2000   Fax: 215 299 2150
Recruitment website: www.foxrothschild.com/careers-for-attorneys/
Linkedin: Fox Rothschild LLP

Twitter: @FoxRothschild
Facebook: Fox Rothschild LLP

Main areas of work

Fox Rothschild has nine primary departments and over 60 practice areas firm-wide. Our departments are: corporate, employee benefits and executive compensation, entertainment, financial restructuring and bankruptcy, intellectual property, labor and employment, litigation, real estate, and taxation and wealth planning.

Firm profile

Fox Rothschild LLP is a national law firm with over 800 lawyers practicing in 21 offices from coast to coast. Our lawyers provide a full range of legal services to public and private companies – from family-run businesses to multinational corporations. We also represent charitable, medical and educational institutions both in the United States and worldwide. Our attorneys have been recognized for their commitment to clients, success in their fields, and diversity.

Recruitment

Law Schools attending for OCIs in 2018:

Berkeley, Boston College, Boston University, Cardozo, Chicago, Columbia, Cornell, Fordham, George Washington, Georgetown, Iowa, Loyola – LA, Michigan, Minnesota, Mitchell Hamline, New York University, Northwestern, Rutgers – Newark and Camden, Penn, Seton Hall, Seattle, SMU, Temple, Texas, UCLA, USC, UVA, Villanova, Washington, Wisconsin

Job Fairs/Consortia Attending in 2018:

Delaware Minority Job Fair, New Jersey Law Firm Group Minority Job Fair, Philadelphia Area Minority Job Fair, Minnesota Minority Recruitment Conference, Northwest Minority Job Fair, Lavender Law Conference and Career Fair

Recruitment outside OCIs:

The firm participates in a number of recruiting events including law school and diversity event sponsorships. The firm also hires 1L summer associates through local diversity organizations.

Summer associate profile:

Our summer program is the foundation of our recruiting efforts. Each summer we invite a diverse group of bright, highly motivated law students to experience the practice of law at Fox Rothschild. Since the majority of our new lawyers come from the pool of second year summer associates who complete our program, we consider the summer program the most important component of the recruiting process.

Summer program components:

Our summer program is designed to expose summer associates to a realistic view of what it is like to practice law at Fox Rothschild. The program provides ongoing interaction with the attorneys on substantive assignments, through trainings, and during varied social events. Summer associates receive work assignments from all departments. We strive to ensure that the assignments given to summer associates are interesting and meaningful, with the results of that work used by our attorneys. Feedback is provided on an assignment-by-assignment basis, as well as through more formal mid-and end-of summer evaluations. In addition, we encourage all summer associates to provide us with a detailed critique of all aspects of the summer program.

Head office: Philadelphia, PA
Number of domestic offices: 21
Partners (US): 497
Associates (US): 241
Counsel (US): 66

Contacts
Main recruitment contact: Natalie Quinn, Director of Associate Recruitment
Diversity officers: Yesenia Gallegos and Prince Thomas, Diversity Committee Co-Chairs

Recruitment details
Entry-level associates starting in 2018: 18
Chicago, IL: 1, Exton, PA: 1, Los Angeles, CA: 2, Minneapolis, MN: 3, Morristown, NJ: 2, New York, NY: 2, Princeton, NJ: 2, Seattle, WA: 1, Washington DC: 2, West Palm Beach, FL: 1, Wilmington, DE: 1
Clerking policy: Yes
Summers joining/anticipated 2018:
1Ls: 7, 2Ls: 26
Summers joining/anticipated 2018 split by office:
Atlantic City, NJ: 1, Blue Bell, PA: 2, Dallas, TX: 1, Denver, CO: 1, Exton, PA: 2, Las Vegas, NV: 1 Los Angeles, CA: 2, Minneapolis, MN: 4, Morristown, NJ: 2, New York, NY: 2, Philadelphia, PA: 4, Pittsburgh, PA: 2, Princeton, NJ: 2, Seattle, WA: 3, Warrington, PA: 2, Washington, DC: 2
Summer salary 2018:
1Ls: $2,211-$3,076/week
2Ls: $2,211-$3,076/week
Split summers offered? No

Firm Profiles

Freshfields Bruckhaus Deringer US LLP

601 Lexington Avenue, 31st Floor, New York, NY 10022

Tel: 212 277 4000　Fax: 212 277 4001
Recruitment website: freshfields.com/en-us/careers/united-states/united-states-careers/
Twitter: @Freshfields

Main areas of work

Freshfields' US offices concentrate on corporate and finance transactions, restructuring and insolvency, antitrust, tax, litigation and international arbitration, while the firm's US attorneys based in Europe and Asia focus on corporate and securities transactions.

Firm profile

Freshfields has nearly 200 lawyers in the US, including 41 partners, with offices in New York and Washington, DC. The US lawyers collaborate with their colleagues in 27 offices around the world, including more than 350 US-qualified lawyers in total. Our US lawyers are internationally recognized as leaders in their respective fields, with four in five US partners cited for their expertise by the leading global directories.

Recruitment

Law Schools attending for OCIs in 2018:

University of Chicago Law School, Columbia University Law School, Cornell, Duke Law School, Emory University, Fordham University School of Law, Georgetown University Law Center, Harvard Law School, University of Michigan Law School, New York University School of Law, Northwestern University School of Law, University of Pennsylvania Law School, Stanford Law School, Vanderbilt Job Fair, UC Berkeley School of Law, University of Virginia, Yale Law School

Recruitment outside OCIs:

Students who do not attend one of the law schools at which we conduct on campus interviews are welcome to submit their materials for consideration.

Summer associate profile:

Freshfields recruits lawyers with many different talents and values individuality. The firm's ability to offer diverse skills locally and across international borders ensures clients have the very best advice possible. Freshfields operates a summer program for US law students in its New York, Washington, DC, Hong Kong, and London offices.

Summer program components:

Freshfields' summer program provides summer associates with exposure to several practice areas. Summer associates get substantive work supported by both formal and informal mentors. Most summer associates spend part of their summer in other Freshfields overseas offices such as London or Hong Kong.

Head Office: New York, NY
Number of domestic offices: 2
Number of international offices: 25
Worldwide revenue: $1.8 billion
Partners (US): 41
Associates (US): 157
(Includes associates, counsel, staff attorneys, contract attorneys, referendar, trainees, and secondees)

Contacts
Main recruitment contact:
Lesley Stumphauzer
Hiring partner: Jerome Ranawake
Diversity officer: Tim Wilkins

Recruitment details
Entry-level associates starting in 2018: 18
Clerking policy: Yes
Summers joining/anticipated 2018:
1Ls: 2, 2Ls: 12, 3Ls: 0, SEO: 1
Summers joining/anticipated 2018 split by office: NY: 12 (including one SEO); DC: 3
Summer salary 2018:
1Ls: $3,462/week
2Ls: $3,462/week
Split summers offered? No
Can summers spend time in an overseas office? Yes

Freshfields Bruckhaus Deringer US LLP

Fried, Frank, Harris, Shriver & Jacobson LLP

One New York Plaza, New York, NY 10004

Tel: 212 859 8000   Fax: 212 859 4000
Recruitment website: www.friedfrank.com/careers
Linkedin: Fried Frank

Twitter: @friedfrank
Facebook: ffhsj
Instagram: @ffhsj

Main areas of work

Antitrust and competition; corporate (asset management, capital markets, corporate governance, derivatives, environmental, finance, mergers and acquisitions, private acquisitions and private equity); energy and energy enforcement; executive compensation and ERISA; financial services; intellectual property and technology; international arbitration; international trade and investment; litigation (antitrust litigation, commercial litigation, government contracts, healthcare fraud and compliance, securities and shareholder litigation, securities enforcement and regulation, white collar criminal defense and securities enforcement); pro bono; real estate (corporate; acquisitions, dispositions and related financings; restructuring and financing; leasing; land use, construction and development); restructuring and insolvency; tax; trusts and estates; white collar criminal defense.

Firm profile

Fried, Frank, Harris, Shriver & Jacobson LLP is a leading international law firm with offices in New York, Washington, DC, Frankfurt and London. Our lawyers regularly advise the world's leading corporations and financial institutions on their most critical legal needs and business opportunities.

Recruitment

Law Schools attending for OCIs in 2018:

American; Boston College; Boston University; Brooklyn; SUNY Buffalo; Cardozo; University of Chicago; Columbia; Cornell; Duke; Fordham; George Mason; Georgetown; George Washington; Harvard; Hofstra; Howard; Michigan; New York Law; Northwestern; NYU; Penn; Rutgers; St. John's; Toronto; UVA and Yale.

Recruitment outside OCIs:

Loyola Patent Job Fair, Lavender Law

Summer associate profile:

Our summer associate program is a critical part of our recruiting process. In hiring summer associates, we look for energetic, motivated candidates who demonstrate a high level of intellectual ability, curiosity, and creativity, as well as a strong interest in working in a collegial setting.

Summer program components:

During the program, summer associates receive meaningful work assignments in a variety of practice areas, as well as attend court, client meetings, drafting and negotiation sessions and closings. They are also given significant opportunities to work on a range of pro bono matters. Each summer associate is matched with one partner mentor and two associate mentors who review and provide feedback on assignments and guide them through the program. Working closely and socializing with partners, counsel and associates, our summer associates leave the program with a clear understanding of what Fried Frank can offer them as a place to begin their legal careers.

Head Office: **New York, NY**
Number of domestic offices: **2**
Number of international offices: **2**
Worldwide revenue: **$634.9 million**
Partners (US): **122**
Associates (US): **298**

Contacts
Main recruitment contact: **Nancy Parker (nancy.parker@friedfrank.com)**
Hiring partners: **Randi Lally and Mark Hayek (NY); Jonathan DeFosse and Michelle Gold (DC)**
Diversity officer: **Asker Saeed**

Recruitment details
Entry-level associates starting in 2018: **60**
Clerking policy: **Yes**
Summers joining/anticipated 2018: **71**
1Ls: **3**, 2Ls: **68**, SEO: **2**
Summers joining/anticipated 2018 split by office: NY: **61**; DC: **10**
Summer salary 2018:
2Ls: **$ 3,462/week**
Split summers offered? **Case by case**
Can summers spend time in an overseas office? **No**

FRIED FRANK

Gibbons P.C.

One Gateway Center, Newark, New Jersey 07102

Tel: 973 596 4500   Fax: 973 596 0545
Recruitment website: www.gibbonslaw.com
Linkedin: gibbons-p.c.

Twitter: @gibbonspc

Main areas of work

The firm's main areas of practice include: commercial and criminal litigation, corporate, employment and labor law, environmental, financial restructuring and creditors' rights, government and regulatory affairs, intellectual property, products liability, and real property.

Firm profile

With 200 attorneys, Gibbons is a leading law firm in New Jersey, New York, Pennsylvania, and Delaware, ranked among the nation's top 200 by The American Lawyer. Gibbons has been recognized nationally for its work — as, for example, one of only 20 law firms on the *National Law Journal's* inaugural *'Midsize Hot List'* — as well as regionally. The *New Jersey Law Journal* has awarded Gibbons a *'Litigation Practice of the Year'* designation four times in recent years, in the class action, products liability, and commercial litigation categories and with the overall *'General Litigation Practice of the Year'* honor. *Law360* has also highlighted the firm's multidisciplinary litigation strength, and its contributions to several high-profile corporate transactions in the public and private sectors, in its *'Regional Powerhouse'* series. The firm has been certified as a great workplace by the independent analysts at the Great Place to Work® organization.

Recruitment

Judicial Clerkship Recruitment:

Gibbons currently focuses its entry-level recruiting efforts exclusively on judicial law clerks for all of the firm's five offices.

Since eliminating the firm's Summer Associate Program in 2003, Gibbons has focused on hiring new associates who have completed a judicial clerkship. Fully 70% of the attorneys in the commercial and criminal litigation department served for federal or state judges. These attorneys provide first-hand insight into the preferences and practices of federal and state judges, in addition to a well-developed knowledge of the inner workings of the courts, adding value for the firm's clients.

Head Office: Newark, NJ
Number of domestic offices: 5
Number of international offices: 0
Worldwide revenue: $99,397,000
Partners (US): 139
Associates (US): 61

Contacts
Main recruitment contacts and hiring partners:
Debra A. Clifford
(dclifford@gibbonslaw.com)
Damian V. Santomauro
(dsantomauro@gibbonslaw.com)
Diversity officer: Robert Johnson

Recruitment details
Clerking policy: Yes

GIBBONS

Gibson, Dunn & Crutcher LLP

33 South Grand Avenue, Los Angeles, CA 90071

Tel: 213 229 7000   Fax: 213 229 7520
Email: lripley@gibsondunn.com
Recruitment website: www.gibsondunn.com

Facebook: GibsonDunnCareers

Main areas of work

Gibson, Dunn & Crutcher is renowned for both its litigation and transactional work. Major practice groups include antitrust, capital markets, class actions, environmental, electronic discovery, information technology, intellectual property, media and entertainment, mergers and acquisitions, securities, transnational litigation and white collar defense. The firm is especially known for its appellate work, particularly in the US Supreme Court.

Firm profile

Gibson, Dunn & Crutcher is a full-service global law firm, with over 1,300 lawyers in 20 offices worldwide, including ten offices in major cities throughout the United States and over 235 lawyers in their London, Paris, Munich, Beijing, Brussels, Dubai, Frankfurt, Hong Kong, Singapore and São Paulo offices. The firm is recognized for excellent legal service and its lawyers routinely represent clients in some of the most high-profile litigation matters and complex transactions in the world.

Recruitment

Law Schools attended for OCIs in 2018:

Berkeley, Chicago, Colorado, Columbia, Cornell, Duke, Fordham, George Washington, Georgetown, Harvard, Houston, Irvine, Loyola, Michigan, NYU, Pennsylvania, Pepperdine, San Diego, SMU, Stanford, Texas, UCLA, USC, Vanderbilt, Virginia, Yale.

Recruitment outside OCIs:

The firm accepts applications from students and graduates from all law schools and not solely from those listed above.

Summer associate profile:

Gibson Dunn's summer program is the single largest means through which new lawyers become a part of our firm. Each summer, Gibson Dunn brings together approximately 135 of the most accomplished and ambitious students from the top law schools across the nation, providing them with real involvement in the high quality legal work that our firm does every day. Summer associates are involved directly in the firm's representation of its clients, maximizing their exposure to the practical aspects of lawyering. In addition to interesting client work, the summer program includes many great social activities giving summer associates the chance to get to know each other and the lawyers of the firm.

Summer program components:

The firm provides significant and substantive training to our select group of summer associates. Each summer associate receives detailed feedback on the projects that they perform plus numerous formal training programs.

Head Office: Los Angeles, CA
Number of domestic offices: 10
Number of international offices: 10
Worldwide revenue: $1,642,000,000
Partners (US): 317
Associates (US): 800

Contacts
Main recruitment contact:
Leslie Ripley, Chief Recruiting Officer
(lripley@gibsondunn.com)
Hiring partner: Steven E Sletten
Diversity officer: Zakiyyah Salim-Williams

Recruitment details
Entry-level associates starting in 2018:
100
Clerking policy: Yes
Summers joining/anticipated 2018:
1Ls: 7, 2Ls: 129, 3Ls: 0, SEO: 1
Summers joining/anticipated 2018 split
by office: Dallas: 6, Denver: 2, Houston:
3, Los Angeles: 23, New York: 44,
Orange County: 12, Palo Alto: 4,
San Francisco: 8, Washington, D:C 34
Summer salary 2018:
1Ls: $3,500
2Ls: $3,500
Split summers offered? Yes
Can summers spend time in an overseas
office? No

GIBSON DUNN

Goodwin

100 Northern Avenue Boston, MA 02210

Tel: 617 570 1000
Email: legalrecruiting@goodwinlaw.com
Recruitment website: www.goodwinlaw.com/careers/law-students
Linkedin: company/goodwin-law

Twitter: @goodwinlaw
Facebook: JoinGoodwin

Main areas of work

Corporate-based practices: private equity, real estate industry (REITS, real estate capital markets, M&A), technology and life sciences, financial industry, intellectual property transactions and strategies, tax.

Litigation-based practices: financial industry, securities, white collar and business litigation, speciality litigation (antitrust, appellate, energy and environmental, global trade, labor and employment, products liability and mass torts).

Firm profile

Goodwin is a Global 50 law firm with offices in Boston, Frankfurt, Hong Kong, London, Los Angeles, New York, Paris, San Francisco, Silicon Valley and Washington, DC. Excelling at complex and sophisticated transactional work and precedent-setting, bet-the company litigation, the firm combines in-depth legal knowledge with practical business experience to help clients maximize opportunities, manage risk and move their business forward. The firm hires talented, motivated people committed to excellence, innovation, collaboration and client service and believes that every lawyer and staff member deserves a supportive, meritocratic environment in which people of all backgrounds are given the opportunity to excel and thrive. Through an extensive and long-standing pro bono program, legal staff is encouraged to assist those unable to afford legal representation.

Recruitment

Law Schools attending for OCIs in 2018:

Berkeley, Boston College, Boston University, Brooklyn, Catholic University of America, Columbia, Cornell, Duke, Emory, Fordham, George Washington, Georgetown, Harvard, Howard, Loyola Law School (Los Angeles), McGill, Northeastern, Northwestern, NYU, Santa Clara, Stanford, Suffolk, UC Davis, UC Hastings, UCLA, UNC, University of Chicago, University of Connecticut, University of Michigan, University of Pennsylvania, University of Texas, USC, UVA, Vanderbilt, Washington University in St. Louis, William & Mary, Yale

Recruitment outside OCIs:

Bay Area Diversity Career Fair, Boston Lawyers Group, Boston Job Fair, Lavender Law Career Fair, Loyola Patent Law Interview Program, NEBLSA Job Fair, Southeastern Minority Job Fair

Goodwin's Asia Track program is designed for summer associates who have a particular interest in pursuing a legal career in Asia. Native fluency in Mandarin Chinese is required. The Asia Track summer program involves spending eight to ten weeks in one of our US offices and two to three weeks in our Hong Kong office.

Summer associate profile:

Goodwin hires summer associates with exceptional academic records, demonstrated leadership abilities and excellent written, verbal and interpersonal skills.

Summer program components:

Goodwin's summer program provides summer associates with a realistic work experience mirroring that of a junior associate. We work closely with summer associates to understand their interests and provide opportunities to work on a broad range of assignments. Summer associates are encouraged to observe client meetings, court hearings, depositions, negotiations and attend practice area meetings. We provide leading litigation and business law training programs throughout the summer. Through our adviser program, summer associates are paired with partners and associates to help them integrate.

Largest Office: Boston, MA
Number of domestic offices: 6
Number of international offices: 4
Worldwide revenue: $1,032,437,000
Partners (US): 318
Counsel (US): 94
Associates (US): 444

Contacts
Main recruitment contact: Ashley Nelson, Director of Legal Recruitment, Associate & Professional Track Hiring
See the full list of office-based recruiting contacts on our website
Hiring partner: Emily Rapalino, National Hiring Partner
Diversity officer: Bernard Guinyard, Director of Diversity & Inclusion

Recruitment details
Entry-level associates starting in 2018: 50
Clerking policy: Yes
Summers joining/anticipated 2018:
1Ls: 1, 2Ls: 58
Summers joining/anticipated 2018 split by office: Boston: 23, New York: 17, Washington, DC: 5, Los Angeles: 2, San Francisco: 5, Silicon Valley: 5, Hong Kong: 2
Summer salary 2018:
1Ls: $3,460/week
2Ls: $3,460/week
Split summers offered? No
Can summers spend time in an overseas office? Case-by-case

GOODWIN

Goulston & Storrs

0 Atlantic Avenue, Boston, MA 02110

el: 617 482 1776 Fax: 617 574 4112
mail: jsmith@goulstonstorrs.com
ecruitment website: www.goulstonstorrs.com
inkedin: goulston-&-storrs

Twitter: @goulstonstorrs
Facebook: GoulstonStorrs

Main areas of work

eal estate, litigation, tax, private clients and trusts, capital markets, bankruptcy, corpo-ate, employment, banking and finance, environmental, intellectual property.

Firm profile

Goulston & Storrs is an Am Law 200 law firm, with offices in Boston, New York and Washington, DC. With over 200 attorneys across multiple disciplines, Goulston & Storrs s nationally recognized for its real estate practice, leading-edge corporate, capital markets nd finance, litigation, and private client and trust practices. Our lawyers employ a proven eam approach that values client outcomes over individual recognition. The firm's dedica-ion to providing prompt, practical legal advice, cost-efficiently and tailored to our clients' business needs, has resulted in Goulston & Storrs being acknowledged for excellence by *Chambers USA*, *BTI's* A-Team for Client Service, *Best Lawyers in America* and other lead-ng industry rankings.

Recruitment

Law Schools attending for OCIs in 2018:

Harvard, Georgetown University, Columbia University, Northeastern University, New York University, Boston College, Boston University, Suffolk University

Recruitment outside OCIs:

We participate in a number of networking events at local law schools; invite students to our office for resume review and mock interviews.

We also host a rising 2L reception every July so students from outside Boston can learn more about G&S in advance of OCI.

Summer associate profile:

We attract and hire people who: seek a sophisticated and challenging legal practice; are concerned about team success; are willing to work hard.

Summer program components:

As a summer associate, you have a unique opportunity to learn about the legal profes-sion and the Boston area. Expect to live the law firm experience with direct partner and client exposure. Work assignments are substantive and include research and writing as-signments, client meetings, conference calls, depositions and attending hearings. Your summer with Goulston & Storrs offers amazing work opportunities throughout several practice areas, assisting the firm's attorneys.

Head Office: Boston, MA
Number of domestic offices: 3
Number of international offices: 0
Worldwide revenue: $176,000,000
Partners (US): 121
Associates (US): 70

Contacts
Main recruitment contacts: Karen Febeo and Jen Smith
Hiring partner: Bill Seuch
Diversity officers: Kevin O'Flaherty and Matt Epstein

Recruitment details
Entry-level associates starting in 2018: 6
Clerking policy: Yes
Summers joining/anticipated 2018:
2Ls: 7
Summers joining/anticipated 2018 split by office: Boston: 6, Washington DC: 1
Summer salary 2018:
1Ls: $3,400 per week
2Ls: $3,400 per week
Split summers offered? Case by case basis
Can summers spend time in overseas office? No

Greenburg Glusker Fields Claman & Machtinger LLP

1900 Avenue of the Stars, 21st Floor, Los Angeles, CA 90067

Tel: 310 553 3610
Email: agafni@greenbergglusker.com
Recruitment website: www.greenbergglusker.com/careers
Linkedin: greenberg-glusker

Twitter: @greenberggluske
Facebook: GreenbergGlusker
Instagram: @greenbergglusker

Main areas of work

Bankruptcy/insolvency, corporate, emerging technology and new media, employment, entertainment, environmental, intellectual property, litigation, private client services, real estate, and taxation.

Firm profile

For nearly 60 years, Greenberg Glusker has held a unique position in Los Angeles as a full-service law firm, with particular expertise in bankruptcy/insolvency, corporate, employment, entertainment, environmental, intellectual property, litigation, private client services, real estate, and taxation.

Committed to providing a wide range of services, we combine the personal attention of a boutique firm with the strength and breadth of services customarily found in a multi-office, international firm.

Results-oriented client service is how we continue to distinguish ourselves today.

Recruitment

Law schools attended for OCI in 2018:

UC Davis, UCLA, UC Berkeley, USC, and Stanford

Summer program components:

The main objective of our summer program is to provide the summer clerks with an honest and real experience of practicing law as a junior attorney at Greenberg Glusker. For purposes of the summer program, we divide the firm into three practice area subgroups. Each summer clerk will spend a minimum of three weeks in each practice subgroup. Typically, the subgroups are organized as follows:

- Litigation/Employment/Entertainment
- Real Estate/Environmental/Trusts & Estates
- Bankruptcy/Business & Tax/Intellectual Property

Our clerks will have the opportunity to attend trials, depositions and business meetings. Also, as a part of the summer program, we plan social events in order to facilitate multiple opportunities for the clerks to interact with each of our attorneys as much as possible. Our summer social calendar includes a mix of formal events such as concerts, sporting events, theater, and cooking classes, as well as informal happy hours and dinners.

Head Office: Los Angeles, CA
Number of domestic offices: 1
Partners US: 63
Associates US: 29

Contacts
Main recruitment contact: Aaron Gafni
(agafni@greenbergglusker.com)
Hiring partner: Aaron Gafni
Diversity officer: Brian Moskal

Recruitment details
Entry-level associates starting in 2018: 3
Clerking policy: No
Summers joining/anticipated 2018:
2Ls: 3
Summers joining/anticipated 2018 split by office: Los Angeles: 3
Summer salary 2018:
1Ls: $3,077/week
2Ls: $3,077/week
Split summers offered? Yes

Greenberg Traurig, LLP

Tel: 212 801 9200 Fax: 212 801 6400
Email: gtrecruiting@gtlaw.com
Recruitment website: www.gtlaw.com/careers/associates
Linkedin: greenberg-traurig-llp

Twitter: @GT_Law
Facebook: GreenbergTraurigLLP
Instagram: @gt_law

Main areas of work

Banking and financial services; blockchain; corporate; cybersecurity, privacy and crisis management; emerging technology; energy and natural resources; entertainment and media; environmental; food, beverage and agribusiness; franchise and distribution; gaming; government contracts; government law and policy; health care and FDA practice; hospitality; immigration and compliance; infrastructure; insurance; intellectual property and technology; international trade; labor and employment; Latin American and Iberian practice; life sciences and medical technology; litigation; marketing, advertising, sweepstakes and promotions law; pharmaceutical, medical device and health care; private wealth services; public finance; real estate; regulatory and compliance; restructuring and bankruptcy; retail; tax; technology, media and telecommunications; transportation and automotive

Firm profile

Greenberg Traurig, LLP (GT) has more than 2,000 attorneys in 38 offices in the United States, Latin America, Europe, Asia, and the Middle East. GT has been recognized for its philanthropic giving, was named the largest firm in the US by *Law360* in 2017, and is among the Top 20 on the 2017 *Am Law* Global 100.

Recruitment

Law Schools attending for OCIs in 2018:

Brooklyn; Chicago-Kent; Columbia; Cornell; Duke; Florida International University; Fordham; Georgetown; George Washington; Harvard; Howard; Indiana University; Loyola; Florida International University; Northwestern; Notre Dame; University of California Los Angeles; University of Chicago; University of Florida; University of Miami; University of Michigan; University of Pennsylvania; University of Southern California; University of Virginia; Vanderbilt

Recruitment outside OCIs:

We also attend a number of job fairs, meet with candidates who contact us directly from schools where do not go on campus, and identify candidates through resume collections.

Job Fairs: Cook County Minority Job Fair; IP Job Fair; Lavender Law Career Fair; Midwest-California-Georgia Consortium in Chicago; Southeastern Minority Job Fair (SEMJF)

Resume Collects: Case Western; Emory; Florida State; Georgia State; Ohio State; Pepperdine; St. Thomas; Stetson; Stanford; University of Georgia; Washington University in St. Louis; Yale

Summer associate profile:

Many of our current firm leaders started their careers as a summer associate at Greenberg Traurig. An important objective of the program is for summer associates to being the transition from law student to practicing lawyers and future leaders by including them on client matters. Key qualities we look for in our attorneys are an entrepreneurial spirit, initiative and willingness to assume responsibility and leadership skills.

Summer program components:

• Corporate deal simulation
• Conflict resolution training
• Litigation training, such as oral advocacy presentation
• Visit to appeals court and Q&A session with a judge
• Firsthand exposure to in-house counsels and their interaction with law firms

---

Head Office: **Global**
Number of domestic offices: **29**
Number of international offices: **9**
Worldwide revenue: **$1,477,180,000**
Partners (US): **992**
Associates (US): **1051**

Contacts
Main recruitment contact:
Janet McKeegan (mckeegan@gtlaw.com)
Hiring partner: Brad Kaufman
Diversity officer: Nikki Lewis Simon

Recruitment details
Entry-level associates starting in 2018: **38**
Clerking policy: **Yes**
Summers joining/anticipated 2018:
1Ls: **5**, 2Ls: **20**, 3Ls: **0**, SEO: **0**
Summer salary 2018:
1Ls: **$ NA**
2Ls: **$ NA**
Split summers offered? **Case-by-case**
Can summers spend time in an overseas office? **Case-by-case**

GT GreenbergTraurig

Hangley Aronchick Segal Pudlin & Schiller

One Logan Square, 27th Floor, Philadelphia, PA 19103

Tel: 215 568 6200 Fax: 215 568 0300
Email: marketingdept@hangley.com
Recruitment website: www.hangley.com/careers/
Linkedin: hangley-aronchick-segal-pudlin-&-schiller

Twitter: @HASPSLaw

Main areas of work

Hangley Aronchick Segal Pudlin & Schiller is a multi-faceted law firm that offers specialized legal solutions to a broad range of local, regional, and national clients. The firm is highly regarded nationally for its quality work, innovative strategies, and excellent results. With offices in Philadelphia, Harrisburg, and Norristown, Pennsylvania, and Cherry Hill, New Jersey, Hangley Aronchick offers a suite of diverse legal services, including litigation, business and corporate, insurance coverage, real estate, bankruptcy, education, antitrust, environmental, family law, and tax and estate planning services.

Firm profile

Hangley Aronchick Segal Pudlin & Schiller is consistently recognized for excellence in legal practice, as well as for its ability to recruit talented attorneys. Founded in 1994, the firm is known for the sophistication of its matters, the roster of its clients and the quality of its work. In the Delaware Valley, the firm is unparalleled in its ability to attract the most highly qualified attorneys, both at the entry level and laterally. The firm includes former Philadelphia City Solicitors; Fellows of the American College of Trial Lawyers, the American College of Bankruptcy, and the American College of Real Estate Lawyers; members of judicial advisory committees; members of the American Law Institute; and adjunct faculty members at area law schools.

For further information on the firm's practice areas and outstanding lawyers, readers are invited to visit the firm's website www.hangley.com

Recruitment

Hangley Aronchick does not participate in OCI. Qualified applicants are encouraged to send their resumes directly to the firm at any time.

Please see www.hangley.com/careers for more details.

Hangley Aronchick Segal Pudlin & Schiller does not have a formal summer associate program, though the firm will consider extraordinary candidates for summer employment on occasion.

Head Office: Philadelphia, PA
Number of domestic offices: 4
Partners (US): 32
Associates (US): 14
Of Counsel (US): 2

Contacts
Main recruitment contact:
Daniel Segal (dsegal@hangley.com)
Hiring Partner: Daniel Segal, Michele Sacks Fenkel
Diversity officer: Sharon McKee

Recruitment details
Entry-level associates starting in 2018: 1
Clerking policy: Yes

HANGLEY
ARONCHICK
SEGAL
PUDLIN
&SCHILLER

Harris, Wiltshire & Grannis LLP

1919 M Street NW, Eighth Floor, Washington, DC 20036

Tel: 202 730 1300   Fax: 202 730 1301

Email: attorneyrecruiting@hwglaw.com

Recruitment website: www.hwglaw.com/recruiting

Linkedin: wiltshire-&-grannis-llp

Facebook: HWGLaw

Main areas of work

Harris, Wiltshire & Grannis is a boutique law firm, meaning we focus on solving fairly specialized legal problems extremely well. We have excellent trial litigators who handle government investigations and criminal defense matters as well as complex civil litigation. We also have an exceptional Supreme Court and appellate litigation group as well as one of the leading legal and government ethics practices. However, the firm started out as a telecom and technology firm and that is still our primary area of practice. We handle just about any kind of matter before the FCC, representing companies both large and small that are involved in all kinds of different technologies, from satellites to wireless phones to undersea cables to the internet.

Firm profile

Work is an integral component of our lives; we gain personal and professional satisfaction from high quality legal advocacy, writing and critical thinking. We enjoy practicing together, working hard and giving our clients the absolute best representation. At the same time, we love our families and our friends and take pleasure in any number of avocations. Harris, Wiltshire & Grannis is a place where smart, dedicated attorneys do work of the highest quality and still live a normal life. Because this is central to the culture of the firm, we have no set billable hours requirement and no aspect of associate compensation is tied to the number of hours billed.

Recruitment

Law Schools attending for OCIs in 2018:

Chicago, Duke, Georgetown, Harvard, Michigan, Stanford, Virginia

Summer associate profile:

We seek associates with superlative writing ability and a record of the very highest academic achievement. We will only hire a summer associate that we fully expect to become a superb lawyer and a trusted colleague.

Summer program components:

We treat summer associates like brand new associates. This means that, although summer associates necessarily require a different level of training and supervision, they will be doing the same work associates do, with the same people and under the same conditions. Harris, Wiltshire & Grannis associates are expected to perform as lawyers, not assistant lawyers and we want our summer associates to aim for the same high level of creativity, initiative and skill. Summer associates can expect to work in our telecommunications and technology, criminal defense and litigation, and appellate practices.

Head Office: Washington, DC
Number of domestic offices: 2
Partners (US): 32
Of Counsel (US): 5
Associates (US): 13

Contacts
Main recruitment contact:
Jonathan Mirsky
Hiring partner: Jonathan Mirsky
Diversity officer: Brita Strandberg

Recruitment details
Entry-level associates starting in 2018: 4
Clerking policy: Yes
Summers joining/anticipated 2018:
2Ls: 3
Summers joining/anticipated 2018 split by office: Washington DC: 3
Summer salary 2018:
2Ls: $3,465/week
Split summers offered? Yes

HWG | HARRIS, WILTSHIRE & GRANNIS LLP

Firm Profiles

Haynes and Boone, LLP

2323 Victory Avenue Suite 700, Dallas, TX 75219

Tel: 214 651 5000
Email: amanda.kelly@haynesboone.com
Recruitment website: www.haynesboone.com
Linkedin: haynes-and-boone-llp

Main areas of work

Corporate/securities/M&A, private equity, hedge funds, business litigation (including IP, insurance coverage, environmental, energy, real estate, securities, healthcare and appellate), restructuring, energy, banking and finance, franchises, intellectual property/technology, labor and employment and real estate.

Firm profile

Haynes and Boone, LLP is an international corporate law firm with offices in Texas, New York, California, Colorado, Washington, DC, London, Shanghai and Mexico City, providing a full spectrum of legal services.

Recruitment

Law Schools attending for OCIs in 2018:

Harvard, Southern Methodist University, Stanford, UC Berkeley, UC Irvine, University of Houston, University of Texas, University of Virginia

Recruitment outside OCIs:

Loyola Patent Law Interview Program, Texas Interview Program, Lavender Law Career Fair, Southeastern IP Job Fair, Sunbelt Minority Job Fair

Summer associate profile:

To sustain what we feel is a blend of culture and sophistication of practice that is unmatched in the market, Haynes and Boone is looking for internally driven law students with a personality that would augment our firm's commitment to teamwork and a long-term approach to the practice of law.

Summer program components:

Our summer associates spend nine to ten weeks (depending on office) with us working in one or two of our practice areas. Each summer associate is given a supervisor who assigns them work and they are able to attend client meetings, negotiations, hearings, etc. Feedback is provided throughout the summer as well as through the mid-clerkship review. Our summer associates also enjoy several social events designed to get to know our attorneys.

Head Office: Dallas, TX
Number of domestic offices: 12
Number of international offices: 3
Worldwide revenue: $397.5 million
Partners (US): 230
Associates (US): 311 (including other attorneys)

Recruitment details
Main recruitment contact: Amanda Kelly, Manager of Entry-Level Recruiting
Hiring partner: Eric Williams
Diversity officer: Kenya Woodruff, Partner of the Attorney Diversity and Inclusion Committee

Recruitment details
Entry-level associates starting in 2018: 26
Clerking policy: Yes
Summers joining/anticipated 2018:
1Ls: 18, 2Ls: 29
Summers joining/anticipated 2018 split by office:
1Ls: Dallas: 4, Denver: 1, Houston: 8, New York: 2, Palo Alto: 1, Richardson: 1, Washington DC: 1
2Ls: Dallas: 16, Houston: 5, New York: 3, Palo Alto: 1, Richardson: 4
Summer salary 2018:
1Ls: $3,462/week
2Ls: $3,462/week
Post 3Ls: $3,462/week
Split summers offered? CBC
Can summers spend time in an overseas office? No

haynes*boone*

Hogan Lovells US LLP

5 13th Street, NW, Washington, DC 20004

el: 202 637 5600   Fax: 202 637 5910
mail: irena.mcgrath@hoganlovells.com
ecruitment website: www.careers-us.hoganlovells.com
nkedin: hoganlovells

Twitter: @HoganLovells
Instagram:
@hoganlovellscareers.americas

Main areas of work

Jorking at the intersection of law, business and government, across a wide range of in-
ustries, Hogan Lovells US LLP's global practices include corporate; finance; government
egulatory; intellectual property, media and technology; litigation, arbitration and em-
loyment; and pro bono.

Firm profile

y joining Hogan Lovells, you will become part of a legal practice with a long tradition of ex-
ellence that is keenly focused on the future. Working as an integrated team, our lawyers help
lients address complex legal issues across a broad spectrum of industries. Our unique global
latform, collaborative culture and commitment to your professional development provide
n exceptional foundation on which to build a legal career. Hogan Lovells' pioneering US Pro
Bono practice began more than 40 years ago when we were the first law firm to establish a
eparate practice exclusively providing pro bono legal services. Our culture of inclusion, which
espects and values the diversity of all of our people, enhances the quality of Hogan Lovells'
workplace and our ability to provide excellent legal services for clients. We prize our friendly,
eam oriented environment, which encourages professional development, good associate-
partner relations and early client contact.

Recruitment

Law Schools attending for OCIs in 2018:

American University, Baltimore, Boston College, Boston University, Catholic University,
Columbia, Colorado, Cornell, Denver, Duke, Florida, Florida International, Florida State,
George Mason, George Washington, Georgetown, Harvard, Howard, Maryland, Miami,
Michigan, Minnesota, Northwestern, NYU, Pennsylvania, Stanford, Texas, UC Berkeley,
UCLA, USC, UVA, Vanderbilt, Washington & Lee, William & Mary, Yale

Summer associate profile:

Hogan Lovells' summer program is very competitive, and we select our participants each year
from among many highly qualified candidates. We seek candidates whose records demonstrate
outstanding academic performance, and excellent written and oral communication skills. We
also look for other indicators of likely success at Hogan Lovells, such as demonstrated leadership skills, strong motivation, good judgment, the ability to work well with others, and an
interest in community involvement.

Summer associate components:

With guidance from lawyer coordinators and mentors, students do meaningful client
work and participate in training programs designed to develop and enhance legal skills.
Summer Associates have opportunities to attend closings, depositions, and legislative and
administrative hearings and meet with alumni and clients serving in prominent roles in
government and business. Five US Summer Associates with strong interest in our transnational practices participated in a two-week program in the London office. All US Summer
Associates attend a conference in Washington where firm leaders share insights about Hogan Lovells' pre-eminent practices and strategic plans for the future, our vision and values,
and commitment to diversity and inclusion. Through group dinners and team building
exercises, US Summer Associates get to know their colleagues from other offices and make
life long connections.

Head Office (US): Washington, DC
Number of domestic offices: 14
Number of international offices: 36
Worldwide revenue: $2.036 billion
Partners (US): 400
Associates (US): 525

Contacts
Main recruitment contact: Irena McGrath,
Chief Recruitment Officer - Americas
(irena.mcgrath@hoganlovells.com)
Hiring partner: Timothy A Lloyd, Esq.
Diversity officer: Leslie Richards-Yellen
Director of Inclusion - Americas

Recruitment details
Entry-level associates starting in 2018: 82
Clerking policy: Yes
Summers joining/anticipated 2018: 102
1Ls: 17, 2Ls: 85, SEO: 2
Summers joining/anticipated 2018 split
by office: Baltimore: 4, Boston: 3,
Denver 6, Houston: 6, Los Angeles: 5,
Miami: 2, Minneapolis: 1, NY: 14,
Northern Virginia: 3, Philadelphia: 3,
San Francisco: 5, Silicon Valley: 1,
Washington: 49
Summer salary 2018:
1Ls: $3,500 per week (in most offices)
2Ls: $3,500 per week (in most offices)
Split summers offered? Case by Case
Can summers spend time in an overseas
office? Case by Case

Firm Profiles

Holland & Knight LLP

701 Brickell Avenue, Suite 3300, Miami, FL 33131

Tel: 305 374 8500   Fax: 305 789 7799
Recruitment website: www.hklaw.com
Linkedin: holland-&-knight-llp

Twitter: @Holland_Knight
Facebook: HollandKnightLLP

Main areas of work

Holland & Knight advises clients in a range of practice areas, including complex commercial litigation, corporate law, intellectual property, private wealth services, mergers and acquisitions, real estate and zoning law, and public policy and regulatory matters. Attorneys work collaboratively across practices and teams, drawing upon their legal and industry knowledge.

Firm profile

Holland & Knight is a global firm with more than 1,250 lawyers and other professionals in 24 U.S. offices, as well as London, Bogotá and Mexico City. Our lawyers provide representation in litigation, business, real estate and governmental law. Interdisciplinary practice groups and industry-based teams provide clients with access to attorneys throughout the firm, regardless of location. Every day, clients call on Holland & Knight to understand their issues, advocate on their behalf and create solutions to accelerate their position.

Recruitment

Law Schools attending for OCIs in 2018:

Boston College, Boston University, Columbia University, Duke University, Emory, Florida State University, Fordham University, George Washington University, Georgetown University, Harvard, Howard, New York University, Northwestern Pritzker School of Law, Stanford, University of California, Berkeley — Boalt Hall, University of California — Los Angeles, University of Chicago, University of Florida, University of Michigan, University of Notre Dame, University of Pennsylvania, University of Virginia and others

Recruitment outside OCIs:

Attracting, retaining and promoting diverse professionals and fostering an inclusive work environment are priorities at Holland & Knight. Harvard BLSA Job Fair 1Ls, 2Ls & 3Ls; Southeastern Minority Job Fair

Summer associate profile:

Holland & Knight seeks students of substance from diverse backgrounds with superior academics, leadership skills, involvement in extracurricular activities and demonstrated commitment to their communities. We look for candidates who have the desire and ethical foundation to make significant contributions as lawyers to the firm, the profession and in the community. We have been very successful in hiring students who meet these criteria, and our firm as a whole reflects these values.

Summer program components:

Holland & Knight's Summer Associate Program is structured to provide exposure to many diverse practice areas. Summer associates work on substantive matters and observe conferences, negotiations, oral arguments, closings, depositions, hearings and trials. These experiences provide a broad foundation to assist them in identifying the areas of practice on which they would like to focus as they begin their legal careers.

Number of domestic offices: **24**
Number of international offices: **3**
Worldwide revenue: **$858.5 million**
Partners (US): **628**
Associates (US): **493**

Contacts
Main recruitment contact:
Carrie Weintraub, Chief Professional Development & Human Resources Officer (carrie.weintraub@hklaw.com)
Hiring partner: Deborah E Barnard
Diversity officer: Tiffani G Lee

Recruitment details
Entry-level associates starting in 2018: **21**
Clerking policy: **No**
Summers joining/anticipated 2018:
1Ls: 3, 2Ls: 31, 3Ls: 0
Summers joining/anticipated 2018 split by office: Austin: 1, Boston: 4, Chicago: 1, Dallas: 3, Denver: 2, Ft. Lauderdale: 1, Houston: 1, Jacksonville: 2, Miami: 7, New York City: 5, San Francisco: 1, Tampa: 1, Tysons: 2, Washington, DC: 3
Summer salary 2018:
1Ls: $3,400/weekly salary
2Ls: $3,400/weekly salary
Split summers offered? **Case by case**
Can summers spend time in an overseas office? **No**

Holland & Knight

Hughes Hubbard & Reed LLP

One Battery Park Plaza

Tel: 212 837 6000 Fax: 212 299 6131
Email: adrian.cockerill@hugheshubbard.com
Recruitment website: www.hugheshubbard.com/careers/associate-recruiting
Linkedin: hughes-hubbard-&-reed-llp

Twitter: @HughesHubbard
Facebook:
Hughes-Hubbard-Reed-LLP

Main areas of work

With offices in New York, Washington, DC, Los Angeles, Miami, Jersey City, Kansas City, Tokyo and Paris, Hughes Hubbard offers expertise in a widerange of practice areas. Our team of more than 350 experienced practitioners works in over 30 specialized practices, from mergers and acquisitions, public offerings, corporate reorganization, real estate and cross-border transactions to general commercial litigation, securities litigation, international trade, anticorruption and internal investigations, international arbitration and dispute resolution, product liability, antitrust, intellectual property, labor, employee benefits and tax, as well as niche practices such as art law, and new media and technology.

Firm profile

The firm has outstanding diversity scores and consistently receives high marks for its pro bono activities. The American Lawyer has consistently recognized Hughes Hubbard on its A-List of the nation's most elite law firms.

Recruitment

Law Schools attending for OCIs in 2018:

Brooklyn Law School, Columbia University Law School, Cornell Law School, Duke University School of Law, Fordham University School of Law, George Washington University Law School, Georgetown University Law Center, Harvard Law School, New York University School of Law, Stanford Law School, University of Chicago Law School, University of Michigan Law School, University of Pennsylvania Law School, University of Virginia School of Law, Yale Law School

Recruitment outside OCIs:

Hughes Hubbard accepts application from students at all law schools.

Summer associate profile:

Hughes Hubbard recognizes that a successful recruiting effort is essential to the long-term success of the firm. We are committed to rendering services of the highest professional quality and, to that end, seek lawyers of exceptional ability, integrity and industry. We actively recruit candidates whose academic performance, energy, personality and character suggest that they possess the ability and desire to meet the challenges presented by a demanding practice and are prepared to develop rapidly and assume responsibility early.

Summer program components:

Summer associates work on real problems, not 'make-work', and those problems often involve far more than library research. In recent years, for example, summer associates have assisted at depositions, court proceedings and closings. Summer associates participate in a wide variety of client meetings, witness interviews, negotiation sessions and fact-gathering projects and, on some occasions, they have traveled to other offices.

Head Office: **New York, NY**
Number of domestic offices: **7**
Number of international offices: **2**
Worldwide revenue: **$322 million**
Partners (US): **82**
Associates (US): **167**

Contacts
Main recruitment contact:
Adrian Cockerill
(adrian.cockerill@hugheshubbard.com)
Hiring partner: Marc Weinstein
Diversity officer: Diane Lifton

Recruitment details
Entry-level associates starting in 2018: **18**
Clerking policy: **Yes**
Summers joining/anticipated
2018: 2Ls: **19**
Summers joining/anticipated 2018 split
by office:
New York: **11**
Washington DC: **8**
Summer salary 2018
1Ls: **$3,461 per week**
2Ls: **$3,461 per week**
Split summers offered? **No**
Can summers spend time in an overseas
office? **Yes**

**Hughes
Hubbard
&Reed**

Hunton Andrews Kurth LLP

2200 Pennsylvania Avenue, NW, Washington, DC 20037

Tel: 202 955 1500
Website: www.huntonak.com
Recruitment website: www.hunton.com/en/careers/join-us/law-students/

Twitter: @HuntonAK
Linkedin: hunton-andrews-kurth

On April 2nd, 2018, Hunton & Williams LLP and Andrews Kurth Kenyon LLP combined to become Hunton Andrews Kurth LLP.

Main areas of work

Hunton Andrews Kurth handles transactional, litigation and regulatory matters, with significant experience in retail and consumer products, energy, financial services, real estate, and privacy and cybersecurity.

Firm profile

Hunton Andrews Kurth blends more than a century of legal experience with a broad view of current business realities and a forward-looking perspective on emerging issues to provide advice that will carry its clients well into the 21st century. The firm is regularly named by legal and business publications as a top firm for client service and a great place to work.

Recruitment

Law Schools attending for OCIs in 2018:

- Columbia
- Cornell
- Duke
- Fordham
- Georgetown
- George Washington
- Harvard
- Howard
- NYU
- SMU
- South Texas
- UCLA
- UC Berkeley
- University of Houston
- University of Michigan
- UNC
- University of Pennsylvania
- University of Richmond
- USC
- University of Texas
- UVA
- Vanderbilt
- Washington & Lee
- Washington University in St. Louis
- William & Mary

Recruitment outside OCIs:

Hunton Andrews Kurth recruits at several diversity-related job fairs each year. Candidates also may apply via the firm's website.

Summer associate profile:

Hunton Andrews Kurth seeks high performing, team-oriented and problem-solving law students. In addition to strong academic credentials and excellent communication skills, applicants should have a solid record of success and leadership. Prior work/professional experience and advanced degrees also are valued.

Summer program components:

Hunton Andrews Kurth's Summer Program is a ten-week immersion in the real-world practice of law. Customized for each summer associate, it generally includes leadership, business development and client service training; career mentoring; client interaction; practical experience; pro bono opportunities; judicial clerkship counseling; and work projects in practice areas of interest.

Head Office: Washington, DC
Number of domestic offices: 15
Number of international offices: 5
Partners (US): 387
Counsel (US): 127
Associates (US): 372

Contacts
Main recruitment contact: Becky Chavez
Hiring partners: Alexis J. Gomez, Rudene Mercer Haynes and Alan J. Marcuis
Diversity co-heads: A. Todd Brown, Gustavo J. Membiela, Shemin V. Proctor and Emily Burkhardt Vicente

Recruitment details
Entry-level associates starting in 2018: 41
Clerking policy: Yes
Summers joining/anticipated 2018: 50
1Ls: 14, 2Ls: 36
Summers joining/anticipated 2018 split by office: Dallas: 8, Houston: 15, Los Angeles: 2, Miami: 2, New York: 5, Richmond: 11, San Francisco: 1, Washington, DC: 6
Summer salary 2018:
1Ls and 2Ls: $3,500/week (major markets) or $3,100/week
Split summers offered? No
Can summers spend time in an overseas office? No

rell & Manella LLP

800 Avenue of the Stars, Suite 900, Los Angeles, CA 90067

el: 310 277 1010   Fax: 310 203 7199

ecruitment website: www.irell.com

inkedin: irell-&-manella

Twitter: @IrellandManella

Main areas of work

antitrust, appellate, art, bankruptcy reorganization and creditors' rights, class action defense, cyber liability and privacy, debt finance, entertainment litigation, insurance, IP litigation, IP transactions, litigation, media and entertainment transactions, mergers and acquisitions, patent, copyright and trademark, private equity and venture capital, professional liability defense, public offerings and private placements, securities law and corporate governance, securities litigation and tax.

Firm profile

Irell & Manella is a full service law firm with offices in Los Angeles and Newport Beach, California. Our unique practice and culture offer opportunities for talented law graduates to excel early in their careers. The quality of our work and the flexibility of our organization attract associates with the highest qualifications.

Irell's preeminent reputation brings clients to us from around the country and abroad and allows us to concentrate our physical presence in a single metropolitan area ensuring firm cohesion and a minimum of bureaucracy.

Recruitment

Law Schools attending for OCIs in 2018:

Law Schools: Berkeley, University of Chicago, Columbia, Harvard, Michigan, Northwestern, NYU, Stanford, UCLA, UC Irvine, USC, Yale.

Recruitment outside OCIs:

Job Fairs & Interview Programs: Loyola University Chicago Patent Law Interview Program, Los Angeles On Tour Interview Program (Otip), Penn Regional Interview Program.

Resume Collections: Cornell, Chapman, Duke, Georgetown, George Washington, Howard, Loyola (Los Angeles), Notre Dame, Pepperdine, Southwestern, Texas, University of Pennsylvania, UVA, Vanderbilt and Wisconsin.

Summer associate profile:

We recruit law students from the top law schools who excel academically. Consideration is given to participation in law school activities, undergraduate record, previous work experience, references and other factors. We look for individuals who are motivated, creative, show leadership, have a strong work ethic and are serious about being a lawyer.

Summer program components:

Our summer program is designed to allow summer associates to explore the various areas of our practice. Summer associates have the opportunity to participate in a mock wrongful death trial that is tried to a jury and presided over by a judge. Each summer associate is assigned a mentor and a work coordinator. Feedback is provided on each project by the assigning attorney and each summer associate has a mid-summer review to deliver additional feedback about his or her progress.

Head Office: Los Angeles, CA
Number of domestic offices: 2
Number of international offices: 0
Partners (US): 46
Associates (US): 48

Contacts
Main recruitment contact:
Alanna Cowan (acowan@irell.com)
Hiring partner: Keith Orso
Diversity officer: Kyle Kawakami

Recruitment details
Entry-level associates starting in 2018: 14
Clerking policy: Yes
Summers joining/anticipated 2018:
2Ls: 20
Summers joining/anticipated 2018 split
by office:
Los Angeles: 18
Newport Beach: 2
Summer salary 2018:
1Ls: $3,462
2Ls: $3,462
Split summers offered? Yes

IRELL & MANELLA
LLP

Jackson Walker LLP

2323 Ross Avenue, Ste.600, Dallas, TX 75201

Tel: 214 953 6000   Fax: 214 953 5822
Recruitment website: www.jw.com/careers
Linkedin: jackson-walker-llp

Facebook: JacksonWalkerLLP

Main areas of work

Corporate and securities; litigation; real estate; bankruptcy; energy; ERISA; environmental and legislative; finance; healthcare; intellectual property; labor and employment; land use; tax; wealth planning.

Firm profile

Jackson Walker is a Texas-based law firm with a national presence and global reach. With more than 350 attorneys, we're one of the largest firms in the state and we provide comprehensive services in a broad range of practice areas. Our practice now spans the globe and our corporate clients include some of the biggest names in business. We represent approximately 237 of the Fortune 500 companies and 69 of the Fortune 100. But we're also a good fit for smaller companies and our clients include family-owned businesses, local and regional government agencies, individuals and nonprofit groups.

Recruitment

Law Schools attending for OCIs in 2018:

Baylor, Chicago, University of Houston, St Mary's, Southern Methodist University, South Texas, Texas Southern, University of Texas, University of Virginia, Texas on Tour Interview Program (Duke, Georgetown and Northwestern Universities), SUNBELT Minority Job Fair, Vanderbilt Job Fair, Notre Dame Texas Interview Program, SWBISA Job Fair, Washington University in St. Louis.

Recruitment outside OCIs:

We collect resumes from the following law schools' career services offices: Louisiana State University, Texas A&M University and Texas Tech University

Summer associate profile:

Candidates with leadership capabilities, academic excellence, strong interpersonal skills, community involvement and dedicated to practicing over the long term.

Summer program components:

We have a first half of summer program. Summers typically are placed in a practice group and work on two or three projects at a time. Feedback is provided from the assigning attorney on each project and each summer has both a partner and associate mentor. Summers have the opportunity to attend client meetings, closings, negotiations, depositions, trials and courtroom hearings.

Head Office: **Dallas, TX**
Number of domestic offices: **7**
Worldwide revenue: **$246,647,013**
Partners (US): **243**
Associates (US): **99**

Contacts
Main recruitment contact:
Bridgette Stahlman
Hiring partner: **Jim Ryan**
Diversity officer: **Bruce Ruzinsky**

Recruitment details
Entry-level associates starting in 2018: **13**
Clerking policy: **Yes**
Summers joining/anticipated 2018:
1Ls: **13**, 2Ls: **14**
Summers joining/anticipated 2018 split by office: **Austin: 7, Dallas: 10, Houston: 8, San Antonio: 2**
Summer salary 2018:
1Ls and 2Ls: **$3,461/week**
Split summers offered? **Yes|**

Firm Profiles

Jenner & Block LLP

53 North Clark Street, Chicago, IL 60654

Tel: 312 222 9350   Fax: 312 527 0484

Recruitment website: www.jenner.com/joinus

Linkedin: jenner-&-block

Twitter: @JennerBlockLLP

Main areas of work

Antitrust and competition; appellate and US Supreme Court; aviation and aerospace; communications; complex commercial litigation; content, media and entertainment; copyright; corporate; data privacy and cybersecurity; election law and redistricting; employee benefits and executive compensation; energy; environmental and workplace health and safety law; government contracts; government controversies and public policy litigation; insurance recovery and counseling; international arbitration; investigations, compliance and defense; media and First Amendment; mergers and acquisitions; patent litigation and counseling; private wealth; professional responsibility; real estate; restructuring and bankruptcy; securities litigation and enforcement; tax; trademark, advertising, and unfair competition.

Firm profile

Jenner & Block is a firm with global reach, comprising more than 500 lawyers and offices in Chicago, London, Los Angeles, New York and Washington, DC. Our lawyers are widely recognized for securing significant litigation victories from the trial level through the US Supreme Court as well as producing results in sophisticated and high-profile corporate transactions. We are a firm with a conscience, committed to pro bono and public service and to creating an unrivaled environment for superior talent. In 2017, *The American Lawyer* named us the number one Pro Bono firm for the eighth time.

Recruitment

Law Schools attending for OCIs in 2018:

Columbia University, Fordham, Georgetown, Harvard University, Howard University, New York University, Northwestern University, Stanford University, University of California-Berkeley, University of California-Los Angeles, University of Chicago, University of Illinois, University of Michigan, University of Notre Dame, University of Pennsylvania, University of Southern California, Yale University

Recruitment outside OCIs:

Loyola Patent Law Interview Program; CCBA Minority Law Student Job Fair; The Midwest-California-Georgia Consortium; Lavender Law; SEO Program. We also accept write-in applications.

Summer associate profile:

We seek summer associates who have excelled in law school, and have exceptional oral and written presentation skills, leadership experience, and strong interpersonal skills.

Summer program components:

Summer associates work with our lawyers and firm clients on a wide variety of complex cases and transactions. Among other things, our summer associates attend court hearings and closings, observe depositions and participate in strategy sessions with firm lawyers and clients. We also offer extensive training programs on a wide range of subjects. Summer associates are encouraged to attend department meetings, firmwide monthly associate lunches and weekly lunch-and-learn sessions. All summer associates have mentors and receive feedback from lawyers with whom they have worked.

Head Office: Chicago
Number of domestic offices: 4
Number of international offices: 1
Worldwide revenue: $448,745,291
Partners (US): 227
Associates (US): 179

Contacts
Main recruitment contacts:
Alexis M. Reed, Director of Lateral Partner Recruiting, (areed@jenner.com)
Amanda Griffin, Legal Recruiting Manager, (agriffin@jenner.com)
Hiring partner: Charlotte L Wager, Chief Talent Officer and Co-Chair of the Hiring Executive Committee
Diversity officers: Courtney Dredden Carter, Associate Director of Diversity and Inclusion

Recruitment details
Entry-level associates starting in 2018: 33
Clerking policy: Yes
Summers joining/anticipated 2018:
2Ls: 39, SEO: 5
Summers joining/anticipated 2018 split by office: Chicago: 24; Los Angeles: 3; New York: 7; Washington DC: 8
Summer salary 2018:
2Ls: $3,461.55/week
Post 3Ls: $3,461.55/week
Split summers offered? Yes
Can summers spend time in overseas office? No

Firm Profiles

JENNER & BLOCK

Jones Day

51 Louisiana Avenue, NW, Washington, DC 20001

Tel: 202 879 3939 Fax: 202 629 1700
Email: recruiting@jonesday.com
Recruitment website: www.jonesdaycareers.com
Linkedin: jones-day

Twitter: @jonesdaycareers
Facebook: JonesDayLawFirm

Main areas of work

Jones Day's practices cover the spectrum of transactional, litigation, regulatory and tax matters. Core practice areas include corporate/M&A, litigation/trial practice, government regulation, real estate, energy, healthcare, cybersecurity, issues and appeals, banking/finance, bankruptcy/restructuring, labor and employment, securities litigation, financial institutions, antitrust, tax and intellectual property.

Firm profile

The firm is a global legal institution based on a set of core principles and values – the most critical of which are integrity, dedication to the profession and a unity of purpose of and relentless focus on client service that transcends individual interests. Each lawyer is committed to the firm's foundation principles and values, which have a social purpose and permanence and ensure the distinctive quality and value of the legal services they provide their clients. This is one important aspect of what makes Jones Day the client service organization that it is. They function seamlessly across the globe and are truly 'One Firm Worldwide'.

Recruitment

Law Schools attending for OCIs in 2018:

American, Benjamin N. Cardozo, Boston College, Boston University, Case Western, Chicago, Cleveland – Marshall, Columbia, Cornell, Dickinson, Duke, Emory, Florida, Fordham, George Mason, George Washington, Georgetown, Georgia, Georgia State, Harvard, Houston, Howard, Illinois, Iowa, Miami, Michigan, Minnesota, New York University, Northwestern, Notre Dame, Ohio State, Pennsylvania, Pittsburgh, San Diego, SMU, Stanford, Texas, UC Berkeley, UC Hastings, UC Irvine, UCLA, U of Southern California, Vanderbilt, Virginia, Wayne State, Wisconsin, Yale

Recruitment outside of OCIs:

The firm participates in several city or regional job fairs and walk-around programs.

Summer associate profile:

Jones Day lawyers share certain fundamental principles: exemplary integrity, a selfless dedication to the firm and its clients and a sense of responsibility and initiative that leads one to take ownership of assignments and to complete them at the highest level of quality legal service. Summer associate candidates are evaluated on their fit with this culture.

Summer program components:

Summer associates do real client work in a variety of practice areas. Mentors are assigned to provide one-on-one guidance. Each summer associate will have formal, mid and end-of-summer reviews. Jones Day's dynamic culture and its global, multidisciplinary practice areas, provide the perfect training ground for summer associates and new lawyers.

Head office: Washington
Number of domestic offices: 18
Number of international offices: 25
Partners (US): 656
Associates (US): 843

Contacts
Main recruitment contact:
Jolie A. Blanchard (202 879 3788, jablanchard@jonesday.com)
Hiring partner: Sharyl A. Reisman (212 326 3405, sreisman@jonesday.com)
Diversity coordinator:
Jennifer Shumaker (202 879 5430, jshumaker@jonesday.com)

Recruitment details
Entry-level associates starting in 2018: 150
Clerking policy: Yes
Summers joining/anticipated 2018: 214
1Ls: 29; 2Ls: 176; SEOs: 9
Summers joining/anticipated 2018 split by office: Atlanta: 15; Boston: 5; Chicago: 24.5; Cleveland: 18; Columbus: 8; Dallas: 20; Detroit: 4; Houston: 7; Irvine: 7; Los Ángeles: 8; Miami: 4; Minneapolis: 5; New York: 33; Pittsburgh: 8; San Diego: 10; San Francisco: 9; Silicon Valley: 6; Washington 22.5
2018 interoffice summer splits:
Atlanta/Washington: 1
Atlanta/New York: 1
Washington/New York: 1
Washington/Chicago: 1
Split arrangements are made on a case-by-case basis.

Firm Profiles

K&L Gates

K&L Gates Center, 210 Sixth Avenue, Pittsburgh, PA 15222-2613

Tel: 412 355 6500
Email: klgatesrecruitment@klgates.com
Recruitment website: www.klgates.com/careers/
Linkedin: k&l-gates

Twitter: @KLGates
Facebook:
klgateslegalrecruitingus

Main areas of work

Corporate and transactional; energy, infrastructure and resources; finance; financial services; intellectual property; labor, employment and workplace safety; litigation and dispute resolution; policy and regulatory; real estate

Firm profile

K&L Gates is a fully integrated global law firm with lawyers located across five continents. Our broad global platform allows us to guide clients through the legal challenges inherent in the ever-changing international landscape. The deep latticework of relationships across our offices and practices enables our clients to respond to diverse legal issues and risks through the services of one law firm with a single communication.

The industry recognition K&L Gates has garnered over the past five years emanates from the foundation of a global community aligned on behalf of our clients. The people at K&L Gates are committed to working together to create a legacy for each other, the firm, our clients, and the communities we serve. We thrive in an inclusive and socially conscious environment that embraces diversity and takes a holistic approach to the career evolution of all our professionals. We take pride in constantly striving for innovation, imagination, and an entrepreneurial spirit. We come up with big ideas and then roll up our sleeves to get the job done, guiding our clients through their most complex issues in a variety of industry sectors and across multiple regions of the world. An indication of the firm's collaborative approach to client service is that our top 20 clients used lawyers from an average of 16.7 K&L Gates offices in 2017, and 470 of the firm's 500 largest clients used lawyers from two or more offices.

Recruitment

Law Schools attending for OCI in 2018:

American, Berkeley, Boston College, Boston U., Catholic, Chapman, Chicago, Columbia, Cornell, Duke, Duquesne, Florida, Fordham, George Washington, Georgetown, Harvard, Houston, Howard, Illinois, Loyola Los Angeles, Maryland, Miami, Michigan, Northwestern, Notre Dame, NYU, Ohio State, Oklahoma, Penn, Penn State, Pepperdine, Pittsburgh, San Diego, Seattle, South Carolina, Southern Methodist, Stanford, Texas, UC - Irvine, UCLA, UNC, USC, UVA, Vanderbilt, Wake Forest, Washington, Washington & Lee, William & Mary

Recruitment outside OCIs:

We welcome applicants who attend law school at campuses other than those we visit for OCI. Please visit www.klgates.com/careers to apply.

Summer associate profile:

Our summer associate program is designed to give law students a full picture of the firm and our culture, all the while giving us the opportunity to get to know and evaluate current law students as a potential associates following graduation. We look for smart, imaginative and hard-working people with diverse backgrounds, experiences and ideas.

Summer program components:

Summer associates sample projects from different practice areas, working as part of a team and participating in pro bono work. We pair our summer associates with mentors, who provide guidance on seeking out and completing substantive work assignments, balancing workload demands, dealing with competing projects, integrating into the firm's culture, and setting and achieving career goals. Through on-the-job experience, a formal training curriculum, regular formal and informal feedback, and opportunities to network and integrate into the fabric of the firm, our summer associates begin to develop the professional skills and competencies that will serve them well throughout their careers.

Number of domestic offices: 23
Number of international offices: 22
Worldwide revenue: $989,861,000
Partners (US): 591
Associates (US): 474

Contacts
Main recruitment contact:
Dyana Barninger, Director of Talent Acquisition and Development (dyana.barninger@klgates.com)
Hiring partner: Craig Budner, Global Client Development, Recruitment and Integration Partner
Diversity officer: Valerie Jackson, Senior Advisor to the Management Committee and Firmwide Director of Diversity & Inclusion

Recruitment details
Entry-level associates starting in 2018: 51
Clerking policy: Yes
Summers joining/anticipated 2018:
1Ls: 8, 2Ls: 39
Summers joining/anticipated 2018 split by office: Boston: 5, Charleston: 2, Charlotte: 3, Chicago: 3, Dallas: 2, Los Angeles: 3, Miami: 1, New York: 3, Orange County: 2, Palo Alto: 2, Pittsburgh: 6, Raleigh: 2, Seattle: 7, Washington, DC: 6
Summer salary 2018:
1Ls: Varies by market
2Ls: Varies by market
Split summers offered? Case by case
Can summers spend time in an overseas office? No

Firm Profiles

K&L GATES

Kasowitz Benson Torres LLP

1633 Broadway, New York, New York 10019

Tel: 212 506 1700   Fax: 212 506 1800
Email: mlindenman@kasowitz.com
Recruitment website: www.kasowitz.com/life-at-the-firm/opportunities/
Linkedin: Kasowitz Benson Torres LLP

Twitter: @KasowitzLLP

Main areas of work

One of the largest litigation firms in the country, representing clients in high-stakes lawsuits, with a particular focus on commercial, securities, antitrust, bankruptcy litigation, and white collar defense and litigation. The firm employs a decidedly aggressive approach to litigation and strives to achieve the most favorable results for its clients by focusing from the beginning of each case on preparation for trial. While litigation remains our core focus, the firm also has a strong real estate transactional practice.

Firm profile

We are known for our creative, aggressive litigators and willingness to take on tough cases. We outthink and outflank our opponents, and understand how to win for our clients. We have extensive trial experience and are always trial-ready, representing both plaintiffs and defendants in every area of litigation. Kasowitz ranked as a 'Top Firm' for Diversity recognized on The American Lawyer's Diversity Scorecard. Our lawyers have been recognized by, among others, Chambers USA, Legal 500, Benchmark Litigation, Law360 and National Law Journal for excellence in their fields. Clients include Fortune 500 companies, private equity and other investment firms across a wide range of industries, including significant experience across financial services, technology, and real estate.

Recruitment

Law Schools attending for OCIs in 2018:

Columbia, Cornell, Fordham, Georgetown, Howard, NYU, NEBLSA Job Fair, Northwestern, and Penn.

Recruitment outside OCIs:

Review all applications received through our online portal. Resume collects.

Summer associate profile:

Strong academic achievement, prior work and leadership experience. Outstanding judgment, character and personal skills. Demonstrated interest in litigation (participation in Moot Court, Law Review and/or other journals preferred).

Summer program components:

We provide our Summer Associates with quality work assignments and professional experiences reflecting the breadth and complexity of our firm. Summer Associates learn first-hand about trying cases and drafting legal documents, motions and agreements, and are exposed to courtroom appearances, depositions and client meetings. Summer Associates participate in formal training programs, a partner lunch series and an associate mentor program.

Summer Associates also attend weekly work assignment meetings, receive ongoing feedback and are provided mid and exit reviews from the lawyers with whom they work. Summer Associates have the opportunity to work on firm pro bono matters and participate in offsite programs offered by legal services organizations, such as The Legal Aid Society, Sanctuary for Families, and New York Lawyers for the Public Interest.

We sponsor a variety of social and cultural events, providing Summer Associates the opportunity to get to know each other and our lawyers in an informal environment. The firm also coordinates a Women's Initiative event and charitable events during Give Back week through Citymeals-on-Wheels 'Eat Cheap for Charity', Sanctuary for Families and St. Luke's Soup Kitchen.

Head Office: New York, NY
Number of domestic offices: 9
Partners (US): 90
Associates (US): 176

Contacts
Main recruitment contact:
Mindy J. Lindenman, Director of Legal Recruiting & Training and Development
Hiring partner: Cindy Caranella Kelly
Diversity officer: Hector Torres, Chair
Jennifer Mercado, Training & Development Manager

Recruitment details
Entry-level associates starting in 2018: 9
Clerking policy: Yes
Summers joining/anticipated 2018:
2Ls: 13
Summers joining/anticipated 2018 split by office: NY 13
Summer salary 2018: 2Ls: $3,462/week
Split summers offered? Case-by-case

KASOWITZ
BENSON TORRES

Katten Muchin Rosenman LLP

25 West Monroe Street, Chicago, IL 60661-3693

Tel: 312 902 5200   Fax: 312 902 1061
Recruitment website: www.kattenlaw.com/careers
Linkedin: katten-muchin-rosenman-llp

Twitter: @KattenLaw
Facebook: KattenLaw

Main areas of work

Corporate, private equity, financial services, litigation, real estate, environmental, commercial finance, intellectual property and trusts and estates.

Firm profile

Katten is a full-service law firm with approximately 650 attorneys in locations across the United States and in London and Shanghai. Clients seeking sophisticated, high value legal services turn to us for counsel locally, nationally and internationally.

Recruitment

Law Schools attending for OCIs in 2018:

Chicago-Kent College of Law, Columbia Law School, Fordham University School of Law, Harvard Law School, Loyola Law School, Los Angeles, Loyola University Chicago School of Law, New York University School of Law, Northwestern Pritzker School of Law, University of California, Los Angeles, School of Law, The University of Chicago Law School, University of Illinois College of Law, University of Michigan Law School, University of North Carolina School of Law, University of Pennsylvania Law School, University of Southern California Gould School of Law, Wake Forest University School of Law

Recruitment outside OCIs:

In addition to OCI, the firm participates in the Lavender Law Career Fair, the Cook County Bar Association Minority Law Student Job Fair and the Chicago On-Tour Interviewing Program.

Summer associate profile:

Katten's summer associate classes are comprised of a diverse group of individuals, who have demonstrated academic achievement, leadership experience and oncampus involvement. The firm seeks candidates who are motivated, entrepreneurial, and possess a high level of critical thinking and interpersonal skills. Katten looks for candidates who are reflective of our culture and values, which includes exhibiting professionalism, commitment to client service and team work.

Summer program components:

Our Summer associate program offers participants a realistic idea of what it is like to be a first year associate. With our diverse client base, summer associates have the opportunity to work in each of our practice areas on a broad spectrum of assignments. We provide programs designed specifically for summer associates, including legal writing, negotiation and professional skills workshops, in addition to presentations introducing the firm's different areas of practice. Summer associates have the opportunity to work directly with our attorneys and interact with clients as part of their training experience. We also encourage our summer associates to participate in all of the attorney training and development programs presented by the firm and our various departments.

Head Office: Chicago, IL
Number of domestic offices: 12
Number of international offices: 2
Partners (US): 393
Associates (US): 263

Contacts
Recruitment website:
For recruitment information and contacts, please visit:
www.kattenlaw.com/careers

Recruitment details
Entry-level associates starting in 2018: 23
Clerking policy: Yes
Summers joining/anticipated 2018:
35 (2Ls: 23, 1Ls: 10)
Summers joining/anticipated 2018 split by office: Charlotte: 5, Chicago: 16, Los Angeles: 5, New York: 6, Washington, DC: 3
Summer salary 2018:
1Ls: $3,461
2Ls: $3,461
Split summers offered? Case by case
Can summers spend time in an overseas office? No

Firm Profiles

King & Spalding LLP

Recruitment website: www.kslaw.com/careers
Linkedin: king-and-spalding

Main areas of work

Antitrust, appellate, banking and finance, corporate, energy, financial restructuring, government investigations, healthcare, intellectual property, international arbitration, international trade, litigation, pharma/biotech/medical device, real estate, tort and environmental, tax/ERISA.

Firm profile

King & Spalding has over 1000 lawyers in 20 offices across the US, Europe, the Middle East and Asia. King & Spalding combines a sophisticated legal practice with a commitment to excellence, collaborative culture, investment in lawyer development, and dedication to pro bono and community service.

Recruitment

Law Schools attending for OCIs in 2018:

Columbia, Cornell, Duke, Emory, Fordham, George Washington, Georgetown, Georgia State, Harvard, Howard, Mercer, NYU, St. Louis, Stanford, UC Berkeley, UC Hastings, UCLA, UChicago, University of Florida – Levin, University of Georgia, University of Houston, University of Maryland, UNC – Chapel Hill, UPenn, University of Texas – Austin, University of Virginia, Vanderbilt, Yale

Summer associate profile:

King & Spalding offers an opportunity to work as part of a team on sophisticated legal matters for top clients in a collaborative environment. We seek well-rounded and intellectually curious candidates who have a demonstrated record of achievement and diverse life and work experiences.

Summer program components:

Summer associates experience what it's like to be a lawyer at King & Spalding and work on challenging matters for real clients in the practice group in which they are interested. Each summer associate is assigned at least one summer advisor who acts as a mentor.

Trainings include weekly luncheon seminars, attendance at practice group meetings, and in-house and external training sessions. Summer associates receive a formal mid-summer and end of summer evaluation, as well as ongoing project feedback.

Summer associates are invited to a variety of events that allow them to build relationships with firm attorneys, clients, and their fellow summer associates.

Number of domestic offices: 10
Number of international offices: 10
Worldwide revenue: $1.14 billion
Partners (US): 338
Associates (US): 317

Contacts
Main recruitment contact:
Michelle L. Carter, Chief Recruiting Officer
Hiring partners:
Michael E. Paulhus (Atlanta)
Adam Gray (Austin)
Mark V. Thigpen (Charlotte)
Peter A. Strotz (Los Angeles)
Brandt Leibe (Houston)
Ellen M. Snare (New York)
Fritz Zimmer, Jr. (San Francisco)
Timothy T. Scott (Silicon Valley)
John H. Fontham (Washington, DC)
Diversity officer: Samuel M Matchett, Partner

Recruitment details
Entry-level associates starting 2018: 35
Clerking policy: Yes
Summers joining/anticipated 2018:
1Ls: 9, 2Ls: 48, 3Ls: 3
Summer salary 2018:
1Ls /2Ls: $ 3,461/week (Austin, Houston, New York, San Francisco, Silicon Valley, Washington, DC)
$2,980/week (Atlanta, Charlotte)
Split summers offered? Yes
Can summer spend time in an overseas office? Generally, no

KING & SPALDING

Firm Profiles

Kirkland & Ellis LLP

00 North LaSalle, Chicago, IL 60654

el: 312 862 2000   Fax: 312 862 2200
mail: info@kirkland.com
ecruitment website: www.kirkland.com/careers
inkedin: Kirkland & Ellis

Twitter: @Kirkland_Ellis

Main areas of work

Kirkland's main practice areas are corporate, intellectual property, litigation and restructuring.

Firm profile

Kirkland & Ellis LLP is a 2,000-attorney law firm representing global clients in private equity, M&A and other complex corporate transactions, litigation and dispute resolution/arbitration, intellectual property, and restructuring matters. The firm has offices in Beijing, Boston, Chicago, Hong Kong, Houston, London, Los Angeles, Munich, New York, Palo Alto, San Francisco, Shanghai and Washington, DC. The firm's principal goals are to provide the highest-quality legal services available anywhere; to be an instrumental part of each client's success; and to recruit, retain and advance the brightest legal talent.

Recruitment

Law Schools attending for OCIs in 2018:

Baylor; UC Berkeley; UC Hastings; UC Davis; UCLA; Boston College; Boston University; Cardozo; University of Chicago; Columbia; Duke; Fordham; George Washington; Georgetown; Harvard; University of Houston; Howard University; University of Illinois; University of Michigan; New York University; Northwestern University; University of Notre Dame; University of Pennsylvania; Santa Clara University; USC; Southern Methodist University; Stanford; University of Texas; Tulane; Vanderbilt University; University of Virginia; Yale.

Recruitment outside OCIs:

Some offices participate in local/regional job fairs for schools we also visit on-campus. They are not included in the list of job fairs below.

University of Arizona/Arizona State University; Brigham Young University; Cornell University; Emory University; Washington University - St. Louis; Bay Area Diversity Career Fair; Boston Lawyers Group (BLG) Diversity Job Fair; Cook County Bar Association (CCBA) Minority Job Fair; Lavender Law Career Fair; Midwest-California-Georgia Consortium (MCGC) Interview Program; NEBLSA Job Fair; On Tour Interview Program (OTIP); Patent Law Interview Program; Southeastern Minority Job Fair; The Law Consortium Recruitment Program.

Summer associate profile:

Kirkland looks for candidates who show a record of outstanding academic achievement, evidence of initiative and a desire to assume early responsibility. Kirkland values individuals from diverse social, economic, cultural and personal backgrounds. The firm looks favorably upon law review, moot court and other indicators of intellectual curiosity and drive.

Summer program components:

Kirkland offers summer associates a realistic view of their future as lawyers at the firm. Summer associates are allowed to choose challenging assignments that are of interest to them through Kirkland's open assignment system, including pro bono matters. Each office offers summer associates substantive, practice-specific training, including a mock trial, negotiation workshops and presentations on a variety of topics. Kirkland also hosts ample social events for summer associates to help them get to know our attorneys and their fellow summer associates. By the end of the summer program, summer associates have an understanding of Kirkland's culture and practices, which gives them a strong foundation on which to begin their career at Kirkland.

Number of domestic offices: 8
Number of international offices: 5
Partners (US): 838
Associates (US): 1,000

Contacts
Hiring partner: Jason Kanner
Diversity officer: Rina Alvarez

Recruitment details
Entry-level associates starting in 2018: 251
Clerking policy: Yes
Summers joining/anticipated 2018:
1Ls: 25, 2Ls: 255, SEO Interns: 3
Summers joining/anticipated 2018 split by office: Boston: 9, Chicago: 66, Hong Kong: 1, Houston: 27, London: 2, Los Angeles: 14, New York: 95, Palo Alto: 9, San Francisco: 33, Washington, DC: 27
Summer salary 2018:
1Ls: $3,462 weekly
2Ls: $3,462 weekly
Split summers offered? No
Can summers spend time in an overseas office? Yes, the London office has a summer program.

KIRKLAND & ELLIS

Kramer Levin Naftalis & Frankel LLP

1177 Avenue of the Americas, New York, NY 10036

Tel: 212 715 9100   Fax: 212 715 8000
Email: legalrecruiting@kramerlevin.com
Recruitment website: www.kramerlevin.com/careers/
Linkedin: kramer-levin-naftalis-&-frankel-llp

Twitter: @kramerlevin
Facebook:
KramerLevinNaftalis&FrankelLLP

Main areas of work

Bankruptcy and restructuring; capital markets and M&A; commercial and white collar litigation; employment litigation; finance and banking; immigration; intellectual property; investment funds; real estate; land use and environmental; securitization; tax, employee benefits and individual clients.

Firm profile

Kramer Levin provides its clients proactive, creative and pragmatic solutions that address today's most challenging legal issues. The firm is headquartered in New York with offices in Silicon Valley and Paris and fosters a strong culture of involvement in public and community service.

Recruitment

Law Schools attending for OCIs in 2018:

- Benjamin N Cardozo
- Brooklyn
- Columbia University
- Duke University
- Fordham University
- Georgetown University
- Harvard
- Hofstra University
- New York University School of Law
- St John's University
- University of California at Berkeley
- Boalt Hall School of Law
- University of Michigan
- University of Pennsylvania
- Yale

Recruitment outside OCIs:

Resume Collects at other Schools

Summer associate profile:

We seek lawyers whose academic achievements, journal writing, and prior work experience demonstrate exceptional ability, motivation and potential for leadership.

Summer program components:

Our summer program offers a realistic experience. We fully involve summer associates in day to day practice and assign work comparable to that given to junior associates.

Summer associates participate in our departmental meetings, firm-wide events and training programs and are given opportunities to attend court hearings, discovery proceedings, negotiating sessions, closings, pro bono matters and client meetings.

Head Office: **New York, NY**
Number of domestic offices: **2**
Number of international offices: **1**
Worldwide revenue: **$387,000,000**
Partners (US): **98**
Associates (US): **217**

Contacts
Main recruitment contact: **Lauren Tapper,
Director of Legal Recruiting**
Hiring partner: **Kerri Ann Law**
Diversity officer: **Lauren Tapper,
Director of Diversity**

Recruitment details
Entry-level associates starting in 2018: **16**
Clerking policy: **Yes**
Summers joining/anticipated 2018:
2Ls: 14, SEO: 1
Summers joining/anticipated 2018 split by office: **NY: 14 2Ls, 1 SEO**
Summer salary 2018:
1Ls: $3,750/week
2Ls: $3,750/week
Split summers offered? **Case by Case**
Can summers spend time in an overseas office? **No**

**KRAMER LEVIN
NAFTALIS & FRANKEL** LLP

Latham & Watkins LLP

85 Third Avenue, New York, NY 10022-4834

Tel: 212 906 1200   Fax: 212 751 4864
Firm website: www.lw.com
Recruitment website: www.lwcareers.com
Linkedin: latham-&-watkins

Twitter: @lathamwatkins
Facebook: lathamwatkins

Main areas of work

Corporate; environment, land and resources; finance; litigation and trial; tax.

Firm profile

Latham & Watkins' extensive practices, one-firm culture, and global footprint provide associates with virtually limitless career opportunities. The firm includes more than 2,600 lawyers across 30 offices and 14 countries. Associates harness the resources of a fully integrated firm that values integrity and diverse perspectives. Every associate receives exceptional training and support to ensure seamless collaboration on projects that span time zones, teams, and offices in the world's major financial, business, and regulatory centers. As a result, associates play an essential role in addressing clients' most important and complex challenges — with the best possible results.

Recruitment

Latham & Watkins recruits students with incredible legal minds who are also incredible people; the firm values transparency, respect, innovation, collaboration, and diversity. As a meritocracy, Latham seeks out candidates who have demonstrated they can contribute to the firm's culture through their initiative, willingness to assume responsibility, maturity, and judgment.

Latham recruits students from more than 90 law schools through campus interviews, job fairs, law school resume collections, and online applications for the firm's 1L Fellowship Program, 2L Diversity Scholars Program, as well as through direct applications.

For more information about campus interview dates and online applications for US offices, visit www.lwcareers.com.

Summer program components:

Latham's Summer Program gives you a sense of life as a junior associate at the firm — for example, by participating in the firm's Unassigned Program, having an assigned mentor, networking and building relationships, and attending Summer Academy — a highlight of the summer program — where you will join summer associates from across Latham's US, London, Hong Kong, and Singapore offices.

Number of domestic offices: 11
Number of international offices: 19
Worldwide revenue: $3.064 billion (FY2016)
Partners (US): 502
Associates (US): 1,087

Contacts
Main recruitment contact:
Debra Clarkson,
Director of Global Recruiting
Hiring partner: Larry Seymour,
Global Recruiting Committee Chair;
Andrea Hogan, Vice-Chair US;
Ross Anderson, Vice-Chair EAME
Diversity officer: BJ Trach, Chair of the
Diversity Leadership Committee

Recruitment details
Entry-level associates starting in 2018:
163 (US)
Clerking policy: Yes
Summers joining/anticipated 2018:
1Ls: 12, 2Ls: 182, 3Ls: 0, SEO Interns: 2
Summer salary 2018:
1Ls: $3,470/week
2Ls: $3,470/week
Split summers offered? First 8 weeks at
Latham required
Can summers spend time in an overseas
office? Case by case

LATHAM & WATKINS LLP

Linklaters

1345 Avenue of the Americas, New York, NY 10105

Tel: 212 903 9000   Fax: 212 903 9100
Email: usrecruit@linklaters.com
Recruitment website: careers.linklaters.com
Linkedin: linklaters

Twitter: @LinklatersLLP

Main areas of work

Antitrust/competition, banking, bankruptcy, restructuring and insolvency, capital markets, corporate/M&A, dispute resolution, energy and infrastructure/project finance, executive compensation and ERISA, financial regulation, investigations and white collar crime, investment funds, structured finance and derivatives, tax

Firm profile

Linklaters has been advising the world's premier companies, financial institutions and governments on their most important and challenging assignments for over 175 years.

With more than 2,600 attorneys based in 29 offices in 20 countries, we deliver an outstanding service to our clients anywhere in the world. Our US practice in New York and Washington, DC, is reinforced by a global network of US lawyers extending across the world's major business and financial centers, including: Frankfurt, Hong Kong, London, Madrid, Moscow, Paris, São Paulo, Seoul, Singapore and Tokyo.

Our team of US-qualified lawyers delivers integrated advice across multiple legal regimes and market practices, covering transactional, regulatory, disclosure, compliance, litigation and liability management issues globally.

Recruitment

Law Schools attending for OCIs in 2018:

Brooklyn, Columbia, Cornell, Duke, Fordham, George Washington, Georgetown, Harvard, Michigan, NYU, Penn, UVA

Recruitment outside OCIs:

Judicial clerks and student applicants from schools where we do not interview on campus are encouraged to apply via our application portal on our website: https://careers.linklaters.com

Summer associate profile:

We look for people who can make the most of all we have to offer: those who will work hard, learn quickly and take responsibility early. You will need analytical intelligence, a high level of attention to detail, creativity, and the people skills required to work well with colleagues and clients. It is also important to have a genuine interest in business and the financial world, a high level of commercial awareness, and the desire to be part of a global network.

Summer program components:

Our summer associates typically rotate through two practice divisions and may have the opportunity to spend time in more than one office. Summers are given real responsibility and are expected to participate in pro bono work in addition to working on billable matters.

In addition to our dedicated summer associate training program, we also encourage our summers to attend training sessions offered to associates. Each summer associate is assigned a partner and associate mentor and receives two formal appraisals, at the midpoint and at the end of the summer.

Number of domestic offices: 2
Number of international offices: 27
Worldwide revenue: £1,438.4 million
Partners (US): 43
Associates (US): 147

Contacts
Main recruitment contact:
Jennifer Katz-Hickman
Hiring partners: Justin Storms and
Douglas Tween
Diversity partner: Peter Cohen-Millstein

Recruitment details
Entry-level associates starting in 2018: 22
Clerking policy: Yes
Summers joining/anticipated 2018: 21
(1Ls: 2, 2Ls: 19, SEO: 2)
Summers joining/anticipated 2018 split
by office: Many of our summers split
time between two offices
NY: 18, London: 7, Washington: 3,
Hong Kong: 1, Singapore: 1
Summer salary 2018:
1Ls: $3,500/week
2Ls: $3,500/week
Split summers offered? No
Can summers spend time in an overseas
office? Yes

Linklaters

Mayer Brown LLP

recruitment website: www.mayerbrown.com/careers
linkedin: mayer-brown

Firm profile

Mayer Brown is a leading global law firm with offices in 26 cities across the Americas, Asia and Europe. The firm's presence in the world's key business and legal centers enables it to offer clients access to local market knowledge and depth combined with a global reach. The firm's practice areas include: banking and finance; corporate and securities; litigation and dispute resolution; antitrust and competition; US Supreme Court and appellate matters; employment and benefits; environmental; financial services regulatory and enforcement; government and global trade; intellectual property; real estate; tax; restructuring, bankruptcy and insolvency; and private clients, trusts, and estates.

Recruitment

Law Schools attending for OCIs in 2018:

Berkeley, Chicago, Columbia, Fordham, Georgetown, Harvard, Houston, Howard, Illinois, Loyola, Michigan, North Carolina, NYU, Northwestern, Penn, Stanford, Texas, Virginia, Wake Forest, Washington & Lee, Yale

Summer associate profile:

Mayer Brown seeks to hire associates of exceptional promise from a variety of backgrounds. Because Mayer Brown seeks to hire associates with the potential to become partners at the firm, its hiring standards are rigorous. Above all, Mayer Brown is interested in candidates who share the firm's dedication to providing high-quality legal services and who have demonstrated superior academic ability and personal achievement.

Summer program components:

Summer Associates at Mayer Brown are not assigned to practice areas and there is no formal rotation between groups. The firm's goal is to expose summer associates to as many practices areas and attorneys as possible during the program. Each summer associate is assigned at least two attorney mentors and receives written reviews on every assignment. Each summer associate will attend development meetings with partners at mid-summer and at the end of summer.

For more information please visit: www.mayerbrownfutures.com/americas/

Number of domestic offices: 8
Number of international offices: 18
Worldwide revenue: $1.313 billion
Partners (US): 401
Counsel (US): 104
Associates (US): 417

Contacts

Main recruitment contacts:
See www.mayerbrown.com/careers for office specific contacts
Hiring partner: J Bradley (Brad) Keck
Diversity officer: Jeremiah DeBerry, Partner Diversity & Inclusion

Recruitment details

Entry-level associates starting in 2018: 50
Clerking policy: Yes
Summers joining/anticipated 2018:
1Ls: 5, 2Ls: 37, 3Ls: 0, Pre-Clerks: 2
Summers joining/anticipated 2018 split by office: Palo Alto: 2, New York: 11, Washington DC: 6, Houston: 3, Charlotte: 3, Chicago:16, Los Angeles: 3
Summer salary 2018:
1Ls: $3,461/week
2Ls: $3,461/week
Post 3Ls: $3,461/week
Split summers offered? Case by case, office by office basis
Can summers spend time in an overseas office? Atypical

MAYER·BROWN

Firm Profiles

McDermott Will & Emery LLP

444 West Lake Street, Suite 4000, Chicago, IL 60606-0029

Tel: 312 372 2000   Fax: 312 984 7700
Recruitment website: www.mwe.com/en/careers/unitedstates
Linkedin: mcdermott-will-&-emery

Facebook:
McDermottWillandEmery

Main areas of work

Antitrust and competition, corporate, employee benefits, energy, financial institutions, government strategies, health, intellectual property, private client, state and local tax, trial, US and international tax, white collar and securities defense.

Firm profile

McDermott Will & Emery is an integrated, international law firm with recognized strength in tax, private equity, mergers and acquisitions, health care, high-stakes litigation and many other key areas of transactional and regulatory law. We emphasize and foster long-term, industry-focused client relationships with multinational companies, rising entrepreneurial firms, investors and capital providers and many of the world's wealthiest families and individuals. In word and deed, we value integrity, efficiency, diversity, pro bono and community service.

Recruitment

Law Schools attending for OCIs in 2018:

American University, Boston College, Boston University, Brooklyn Law School, Columbia, Duke, Fordham, George Mason, George Washington, Georgetown University, Harvard, Howard, Illinois, Loyola Chicago, New York University, Northwestern, Santa Clara, Stanford, University of California (Berkeley, Hastings, Irvine, Los Angeles), University of Chicago, University of Florida, University of Miami, University of Michigan, University of Notre Dame, University of Pennsylvania, University of Southern California, University of Virginia, Vanderbilt, Washington University, William & Mary, Yale.

Recruitment outside OCIs:

We attend several regional and IP focused job fairs outside of OCI programs at law schools. We also accept write-in applications.

Summer associate profile:

McDermott strives to hire well-rounded candidates who maintain a balance of academic, as well as personal and professional successes. The ideal summer associate candidate is someone who possesses the drive to tackle new challenges and embrace new experiences, takes an active approach to building relationships with attorneys and staff, has a collegial attitude and acts with integrity.

Summer program components:

Our program offers summer associates a realistic introduction to the practice of law and day-to-day life as a McDermott associate. The summer associate program provides meaningful responsibility and feedback that is consistent with a junior associate experience. Summer associates are given the opportunity to accept assignments with many of our practice groups during the summer. This allows summers to experience the type of work they are interested in first-hand and ultimately steer them toward the type of work they enjoy. Our conservative hiring approach allows students to access a number of substantive assignments and matters. Summer associates receive formal feedback during mid-summer evaluation and final review in addition to information feedback over the course of the summer. Each summer associate is assigned an associate and partner level mentor to provide guidance throughout the summer, explain firm policies, address any questions or concerns and to assist in the transition from law school to life in a law firm.

Head Office: Chicago, IL
Number of domestic offices: 10
Number of international offices: 8
(plus a strategic alliance in Shanghai)
Worldwide revenue: $925,470,000
Partners (US): 472
Associates (US): 245

Contacts
Main recruitment contact: Erika Gardiner, Senior Legal Recruiting Manager (egardiner@mwe.com)
Hiring partner: Eric Gilbert
Diversity officer: Anthony Upshaw, Global Head of Diversity & Inclusion

Recruitment details
Entry-level associates starting in 2018: 34
Clerking policy: Yes
Summers joining/anticipated 2018: 48
(1Ls: 6, 2Ls: 41, 3Ls: 1)
Summers joining/anticipated 2018 split by office: Boston: 3, Chicago: 14, Dallas: 1, Los Angeles: 2, Miami: 3, New York: 10, Silicon Valley: 3, Washington, DC: 13
Summer salary 2018:
1Ls: $ 3,461/week
2Ls: $ 3,461/week
Split summers offered? Yes
Can summers spend time in an overseas office? No

McDermott
Will & Emery

Milbank, Tweed, Hadley & McCloy LLP

8 Liberty Street, New York, NY 10005

Tel: 212 530 5000   Fax: 212 530 5219   Twitter: @MilbankLaw
Recruitment website: www.milbank.com/careers
Linkedin: milbank-tweed-hadley-&-mccloy-llp

Main areas of work

Milbank's practice areas include alternative investments, capital markets, corporate, financial restructuring, leveraged finance, litigation (complex commercial, white collar and regulatory, securities and IP), pro bono, project, energy and infrastructure finance, real estate, structured finance, tax, transportation and space finance and trusts and estates.

Firm profile

Milbank is a premier international law firm handling high-profile cases and complex business transactions. We are a leader in corporate/finance work, including banking, capital markets, project and transportation, finance and M&A. Our litigation group handles complex and high profile civil actions, SEC enforcements and white collar criminal matters. Our financial restructuring attorneys have been involved in every recent major reorganization in the US.

Recruitment

Law Schools attending for OCIs in 2018:

Albany, Berkeley, Boston University, Cardozo, Chicago, Columbia, Cornell Job Fair, Duke, Emory Job Fair, Fordham, Georgetown, George Washington, Harvard, Howard, Lavender Law Job Fair, Loyola Los Angeles (LA), Michigan, Midwest-California-Georgia Recruiting Consortium, New York University, New York Law School, Northwestern, Pennsylvania, Stanford, St. John's, Texas Job Fair, Tulane/Washington University Job Fair, UCI (LA), UCLA (LA), USC (LA), Vanderbilt, Virginia, Yale

Recruitment outside OCIs:

Our 1L Diversity Fellowship Program hires exceptionally talented 1L students for the New York office and we begin accepting applications for the following summer on December 1st. Milbank actively recruits judicial clerks from courts in the United States and from the Supreme Court of Canada.

Summer associate profile:

We are looking for summer associates with diverse backgrounds who demonstrate a high level of intelligence, creativity, leadership, determination and enthusiasm.

Summer program components:

Milbank's summer program is a microcosm of life at the firm. Professional development is fundamental to the program, and our comprehensive summer-long training program follows a company's lifecycle from inception to restructuring. Summer associates rotate through practice groups and are assigned partner and associate mentors who help ensure direct exposure to the firm's work and culture. Summer associates receive constructive and substantive feedback from partners at mid-summer and end-of-summer reviews.

Head Office: New York, NY
Number of domestic offices: 3
Number of international offices: 9
Worldwide revenue: $916,538,000
Partners (US): 114
Counsel (US): 29
Associates (US): 356

Contacts
Main recruitment contact: Ann Bjornstad
(abjornstad@milbank.com)
Hiring partner: Rod Miller
Diversity officer: Salila Yohn

Recruitment details
Entry-level associates starting in 2018: 79
Clerking policy: Yes
Summers joining/anticipated 2018:
1Ls: 2, 2Ls: 59, 3Ls: 0, SEO: 2
Summers joining/anticipated 2018 split
by office: NY 49, LA 8, Washington, DC 4
Summer salary 2018:
1Ls: $ 3,462
2Ls: $3,462
Split summers offered? No
Can summers spend time in an overseas
office? Yes

Mintz Levin

One Financial Center, Boston, MA 02127

Tel: 617 542 6000   Fax: 617 542 2241
Email: jcarrion@mintz.com
Recruitment website: www.mintz.com/careers
Linkedin: mintz-levin

Twitter: @MintzLevin
Facebook: MintzLevin

Main areas of work

Antitrust; bankruptcy, restructuring and commercial law; communications; consumer product safety, corporate and securities; corporate compliance and investigations; crisis response, risk management and executive protection; employment, labor and benefits; environmental law; health law; immigration; intellectual property; international; litigation; privacy and security; private client; private equity; product risk management and response; project development and finance; public finance; real estate; start-ups; tax; venture capital and emerging companies; white collar defense; government investigations and enforcement.

Firm profile

Mintz Levin is a multidisciplinary firm, characterized by innovation and an entrepreneurial drive that attracts interesting clients, from startups to large public companies, universities, non-profits and family-run businesses. Mintz Levin is dedicated to the continued professional growth of its attorneys at all levels. Incoming associates benefit from a formal orientation program that acclimates them to the firm. New associates participate in an intensive three-day 'base camp' to learn the substantive law of the area of practice in which they will be concentrating. This is followed by a curriculum designed to meet the professional development needs of each attorney at every step of his/her career.

Mintz Levin is proud of its formal mentoring programs that complement the collegiality of our firm. The firm has an extensive associate mentoring program run by a firm-wide mentoring coordinator and on-site mentoring coordinators in each office.

Recruitment

Law Schools attending for OCIs in 2018:

Boston College Law School, Boston University School of Law, Georgetown Law School, Harvard Law School, University of California Los Angeles School of Law, University of San Diego School of Law, UCLA School of Law, USC Gould School of Law, University of Pennsylvania Law School, and Suffolk University Law School.

Recruitment outside OCIs:

Northeastern University School of Law – resume drop, Northeast BLSA Job Fair, Lavender Law Job Fair, and Boston Lawyers Group Job Fair.

Summer associate profile:

Mintz Levin's summer associate program is an eagerly anticipated and vital program. Summer associates are encouraged to work on assignments from a variety of practice areas. They attend trials, depositions and negotiations. They participate in legal writing workshops, a transactional case study, and a mock trial. Each summer associate is assigned an associate mentor, a member mentor and a writing mentor. Mentors are available for questions, and they facilitate informal feedback on work projects. Through work assignments and social events, our attorneys strive to provide each summer associate with an opportunity to get to know what a career at Mintz has to offer.

Summer program components:

Mintz offers a summer associate program in their Boston and San Diego office. Summer associates are exposed to a variety of practice areas. This provides them with the opportunity to explore new and current interest areas.

Head Office: Boston, MA
Number of domestic offices: 7
Number of international offices: 2
Worldwide revenue: $400m
Partners (US): 239
Associates (US): 219

Contacts
Main recruitment contact:
Jennifer Carrion, (jcarrion@mintz.com)
Hiring partner: Bret Leone-Quick
Diversity officer: Tyrone Thomas

Recruitment details
Entry-level associates starting in 2018: 14
Clerking policy: Yes (depending on the situation)
Summers joining/anticipated 2018:
1Ls: 4, 2Ls: 12
Summers joining/anticipated 2018 split by office: New York: 2, Boston: 11, San Diego: 3
Summer salary 2018:
1Ls: $3,461 bi-weekly
2Ls: $3,461 bi-weekly
Split summers offered? No
Can summers spend time in overseas office? No

MINTZ LEVIN
Mintz Levin Cohn Ferris Glovsky and Popeo PC

Firm Profiles

Morgan, Lewis & Bockius LLP

701 Market Street, Philadelphia, PA 19103-2921

Tel: 215 963 5000   Fax: 215 963 5001
Email: firmattorneyrecruiting@morganlewis.com
Recruitment website: www.morganlewis.com
Linkedin: Morgan Lewis

Twitter: @MorganLewisLaw
@mlrecruit
Facebook: Morgan Lewis
Instagram: @mlrecruit

Main areas of work

At Morgan Lewis, we work around the world and around the clock to respond to the needs of our clients. We provide comprehensive corporate, transactional, litigation and regulatory services that address and anticipate challenges across rapidly changing landscapes. Our international team of lawyers and other specialists support clients across a wide range of industries, including financial services, energy and environmental, healthcare and life sciences, retail, and technology.

Firm profile

From our 30 offices in the United States, Asia, Europe, and the Middle East, we work across all major industries with clients that range from established, global Fortune 100 companies to enterprising startups. Our team comprises more than 2,000 legal professionals including lawyers, patent agents, employee benefits advisors, regulatory scientists, and other specialists. We focus on immediate concerns and long-term goals, harnessing our resources from strategic hubs of commerce, law, and government around the world. Founded in 1873, we stand on the shoulders of more than 140 years of excellence.

Recruitment

Law Schools attending for OCIs in 2018:

American, BC, Berkeley, BU, Catholic, Chicago, Columbia, Cornell, Davis, Duke, Fordham, GW, Georgetown, Harvard, Hastings, Houston, Howard, Illinois, Irvine, Michigan, NYU, Northwestern, Pennsylvania, Rutgers, Santa Clara, Stanford, Temple, Texas, UCLA, USC, USF, UVA, Vanderbilt, and Villanova

Recruitment outside OCIs:

The firm participates in a number of diversity and practice-related job fairs.

Summer associate profile:

Highly motivated individuals from diverse backgrounds who have a record of outstanding academic achievement; superior writing and analytical skills; a commitment to client service; demonstrate initiative; and an ability to succeed in a challenging, collaborative workplace.

Summer program components:

Our program provides insight into Morgan Lewis, its practices and culture through professional and social experiences. The summer program launches with a multiday kickoff that brings summer associates from all offices together with firm leaders, other partners, and associates. Summer associates have the unique opportunity to tailor their summer experiences with the option of either spending the entire summer at the firm or spending a portion of the summer working on-site with a public interest organization. While at the firm, summer associates work on matters typically assigned to first-year associates and participate in a generous mix of training opportunities to hone skills such as legal writing and presentation style. After joining the firm fulltime, associates are offered Student Loan Repayment services, an innovative Remote Working Program and a Ramp-Up Programs, including a reduced-hours expectation for six months, for associates returning from an extended leave of absence.

Head Office: Philadelphia, PA
Number of domestic offices: 17
Number of international offices: 13
Partners (US): 633
Associates (US): 762

Contacts
Main recruitment contact: Noelani Walser
(noelani.walser@morganlewis.com)
Hiring partner: Christina Edling Melendi
Diversity officer: MaLora McCullough

Recruitment details
Entry-level associates starting in 2018: 56
Clerking policy: Yes
Summers joining/anticipated 2018:
1Ls: 11, 2Ls: 76
Summers joining/anticipated 2018 split by office: Boston: 8; Chicago: 3;
Houston: 5; Los Angeles: 5;
New York: 19; Philadelphia: 17;
San Francisco: 7; Silicon Valley: 8;
Washington, DC: 15
Summer salary 2018:
1Ls: $3,500/week
2Ls: $3,500/week
Split summers offered? Case by case
Can summers spend time in an overseas office? No

Morgan Lewis

Morrison & Foerster

425 Market Street, San Francisco, CA 94105

Tel: 415 268 7000　Fax: 415 268 7522
Email: fwattorneyrecruiting@mofo.com
Recruitment website: www.mofocareers.com
Linkedin: Morrison Foerster LLP

Twitter: @MoFoLLP
Facebook: MoFoLLP
Instagram: @MoFoLLP

Main areas of work

Appellate; business restructuring and insolvency; capital markets; clean technology and alternative energy; commercial litigation; emerging companies and venture capital; energy; financial transactions; global risk and crisis management; intellectual property; life sciences; mergers and acquisitions; national security; privacy and data security; private equity; real estate; securities litigation, enforcement and white-collar criminal defense; tax; and technology transactions.

Firm profile

Morrison & Foerster is a global firm of exceptional credentials. With more than 950 lawyers in 16 offices in key technology and financial centers in the United States, Europe and Asia, the firm advises the world's leading financial institutions, investment banks and technology, telecommunications, life sciences and Fortune 100 companies.

Recruitment

Law Schools attending for OCIs in 2018:

Berkeley, Cardozo, Chicago, Columbia, Cornell, UC Davis, Duke, Fordham, George Washington, Georgetown, Harvard, Howard, McGill, Michigan, Northwestern, New York University, Penn, USD, Santa Clara, Stanford, UCLA, USC, Virginia, Yale

Recruitment outside OCIs:

Generally, about 20% of our summer class is made up of 1Ls who were hired outside of OCI. We also recruit a small number of 2Ls in advance of OCI on a write-in basis.

Summer associate profile:

Morrison & Foerster looks for individuals of exceptional intelligence whose academic and other achievements evidence their talent, motivation, energy and creativity.

Summer program components:

The summer program is intended to give summer associates a real sense of what it means to practice at MoFo.

Work is distributed using a central assignment system, taking into account your areas of interest. Typical assignments include writing briefs, motions, contracts and client memoranda, assisting in drafting and negotiation sessions, assisting in depositions and witness preparation and performing due diligence in corporate transactions, as well as pro bono assignments.

A variety of training programs are designed specifically for summer associates, including practice area presentations.

Each summer associate is assigned one or more mentors to help acclimate him or her to the firm. Mentors take their summer associates out to lunch, introduce their summer associates to the lawyers and staff in their practice group and office and act as a sounding board for any questions or concerns summer associates may have throughout the summer.

Largest Office: San Francisco, CA
Number of domestic offices: 8
Number of international offices: 8
Worldwide revenue: $1,062,700,000
Partners (US): 237
Associates (US): 404

Contacts
Main recruitment contact: Nicole Wanzer, Director of Attorney Recruiting (nwanzer@mofo.com)
Hiring partner: Craig Martin, Managing Partner
Diversity officer: Natalie Kernisant, Director of Diversity and Inclusion

Recruitment details
Entry-level associates starting in 2018: 58
Clerking policy: Yes
Summers joining/anticipated 2018:
1Ls 17, 2Ls 69
Summers joining/anticipated 2018 split by office: Los Angeles: 15, New York: 15, San Diego: 7, San Francisco: 30, Palo Alto: 10, Northern Virginia: 3, Washington, DC: 9
Summer salary 2018:
1Ls: $3,750/week
2Ls: $3,750/week
Split summers offered? Yes, on a case by case basis
Can summers spend time in an overseas office? Yes

MORRISON FOERSTER

Munger, Tolles & Olson LLP

50 South Grand Avenue, 50th Floor, Los Angeles, CA 90071

Tel: 213 683 9100   Fax: 213 687 3702

Email: kevinn.villard@mto.com

Recruitment website: www.mto.com/careers

Linkedin: munger-tolles-&-olson

Twitter: @mungertolles

Main areas of work

For over a half a century, attorneys from Munger, Tolles & Olson have been partnering with clients on their most important and complex cases and business deals. We maintain a national and international practice. Our principal areas of practice include bet-the-company litigation (from the outset of the case through trial and any appeals), internal investigations, white collar defense, corporate advice, labor and employment, environmental, real estate, financial restructuring and tax.

Firm profile

Munger Tolles has for decades intentionally maintained low-leverage. We believe our roughly one-to-one partner-to-associate ratio empowers all of our approximately 200 lawyers to make an impact in the work we do for our clients. We are involved in some of the highest profile cases in the country and count among our clients Bank of America, Wells Fargo, LinkedIn, Facebook, the major motion picture studios, Verizon, Intel, KB Home, LG Display, and Berkshire Hathaway.

Recruitment

Law Schools attending for OCIs in 2018:

Berkeley, Chicago, Columbia, Harvard, Howard, Michigan, NYU, Stanford, UCLA, USC and Yale

Recruitment outside OCIs:

Job Fairs: Bay Area Diversity Career Fair and Penn LA Regional Interview Program

Resume Collections: Duke, Georgetown, Loyola (LA), Northwestern, Texas, UC Irvine, and UVA

Summer associate profile:

We want to hire problem solvers. We look for law students who have demonstrated excellence and leadership in their prior pursuits and who bring both leadership, intellectual curiosity, and a sense of individuality to an already extremely talented and diverse group of lawyers. Unlike other law firms, where it has become common to expect that young lawyers will stay only a short time before moving on to other endeavours, we only hire lawyers we believe have the potential to ultimately join our (one-tier) partnership.

Summer program components:

Our summer program will provide you a realistic idea of what it is like to practice law at our firm. You will work closely with attorneys in various practice areas, doing meaningful assignments. Each summer associate is assigned a work coordinator and social advisor. Your work coordinator will find assignments that are of interest to you and provide guidance and feedback during the summer. Your summer will include invitations to attend our weekly lunches, training programs, social events and practice group meetings.

Offices: Los Angeles, CA; San Francisco, CA; Washington, DC

Number of domestic offices: 3

Partners (US): 84

Associates (US): 106

Contacts

Main recruitment contact: Kevinn Villard, kevinn.villard@mto.com

Hiring partners: Daniel Levin and Carolyn Luedtke

Diversity director: Chantel Moore

Recruitment details

Entry-level associates starting in 2018: 22-25

Clerking policy: Yes

Summers joining/anticipated 2018:
1Ls: 2, 2Ls: 10

Summers joining/anticipated 2018 split by office: Los Angeles: 18, San Francisco: 2 (1L Summer Program)

Summer salary 2018:
1Ls: $3,461/week
2Ls: $3,461/week

Split summers offered? Yes

Nelson Mullins Riley & Scarborough LLP

Meridian, 17th Floor, 1320 Main Street, Columbia, SC 29201

Tel: 803 799 2000
Email: nm.recruiting@nelsonmullins.com
Recruitment website: www.nelsonmullins.com/careers
Linkedin: Nelson Mullins Riley & Scarborough LLP

Twitter: @NelsonMullins
Instagram: @Nelson_Mullins
Facebook: Nelson Mullins Riley & Scarborough LLP

Main areas of work

Banking and financial services, corporate and securities, cybersecurity and privacy, e-discovery, education, energy and environment, government relations, healthcare, insurance, intellectual property, international, litigation, real estate, tax, technology, transportation.

Firm profile

Established in 1897, Nelson Mullins has more than 575 attorneys and government relations professionals with offices in 11 states and Washington, DC. For more information on the firm, go to www.nelsonmullins.com.

Recruitment

Law Schools attending for OCIs in 2018:

- Boston College
- Boston University
- Charleston School of Law
- Columbia
- Duke
- Emory University
- Florida State
- Fordham
- George Mason
- George Washington
- Georgia State
- Harvard
- Mercer University
- New York University
- Ohio State
- Suffolk
- University of Florida
- University of Georgia
- University of Kentucky
- University of Mississippi
- University of North Carolina
- University of South Carolina
- University of Tennessee
- University of Virginia
- Vanderbilt University
- Wake Forest University
- Washington & Lee
- West Virginia University
- William & Mary

Summer associate profile:

Job description: The firm's summer program is designed to give summer associates a comprehensive view of the firm's practice while giving the firm an opportunity to evaluate the skills of the summer associates. In evaluating applicants, consideration is given to undergraduate and law school academic performance, extracurricular activities and leadership skills, as well as other experiences and accomplishments.

Qualifications: In evaluating applicants, consideration is given to undergraduate and law school academic performance, extracurricular activities and leadership skills, as well as other experiences and accomplishments.

Summer program components:

For associates who join us post-law school graduation, our associate development process includes bringing new associates onto established practice teams, a formal mentor program pairing new associates with experienced attorneys, and robust programming developed by our Associates Committee designed to advance professional development of associates across the firm. Associates receive training on business, marketing, and a range of substantive issues, and work side-by-side with experienced colleagues.

Head office: Columbia, SC
Number of domestic offices: 18
Number of international offices: 0
Worldwide revenue: $ 405,426,258
Partners (US): 362
Associates (US): 235

Contacts
Main recruitment contact: Emily Martin (emily.martin@nelsonmullins.com)
Hiring partner: Dell Chappell

Recruitment details
Entry-level associates starting in 2018: 13
Clerking policy: Yes
Summers joining/anticipated 2018:
1Ls: 28, 2Ls: 20
Summers joining/anticipated 2018 split by office: ATL: 7; CHAS: 5; CHLT: 2; CAE: 17; GV: 4; HUNT: 4; JAX: 1; NASH: 2; NY: 1; DC: 4; WS: 1
Summer salary 2018:
Georgia: 1L $1,600/2L $2,600
Florida: 1L $1,500/2L $1,800
Massachusetts: 1L $2,600/2L $2,600
New York: 1LS $2,600/2L $2,600
North Carolina: 1L $1,600/2L $1,750
South Carolina: 1L $1,400/2L $1,500
Tennessee: 1L $1,500/2L $1,800
Washington, DC: 1L $2,600/2L $2,600
West Virginia: 1L $1,000/2L $1,150
Split summers offered? Yes
Can summers spend time in an overseas office? No

Norton Rose Fulbright

301 McKinney, Suite 5100, Houston, TX 77010

Tel: 713 651 5151
Email: USLegalRecruiting@nortonrosefulbright.com
Recruitment website: joinus.nortonrosefulbright.com
Linkedin: nortonrosefulbright

Main areas of work

Antitrust and competition; banking and finance; corporate, M&A and securities; dispute resolution and litigation; employment and labor; financial restructuring and insolvency; intellectual property; real estate; regulations and investigations; risk advisory; and tax.

Firm profile

Norton Rose Fulbright provides the world's preeminent corporations and financial institutions with a full business law service. It has more than 4,000 lawyers and other legal staff based in Europe, the United States, Canada, Latin America, Asia, Australia, Africa and the Middle East.

Recognized for its industry focus, Norton Rose Fulbright is strong across all the key industry sectors: financial institutions; energy; infrastructure, mining and commodities; transport; technology and innovation; and life sciences and healthcare. Through its global risk advisory group, Norton Rose Fulbright leverages its industry experience with its knowledge of legal, regulatory, compliance and governance issues to provide clients with practical solutions to the legal and regulatory risks facing their businesses.

Recruitment

Law Schools attending for OCIs in 2018:

Baylor, Cardozo, Columbia, Duke, Fordham, George Washington, Georgetown, Harvard, Hofstra, Howard, Loyola (CA), NYU, Penn, South Texas College of Law, SMU, Texas Southern, Texas Tech, UC-Irvine, UCLA, University of Chicago, University of Southern California, University of Texas, University of Virginia, Washington University, Yale

Recruitment outside OCIs:

Cornell (DC and NY job fairs), Emory Job Fair, Lavender Law, Loyola Patent Law, National Law School Consortium, NEBLSA Job fair, Notre Dame Interview Program, Penn Regional Job Fairs, SEMJF, Sunbelt, Vanderbilt Career Fairs, Washington University Walkaround Programs.

Summer associate profile:

We recruit motivated, energetic and personable individuals with whom we will enjoy practicing law. Candidates should have high academic achievement, maturity, and initiative. We also value other indicators of likely success at Norton Rose Fulbright, such as demonstrated leadership skills and an entrepreneurial outlook.

Summer program components:

Your summer experience will provide you with a realistic preview of what it is like to practice at Norton Rose Fulbright. You will do real work for real clients.

We offer sophisticated work, world-class learning and development and our lawyers are committed to teaching and mentoring. Our US Summer Associates are invited to participate in the Summer Associate Academy, a two day induction into the firm.

Head Office: N/A
Number of domestic offices: 11
Number of international offices: 47
Worldwide revenue: $1.958 billion
Partners (US): 309
Associates (US): 325

Contacts
Main recruitment contact: Jaimee Slovak
(jaimee.slovak@nortonrosefulbright.com)
Hiring partner: Doug Wabner
Diversity officer: Lisa Genecov

Recruitment details
Entry-level associates starting in 2018: 38
Clerking policy: Yes
Summers joining/anticipated 2018: 83
1Ls: 14; 2Ls: 69
Summers joining/anticipated 2018 split
by office: Austin: 10, Dallas: 12,
Houston: 26, Los Angeles: 2,
Minneapolis: 1, New York: 24,
St. Louis: 1, Washington: 7
Summer salary 2018:
1Ls: $3,500/wk (CA, DC, NY, TX)
2Ls: $3,500/wk (CA, DC, NY, TX)
Split summers offered? Case by case
Can summers spend time in an overseas
office? No

NORTON ROSE FULBRIGHT

Nutter McClennen & Fish LLP

155 Seaport Blvd, Seaport West, Boston, MA 02210

Tel: 617 439 2000
Recruitment website: www.nutter.com/careers
Linkedin: nutter-mcclennen-&-fish-llp

Twitter: @NutterLaw
Facebook: NutterLaw
Instagram: @NutterLaw

Main areas of work
Corporate and transactions, intellectual property, litigation, private client, real estate and tax.

Firm profile
Nutter McClennen & Fish LLP has deep roots in Boston and a long-standing reputation for business savvy and pragmatism. Nutter advises clients across a wide range of industries, including life sciences, medical devices, pharmaceuticals, banking and financial services, real estate, energy, and technology. The firm regularly represents major US global corporations and financial institutions, research universities, high technology and emerging companies, investors, developers, foundations, and families that select Nutter for the quality of its lawyers and its depth as a multi-service firm. Nutter was co-founded by Louis D. Brandeis, who later became a renowned justice of the US Supreme Court. The founding partners' rich legacy continues to inspire and set an example for the firm. Today Nutter upholds the same standard of focused dedication, innovation, and unwavering commitment to client service that they set over a century ago.

Recruitment

Law Schools attending for OCIs in 2018:
Boston College Law School, Boston University School of Law, Harvard Law School, New England Law | Boston, Northeastern University School of Law, and Suffolk University Law School

Recruitment outside OCIs:
Job Fairs: Boston Lawyers Group Job Fair (diversity fair) and Patent Law Interview Program
Resume Drops: Top 20 Law Schools

Summer associate profile:
Strong academic record. Intelligent, enthusiastic, confident and results-oriented team players with demonstrated interpersonal and communication skills.

Summer program components:
Our approach to the summer experience at Nutter is to provide our summer associates with as complete and accurate a view of the firm and our practice as possible. Summer associates divide their ten weeks between two departments. For those who desire exposure to other areas, assignment coordinators endeavor to provide them with projects tailored to their individual interests. Each summer associate receives two formal reviews, one at midsummer and the other at the end of the program. These reviews are intended to provide the summer associate with guidance and are based upon written evaluations by supervising attorneys. We expect attorneys to provide individual, ongoing, informal feedback to summer associates and encourage summer associates to solicit feedback directly from attorneys. Each summer associate is assigned mentors, from each department to which he or she is assigned. By the end of the program, our goal is for summer associates to have a thorough understanding of our client-base and the work environment they will encounter as full-time associates.

Head Office: Boston, MA
Number of domestic offices: 2
Worldwide revenue: $90 million
Partners (US): 79
Associates (US): 39

Contacts
Main recruitment contact:
Donna M Yergeau,
Director of Legal Recruiting
Hiring partner: Christopher H Lindstrom
Diversity officers: Julia S Cosentino,
David L. Ferrera, Co-Chairs,
Diversity and Inclusion Committee

Recruitment details
Entry-level associates starting in 2018: 7
Clerking policy: Case-by-case
Summers joining/anticipated 2018:
1Ls: 1, 2Ls: 6
Summers joining/anticipated 2018 split by office: Boston: 7
Summer salary 2018:
1Ls: $1,500/week
2Ls: $3,077/week
Split summers offered? No

O'Melveny & Myers LLP

Tel: 212 326 2000
Recruitment website: www.omm.com/careers
Linkedin: o'melveny-&-myers-llp

Twitter: @omelvenymyers
Facebook:
OMelvenyandMyersLLP
Instagram: omelvenymyers

Main areas of work

O'Melveny is a multidisciplinary firm with approximately 800 lawyers in 15 offices worldwide. Our wide-ranging legal services encompass litigation, business deals, risk management, regulatory compliance, and government relations. The firm advises clients on a full range of cutting-edge litigation and corporate matters that arise in various industries, including aviation, consumer products, energy, entertainment and media, financial services, health care, insurance, life sciences, natural resources, private equity, sports, and emerging technologies. For a complete listing of our client services and locations, visit omm.com.

Firm profile

It's more than what you do: it's how you do it. That's why O'Melveny is counsel of choice to an ever-expanding list of market leaders. Opportunity at O'Melveny means working alongside exceptional lawyers — recognized legal authorities who counsel industry leaders on their most significant and sensitive matters with a blend of creativity, passion, and commitment. It's a place to build a rewarding career and create lasting connections by tackling new challenges while feeling appreciated, included, and supported. So, tell us. What do you want to achieve?

Recruitment

Law Schools attending for OCIs in 2018:

Berkeley, Brooklyn, Chapman, Chicago, Columbia, Duke, Fordham, Georgetown, George Washington, Harvard, Hastings, Howard, Lavender Law, Loyola, Michigan, Northwestern, NYU, Penn, Santa Clara, Stanford, UCI, UCLA, University of Washington, USC, UVA, Yale

Recruitment outside OCIs:

Last year, O'Melveny recruited on campus at more than 25 schools, in addition to accepting write-in applications and conducting resume collections. We aim to strike a balance between recruiting at national schools and regional schools within our various markets. We also participate in diversity career fairs and initiatives, such as Lavender Law and veteran recruiting events. We continue to connect with a variety of law student organizations for speaking engagements, networking events, and sponsorships.

Summer associate profile:

We're looking for candidates who are enthusiastic about O'Melveny. We consider a variety of criteria when making hiring decisions, including high academic achievement, extracurricular activities, prior professional work, and a diverse set of experiences.

Summer program components:

Our summer program offers an inside look at what it is like to practice at O'Melveny. During our ten-week program, summer associates work on major cases and deals, support ongoing pro bono matters, participate in targeted training and development programs, and join in social events to get to know our attorneys. Experiential training includes our Advocacy Institute, Mock Deal Program, and opportunities to accompany O'Melveny lawyers to deal closings, client meetings, depositions, and court appearances. Our work coordination system ensures our summers are exposed to a variety of practice areas, attorneys, and types of work. Mentors, ongoing feedback, and a midsummer review help our summer associates make the most of their experiences.

Number of domestic offices: **7**
Number of international offices: **8**
Worldwide revenue: **$738 million**
Partners (US): **186**
Associates (US): **438**

Contacts
Main recruitment contact: **Tina Metis**
Hiring partner: **Allen Burton**
Diversity officer: **Mary Ellen Connerty**

Recruitment details
Entry-level associates starting in 2018: **44**
Clerking policy: **Yes**
Summers joining/anticipated 2018:
1Ls: **4**, 2Ls: **70**, 3Ls: **0**, SEO: **6**
Summers joining/anticipated 2018 split by office: **Century City: 11,
Los Angeles: 20, Newport Beach: 8,
New York: 13, San Francisco: 10,
Silicon Valley: 3, Washington, DC: 10**
Summer salary 2018:
1Ls: **$3,500/week**
2Ls: **$3,500/week**
Split summers offered? **Case by case**
Can summers spend time in an overseas office? **No**

Firm Profiles

Orrick, Herrington & Sutcliffe LLP

51 West 52nd Street, New York, NY 10019

The Orrick Building, 405 Howard Street, San Francisco, CA 94105-2669

Tel: 212 506 5000 (New York) / 415 773 5700 (San Francisco)
Recruitment website: www.orrick.com/careers
Twitter: @Orrick, @OrrickCareers, @MitchZuklie

Facebook: @Orrick
Instagram: @OrrickCareers,
@mzuklie

Main areas of work

Technology and innovation, energy and infrastructure, finance, corporate, litigation, appellate and intellectual property.

Firm profile

At Orrick, we focus on serving the technology and innovation, energy and infrastructure and finance sectors globally. Founded more than 150 years ago in San Francisco, Orrick today as 1000+ lawyers and offices in 25 markets worldwide including our newest offices in Houston and Santa Monica. Our clients include 1600+ high-growth companies, 20% of today's unicorns, public companies, global financial institutions, funds and government entities.

Recruitment

Law Schools attending for OCIs in 2018:

- Boston College
- Columbia
- Duke
- Fordham
- George Mason University
- George Washington
- Georgetown
- Harvard
- McGeorge
- Northwestern
- Notre Dame
- NYU
- Santa Clara
- Stanford
- Tulane

- UC Davis
- UC Hastings
- UC Irvine
- UCLA
- University of Chicago
- University of Houston
- University of Michigan
- University of North Carolina
- University of Pennsylvania
- University of Texas
- University of Washington
- USC
- UVA
- Vanderbilt
- Yale

Summer associate profile:

We seek candidates who have diverse backgrounds and interests, and who bring interesting life experiences and perspectives that shape their world view. We've identified three qualities our most successful lawyers have in common: grit, EQ and teamplay. We believe in having fun while working hard on projects that make a tangible impact on the world, locally and globally.

Summer program components:

Your first day as a summer associate is the beginning of your Orrick career. Our goal is to immerse you in the firm, introduce you to our clients, engage you in the issues on which we are working and create opportunities for you to start building relationships that we hope will last a lifetime. Our summer associate classes are small which means focused and personal attention, practical training, varied assignments spanning different transactional and litigation practice area, extensive feedback and hands-on experience with real client matters.

Head Office: New York/San Francisco
Number of domestic offices: 12
Number of international offices: 13
Worldwide revenue: $975 million
Partners (US): 299
Associates (US): 541

Contacts
Main recruitment contact:
Siobhan Handley (shandley@orrick.com)
Hiring partner: Eric Hairston
Diversity officer: Joi Y. Bourgeois

Recruitment details
Entry-level associates starting in 2018: 51
Clerking policy: Yes
Summers joining/anticipated 2018: 64
1Ls: 10, 2Ls: 53 SEO: 1
Summers joining/anticipated 2018 split
by office: Houston: 3, Los Angeles: 4,
New York: 17, Orange County: 4.
Portland: 1, Sacramento: 4,
Santa Monica: 1, San Francisco: 15
Seattle: 1, Silicon Valley: 8,
Washington, DC: 6
Summer salary 2018:
1Ls: $3,400
2Ls: $3,400
Split summers offered? Yes. Must spend
a minimum of 8 weeks at Orrick.
Can summers spend time in an overseas
office? No

Patterson Belknap Webb & Tyler LLP

133 Avenue of the Americas, New York, NY 10036

Tel: 212 336 2000
Email: rlklum@pbwt.com
Recruitment website: www.pbwt.com/careers/
Linkedin: patterson-belknap-webb-&-tyler-llp

Main areas of work

Our clients are at the forefront of their industries, whether in white collar investigations, privacy and data security, pharmaceuticals, biosimilars or medical devices, finance or philanthropy, music, museums or sports, the Internet or newspapers. 100% of our lawyers and paralegals work on pro bono cases each year and our contributions have repeatedly put us first among New York City-based firms. The firm is regularly recognized in industry publications as a leader in litigation areas including intellectual property and false advertising. In addition, the firm has the leading personal planning and tax-exempt organizations practices in New York City.

Firm profile

About to celebrate its centennial year, Patterson Belknap Webb & Tyler LLP, is a law firm based in New York City with more than 200 lawyers committed to maintaining its independence, its diversity and its focus of providing superior legal advice and service to clients. The firm delivers a full range of services across more than 20 practice groups in both litigation and commercial law. *The National Law Journal* has included Patterson Belknap on a list of firms which it considers to have 'the nimbleness and adaptability that come from lean operations and strong client ties.' The firm highly values public service and has consistently ranked at or near the top of *The American Lawyer*'s annual pro bono survey.

Recruitment

Law Schools attending for OCIs in 2018:

For 3Ls: Columbia, Harvard, NYU, Yale.

Recruitment outside OCIs:

Patterson Belknap hires associates directly from judicial clerkships. We will also recruit in August 2018 to hire a select group of 3L law students graduating at the end of the 2019 school year. We look forward to meeting with outstanding law students through both clerkship and 3L recruiting.

Diversity Fellowship for Judicial Clerks:

Patterson Belknap believes that a workforce made up of people from diverse social, racial, economic and cultural backgrounds results in a dynamic and supportive workplace for our attorneys and staff and enhances our ability to provide the highest quality representation for and service to our clients. As part of our ongoing commitment to recruiting, retaining and promoting attorneys who contribute to the diversity of our firm and our profession, we are pleased to offer the Patterson Belknap Webb & Tyler LLP Diversity Fellowship to a current judicial law clerk planning to start practicing at the firm as an associate in the fall of 2019. In addition to our standard clerk bonus, the Fellowship includes:

- $25,000 as a financial award
- The firm will make a $5,000 contribution in the Fellow's honor to a non-profit organization that supports diversity (to be selected by the Fellow, with input from the firm)

Head Office: New York
Worldwide revenue: $192,000
Partners (US): 50
Associates (US): 105

Contacts
Main recruitment contact:
Robin L Klum, rlklum@pbwt.com
Hiring partners: Catherine Williams and Josh Goldberg
Diversity officers: Peter Harvey, TJ Tu, Co Chairs, Diversity Committee

Recruitment details
Entry-level associates starting in 2018: 2
Clerking policy: We hire directly from clerkships

Patterson Belknap Webb & Tyler LLP

Paul Hastings

200 Park Avenue, New York, NY10166

Email: attorneyrecruiting@paulhastings.com
Recruitment website: www.paulhastings.com/carrers/law-students
Linkedin: paul-hastings

Twitter: @PH_Recruiting
Facebook: paulhastingsllp

Main areas of work

We understand the imperative for innovation, efficiency and breakthrough performance facing today's leading companies – and what it takes to help them succeed.

Our practice areas include: anticorruption and compliance, antitrust and competition, complex commercial litigation, employment, finance and restructuring, global banking and payment systems, intellectual property, investment management, mergers and acquisitions, privacy and data security, private equity, real estate, securities and capital markets, securities litigation, tax, white collar defense and investigations.

Firm profile

At Paul Hastings, our purpose is clear — to help our clients and people navigate new paths to growth. With a strong presence throughout Asia, Europe, Latin America and the US, Paul Hastings is recognized as one of the world's most innovative global law firms and a great place to work. The firm has been named *Vault*'s #1 'Place to Work' four times in the last five years.

At Paul Hastings, we are committed to the professional development and career aspirations of our associates. We hire great people and provide them with opportunities to broaden their skills from day one.

Recruitment

Law Schools attending for OCIs in 2018:

Berkeley, University of Chicago, Columbia, Cornell, Duke, Emory, Fordham, Georgia, Georgetown, GW, Harvard, Howard, Michigan, Northwestern, NYU, Penn, Santa Clara, Stanford, UC Hastings, University of Houston, UC Irvine, UCLA, USC, University of San Diego, University of Texas, UVA, Vanderbilt, Yale.

Recruitment outside of OCIs:

Paul Hastings provides numerous opportunities for students to connect with our lawyers throughout the year. We sponsor student groups, host panels and events on campus and may also offer informational interviews.

Summer associate profile:

At Paul Hastings, it's smart business to build diverse teams rich in talent, experiences, and creativity. We seek students who exemplify the hallmarks of successful Paul Hastings associates: innovative, strong communication skills, achievement drive, interpersonal savvy, client service excellence and ability to be collaborative team members. Students should be committed to work for a dynamic and entrepreneurial law firm on complex legal matters across practices and offices to help our clients overcome challenges and move their business forward. Law students with outstanding academic credentials, superior writing skills, law review, journal or Moot Court membership are preferred.

Summer program components:

Our summer program serves as a cornerstone for the recruitment of outstanding associates and the future success of our firm. We are fully committed to the professional development and advancement of each summer associate. Summer associates are given substantive and challenging work with a variety of lawyers and a realistic view of practicing law at Paul Hastings. Our summer associates observe and, when possible, assist in trials, hearings, depositions and negotiations, and participate in client meetings and closings. Summer associates can also expect exceptional training and development in a collaborative work environment.

Largest Office: **New York, NY**
Number of domestic offices: **11**
Number of international offices: **11**
Worldwide revenue: **$1,118,100,000**
Partners (US): **232**
Counsel (US): **58**
Associates (US): **469**

Contacts
Main recruitment contact:
**Cynthia Hasson, Director,
Talent Acquisition**
Hiring partners: **Talent Advisory Council**
Diversity manager: **Karlie Ilaria**

Recruitment details
Entry-level associates starting in 2018: **59**
Clerking policy: **Yes**
Summers joining/anticipated 2018: **82**
1Ls: **7,** 2Ls: **75**
Summer salary 2018:
1Ls: **$3,500**
2Ls: **$3,500**
Split summers offered? **Case by case**
Can summers spend time in an overseas office? **In special cases, we may offer the opportunity to spend two weeks in one of our offices in Asia. The summer associate must have the appropriate language skills.**

PAUL
HASTINGS

Firm Profiles

Paul, Weiss, Rifkind, Wharton & Garrison LLP

1285 Avenue of the Americas, New York, NY 10019-6064

Tel: 212 373 3000

Email: summerprogram@paulweiss.com, lateralhiring@paulweiss.com

Recruitment website: www.paulweiss.com/careers

Main areas of work

Paul, Weiss is widely recognized as having leading litigation and corporate capabilities, and the firm has developed equally strong practices in the areas of bankruptcy and corporate reorganization, employee benefits and executive compensation, intellectual property, personal representation, real estate and tax law.

Firm profile

Paul, Weiss, Rifkind, Wharton & Garrison LLP is a firm of more than 900 lawyers, with diverse backgrounds, personalities, ideas and interests, who collaborate with clients to help them conquer their most critical legal challenges and business goals. Our long-standing clients include many of the largest publicly and privately held corporations and financial institutions in the United States and throughout the world. We have an unwavering dedication to representing those in need through our pro bono efforts, and have long been a leader in promoting diversity within our firm and the legal profession.

Recruitment

Law Schools attending for OCIs in 2018:

Boston College, Boston University, Berkeley, Brooklyn, Cardozo, Chicago, Columbia, Cornell, Duke, Fordham, Georgetown, George Washington, Harvard, Howard, McGill, Michigan, Northwestern, NYU, Patent Law Job Fair at Loyola, Penn, Stanford, Texas, Toronto, Vanderbilt, Virginia, Washington University in St. Louis, Yale.

Recruitment outside OCIs:

In addition to participating in on-campus recruiting programs, Paul, Weiss also interviews select strong candidates who submit their applications directly.

Summer associate profile:

You should have a strong academic record, life experience, and initiative and commitment to excellence in the practice of law.

Summer program components:

The summer associate program at Paul, Weiss is more than just legal training. It's your introduction to life in one of New York's most unique law firms. You'll have the opportunity to shape your summer experience at Paul, Weiss. Choose one department to call your home, or select a variety of work from a number of different practice areas. You'll be mentored by a team of lawyers including associates, counsel and partners. Your mentors will help you make connections with other lawyers at the firm and make informed decisions about the work you choose. You'll receive training in both substantive areas of law and practical legal skills in a mix of highly interactive small group trainings, individual skills development workshops and more traditional classroom-style presentations.

Head Office: New York, NY
Number of domestic offices: 3
Number of international offices: 5
Worldwide revenue: $1,301,773,000
Partners (US): 132
Associates (US): 612

Contacts
Main recruitment contact:
Pamela Davidson, Chief Legal Personnel & Recruitment Officer
Hiring partners: Neil Goldman and Catherine Nyarady
Chief Inclusion Officer: Danyale Price
Women's Initiative Director:
Anne Weisberg

Recruitment details
Entry-level associates starting in 2018:
101
Clerking policy: Yes
Summers joining/anticipated 2018:
1Ls: 7; 2Ls: 136; 3Ls: 2; SEO 1Ls: 3
Summers joining/anticipated 2018 split by office: NY: 138; DC: 10
Summer salary 2018:
1Ls: $3,500/week
2Ls: $3,500/week
3Ls: $3,500/week
Split summers offered? Yes
Can summers spend time in an overseas office? Yes

Paul | Weiss

Perkins Coie LLP

1201 Third Avenue, Suite 4900, Seattle, WA 98101-3099

Tel: 206 359 8000
Email: lawschoolinfo@perkinscoie.com
Recruitment website: www.perkinscoie.com/en/about-us/careers/entry-level/overview.html
Linkedin: PerkinsCoieLLP

Twitter: @PerkinsCoieLLP
Facebook: Perkins Coie LLP

Main areas of work

Perkins Coie's practice areas include:

- Intellectual Property
- Commercial Litigation
- Business (M&A, Emerging Companies, Corporate & Securities)
- Environmental Law
- Political Law
- Real Estate & Land Use
- Labor Law
- Privacy & Data Security

Firm profile

With more than 1,000 lawyers in 19 offices across the United States and Asia, Perkins Coie LLP represents companies across a wide range of industries and stages of growth—from startups to Fortune 500 corporations. This year 281 of the firm's attorneys were listed among the 'Best Lawyers in America' and the firm was named 'Law Firm of the Year' in patent law for the third time. Perkins Coie is very proud to have been named one of *Fortune magazine*'s 'Best Companies to Work for' for the past 16 years.

Recruitment

Law Schools attending for OCIs in 2018:

Arizona State, Columbia, Cornell, Duke, Georgetown, GWU, Gonzaga, Harvard, Howard, Lewis & Clark, Loyola (LA), Northwestern, NYU, Santa Clara, Seattle U., SMU, Stanford, UC Berkeley, UC Davis, UC Hastings, UC Irvine, UCLA, Univ. of Chicago, Univ. of Illinois, Univ. of Michigan, Univ. of Oregon, U Penn, USD, Univ. of Arizona, Univ. of Texas, Univ. of Washington, Univ. of Wisconsin, USC, UVA, Vanderbilt, Wash U (St. Louis), Willamette, Yale

Recruitment outside OCIs:

Each year Perkins Coie attends a number of interview or job fairs including the Patent Law Interview Program (PLIP); Lavender Law, the Northwest Minority Job Fair, the Bay Area Diversity Fair and the Cook County Bar Association Minority Job Fair.

Summer associate profile:

Perkins Coie seeks self-starters who have demonstrated academic excellence, leadership in and service to the community, and dedication to excellence in the legal profession.

Summer program components:

Perkins Coie's summer associate program provides varied work opportunities and social events designed to promote interaction among summer associates, attorneys and staff. Summer associates work on a wide range of challenging legal assignments similar to those given to new associates which typically include legal research, analysis and drafting. Summer associates are invited to attend depositions, mediations, deal closings, client meetings, trials and other professional activities and events. They are welcome and encouraged to work on pro bono projects.

Head Office: Seattle, WA
Number of domestic offices: 16
Number of international offices: 3
Worldwide revenue: $785,991,000
Partners (US): 513
Associates (US): 497

Contacts
Main recruitment contact:
Michael Gotham, Director of Legal Recruiting and Retention (mgotham@perkinscoie.com)
Diversity officer: Theresa Cropper

Recruitment details
Entry-level associates starting in 2018: 42
Clerking policy: Yes
Summers joining/anticipated 2018:
1Ls: 18; 2Ls: 44
Summers joining/anticipated 2018 split by office: Bellevue: 1; Chicago: 8; Dallas: 3; Madison: 2; Palo Alto: 9; Phoenix: 4; Portland: 5; San Diego: 2; San Francisco: 4; Seattle: 16; Washington, DC: 8
Summer salary 2018:
1Ls: $2,693—$3,462 (depending on location)
2Ls: $ $2,693—$3,462 (depending on location)
Split summers offered? Case by case
Can summers spend time in an overseas office? No

Pillsbury Winthrop Shaw Pittman LLP

1540 Broadway, New York, NY 10036

Tel: 212 858 1000   Fax: 212 858 1500
Recruitment website: www.careers.pillsburylaw.com
Linkedin: Pillsbury Winthrop Shaw Pittman LLP

Twitter: @pillsburylaw
Facebook: @PillsburyLawfirm
Instagram: @pillsburylawfirm

Main areas of work

Pillsbury's firm-wide practices can be broadly grouped into three categories:

Regulatory: Whether working with a startup, a company in growth mode or a market leader, Pillsbury's lawyers help companies limit risk, achieve compliance, defend against investigations, advocate for new laws and challenge restrictions.

Litigation: Pillsbury's litigators handle complex commercial cases, matters of public interest, intellectual property challenges, tax controversies, insurance policyholder disputes, environmental claims, securities class actions, construction disputes and a wide variety of other assignments.

Business: Pillsbury's business teams partner with clients to help find capital, organize new companies, secure patents, purchase real estate, negotiate contracts, challenge competitors, guide investments, protect data, limit liability, outsource support services, minimize taxes, establish policies and expand markets.

Firm profile

Pillsbury is a leading international law firm with a particular focus on the technology, energy and natural resources, financial services, real estate and construction, and travel and hospitality sectors. Recognized by legal research firm BTI as one of the top 20 firms for client service, Pillsbury and its lawyers are highly regarded for their forward-thinking approach, their enthusiasm for collaborating across disciplines and their unsurpassed commercial awareness.

Recruitment

Law Schools attending for OCIs in 2018:

University of California, Berkeley; University of California, Hastings; University of California, Irvine; University of California, Los Angeles; University of Chicago; Columbia; Duke; Fordham; George Washington; Georgetown; Harvard; Hofstra; Howard University; Loyola Law School; University of Michigan; Northwestern; New York University; University of Pennsylvania; Stanford; University of Southern California; University of Texas; University of Virginia

Recruitment outside OCIs:

Cornell DC and NY Fairs; Duke in San Francisco; Lavender Law; Loyola Chicago (Patent); MABLSA; West Coast BLSA; Vanderbilt Fair; William & Mary Greater DC interviews; National Law Consortium DC

Summer associate profile:

Pillsbury seeks energetic, high-performing students who possess sound judgment, determination, common sense, excellent interpersonal skills, the ability to inspire confidence and the drive to produce high quality work and achieve outstanding results.

Summer program components:

Pillsbury's summer associates experience the firm's collaborative style by working side-by-side with attorneys in a variety of practice areas, on industry and client teams and on issue-specific projects. Pillsbury University offers training on everything from legal writing to client service basics to effective networking. Formal reviews supplement the extemporaneous feedback provided to summer associates by our lawyers.

Head Office: New York, NY
Number of domestic offices: 14
Number of international offices: 7
Worldwide revenue: $589,472,000
Partners (US): 297
Associates (US): 245

Contacts
Main recruitment contact: Charles Curtis,
Firmwide Director of Attorney Recruiting
(charles.curtis@pillsburylaw.com)
Hiring partner: Mariah Brandt
Diversity officer: Rosa Walker,
Director of Diversity and Inclusion

Recruitment details
Entry-level associates starting in 2018: 37
Clerking policy: Yes
Summers joining/anticipated 2018:
2Ls: 33
Summers joining/anticipated 2018 split
by office: Austin: 2; LA: 2; NYC: 7;
San Francisco: 5; Silicon Valley: 2;
Northern Virginia: 3; DC: 12
Summer salary 2018:
1Ls: $3,462/week
2Ls: $3,462/week
Split summers offered? Yes, but not
preferred
Can summers spend time in an overseas
office? Case-by-case

Firm Profiles

Proskauer Rose LLP

Eleven Times Square, New York, NY 10036

Tel: 212 969 3000
Email: nyrecruiting@proskauer.com
Recruitment website: www.proskauer.com/careers/
Linkedin: proskauer-rose-llp

Twitter: @proskauer
Facebook: proskauerlife
Instagram: @proskauer_rose

Main areas of work

Private equity; corporate finance and securities; mergers and acquisitions; capital markets; litigation, trials and dispute resolution; white collar defense and investigations; intellectual property; labor and employment; employee benefits and executive compensation; real estate; privacy and cybersecurity; bankruptcy and restructuring; and wealth management. The firm also has significant industry-focused experience across many fields, including asset management; health care; financial institutions; technology, media and telecommunications; private equity real estate; life sciences; sports; and media and entertainment.

Firm profile

We are 725+ lawyers serving clients from 13 offices located in the leading financial and business centers in North and South America, Europe and Asia. The world's leading organizations, companies and corporations choose us to be their representatives in their most critical situations. We work with alternative capital providers, major sports leagues, Fortune 500 companies, entertainment industry legends, many of the world's most successful asset managers and other industry-redefining companies.

Recruitment

Law Schools attending for OCIs in 2018:

Boston College, Boston University, Columbia, Cornell, Duke, Emory, Fordham, George Washington University, Georgetown, Harvard, Howard, New York University, Northwestern, Notre Dame, Rutgers, Stanford, Suffolk, Tulane, University of California (Berkeley, Los Angeles), University of Chicago, University of Connecticut, University of Illinois, University of Michigan, University of Pennsylvania, University of Southern California, University of Texas, University of Virginia, Vanderbilt, Washington University in St Louis, Yale.

If we do not visit your law school, or you are unable to participate in one of the many career fairs in which we participate, please submit your cover letter, resume and transcript directly to the recruiting mailbox of the office in which you are interested.

Summer associate profile:

We look for well-rounded students who have demonstrated academic excellence, leadership, community service, intellectual curiosity, maturity and strong motivation to succeed. Our environment is challenging, rewarding, entrepreneurial and inclusive. Associates receive early exposure to high levels of responsibility, so the people who thrive here are those who can engage with clients, have a sense of humor, and some worldliness.

Summer program components:

Our summer program is designed to replicate, as closely as possible, the experience of being a lawyer at Proskauer. You will work on challenging matters alongside some of the top lawyers in the field while building relationships with your colleagues. You might find yourself attending a deposition, courtroom argument or administrative hearing. Or being at the table in a labor arbitration. You might help in the formation of companies or be part of a team handling a merger or acquisition. Every day of your time with us represents part of your training – as you work with experienced professionals on client matters and gain their real-time feedback and direction. You will also have the chance to up your game in key areas through partner-led, interactive training workshops throughout your summer. You will have many opportunities to join in social, cultural and recreational activities to get better acquainted with your fellow summers and lawyers at Proskauer. In recent years our summer associates have joined in a an array of activities including Major League Baseball games, mixology events, the Tony Awards, scavenger hunts, private movie screenings and community service team projects, to name a few.

Head Office: **New York, NY**
Number of domestic offices: **8**
Number of international offices: **5**
Worldwide revenue: **$890,300,000**
Partners (US): **235**
Associates (US): **386**

Contacts
Main recruitment contact:
Caroline K Menes
Hiring partner: **Michael T Mervis**
Diversity officer: **Peter Wilson, Jr.**

Recruitment details
Entry-level associates starting in 2018: **74**
Clerking policy: **Yes**
Summers joining/anticipated 2018:
1Ls: 6, 2Ls: 55, SEOs: 2
Summers joining/anticipated 2018 split by office:
Boston: 14, Chicago: 2, LA: 9, New Orleans: 3, New York: 29 (not including 2 SEOs), Newark: 3 Washington DC: 1
Summer salary 2018:
1Ls: $3,462/week (except Boca Raton, New Orleans and Newark)
2Ls: $3,462/week (except Boca Raton, New Orleans and Newark)
Split summers offered? Case by case
Can summers spend time in an overseas office? No

Reed Smith LLP

25 Fifth Avenue, Pittsburgh, PA 15222

Tel: 412 288 313
Email: jross@reedsmith.com
Recruitment website: www.reedsmith.com
Linkedin: reed-smith-llp

Twitter: @reedsmithllp
Facebook: Reed-Smith-LLP

Main areas of work

Reed Smith is a global relationship law firm with more than 1,500 lawyers in 27 offices throughout the United States, Europe, Asia and the Middle East. Its lawyers provide litigation and other dispute-resolution services in multi-jurisdictional and other high stakes matters; deliver regulatory counsel; and execute the full range of strategic domestic and cross-border transactions. Reed Smith is a preeminent advisor to industries including financial services, life sciences, healthcare, advertising, technology and media, shipping, energy and natural resources, real estate, manufacturing and education.

Firm profile

Reed Smith has been ranked consistently among the top law firms for client service and has been identified as one of the few large firms with a strategic focus on client satisfaction. Reed Smith has grown in large part because of its commitment to delivering high-quality service and developing long-term client relationships. Reed Smith is united by a culture that is defined by core values of quality, integrity, teamwork and respect, performance and innovation and improvement. These are further demonstrated through a firmwide commitment to diversity, pro bono and community support activity and the professional development of the firm's lawyers.

Recruitment

Law Schools attending for OCIs in 2018:

Reed Smith visits numerous local and national schools for On-Campus Interviews. A full list of schools and OCI events can be found on the firm's website here: www.reedsmith.com

Recruitment outside OCIs:

Reed Smith does resume collection at a number of schools and connects with potential candidates through diversity events, employer receptions and through 1L fellowships like LCLD and client partnerships.

Summer associate profile:

Reed Smith is looking for summer associates who have a combination of top academics, practical experience and superior analytical and writing skills. The firm values people who are mature and engaging and who demonstrate leadership capabilities and community involvement.

Summer program components:

Reed Smith offers law students first-rate work in a challenging and busy atmosphere where their contributions count from day one. Summer associates will become immersed in law firm life by completing assignments relating to actual client situations. Each assignment presents a fresh opportunity for summer associates to hone their research, writing, judgment, communication and analytical skills.

CareeRS is Reed Smith's competency-based career development program with a focus on role-specific professional training and development, including mentoring, and more developmentally oriented assessments tailored to the needs of associates. The firm offers its summer associates numerous chances to participate in both formal and informal training programs, such as: managing partner's forum, mediation and mergers and acquisitions clinics, law firm economics, cross-cultural training and legal writing. Summer associates also have numerous opportunities to participate in pro bono and community service projects and become acquainted with our Women's Initiative Network and Diversity and Inclusion Committees.

Please visit www.reedsmith.com for more information about each of these initiatives.

Head Office: Pittsburgh, PA
Number of domestic offices: 15
Number of international offices: 12
Worldwide revenue: $1.119 billion
Partners (US): 448
Associates (US): 395

Contacts
Main recruitment contact:
Jen Ross, US Director of Legal Recruiting
(jross@reedsmith.com)
Diversity officer: John Iino
Partner and Director of Global Diversity
& Inclusion

Recruitment details
Entry-level associates starting in 2018: 46
Clerking policy: Yes
Summers joining/anticipated 2018:
1Ls: 9, 2Ls: 50
Summers joining/anticipated 2018 split
by office: CHI: 10, HOU: 4, LA: 5, MIA:
1, NY: 8, PGH: 9, PHL: 8, PRC: 2, SF: 6,
TYS: 2, WDC: 3, WIL: 1
Summer salary 2018:
1Ls: $5,208-$6,667 semi-monthly
2Ls: $5,208-$6,667 semi-monthly
Split summers offered? Case by Case
Can summers spend time in an overseas
office? No

Firm Profiles

Ropes & Gray LLP

Prudential Tower, 800 Boylston Street, Boston, MA 02119

Tel: 617 951 7000
Email: hiringprogram@ropesgray.com
Recruitment website: www.ropesgray.com
Linkedin: ropes-&-gray-llp

Twitter: @ropesgray

Main areas of work

From the boardroom to the courtroom, Ropes & Gray represents the world's leading companies on their most critical matters. On corporate transactional issues, the firm has been recognized as having top-ranked practices in private equity, M&A, finance, investment management, bankruptcy, healthcare, life sciences and intellectual property, among others. The firm also has been cited for its litigation experience and successful track record, including antitrust, appellate, complex business litigation, securities litigation and regulation, government enforcement and white collar criminal defense, IP litigation and privacy and cybersecurity.

Firm profile

Ropes & Gray, an international law firm with more than 1,200 attorneys and professionals in 11 offices in the United States, Europe and Asia, provides comprehensive legal services to leading businesses and individuals around the world. Clients benefit from the firm's unwavering standards of integrity, service and responsiveness. The firm is ideally positioned to address its clients' most pressing legal and business issues. In 2017, lawyers, paralegals and other Ropes & Gray professionals worldwide logged more than 160,000 hours toward assisting our pro bono clients.

Recruitment

Law Schools attending for OCIs in 2018:

American, Berkeley, Boston College, Boston University, Brooklyn, Chicago, Columbia, Cornell, Duke, Fordham, George Washington, Georgetown, Harvard, Howard, Illinois, Maryland, Michigan, North Carolina, Northeastern, Northwestern, Notre Dame, NYU, Penn, Santa Clara, Stanford, Suffolk, Texas, UC Davis, UCLA, USC, UVA, Vanderbilt, Washington University in St Louis, Yale. The firm also attends various job fairs.

Roscoe Trimmier Jr. Diversity Scholarship:

Award: This scholarship provides a $25,000* award to five outstanding second-year law students and includes a paid summer associate position following completion of the second year of law school. *payable in installments, less all required income and payroll taxes*

Eligibility requirements: Outstanding undergraduate and law school academic achievement; member of a historically underrepresented group in the legal profession; 2L, enrolled in an ABA-accredited law school; US citizen or authorized to work in the United States.

To find out more about this scholarship and how to apply, please visit:
www.ropesgray.com/en/legalhiring/The-Culture/Commitment-to-Diversity/Roscoe-Trimmier-Jr-Diversity-Scholarship.

Summer associate profile:

Ropes & Gray chooses summer associates based on academic performance, personal skills, motivation, work and leadership experience, practice area interests and the ability to work well in a highly collaborative environment.

Summer program components:

Our goal is to provide summer associates with a realistic sense of what it is like to work at the firm by having them work on actual client matters and by giving them opportunities to get to know our attorneys through a variety of social events, activities and lunches. Our attorneys provide meaningful and timely feedback on work assignments and offer additional perspective through an end-of-summer formal review.

Summer associates also benefit from our highly regarded training program, which provides both practice-specific and general soft-skills training designed to support summer associates' professional growth and development.

Head Office: Boston, MA
Number of domestic offices: 6
Number of international offices: 5
Partners (US): 235
Associates (US): 879

Contacts
Main recruitment contact: Amy Ross
(amy.ross@ropesgray.com)
Hiring partner: Peter Erichsen
Diversity officer: Lindsay Kendrick

Recruitment details
Entry-level associates starting in 2018: 135
Summers joining/anticipated 2018:
1Ls: 6, 2Ls: 164, 3Ls: 3, SEOs: 2
Summers joining/anticipated 2018 split by office: Boston: 74; NY: 55
Chicago: 12; DC: 13; SF: 13; SV: 3
Summer salary 2018:
1Ls: $3,500
2Ls: $3,500
Split summers offered? Yes

ROPES & GRAY

Firm Profiles

Schulte Roth & Zabel LLP

9 Third Avenue, New York, NY 10022

Tel: 212 756 2000
Email: recruiting.department@srz.com
Recruitment website: www.srz.com/careers
Linkedin: Schulte Roth & Zabel LLP

Twitter: @SRZLawFirm

Main areas of work

Our specialties include bank regulatory; bankruptcy and creditors' rights litigation; blockchain technology and digital assets; broker-dealer regulatory and enforcement; business reorganization; complex commercial litigation; cybersecurity; distressed debt and claims trading; distressed investing; education law; employment and employee benefits; energy; environmental; finance; financial institutions; hedge funds; individual client services; insurance; intellectual property, sourcing and technology; investment management; litigation; litigation finance; mergers and acquisitions; PIPEs; private equity; real estate; real estate capital markets and REITs; real estate litigation; regulated funds; regulatory and compliance; securities and capital markets; securities enforcement; securities litigation; securitization; shareholder activism; structured finance and derivatives; tax; and white collar defense and government investigations.

Firm profile

Schulte Roth & Zabel is a premier law firm serving the financial services industry from strategically located offices in New York, Washington, DC and London. We take a multidisciplinary approach in our work with a large and impressive array of global and forward-thinking institutional, entrepreneurial and individual clients, from advising clients on investment management, corporate and transactional matters, to providing counsel on regulatory, compliance, enforcement and investigative issues.

Recruitment

Law Schools attending for OCIs in 2018:

Cardozo, Columbia, Cornell, Duke, Emory, Fordham, Georgetown, George Washington, Harvard, Howard, Michigan, NYU, Penn, Tulane, UVA, Wash U.

Recruitment outside OCIs:

Lav Law, NEBLSA Job Fair, Resume Collections from Syracuse, UCLA, William & Mary, interview write-in candidates from many additional law schools.

Summer associate profile:

SRZ hires attorneys who are bright, personable and enthusiastic about early substantive responsibility and client contact. We seek candidates with outstanding academic achievement, high motivation and strong interpersonal skills.

Summer program components:

Our summer associate program allows students to receive substantive assignments from practice groups of their choice during two assigning periods. Summer associates have interaction with our clients, attend meetings and depositions and work on complex projects. Training and feedback are emphasized through regular departmental training sessions, a writing seminar, a corporate negotiation workshop, a trial advocacy program, and a pro bono week. These experiences are all designed to allow students to explore various areas of interest, get immersed in the firm culture and gain first-hand knowledge of what they will see as a junior associate. In addition to our top-notch training programs and hands-on work experience, we offer fun and exciting social activities that allow summer associates to spend time with their associate and partner mentors, develop relationships with our attorneys and get to know everyone outside of the office.

Head Office: New York
Number of domestic offices: 2
Number of international offices: 1
Worldwide revenue: $424,100,000 (2017)
Partners (US): 86
Other lawyers (US): 250

Contacts
Main recruitment contact:
Alissa K Golden (alissa.golden@srz.com)
Hiring partners: William H Gussman, Jr,
Taleah E Jennings, Jason S Kaplan
Diversity officer: Taleah E Jennings

Recruitment details
Entry-level associates starting in 2018: 38
Clerking policy: Yes
Summers joining/anticipated 2018:
2Ls: 41
Summers joining/anticipated 2018 split
by office: NY: 41
Summer salary 2018:
2Ls: $3,462
Split summers offered? No
Can summers spend time in an overseas
office? No

Firm Profiles

Schulte Roth & Zabel

Seward & Kissel LLP

One Battery Park Plaza, New York, NY 10004

Tel: 212 574 1200   Email: akiva@sewkis.com
Recruitment website: www.sewkis.com
Linkedin: Seward & Kissel LLP

Facebook: Seward & Kissel LLP

Main areas of work

Investment management, corporate finance, global bank and institutional finance, litigation, maritime and transportation finance, capital markets and securities, business transactions, bankruptcy and corporate reorganization, real estate, taxation, trusts and estates, employee benefits, aviation finance, employment law, government enforcement and internal investigations and executive compensation.

Firm profile

Seward & Kissel offers our New York associates the broad experience and training of a large practice in the context of a moderately sized firm. We offer our Washington, DC associates a focused experience concentrating on our investment management, corporate finance and capital markets practices in the context of a small office environment. Our associates have the opportunity to work on a wide range of challenging and stimulating matters within the practice areas of our particular offices.

Recruitment

Law Schools attending for OCIs in 2018:

Our New York office participates in the following OCI programs:

- Albany
- American
- Boston College
- Boston University
- Brooklyn
- Cardozo
- Columbia
- Cornell
- Duke
- Fordham
- Georgetown
- George Washington
- Harvard
- Midwest California
- Consortium
- New York University
- Tulane/Washington University/ Vanderbilt Job Fair
- Michigan
- University of North Carolina
- University of Pennsylvania
- University of Virginia
- Vanderbilt

Our Washington, DC office participates in the following OCI programs:

- Boston College
- Boston University
- Georgetown
- George Washington
- University of Virginia
- Washington & Lee

Summer associate profile:

We rely heavily on our summer program for our hiring needs. The primary goals of the program are to provide summer associates with a realistic, broad-based view of our practice and an opportunity to become acquainted with our attorneys through our informal mentoring program, training sessions and social events.

Summer program components:

Assignments are from our practice areas. Training: weekly seminars, practice group meetings and in-house training sessions. Feedback is given formally at the middle and end of the summer program.

Head Office: New York, NY
Number of domestic offices: 2
Partners (US): 53
Counsel (US): 20
Associates (US): 92

Contacts
Main recruitment contact:
Royce Akiva (akiva@sewkis.com)
Hiring partners: Christopher Riccardi, Jack Yoskowitz, Sharan Calay
Diversity officer: Marlon Q Paz

Recruitment details
Entry-level associates starting in 2018:
11 (NY: 10, DC: 1)
Clerking policy: Case by case
Summers joining/anticipated 2018:
2Ls: 11 (NY: 10, DC: 1)
Summer salary 2018:
2Ls: $3,461
Split summers offered? No

SEWARD & KISSEL LLP

Firm Profiles

Shearman & Sterling LLP

9 Lexington Avenue, New York, NY 10022

Tel: 212 848 4000
Email: newyork.recruiting@shearman.com
Recruitment website: usrecruiting.shearman.com

Main areas of work

Anti-Corruption and Foreign Corrupt Practices Act, antitrust, capital markets, corporate governance, derivatives and structured products, environmental, executive compensation and employee benefits, finance, financial institutions advisory and financial regulatory, financial restructuring and insolvency, intellectual property, international arbitration, international trade and government relations, investment funds, litigation, mergers and acquisitions, patent litigation, project development and finance, real estate, sports, tax

Firm profile

Shearman & Sterling LLP is a leading global law firm with approximately 850 lawyers in 21 offices in 13 countries around the world. Founded in 1873, Shearman & Sterling distinguishes itself by the way in which it harnesses the intellectual strength and deep experience of its lawyers across its extensive global footprint. The firm represents many of the world's leading corporations, financial institutions, emerging growth companies, governments and state-owned enterprises.

Recruitment

Law Schools attending for OCIs in 2018:

Shearman & Sterling will be recruiting at the following schools or regional job fairs: American, BC, BU, Cardozo, Chicago, Columbia, Cornell, Duke, Fordham, Georgetown, George Washington, Harvard, Howard, Michigan, NEBLSA job fair, Northwestern, NYU, Osgoode, Penn, Stanford, St. John's, Texas, Toronto, Tulane, Washington University, Vanderbilt, UC- Berkeley, UCLA, USC, UVA, Yale.

Recruitment outside OCIs:

The firm conducts a number of resume collections and considers write-in applicants as well.

Summer associate profile:

We seek candidates who are bright, confident and enthusiastic about the practice of law and bring with them life, work, and educational experiences that will be highly valued by clients and colleagues alike. We also remain strongly committed to diversity and inclusion and overall excellence in our hiring. Finally, we expect that our associates will view collegiality and teamwork as important personal and firm values.

Summer program components:

Summer associates are given the opportunity to rotate through two practice groups. Senior and junior advisors are assigned during each rotation and, depending on the group, summer associates may attend client meetings, court hearings, depositions, or business trips. The firm has a robust training program for summer associates and also hosts a variety of social events.

Head Office: New York, NY
Number of domestic offices: 5
Number of international offices: 16
Worldwide revenue: $917 million

Contacts
Main recruitment contact:
Trisha Weiss
(trisha.weiss@shearman.com)
Director of Legal Recruiting
Hiring partners: John Nathanson,
Linda Rappaport
Diversity officer: Jessica Maroney Shillito,
Director of Global Diversity & Inclusion

Recruitment details
Entry-level associates starting in 2018:
58 approx. (some offers still pending due
to clerkships/other post-graduate plans)
Clerking policy: Yes
Summers joining/anticipated 2018: 53
1Ls: 2; 2Ls: 51; SEOs: 3
Summers joining/anticipated 2018 split
by office:
New York: 48, Washington, DC: 2,
Austin: 1, Paris: 1, San Francisco: 1
Summer salary 2018:
1Ls: $ 3500/week
2Ls: $ 3500/week
Split summers offered? No
Can summers spend time in an overseas
office? Yes, on a case by case basis
depending on level of interest, business
need, language skills, and other factors

SHEARMAN & STERLING LLP

Firm Profiles

Sheppard, Mullin, Richter & Hampton LLP

333 South Hope Street, 43rd Floor, Los Angeles, CA 90071-1422

Tel: 213 620 1780
Recruitment website: www.sheppardmullin.com/careers
Linkedin: sheppard-mullin-richter-&-hampton-llp

Twitter: @SheppardMullin
Facebook: SheppardMullin

Main areas of work

Major Practice Areas: Antitrust; corporate; entertainment and digital media; finance and bankruptcy; government contracts; intellectual property; labor and employment; litigation; privacy and cybersecurity; real estate, land use, environmental; tax.

Major Industry Focus: Aerospace and defense; blockchain technology and digital currency; construction; energy; fashion, apparel and beauty; food and beverage; healthcare; hospitality; insurance; life sciences; private wealth; retail.

Firm profile

Founded in Los Angeles in 1927, there are now about 800 attorneys practicing in 15 offices (seven in California, plus Chicago, New York, Washington, DC, Shanghai, Beijing, Seoul, Brussels and London). The firm remains a true partnership which governs itself through an elected, representative democracy. Stability is enhanced by skillful administration, excellent cost control and no firm debt. Core values include transparency in financial operations and governance, civility in the daily conduct of its business, advancement and celebration of diversity and inclusiveness, and a vigorous pro bono program.

Recruitment

Law Schools attending for OCIs in 2018:

Columbia, George Washington, Georgetown, Harvard, Hastings, Howard, U. of Illinois, Loyola (L.A.), U. of Michigan, Notre Dame, Southwestern, Stanford, UC Berkeley, UC Davis, UC Irvine, UCLA, USC, USD, USF, Virginia, Vanderbilt; plus several regional/national/diversity job fairs.

Summer associate profile:

High academic achievement is a precondition to employment. But the firm is interested in more than that: it seeks associates who will succeed over the long term. It looks for associates who have the personal traits needed to become outstanding practicing lawyers: self-awareness, drive to succeed, capacity for hard work and an ability to work well with other people.

Summer program components:

The firm's ten week summer program is structured to give students an idea of what life is like as an associate with the firm. Our summer associates do meaningful, billable work and work closely with partners and associates in various practice groups. Summer associates are given opportunities to attend depositions and court appearances, participate in conference calls and negotiations, draft documents and sit in on meetings. All summer associates work on at least one pro bono project. We also offer comprehensive transactional and litigation training programs. Attorney mentors assist the students in a variety of ways throughout the summer, and we plan a well-balanced calendar of social events that gives students the opportunity to get to know our attorneys outside of the office as well as enjoy the geographic area in which they are working.

Head Office: Los Angeles, CA
Number of domestic offices: 10
Number of international offices: 5
Worldwide revenue: $671,101,000
Partners (US): 324
Associates (US): 281
Special counsel (US): 75
Staff attorneys (US): 52
Of counsel (US): 49

Contacts
Main recruitment contact: Sally Bucklin (sbucklin@sheppardmullin.com)
Hiring partner: Bess Sully (Chief Human Resources Officer)
Diversity officer: Carol Ross-Burnett (Manager of Diversity & Inclusion)

Recruitment details
Entry-level associates starting in 2018: 30
Clerking policy: Yes
Summers joining/anticipated 2018:
1L: 1-2; 2Ls: 28
Summers joining/anticipated 2018 split by office: LA (Downtown): 6, LA (Century City): 4, Costa Mesa, CA: 2, San Diego, CA (Downtown): 3, San Diego, CA (Del Mar): 4, San Francisco, CA: 3, Palo Alto, CA: 1, Chicago, IL: 1, Washington, DC: 4, New York, NY: 1-2
Summer salary 2018:
1Ls: $3,462 per week
2Ls: $3,462 per week
Split summers offered? No
Can summers spend time in an overseas office? No

SheppardMullin

Sidley Austin LLP

One South Dearborn, Chicago, IL 60603 / 787 Seventh Avenue, New York, NY 10019

Tel: 312 853 7000/212 839 5300
Email: lrch@sidley.com
Recruitment website: sidley.com/careers
Linkedin: sidley-austin

Twitter: @SidleyLaw
Facebook: sidleyaustinllpofficial

Main areas of work

Services: Corporate and finance; employment; international trade; IP and technology; litigation, disputes and investigations; regulatory and government affairs; restructuring, tax
Industries: Agribusiness; energy; financial services; hospitality; insurance; investment funds; life sciences; media and entertainment; real estate; REITs; technology

Firm profile

Sidley provides a broad range of legal services to meet the needs of our diverse client base. The strategic establishment of our offices in the key corporate and financial centers of the world has enabled us to represent a broad range of clients that includes multinational and domestic corporations, banks, funds and financial institutions. With over 2,000 lawyers in 20 offices around the world, talent and teamwork are central to Sidley's successful results for clients in all types of legal matters, from complex transactions to 'bet the company' litigation to cutting-edge regulatory issues.

Recruitment

Law Schools attending for OCIs in 2018:

University of California, Berkeley, School of Law; The University of Chicago Law School; Columbia Law School; DePaul University College of Law; Duke University School of Law; Fordham Law School; Georgetown University Law Center; The George Washington University Law School; Harvard Law School; University of California - Hasting; Howard University School of Law; University of Houston Law Center; University of Illinois College of Law; University of Iowa College of Law; Chicago-Kent College of Law; University of California, Los Angeles, School of Law; Loyola University Chicago; Loyola University – Los Angeles; University of Michigan Law School; University of Minnesota Law School; New York University School of Law; Northwestern University School of Law; University of Notre Dame Law School; University of Pennsylvania Law School; Santa Clara University School of Law; University of Southern California Gould School of Law; Southern Methodist; Stanford Law School; The University of Texas School of Law; University of Virginia School of Law; University of Wisconsin Law School; Yale Law School

Recruitment outside OCIs:

Southeastern Minority Job Fair, Penn Regional Job Fair, On Tour Interview Program, Vanderbilt Job Fair, Bay Area Diversity Career Fair, Cornell Job Fair, Loyola Patent Job Fair, Lavender Law Career Fair, NEBLSA Job Fair, Midwest-California-Georgia Consortium, CCBA Minority Job Fair, BC/BU Job Fair

Summer associate profile:

Sidley seeks candidates who have demonstrated academic success and possess strong leadership and interpersonal qualities. The firm looks for a diverse group of individuals who are motivated by highly sophisticated legal work practiced in a collegial and supportive environment.

Summer program components:

Sidley's summer associate program is an invaluable window into its practice and firm culture. Participants select projects that interest them and perform legal work under lawyer supervision. An essential component of Sidley's summer program is the opportunity to learn and develop professional skills. Hands-on training includes detailed reviews of each summer associate's work product, as well as more formal training programs such as writing seminars, a mock trial and a mock negotiation exercise. Each summer associate is assigned senior associates and partners to provide guidance and each participant receives a formal review at the midpoint of the summer program.

Head offices: Chicago, Il ; New York, NY
Number of domestic offices: 10
Number of international offices: 10
Worldwide revenue: $2.036 billion
Partners (US): 577
Associates (US): 808

Contacts
Main recruitment contact:
Jennifer L Connelly
(jlconnelly@sidley.com)
Diversity officer: Sally L Olson

Recruitment details
Entry-level associates starting in 2018: 155
Clerking policy: Yes
Summers joining/anticipated 2018: 168
Summer salary 2018:
1Ls: $3,500
2Ls: $3,500
Split summers offered? Case by case

Simpson Thacher & Bartlett LLP

425 Lexington Avenue, New York, NY

Tel: 212 465 2000
Email: attorneyrecruiting@stblaw.com
Recruitment website: www.simpsonthacher.com
Linkedin: simpson-thacher-&-bartlett-llp

Main areas of work

Clients in a wide array of industries and in jurisdictions around the world turn to Simpson Thacher to help them address their evolving business challenges. The firm is consistently ranked as one of the world's leading advisors for M&A, capital markets and banking activity, as well as private equity fund formation and investment management. The firm's litigation practice encompasses every type of complex litigation and is recognized as one of the most comprehensive, trial-ready litigation practices in the country.

Simpson Thacher also has leading innovative practices in the areas of antitrust, IP, tax, bankruptcy, real estate, executive compensation and employee benefits, exempt organizations and personal planning. Further, pro bono work is critical to the firm's identity and its record in this area is unparalleled.

Firm profile

Simpson Thacher & Bartlett LLP is one of the world's leading international law firms. The firm was established in 1884 and has more than 900 lawyers worldwide. Headquartered in New York City, the firm has offices in Beijing, Hong Kong, Houston, London, Los Angeles, Palo Alto, São Paulo, Seoul, Tokyo and Washington, DC. The firm provides coordinated legal advice and transactional capability to clients around the globe. Our focus on client needs is the hallmark of our practice and we value excellence in client service in all respects.

Recruitment

Law Schools attending for OCIs in 2018:

Berkeley, Brooklyn, Cardozo, Chicago, Columbia, Cornell, Davis, Duke, Emory, Fordham, George Washington, Georgetown, Harvard, Howard, Michigan, NYU, Northwestern, Notre Dame, Pennsylvania, Santa Clara, St. John's, Seton Hall, Stanford, Texas, Tulane, UCLA, USC, Vanderbilt, Virginia, Washington University, Yale.

Recruitment outside OCIs:

1L Summer Diversity Program, resume collects at various schools, Regional job fairs including, but not limited to: Bay Area Diversity, Northeast BLSA, Lavender Law, Midwest-California-Georgia Consortium, Notre Dame NY Interview Program, Patent Law Interview Program.

Summer associate profile:

The firm looks for candidates with distinguished records of achievement, demonstrated leadership potential, a commitment to excellence and the ability to work cooperatively with clients and colleagues.

Summer program components:

The Simpson Thacher Summer Program is both challenging and satisfying. Summer associates work on assignments from all practice areas side by side with partners and associates on client projects of substantial complexity. Summer associates participate in frequent formal training programs geared to their needs and are also invited to attend other firmwide training programs. Summer associates have partner and associate mentors and are given prompt and specific feedback. At the end of the summer program, summer associates will have a thorough understanding of the firm's work and culture.

Head Office: New York, NY
Number of domestic offices: 5
Number of international offices: 6
Worldwide revenue: $1,375,661,814
Partners (US): 155
Associates (US): 602

Contacts
Main recruitment contacts:
Susan Osnato, Chief, Legal Recruiting & Professional Development;
Michelle Las, Legal Recruiting Director
Hiring partners: Rajib Chanda, Nick Goldin, Krista Miniutti
Diversity officer: Natalia Martín, Director of Diversity

Recruitment details
Entry-level associates starting in 2018: 105
Clerking policy: Yes
Summers joining/anticipated 2018:
1Ls: 10, 2Ls: 98
Summers joining/anticipated 2018 split by office:
US: NY: 79, Palo Alto: 10, Houston: 8, Los Angeles: 4, Washington: 6
UK: London: 1
Summer salary 2018:
1Ls: $3,500
2Ls: $3,500
Split summers offered? Case by case
Can summers spend time in an overseas office? Yes, subject to need and relevant language skills

Simpson Thacher

Skadden, Arps, Slate, Meagher & Flom LLP

Times Square, New York, NY 10036

Tel: 212 735 3000   Fax: 212 735 2000
Recruitment website: www.skadden.com/careers/attorneys/carve-your-path
Twitter: @skaddenrecruit

Main areas of work

Antitrust, banking, complex litigation and trials, complex mass torts/insurance litigation, corporate finance, corporate restructuring, energy and infrastructure projects, executive compensation and benefits, government enforcement and white collar crime, intellectual property and technology, international arbitration, investment management, mergers and acquisitions, real estate, regulatory, structured finance, tax, trusts and estates.

Firm profile

Skadden attorneys work on bet-the-company issues around the world for leading Fortune 500 corporations, financial institutions, governments and cultural, educational and charitable organizations. Communication and expertise across our offices enable us to provide unparalleled service to our clients. Our attorneys, spread among 22 interconnected offices around the world, are engaged in more than 60 practice areas, many of which are specialized. We also encourage pro bono work, providing chargeable time credit. With fostering professional growth as a primary goal, our attorney development partners and Training Committee ensure that associates receive appropriate training and mentoring from the start of their careers. Our Diversity Committee promotes cross-cultural appreciation and competency through diversity and inclusion seminars, lunches, and our facets diversity publication and lecture series. Our widely regarded summer associate program is designed to provide substantive practical skills training, exposure to various practices, as well as a sense of what it is like to be an attorney at Skadden.

Recruitment

Law Schools attended for OCI in 2018:

Berkeley, Boston University, Brooklyn, Chicago, Columbia, Cornell, Duke, Fordham, Georgetown, George Washington, Harvard, Iowa, Michigan, NYU, Northwestern, Penn, Stanford, Texas, UCLA, USC, Vanderbilt, Virginia, Yale.

Recruitment outside OCIs:

In addition to participating in OCIs, the firm accepts summer associate applications directly from students starting 1st June. Interested applicants may submit their resume and full 1L transcript through the Skadden online system: skadden.com/recruiting.

Summer associate profile:

The breadth of our practice and the success it has enjoyed is largely due to the capabilities of our attorneys. We look for candidates who combine intellectual ability with enthusiasm and creativity. Successful candidates display high academic achievement in their law school and undergraduate education. Law Journal and/or Moot Court participation are preferred.

Summer program components:

One of the most comprehensive programs of its kind, our Summer Associate Program (offered in our Boston, Chicago, Houston, Los Angeles, New York, Palo Alto, Washington, DC, Wilmington, London, Hong Kong, Toronto and Tokyo offices) drives our hiring efforts. Summer associates are assigned to active deals and litigations, providing them with work experiences similar to those of full time associates.

For more information visit: www.skadden.com/recruiting.

Head Office: New York, NY
Number of domestic offices: 8
Number of international offices: 14
Partners (US): 289
Associates (US): 900

Contacts
Main recruitment contact:
Carol Lee H Sprague
Hiring partner: Howard Ellin
Diversity officer: Melique Jones

Recruitment details
Entry-level associates starting in 2018:
187
Clerking policy: Yes
Summers joining/anticipated 2018:
1Ls: 32, 2Ls: 171
Summers joining/anticipated 2018 split
by office: New York: 6, Chicago: 2,
Los Angeles: 2, London: 6,
Palo Alto: 2, Paris: 1, Toronto: 1,
Washington, DC: 4
Summer salary 2018:
1Ls: $3,500
2Ls: $3,500
Split summers offered? Yes — splits must
spend at least 8 weeks with Skadden for
first half
Can summers spend time in an overseas
office? Case by case

Snell & Wilmer L.L.P

One Arizona Center, Phoenix, Arizona 85004

Tel: 602 382 6000
Email: attyrecruit@swlaw.com
Recruitment website: www.swlaw.com/careers
Linkedin: snell-&-wilmer

Twitter: @SWLawNews
Facebook: swlawnews

Main areas of work

Appellate, banking, bankruptcy, business and finance, class action, commercial litigation, construction, election and political law, emerging businesses, employee benefits and executive compensation, environmental and natural resources, estate planning and taxation, financial services and securities, franchise, government investigations/criminal defense and government related litigation, healthcare, intellectual property, international, labor, mergers and acquisitions, municipal finance, professional liability, product liability, professional liability and tort liability, public utilities, legislation and real estate/land use.

Firm profile

Founded in 1938, Snell & Wilmer is a full service business law firm with more than 400 lawyers practicing in nine locations throughout the western United States and in Mexico, including Phoenix and Tucson, Arizona; Los Angeles and Orange County, California; Denver, Colorado; Las Vegas and Reno, Nevada; Salt Lake City, Utah; and Los Cabos, Mexico. The firm represents clients ranging from large, publicly traded corporations to small businesses, individuals and entrepreneurs. Snell & Wilmer and its lawyers have been recognized by clients and peers for exceptional legal skills, ethical and exemplary business practices with various distinguished awards.

Recruitment

Law Schools attending for OCIs in 2018:

Arizona State; Brigham Young; Notre Dame; University of Arizona; UC Irvine; UCLA; University of Colorado; University of Denver; Iowa; Kansas; University of San Diego; University of Nevada Las Vegas; USC; University of Utah; Vanderbilt; Virginia; Pepperdine; Loyola Los Angeles; Washington University (St. Louis); University of Michigan.

Recruitment outside OCIs:

Candidates at non-OCI schools may apply directly through our website. We participate in resume collections at many schools and in the Rocky Mountain Diversity Job Fair. We are not committed to only hiring from schools where we go on-campus.

Summer associate profile:

Snell & Wilmer seeks candidates who not only demonstrate high academic achievement, but also are social, energetic, unique, genuine, motivated, have a sense of humor, and enjoy working with their friends and colleagues and are committed to their communities. We desire diverse individuals who want to resolve new and exciting legal challenges, who enjoy working as part of a team and who will uphold our valued firm culture. In other words, we want great people who will become great lawyers.

Summer program components:

The firm appoints several senior associates to coordinate the program and assign summer associate projects. In addition, each summer associate is assigned a mentor, a partner reader and a reality partner. Summer associate mentors are responsible for making the summer a positive experience for each summer associate. Partner readers provide invaluable feedback on two written assignments a summer associate completes. The 'Reality Snell & Wilmer' program matches summer associates with a partner who brings them into other cases and transactions, as needed, to simulate the day-to-day reality of working as an attorney.

Head Office: Phoenix, AZ
Number of domestic offices: 8
Number of international offices: 1
Partners (US): 202
Associates (US): 153

Contacts
Main recruitment contact:
Abigail Raddatz, Director of Attorney Recruiting and Development
Hiring partners: Adam E Lang, Craig O'Loughlin, Rebecca Winterscheidt
Diversity officer: Mina Mendez

Recruitment details
Entry-level associates starting in 2018: 21
Clerking policy: Yes
Summers joining/anticipated 2018:
1Ls: 5, 2Ls: 20
Summers joining/anticipated 2018 split by office: Denver: 4; Las Vegas: 2, Los Angeles: 2; Orange County: 2, Phoenix: 12; SLC: 2, Tucson: 1
Summer salary 2018:
1Ls: $2,211-$3,077/week
2Ls: $2,211-$3,077/week
Split summers offered? No
Can summers spend time in an overseas office? No

Squire Patton Boggs

900 Key Tower, 127 Public Square, Cleveland, Ohio 44114

Tel: 216 479 8500
Email: careers@squirepb.com
Website: www.squirepattonboggs/careers
Linkedin: squire-patton-boggs

Twitter: @SPB_Careers
Facebook:
SquirePattonBoggsCareers
Instagram: @squirepattonboggs

Main areas of work

Aerospace, defense and government services; automotive; aviation; brands and consumer products; business immigration; chemicals; communications, competition – antitrust; construction and engineering; corporate; data privacy and cybersecurity; energy and natural resources; environmental, safety and health; financial services; government investigations and white collar; healthcare; hospitality and leisure; industrial products; infrastructure; institutional investors; insurance; intellectual property and technology; international dispute resolution; international trade; labor and employment; life sciences; litigation; media and advertising; pensions; public and infrastructure finance; public policy; real estate; restructuring and insolvency; retail; sports and entertainment; tax credit finance and community development; tax strategy and benefits; transportation, shipping and logistics.

Firm profile

One of the strongest, most geographically diverse law firms in the world, with 47 offices in 20 countries and a team of more than 1,500 lawyers. Our client base spans every type of business, both private and public. We advise a diverse mix of clients, from Fortune 100 and FTSE 100 corporations to emerging companies and from individuals to local and national governments.

Recruitment

Law Schools attending for OCIs in 2018:

American, Arizona, ASU, Case, Cincinnati, Cleveland-Marshall, Colorado, CUA, Denver, George Mason, Georgetown, GW Law, Harvard, Howard, Maryland, Michigan, Ohio State, UNC, UVA

Recruitment outside OCIs:

We participate in job fairs, law student and bar association events, and meet law students both on-campus and in our offices.

Summer associate profile:

We seek outstanding academic credentials, excellent communication skills, common sense, creativity, a strong work ethic and an ability to cultivate long-term relationships with our clients and colleagues.

Summer program components:

A range of valuable experiences structured around three global themes:

Commercial: Work side by side with our partners, attending depositions, hearings, deal negotiations and trials. In addition, you will cover legal writing and research, public speaking, negotiations and advocacy techniques.

Connected: Attend practice group meetings and associate training programs to build your network of contacts within the business.

Committed: Enjoy a collegial atmosphere with the support of a mentor for the duration of your summer with us.

Founding Office: Cleveland, OH
Number of domestic offices: 18
Number of international offices: 29
Worldwide revenue: $1,000,000,000
Partners (US): 262
Associates (US): 244
Other Attorneys (US): 161

Contacts
Main recruitment contact:
Crystal L Arnold
(crystal.arnold@squirepb.com)
Hiring partner: Aneca E Lasley
Inclusion & Diversity Committee Leadership: Frederick R Nance, Alethia N Nancoo, Traci H Rollins
Women's Enterprise Leadership: Aneca E Lasley

Recruitment details
Entry-level associates starting in 2018: 15
Clerking policy: Yes
Summers joining/anticipated 2018: 30
1Ls: 7, 2Ls: 23, 3Ls: 0, SEO: 0
Split summers offered? Case by case
Can summers spend time in an overseas office? Yes

Sterne, Kessler, Goldstein & Fox P.L.L.C

1100 New York Avenue NW, Suite 600, Washington, D.C. 20005

Tel: 202 371 2600
Email: kobrien@sternekessler.com
Recruitment website: www.sternekessler.com/careers
Linkedin: sternekessler

Twitter: @sternekessler

Main areas of work

Sterne, Kessler, Goldstein & Fox is an intellectual property specialty firm. The firm is organized into five primary areas: biotechnology/chemical; electronics; mechanical and design; trial and appellate; and trademark and brand protection. The firm provides full-service IP support for clients in every sector of the economy.

Firm profile

We were founded in 1978 and are proud to be a leading IP firm in Washington, DC, with decades of experience helping companies strategize and build global IP portfolios. We have over 170 professionals, most of whom hold an advanced technical degree, including over 50 with masters degrees and more than 50 with a doctorate degree in science and engineering. We deliver integrated IP services, including top-tier patent prosecution, PTAB litigation, design patents, trademark, advertising and anti-counterfeiting, ITC investigations, and district court and appellate litigation. Our attorneys and staff consistently vote our firm as a *great place to work.*

Recruitment

Law Schools attending for OCIs in 2018:

American University College of Law, George Mason University Antonin Scalia Law School, George Washington University School of Law, Howard University School of Law, Catholic University of America Columbus School of Law, University of Baltimore School of Law, University of Maryland School of Law, Georgetown University Law Center.

Recruitment outside OCIs:

Loyola University Chicago, School of Law (Patent Law Interview 'PLI' Program), MBLSA Regional Job Fair, Southeastern Minority Job Fair (SEMJF), Lavender Law.

Summer associate profile:

Sterne Kessler seeks students in science and/or engineering. Advanced degrees are required for our biotechnology/chemical group. We strongly prefer advanced degrees for our mechanical and electronics groups. All applicants must have at least a 3.0 cumulative GPA in undergraduate, graduate, and law school studies. United States Patent and Trademark Office and/or other industry work experience is a plus. Teamwork, motivation, collaboration, work ethic, and universal respect are core values of the firm.

Summer program components:

Our summer associate program begins with a full week of orientation training comprised of IP-focused informational sessions as well as introductions to our firm departments and practice groups. Additionally, the professional development department conducts firm-wide training throughout the summer including topics such as legal writing, presentation skills, ethics, time management, and more. Our summer associates also have the opportunity to attend practice group lunches where substantive topics are presented and discussed.

Each summer associate is also assigned a point person and buddy. A point person is typically a senior level associate responsible for regulating workload and providing guidance throughout the program. A buddy is a junior associate, usually a former summer associate, who helps acclimate you to the firm and answer any questions you may have.

Over the past several years, the firm has been consistently rated as a 'best place to work' based on attorney and staff surveys conducted by *The Washington Post* and *The Washington Business Journal.*

Head Office: Washington, D.C.
Number of domestic offices: 1
Partners (US): 54
Associates (US): 63

Contacts
Main recruitment contact: Kerrie O'Brien (kobrien@sternekessler.com)
Hiring partner: Paul Ainsworth
Diversity officer: Gaby Longsworth, Chair, Diversity Committee

Recruitment details
Entry-level associates starting in 2018: 4
Clerking policy: Yes
Summers joining/anticipated 2018:
1Ls: 0, 2Ls: 6
Summer salary 2018:
1Ls: $3,500/week
2Ls: $3,500/week
Split summers offered? Case by case

Sterne Kessler
STERNE KESSLER
GOLDSTEIN & FOX

Firm Profiles

Stroock & Stroock & Lavan LLP

180 Maiden Lane, New York, NY 10038
Tel: 212 806 5400
Email: legalrecruiting@stroock.com
Recruitment website: www.stroock.com
Linkedin: Stroock & Stroock & Lavan LLP

Twitter: @Stroock

Main areas of work

Primary practice areas include real estate; financial restructuring; corporate transactions; commodities; private funds; insurance and reinsurance; financial services litigation, regulation and enforcement; government affairs; government contracts and national security; entertainment; intellectual property; private client services; and regulatory support.

Firm profile

With deep roots, dating back more than 140 years, and at 250 lawyers strong, Stroock is a multidisciplinary law firm, known as a market-leading advisor to the financial services and investment communities and for its special focus in financial restructuring, real estate, private funds and litigation/enforcement.

Recruitment

Law Schools attending for OCIs in 2018:

New York Office:

- Boston College
- Boston University
- Brooklyn
- Cardozo
- Columbia
- Cornell
- Fordham
- Georgetown
- Harvard
- Howard
- Michigan
- New York Law School
- NYU
- Penn

Los Angeles Office:

- Loyola
- UCLA
- USC

Head Office: New York, NY
Number of domestic offices: 4
Worldwide revenue: $251,000,000
Partners (US): 75
Associates (US): 172

Contacts
Main recruitment contacts: Halle Schargel
Hiring partner: Marissa Holob
Diversity officer: Yakiry Adal

Recruitment details
Entry-level associates starting in 2018: 13
Clerking policy: Yes
Summers joining/anticipated 2018:
1Ls: 1, 2Ls: 16
Summers joining/anticipated 2018 split
by office: New York: 15, LA: 2
Summer salary 2018:
1Ls: $3,461/week
2Ls: $3,461/week
Split summers offered? No
Can summers spend time in an overseas
office? No

Recruitment outside OCIs:

In addition to visiting a number of law schools throughout the fall to interview students for our summer associate program, we also recruit at a number of diversity, regional, and/or practice specific job fairs. We begin accepting resumes from those law students entering their second year of law school in early July with whom we are not able to meet during OCI or at a job fair. Stroock is also proudly participating in the Leadership Council on Legal Diversity 1L Scholar Program.

Summer associate profile:

Successful summer associates at Stroock are self-starters who quickly take ownership of their matters and are able to function at a high level early in their career. While not a prerequisite, those with prior work experience and those who have held leadership positions typically do very well with us.

Summer program components:

The firm's program includes a flexible work assignment system, billable work across different practice areas, extensive training programs, pro bono opportunities, access to Diversity/Affinity Group activities and social events. In addition, each summer associate has a partner and an associate mentor, as well as a first-year office mate, which allows summer associates to quickly build relationships with our lawyers. Summer associates receive formal feedback at the mid-point and at the end of the summer, as well as when they complete assignments.

STROOCK

Sullivan & Cromwell LLP

125 Broad Street, New York, NY 10004

Tel: 212 558 4000   Fax: 212 558 3588
Email: legalrecruiting@sullcrom.com
Recruitment website: careers.sullcrom.com

Twitter: @sullcrom

Main areas of work

Sullivan & Cromwell brings a multidisciplinary approach to providing the fullest and most comprehensive legal advice to our clients. Our global practice includes four main groups: general practice (corporate), litigation, tax and estates and personal.

Our lawyers are trained to be generalists through broad exposure to a wide range of challenging legal matters, many of which have a significant cross-border component. A substantial number of S&C's clients are non-US commercial enterprises and government entities and many of our US clients retain us for international matters. Our lawyers serve our clients through a network of 13 offices in New York, Washington, DC, Los Angeles, Palo Alto, London, Paris, Frankfurt, Brussels, Tokyo, Hong Kong, Beijing, Melbourne and Sydney.

Firm profile

S&C has the most broadly and deeply trained collection of lawyers in the world. They thrive in our working environment, which is characterized by commitment to clients, leadership, professional development, broad experience, teamwork and commitment to community. Associates at S&C typically acquire leadership skills as lawyers more quickly than they would at other law firms, as they are given early responsibility for managing transactions, counseling clients and representing their interests in dealings with other parties. To supplement this on-the-job experience, we provide comprehensive training programs for associates as well as formal mentoring programs.

Recruitment

Law Schools attending for OCIs in 2018:

S&C interviews at top law schools around the country. Our lawyers are alumni of more than 135 law schools.

Recruitment outside OCIs:

Hiring for Sullivan & Cromwell's US offices is handled by each individual office. Hiring for S&C's Asia and Australia offices, and of US-trained applicants to our European offices, is coordinated out of the New York office. Please send an application package consisting of a cover letter, resume and transcript to the appropriate office:

- New York, Europe, Asia, Australia: legalrecruiting@sullcrom.com
- Los Angeles: whitejak@sullcrom.com
- Palo Alto: moralesm@sullcrom.com
- Washington, DC: rochek@sullcrom.com

Summer associate profile:

We are actively seeking people whose intellect, character, motivation and other attributes promise to make them outstanding lawyers.

Summer program components:

Training/Orientation: All summer associates participate in a formal orientation program, as well as a wide variety of training programs and skills workshops.

Advising/Assigning/Evaluations: Summer associates are assigned a partner advisor and an associate advisor, from whom they receive assignments. They are also matched with a junior associate, who is there to help with day-to-day matters at the firm. In addition, each summer associate is assigned to an associate development partner, who oversees the distribution of summer associate assignments.

Events: Every summer, S&C organizes a variety of events, including professional opportunities, social events and charitable events.

Head Office: New York, NY
Number of domestic offices: 4
Number of international offices: 9
Partners (US): 137
Associates (US): 476

Contacts
Main recruitment contact: Milana L Hogan, Chief Legal Talent Officer
Hiring partner: Sergio J Galvis
Diversity officers: David Braff and Tracy Richelle High, Partners, Co-Chairs of the Diversity Committee

Recruitment details
Entry-level associates starting in 2018: 79
Clerking policy: Yes
Summers joining/anticipated 2018:
1Ls: 5, 2Ls: 129
3Ls (pre-clerks): 15
SEOs: 3 (anticipated)
Summer salary 2018:
1Ls: $3,500/week
2Ls: $3,500/week
Split summers offered? Yes
Can summers spend time in an overseas office? Yes

SULLIVAN & CROMWELL LLP

Thompson & Knight LLP

722 Routh Street Suite 1500 Dallas, TX 75201

Tel: 214 969 1700
Email: hattie.wheeler@tklaw.com
Recruitment website: www.tklaw.com
Linkedin: Thompson & Knight LLP

Twitter: @ThompsonKnight
Facebook: ThompsonKnightLLP
Instagram:
@thompsonknightrecruiting

Main areas of work

Bankruptcy and restructuring; chemical; consumer products; corporate and securities; data privacy and cybersecurity; employment and labor, environmental; finance; financial institutions; government and regulatory; healthcare; insurance; intellectual property; manufacturing; nonprofits; oil, gas, and energy; real estate and real estate finance; restaurants/hospitality; retail; sports, entertainment, and media law; tax; technology/semiconductors; telecommunications; transportation; trial.

Firm profile

Established in 1887, Thompson & Knight is a full-service law firm with more than 300 attorneys who provide legal solutions to clients and communities around the world. Our summer associate program is the principal source of hiring new associates and offers a collegial, team-oriented, and supportive culture, as well as challenging and fulfilling work.

Recruitment

Law Schools attending for OCIs in 2018:

- SMU
- UT
- LSU
- Duke
- Baylor
- Texas Tech
- OU
- Harvard
- University of Houston
- Vanderbilt Job Fair
- Tulane
- South Texas
- Southern Legal Interview Program (UNC, Wake Forest, Washington & Lee, William & Mary)
- On Tour Interview Program (Northwestern, UVA)

Recruitment outside OCIs:

Visit local law school campuses during finals to host lunches, happy hours, etc. Attend job fairs hosted by law schools and send attorneys to speak on law school panels to represent the firm.

Summer associate profile:

Individuals who are a cultural fit, intelligent, hardworking, team-players, self-starters, service oriented, honest, and have a genuine interest in the firm. Having long term goals, a commitment to his/her career, prior work experience, involvement in the community, a strong academic record, and moot court, mock trial, law review experience can all make a candidate stand out.

Summer program components:

Summer associates work in two practice areas and have partner and associate advisors who assist with work assignments, provide feedback, and ensure a rewarding experience with T&K. Formalized training opportunities such as 'Anatomy of a Deal' and 'Trial Academy' (i.e. completing a deal or trial start to finish under the mentorship of senior associates and partners) are provided. Events include scavenger hunts, casino parties, cultural events, firm's Management Committee dinner, and sporting events. Volunteer opportunities with organizations such as Habitat for Humanity, the Housing Crisis Center, and Amazing Place are also offered.

Head Office: Dallas, TX
Number of domestic offices: 6
Number of international offices: 4
Worldwide revenue: $212.02 million
Partners (US): 148
Associates (US): 79

Contacts
Main recruitment contact:
Hattie Wheeler (hattie.wheeler@tklaw.com)
Hiring partner: Jessica Hammons
Diversity officer: Nichole Dotson-Olajuwon

Recruitment details
Entry-level associates starting in 2018: 7
Clerking policy: Yes
Summers joining/anticipated 2018:
1Ls: 3, 2Ls: 8
Summer salary 2018:
1Ls: $3,462 per week
2Ls: $3,462 per week
Split summers offered? No, first half only
Can summers spend time in an overseas office? No

Firm Profiles

Thompson & Knight Impact
ATTORNEYS AND COUNSELORS

Troutman Sanders LLP

600 Peachtree Street, NE Suite 3000 Atlanta, GA 30308

Tel: 404 885 3000
Email: recruiting@troutman.com
Recruitment website: www.troutman.com/laterals/summer_program/
Linkedin: troutman-sanders-llp

Twitter: @TStweets
Facebook:
TroutmanSandersLawFirm

Main areas of work

Some of the firm's main areas of practice include:
Corporate, financial institution, tax and benefits, finance and restructuring, multifamily housing finance, real estate, business litigation, construction, government investigations, compliance and enforcement, intellectual property, financial services litigation, insurance, labor and employment, energy, capital projects and infrastructure, environmental and natural resources, government and regulatory.

Firm profile

Founded in 1897, Troutman Sanders LLP is an international law firm with more than 650 attorneys practicing in 15 offices located throughout the United States and Asia. The firm's clients range from large multinational corporations to individual entrepreneurs and reflect virtually every sector and industry. The firm's heritage of extensive experience, exceptional responsiveness and an unwavering commitment to service has resulted in strong, long-standing relationships with clients across the globe. In recognition of the firm's strong service culture, Troutman Sanders has been on the *BTI* Client Service A-Team for 13 consecutive years.

Recruitment

Law Schools attending for OCIs in 2018:

Law Schools: Cardozo University, Emory University, Fordham University, Georgia State University, Howard University, Kent University, Mercer University, University of Alabama, University of Georgia, University of Illinois, University of North Carolina, University of North Carolina, University of South Carolina, University of Virginia, Vanderbilt University, Wake Forest University, American University, College of William & Mary, Columbia University, Georgetown University, New York University, University of California, Berkeley, University of California, Hastings, University of California, Irvine, University of California, Los Angeles, University of Richmond, University of San Diego, University of Southern California, Washington & Lee University.

Job Fairs: Loyola Patent Program, Lavender Law Job Fair, Southeastern Intellectual Property Job Fair, Southeastern Minority Job Fair.

Summer associate profile:

Troutman Sanders seeks highly motivated, personable individuals with outstanding intellectual ability, academic credentials, and extracurricular accomplishments. Non-legal work experiences are also desirable, as they can greatly enhance insight for client issues. Because effective, clear writing is an indispensable legal skill, significant journal experience during law school is another favorable asset. Evidence of motivation, energy and the ability to effectively manage the competing demands of a rigorous schedule are essential.

Summer program components:

Our summer program strives to give our summer associates a realistic view of the culture at Troutman Sanders and help them bridge the gap between academia and practice. Our summer associates work on current projects for actual clients. They participate in meetings as well as attend strategy sessions and closings. They draft documents, write briefs, and help prepare for trials. The workload in our summer program can be intense, but our summer associates value this fast pace and view it as preparation for a lucrative and successful career in law. An abundant and diverse mix of social events complements the rigorous workload in the summer program. The social element of our program aims to provide relaxing opportunities for summer associates to get acquainted with our attorneys.

Head office: Atlanta, GA
Number of domestic offices: 13
Worldwide revenue: $509,000,000
Partners (US): 295
Associates (US): 267

Contacts
Main recruitment contact: Clare M Roath (clare.roath@troutman.com)
Hiring partner: Steve Riddell
Diversity officer: Sallie Daniel

Recruitment details
Entry-level associates starting in 2018: 27
Clerking policy: Yes
Summers joining/anticipated 2018:
1Ls: 17, 2Ls: 39
Summers joining/anticipated 2018 split by office: Atlanta: 29, Charlotte: 3, Chicago: 1, New York: 6, Orange County: 4, Raleigh: 1, Richmond: 7, San Diego: 1, San Francisco: 1, Virginia Beach: 1, Washington, DC: 2
Summer salary 2018:
1Ls: $3,000/week
2Ls: $3,000/week
Split summers offered? Yes
Can summers spend time in an overseas office? No

Firm Profiles

Vedder Price

'22 North LaSalle Street, Chicago, IL 60601

Tel: 312 609 7500
Email: info@vedderprice.com
Recruitment website: www.vedderprice.com/careers
Linkedin: vedder-price-pc/vedder-price-pc/jobs

Twitter: @vedderlaw
Facebook: VedderLaw

Main areas of work

Corporate, labor and employment, litigation.

Firm profile

Vedder Price is a business-focused law firm with a global reach and a proud tradition of maintaining long-term client relationships. With approximately 300 attorneys and growing, Vedder Price serves clients of all sizes and in virtually all industries from offices in Chicago, New York, Washington, DC, London, San Francisco, Los Angeles and Singapore.

Recruitment

Law Schools attending for OCIs in 2018:

- Brooklyn
- Chicago-Kent
- Cornell
- Fordham
- George Washington
- Georgetown
- Loyola
- Northwestern
- Notre Dame
- University of Chicago
- University of Illinois
- University of Michigan
- Washington University in St. Louis

Recruitment outside OCIs:

Participation in Cook County Minority Job Fair and Loyola Patent Law Program; 2L write-in applications accepted after July 15th.

Summer associate profile:

Vedder Price recruits candidates with strong academic credentials, excellent verbal and written communication skills, initiative and enthusiasm. Ideal candidates have a demonstrated interest in the practice area they are applying for, as evidenced by relevant course work and/or prior work experience. As summer associates will interact immediately with senior shareholders and clients, executive presence and maturity are valued.

Summer program components:

Summer associates are integrated quickly into the practice area they are joining, through substantive work assignments, observation opportunities and training sessions. Summer associates will work with an assigned associate advisor to receive practical advice and guidance. A firm-wide summer program orientation is hosted in Chicago during the first week of the program for the full summer class to meet each other and engage with firm management. There are two formal review sessions, one at mid-summer and the other at the completion of the program, incorporating written attorney feedback regarding each completed project. Social events are frequent, both office-wide and in small groups, to ensure summer associates enjoy the collegiality of the firm.

Head Office: Chicago, IL
Number of domestic offices: 5
Number of international offices: 2
Worldwide revenue: $252 million
Shareholders (US): 160
Associates (US): 126

Contacts
Main recruitment contacts:
Amanda Brummel
(abrummel@vedderprice.com)
Elise Rippe (erippe@vedderprice.com)
Managers of Legal Recruiting
Hiring shareholder: Michael J. Waters
Diversity officer: Jeanah Park,
Shareholder

Recruitment details
Entry-level associates starting in 2018: 12
Clerking policy: No
Summers joining/anticipated 2018:
1Ls: 2, 2Ls: 11
Summers joining/anticipated 2018 split
by office: CH: 9, NY: 4
Summer salary 2018:
1Ls: $3,462/wk
2Ls: $3,462/wk
Split summers offered? No
Can summers spend time in an overseas
office? No

VedderPrice

Venable LLP

600 Massachusetts Ave, NW, Washington, DC 20001

Tel: 202 344 8300
Recrutment website: www.venable.com

Main areas of work

Our clients rely on Venable's proven capabilities in all areas of corporate and business law, complex litigation, intellectual property, and regulatory and government affairs.

Firm profile

With more than 700 attorneys in nine offices across the country, we are strategically positioned to advance our clients' business objectives in the United States and abroad. Clients choose Venable for the skill, dedication, creativity and superior service that our legal and professional staff provide. We firmly believe that a talented and diverse legal team delivers the best results and strive to recruit, retain and promote a diverse group of attorneys and staff throughout the firm.

Recruitment

Law Schools attending for OCIs in 2018:

American University, Benjamin N. Cardozo School of Law, Berkeley Law, Brooklyn Law School, Univ. of Baltimore, Catholic University, UC Davis, Duke, Fordham, George Mason, Georgetown, George Washington, Harvard, UC Hastings, Howard, UCI Law, Loyola Law (LA), UCLA, Univ. of Maryland, Univ. of Michigan, New York Law School, NYU, Univ. of Pennsylvania, Univ. of Richmond, USC, Stanford, Vanderbilt, UVA, and William & Mary. We will also attend the Southeastern Minority Job Fair, Mid-Atlantic BLSA, Western Region BLSA Job Fair, Northeast Region BLSA Job Fair, and Lavender Law Job Fair.

Summer associate profile:

We typically fill our entry-level class with hires from our summer associate program.

We give careful attention to all aspects of a candidate's experience and abilities and like to see the following:
• Demonstrated record of academic achievement with an emphasis on strong undergrad and 1L performance
• Participation in various extracurricular activities highlighting leadership skills, commitment, and time management
• Excellent written and oral communication skills
• Ability to work well with others and independently
• We look particularly favorably on law journal and moot court participation. Previous job experience is a plus

Summer program components:

Summer associates receive real work assignments on behalf of real clients — the same type of assignments our junior associates receive throughout the year, ranging from research and memos to presentations for a client. We strive to maintain a balance between work and social events for the duration of the summer program. Informal dinners, lunches, happy hours, and city-specific events are some of the best ways for our summers to get to know the firm.

Leadership Council on Legal Divesity Scholarship Program:

Venable's 2018 1L LCLD Scholars Program, available in our Washington, Baltimore, New York and Los Angeles offices, offers diverse law students who will have completed their first year of law school by May 2018 the opportunity to spend a summer working side-by-side with attorneys from LCLD Member Organizations. Our 1L LCLD scholars split their time between Venable and a corporate partner in each of our offices. Scholars pull from the same project pool as our 2L summers and participate in an assortment of professional development and social programming. Applications can be submitted through: www.venable.com/careers/laterals/positions/.

Head Office: Washington, DC
Number of domestic offices: 9
Worldwide revenue: $540.5 million
Partners (US): 306
Associates (US): 272

Contacts
Main recruitment contact: Kera Wise, Senior Director of Legal Personnel & Attorney Recruiting, (kwise@venable.com)
Hiring partner: Bob Bolger
Diversity officers: Nora Garrote, Kathleen Hardway

Recruitment details
Entry-level associates starting in 2018: 32
Clerking policy: Yes
Summers joining/anticipated 2018:
1L LCLD Scholars: 4
2Ls: 38, 3Ls: N/A
Summers joining/anticipated 2018 split by office:
DC: 15; BA: 8; NY: 5; LA: 5; TY: 3; SF: 2
Summer salary 2018:
1L LCLD Scholars: $3,460 (for the first 5 weeks at Venable)
2Ls: $3,460
Split summers offered? Determined on a case-by-case basis; must spend the first 8 weeks of the summer with Venable
Can summers spend time in an overseas office? No

Vinson & Elkins LLP

001 Fannin Street, Suite 2500, Houston, TX 77002-6760

Tel: 713 758 2222   Fax: 713 758 2346
Recruitment website: www.velaw.com/join-us/

Twitter: @VECareers;
@VinsonandElkins; @VEAlums
Instagram: @vecareers

Main areas of work

Antitrust; appellate; complex commercial litigation; condemnation; construction; employment, labor and OSHA; energy litigation; energy regulatory; energy transactions/projects; environmental and natural resources; finance; government contracts; government investigations and white collar; intellectual property; international dispute resolution; M&A/capital markets; media and entertainment; private equity; professional liability; real estate; REITs, restructuring and reorganization; securities litigation/regulation; tax — executive compensation and benefits.

Firm profile

Vinson & Elkins LLP delivers competitive strength, insight and know-how to guide our clients through complex transactions and litigation. We collaborate seamlessly across 16 offices worldwide to provide outstanding client service. Our lawyers are committed to excellence, offering clients deep and broad experience handling sophisticated transactions, investments, projects and disputes across the globe. Established in 1917, the firm's time-tested role as trusted advisor has made V&E a go-to law firm for many of the world's leading corporations, investment firms and organizations.

Recruitment

Law Schools attending for OCIs in 2018:

Brooklyn, Columbia, Cornell, Duke, Fordham, George Washington, Georgetown, Harvard, Howard, LSU, NYU, Northwestern, South Texas, SMU, Stanford, The University of Texas, Tulane, UC Berkeley, The University of Chicago, University of Houston, University of Maryland, University of Michigan, University of Pennsylvania, University of Richmond, UVA, Vanderbilt, Washington University, Washington & Lee, William & Mary, Yale.

Recruitment outside OCIs:

V&E participates in job fairs such as: Bay Area Diversity Career Fair, Bay Area Walk Around Program, Lavender Law Career Fair, Loyola University Patent Law Program, and Sunbelt Minority Recruitment Program. V&E accepts write-in applications from 2L students and awards several Diversity Fellowships to 1L and 2L law students. We also consider 3L applicants and judicial clerks for associate positions.

Summer associate profile:

Vinson & Elkins hires talented and highly motivated individuals who desire a sophisticated legal practice. We look for candidates who take initiative, offer diverse perspectives, are innovative and will enjoy working alongside top lawyers in a friendly and collegial environment.

Summer program components:

V&E's 'one firm' mentality offers summer associates the opportunity to work on cross-office projects from a variety of practice areas of interest. As a summer associate, you'll experience hands-on legal training, develop mentoring relationships and get an understanding of what it is like to practice law at Vinson & Elkins.

Head Office: Houston, TX
Number of domestic offices: 8
Number of international offices: 8
Worldwide revenue: $727,475,000
Partners (US): 201
Associates (US): 340

Contacts
Main recruitment contact:
Gretchen Rollins,
Director of Entry-Level Hiring
Hiring partner: Doug Bland
Diversity officer: Julie Tran,
Senior Inclusion & Alumni Relations
Manager

Recruitment details
Entry-level associates starting in 2018: 68
Clerking policy: Yes
Summers joining/anticipated 2018: 113
1Ls: 30, 2Ls: 82, SEOs:1
Summers joining/anticipated 2018 split
by office: Austin: 6; Dallas: 26;
Houston: 55; New York: 13;
Richmond: 2; San Francisco: 4;
Washington: 6
Summer salary 2018:
1Ls: $3,462
2Ls: $3,462
Split summers offered? 10 week
program, varies by office
Can summers spend time in an overseas
office? Case by case

Vinson&Elkins LLP

Waller

511 Union Street, Suite 2700, Nashville, TN 37219

Tel: 615 244 6380   Fax: 615 244 6804
Email: michelle.parsons@wallerlaw.com
Recruitment website: www.wallerlaw.com/join-us
Linkedin: waller-lansden-dortch-and-davis

Twitter: @WallerLansden

Main areas of work

Waller is a full-service general practice firm advising clients across a spectrum of industries including healthcare, financial services, retail, hospitality, advanced manufacturing, technology, real estate and beyond. Our attorneys thrive in the space where heavily regulated industries are faced with complex transactions and bet-the-company matters, counselling clients through these most important issues day in and day out. Core practices include M&A and capital markets, tax, litigation, commercial finance, bankruptcy and restructuring, environmental, real estate, intellectual property, regulatory compliance and government relations.

Firm profile

A mid-market powerhouse with nationally recognized healthcare and financial services industry teams, Waller is a law firm built to help clients weather any storm. Waller attorneys maintain a laid-back, family oriented culture while working hard in a collaborative environment. We provide seamless staffing across offices, and clients benefit from our deep bench. To accomplish this, Waller has an unrelenting drive to recruit, retain, train, and promote the top attorneys in each of our markets.

Recruitment

Law Schools attending for OCIs in 2018:

Duke University, Columbia University, University of Alabama, Vanderbilt University, Belmont University, University of Texas, University of Tennessee

Recruitment outside OCIs:

We offer resume drops at Howard, Pepperdine, Georgetown, University of North Carolina, University of Florida, Wake Forest, Washington & Lee, University of Virginia, Yale, Kentucky, and Harvard. We attend the Southeastern Minority Job fair, the Cook County Bar Association Minority Job Fair, and we present to law schools and participate in panels across the country.

Summer associate profile:

Waller recruits students who are diverse in thought, background and education, especially those with strong ties to the five Southeastern cities in which we are located. Individuals who have a record of academic excellence and are motivated to learn and be integrated in a collegial environment excel at Waller.

Summer program components:

Waller's Summer Program combines mentoring and learning based core practice projects with the opportunity to engage in live matters and other assignments with attorneys across all practice groups and offices.

Based on completed client matters, the core practice projects offer students first-hand experience with actual assignments and client relationships, providing unique insight into the students' future roles at the firm.

Head Office: Nashville, TN
Number of domestic offices: 5
Partners (US): 133
Associates (US): 104

Contacts
Main recruitment contacts:
Michelle Parsons
(michelle.parsons@wallerlaw.com)
Bobby Weiss (raweiss@wallerlaw.com)
Hiring partner: **Tera Rica Murdock**
Diversity officer: **Michelle Parsons**

Recruitment details
Entry-level associates starting in 2018: **7**
Clerking Policy: **One year of credit for relevant practice areas (Evaluated on case by case basis)**
Summers joining/anticipated 2018:
1Ls: 3, 2Ls: 14
Summers joining/anticipated 2018 split by office: **Austin: 3, Birmingham: 2, Nashville: 12**
Summer salary 2018:
1Ls: $1,650/week
2Ls: $2,000/week
Split summers offered? **Yes**

Weil, Gotshal & Manges LLP

67 Fifth Avenue, New York, NY 10153

Tel: 212 310 8000   Fax: 212 310 8007
Email: recruit@weil.com
Recruitment website: careers.weil.com
Linkedin: Weil, Gotshal & Manges LLP

Twitter: @WeilGotshal
Facebook: WeilGotshal
Instagram: @weilgotshal

Main areas of work

The firm offers legal counsel in more than two dozen practice areas categorized by the following groups: business finance and restructuring, corporate, litigation and tax.

Firm profile

Founded in 1931, Weil, Gotshal & Manges LLP has been a preeminent provider of legal services for more than 80 years. With approximately 1,100 lawyers in offices on three continents, Weil has been a pioneer in establishing a geographic footprint that has allowed the firm to partner with clients wherever they do business. The firm's four departments, corporate, litigation, business finance and restructuring, and tax, executive compensation and benefits, and more than two dozen practice groups are consistently recognized as leaders in their respective fields. Weil has become a highly visible leader among major law firms for its innovative diversity and pro bono initiatives, the product of a comprehensive and long-term commitment which has ingrained these values into our culture. Our proven, demonstrated experience allows the firm to provide clients with unmatched legal services.

Please see www.weil.com for more information, including awards and rankings.

Recruitment

Law Schools attending for OCIs in 2018:

Benjamin N. Cardozo, Boston College, Boston University, Brooklyn, University of Chicago, Columbia, Cornell, Duke, Emory, Fordham, George Mason, Georgetown, George Washington, Harvard, Lavender Law Job Fair, New York University, Northwestern, New York Law School, Northeast Interview Program (Washington and Lee /William & Mary Law Job Fair), On Tour Regional Program, Santa Clara, SMU, Stanford, St. John's, Suffolk, Sunbelt Job Fair, Tulane /University of Washington New York Interview Program, UCLA, University of Pennsylvania, UC Berkeley, University of Miami, University of Michigan, University of San Francisco, University of Texas, University of Virginia, USC Gould, Vanderbilt, Yale.

Recruitment outside OCIs:

Weil has a diversified approach to its recruiting process. Firm-wide, Weil interviews at 40 law schools and job fairs and participates in resume collection programs at more than ten other law schools. For a complete list, please visit careers.weil.com.

Summer associate profile:

Weil's summer associate program provides an exceptional opportunity for outstanding law students from across the nation to explore a career in the practice of law. Weil seeks candidates with exceptional credentials, both in terms of qualifications and character.

Summer program components:

Summer associates may work in a total of one to three departments of their choice. They are assigned to active transactional and litigation matters and attend client meetings, negotiations, depositions and court hearings. This enables them to gain a much clearer idea of their choice of future practice area and obtain a realistic view of what it is like to practice law at the firm. Weil organizes special seminars during the summer to discuss particular fields of specialization and topics of interest to law students and to provide training in such areas as negotiation, litigation and writing skills. The firm assigns both associate and partner mentors whose role is to guide the summer associate throughout their summer experience, both personally and professionally. Feedback is a critical element of the summer experience. Assigning attorneys regularly evaluate the summer associate's performance and written product, in much the same way that a senior attorney reviews a junior attorney's work. The summer associate's performance is formally evaluated twice during the summer.

Head Office: New York, NY
Number of domestic offices: 8
Number of international offices: 9
Worldwide revenue: $1.39 billion
Partners (US): 181
Associates (US): 538

Contacts
Main recruitment contact:
Wesley Powell (wesley.powell@weil.com)
Hiring partners: Joshua Amsel,
Jackie Cohen
Diversity officer: Meredith Moore

Recruitment details
Entry-level associates starting in 2018:
102
Clerking policy: Yes
Summers joining/anticipated 2018:
1Ls: 14, 2Ls: 119, 3Ls: 1, SEOs: 2
Summers joining/anticipated 2018 split
by office:
Boston: 10, Dallas: 11, Miami: 2,
New York: 98*, Silicon Valley: 9*,
Washington, DC: 7*
(*includes candidates splitting offices)
Summer salary 2018:
1Ls: $3,462
2Ls: $3,462
Split summers offered? Case by case
Can summers spend time in an overseas
office? Case by case

White & Case LLP

1221 Avenue of the Americas, New York, NY 10020

Tel: 212 819 8200
Email: recruit@whitecase.com
Recruitment website: www.whitecase.com/careers
Linkedin: white-&-case

Twitter: WhiteCase
Facebook: whitecase
YouTube: @whitecaseglobal

Main areas of work

Antitrust, asset finance, banking, capital markets, commercial litigation, financial restructuring and insolvency, intellectual property, international arbitration, mergers and acquisitions, private equity, pro bono, project finance, sourcing and technology transactions, tax, trade and white collar.

Firm profile

We are a truly global firm, with an unrivaled network of 43 offices in 30 countries. It's the reason many of our global clients choose to work with us, and why they trust us with their most challenging cross-border matters. From day one, our lawyers work on cutting-edge and complex multi jurisdictional projects, experiencing the operational realities of cross-border law. We will help you become a great lawyer, with training and mentoring programs to support you at every stage of your career. We are proud of our achievements — revenue of more than US$1.8 billion and top ranked for diversity and pro bono programs — but we will not rest on our laurels. In 2015, we launched an ambitious five-year growth strategy that will strengthen our position as a top-of-mind firm for global clients — and an employer of choice for top talent.

Recruitment

Law Schools attending for OCIs in 2018:

American, Bay Area Diversity Job Fair, Berkeley, Chicago, Columbia, Cornell, Duke, Florida, Fordham, Georgetown, Harvard, Howard, Irvine, Loyola, Loyola Patent Job Fair, McGill, Miami, Michigan, Mid-Atlantic BLSA, Northeast BLSA, Northwestern, Notre Dame, NYU, Penn, Pepperdine, San Francisco IP Job Fair, Stanford, Toronto, UCLA, USC, Virginia, Yale.

Recruitment outside OCIs:

Brooklyn, Emory, Hastings, Hofstra, Houston, NYLS, Rutgers, Santa Clara, Suffolk, Tennessee, Texas, Tulane, Wash U.

Summer associate profile:

We look for highly motivated individuals with excellent academic credentials, significant personal achievements and a strong commitment to the practice of law in a global and diverse environment. A successful candidate will be able to demonstrate evidence of our core competencies which include excellent judgment, client readiness, drive, initiative and an entrepreneurial mindset. We are looking for those with the ability to work collaboratively in high pace, high stakes situations.

Summer program components:

We pride ourselves on giving summer associates real work for real clients with real deadlines. We include a full curriculum of training programs in addition to hands-on training working side-by-side with our lawyers. Our assignment coordinators ensure that each summer associate is exposed to a variety of work, including pro bono matters. Mentors are assigned to provide guidance. One of the highlights is the US Summer Associate Conference in New York, which provides an opportunity for our summer associates across the US to network with their peers and learn more about the firm, our people and our culture. At the end of the program, our summer associates will have a thorough understanding of what it is like to be an associate at White & Case.

Head office: New York, NY
Number of domestic offices: 7
Number of international offices: 43
Worldwide revenue: $1.8 billion
Partners (US): 186
Associates (US): 477

Contacts
Main recruitment contact: Antonia Choi
Hiring partner: Brenda Dieck
Diversity officer: Maja Hazell

Recruitment details
Entry-level associates starting in 2018: 108
Clerking policy: Yes
Summers joining/anticipated 2018:
1Ls: 8, 2Ls: 109, SEOs: 2
Summers joining/anticipated 2018 split by office: BOS: 2, LA: 8, MI: 8, NY: 68, SV: 4, DC: 27 (includes 1Ls; not SEOs)
Summer salary 2018:
1Ls: $ 3,500/week
2Ls: $ 3,500/week
Split summers offered? Case-by-case
Can summers spend time in an overseas office? Yes

WHITE & CASE

Firm Profiles

Wiley Rein LLP

1776 K Street NW, Washington, DC 20006

Tel: 202 719 7000   Fax: 202 719 7049
Recruitment website: www.wileyrein.com/careers.cfm
LinkedIn: wiley-rein-llp

Twitter: @WileyRein
Facebook: WileyReinLLP
Instagram: @wileyrein

Main areas of work

- Government Contracts
- Insurance
- International Trade
- Intellectual Property
- Telecom, Media & Technology
- Litigation

Firm profile

Wiley Rein operates at the intersection of politics, law, government, business, and technological innovation, representing a wide range of clients — from Fortune 500 corporations to trade associations to individuals — in virtually all industries. We believe consistent and successful results are achieved through building true partnerships with our clients. We do this by understanding the industries and economic climate in which they operate and the current and potential legal issues that impact their business. Most importantly, because Wiley Rein remains a Washington, DC-based firm that largely operates out of a single office, we are able to control costs and billing rates in a manner that is nearly impossible in large, multi-office or multinational law firms. In addition, Wiley Rein generously gives back to the community, providing significant pro bono legal services and charitable contributions to more than 450 local and national organizations every year.

Recruitment

Law Schools attending for OCIs in 2018:

Antonin Scalia Law School — George Mason University, The George Washington University Law School, Georgetown University Law Center, Harvard Law School, Howard University School of Law, University of Michigan Law School, University of Pennsylvania Law School, University of Virginia School of Law, Vanderbilt University Law School, Washington and Lee University School of Law.

Summer associate profile:

Wiley Rein's summer associate program is the foundation of our recruiting efforts. We ensure that summer associates experience the excellence and diversity of our firm and we provide opportunities for each student to handle responsibilities typically assumed by first year associates.

Summer program components:

The defining feature of our program is the flexibility of work assignments. We assist students in tailoring their assignments so that they gain significant exposure to a wide variety of practice areas through our interactive database of assignments. In addition, summer associates receive an associate mentor to help integrate them into the firm and our practices. We host an extensive litigation skills training program in addition to other professional development and social events throughout the summer.

Head Office: Washington, DC
Number of domestic offices: 1
Partners (US): 113
Associates (US): 57

Contacts
Main recruitment contact:
Janell Mallard, Senior Recruiting & Diversity Manager
Hiring partner: Rachel A. Alexander
Diversity officer: Anna Gomez

Recruitment details
Entry-level associates starting in 2018: 8
Clerking policy: Yes
Summers joining/anticipated 2018:
1Ls: 1
2Ls: 11
Summer salary 2018:
1Ls: $3,465
2Ls: $3,465
Split summers offered? No

...rr & Gallagher LLP

..., New York, NY 10019

...0 Fax: 212 728 8111
...t website: www.willkie.com/careers

Main areas of work

Antitrust and competition; asset management; business reorganization and restructuring; communications, media and privacy; commodities and derivatives; corporate and financial services; environmental; energy; health and safety; executive compensation and employee benefits; government relations; insurance; intellectual property; litigation; private clients; real estate; and tax.

Firm profile

Willkie Farr & Gallagher LLP was founded 130 years ago upon principles that still characterize our practice today. Our founders and memorable colleagues, like Wendell Willkie and Felix Frankfurter, established a strong foundation of integrity, innovation, pragmatism, flexibility and intellectual agility designed to continually meet the ever changing business needs of our clients. We continue our tradition of excellence by keeping nimble, working collaboratively, with respect and professionalism, and by integrating our philosophy into our client relationships. Our clients rely on us not only for our creativity, skill, leadership, decisiveness and high quality of work, but because they know we are solution-oriented and we get the job done effectively and efficiently.

Recruitment

Law Schools attending for OCIs in 2018:

Brooklyn, Columbia University, Cornell, Duke, Emory Fordham University, GWU, Georgetown University, Harvard, Howard University, NYU, Northwestern University, St. John's University, Tulane, University of Michigan, University of Pennsylvania, University of Texas, UCLA, UVA, Vanderbilt, Washington University, and Yale.

Summer associate profile:

Willkie seeks motivated individuals who have excelled academically. We are looking for candidates who possess ambition, maturity, strong communication skills and the ability to work collaboratively.

Summer program components:

Willkie's summer program is a terrific introduction to the firm. We offer summer associates the opportunity to work side by side with our attorneys in practice areas of their choice. We offer departmental rotations during the course of the summer. In addition, summer associates participate in a presentation-skills workshop, mock arbitration and corporate negotiation training seminars and attend department overviews. Summer associates are evaluated twice during the program: once at mid-summer and then at the end of the program. In addition to giving an introduction to life as an associate, we offer a wide array of social events with the goal of helping our summer associates to get to know one another, our lawyers and the city.

Head Office: New York, NY
Number of domestic offices: 3
Number of international offices: 6
Partners (US): 167
Associates (US): 476

Contacts
Main recruitment contacts:
Christie Bonasera, Associate Director of Legal Recruiting (NY/TX),
Jeanine Thomas, Legal Personnel & Recruiting Manager (DC)
Hiring partners: Jeffrey Clark (DC); Rajab Abbassi; Sameer Advani; Amelia Cottrell; David Drewes; Matthew Guercio; Benjamin McCallen; Carly Saviano; Danielle Scalzo; Robert Jocabson (TX)
Angela Olivarez (TX)
Diversity officer: Kim Walker, Chief Diversity & Inclusion Officer

Recruitment details
Entry-level associates starting in 2018: 52
Summers joining/anticipated 2018:
1Ls: 6 , 2Ls: 49
Summers joining/anticipated 2018 split by office: NY: 40, DC: 7, Houston: 8
Summer salary 2018:
1Ls: $3,462
2Ls: $3,462
Split summers offered? No
Can summers spend time in an overseas office? Case-by-case

WILLKIE FARR & GALLAGHER LLP

WilmerHale

0 State Street, Boston, MA / 1875 Pennsylvania Ave, NW, Washington, DC

el: 617 526 6000/202 663 6000
Recruitment website: www.wilmerhalecareers.com

Linkedin: WilmerHale
Twitter: @WilmerHale

Main areas of work

Our global practice includes over 500 litigators with unmatched trial, appellate and Supreme Court experience; a preeminent securities law practice with over 200 lawyers; a regulatory practice that includes more than 100 lawyers who have held high-level government positions; an intellectual property practice enriched by the expertise of more than 200 attorneys and technology specialists with more than 120 who hold scientific, engineering or technical degrees; more than 160 seasoned corporate transactional lawyers and business counselors; and lawyers who focus on bankruptcy, environmental, labor and employment, private client, real estate and tax matters.

Firm profile

WilmerHale offers unparalleled legal representation across a comprehensive range of practice areas that are critical to the success of our clients. We practice at the very top of the legal profession and offer a cutting-edge blend of capabilities that enables us to handle deals and cases of any size and complexity. With a practice unsurpassed in depth and scope by any other major firm, we have the ability to anticipate obstacles, seize opportunities and get the case resolved or the deal done —a nd the experience and know-how to prevent it from being undone. Our heritage includes involvement in the foundation of legal aid work early in the 20th century, and today we consistently distinguish ourselves as leaders in pro bono representation. Many of our lawyers have played, and continue to play, prominent roles in public service activities of national and international importance — from counseling US presidents to opposing discrimination and defending human rights around the world. Most importantly, our firm stands for a steadfast commitment to quality and excellence in everything we do — a commitment reflected in the continued success of our clients across the globe and our dedication to the development of our attorneys.

Recruitment

Law Schools attending for OCIs in 2018:

University of California-Berkeley, Boston College, Boston University, University of Chicago, Columbia, Cornell, Duke, Fordham, George Washington, Georgetown, Harvard, Howard, Loyola Law School - LA, Michigan, Northwestern, Northeastern, NYU, University of Pennsylvania, Santa Clara, Stanford, Suffolk, University of California-LA (UCLA), University of Colorado-Boulder, University of Denver, University of Southern California (USC), University of Texas, University of Virginia, Yale.

Recruitment outside OCIs:

Bay Area Diversity Career Fair, Boston Lawyers Group Diversity Job Fair, BU/BC Job Fair, Harvard Law School BLSA Job Fair, Lavender Law, Loyola Patent Law Program, Rocky Mountain Diversity Legal Career Fair.

Head offices: Boston, MA and Washington, DC
Number of domestic offices: 7
Number of international offices: 5
Worldwide revenue: $1,137,000,000
Partners (US): 249
Associates (US): 538

Contacts
Main recruitment contacts:
Beth Miller (firmwide)
Karen Rameika (Boston)
Terri Janezeck (Denver and Los Angeles)
Nancy Gray (New York)
Nancy Lam (Palo Alto)
Melissa Grossman (Washington, DC)
Hiring partners:
Mark Ford (Boston)
Natalie Hanlon Leh & Andy Spielman (Denver)
Randall Lee (Los Angeles)
Erin Sloane & Alan Schoenfeld (New York)
Mark Flanagan (Palo Alto)
Jonathan Paikin (Washington, DC)
Diversity officer: Nimesh Patel

⌐le (continued)

...on, MA

...nia Ave, NW, Washington, DC

Summer associate profile:

We seek to hire an extraordinarily talented and diverse group of students whose academic and personal record of achievement demonstrates a commitment to excellence and who want to practice law at the highest and most demanding levels, while still enjoying lives enriched by public, professional and personal pursuits outside the firm. We have identified six competencies — commitment, confidence, oral communication, problem solving, teamwork and writing — that outline what constitutes outstanding performance at WilmerHale and are used to align our selection criteria and evaluations of candidates and summer associates with our expectations of attorneys. In addition, we seek individuals whose character, intelligence, judgment and training will inspire their colleagues and clients to have confidence in their advice and representation.

Summer program components:

By providing a realistic view of the firm through interesting work assignments, practical training and the opportunity to work and socialize with many of our lawyers, we give summer associates the insight needed to make an informed decision to join the firm after graduation or a clerkship. Summer associates do substantive client work and have the opportunity to try a broad range of practices or focus on a few, depending on their interests. Summer associates also have the opportunity to attend client meetings and trials whenever possible. Our mentors provide guidance and constructive feedback throughout the summer and make themselves available to their mentees as resources in the firm. We have developed training programs specifically for our summer associates designed to assist in their professional development by introducing the practical skills lawyers need and provide a sample of our training programs for our attorneys. Summer training topics include: research skills, leadership, negotiation skills, deposition skills, presentation skills/oral communication skills, legal writing, departmental panels and meetings, case studies and mock trials. In addition, summer associates receive a review of their work and are encouraged to provide feedback about their experience.

Recruitment details

Entry-level associates starting in 2018: 75

Clerking policy: Yes

Summers joining/anticipated 2018:

1Ls: 3, 2Ls: 85, SEOs: 4

Summers joining/anticipated 2018 split by office: Boston: 23, Denver: 4, LA: 4, NY: 23, Palo Alto: 7, Washington DC: 27

Summer salary 2018:

1Ls: $3,500/week

2Ls: $3,500/week

Split summers offered? Yes

Can summers spend time in overseas office? Yes

WILMERHALE®

Wilson Sonsini Goodrich & Rosati

650 Page Mill Road, Palo Alto, CA 94304

Tel: 650 493 9300   Fax: 650 493 6811
Email: wsgr@wsgr.com
Recruitment website: www.wsgr.com/attorneyrecruiting
Linkedin: wilson-sonsini-goodrich-&-rosati

Twitter: @wilsonsonsini
Facebook: wilsonsonsini

Main areas of work

Corporate governance, corporate finance, mergers and acquisitions, shareholder activism, litigation, IP counseling and transactions, antitrust counseling and litigation, employee benefits and compensation, export control and sanctions, FCPA and anti-corruption, energy and infrastructure, privacy and data protection, national security/CFIUS, cybersecurity, Federal Trade Commission, real estate, and tax. You can view the full practice group list by visiting www.wsgr.com

Firm profile

Wilson Sonsini Goodrich & Rosati is the premier provider of legal services to technology, life sciences, and other growth enterprises worldwide, as well as the venture firms, private equity firms, and investment banks that finance and advise them. The firm represents clients in a vast array of industries at all stages of development, from venture-backed start-ups to multibillion-dollar global corporations. We are nationally recognized as a leader in the fields of corporate governance and finance, mergers and acquisitions, private equity, securities litigation, IP, and antitrust, among many other areas of law. Over the past 50-plus years, since its inception in Silicon Valley, the firm has established its reputation by having a superior knowledge of its clients' industries, as well as deep and longstanding contacts throughout the technology and life sciences sectors.

Recruitment

Law Schools attending for OCIs in 2018:

Berkeley, Boston College, Boston University, Chicago, Cornell, Columbia, Duke, George Mason, George Washington, Georgetown, Penn, Harvard, Hastings, Michigan, Northwestern, NYU, Santa Clara, Stanford, University of Texas, UC Irvine, UCLA, USC, USD, UVA, UW, Yale.

Recruitment outside OCIs:

Candidates are welcome to apply directly by sending their materials (cover letter, resume and law school transcript) to www.wsgr.com/attorneyrecruiting

Summer associate profile:

We look for candidates who are enthusiastic about working at our firm and for our client base, and have a solid understanding of what we do and the practices we have. Given our extensive work for technology, life sciences, renewable energy, and other growth companies at all stages of development, we are particularly interested in candidates who want to work for those companies. We are also interested in candidates who have the requisite scientific expertise for one of our IP practices. Depending on the experience, we typically prefer candidates with prior work experience. Given our particular client base and entrepreneurial orientation, work experience for technology, life sciences, renewable energy, or other growth companies is particularly valuable, as is experience starting a company or student organization. We also value experience in management consulting, accounting, paralegal and similar types of backgrounds.

Summer associate components:

Our summer program offers law students an opportunity to observe and participate in the work of the leading provider of legal services to technology, life sciences, and other growth enterprises worldwide. The summer period at our firm incorporates many of the things important to our culture: challenging and varied assignments, direct working relationships with our innovative clients, meeting a wide range of attorneys, and exciting social activities that take advantage of our locations in technology centers around the country.

Head Office: Palo Alto, CA
Number of domestic offices: 11
Number of international offices: 4
Worldwide revenue: $797 million
Partners (US): 204
Associates (US): 438

Contacts
Main recruitment contact: Elizabeth Pond (epond@wsgr.com)
Hiring partners: Lisa Stimmell, Maura Rees, Andrew Hoffman
Diversity officer: Chris Boyd

Recruitment details
Entry-level associates starting in 2018: 53
Clerking policy: Yes
Summers joining/anticipated 2018:
2Ls: 48
Summers joining/anticipated 2018 split by office:
Palo Alto: 21   San Francisco: 6.5
San Diego: 4.5   Los Angeles: 2
Seattle: 2   Boston: 4
NY: 2   Washington, DC: 6
Summer salary 2018:
2Ls: $3,462 per week
Split summers offered? On a case-by-case basis
Can summers spend time in an overseas office? On a case-by-case basis

---

WSGR
Wilson Sonsini Goodrich & Rosati
PROFESSIONAL CORPORATION

Firm Profiles

n & Strawn LLP

Drive, Chicago, IL 60601

5600 Fax: 312 558 5700

ent website: www.winston.com

din: winston-&-strawn-llp

Twitter: @winstonlaw
Facebook: WinstonStrawnLLP
Instagram: @winstonstrawnllp

Main areas of work

Litigation, corporate and financial, intellectual property, labor and employment relations, tax, employee benefits and executive compensation, energy, environmental, government relations and regulatory affairs, healthcare, maritime, real estate, trusts and estates.

Firm profile

Throughout its more than 160 year history, Winston & Strawn LLP has handled many significant, high profile matters for its clients — from antitrust litigation to cross-border mergers, energy transactions to labor negotiations. The firm is a global law firm with more than 875 attorneys across the US, Europe and Asia. The firm's mission is to provide the highest quality legal services to meet the difficult legal challenges of the world's most important companies and organizations. Winston & Strawn is consistently honored by its clients for outstanding legal service.

Recruitment

Law Schools attending for OCIs in 2018:

Please visit the Careers section of winston.com for a list of OCI Schools.

Summer associate profile:

Winston & Strawn prefers strong academic performance, participation in law review or other law school publications or competitive endeavors and a good balance of academic and interpersonal skills.

Summer program components:

Summer associates have the opportunity to learn about a wide range of Winston practice areas and the specialized skills each one demands. Individual department presentations allow summer associates to meet lawyers from specific practice groups who detail what they do in their daily practice. The firm's 'Highlights Lecture' series gives an inside look at some of the most publicized and interesting cases that the firm handled in the past year. In addition, the firm offers a practical training component that provides hands-on experience with activities such as drafting a legal research memorandum, negotiating a deal, drafting an IPO document, taking a deposition and trying a case in a mock trial. Summer associates learn from veteran Winston attorneys with years of experience and insight, who make the law come alive through examples, personal experience and anecdotes. In addition, summer associates have the opportunity to build relationships with attorneys through a variety of social activities throughout the summer.

Head Office: Chicago, IL
Number of domestic offices: 9
Number of international offices: 7
Worldwide revenue: $978,500,000
Partners (US): 398
Associates (US): 428

Contacts

Main recruitment contact:
Lisa A McLafferty, Director of Attorney Recruiting & Development
lmclafferty@winston.com
Hiring partners: Suzanne Jaffe Bloom, William C O'Neil, Co-Chairs, Hiring Committee
Diversity officer: Sylvia James, Director of Diversity & Inclusion

Recruitment Details

Entry-level associates starting in 2018: 58
Clerking policy: Yes
Summers joining/anticipated 2018: 83
(1Ls: 8, 2Ls: 76)
Summers joining/anticipated 2018 split by office: Charlotte 2, Chicago 26, Dallas 9, Houston 7, Los Angeles 7, New York 22, San Francisco 5, Washington DC 5
Summer salary 2018
1Ls: $3,461/week
2Ls: $3,461/week
Split summers offered? No
Can summers spend time in an overseas office? No